2

THE BEST OF
HERMAN MELVILLE

Moby Dick
Omoo
Typee
Israel Potter

THE BEST OF
HERMAN MELVILLE

CASTLE

CONTENTS

MOBY DICK
or The Whale
1

OMOO
A Narrative of Adventure
in the South Seas
361

TYPEE
A Peep at Polynesian
Life
543

ISRAEL POTTER
His Fifty Years in Exile
729

BOOK ONE

MOBY-DICK: *Or the Whale*

CONTENTS

3

4

ETYMOLOGY

(SUPPLIED BY A LATE CONSUMPTIVE USHER TO A GRAMMAR SCHOOL)

The pale Usher—threadbare in coat, heart, body, and brain; I see him now. He was ever dusting his old lexicons and grammars, with a queer handkerchief, mockingly embellished with all the gay flags of all the known nations of the world. He loved to dust his old grammars; it somehow mildly reminded him of his mortality.

"WHILE you take in hand to school others, and to teach them by what name a whale-fish is to be called in our tongue, leaving out, through ignorance, the letter H, which almost alone maketh up the signification of the word, you deliver that which is not true." *Hackluyt.*

"WHALE. * * * Sw. and Dan. *hval.* This animal is named from roundness or rolling; for in Dan. *hvalt* is arched or vaulted." *Webster's Dictionary.*

"WHALE. * * * It is more immediately from the Dut. and Ger. *Wallen;* A.S. *Walw-ian,* to roll, to wallow." *Richardson's Dictionary."*

חך,	*Hebrew.*
κητος,	*Greek,*
CETUS,	*Latin.*
WHŒL,	*Anglo-Saxon.*
HVALT,	*Danish.*
WAL,	*Dutch.*
HWAL,	*Swedish.*
WHALE,	*Icelandic.*
WHALE,	*English.*
BALEINE,	*French.*
BALLENA,	*Spanish.*
PEKEE-NUEE-NUEE,	*Fegee.*
PEHEE-NUEE-NUEE,	*Erromangoan.*

EXTRACTS

(SUPPLIED BY A SUB-SUB-LIBRARIAN)

It will be seen that this mere painstaking burrower and grub-worm of a poor devil of a Sub-Sub appears to have gone through the long Vaticans and street-stalls of the earth, picking up whatever random allusions to whales he could anyways find in any book whatsoever, sacred or profane. Therefore you must not, in every case at least, take the higgledy-piggledy whale statements, however authentic, in these extracts, for veritable gospel cetology. Far from it. As touching the ancient authors generally, as well as the poets here appearing,

7

these extracts are solely valuable or entertaining, as affording a glancing bird's eye view of what has been promiscuously said, thought, fancied and sung of Leviathan, by many nations and generations, including our own.

So fare thee well, poor devil of a Sub-Sub, whose commentator I am. Thou belongest to that hopeless, sallow tribe which no wine of this world will ever warm; and for whom even Pale Sherry would be too rosy-strong; but with whom one sometimes loves to sit, and feel poor-devilish, too; and grow convivial upon tears; and say to them bluntly, with full eyes and empty glasses, and in not altogether unpleasant sadness—Give it up, Sub-Subs! For by how much the more pains ye take to please the world, by so much the more shall ye for ever go thankless! Would that I could clear out Hampton Court and the Tuileries for ye! But gulp down your tears and hie aloft to the royal-mast with your hearts; for your friends who have gone before are clearing out the seven-storied heavens, and making refugees of long-pampered Gabriel, Michael, and Raphael, against your coming. Here ye strike but splintered hearts together —there, ye shall strike unsplinterable glasses!

"And God created great whales." *Genesis.*

"Leviathan maketh a path to shine after him;
One would think the deep to be hoary." *Job.*

"Now the Lord had prepared a great fish to swallow up Jonah." *Jonah.*

"There go the ships; there is that Leviathan whom thou hast made to play therein." *Psalms.*

"In that day, the Lord with his sore, and great, and strong sword, shall punish Leviathan the piercing serpent, even Leviathan that crooked serpent; and he shall slay the dragon that is in the sea." *Isaiah.*

"And what thing soever besides cometh within the chaos of this monster's mouth, be it beast, boat, or stone, down it goes all incontinently that foul great swallow of his, and perisheth in the bottomless gulf of his paunch." *Holland's Plutarch's Morals.*

"The Indian Sea breedeth the most and the biggest fishes that are: among which the Whales and Whirlpooles called Balæne, take up as much in length as four acres or arpens of land." *Holland's Pliny.*

"Scarcely had we proceeded two days on the sea, when about sunrise a great many Whales and other monsters of the sea, appeared. Among the former, one was of a most monstrous size. * * This came towards us, open-mouthed, raising the waves on all sides, and beating the sea before him into a foam." *Tooke's Lucian.*
"The True History."

"He visited this country also with a view of catching horse-whales, which had bones of very great value for their teeth, of which he brought some to the king. * * * The best whales were catched in his own country, of which some were forty-eight, some fifty yards long. He said that he was one of six who had killed sixty in two days." *Other or Octher's verbal narrative taken down from his mouth by King Alfred, A. D. 890.*

"And whereas all the other things, whether beast or vessel, that enter into the dreadful gulf of this monster's (whale's) mouth, are immediately lost and swallowed up, the sea-gudgeon retires into it in great security, and there sleeps." MONTAIGNE.—*Apology for Raimond Sebond.*

"Let us fly, let us fly! Old Nick take me if it is not Leviathan described by the noble prophet Moses in the life of patient Job."   *Rabelais.*

"This whale's liver was two cart-loads."   *Stowe's Annals.*

"The great Leviathan that maketh the seas to seethe like boiling pan."
Lord Bacon's Version of the Psalms.

"Touching that monstrous bulk of the whale or ork we have received nothing certain. They grow exceeding fat, insomuch that an incredible quantity of oil will be extracted out of one whale."   *Ibid "History of Life and Death."*

"The sovereignest thing on earth is parmacetti for an inward bruise."
King Henry.

"Very like a whale."   *Hamlet.*

> "Which to secure, no skill of leach's art
> Mote him availle, but to returne againe
> To his wound's worker, that with lowly dart,
> Dinting his breast, had bred his restless paine,
> Like as the wounded whale to shore flies thro' the maine.
> *The Fairie Queen.*

"Immense as whales, the motion of whose vast bodies can in a peaceful calm trouble the ocean till it boil."   *Sir William Davenant. Preface to Gondibert.*

"What spermacetti is, men might justly doubt, since the learned Hosmannus in his work of thirty years, saith plainly, *Nescio quid sit.*"
*Sir T. Browne. Of Sperma Ceti and the
Sperma Ceti Whale. Vide his V. E.*

> "Like Spencer's Talus with his modern flail
> He threatens ruin with his ponderous tail.
> *   *   *   *   *
> Their fixed jav'lins in his side he wears,
> And on his back a grove of pikes appears."
> *Waller's Battle of the Summer Islands.*

"By art is created that great Leviathan, called a Commonwealth or State—(in Latin. Civitas) which is but an artificial man."
Opening sentence of Hobbes's Leviathan.

"Silly Mansoul swallowed it without chewing, as if it had been a sprat in the mouth of a whale."   *Pilgrim's Progress.*

> "That sea beast
> Leviathan, which God of all his works
> Created hugest that swim the ocean stream."
> *Paradise Lost.*

> ——"There Leviathan,
> Hugest of living creatures, in the deep
> Stretched like a promontory sleeps or swims,
> And seems a moving land; and at his gills
> Draws in, and at his breath spouts out a sea."
> *Ibid.*

"The mighty whales which swim in a sea of water, and have a sea of oil swimming in them."   *Fuller's Profane and Holy State.*

> "So close behind some promontory lie
> The huge Leviathans to attend their prey,
> And give no chace, but swallow in the fry,
> Which through their gaping jaws mistake the way."
>   *Dryden's Annus Mirabilis.*

"While the whale is floating at the stern of the ship, they cut off his head, and tow it with a boat as near the shore as it will come; but it will be aground in twelve or thirteen feet water."   *Thomas Edge's Ten Voyages to Spitzbergen, in Purchass.*

"In their way they saw many whales sporting in the ocean, and in wantonness fuzzing up the water through their pipes and vents, which nature has placed on their shoulders."
>   *Sir T. Herbert's Voyages into Asia and Africa.*
>   *Harris Coll.*

"Here they saw such huge troops of whales, that they were forced to proceed with a great deal of caution for fear they should run their ship upon them."
>   *Schouten's Sixth Circumnavigation.*

"We set sail from the Elbe, wind N. E. in the ship called The Jonas-in-the-Whale.
* * *
Some say the whale can't open his mouth, but that is a fable. * * *
They frequently climb up the masts to see whether they can see a whale, for the first discoverer has a ducat for his pains. * * *
I was told of a whale taken near Shetland, that had above a barrel of herrings in his belly. * * *
One of our harpooneers told me that he caught once a whale in Spitzbergen that was white all over."
>   *A Voyage to Greenland, A. D.* 1671.
>   *Harris Coll.*

"Several whales have come in upon this coast (Fife) Anno 1652, one eighty feet in length of the whale-bone kind came in, which, (as I was informed) besides a vast quantity of oil, did afford 500 weight of baleen. The jaws of it stand for a gate in the garden of Pitferren."   *Sibbald's Fife and Kinross.*

"Myself have agreed to try whether I can master and kill this Sperma-ceti whale, for I could never hear of any of that sort that was killed by any man, such is his fierceness and swiftness."   *Richard Strafford's Letter from the Bermudas.*
>   *Phil. Trans. A. D.* 1668.

> "Whales in the sea
> God's voice obey."
>
>   *N. E. Primer.*

"We saw also abundance of large whales, there being more in those southern seas, as I may say, by a hundred to one; than we have to the northward of us."
>   *Captain Cowley's Voyage round the Globe, A. D.* 1729.

* * * * * "and the breath of the whale is frequently attended with such an insupportable smell, as to bring on a disorder of the brain."   *Ulloa's South America.*

"To fifty chosen sylphs of special note,
We trust the important charge, the petticoat.
Oft have we known that seven-fold fence to fail,
Tho' stuffed with hoops and armed with ribs of whale.

Rape of the Lock.

"If we compare land animals in respect to magnitude, with those that take up their abode in the deep, we shall find they will appear contemptible in the comparison. The whale is doubtless the largest animal in creation." *Goldsmith, Nat. Hist.*

"If you should write a fable for little fishes, you would make them speak like great whales." *Goldsmith to Johnson.*

"In the afternoon we saw what was supposed to be a rock, but it was found to be a dead whale, which some Asiatics had killed, and were then towing ashore. They seemed to endeavor to conceal themselves behind the whale, in order to avoid being seen by us." *Cook's Voyages.*

"The larger whales, they seldom venture to attack. They stand in so great dread of some of them, that when out at sea they are afraid to mention even their names, and carry dung, lime-stone, juniper-wood, and some other articles of the same nature in their boats, in order to terrify and prevent their too near approach."
*Uno Von Troil's Letters on Banks's and
Solander's Voyage to Iceland in 1772.*

"The Spermacetti Whale found by the Nantuckois, is an active, fierce animal, and requires vast address and boldness in the fishermen."
Thomas Jefferson's Whale Memorial to the French Minister in 1778.

"And pray, sir, what in the world is equal to it?"
Edmund Burke's reference in Parliament to the Nantucket Whale-Fishery.

"Spain——a great whale stranded on the shores of Europe."
Edmund Burke. (*somewhere.*)

"A tenth branch of the king's ordinary revenue, said to be grounded on the consideration of his guarding and protecting the seas from pirates and robbers, is the right to *royal* fish, which are whale and sturgeon. And these, when either thrown ashore or caught near the coast, are the property of the king." *Blackstone.*

"Soon to the sport of death the crews repair:
Rodmond unerring o'er his head suspends
The barbed steel, and every turn attends.

Falconer's Shipwreck.

"Bright shone the roofs, the domes, the spires,
    And rockets blew self driven,
To hang their momentary fire
    Around the vault of heaven.

"So fire with water to compare,
    The ocean serves on high,
Up-spouted by a whale in air,
    To express unwieldy joy."

Cowper, on the Queen's Visit to London.

"Ten or fifteen gallons of blood are thrown out of the heart at a stroke, with immense velocity."

John Hunter's account of the dissection of a whale. (*A small sized one.*)

"The aorta of a whale is larger in the bore than the main pipe of the water-works at London Bridge, and the water roaring in its passage through that pipe is inferior in impetus and velocity to the blood gushing from the whale's heart."

Paley's Theology.

"The whale is a mammiferous animal without hind feet."

Baron Cuvier.

"In 40 degrees south, we saw Spermacetti Whales, but did not take any till the first of May, the sea being then covered with them."

Colnett's Voyage for the Purpose of Extending the Spermacetti Whale Fishery.

"In the free element beneath me swam,
Floundered and dived, in play, in chace, in battle,
Fishes of every color, form, and kind;
Which language cannot paint, and mariner
Had never seen; from dread Leviathan
To insect millions peopling every wave:
Gather'd in shoals immense, like floating islands,
Led by mysterious instincts through that waste
And trackless region, though on every side
Assaulted by voracious enemies,
Whales, sharks, and monsters, arm'd in front or jaw,
With swords, saws, spiral horns, or hooked fangs."

Montgomery's World before the Flood.

"Io! Pæan! Io! sing,
To the finny people's king.
Not a mightier whale than this
In the vast Atlantic is;
Not a fatter fish than he,
Flounders round the Polar Sea."

Charles Lamb's Triumph of the Whale.

"In the year 1690 some persons were on a high hill observing the whales spouting and sporting with each other, when one observed; there—pointing to the sea—is a green pasture where our children's grandchildren will go for bread."

Obed Macy's History of Nantucket.

"I built a cottage for Susan and myself and made a gateway in the form of a Gothic Arch, by setting up a whale's jawbones."   *Hawthorne's Twice Told Tales.*

"She came to bespeak a monument for her first love, who had been killed by a whale in the Pacific ocean, no less than forty years ago."   *Ibid.*

"No, Sir, 'tis a Right Whale," answered Tom; "I saw his spout; he threw up a pair of as pretty rainbows as a Christian would wish to look at. He's a raal oil-butt, that fellow!"   *Cooper's Pilot.*

"The papers were brought in, and we saw in the Berlin Gazette that whales had been introduced on the stage there."   *Eckermann's Conversations with Goethe.*

"My God! Mr. Chace, what is the matter?" I answered, "we have been stove by a whale."

> *Narrative of the Shipwreck of the Whale Ship Essex of Nantucket, which was attacked and finally destroyed by a large Sperm Whale in the Pacific Ocean.. By Owen Chace of Nantucket, first mate of said vessel. New York, 1821.*

"A mariner sat in the shrouds one night,
  The wind was piping free;
Now bright, now dimmed, was the moonlight pale,
And the phospher gleamed in the wake of the whale,
  As it floundered in the sea."

> *Elizabeth Oakes Smith.*

"The quantity of line withdrawn from the different boats engaged in the capture of this one whale, amounted altogether to 10,440 yards or nearly six English miles." * * *
"Sometimes the whale shakes its tremendous tail in the air, which, cracking like a whip, resounds to the distance of three or four miles." *Scoresby.*

"Mad with the agonies he endures from these fresh attacks, the infuriated Sperm Whale rolls over and over; he rears his enormous head, and with wide expanded jaws snaps at everything around him; he rushes at the boats with his head; they are propelled before him with vast swiftness, and sometimes utterly destroyed.
* * * It is a matter of great astonishment that the consideration of the habits of so interesting, and, in a commercial point of view, of so important an animal (as the Sperm Whale) should have been so entirely neglected, or should have excited so little curiosity among the numerous, and many of them competent observers, that of late years must have possessed the most abundant and the most convenient opportunities of witnessing their habitudes."

> *Thomas Beale's History of the Sperm Whale, 1839.*

"The Cachalot" (Sperm Whale) "is not only better armed than the True Whale" (Greenland or Right Whale) "in possessing a formidable weapon at either extremity of its body, but also more frequently displays a disposition to employ these weapons offensively, and in a manner at once so artful, bold, and mischievous, as to lead to its being regarded as the most dangerous to attack of all the known species of the whale tribe."

> *Frederick Debell Bennett's Whaling Voyage Round the Globe, 1840.*

October 13. "There she blows," was sung out from the mast-head.
"Where away?" demanded the captain.
"Three points off the lee bow, sir."
"Raise up your wheel. Steady!"
"Steady, sir."
"Mast-head ahoy! Do you see that whale now?"
"Ay ay, sir! A shoal of Sperm Whales! There she blows! There she breaches!"
"Sing out! sing out every time!"
"Ay ay, sir! There she blows! there—there—*thar* she blows—bowes—bo-o-o-s!"
"How far off?"
"Two miles and a half."
"Thunder and lightning! so near! Call all hands!"

> *J. Ross Browne's Etchings of a Whaling Cruize. 1846.*

"The Whale-ship Globe, on board of which vessel occurred the horrid transactions we are about to relate, belonged to the island of Nantucket."

> *"Narrative of the Globe Mutiny, by Lay and Hussey survivors. A. D. 1828.*

"Being once pursued by a whale which he had wounded, he parried the assault for some time with a lance; but the furious monster at length rushed on the boat; himself

and comrades only being preserved by leaping into the water when they saw the onset
was inevitable." *Missionary Journal of Tyerman and Bennett.*

"Nantucket itself," said **Mr. Webster**, "is a very striking and peculiar portion of the
National interest. There is a population of eight or nine thousand persons, living
here in the sea, adding largely every year to the National wealth by the boldest and
most persevering industry."
*Report of Daniel Webster's Speech in the U. S. Senate, on
the application for the Erection of a Breakwater at Nantucket.* 1828.

"The whale fell directly over him, and probably killed him in a moment."
*"The Whale and his Captors, or The Whaleman's Adventures
and the Whale's Biography, gathered on the Homeward
Cruise of the Commodore Preble." By Rev. Henry T.
Cheever.*

"If you make the least damn bit of noise," replied Samuel, "I will send you to hell."
*Life of Samuel Comstock (the mutineer), by his brother,
William Comstock. Another Version of the whale-ship
Globe narrative.*

"The voyages of the Dutch and English to the Northern Ocean, in order, if possible,
to discover a passage through it to India, though they failed of their main object, laid
open the haunts of the whale." *McCulloch's Commercial Dictionary.*

"These things are reciprocal; the ball rebounds, only to bound forward again; for
now in laying open the haunts of the whale, the whalemen seem to have indirectly hit
upon new clews to that same mystic North-West Passage."
From "Something" unpublished.

"It is impossible to meet a whale-ship on the ocean without being struck by her near
appearance. The vessel under short sail, with look-outs at the mast-heads, eagerly
scanning the wide expanse around them, has a totally different air from those engaged
in a regular voyage." *Currents and Whaling. U. S. Ex. Ex.*

"Pedestrians in the vicinity of London and elsewhere may recollect having seen
large curved bones set upright in the earth, either to form arches over gateways, or
entrances to alcoves, and they may perhaps have been told that these were the ribs of
whales." *Tales of a Whale Voyager to the Arctic Ocean.*

"It was not till the boats returned from the pursuit of these whales, that the whites
saw their ship in bloody possession of the savages enrolled among the crew."
Newspaper Account of the Taking and Retaking of the Whale-ship Hobomack.

"It is generally well known that out of the chews of Whaling vessels (American)
few ever return in the ships on board of which they departed."
Cruise in a Whale Boat.

"Suddenly a mighty mass emerged from the water, and shot up perpendicularly into
the air. It was the whale." *Miriam Coffin or the Whale Fisherman.*

"The Whale is harpooned to be sure; but bethink you, how you would manage a
powerful unbroken colt, with the mere appliance of a rope tied to the root of his tail."
A Chapter on Whaling in Ribs and Trucks.

"On one occasion I saw two of these monsters (whales) probably male and female,
slowly swimming, one after the other, within less than a stone's throw of the shore"
(Terra Del Fuego), "over which the beach tree extended its branches."
Darwin's Voyage of a Naturalist.

"'Stern all!' exclaimed the mate, as upon turning his head, he saw the distended jaws of a large Sperm Whale close to the head of the boat, threatening it with instant destruction;—'Stern all, for your lives!'"

Wharton the Whale Killer.

"So be cheery, my lads, let your hearts never fail,
While the bold harpooneer is striking the whale!"

Nantucket Song.

"Oh, the rare old Whale, mid storm and gale
In his ocean home will be
A giant in might, where might is right,
And King of the boundless sea."

Whale Song.

MOBY-DICK

CALL me Ishmael. Some years ago—never mind how long precisely—having little or no money in my purse, and nothing particular to interest me on shore, I thought I would sail about a little and see the watery part of the world. It is a way I have of driving off the spleen, and regulating the circulation. Whenever I find myself growing grim about the mouth; whenever it is a damp, drizzly November in my soul; whenever I find myself involuntarily pausing before coffin warehouses, and bringing up the rear of every funeral I meet; and especially whenever my hypos get such an upper hand of me, that it requires a strong moral principle to prevent me from deliberately stepping into the street, and methodically knocking people's hats off—then, I account it high time to get to sea as soon as I can. This is my substitute for pistol and ball. With a philosophical flourish Cato throws himself upon his sword; I quietly take to the ship. There is nothing surprising in this. If they but knew it, almost all men in their degree, some time or other, cherish very nearly the same feelings towards the ocean with me.

There now is your insular city of the Manhattoes, belted round by wharves as Indian isles by coral reefs—commerce surrounds it with her surf. Right and left, the streets take you waterward. Its extreme down-town is the battery, where that noble mole is washed by waves, and cooled by breezes, which a few hours previous were out of sight of land. Look at the crowds of water-gazers there.

Circumambulate the city of a dreamy Sabbath afternoon. Go from Corlears Hook to Coenties Slip, and from thence, by Whitehall, northward. What do you see?—Posted like silent sentinels all around the town, stand thousands upon thousands of mortal men fixed in ocean reveries. Some leaning against the spiles; some seated upon the pier-heads; some looking over the bulwarks of ships from China; some high aloft in the rigging, as if striving to get a still better seaward peep. But these are all landsmen; of week days pent up in lath and plaster—tied to counters, nailed to benches, clinched to desks. How then is this? Are the green fields gone? What do they here?

But look! here come more crowds, pacing straight for the water, and seemingly bound for a dive. Strange! Nothing will content them but the extremest limit of the land; loitering under the shady lee of yonder warehouses will not suffice. No. They must get just as nigh the water as they possibly can without falling in. And there they stand—miles of them—leagues. Inlanders all, they come from lanes and alleys, streets and avenues—north, east, south, and west. Yet here they all unite. Tell me, does the magnetic virtue of the needles of the compasses of all those ships attract them thither?

Once more. Say, you are in the country; in some high land of lakes. Take almost any path you please, and ten to one it carries you down in a dale, and leaves you there by a pool in the stream. There is magic in it. Let the most absent-minded of men be plunged in his deepest reveries—stand that man on his legs, set his feet a-going, and he will infallibly lead you to water, if water there be in all that region. Should you ever be athirst in the great American desert, try this experiment, if your caravan happen to be supplied with a metaphysical professor. Yes, as every one knows, meditation and water are wedded for ever.

But here is an artist. He desires to paint you the dreamiest, shadiest, quietest, most enchanting bit of romantic landscape in all the valley of the Saco. What is the chief element he employs? There stand his trees, each with a hollow trunk, as if a hermit and a crucifix were within; and here sleeps his meadow, and there sleep his cattle; and up from yonder cottage goes a sleepy smoke. Deep into distant woodlands winds a mazy way, reaching to overlapping spurs of mountains bathed in their hill-side blue. But though the picture lies thus tranced, and though this pine-tree shakes down its sighs like leaves upon this shepherd's head, yet all were vain, unless the shepherd's eye were fixed upon the magic stream before him. · Go visit the Prairies in June, when for scores on scores of miles you wade knee-deep among Tiger-lilies— what is the one charm wanting?—Water—there is not a drop of water there! Were Niagara but a cataract of sand, would you travel your thousand miles to see it? Why did the poor poet of Tennessee, upon suddenly receiving two handfuls of silver, deliberate whether to buy him a coat, which he sadly needed, or invest his money in a pedestrian trip to Rockaway Beach? Why is almost every robust healthy boy with a robust healthy soul in him, at some time or other crazy to go to sea? Why upon your first voyage as a passenger, did you yourself feel such a mystical vibration, when first told that you and your ship were now out of sight of land? Why did the old Persians hold the sea holy? Why did the Greeks give it a separate deity, and own brother of Jove? Surely all this is not without meaning. And still deeper the meaning of that story of Narcissus, who because he could not grasp the tormenting, mild image he saw in the fountain, plunged into it and was drowned. But that same image, we ourselves see in all rivers and oceans. It is the image of the ungraspable phantom of life; and this is the key to it all.

Now, when I say that I am in the habit of going to sea whenever I begin to grow hazy about the eyes, and begin to be over-conscious of my lungs, I do not mean to have it inferred that I ever go to sea as a passenger. For to go as a passenger you must needs have a purse, and a purse is but a rag unless you have something in it. Besides, passengers get sea-sick—grow quarrelsome —don't sleep of nights—do not enjoy themselves much, as a general thing; no, I never go as a passenger; nor, though I am something of a salt, do I ever go to sea as a Commodore, or a Captain, or a Cook. I abandon the glory and distinction of such offices to those who like them. For my part, I abominate all honorable respectable toils, trials, and tribulations of every kind whatsoever. It is quite as much as I can do to take care of myself, without taking care of ships, barques, brigs, schooners, and what not. And as for going as cook,— though I confess there is considerable glory in that, a cook being a sort of officer on ship-board—yet, somehow, I never fancied broiling fowls;—though once broiled, judiciously buttered, and judgmatically salted and peppered, there is no one who will speak more respectfully, not to say reverentially, of a broiled fowl than I will. It is out of the idolatrous dotings of the old Egyptians upon broiled ibis and roasted river horse, that you see the mummies of those creatures in their huge bake-houses the pyramids.

No, when I go to sea, I go as a simple sailor, right before the mast, plumb down into the forecastle, aloft there to the royal mast-head. True, they rather order me about some, and make me jump from spar to spar, like a grasshopper in a May meadow. And at first, this sort of thing is unpleasant enough. It touches one's sense of honor, particularly if you come of an old established family in the land, the Van Rensselaers, or Randolphs, or Hardicanutes. And more than all, if just previous to putting your hand into the tar-pot, you have been lording it as a country schoolmaster, making the tallest boys stand in awe of you. The transition is a keen one, I assure you, from a schoolmaster to a sailor, and requires a strong decoction of Seneca and the Stoics to enable you to grin and bear it. But even this wears off in time.

What of it, if some old hunks of a sea-captain orders me to get a broom and sweep down the decks? What does that indignity amount to, weighed, I mean, in the scales of the New Testament? Do you think the archangel Gabriel thinks anything the less of me, because I promptly and respectfully obey that old hunks in that particular instance? Who ain't a slave? Tell me that. Well, then, however the old sea-captains may order me about—however they may thump and punch me about, I have the satisfaction of knowing that it is all right; that everybody else is one way or other served in much the same way —either in a physical or metaphysical point of view, that is; and so the universal thump is passed round, and all hands should rub each other's shoulder-blades, and be content.

Again, I always go to sea as a sailor, because they make a point of paying me for my trouble, whereas they never pay passengers a single penny that I ever heard of. On the contrary, passengers themselves must pay. And there is all the difference in the world between paying and being paid. The act of paying is perhaps the most uncomfortable infliction that the two orchard thieves entailed upon us. But *being paid*,—what will compare with it? The urbane activity with which a man receives money is really marvellous, considering that we so earnestly believe money to be the root of all earthly ills, and that on no account can a monied man enter heaven. Ah! how cheerfully we consign ourselves to perdition!

Finally, I always go to sea as a sailor, because of the wholesome exercise and pure air of the forecastle deck. For as in this world, head winds are far more prevalent than winds from astern (that is, if you never violate the Pythagorean maxim), so for the most part the Commodore on the quarter-deck gets his atmosphere at second hand from the sailors on the forecastle. He thinks he breathes it first; but not so. In much the same way do the commonalty lead their leaders in many other things, at the same time that the leaders little suspect it. But wherefore it was that after having repeatedly smelt the sea as a merchant sailor, I should now take it into my head to go on a whaling voyage; this the invisible police officer of the Fates, who has the constant surveillance of me, and secretly dogs me, and influences me in some unaccountable way— he can better answer than any one else. And, doubtless, my going on this whaling voyage, formed part of the grand programme of Providence that was drawn up a long time ago. It came in as a sort of brief interlude and solo between more extensive performances. I take it that this part of the bill must have run something like this:

"Grand Contested Election for the Presidency of the United States.

"WHALING VOYAGE BY ONE ISHMAEL.

"BLOODY BATTLE IN AFGHANISTAN."

Though I cannot tell why it was exactly that those stage managers, the Fates, put me down for this shabby part of a whaling voyage, when others were set down for magnificent parts in high tragedies, and short and easy parts in genteel comedies, and jolly parts in farces—though I cannot tell why this was exactly; yet, now that I recall all the circumstances, I think I can see a little into the springs and motives which being cunningly presented to me under various disguises, induced me to set about performing the part I did, besides cajoling me into the delusion that it was a choice resulting from my own unbiased freewill and discriminating judgment.

Chief among these motives was the overwhelming idea of the great whale himself. Such a portentous and mysterious monster roused all my curiosity. Then the wild and distant seas where he rolled his island bulk; the undeliverable, nameless perils of the whale; these, with all the attending marvels of a thousand Patagonian sights and sounds, helped to sway me to my wish. With other men, perhaps, such things would not have been inducements; but as for me, I am tormented with an everlasting itch for things remote. I love to sail forbidden seas, and land on barbarous coasts. Not ignoring what is good, I am quick to perceive a horror, and could still be social with it—would they let me —since it is but well to be on friendly terms with all the inmates of the place one lodges in.

By reason of these things, then, the whaling voyage was welcome; the great flood-gates of the wonder-world swung open, and in the wild conceits that swayed me to my purpose, two and two there floated into my inmost soul, endless processions of the whale, and, mid most of them all, one grand hooded phantom, like a snow hill in the air.

CHAPTER II

THE CARPET-BAG

I STUFFED a shirt or two into my old carpet-bag, tucked it under my arm, and started for Cape Horn and the Pacific. Quitting the good city of old Manhatto, I duly arrived in New Bedford. It was on a Saturday night in December. Much was I disappointed upon learning that the little packet for Nantucket had already sailed, and that no way of reaching that place would offer, till the following Monday.

As most young candidates for the pains and penalties of whaling stop at this same New Bedford, thence to embark on their voyage, it may as well be related that I, for one, had no idea of so doing. For my mind was made up to sail in no other than a Nantucket craft, because there was a fine, boisterous something about everything connected with that famous old island, which amazingly pleased me. Besides though New Bedford has of late been gradually monopolizing the business of whaling, and though in this matter poor old Nantucket is now much behind her, yet Nantucket was her great original—the Tyre of this Carthage;—the place where the first dead American whale was stranded. Where else but from Nantucket did those aboriginal whalemen, the Red-Men, first sally out in canoes to give chase to the Leviathan? And where but from Nantucket, too, did that first adventurous little sloop put forth, partly laden with imported cobble-stones—so goes the story—to throw at the whales, in order to discover when they were nigh enough to risk a harpoon from the bowsprit?

Now having a night, a day, and still another night following before me in New Bedford, ere I could embark for my destined port, it became a matter of concernment where I was to eat and sleep meanwhile. It was a very dubious-looking, nay, a very dark and dismal night, bitingly cold and cheerless. I knew no one in the place. With anxious grapnels I had sounded my pocket, and only brought up a few pieces of silver,—So, wherever you go, Ishmael, said I to myself, as I stood in the middle of a dreary street shouldering my bag, and comparing the gloom towards the north with the darkness towards the south—wherever in your wisdom you may conclude to lodge for the night, my dear Ishmael, be sure to inquire the price, and don't be too particular.

With halting steps I paced the streets, and passed the sign of "The Crossed Harpoons"—but it looked too expensive and jolly there. Farther on, from the bright red windows of the "Sword-Fish Inn," there came such fervent rays, that it seemed to have melted the packed snow and ice from before the house, for everywhere else the congealed frost lay ten inches thick in a hard, asphaltic pavement,—rather weary for me, when I struck my foot against the flinty pro-jections, because from hard, remorseless service the soles of my boots were in a most miserable plight. Too expensive and jolly, again thought I, pausing one moment to watch the broad glare in the street, and hear the sounds of the tinkling glasses within. But go on, Ishmael, said I at last; don't you hear? get away from before the door; your patched boots are stopping the way. So on I went. I now by instinct followed the streets that took me waterward, for there, doubtless, were the cheapest, if not the cheeriest inns.

Such dreary streets! blocks of blackness, not houses, on either hand, and here and there a candle, like a candle moving about in a tomb. At this hour of the night, of the last day of the week, that quarter of the town proved all but deserted. But presently I came to a smoky light proceeding from a low, white building, the door of which stood invitingly open. It had a careless look, as if it were meant for the uses of the public; so, entering, the first thing I did was to stumble over an ash-box in the porch. Ha! thought I, ha, as the flying particles almost choked me, are these ashes from that destroyed city, Gomorrah? But "The Crossed Harpoons," and "The Sword-Fish?"—this, then, must needs be the sign of "The Trap." However, I picked myself up and hearing a loud voice within, pushed on and opened a second, interior door.

It seemed the great Black Parliament sitting in Tophet. A hundred black faces turned round in their rows to peer; and beyond, a black Angel of Doom was beating a book in a pulpit. It was a negro church; and the preacher's text was about the blackness of darkness, and the weeping and wailing and teeth-gnashing there. Ha, Ishmael, muttered I, backing out, Wretched entertainment at the sign of "The Trap!"·

Moving on, I at last came to a dim sort of light not far from the docks, and heard a forlorn creaking in the air; and looking up, saw a swinging sign over the door with a white painting upon it, faintly representing a tall straight jet of misty spray, and these words underneath—"The Spouter-Inn:—Peter Coffin."

Coffin?—Spouter?—Rather ominous in that particular connexion, thought I. But it is a common name in Nantucket, they say, and I suppose this Peter here is an emigrant from there. As the light looked so dim, and the place, for the time, looked quiet enough, and the dilapidated little wooden house itself looked as if it might have been carted here from the ruins of some burnt district, and as the swinging sign had a poverty-stricken sort of creak to it, I thought that here was the very spot for cheap lodgings, and the best of pea coffee.

It was a queer sort of place—a gable-ended old house, one side palsied as it were, and leaning over sadly. It stood on a sharp bleak corner, where that tempestuous wind Euroclydon kept up a worse howling than ever it did about poor Paul's tossed craft. Euroclydon, nevertheless, is a mighty pleasant zephyr to any one in-doors, with his feet on the hob quietly toasting for bed. "In judging of that tempestuous wind called Euroclydon," says an old writer—of whose works I possess the only copy extant—"it maketh a marvellous difference, whether thou lookest out at it from a glass window where the frost is all on the outside, or whether thou observest it from that sashless window, where the frost is on both sides, and of which the wight Death is the only glazier." True enough, thought I, as this passage occurred to my mind—old black-letter, thou reasonest well. Yes, these eyes are windows, and this body of mine is the house. What a pity they didn't stop up the chinks and the crannies though, and thrust in a little lint here and there. But it's too late to make any improvements now. The universe is finished; the copestone is on, and the chips were carted off a million years ago. Poor Lazarus there, chattering his teeth against the curbstone for his pillow, and shaking off his tatters with his shiverings, he might plug up both ears with rags, and put a corn-cob into his mouth, and yet that would not keep out the tempestuous Euroclydon. Euroclydon! says old Dives, in his red silken wrapper—(he had a redder one afterwards) pooh, pooh! What a fine frosty night; how Orion glitters; what northern lights! Let them talk of their oriental summer climes of everlasting conservatories; give me the privilege of making my own summer with my own coals.

But what thinks Lazarus? Can he warm his blue hands by holding them up to the grand northern lights? Would not Lazarus rather be in Sumatra than here? Would he not far rather lay him down lengthwise along the line of the equator; yea, ye gods! go down to the fiery pit itself, in order to keep out this frost?

Now, that Lazarus should lie stranded there on the curbstone before the door of Dives, this is more wonderful than that an iceberg should be moored to one of the Moluccas. Yet Dives himself, he too lives like a Czar in an ice palace made of frozen sighs, and being a president of a temperance society, he only drinks the tepid tears of orphans.

But no more of this blubbering now, we are going a-whaling, and there is plenty of that yet to come. Let us scrape the ice from our frosted feet, and see what sort of a place this "Spouter" may be.

CHAPTER III

THE SPOUTER-INN

ENTERING that gable-ended Spouter-Inn, you found yourself in a wide, low, straggling entry with old-fashioned wainscots, reminding one of the bulwarks of some condemned old craft. On one side hung a very large oil-painting so thoroughly besmoked, and every way defaced, that in the unequal cross-lights by which you viewed it, it was only by diligent study and a series of systematic visits to it, and careful inquiry of the neighbors, that you could any way arrive at an understanding of its purpose. Such unaccountable masses of shades and shadows, that at first you almost thought some ambitious young artist, in the time of the New England hags, had endeavored to delineate chaos bewitched. But by dint of much and earnest contemplation, and oft repeated ponderings, and especially by throwing open the little window towards the back of the entry, you at last come to the conclusion that such an idea, however wild, might not be altogether unwarranted.

But what most puzzled and confounded you was a long, limber, portentous, black mass of something hovering in the centre of the picture over three blue, dim, perpendicular lines floating in a nameless yeast. A boggy, soggy, squitchy picture truly, enough to drive a nervous man distracted. Yet was there a sort of indefinite, half-attained, unimaginable sublimity about it that fairly froze you to it, till you involuntarily took an oath with yourself to find out what that marvellous painting meant. Ever and anon a bright, but, alas, deceptive idea would dart you through.—It's the Black Sea in a midnight gale.—It's the unnatural combat of the four primal elements.—It's a blasted heath.—It's a Hyperborean winter scene.—It's the breaking-up of the ice-bound stream of Time. But at last all these fancies yielded to that one portentous something in the picture's midst. *That* once found out, and all the rest were plain. But stop; does it not bear a faint resemblance to a gigantic fish? even the great leviathan himself?

In fact, the artist's design seemed this: a final theory of my own, partly based upon the aggregated opinions of many aged persons with whom I conversed upon the subject. The picture represents a Cape-Horner in a great hurricane; the half-foundered ship weltering there with its three dismantled masts alone visible; and an exasperated whale, purposing to spring clean over the craft, is in the enormous act of impaling himself upon the three mast-heads.

The opposite wall of this entry was hung all over with a heathenish array of monstrous clubs and spears. Some were thickly set with glittering teeth resembling ivory saws; others were tufted with knots of human hair; and one was sickle-shaped, with a vast handle sweeping round like the segment made in the new-mown grass by a long-armed mower. You shuddered as you gazed, and wondered what monstrous cannibal and savage could ever have gone a deathharvesting with such a hacking, horrifying implement. Mixed with these were rusty old whaling lances and harpoons all broken and deformed. Some were storied weapons. With this once long lance, now wildly elbowed, fifty years ago did Nathan Swain kill fifteen whales between a sunrise and a sunset. And that harpoon—so like a corkscrew now—was flung in Javan seas, and run away with by a whale, years afterwards slain off the Cape of Blanco. The original iron entered nigh the tail, and, like a restless needle sojourning in the body of a man, travelled full forty feet, and at last was found imbedded in the hump.

Crossing this dusky entry, and on through yon low-arched way—cut through what in old times must have been a great central chimney with fireplaces all round—you enter the public room. A still duskier place is this, with such low ponderous beams above, and such old wrinkled planks beneath, that you would almost fancy you trod some old craft's cockpits, especially of such a howling night, when this corner-anchored old ark rocked so furiously. On one side stood a long, low, shelf-like table covered with cracked glass cases, filled with dusty rarities gathered from this wide world's remotest nooks. Projecting from the farther angle of the room stands a dark-looking den—the bar—a rude attempt at a right whale's head. Be that how it may, there stands the vast arched bone of the whale's jaw, so wide, a coach might almost drive beneath it. Within are shabby shelves, ranged round with old decanters, bottles, flasks; and in those jaws of swift destruction, like another cursed Jonah (by which name indeed they called him), bustles a little withered old man, who, for their money, dearly sells the sailors deliriums and death.

Abominable are the tumblers into which he pours his poison. Though true cylinders without—within, the villanous green goggling glasses deceitfully tapered downwards to a cheating bottom. Parallel meridians rudely pecked into the glass, surround these footpads' goblets. Fill to *this* mark, and your charge is but a penny; to *this* a penny more; and so on to the full glass—the Cape Horn measure, which you may gulp down for a shilling.

Upon entering the place I found a number of young seamen gathered about a table, examining by a dim light divers specimens of *skrimshander*. I sought the landlord, and telling him I desired to be accommodated with a room, received for answer that his house was full—not a bed unoccupied. "But avast," he added, tapping his forehead, "you hain't no objections to sharing a harpooneer's blanket, have ye? I s'pose you are goin' a whalin', so you'd better get used to that sort of thing."

I told him that I never liked to sleep two in a bed; that if I should ever do so, it would depend upon who the harpooneer might be, and that if he (the landlord) really had no other place for me, and the harpooneer was not decidedly objectionable, why rather than wander farther about a strange town on so bitter a night, I would put up with the half of any decent man's blanket.

"I thought so. All right; take a seat. Supper?—you want supper? Supper'll be ready directly."

I sat down on an old wooden settle, carved all over like a bench on the Battery. At one end a ruminating tar was still further adorning it with his jack-knife, stooping over and diligently working away at the space between his legs. He was trying his hand at a ship under full sail, but he didn't make much headway, I thought.

At last some four or five of us were summoned to our meal in an adjoining room. It was cold as Iceland—no fire at all—the landlord said he couldn't afford it. Nothing but two dismal tallow candles, each in a winding sheet. We were fain to button up our monkey jackets, and hold to our lips cups of scalding tea with our half frozen fingers. But the fare was of the most substantial kind—not only meat and potatoes, but dumplings; good heavens! dumplings for supper! One young fellow in a green box coat, addressed himself to these dumplings in a most direful manner.

"My boy," said the landlord, "you'll have the nightmare to a dead sartainty."

"Landlord," I whispered, "that ain't the harpooneer, is it?"

"Oh, no," said he, looking a sort of diabolically funny, "the harpooneer is a dark complexioned chap. He never eats dumplings, he don't—he eats nothing but steaks, and likes 'em rare."

"The devil he does," says I. "Where is that harpooneer? Is he here?"

"He'll be here afore long," was the answer.

I could not help it, but I began to feel suspicious of this "dark complexioned" harpooneer. At any rate, I made up my mind that if it so turned out that we should sleep together, he must undress and get into bed before I did.

Supper over, the company went back to the bar-room, when, knowing not what else to do with myself, I resolved to spend the rest of the evening as a looker on.

Presently a rioting noise was heard without. Starting up, the landlord cried, "That's the Grampus's crew. I seed her reported in the offing this morning; a three years' voyage, and a full ship. Hurrah, boys; now we'll have the latest news from the Feegees."

A tramping of sea boots was heard in the entry; the door was flung open, and in rolled a wild set of mariners enough. Enveloped in their shaggy watch coats, and with their heads muffled in woollen comforters, all bedarned and ragged, and their beards stiff with icicles, they seemed an eruption of bears from Labrador. They had just landed from their boat, and this was the first house they entered. No wonder, then, that they made a straight wake for the whale's mouth—the bar—when the wrinkled little old Jonah, there officiating, soon poured them out brimmers all round. One complained of a bad cold in his head, upon which Jonah mixed him a pitch-like potion of gin and molasses, which he swore was a sovereign cure for all colds and catarrhs whatsoever, never mind of how long standing, or whether caught off the coast of Labrador, or on the weather side of an ice-island.

The liquor soon mounted into their heads, as it generally does even with the arrantest topers newly landed from sea, and they began capering about most obstreperously.

I observed, however, that one of them held somewhat aloof, and though he seemed desirous not to spoil the hilarity of his shipmates by his own sober face, yet upon the whole he refrained from making as much noise as the rest. This man interested me at once; and since the sea-gods had ordained that he should soon become my shipmate (though but a sleeping-partner one, so far as this narrative is concerned), I will here venture upon a little description of him. He stood full six feet in height, with noble shoulders, and a chest like a coffer-dam. I have seldom seen such brawn in a man. His face was deeply brown and burnt, making his white teeth dazzling by the contrast; while in the deep shadows of his eyes floated some reminiscences that did not seem to give him much joy. His voice at once announced that he was a Southerner, and from his fine stature, I thought he must be one of those tall mountaineers from the Alleganian Ridge in Virginia. When the revelry of his companions had mounted to its height, this man slipped away unobserved, and I saw no more of him till he became my comrade on the sea. In a few minutes, however, he was missed by his shipmates, and being, it seems, for some reason a huge favorite with them, they raised a cry of "Bulkington! Bulkington! where's Bulkington?" and darted out of the house in pursuit of him.

It was now about nine o'clock, and the room seeming almost supernaturally quiet after these orgies, I began to congratulate myself upon a little plan that had occurred to me just previous to the entrance of the seamen.

No man prefers to sleep two in a bed. In fact, you would a good deal rather not sleep with your own brother. I don't know how it is, but people like to be private when they are sleeping. And when it comes to sleeping with an unknown stranger, in a strange inn, in a strange town, and that stranger a harpooneer, then your objections indefinitely multiply. Nor was there any earthly reason why I as a sailor should sleep two in a bed, more than anybody else; for sailors no more sleep two in a bed at sea, than bachelor Kings do ashore. To be sure they all sleep together in one apartment, but you have your own hammock, and cover yourself with your own blanket, and sleep in your own skin.

The more I pondered over this harpooneer, the more I abominated the thought of sleeping with him. It was fair to presume that being a harpooneer, his linen or woollen, as the case might be, would not be of the tidiest, certainly none of the finest. I began to twitch all over. Besides, it was getting late, and my decent harpooneer ought to be home and going bedwards. Suppose now, he should tumble in upon me at midnight—how could I tell from what vile hole he had been coming?

"Landlord! I've changed my mind about that harpooneer.—I shan't sleep with him. I'll try the bench here."

"Just as you please; I'm sorry I can't spare ye a tablecloth for a mattress, and it's a plaguy rough board here"—feeling of the knots and notches. "But wait a bit, Skrimshander; I've got a carpenter's plane there in the bar—wait, I say, and I'll make ye snug enough." So saying he procured the plane; and with his old silk handkerchief first dusting the bench, vigorously set to planing away at my bed, the while grinning like an ape. The shavings flew right and left; till at last the plane-iron came bump against an indestructible knot. The landlord was near spraining his wrist, and I told him for heaven's sake to quit—the bed was soft enough to suit me, and I did not know how all the planing in the world could make eider down of a pine plank. So gathering up the shavings with another grin, and throwing them into the great stove in the middle of the room, he went about his business, and left me in a brown study.

I now took the measure of the bench, and found that it was a foot too short; but that could be mended with a chair. But it was a foot too narrow, and the other bench in the room was about four inches higher than the planed one—so there was no yoking them. I then placed the first bench lengthwise along the only clear space against the wall, leaving a little interval between, for my back to settle down in. But I soon found that there came such a draught of cold air over me from under the sill of the window, that this plan would never do at all, especially as another current from the rickety door met the one from the window, and both together formed a series of small whirlwinds in the immediate vicinity of the spot where I had thought to spend the night.

The devil fetch that harpooneer, thought I, but stop, couldn't I steal a march on him—bolt his door inside, and jump into his bed, not to be wakened by the most violent knockings? It seemed no bad idea; but upon second thoughts I dismissed it. For who could tell but what the next morning, so soon as I popped out of the room, the harpooneer might be standing in the entry, all ready to knock me down!

Still, looking round me again, and seeing no possible chance of spending a sufferable night unless in some other person's bed, I began to think that after all I might be cherishing unwarrantable prejudices against this unknown harpooneer. Thinks I, I'll wait awhile; he must be dropping in before long. I'll have a good look at him then, and perhaps we may become jolly good bedfellows after all—there's no telling.

But though the other boarders kept coming in by ones, twos, and threes, and going to bed, yet no sign of my harpooneer.

"Landlord!" said I, "what sort of a chap is he—does he always keep such late hours?" It was now hard upon twelve o'clock.

The landlord chuckled again with his lean chuckle, and seemed to be mightily tickled at something beyond my comprehension. "No," he answered, "generally he's an early bird—airley to bed and airley to rise—yea, he's the bird what catches the worm.—But to-night he went out a peddling, you see, and I don't see what on airth keeps him so late, unless, may be, he can't sell his head."

"Can't sell his head?—What sort of a bamboozling story is this you are telling me?" getting into a towering rage. "Do you pretend to say, landlord, that this harpooneer is actually engaged this blessed Saturday night, or rather Sunday morning, in peddling his head around this town?"

"That's precisely it," said the landlord, "and I told him he couldn't sell it here, the market's overstocked."

"With what?" shouted I.

"With heads to be sure; ain't there too many heads in the world?"

"I tell you what it is, landlord," said I, quite calmly, "you'd better stop spinning that yarn to me—I'm not green."

"Maybe not," taking out a stick and whittling a toothpick, "but I rayther guess you'll be done *brown* if that ere harpooneer hears you a slanderin' his head."

"I'll break it for him," said I, now flying into a passion again at this unaccountable farrago of the landlord's.

"It's broke a'ready," said he.

"Broke," said I—"*broke,* do you mean?"

"Sartain, and that's the very reason he can't sell it, I guess."

"Landlord," said I, going up to him as cool as Mt. Hecla in a snow storm—"landlord, stop whittling. You and I must understand one another, and that too without delay. I come to your house and want a bed; you tell me you can only give me half a one; that the other half belongs to a certain harpooneer. And about this harpooneer, whom I have not yet seen, you persist in telling me the most mystifying and exasperating stories, tending to beget in me an uncomfortable feeling towards the man whom you design for my bedfellow—a sort of connexion, landlord, which is an intimate and confidential one in the highest degree. I now demand of you to speak out and tell me who and what this harpooneer is, and whether I shall be in all respects safe to spend the night with him. And in the first place, you will be so good as to unsay that story about selling his head, which if true I take to be good evidence that this harpooneer is stark mad, and I've no idea of sleeping with a madman; and you, sir, *you* I mean, landlord, *you,* sir, by trying to induce me to do so knowingly, would thereby render yourself liable to a criminal prosecution."

"Wall," said the landlord, fetching a long breath, "that's a purty long sarmon for a chap that rips a little now and then. But be easy, be easy, this here harpooneer I have been tellin' you of has just arrived from the south seas, where he bought up a lot of 'balmed New Zealand heads (great curios, you know), and he's sold all on 'em but one, and that one he's trying to sell to-night, cause to-morrow's Sunday, and it would not do to be sellin' human heads about the streets when folks is goin' to churches. He wanted to, last Sunday, but I stopped him just as he was goin' out of the door with four heads strung on a string, for all the airth like a string of inions."

This account cleared up the otherwise unaccountable mystery, and showed that the landlord, after all, had no idea of fooling me—but at the same time what could I think of a harpooneer who stayed out of a Saturday night clean into the holy Sabbath, engaged in such a cannibal business as selling the heads of dead idolators?

"Depend upon it, landlord, that harpooneer is a dangerous man."

"He pays reg'lar," was the rejoinder. "But come, it's getting dreadful late, you had better be turning flukes—it's a nice bed: Sal and me slept in that ere bed the night we were spliced. There's plenty room for two to kick about in that bed; it's an almighty big bed that. Why, afore we give it up, Sal used to put our Sam and little Johnny in the foot of it. But I got a dreaming and sprawling about one night, and somehow, Sam got pitched on the floor, and came near breaking his arm. Arter that, Sal said it wouldn't do. Come along here, I'll give ye a glim in a jiffy;" and so saying he lighted a candle and held it towards me, offering to lead the way. But I stood irresolute; when looking at a clock in the corner, he exclaimed "I vum it's Sunday—you won't see that harpooneer to-night; he's come to anchor somewhere—come along then; *do* come; *won't* ye come?"

I considered the matter a moment, and then up stairs we went, and I was ushered into a small room, cold as a clam, and furnished, sure enough, with a prodigious bed, almost big enough indeed for any four harpooneers to sleep abreast.

"There," said the landlord, placing the candle on a crazy old sea chest that did double duty as a wash-stand and centre table; "there, make yourself comfortable now, and good night to ye." I turned round from eyeing the bed, but he had disappeared.

Folding back the counterpane, I stooped over the bed. Though none of the most elegant, it yet stood the scrutiny tolerably well. I then glanced round the room; and besides the bedstead and centre table, could see no other furniture belonging to the place, but a rude shelf, the four walls, and a papered fireboard representing a man striking a whale. Of things not properly belonging to the room, there was a hammock lashed up, and thrown upon the floor in one corner; also a large seaman's bag, containing the harpooneer's wardrobe, no doubt in lieu of a land trunk. Likewise, there was a parcel of outlandish bone fish hooks on the shelf over the fire-place, and a tall harpoon standing at the head of the bed.

But what is this on the chest? I took it up, and held it close to the light, and felt it, and smelt it, and tried every way possible to arrive at some satisfactory conclusion concerning it. I can compare it to nothing but a large door mat, ornamented at the edges with little tinkling tags something like the stained porcupine quills round an Indian moccasin. There was a hole or slit in the middle of this mat, as you see the same in South American ponchos. But could it be possible that any sober harpooneer would get into a door mat, and parade the streets of any Christian town in that sort of guise? I put it on, to try it; and it weighed me down like a hamper, being uncommonly shaggy and thick, and I thought a little damp, as though this mysterious harpooneer had been wearing it of a rainy day. I went up in it to a bit of glass stuck against the wall, and I never saw such a sight in my life. I tore myself out of it in such a hurry that I gave myself a kink in the neck.

I sat down on the side of the bed, and commenced thinking about this head-peddling harpooneer, and his door mat. After thinking some time on the bedside, I got up and took off my monkey jacket, and then stood in the middle of the room thinking. I then took off my coat, and thought a little more in my shirt sleeves. But beginning to feel very cold now, half undressed as I was, and remembering what the landlord said about the harpooneer's not coming home at all that night, it being so very late, I made no more ado, but jumped out of my pantaloons and boots, and then blowing out the light tumbled into bed, and commended myself to the care of heaven.

Whether that mattress was stuffed with corn-cobs or broken crockery, there is no telling, but I rolled about a good deal, and could not sleep for a long time. At last I slid off into a light doze, and had pretty nearly made a good offing towards the land of Nod, when I heard a heavy footfall in the passage, and saw a glimmer of light come into the room from under the door.

Lord save me, thinks I, that must be the harpooneer, the infernal head-peddler. But I lay perfectly still, and resolved not to say a word till spoken to. Holding a light in one hand, and that identical New Zealand head in the other, the stranger entered the room, and without looking towards the bed, placed his candle a good way off from me on the floor in one corner, and then began working away at the knotted cords of the large bag I before spoke of as being in the room. I was all eagerness to see his face, but he kept it averted for some time while employed in unlacing the bag's mouth. This accomplished, however, he turned round—when, good heavens! what a sight! Such a face! It was of a dark, purplish, yellow color, here and there stuck over with large, blackish looking squares. Yes, it's just as I thought, he's a terrible bedfellow; he's been in a fight, got dreadfully cut, and here he is, just from the surgeon. But at that moment he chanced to turn his face so towards the light, that I plainly saw they could not be sticking-plasters at all, those black squares on his cheeks. They were stains of some sort or other. At first I knew not what to make of this; but soon an inkling of the truth occurred to me. I remembered a story of a white man—a whaleman too—who, falling among the cannibals, had been tattooed by them. I concluded that this harpooneer, in the course of his distant voyages, must have met with a similar adventure. And what is it, thought I, after all? It's only his outside; a man can be honest in any sort of skin. But then, what to make of his unearthly complexion, that part of it, I mean, lying round about, and completely independent of the squares of tattooing. To be sure, it might be nothing but a good coat of tropical tanning; but I never heard of a hot sun's tanning a white man into a purplish yellow one. However, I had never been in the South Seas; and perhaps the sun there produced these extraordinary effects upon the skin. Now, while all these ideas were passing through me like lightning, this harpooneer never noticed me at all. But, after some difficulty having opened his bag, he commenced fumbling in it, and presently pulled out a sort of tomahawk, and a seal-skin wallet with the hair on. Placing these on the old chest in the middle of the room, he then took the New Zealand head—a ghastly thing enough—and crammed it down into the bag. He now took off his hat—a new beaver hat—when I came nigh singing out with fresh surprise. There was no hair on his head—none to speak of at least—nothing but a small scalp-knot twisted up on his forehead. His bald purplish head now looked for all the world like a mildewed skull. Had not the stranger stood between me and the door, I would have bolted out of it quicker than ever I bolted a dinner.

Even as it was, I thought something of slipping out of the window, but it was the second floor back. I am no coward, but what to make of this head-peddling purple rascal altogether passed my comprehension. Ignorance is the parent of fear, and being completely nonplussed and confounded about the stranger, I confess I was now as much afraid of him as if it was the devil himself who had thus broken into my room at the dead of night. In fact, I was so afraid of him that I was not game enough just then to address him, and demand a satisfactory answer concerning what seemed inexplicable in him.

Meanwhile, he continued the business of undressing, and at last showed his chest and arms. As I live, these covered parts of him were checkered with the same squares as his face; his back, too, was all over the same dark squares; he seemed to have been in a Thirty Years' War, and just escaped from it with a sticking-plaster shirt. Still more, his very legs were marked, as if a parcel of dark green frogs were running up the trunks of young palms. It was now quite plain that he must be some abominable savage or other shipped aboard of a whaleman in the South Seas, and so landed in this Christian country. I quaked to think of it. A peddler of heads too—perhaps the heads of his own brothers. He might take a fancy to mine—heavens! look at that tomahawk!

But there was no time for shuddering, for now the savage went about something that completely fascinated my attention, and convinced me that he must indeed be a heathen. Going to his heavy grego, or wrapall, or dreadnaught, which he had previously hung on a chair, he fumbled in the pockets, and produced at length a curious little deformed image with a hunch on its back, and exactly the color of a three days' old Congo baby. Remembering the embalmed head, at first I almost thought that this black manikin was a real baby preserved in some similar manner. But seeing that it was not at all limber, and that it glistened a good deal like polished ebony, I concluded that it must be nothing but a wooden idol, which indeed it proved to be. For now the savage goes up to the empty fire-place, and removing the papered fire-board, sets up this little hunch-backed image, like a tenpin, between the andirons. The chimney jambs and all the bricks inside were very sooty, so that I thought this fire-place made a very appropriate little shrine or chapel for his Congo idol.

I now screwed my eyes hard towards the half hidden image, feeling but ill at ease meantime—to see what was next to follow. First he takes about a double handful of shavings out of his grego pocket, and places them carefully before the idol; then laying a bit of ship biscuit on top and applying the flame from the lamp, he kindled the shavings into a sacrificial blaze. Presently, after many hasty snatches into the fire, and still hastier withdrawals of his fingers (whereby he seemed to be scorching them badly), he at last succeeded in drawing out the biscuit; then blowing off the heat and ashes a little, he made a polite offer of it to the little negro. But the little devil did not seem to fancy such dry sort of fare at all; he never moved his lips. All these strange antics were accompanied by still stranger guttural noises from the devotee, who seemed to be praying in a sing-song or else singing some pagan psalmody or other, during which his face twitched about in the most unnatural manner. At last extinguishing the fire, he took the idol up very unceremoniously, and bagged it again in his grego pocket as carelessly as if he were a sportsman bagging a dead woodcock.

All these queer proceedings increased my uncomfortableness, and seeing him now exhibiting strong symptoms of concluding his business operations, and jumping into bed with me, I thought it was high time, now or never, before the light was put out, to break the spell in which I had so long been bound.

But the interval I spent in deliberating what to say, was a fatal one. Taking up his tomahawk from the table, he examined the head of it for an instant, and then holding it to the light, with his mouth at the handle, he puffed out great clouds of tobacco smoke. The next moment the light was extinguished, and this wild cannibal, tomahawk between his teeth, sprang into bed with me. I sang out, I could not help it now; and giving a sudden grunt of astonishment he began feeling me.

Stammering out something, I knew not what, I rolled away from him against the wall, and then conjured him, whoever or whatever he might be, to keep quiet, and let me get up and light the lamp again. But his guttural responses satisfied me at once that he but ill comprehended my meaning.

"Who-e debel you?"—he at last said—"you no speak-e, dam-me, I kill-e." And so saying the lighted tomahawk began flourishing about me in the dark.

"Landlord, for God's sake, Peter Coffin!" shouted I. "Landlord! Watch! Coffin! Angels! Save me!"

"Speak-e! tell-ee me who-ee be, or dam-me, I kill-e!" again growled the cannibal, while his horrid flourishings of the tomahawk scattered the hot tobacco ashes about me till I thought my linen would get on fire. But thank heaven, at that moment the landlord came into the room light in hand, and leaping from the bed I ran up to him.

"Don't be afraid now," said he, grinning again. "Queequeg here wouldn't harm a hair of your head."

"Stop your grinning," shouted I, "and why didn't you tell me that that infernal harpooneer was a cannibal?"

"I thought ye know'd it;—didn't I tell ye, he was a peddlin' heads around town?—but turn flukes again and go to sleep. Queequeg, look here—you sabbee me, I sabbee you—this man sleepe you—you sabbee?"

"Me sabbee plenty"—grunted Queequeg, puffing away at his pipe, and sitting up in bed.

"You gettee in," he added, motioning to me with his tomahawk, and throwing the clothes to one side. He really did this in not only a civil but a really kind and charitable way. I stood looking at him a moment. For all his tattooings he was on the whole a clean, comely looking cannibal. What's all this fuss I have been making about, thought I to myself—the man's a human being just as I am: he has just as much reason to fear me, as I have to be afraid of him. Better sleep with a sober cannibal than a drunken Christian.

"Landlord," said I, "tell him to stash his tomahawk there, or pipe, or whatever you call it; tell him to stop smoking, in short, and I will turn in with him. But I don't fancy having a man smoking in bed with me. It's dangerous. Besides, I ain't insured."

This being told to Queequeg, he at once complied, and again politely motioned me to get into bed—rolling over to one side as much as to say—I won't touch a leg of ye.

"Good night, landlord," said I, "you may go."

I turned in, and never slept better in my life.

CHAPTER IV

THE COUNTERPANE

Upon waking next morning about daylight, I found Queequeg's arm thrown over me in the most loving and affectionate manner. You had almost thought I had been his wife. The counterpane was of patchwork, full of odd little parti-colored squares and triangles; and this arm of his tattooed all over with an interminable Cretan labyrinth of a figure, no two parts of which were of one precise shade—owing I suppose to his keeping his arm at sea unmethodically in sun and shade, his shirt sleeves irregularly rolled up at various times—this same arm of his, I say, looked for all the world like a strip of that same patchwork quilt. Indeed, partly lying on it as the arm did when I first awoke, I could hardly tell it from the quilt, they so blended their hues together; and it was only by the sense of weight and pressure that I could tell that Queequeg was hugging me.

My sensations were strange. Let me try to explain them. When I was a child, I well remember a somewhat similar circumstance that befell me; whether it was a reality or a dream, I never could entirely settle. The circumstance was this. I had been cutting up some caper or other—I think it was trying to crawl up the chimney, as I had seen a little sweep do a few days previous; and my stepmother who, somehow or other, was all the time whipping me, or sending me to bed supperless,—my mother dragged me by the legs out of the chimney and packed me off to bed, though it was only two o'clock in the afternoon of the 21st June, the longest day in the year in our hemisphere. I felt dreadfully. But there was no help for it, so up stairs I went to my little room in the third floor, undressed myself as slowly as possible so as to kill time, and with a bitter sigh got between the sheets.

I lay there dismally calculating that sixteen entire hours must elapse before I could hope for a resurrection. Sixteen hours in bed! the small of my back ached to think of it. And it was so light too; the sun shining in at the window, and a great rattling of coaches in the streets, and the sound of gay voices all over the house. I felt worse and worse—at last I got up, dressed, and softly going down in my stockinged feet, sought out my stepmother, and suddenly threw myself at her feet, beseeching her as a particular favour to give me a good slippering for my misbehavior; anything indeed but condemning me to lie abed such an unendurable length of time. But she was the best and most conscientious of stepmothers, and back I had to go to my room. For several hours I lay there broad awake, feeling a great deal worse than I have ever done since, even from the greatest subsequent misfortunes. At last I must have fallen into a troubled nightmare of a doze; and slowly waking from it— half steeped in dreams—I opened my eyes, and the before sunlit room was now wrapped in outer darkness. Instantly I felt a shock running through all my frame; nothing was to be seen, and nothing was to be heard; but a supernatural hand seemed placed in mine. My arm hung over the counterpane, and the nameless, unimaginable, silent form or phantom, to which the hand belonged, seemed closely seated by my bedside. For what seemed ages piled on ages, I lay there, frozen with the most awful fears, not daring to drag away my hand; yet ever thinking that if I could but stir it one single inch, the horrid spell would be broken. I knew not how this consciousness at last glided away from me; but waking in the morning, I shudderingly remembered it all, and for days and weeks and months afterwards I lost myself in confounding attempts to explain the mystery. Nay, to this very hour, I often puzzle myself with it.

Now, take away the awful fear, and my sensations at feeling the supernatural hand in mine were very similar, in their strangeness, to those which I experienced on waking up and seeing Queequeg's pagan arm thrown round me. But at length all the past night's events soberly recurred, one by one, in fixed reality, and then I lay only alive to the comical predicament. For though

I tried to move his arm—unlock his bridegroom clasp—yet, sleeping as he was, he still hugged me tightly, as though naught but death should part us twain. I now strove to rouse him—"Queequeg!"—but his only answer was a snore. I then rolled over, my neck feeling as if it were in a horse-collar; and suddenly felt a slight scratch. Throwing aside the counterpane, there lay the tomahawk sleeping by the savage's side, as if it were a hatchet-faced baby. A pretty pickle, truly, thought I; abed here in a strange house in the broad day, with a cannibal and a tomahawk! "Queequeg!—in the name of goodness, Queequeg, wake!" At length, by dint of much wriggling, and loud and incessant expostulations upon the unbecomingness of his hugging a fellow male in that matrimonial sort of style, I succeeded in extracting a grunt; and presently, he drew back his arm, shook himself all over like a Newfoundland dog just from the water, and sat up in bed, stiff as a pike-staff, looking at me, and rubbing his eyes as if he did not altogether remember how I came to be there, though a dim consciousness of knowing something about me seemed slowly dawning over him. Meanwhile, I lay quietly eyeing him, having no serious misgivings now, and bent upon narrowly observing so curious a creature. When, at last, his mind seemed made up touching the character of his bedfellow, and he became, as it were, reconciled to the fact; he jumped out upon the floor, and by certain signs and sounds gave me to understand that, if it pleased me, he would dress first and then leave me to dress afterwards, leaving the whole apartment to myself. Thinks I, Queequeg, under the circumstances, this is a very civilized overture; but, the truth is, these savages have an innate sense of delicacy, say what you will; it is marvellous how essentially polite they are. I pay this particular compliment to Queequeg, because he treated me with so much civility and consideration, while I was guilty of great rudeness; staring at him from the bed, and watching all his toilette motions; for the time my curiosity getting the better of my breeding. Nevertheless, a man like Queequeg you don't see every day, he and his ways were well worth unusual regarding.

He commenced dressing at top by donning his beaver hat, a very tall one, by the by, and then—still minus his trousers—he hunted up his boots. What under the heavens he did it for, I cannot tell, but his next movement was to crush himself—boots in hand, and hat on—under the bed; when, from sundry violent gaspings, and strainings, I inferred he was hard at work booting himself; though by no law of propriety that I ever heard of, is any man required to be private when putting on his boots. But Queequeg, do you see, was a creature in the transition stage—neither caterpillar nor butterfly. He was just enough civilized to show off his outlandishness in the strangest possible manner. His education was not yet completed. He was an undergraduate. If he had not been a small degree civilized, he very probably would not have troubled himself with boots at all; but then, if he had not been still a savage, he never would have dreamt of getting under the bed to put them on. At last, he emerged with his hat very much dented and crushed down over his eyes, and began creaking and limping about the room, as if, not being much accustomed to boots, his pair of damp, wrinkled cowhide ones—probably not made to order either—rather pinched and tormented him at the first go off of a bitter cold morning.

Seeing, now, that there were no curtains to the window, and that the street being very narrow, the house opposite commanded a plain view into the room, and observing more and more the indecorous figure that Queequeg made, staving about with little else but his hat and boots on; I begged him as well as I could, to accelerate his toilet somewhat, and particularly to get into his pantaloons as soon as possible. He complied, and then proceeded to wash himself. At that time in the morning any Christian would have washed his face; but Queequeg, to my amazement, contented himself with restricting his ablutions to his chest, arms, and hands. He then donned his waistcoat, and taking up a piece of hard soap on the wash-stand centre-table, dipped it into water and commenced lathering his face. I was watching to see where he kept his razor, when lo and behold, he takes the harpoon from the bed corner, slips out the long wooden stock, unsheathes the head, whets it a little on his boot, and striding up to the bit of mirror against the wall, begins a vigorous scraping, or rather harpooning of his cheeks. Thinks I, Queequeg, this is using Rogers's best cutlery with a vengeance. Afterwards I wondered the less at this operation when I came to know of what fine steel the head of a harpoon is made, and how exceedingly sharp the long straight edges are always kept.

The rest of his toilet was soon achieved, and he proudly marched out of the room, wrapped up in his great pilot monkey jacket, and sporting his harpoon like a marshal's baton.

CHAPTER V

BREAKFAST

I quickly followed suit, and descending into the bar-room accosted the grinning landlord very pleasantly. I cherished no malice towards him, though he had been skylarking with me not a little in the matter of my bedfellow.

However, a good laugh is a mighty good thing, and rather too scarce a good thing; the more's the pity. So, if any one man, in his own proper person, afford stuff for a good joke to anybody, let him not be backward, but let him cheerfully allow himself to spend and to be spent in that way. And the man that has anything bountifully laughable about him, be sure there is more in that man than you perhaps think for.

The bar-room was now full of the boarders who had been dropping in the night previous, and whom I had not as yet had a good look at. They were nearly all whalemen; chief mates, and second mates, and third mates, and sea carpenters, and sea coopers, and sea blacksmiths, and harpooneers, and ship keepers; a brown and brawny company, with bosky beards; an unshorn, shaggy set, all wearing monkey jackets for morning gowns.

You could pretty plainly tell how long each one had been ashore. This young fellow's healthy cheek is like a sun-toasted pear in hue, and would seem to smell almost as musky; he cannot have been three days landed from his Indian voyage. That man next him looks a few shades lighter; you might say a touch of satin wood is in him. In the complexion of a third still lingers a tropic tawn, but slightly bleached withal; he doubtless has tarried whole weeks ashore. But who could show a cheek like Queequeg? which, barred with various tints, seemed like the Andes' western slope, to show forth in one array, contrasting climates, zone by zone.

"Grub, ho!" now cried the landlord, flinging open a door, and in we went to breakfast.

They say that men who have seen the world, thereby become quite at ease in manner, quite self-possessed in company. Not always, though: Ledyard, the great New England traveller, and Mungo Park, the Scotch one; of all men, they possessed the least assurance in the parlor. But perhaps the mere crossing of Siberia in a sledge drawn by dogs as Ledyard did, or the taking a long solitary walk on an empty stomach, in the negro heart of Africa, which was the sum of poor Mungo's performances—this kind of travel, I say, may not be the very best mode of attaining a high social polish. Still, for the most part, that sort of thing is to be had anywhere.

These reflections just here are occasioned by the circumstance that after we were all seated at the table, and I was preparing to hear some good stories about whaling; to my no small surprise nearly every man maintained a profound silence. And not only that, but they looked embarrassed. Yes, here were a set of sea-dogs, many of whom without the slightest bashfulness had boarded great whales on the high seas—entire strangers to them—and duelled them dead without winking; and yet, here they sat at a social breakfast table—all of the same calling, all of kindred tastes—looking round as sheepishly at each other as though they had never been out of sight of some sheepfold among the Green Mountains. A curious sight; these bashful bears, these timid warrior whalemen!

But as for Queequeg—why, Queequeg sat there among them—at the head of the table, too, it so chanced; as cool as an icicle. To be sure I cannot say much for his breeding. His greatest admirer could not have cordially justified his bringing his harpoon into breakfast with him, and using it there without ceremony; reaching over the table with it, to the imminent jeopardy of many heads, and grappling the beefsteaks towards him. But *that* was certainly very coolly done by him, and every one knows that in most people's estimation, to do anything coolly is to do it genteelly.

We will not speak of all Queequeg's peculiarities here; how he eschewed coffee and hot rolls, and applied his undivided attention to beefsteaks, done rare. Enough, that when breakfast was over he withdrew like the rest into the public room, lighted his tomahawk-pipe, and was sitting there quietly digesting and smoking with his inseparable hat on, when I sallied out for a stroll.

CHAPTER VI

THE STREET

IF I had been astonished at first catching a glimpse of so outlandish an individual as Queequeg circulating among the polite society of a civilized town, that astonishment soon departed upon taking my first daylight stroll through the streets of New Bedford.

In thoroughfares nigh the docks, any considerable seaport will frequently offer to view the queerest looking nondescripts from foreign parts. Even in Broadway and Chestnut streets, Mediterranean mariners will sometimes jostle the affrighted ladies. Regent Street is not unknown to Lascars and Malays; and at Bombay, in the Apollo Green, live Yankees have often scared the natives. But New Bedford beats all Water Street and Wapping. In these last-mentioned haunts you see only sailors; but in New Bedford, actual cannibals stand chatting at street corners; savages outright; many of whom yet carry on their bones unholy flesh. It makes a stranger stare.

But, besides the Feegeeans, Tongatobooarrs, Erromanggoans, Pannangians, and Brighggians, and, besides the wild specimens of the whaling-craft which unheeded reel about the streets, you will see other sights still more curious, certainly more comical. There weekly arrive in this town scores of green Vermonters and New Hampshire men, all athirst for gain and glory in the fishery. They are mostly young, of stalwart frames; fellows who have felled forests, and now seek to drop the axe and snatch the whale-lance. Many are as green as the Green Mountains whence they came. In some things you would think them but a few hours old. Look there! that chap strutting round the corner. He wears a beaver hat and swallow-tailed coat, girdled with a sailor-belt and a sheath-knife. Here comes another with a sou'-wester and a bombazine cloak.

No town-bred dandy will compare with a country-bred one—I mean a downright bumpkin dandy—a fellow that, in the dog-days, will mow his two acres in buckskin gloves for fear of tanning his hands. Now when a country dandy like this takes it into his head to make a distinguished reputation, and joins the great whale-fishery, you should see the comical things he does upon reaching the seaport. In bespeaking his sea-outfit, he orders bell-buttons to his waistcoats; straps to his canvas trousers. Ah, poor Hay-Seed! how bitterly will burst those straps in the first howling gale, when thou art driven, straps, buttons, and all, down the throat of the tempest.

But think not that this famous town has only harpooneers, cannibals, and bumpkins to show her visitors. Not at all. Still New Bedford is a queer place. Had it not been for us whalemen, that tract of land would this day perhaps have been in as howling condition as the coast of Labrador. As it is, parts of her back country are enough to frighten one, they look so bony. The town itself is perhaps the dearest place to live in, in all New England. It is a land of oil, true enough: but not like Caanan; a land, also, of corn and wine. The streets do not run with milk; nor in the springtime do they pave them with fresh eggs. Yet, in spite of this, nowhere in all America will you find more patrician-like houses; parks and gardens more opulent, than in New Bedford. Whence came they? how planted upon this once scraggy scoria of a country?

Go and gaze upon the iron emblematical harpoons round yonder lofty mansion, and your question will be answered. Yes; all these brave houses and flowery gardens came from the Atlantic, Pacific, and Indian oceans. One and all, they were harpooned and dragged up hither from the bottom of the sea. Can Herr Alexander perform a feat like that?

In New Bedford, fathers, they say, give whales for dowers to their daughters, and portion off their nieces with a few porpoises a-piece. You must go to New Bedford to see a brilliant wedding; for, they say, they have reservoirs of oil in every house, and every night recklessly burn their lengths in spermaceti candles.

In summer time, the town is sweet to see; full of fine maples—long avenues of green and gold. And in August, high in air, the beautiful and bountiful horse-chestnuts, candelabra-wise, proffer the passer-by their tapering upright cones of congregated blossoms. So omnipotent is art; which in many a district of New Bedford has superinduced bright terraces of flowers upon the barren refuse rocks thrown aside at creation's final day.

And the women of New Bedford, they bloom like their own red roses. But roses only bloom in summer; whereas the fine carnation of their cheeks is perennial as sunlight in the seventh heavens. Elsewhere match that bloom of theirs, ye cannot, save in Salem, where they tell me the young girls breathe such musk, their sailor sweethearts smell them miles off shore, as though they were drawing nigh the odorous Moluccas instead of the Puritanic sands.

CHAPTER VII

THE CHAPEL

IN the same New Bedford there stands a Whaleman's Chapel, and few are the moody fishermen, shortly bound for the Indian Ocean or Pacific, who fail to make a Sunday visit to the spot. I am sure that I did not.

Returning from my first morning stroll, I again sallied out upon this special errand. The sky had changed from clear, sunny cold, to driving sleet and mist. Wrapping myself in my shaggy jacket of the cloth called bearskin, I fought my way against the stubborn storm. Entering, I found a small scattered congregation of sailors, and sailors' wives and widows. A muffled silence reigned, only broken at times by the shrieks of the storm. Each silent worshipper seemed purposely sitting apart from the other, as if each silent grief were insular and incommunicable. The chaplain had not yet arrived; and there these silent islands of men and women sat steadfastly eyeing several marble tablets, with black borders, masoned into the wall on either side the pulpit. Three of them ran something like the following, but I do not pretend to quote:—

SACRED
To the Memory
OF
JOHN TALBOT,
Who, at the age of eighteen, was lost overboard,
Near the Isle of Desolation, off Patagonia,
November 1st, 1836.
THIS TABLET
Is erected to his Memory
BY HIS SISTER.

SACRED
To the Memory
OF
ROBERT LONG, WILLIS ELLERY,
NATHAN COLEMAN, WALTER CANNY, SETH MACY,
AND SAMUEL GLEIG,
Forming one of the boats' crews
OF
THE SHIP ELIZA,
Who were towed out of sight by a Whale,
On the Off-shore Ground in the
PACIFIC,
December 31st, 1839.
THIS MARBLE
Is here placed by their surviving
SHIPMATES.

SACRED
To the Memory
OF
The late
CAPTAIN EZEKIEL HARDY,
Who in the bows of his boat was killed by a
Sperm Whale on the coast of Japan,
August 3d, 1833.
THIS TABLET
Is erected to his Memory
BY
HIS WIDOW.

Shaking off the sleet from my ice-glazed hat and jacket, I seated myself near the door, and turning sideways was surprised to see Queequeg near me. Affected by the solemnity of the scene, there was a wondering gaze of incredulous curiosity in his countenance. This savage was the only person present who seemed to notice my entrance; because he was the only one who could not read, and, therefore, was not reading those frigid inscriptions on the wall. Whether any of the relatives of the seamen whose names appeared there were now among the congregation, I knew not; but so many are the unrecorded accidents in the fishery, and so plainly did several women present wear the countenance if not the trappings of some unceasing grief, that I feel sure that here before me were assembled those, in whose unhealing hearts the sight of those bleak tablets sympathetically caused the old wounds to bleed afresh.

Oh! ye whose dead lie buried beneath the green grass; who standing among flowers can say—here, *here* lies my beloved; ye know not the desolation that broods in bosoms like these. What bitter blanks in those black-bordered marbles which cover no ashes! What despair in those immovable inscriptions! What deadly voids and unbidden infidelities in the lines that seem to gnaw upon all Faith, and refuse resurrections to the beings who have placelessly perished without a grave. As well might those tablets stand in the cave of Elephanta as here.

In what census of living creatures, the dead of mankind are included; why it is that a universal proverb says of them, that they tell no tales, though containing more secrets than the Goodwin Sands; how it is that to his name who yesterday departed for the other world, we prefix so significant and infidel a word, and yet do not thus entitle him, if he but embarks for the remotest Indies of this living earth; why the Life Insurance Companies pay death-forfeitures upon immortals; in what eternal, unstirring paralysis, and deadly, hopeless trance, yet lies antique Adam who died sixty round centuries ago; how is it that we still refuse to be comforted for those who we nevertheless maintain are dwelling in unspeakable bliss; why all the living so strive to hush all the dead; wherefore but the rumor of a knocking in a tomb will terrify a whole city. All these things are not without their meanings.

But Faith, like a jackal, feeds among the tombs, and even from these dead doubts she gathers her most vital hope.

It needs scarcely to be told, with what feelings, on the eve of a Nantucket voyage, I regarded those marble tablets, and by the murky light of that darkened, doleful day read the fate of the whalemen who had gone before me. Yes, Ishmael, the same fate may be thine. But somehow I grew merry again. Delightful inducements to embark, fine chance for promotion, it seems—aye, a stove boat will make me an immortal by brevet. Yes, there is death in this business of whaling—a speechlessly quick chaotic bundling of a man into Eternity. But what then? Methinks we have hugely mistaken this matter of Life and Death. Methinks that what they call my shadow here on earth is my true substance. Methinks that in looking at things spiritual, we are too much like oysters observing the sun through the water, and thinking that thick water the thinnest of air. Methinks my body is but the lees of my better being. In fact, take my body who will, take it I say, it is not me. And therefore three cheers for Nantucket; and come a stove boat and stove body when they will, for stave my soul, Jove himself cannot.

CHAPTER VIII

THE PULPIT

I HAD not been seated very long ere a man of a certain venerable robustness entered; immediately as the storm-pelted door flew back upon admitting him, a quick regardful eyeing of him by all the congregation, sufficiently attested that this fine old man was the chaplain. Yes, it was the famous Father Mapple, so called by the whalemen, among whom he was a very great favorite. He had been a sailor and a harpooneer in his youth, but for many years past had dedicated his life to the ministry. At the time I now write of, Father Mapple was in the hardy winter of a healthy old age; that sort of old age which seems merging into a second flowering youth, for among all the fissures of his wrinkles, there shone certain mild gleams of a newly developing bloom—the spring verdure peeping forth even beneath February's snow. No one having previously heard his history, could for the first time behold Father Mapple without the utmost interest, because there were certain engrafted clerical peculiarities about him, imputable to that adventurous maritime life he had led. When he entered I observed that he carried no umbrella, and certainly had not come in his carriage, for his tarpaulin hat ran down with melting sleet, and his great pilot cloth jacket seemed almost to drag him to the floor with the weight of the water it had absorbed. However, hat and coat and overshoes were one by one removed, and hung up in a little space in an adjacent corner; when, arrayed in a decent suit, he quietly approached the pulpit.

Like most old fashioned pulpits, it was a very lofty one, and since a regular stairs to such a height would, by its long angle with the floor, seriously contract the already small area of the chapel, the architect, it seemed, had acted upon the hint of Father Mapple, and finished the pulpit without a stairs, substituting a perpendicular side ladder, like those used in mounting a ship from a boat at sea. The wife of a whaling captain had provided the chapel with a handsome pair of red worsted man-ropes for this ladder, which, being itself nicely headed, and stained with a mahogany color, the whole contrivance, considering what manner of chapel it was, seemed by no means in bad taste. Halting for an instant at the foot of the ladder, and with both hands grasping the ornamental knobs of the man-ropes, Father Mapple cast a look upwards, and then with a true sailor-like but still reverential dexterity, hand over hand, mounted the steps as if ascending the main-top of his vessel.

The perpendicular parts of this side ladder, as is usually the case with swinging ones, were of cloth-covered rope, only the rounds were of wood, so that at every step there was a joint. At my first glimpse of the pulpit, it had not escaped me that however convenient for a ship, these joints in the present instance seemed unnecessary. For I was not prepared to see Father Mapple after gaining the height, slowly turn round, and stooping over the pulpit, deliberately drag up the ladder step by step, till the whole was deposited within, leaving him impregnable in his little Quebec.

I pondered some time without fully comprehending the reason for this. Father Mapple enjoyed such a wide reputation for sincerity and sanctity, that I could not suspect him of courting notoriety by any mere tricks of the stage. No, thought I, there must be some sober reason for this thing; furthermore, it must symbolize something unseen. Can it be, then, that by that act of physical isolation, he signifies his spiritual withdrawal for the time, from all outward worldly ties and connexions? Yes, for replenished with the meat and wine of the world, to the faithful man of God, this pulpit, I see, is a self-containing stronghold—a lofty Ehrenbreitstein, with a perennial well of water within the walls.

But the side ladder was not the only strange feature of the place, borrowed from the chaplain's former sea-farings. Between the marble cenotaphs on either hand of the pulpit, the wall which formed its back was adorned with a large painting representing a gallant ship beating against a terrible storm off a lee coast of black rocks and snowy breakers. But high above the flying scud and dark-rolling clouds, there floated a little isle of sunlight, from which beamed forth an angel's face; and this bright face shed a distinct spot of radiance upon the ship's tossed deck, something like that silver plate now inserted into the Victory's plank where Nelson fell. "Ah, noble ship," the angel seemed to say, "beat on, beat on, thou noble ship, and bear a hardy helm; for lo! the sun is breaking through; the clouds are rolling off—serenest azure is at hand."

Nor was the pulpit itself without a trace of the same sea-taste that had achieved the ladder and the picture. Its panelled front was in the likeness of a ship's bluff bows, and the Holy Bible rested on a projecting piece of scroll work, fashioned after a ship's fiddle-headed beak.

What could be more full of meaning?—for the pulpit is ever this earth's foremost part; all the rest comes in its rear; the pulpit leads the world. From thence it is the storm of God's quick wrath is first descried, and the bow must bear the earliest brunt. From thence it is the God of breezes fair or foul is first invoked for favorable winds. Yes, the world's a ship on its passage out, and not a voyage complete; and the pulpit is its prow.

CHAPTER IX

THE SERMON

FATHER MAPPLE rose, and in a mild voice of unassuming authority ordered the scattered people to condense. "Starboard gangway, there! side away to larboard—larboard gangway to starboard! Midships! midships!"

There was a low rumbling of heavy sea-boots among the benches, and a still slighter shuffling of women's shoes, and all was quiet again, and every eye on the preacher.

He paused a little; then kneeling in the pulpit's bows, folded his large brown hands across his chest, uplifted his closed eyes, and offered a prayer so deeply devout that he seemed kneeling and praying at the bottom of the sea.

This ended, in prolonged solemn tones, like the continual tolling of a bell in a ship that is foundering at sea in a fog—in such tones he commenced reading the following hymn; but changing his manner towards the concluding stanzas, burst forth with a pealing exultation and joy—

> "The ribs and terrors in the whale,
>   Arched over me a dismal gloom,
> While all God's sun-lit waves rolled by,
>   And lift me deepening down to doom.
>
> "I saw the opening maw of hell,
>   With endless pains and sorrows there;
> Which none but they that feel can tell—
>   Oh, I was plunging to despair.
>
> "In black distress, I called my God,
>   When I could scarce believe him mine,
> He bowed his ear to my complaints—
>   No more the whale did me confine.
>
> "With speed he flew to my relief,
>   As on a radiant dolphin borne;
> Awful, yet bright, as lightning shone
>   The face of my Deliverer God.
>
> "My song for ever shall record
>   That terrible, that joyful hour;
> I give the glory to my God,
>   His all the mercy and the power."

Nearly all joined in singing this hymn, which swelled high above the howling of the storm. A brief pause ensued; the preacher slowly turned over the leaves of the Bible, and at last, folding his hand down upon the proper page, said: "Beloved shipmates, clinch the last verse of the first chapter of Jonah—'And God had prepared a great fish to swallow up Jonah.'"

"Shipmates, this book, containing only four chapters—four yarns—is one of the smallest strands in the mighty cable of the Scriptures. Yet what depths of the soul does Jonah's deep sealine sound! what a pregnant lesson to us is this prophet! What a noble thing is that canticle in the fish's belly! How billow-like and boisterously grand! We feel the floods surging over us, we sound with him to the kelpy bottom of the waters; sea-weed and all the slime of the sea is about us! But *what* is this lesson that the book of Jonah teaches? Shipmates, it is a two-stranded lesson; a lesson to us all as sinful men, and a lesson to me as a pilot of the living God. As sinful men, it is a lesson to us all, because it is a story of the sin, hard-heartedness, suddenly awakened fears, the swift punishment, repentance, prayers, and finally the deliverance and joy of Jonah. As with all sinners among men, the sin of this son of Amittai was in his wilful disobedience of the command of God—never mind now what that command was, or how conveyed—which he found a hard command. But all the things that God would have us do are hard for us to do—remember that —and hence, he oftener commands us than endeavors to persuade. And if we obey God, we must disobey ourselves; and it is in this disobeying ourselves, wherein the hardness of obeying God consists.

"With this sin of disobedience in him, Jonah still further flouts at God, by seeking to flee from Him. He thinks that a ship made by men, will carry him into countries where God does not reign, but only the Captains of this earth. He skulks about the wharves of Joppa, and seeks a ship that's bound for Tarshish. There lurks, perhaps, a hitherto unheeded meaning here. By all accounts Tarshish could have been no other city than the modern Cadiz. That's the opinion of learned men. And where is Cadiz, shipmates? Cadiz is in Spain; as far by water, from Joppa, as Jonah could possibly have sailed in those ancient days, when the Atlantic was an almost unknown sea. Because Joppa, the modern Jaffa, shipmates, is on the most easterly coast of the Mediterranean, the Syrian; and Tarshish or Cadiz more than two thousand miles to the westward from that, just outside the Straits of Gibraltar. See ye not then, shipmates, that Jonah sought to flee world-wide from God? Miserable man! Oh! most contemptible and worthy of all scorn; with slouched hat and guilty eye, skulking from his God; prowling among the shipping like a vile burglar hastening to cross the seas. So disordered, self-condemning is his look, that had there been policemen in those days, Jonah, on the mere suspicion of something wrong, had been arrested ere he touched a deck. How plainly he's a fugitive! no baggage, not a hat-box, valise, or carpet-bag,—no friends accompany him to the wharf with their adieux. At last, after much dodging search, he finds the Tarshish ship receiving the last items of her cargo; and as he steps on board to see its Captain in the cabin, all the sailors for the moment desist from hoisting in the goods; to mark the stranger's evil eye. Jonah sees this; but in vain he tries to look all ease and confidence; in vain essays his wretched smile. Strong intuitions of the man assure the mariners he can be no innocent. In their gamesome but still serious way, one whispers to the other—"Jack, he's robbed a widow;" or, "Joe, do you mark him; he's a bigamist;" or, "Harry lad, I guess he's the adulterer that broke jail in old Gomorrah, or belike, one of the missing murderers from Sodom." Another runs to read the bill that's stuck against the spile upon the wharf to which the ship is moored, offering five hundred gold coins for the apprehension of a parricide, and containing a description of his person. He reads, and looks from Jonah to the bill; while all his sympathetic shipmates now crowd round Jonah, prepared to lay their hands upon him. Frighted Jonah trembles, and summoning all his boldness to his face, only looks so much the more a coward. He will not confess himself suspected; but that itself is strong suspicion. So he makes the best of it; and when the sailors find him not to be the man that is advertised, they let him pass, and he descends into the cabin.

" 'Who's there?' cries the Captain at his busy desk, hurriedly making out his papers for the Customs—'Who's there?' Oh! how that harmless question mangles Jonah! For the instant he almost turns to flee again. But he rallies. 'I seek a passage in this ship to Tarshish; how soon sail ye, sir?' Thus far the busy Captain had not looked up to Jonah, though the man now stands before him; but no sooner does he hear that hollow voice, than he darts a scrutinizing glance. "We sail with the next coming tide,' at last he slowly answered, still intently eyeing him. 'No sooner, sir?'—'Soon enough for any honest man that goes a passenger.' Ha! Jonah, that's another stab. But he swiftly calls away the Captain from that scent. 'I'll sail with ye,'—he says, —'the passage money, how much is that?—I'll pay now.' For it is particularly written, shipmates, as if it were a thing not to be overlooked in this history, 'that he paid the fare thereof' ere the craft did sail. And taken with the context, this is full of meaning.

"Now Jonah's Captain, shipmates, was one whose discernment detects crime in any, but whose cupidity exposes it only in the penniless. In this world, shipmates, sin that pays its way can travel freely, and without a passport; whereas Virtue, if a pauper, is stopped at all frontiers. So Jonah's Captain prepares to test the length of Jonah's purse, ere he judge him openly. He charges him thrice the usual sum; and it's assented to. Then the Captain knows that Jonah is a fugitive; but at the same time resolves to help a flight that paves its rear with gold. Yet when Jonah fairly takes out his purse, prudent suspicions still molest the Captain. He rings every coin to find a counterfeit. Not a forger, any way, he mutters; and Jonah is put down for his passage. 'Point out my state-room, Sir,' says Jonah now, 'I'm travelweary; I need sleep.' 'Thou look'st like it,' says the Captain, 'there's thy room.' Jonah enters, and would lock the door, but the lock contains no key. Hearing him foolishly fumbling there, the Captain laughs lowly to himself, and mutters something about the doors of convicts' cells being never allowed to be locked within. All dressed and dusty as he is, Jonah throws himself into his berth, and finds the little state-room ceiling almost resting on his forehead. The air is close, and Jonah gasps. Then, in that contracted hole, sunk, too, beneath the ship's water-line, Jonah feels the heralding presentiment of that stifling hour, when the whale shall hold him in the smallest of his bowels' wards.

"Screwed at its axis against the side, a swinging lamp slightly oscillates in Jonah's room; and the ship, heeling over towards the wharf with the weight of the last bales received, the lamp, flame and all, though in slight motion, still maintains a permanent obliquity with reference to the room; though, in truth, infallibly straight itself, it but made obvious the false, lying levels among which it hung. The lamp alarms and frightens Jonah; as lying in his berth his tormented eyes roll round the place, and this thus far successful fugitive finds no refuge for his restless glance. But that contradiction in the lamp more and more appals him. The floor, the ceiling, and the side, are all awry. 'Oh! so my conscience hangs in me!' he groans, 'straight upward, so it burns; but the chambers of my soul are all in crookedness!'

"Like one who after a night of drunken revelry hies to his bed, still reeling, but with conscience yet pricking him, as the plungings of the Roman racehorse but so much the more strike his steel tags into him; as one who in that miserable plight still turns and turns in giddy anguish, praying God for annihilation until the fit be passed; and at last amid the whirl of woe he feels, a deep stupor steals over him, as over the man who bleeds to death, for conscience is the wound, and there's naught to staunch it; so, after sore wrestlings in his berth, Jonah's prodigy of ponderous misery drags him drowning down to sleep.

"And now the time of tide has come; the ship casts off her cables; and from the deserted wharf the uncheered ship for Tarshish, all careening, glides to sea. That ship, my friends, was the first of recorded smugglers! the contraband was Jonah. But the sea rebels; he will not bare the wicked burden. A dreadful storm comes on, the ship is like to break. But now when the boatswain calls all hands to lighten her; when boxes, bales, and jars are clattering overboard; when the wind is shrieking, and the men are yelling, and every plank thunders with trampling feet right over Jonah's head; in all this raging tumult, Jonah sleeps his hideous sleep. He sees no black sky and raging sea, feels not the reeling timbers, and little hears he or heeds he the far rush of the mighty whale, which even now with open mouth is cleaving the seas after him. Aye, shipmates, Jonah was gone down into the sides of the ship—a berth in the cabin as I have taken it, and was fast asleep. But the frightened master comes to him, and shrieks in his dead ear, 'What meanest thou, O sleeper! arise!' Startled from his lethargy by that direful cry, Jonah staggers to his feet, and stumbling to the deck, grasps a shroud, to look out upon the sea. But at that moment he is sprung upon by a panther billow leaping over the bulwarks. Wave after wave thus leaps into the ship, and finding no speedy vent runs roaring fore and aft, till the mariners come nigh to drowning while yet afloat. And ever, as the white moon shows her affrighted face from the steep gullies in the blackness overhead, aghast Jonah sees the rearing bowsprit pointing high upward, but soon beat downward again towards the tormented deep.

"Terrors upon terrors run shouting through his soul. In all his cringing attitudes, the God-fugitive is now too plainly known. The sailors mark him; more and more certain grow their suspicions of him, and at last, fully to test the truth, by referring the whole matter to high Heaven, they fall to casting lots, to see for whose cause this great tempest was upon them. The lot is Jonah's; that discovered, then how furiously they mob him with their questions. 'What is thine occupation? Whence comest thou? Thy country? What people?' But mark now, my shipmates, the behavior of poor Jonah. The eager mariners but ask him who he is, and where from; whereas, they not only receive an answer to those questions, but likewise another answer to a question not put by them, but the unsolicited answer is forced from Jonah by the hard hand of God that is upon him.

" 'I am a Hebrew,' he cries—and then—'I fear the Lord the God of Heaven who hath made the sea and the dry land!' Fear him, O Jonah? Aye, well mightest thou fear the Lord God *then!* Straightway he now goes on to make a full confession; whereupon the mariners became more and more appalled, but still are pitiful. For when Jonah, not yet supplicating God for mercy, since he but too well knew the darkness of his deserts,—when wretched Jonah cries out to them to take him and cast him forth into the sea, for he knew that for *his* sake this great tempest was upon them; they mercifully turn from him, and seek by other means to save the ship. But all in vain; the indignant gale howls louder; then, with one hand raised invokingly to God, with the other they not unreluctantly lay hold of Jonah.

"And now behold Jonah taken up as an anchor and dropped into the sea; when instantly an oily calmness floats out from the east, and the sea is still, as Jonah carries down the gale with him, leaving smooth water behind. He goes down in the whirling heart of such a masterless commotion that he scarce heeds the moment when he drops seething into the yawning jaws awaiting him; and the whale shoots-to all his ivory teeth, like so many white bolts, upon his prison. Then Jonah prayed unto the Lord out of the fish's belly. But observe his prayer, and learn a weighty lesson. For sinful as he is, Jonah does not weep and wail for direct deliverance. He feels that his dreadful punishment is just. He leaves all his deliverance to God, contenting himself with this, that spite of all his pains and pangs, he will still look towards His holy temple. And here, shipmates, is true and faithful repentance; not clamorous for pardon, but grateful for punishment. And how pleasing to God was this conduct in Jonah, is shown in the eventual deliverance of him from the sea and the whale. Shipmates, I do not place Jonah before you to be copied for his sin but I do place him before you as a model for repentance. Sin not; but if you do, take heed to repent of it like Jonah."

While he was speaking these words, the howling of the shrieking, slanting storm without seemed to add new power to the preacher, who, when describing Jonah's sea-storm, seemed tossed by a storm himself. His deep chest heaved as with a ground-swell; his tossed arms seemed the warring elements at work; and the thunders that rolled away from off his swarthy brow, and the light leaping from his eye, made all his simple hearers look on him with a quick fear that was strange to them.

There now came a lull in his look, as he silently turned over the leaves of the Book once more; and, at last, standing motionless, with closed eyes, for the moment, seemed communing with God and himself.

But again he leaned over towards the people, and bowing his head lowly, with an aspect of the deepest yet manliest humility, he spake these words:

"Shipmates, God has laid but one hand upon you; both his hands press upon me. I have read ye by what murky light may be mine the lesson that Jonah teaches to all sinners; and therefore to ye, and still more to me, for I am a greater sinner than ye. And now how gladly would I come down from this mast-head and sit on the hatches there where you sit, and listen as you listen, while some one of you reads *me* that other and more awful lesson which Jonah teaches to *me*, as a pilot of the living God. How being an anointed pilot-prophet, or speaker of true things, and bidden by the Lord to sound those unwelcome truths in the ears of a wicked Nineveh, Jonah, appalled at the hostility he should raise, fled from his mission, and sought to escape his duty and his God by taking ship at Joppa. But God is everywhere; Tarshish he never reached. As we have seen, God came upon him in the whale, and swallowed him down to living gulfs of doom, and with swift slantings tore him along 'into the midst of the seas,' where the eddying depths sucked him ten thousand fathoms down, and 'the weeds were wrapped about his head,' and all the watery world of woe bowled over him. Yet even then beyond the reach of any plummet—'out of the belly of hell'—when the whale grounded upon the ocean's utmost bones, even then, God heard the engulphed, repenting prophet when he cried. Then God spake unto the fish; and from the shuddering cold and blackness of the sea, the whale came breeching up towards the warm and pleasant sun, and all the delights of air and earth; and 'vomited out Jonah upon the dry land;' when the word of the Lord came a second time; and Jonah, bruised and beaten—his ears, like two sea-shells, still multitudinously murmuring of the ocean—Jonah did the Almighty's bidding. And what was that, shipmates? To preach the Truth to the face of Falsehood! That was it!

"This, shipmates, this is that other lesson; and woe to that pilot of the living God who slights it. Woe to him whom this world charms from Gospel duty! Woe to him who seeks to pour oil upon the waters when God has brewed them into a gale! Woe to him who seeks to please rather than to appal! Woe to him whose good name is more to him than goodness! Woe to him who, in this world, courts not dishonor! Woe to him who would not be true, even though to be false were salvation! Yea, woe to him who, as the great Pilot Paul has it, while preaching to others is himself a castaway!"

He drooped and fell away from himself for a moment; then lifting his face to them again, showed a deep joy in his eyes, as he cried out with a heavenly enthusiasm—"But oh! shipmates! on the starboard hand of every woe, there is a sure delight; and higher the top of that delight, than the bottom of the woe is deep. Is not the maintruck higher than the kelson is low? Delight is to him—a far, far upward, and inward delight—who against the proud gods and commodores of this earth, ever stands forth his own inexorable self. Delight is to him whose strong arms yet support him, when the ship of this base treacherous world has gone down beneath him. Delight is to him, who gives no quarter in the truth, and kills, burns, and destroys all sin though he pluck it out from under the robes of Senators and Judges. Delight,—topgallant delight is to him, who acknowledges no law or lord, but the Lord his God, and is only a patriot to heaven. Delight is to him, whom all the waves of the billows of the seas of the boisterous mob can never shake from this sure Keel of the Ages. And eternal delight and deliciousness will be his, who coming to lay him down, can say with his final breath—O Father!—chiefly known to me by Thy rod—mortal or immortal, here I die. I have striven to be Thine, more than to be this world's, or mine own. Yet this is nothing: I leave eternity to Thee; for what is man that he should live out the lifetime of his God?"

He said no more, but slowly waving a benediction, covered his face with his hands, and so remained kneeling, till all the people had departed, and he was left alone in the place.

CHAPTER X

A BOSOM FRIEND

RETURNING to the Spouter-Inn from the Chapel, I found Queequeg there quite alone; he having left the Chapel before the benediction some time. He was sitting on a bench before the fire, with his feet on the stove hearth, and in one hand was holding close up to his face that little negro idol of his; peering hard into its face, and with a jack-knife gently whittling away at its nose, meanwhile humming to himself in his heathenish way.

But being now interrupted, he put up the image; and pretty soon, going to the table, took up a large book there, and placing it on his lap began counting the pages with deliberate regularity; at every fiftieth page—as I fancied —stopping for a moment, looking vacantly around him, and giving utterance to a long-drawn gurgling whistle of astonishment. He would then begin again at the next fifty; seeming to commence at number one each time, as though he could not count more than fifty, and it was only by such a large number of fifties being found together, that his astonishment at the multitude of pages was excited.

With much interest I sat watching him. Savage though he was, and hideously marred about the face—at least to my taste—his countenance yet had a something in it which was by no means disagreeable. You cannot hide the soul. Through all his unearthly tattooings, I thought I saw the traces of a simple honest heart; and in his large, deep eyes, fiery black and bold, there seemed tokens of a spirit that would dare a thousand devils. And besides all this, there was a certain lofty bearing about the Pagan, which even his uncouthness could not altogether maim. He looked like a man who had never cringed and never had had a ·creditor. Whether it was, too, that his head being shaved, his forehead was drawn out in freer and brighter relief, and looked more expansive than it otherwise would, this I will not venture to decide; but certain it was his head was phrenologically an excellent one. It may seem ridiculous, but it reminded me of General Washington's head, as seen in the popular busts of him. It had the same long regularly graded retreating slope from above the brows, which were likewise very projecting, like two long promontories thickly wooded on top. Queequeg was George Washington cannibalistically developed.

Whilst I was thus closely scanning him, half-pretending meanwhile to be looking out at the storm from the casement, he never heeded my presence, never troubled himself with so much as a single glance; but appeared wholly occupied with counting the pages of the marvellous book. Considering how sociably we had been sleeping together the night previous, and especially considering the affectionate arm I had found thrown over me upon waking in the morning, I thought this indifference of his very strange. But savages are strange beings; at times you do not know exactly how to take them. At first they are overawing; their calm self-collectedness of simplicity seems a Socratic wisdom. I had noticed also that Queequeg never consorted at all, or but very little, with the other seamen in the inn. He made no advances whatever; appeared to have no desire to enlarge the circle of his acquaintances. All this struck me as mighty singular; yet, upon second thoughts, there was something almost sublime in it. Here was a man some twenty thousand miles from home, by the way of Cape Horn, that is—which was the only way he could get there—thrown among people as strange to him as though he were in the planet Jupiter; and yet he seemed entirely at his ease; preserving the utmost serenity; content with his own companionship; always equal to himself. Surely this was a touch of fine philosophy; though no doubt he had never heard there was such a thing as that. But, perhaps, to be true philosophers, we mortals should not be conscious of so living or so striving. So soon as I hear that such or such a man gives himself out for a philosopher, I conclude that, like the dyspeptic old woman, he must have "broken his digester."

As I sat there in that now lonely room; the fire burning low, in that mild stage when, after its first intensity has warmed the air, it then only glows to be looked at; the evening shades and phantoms gathering round the casements, and peering in upon us silent, solitary twain; the storm booming without in solemn swells; I began to be sensible of strange feelings. I felt a melting in me. No more my splintered heart and maddened hand were turned against the wolfish world. This soothing savage had redeemed it. There he sat, his very indifference speaking a nature in which there lurked no civilized hypocrisies and bland deceits. Wild he was; a very sight of sights to see; yet I began to feel myself mysteriously drawn towards him. And those same things that would have repelled most others, they were the very magnets that thus drew me. I'll try a Pagan friend, thought I, since Christian kindness has proved but hollow courtesy. I drew my bench near him, and made some friendly signs and hints, doing my best to talk with him meanwhile. At first he little noticed these advances; but presently, upon my referring to his last night's hospitalities, he made out to ask me whether we were again to be bedfellows. I told him yes; whereat I thought he looked pleased, perhaps a little complimented.

We then turned over the book together, and I endeavored to explain to him the purpose of the printing, and the meaning of the few pictures that

were in it.   Thus I soon engaged his interest; and from that we went to jabbering the best we could about the various outer sights to be seen in this famous
town.   Soon I proposed a social smoke; and, producing his pouch and tomahawk, he quietly offered me a puff.   And then we sat exchanging puffs from
that wild pipe of his, and keeping it regularly passing between us.

If there yet lurked any ice of indifference towards me in the Pagan's breast,
this pleasant, genial smoke we had, soon thawed it out, and left us cronies.   He
seemed to take to me quite as naturally and unbiddenly as I to him; and when
our smoke was over, he pressed his forehead against mine, clasped me round
the waist, and said that henceforth we were married; meaning, in his country's
phrase, that we were bosom friends; he would gladly die for me, if need should
be.   In a countryman, this sudden flame of friendship would have seemed
far too premature, a thing to be much distrusted; but in this simple savage
those old rules would not apply.

After supper, and another social chat and smoke, we went to our room
together.   He made me a present of his embalmed head; took out his enormous
tobacco wallet, and groping under the tobacco, drew out some thirty dollars
in silver; then spreading them on the table, and mechanically dividing them
into two equal portions, pushed one of them towards me, and said it was mine.
I was going to remonstrate; but he silenced me by pouring them into my
trousers pockets.   I let them stay.   He then went about his evening prayers,
took out his idol, and removed the paper firebrand.   By certain signs and
symptoms, I thought he seemed anxious for me to join him; but well knowing
what was to follow, I deliberated a moment whether, in case he invited me,
I would comply or otherwise.

I was a good Christian; born and bred in the bosom of the infallible Presbyterian Church.   How then could I unite with this wild idolator in worshipping
his piece of wood?   But what is worship? thought I.   Do you suppose now,
Ishmael, that the magnanimous God of heaven and earth—pagans and all included—can possibly be jealous of an insignificant bit of black wood?   Impossible!   But what is worship?—to do the will of God?—*that* is worship.
And what is the will of God?—to do to my fellow man what I would have
my fellow man to do to me—*that* is the will of God.   Now, Queequeg is my
fellow man.   And what do I wish that this Queequeg would do to me?   Why,
unite with me in my particular Presbyterian form of worship.   Consequently,
I must then unite with him in his; ergo, I must turn idolator.   So I kindled
the shavings; helped prop up the innocent little idol; offered him burnt biscuit
with Queequeg; salaamed before him twice or thrice; kissed his nose; and that
done, we undressed and went to bed, at peace with our own consciences and all
the world.   But we did not go to sleep without some little chat.

How it is I know not; but there is no place like a bed for confidential disclosures between friends.   Man and wife, they say, there open the very bottom of their souls to each other; and some old couples often lie and chat over
old times till nearly morning.   Thus, then, in our hearts' honeymoon, lay I
and Queequeg—a cosy, loving pair.

CHAPTER XI

NIGHTGOWN

WE had lain thus in bed, chatting and napping at short intervals, and Queequeg now and then affectionately throwing his brown tattooed legs over mine, and then drawing them back; so entirely sociable and free and easy were we; when, at last, by reason of our confabulations, what little nappishness remained in us altogether departed, and we felt like getting up again, though day-break was yet some way down the future.

Yes, we became very wakeful; so much so that our recumbent position began to grow wearisome, and by little and little we found ourselves sitting up; the clothes well tucked around us, leaning against the head-board with our four knees drawn up close together, and our two noses bending over them, as if our knee-pans were warming-pans. We felt very nice and snug, the more so since it was so chilly out of doors; indeed out of bed-clothes too, seeing that there was no fire in the room. The more so, I say, because truly to enjoy bodily warmth, some small part of you must be cold, for there is no quality in this world that is not what it is merely by contrast. Nothing exists in itself. If you flatter yourself that you are all over comfortable, and have been so a long time, then you cannot be said to be comfortable any more. But if, like Queequeg and me in the bed, the tip of your nose or the crown of your head be slightly chilled, why then, indeed, in the general consciousness you feel most delightfully and unmistakably warm. For this reason a sleeping apartment should never be furnished with a fire, which is one of the luxurious discomforts of the rich. For the height of this sort of deliciousness is to have nothing but the blanket between you and your snugness and the cold of the outer air. Then there you lie like the one warm spark in the heart of an arctic crystal.

We had been sitting in this crouching manner for some time, when all at once I thought I would open my eyes; for when between sheets, whether by day or by night, and whether asleep or awake, I have a way of always keeping my eyes shut, in order the more to concentrate the snugness of being in bed. Because no man can ever feel his own identity aright except his eyes be closed; as if darkness were indeed the proper element of our essences, though light be more congenial to our clayey part. Upon opening my eyes then, and coming out of my own pleasant and self-created darkness into the imposed and coarse outer gloom of the unilluminated twelve-o'clock-at-night, I experienced a disagreeable revulsion. Nor did I at all object to the hint from Queequeg that perhaps it were best to strike a light, seeing that we were so wide awake; and besides he felt a strong desire to have a few quiet puffs from his Tomahawk. Be it said, that though I had felt such a strong repugnance to his smoking in the bed the night before, yet see how elastic our stiff prejudices grow when once love comes to bend them. For now I liked nothing better than to have Queequeg smoking by me, even in bed, because he seemed to be full of such serene household joy then. I no more felt unduly concerned for the landlord's policy of insurance. I was only alive to the condensed confidential comfortableness of sharing a pipe and a blanket with a real friend. With our shaggy jackets drawn about our shoulders, we now passed the Tomahawk from one to the other, till slowly there grew over us a blue hanging tester of smoke, illuminated by the flame of the new-lit lamp.

Whether it was that this undulating tester rolled the savage away to far distant scenes, I know not, but he now spoke of his native island; and, eager to hear his history, I begged him to go on and tell it. He gladly complied. Though at the time I but ill comprehended not a few of his words, yet subsequent disclosures, when I had become more familiar with his broken phraseology, now enable me to present the whole story such as it may prove in the mere skeleton I give.

CHAPTER XII

BIOGRAPHICAL

QUEEQUEG was a native of Rokovoko, an island far away to the West and South. It is not down in any map; true places never are.

When a new-hatched savage running wild about his native woodlands in a grass clout, followed by the nibbling goats, as if he were a green sapling; even then, in Queequeg's ambitious soul, lurked a strong desire to see something more of Christendom than a specimen whaler or two. His father was a High Chief, a King; his uncle a High Priest; and on the maternal side he boasted aunts who were the wives of unconquerable warriors. There was excellent blood in his veins—royal stuff; though sadly vitiated, I fear, by the cannibal propensity he nourished in his untutored youth.

A Sag Harbor ship visited his father's bay, and Queequeg sought a passage to Christian lands. But the ship, having her full complement of seamen, spurned his suit; and not all the King his father's influence could prevail. But Queequeg vowed a vow. Alone in his canoe, he paddled off to a distant strait, which he knew the ship must pass through when she quitted the island. On one side was a coral reef; on the other a low tongue of land, covered with mangrove thickets that grew out into the water. Hiding his canoe, still afloat, among these thickets, with its prow seaward, he sat down in the stern, paddle low in hand; and when the ship was gliding by, like a flash he darted out; gained her side; with one backward dash of his foot capsized and sank his canoe; climbed up the chains; and throwing himself at full length upon the deck, grappled a ring-bolt there, and swore not to let it go, though hacked in pieces.

In vain the captain threatened to throw him overboard; suspended a cutlass over his naked wrists; Queequeg was the son of a King, and Queequeg budged not. Struck by his desperate dauntlessness, and his wild desire to visit Christendom, the captain at last relented, and told him he might make himself at home. But this fine young savage—this sea Prince of Wales, never saw the captain's cabin. They put him down among the sailors, and made a whaleman of him. But like Czar Peter content to toil in the shipyards of foreign cities, Queequeg disdained no seeming ignominy, if thereby he might happily gain the power of enlightening his untutored countrymen. For at bottom—so he told me—he was actuated by a profound desire to learn among the Christians, the arts whereby to make his people still happier than they were; and more than that, still better than they were. But, alas! the practices of whalemen soon convinced him that even Christians could be both miserable and wicked; infinitely more so, than all his father's heathens. Arrived at last in old Sag Harbor; and seeing what the sailors did there; and then going on to Nantucket, and seeing how they spent their wages in *that* place also, poor Queequeg gave it up for lost. Thought he, it's a wicked world in all meridians; I'll die a pagan.

And thus an old idolator at heart, he yet lived among these Christians, wore their clothes, and tried to talk their gibberish. Hence the queer ways about him, though now some time from home.

By hints I asked him whether he did not propose going back, and having a coronation; since he might now consider his father dead and gone, he being very old and feeble at the last accounts. He answered no, not yet; and added that he was fearful Christianity, or rather Christians, had unfitted him for ascending the pure and undefiled throne of thirty pagan Kings before him. But by and by, he said, he would return,—as soon as he felt himself baptized again. For the nonce, however, he proposed to sail about, and sow his wild oats in all four oceans. They had made a harpooneer of him, and that barbed iron was in lieu of a sceptre now.

I asked him what might be his immediate purpose, touching his future movements. He answered, to go to sea again, in his old vocation. Upon this, I told him that whaling was my own design, and informed him of my intention to sail out of Nantucket, as being the most promising port for an adventurous whaleman to embark from. He at once resolved to accompany me to that island, ship aboard the same vessel, get into the same watch, the same boat, the same mess with me, in short to share my every hap; with both my hands in his, boldly dip into the Potluck of both worlds. To all this I joyously assented; for besides the affection I now felt for Queequeg, he was an experienced harpooneer, and as such, could not fail to be of great usefulness to one, who, like me, was wholly ignorant of the mysteries of whaling, though well acquainted with the sea, as known to merchant seamen.

His story being ended with his pipe's last dying puff, Queequeg embraced me, pressed his forehead against mine, and blowing out the light, we rolled over from each other, this way and that, and very soon were sleeping.

CHAPTER XIII

WHEELBARROW

Next morning, Monday, after disposing of the embalmed head to a barber, for a block, I settled my own and comrade's bill; using, however, my comrade's money. The grinning landlord, as well as the boarders, seemed amazingly tickled at the sudden friendship which had sprung up between me and Queequeg—especially as Peter Coffin's cock and bull stories about him had previously so much alarmed me concerning the very person whom I now companied with.

We borrowed a wheelbarrow, and embarking our things, including my own poor carpet-bag, and Queequeg's canvas sack and hammock, away we went down to "the Moss," the little Nantucket packet schooner moored at the wharf. As we were going along the people stared; not at Queequeg so much —for they were used to seeing cannibals like him in their streets,—but at seeing him and me upon such confidential terms. But we heeded them not, going along wheeling the barrow by turns, and Queequeg now and then stopping to adjust the sheath on his harpoon barbs. I asked him why he carried such a troublesome thing with him ashore, and whether all whaling ships did not find their own harpoons. To this, in substance, he replied, that though what I hinted was true enough, yet he had a particular affection for his own harpoon, because it was of assured stuff, well tried in many a mortal combat, and deeply intimate with the hearts of whales. In short, like many reapers and mowers, who go into the farmer's meadows armed with their own scythes —though in no wise obliged to furnish them—even so, Queequeg, for his own private reasons, preferred his own harpoon.

Shifting the barrow from my hand to his, he told me a funny story about the first wheelbarrow he had ever seen. It was in Sag Harbor. The owners of his ship, it seems, had lent him one, in which to carry his heavy chest to his boarding house. Not to seem ignorant about the thing—though in truth he was entirely so, concerning the precise way in which to manage the barrow —Queequeg puts his chest upon it; lashes it fast; and then shoulders the barrow and marches up the wharf. "Why," said I, "Queequeg, you might have known better than that, one would think. Didn't the people laugh?"

Upon this, he told me another story. The people of his island of Roko-voko, it seems, at their wedding feasts express the fragrant water of young cocoanuts into a large stained calabash like a punchbowl; and this punchbowl always forms the great central ornament on the braided mat where the feast is held. Now a certain grand merchant ship once touched at Rokovoko, and its commander—from all accounts, a very stately punctilious gentleman, at least for a sea captain—this commander was invited to the wedding feast of Queequeg's sister, a pretty young princess just turned of ten. Well; when all the wedding guests were assembled at the bride's bamboo cottage, this Captain marches in, and being assigned the post of honor, placed himself over against the punchbowl, and between the High Priest, and his majesty the King, Queequeg's father. Grace being said,—for those people have their grace as well as we—though Queequeg told me that unlike us, who at such times look downwards to our platters, they, on the contrary, copying the ducks, glance upwards to the great Giver of all feasts—Grace, I say, being said, the High Priest opens the banquet by the immemorial ceremony of the island; that is, dipping his consecrated and consecrating fingers into the bowl before the blessed beverage circulates. Seeing himself placed next the Priest, and noting the ceremony, and thinking himself—being Captain of a ship—as having plain precedence over a mere island King, especially in the King's own house— the Captain coolly proceeds to wash his hands in the punch bowl;—taking it I suppose for a huge finger-glass. "Now," said Queequeg, "what you tink now? —Didn't our people laugh?"

As last, passage paid, and luggage safe, we stood on board the schooner. Hoisting sail, it glided down the Acushnet river. On one side, New Bedford rose in terraces of streets, their ice-covered trees all glittering in the clear, cold air. Huge hills and mountains of casks on casks were piled upon her wharves, and side by side the world-wandering whale ships lay silent and safely moored at last; while from others came a sound of carpenters and coopers, with blended noises of fires and forges to melt the pitch, all betokening that new cruises were on the start; that one most perilous and long voyage ended, only begins a second; and a second ended, only begins. a third, and so on, for ever and for aye. Such is the endlessness, yea, the intolerableness of all earthly effort.

Gaining the more open water, the bracing breeze waxed fresh; the little

Moss tossed the quick foam from her bows, as a young colt his snortings. How I snuffed that Tartar air!—how I spurned that turnpike earth!—that common highway all over dented with the marks of slavish heels and hoofs; and turned me to admire the magnanimity of the sea which will permit no records.

At the same foam-fountain, Queequeg seemed to drink and reel with me. His dusky nostrils swelled apart; he showed his filed and pointed teeth. On, on we flew; and our offing gained, the Moss did homage to the blast; ducked and dived her brows as a slave before the Sultan. Sideways leaning, we sideways darted; every ropeyarn tingling like a wire; the two tall masts buckling like Indian canes in land tornadoes. So full of this reeling scene were we, as we stood by the plunging bowsprit, that for some time we did not notice the jeering glances of the passengers, a lubber-like assembly, who marvelled that two fellow beings should be so companionable; as though a white man were anything more dignified than a whitewashed negro. But there were some boobies and bumpkins there, who, by their intense greenness, must have come from the heart and centre of all verdure. Queequeg caught one of these young saplings mimicking him behind his back. I thought the bumpkin's hour of doom was come. Dropping his harpoon, the brawny savage caught him in his arms, and by an almost miraculous dexterity and strength, sent him high up bodily into the air; then slightly tapping his stern in mid-somerset, the fellow landed with bursting lungs upon his feet, while Queequeg, turning his back upon him, lighted his tomahawk pipe and passed it to me for a puff.

"Capting! Capting!" yelled the bumpkin, running towards that officer; "Capting, Capting, here's the devil."

"Hallo, *you* sir," cried the Captain, a gaunt rib of the sea, stalking up to Queequeg, "what in thunder do you mean by that? Don't you know you might have killed that chap?"

"What him say?" said Queequeg, as he mildly turned to me.

"He say," said I, "that you came near kill-e that man there," pointing to the still shivering greenhorn.

"Kill-e," cried Queequeg, twisting his tattooed face into an unearthly expression of disdain, "ah! him bevy small-e fish-e; Queequeg no kill-e so small-e fish-e; Queequeg kill-e big whale!"

"Look you," roared the Captain, "I'll kill-e *you*, you cannibal, if you try any more of your tricks aboard here; so mind your eye."

But it so happened just then, that it was high time for the Captain to mind his own eye. The prodigious strain upon the main-sail had parted the weather-sheet, and the tremendous boom was now flying from side to side, completely sweeping the entire after part of the deck. The poor fellow whom Queequeg had handled so roughly, was swept overboard; all hands were in a panic; and to attempt snatching at the boom to stay it, seemed madness. It flew from right to left, and back again, almost in one ticking of a watch, and every instant seemed on the point of snapping into splinters. Nothing was done, and nothing seemed capable of being done; those on deck rushed toward the bows, and stood eyeing the boom as if it were the lower jaw of an exasperated whale. In the midst of this consternation, Queequeg dropped deftly to his knees, and crawling under the path of the boom, whipped hold of a rope, secured one end to the bulwarks, and then flinging the other like a lasso, caught it round the boom as it swept over his head, and at the next jerk, the spar was that way trapped, and all was safe. The schooner was run into the wind, and while the hands were clearing away the stern boat, Queequeg, stripped to the waist, darted from the side with a long living arc of a leap. For three minutes or more he was seen swimming like a dog, throwing his long arms straight out before him, and by turns revealing his brawny shoulders through the freezing foam. I looked at the grand and glorious fellow, but saw no one to be saved. The greenhorn had gone down. Shooting himself perpendicularly from the water, Queequeg now took an instant's glance around him, and seeming to see just how matters were, dived down and disappeared. A few minutes more, and he rose again, one arm still striking out, and with the other dragging a lifeless form. The boat soon picked them up. The poor bumpkin was restored. All hands voted Queequeg a noble trump; the captain begged his pardon. From that hour I clove to Queequeg like a barnacle; yea, till poor Queequeg took his last long dive.

Was there ever such unconsciousness? He did not seem to think that he at all deserved a medal from the Humane and Magnanimous Societies. He only asked for water—fresh water—something to wipe the brine off; that done, he put on dry clothes, lighted his pipe, and leaning against the bulwarks, and mildly eyeing those around him, seemed to be saying to himself—"It's a mutual, joint-stock world, in all meridians. We cannibals must help these Christians."

CHAPTER XIV

NANTUCKET

NOTHING more happened on the passage worthy the mentioning; so, after a fine run, we safely arrived in Nantucket.

Nantucket! Take out your map and look at it. See what a real corner of the world it occupies; how it stands there, away off shore, more lonely than the Eddystone lighthouse. Look at it—a mere hillock, and elbow of sand; all beach, without a background. There is more sand there than you would use in twenty years as a substitute for blotting paper. Some gamesome wights will tell you that they have to plant weeds there, they don't grow naturally; that they import Canada thistles; that they have to send beyond seas for a spile to stop a leak in an oil cask; that pieces of wood in Nantucket are carried about like bits of the true cross in Rome; that people there plant toadstools before their houses, to get under the shade in summer time; that one blade of grass makes an oasis, three blades in a day's walk a prairie; that they wear quicksand shoes, something like Laplander snow-shoes; that they are so shut up, belted about, every way inclosed, surrounded, and made an utter island of by the ocean, that to their very chairs and tables small clams will sometimes be found adhering, as to the backs of sea turtles. But these extravaganzas only show that Nantucket is no Illinois.

Look now at the wondrous traditional story of how this island was settled by the red-men. Thus goes the legend. In olden times an eagle swooped down upon the New England coast, and carried off an infant Indian in his talons. With loud lament the parents saw their child borne out of sight over the wide waters. They resolved to follow in the same direction. Setting out in their canoes, after a perilous passage they discovered the island, and there they found an empty ivory casket,—the poor little Indian's skeleton.

What wonder, then, that these Nantucketers, born on a beach, should take to the sea for a livelihood! They first caught crabs and quohogs in the sand;

grown bolder, they waded out with nets for mackerel; more experienced, they pushed off in boats and captured cod; and at last, launching a navy of great ships on the sea, explored this watery world; put an incessant belt of circumnavigations round it; peeped in at Behring's Straits; and in all seasons and all oceans declared everlasting war with the mightiest animated mass that has survived the flood; most monstrous and most mountainous! That Himmalehan, salt-sea Mastodon, clothed with such portentousness of unconscious power, that his very panics are more to be dreaded than his most fearless and malicious assaults!

And thus have these naked Nantucketers, these sea hermits, issuing from their ant-hill in the sea, overrun and conquered the watery world like so many Alexanders; parcelling out among them the Atlantic, Pacific, and Indian oceans, as the three pirate powers did Poland. Let America add Mexico to Texas, and pile Cuba upon Canada; let the English overswarm all India, and hang out their blazing banner from the sun; two thirds of this terraqueous globe are the Nantucketer's. For the sea is his; he owns it, as Emperors own empires; other seamen having but a right of way through it. Merchant ships are but extension bridges; armed ones but floating forts; even pirates and privateers, though following the sea as highwaymen the road, they but plunder other ships, other fragments of the land like themselves, without seeking to draw their li/ing from the bottomless deep itself. The Nantucketer, he alone resides and riots on the sea; he alone, in Bible language, goes down to it in ships; to and fro ploughing it as his own special plantation. *There* is his home; *there* lies his business, which a Noah's flood would not interrupt, though it overwhelmed all the millions in China. He lives on the sea, as prairie cocks in the prairie; he hides among the waves, he climbs them as chamois hunters climb the Alps. For years he knows not the land; so that when he comes to it at last, it smells like another world, more strangely than the moon would to an Earthsman. With the landless gull, that at sunset folds her wings and is rocked to sleep between billows; so at nightfall, the Nantucketer, out of sight of land, furls his sails, and lays him to his rest, while under his very pillow rush herds of walruses and whales.

CHAPTER XV

CHOWDER

It was quite late in the evening when the little Moss came snugly to anchor, and Queequeg and I went ashore; so we could attend to no business that day, at least none but a supper and a bed. The landlord of the Spouter-Inn had recommended us to his cousin Hosea Hussey of the Try Pots, whom he asserted to be the proprietor of one of the best kept hotels in all Nantucket, and moreover he had assured us that Cousin Hosea, as he called him, was famous for his chowders. In short, he plainly hinted that we could not possibly do better than try pot-luck at the Try Pots. But the directions he had given us about keeping a yellow warehouse on our starboard hand till we opened a white church to the larboard, and then keeping that on the larboard hand till we made a corner three points to the starboard, and that done, then ask the first man we met where the place was; these crooked directions of his very much puzzled us at first, especially as, at the outset, Queequeg insisted that the yellow warehouse—our first point of departure—must be left on the larboard hand, whereas I had understood Peter Coffin to say it was on the starboard. However, by dint of beating about a little in the dark, and now and then knocking up a peaceful inhabitant to inquire the way, we at last came to something which there was no mistaking.

Two enormous wooden pots painted black, and suspended by asses' ears, swung from the cross-trees of an old top-mast, planted in front of an old doorway. The horns of the cross-trees were sawed off on the other side, so that this old top-mast looked not a little like a gallows. Perhaps I was oversensitive to such impressions at the time, but I could not help staring at this gallows with a vague misgiving. A sort of crick was in my neck as I gazed up to the two remaining horns; yes, *two* of them, one for Queequeg, and one for me. It's ominous, thinks I. A Coffin my Innkeeper upon landing in my first whaling port; tombstones staring at me in the whalemen's chapel; and here a gallows! and a pair of prodigious black pots too! Are these last throwing out oblique hints touching Tophet?

I was called from these reflections by the sight of a freckled woman with yellow hair and a yellow gown, standing in the porch of the inn, under a dull red lamp swinging there, that looked much like an injured eye, and carrying on a brisk scolding with a man in a purple woollen shirt.

"Get along with ye," said she to the man, "or I'll be combing ye!"

"Come on, Queequeg," said I, "all right. There's Mrs. Hussey."

And so it turned out; Mr. Hosea Hussey being from home, but leaving Mrs. Hussey entirely competent to attend to all his affairs. Upon making known our desires for a supper and a bed, Mrs. Hussey, postponing further scolding for the present, ushered us into a little room, and seating us at a table spread with the relics of a recently concluded repast, turned round to us and said —"Clam or Cod?"

"What's that about Cods, ma'am?" said I, with much politeness.

"Clam or Cod?" she repeated.

"A clam for supper? a cold clam; is *that* what you mean, Mrs. Hussey?" says I; "but that's a rather cold and clammy reception in the winter time, ain't it, Mrs. Hussey?"

But being in a great hurry to resume scolding the man in the purple shirt, who was waiting for it in the entry, and seeming to hear nothing but the word "clam," Mrs. Hussey hurried towards an open door leading to the kitchen, and bawling out "clam for two," disappeared.

"Queequeg," said I, "do you think that we can make out a supper for us both on one clam?"

However, a warm savory steam from the kitchen served to belie the apparently cheerless prospect before us. But when that smoking chowder came in, the mystery was delightfully explained. Oh! sweet friends, hearken to me. It was made of small juicy clams, scarcely bigger than hazel nuts, mixed with pounded ship biscuits, and salted pork cut up into little flakes; the whole enriched with butter, and plentifully seasoned with pepper and salt. Our appetites being sharpened by the frosty voyage, and in particular, Queequeg seeing his favourite fishing food before him, and the chowder being surpassingly excellent, we despatched it with great expedition: when leaning back a moment and bethinking me of Mrs. Hussey's clam and cod announcement, I thought I would try a little experiment. Stepping to the kitchen door, I uttered the word "cod" with great emphasis, and resumed my seat. In a few moments the savoury steam came forth again, but with a different flavor, and in good time a fine cod-chowder was placed before us.

We resumed business; and while plying our spoons in the bowl, thinks I to myself, I wonder now if this here has any effect on the head? What's that stultifying saying about chowder-headed people? "But look, Queequeg, ain't that a live eel in your bowl? Where's your harpoon?"

Fishiest of all fishy places was the Try Pots, which well deserved its name; for the pots there were always boiling chowders. Chowder for breakfast, and chowder for dinner, and chowder for supper, till you began to look for fish-bones coming through your clothes. The area before the house was paved with clam-shells. Mrs. Hussey wore a polished necklace of codfish vertebra; and Hosea Hussey had his account books bound in superior old shark-skin. There was a fishy flavor to the milk, too, which I could not at all account for, till one morning happening to take a stroll along the beach among some fishermen's boats, I saw Hosea's brindled cow feeding on fish remnants, and marching along the sand with each foot in a cod's decapitated head, looking very slip-shod, I assure ye.

Supper concluded, we received a lamp, and directions from Mrs. Hussey concerning the nearest way to bed; but, as Queequeg was about to precede me up the stairs, the lady reached forth her arm, and demanded his harpoon; she allowed no harpoon in her chambers. "Why not?" said I; "every true whaleman sleeps with his harpoon—but why not?" "Because it's dangerous," says she. "Ever since young Stiggs coming from the unfort'nt v'y'ge of his when he was gone four years and a half, with only three barrels of *ile*, was found dead in my first floor back, with his harpoon in his side; ever since then I allow no boarders to take sich dangerous weepons in their rooms at night. So, Mr. Queequeg" (for she had learned his name), "I will just take this here iron, and keep it for you till morning. But the chowder; clam or cod to-morrow for breakfast, men?"

"Both," says I; "and let's have a couple of smoked herring by way of variety."

CHAPTER XVI

THE SHIP

In bed we concocted our plans for the morrow. But to my surprise and no small concern, Queequeg now gave me to understand, that he had been dili-gently consulting Yojo—the name of his black little god—and Yojo had told him two or three times over, and strongly insisted upon it everyway, that instead of our going together among the whaling-fleet in harbor, and in concert selecting our craft; instead of this, I say, Yojo earnestly enjoined that the selection of the ship should rest wholly with me, inasmuch as Yojo purposed befriending us; and, in order to do so, had already pitched upon a vessel, which, if left to myself, I, Ishmael, should infallibly light upon, for all the world as though it had turned out by chance; and in that vessel I must imme-diately ship myself, for the present irrespective of Queequeg.

I have forgotten to mention that, in many things, Queequeg placed great confidence in the excellence of Yojo's judgment and surprising forecast of things; and cherished Yojo with considerable esteem, as a rather good sort of god, who perhaps meant well enough upon the whole, but in all cases did not succeed in his benevolent designs.

Now, this plan of Queequeg's, or rather Yojo's, touching the selection of our craft; I did not like that plan at all. I had not a little relied upon Queequeg's sagacity to point out the whaler best fitted to carry us and our fortunes securely. But as all my remonstrances ·produced no effect upon Queequeg, I was obliged to acquiesce; and accordingly prepared to set about this business with a determined rushing sort of energy and vigor, that should quickly settle that trifling little affair. Next morning early, leaving Queequeg shut up with Yojo in our little bedroom—for it seemed that it was some sort of Lent or Ramadan, or day of fasting, humiliation, and prayer with Queequeg and Yojo that day; *how* it was I never could find out, for, though I applied myself to it several times, I never could master his liturgies and XXXIX Articles— leaving Queequeg, then, fasting on his tomahawk pipe, and Yojo warming himself at his sacrificial fire of shavings, I sallied out among the shipping. After much prolonged sauntering and many random inquiries, I learned that there were three ships up for three-years' voyages—The Devil-dam, the Tit-bit, and the Pequod. ·*Devil-Dam,* I do not know the origin of; *Tit-bit* is obvious; *Pequod,* you will no doubt remember, was the name of a celebrated tribe of Massachusetts Indians, now extinct as the ancient Medes. I peered and pryed about the Devil-Dam; from her, hopped over to the Tit-bit; and, finally, going on board the Pequod, looked around her for a moment, and then decided that this was the very ship for us.

You may have seen many a quaint craft in your day, for aught I know; —square-toed luggers; mountainous Japanese junks; butter-box galliots, and what not; but take my word for it, you never saw such a rare old craft as this same rare old Pequod. She was a ship of the old school, rather small if anything; with an old fashioned claw-footed look about her. Long seasoned and weather-stained in the typhoons and calms of all four oceans, her old hull's complexion was darkened like a French grenadier's who has alike fought in Egypt and Siberia. Her venerable bows looked bearded. Her masts —cut somewhere on the coast of Japan, where her original ones were lost overboard in a gale—her masts stood stiffly up like the spines of the three old kings of Cologne. Her ancient decks were worn and wrinkled, like the pilgrim-worshipped flag-stone in Canterbury Cathedral where Becket bled. But to all these her old antiquities, were added new and marvellous features, pertaining to the wild business that for more than half a century she had followed. Old Captain Peleg, many years her chief-mate, before he commanded another vessel of his own, and now a retired seaman, and one of the principal owners of the Pequod,—this old Peleg, during the term of his chief-mateship, had built upon her original grotesqueness, and inlaid it, all over, with a quaintness both of material and device, unmatched by anything except it be Thorkill-Hake's carved buckler or bedstead. She was apparelled like any barbaric Ethiopian emperor, his neck heavy with pendants of polished ivory. She was a thing of trophies. A cannibal of a craft, tricking herself forth in the chased bones of her enemies. All round, her unpanelled, open bulwarks were garnished like one continuous jaw, with the long sharp teeth of the sperm whale, inserted there for pins, to fasten her old hempen thews and tendons to. Those thews ran not through base blocks of land wood, but deftly travelled over sheaves of sea-ivory. Scorning a turnstile wheel at her reverend helm, she sported there a tiller; and that tiller was in one mass, curiously carved from the long narrow lower jaw of her hereditary foe. The helmsman who steered by that tiller in a tempest, felt like the Tartar, when he holds back his fiery steed by clutching its jaw. A noble craft, but somehow a most melancholy! All noble things are touched with that.

Now when I looked about the quarter-deck, for some one having authority, in order to propose myself as a candidate for the voyage, at first I saw nobody; but I could not well overlook a strange sort of tent, or rather wigwam, pitched a little behind the main-mast. It seemed only a temporary erection used in port. It was of a conical shape, some ten feet high; consisting of the long, huge slabs of limber black bone taken from the middle and highest part of the jaws of the right-whale. Planted with their broad ends on the deck, a circle of these slabs laced together, mutually sloped towards each other, and at the apex united in a tufted point, where the loose hairy fibres waved to and fro like the top-knot on some old Pottowotamie Sachem's head. A triangular opening faced towards the bows of the ship, so that the insider commanded a complete view forward.

And half concealed in this queer tenement, I at length found one who by his aspect seemed to have authority; and who, it being noon, and the ship's work suspended, was now enjoying respite from the burden of command. He was seated on an old-fashioned oaken chair, wriggling all over with curious carving; and the bottom of which was formed of a stout interlacing of the same elastic stuff of which the wigwam was constructed.

There was nothing so very particular, perhaps, about the appearance of the elderly man I saw; he was brown and brawny, like most old seamen, and heavily rolled up in blue pilot-cloth, cut in the Quaker style; only there was a fine and almost microscopic net-work of the minutest wrinkles interlacing round his eyes, which must have arisen from his continual sailings in many hard gales, and always looking to windward;—for this causes the muscles about the eyes to become pursed together. Such eye-wrinkles are very effectual in a scowl.

"Is this the Captain of the Pequod?" said I, advancing to the door of the tent.

"Supposing it be the Captain of the Pequod, what dost thou want of him?" he demanded.

"I was thinking of shipping."

"Thou wast, wast thou? I see thou art no Nantucketer—ever been in a stove boat?"

"No, Sir, I never have."

"Dost know nothing at all about whaling, I dare say—eh?"

"Nothing, Sir; but I have no doubt I shall soon learn. I've been several voyages in the merchant service, and I think that——"

"Marchant service be damned. Talk not that lingo to me. Dost see that leg?—I'll take that leg away from thy stern, if ever thou talkest of the marchant service to me again. Marchant service indeed! I suppose now ye feel considerable proud of having served in those marchant ships. But flukes! man, what makes thee want to go a whaling, eh?—it looks a little suspicious, don't it, eh?—Hast not been a pirate, hast thou?—Didst not rob thy last Captain, didst thou?—Dost not think of murdering the officers when thou gettest to sea?"

I protested my innocence of these things. I saw that under the mask of these half humorous inuendoes, this old seaman, as an insulated Quakerish Nantucketer, was full of his insular prejudices, and rather distrustful of all aliens, unless they hailed from Cape Cod or the Vineyard.

"But what takes thee a-whaling? I want to know that before I think of shipping ye."

"Well, sir, I want to see what whaling is. I want to see the world."

"Want to see what whaling is, eh? Have ye clapped eye on Captain Ahab?"

"Who is Captain Ahab, sir?"

"Aye, aye, I thought so. Captain Ahab is the Captain of this ship."

"I am mistaken then. I thought I was speaking to the Captain himself."

"Thou art speaking to Captain Peleg—that's who ye are speaking to, young man. It belongs to me and Captain Bildad to see the Pequod fitted out for the voyage, and supplied with all her needs, including crew. We are part owners and agents. But as I was going to say, if thou wantest to know what whaling is, as thou tellest ye do, I can put ye in a way of finding it out before ye bind yourself to it, past backing out. Clap eye on Captain Ahab, young man, and thou wilt find that he has only one leg."

"What do you mean, sir? Was the other one lost by a whale?"

"Lost by a whale! Young man, come nearer to me: it was devoured, chewed up, crunched by the monstrousest parmacetty that ever shipped a boat!—ah, ah!"

I was a little alarmed by his energy, perhaps also a little touched by the hearty grief in his concluding exclamation, but said as calmly as I could, "What you say is no doubt true enough, sir; but how could I know there was any peculiar ferocity in that particular whale, though indeed I might have inferred as much from the simple fact of the accident."

"Look ye now, young man, thy lungs are a sort of soft, d'ye see; thou dost not talk shark a bit. *Sure,* ye've been to sea before now; sure of that?"

"Sir," said I, "I thought I told you that I had been four voyages in the merchant——"

"Hard down out of that! Mind what I said about the marchant service —don't aggravate me—I won't have it. But let us understand each other. I have given thee a hint about what whaling is; do ye yet feel inclined for it?"

"I do, sir."

"Very good. Now, art thou the man to pitch a harpoon down a live whale's throat, and then jump after it? Answer, quick!"

"I am, sir, if it should be positively indispensable to do so; not to be got rid of, that is; which I don't take to be the fact."

"Good again. Now then, thou not only wantest to go a-whaling, to find out by experience what whaling is, but ye also want to go in order to see the world? Was not that what ye said? I thought so. Well then, just step forward there, and take a peep over the weather-bow, and then back to me and tell me what ye see there."

For a moment I stood a little puzzled by this curious request, not knowing exactly how to take it, whether humorously or in earnest. But concentrating all his crow's feet into one scowl, Captain Peleg started me on the errand.

Going forward and glancing over the weather bow, I perceived that the ship swinging to her anchor with the flood-tide, was now obliquely pointing towards the open ocean. The prospect was unlimited, but exceedingly monotonous and forbidding; not the slightest variety that I could see.

"Well, what's the report?" said Peleg when I came back; "what did ye see?"

"Not much," I replied—"nothing but water; considerable horizon though, and there's a squall coming up, I think."

"Well, what dost thou think then of seeing the world? Do ye wish to go round Cape Horn to see any more of it, eh? Can't ye see the world where you stand?"

I was a little staggered, but go a-whaling I must, and I would; and the Pequod was as good a ship as any—I thought the best—and all this I now repeated to Peleg. Seeing me so determined, he expressed his willingness to ship me.

"And thou mayest as well sign the papers right off," he added—"come along with ye." And so saying, he led the way below deck into the cabin.

Seated on the transom was what seemed to me a most uncommon and surprising figure. It turned out to be Captain Bildad, who along with Captain Peleg was one of the largest owners of the vessel; the other shares, as is sometimes the case in these ports, being held by a crowd of old annuitants; widows, fatherless children, and chancery wards; each owning about the value of a timber head, or a foot of plank, or a nail or two in the ship. People in Nantucket invest their money in whaling vessels, the same way that you do yours in approved state stocks bringing in good interest.

Now, Bildad, like Peleg, and indeed many other Nantucketers, was a Quaker, the island having been originally settled by that sect; and to this day its inhabitants in general retain in an uncommon measure the peculiarities of the Quaker, only variously and anomalously modified by things altogether alien and heterogeneous. For some of these same quakers are the most sanguinary of all sailors and whale-hunters. They are fighting Quakers; they are Quakers with a vengeance.

So that there are instances among them of men, who, named with Scripture names—a singularly common fashion on the island—and in childhood naturally imbibing the stately dramatic thee and thou of the Quaker idiom; still, from the audacious, daring, and boundless adventure of their subsequent lives, strangely blend with these unoutgrown peculiarities, a thousand bold dashes of character, not unworthy a Scandinavian sea-king, or a poetical Pagan Roman. And when these things unite in a man of greatly superior natural force, with a globular brain and a ponderous heart; who has also by the stillness and seclusion of many long night-watches in the remotest waters, and beneath constellations never seen here at the north, been led to think untraditionally and independently; receiving all nature's sweet or savage impressions fresh from her own virgin voluntary and confiding breast, and thereby chiefly, but with some help from accidental advantages, to learn a bold and nervous lofty language—that man makes one in a whole nation's census—a mighty pageant creature, formed for noble tragedies. Nor will it at all detract from him, dramatically regarded, if either by birth or other circumstances, he have what seems a half wilful over-ruling morbidness at the bottom of his nature. For all men tragically great are made so through a certain morbidness. Be sure of this, O young ambition, all mortal greatness is but disease. But, as yet we have not to do with such an one, but with quite another; and still a man, who, if indeed peculiar, it only results again from another phase of the Quaker, modified by individual circumstances.

Like Captain Peleg, Captain Bildad was a well-to-do, retired whaleman. But unlike Captain Peleg—who cared not a rush for what are called serious things, and indeed deemed those self-same serious things the veriest of all trifles —Captain Bildad had not only been originally educated according to the strictest sect of Nantucket Quakerism, but all his subsequent ocean life, and the sight of many unclad, lovely island creatures, round the Horn—all that had not moved this native born Quaker one single jot, had not so much as altered one angle of his vest.   Still, for all this immutableness, was there some lack of common consistency about worthy Captain Peleg.   Though refusing, from conscientious scruples, to bear arms against land invaders, yet himself had illimitably invaded the Atlantic and Pacific; and though a sworn foe to human bloodshed, yet had he in his straight-bodied coat, spilled tuns upon tuns of leviathan gore.   How now in the contemplative evening of his days, the pious Bildad reconciled these things in the reminiscence, I do not know; but it did not seem to concern him much, and very probably he had long since come to the sage and sensible con- clusion that a man's religion is one thing, and this practical world quite another. This world pays dividends.   Rising from a little cabin-boy in short clothes of the drabbest drab, to a harpooneer in a broad shad-bellied waistcoat; from that be- coming boat-header, chief-mate, and captain, and finally a shipowner; Bildad, as I hinted before, had concluded his adventurous career by wholly retiring from active life at the goodly age of sixty, and dedicating his remaining days to the quiet receiving of his well-earned income.

Now Bildad, I am sorry to say, had the reputation of being an incorrigible old hunk, and in his sea-going days, a bitter, hard task-master.   They told me in Nantucket, though it certainly seems a curious story, that when he sailed the old Categut whaleman, his crew, upon arriving home, were mostly all carried ashore to the hospital, sore exhausted and worn out.   For a pious man, espe- cially for a Quaker, he was certainly rather hard-hearted, to say the least. He never used to swear, though, at his men, they said; but somehow he got an inordinate quantity of cruel, unmitigated hard work out of them.   When Bildad was a chief-mate, to have his drab-colored eye intently looking at you, made you feel completely nervous, till you could clutch something—a hammer or a marling-spike, and go to work like mad, at something or other, never mind what. Indolence and idleness perished from before him.   His own person was the exact embodiment of his utilitarian character.   On his long, gaunt body, he carried no spare flesh, no superfluous beard, his chin having a soft, economical nap to it, like the worn nap of his broad-brimmed hat.

Such, then, was the person that I saw seated on the transom when I fol- lowed Captain Peleg down into the cabin.   The space between the decks was small; and there, bolt upright, sat old Bildad, who always sat so, and never leaned, and this to save his coat-tails.   His broad-brim was placed beside him; his legs were stiffly crossed; his drab vesture was buttoned up to his chin; and spectacles on nose, he seemed absorbed in reading from a ponderous volume.

"Bildad," cried Captain Peleg, "at it again, Bildad, eh?   Ye have been studying those Scriptures, now, for the last thirty years, to my certain knowl- edge.   How far ye got, Bildad?"

As if long habituated to such profane talk from his old shipmate, Bildad, without noticing his present irreverence, quietly looked up, and seeing me, glanced again inquiringly towards Peleg.

"He says he's our man, Bildad," said Peleg, "he wants to ship."

"Dost thee?" said Bildad, in a hollow tone, and turning round to me.

"I *dost*," said I unconsciously, he was so intense a Quaker.

"What do ye think of him, Bildad?" said Peleg.

"He'll do," said Bildad, eyeing me, and then went on spelling away at his book in a mumbling tone quite audible.

I thought him the queerest old Quaker I ever saw, especially as Peleg, his friend and old shipmate, seemed such a blusterer. But I said nothing, only looking round me sharply. Peleg now threw open a chest, and drawing forth the ship's articles, placed pen and ink before him, and seated himself at a little table. I began to think it was high time to settle with myself at what terms I would be willing to engage for the voyage. I was already aware that in the whaling business they paid no wages; but all hands, including the captain, received certain shares of the profits called *lays*, and that these lays were proportioned to the degree of importance pertaining to the respective duties of the ship's company. I was also aware that being a green hand at whaling, my own lay would not be very large; but considering that I was used to the sea, could steer a ship, splice a rope, and all that, I made no doubt that from all I had heard I should be offered at least the 275th lay—that is, the 275th part of the clear nett proceeds of the voyage, whatever that might eventually amount to. And though the 275th lay was what they call a rather *long lay*, yet it was better than nothing; and if we had a lucky voyage, might pretty nearly pay for the clothing I would wear out on it, not to speak of my three years' beef and board, for which I would not have to pay one stiver.

It might be thought that this was a poor way to accumulate a princely fortune—and so it was, a very poor way indeed. But I am one of those who never take on about princely fortunes, and am quite content if the world is ready to board and lodge me, while I am putting up at this grim sign of the Thunder Cloud. Upon the whole, I thought the 275th lay would be about the fair thing, but would not have been surprised had I been offered the 200th, considering I was of a broad-shouldered make.

But one thing, nevertheless, that made me a little distrustful about receiving a generous share of the profits was this: Ashore, I had heard something of both Captain Peleg and his unaccountable old crony Bildad; how that they being the principal proprietors of the Pequod, therefore the other and more inconsiderable and scattered owners, left nearly the whole management of the ship's affairs to these two. And I did not know but what the stingy old Bildad might have a mighty deal to say about shipping hands, especially as I now found him on board the Pequod, quite at home there in the cabin, and reading his Bible as if at his own fireside. Now while Peleg was vainly trying to mend a pen with his jack-knife, old Bildad, to my no small surprise, considering that he was such an interested party in these proceedings; Bildad never heeded us, but went on mumbling to himself out of his book, "*Lay* not up for yourselves treasures upon earth, where moth—"

"Well, Captain Bildad," interrupted Peleg, "what d'ye say, what lay shall we give this young man?"

"Thou knowest best," was the sepulchral reply, "the seven hundred and seventy-seventh wouldn't be too much, would it?—'where moth and rust do corrupt, but *lay*—'"

Lay, indeed, thought I, and such a lay! the seven hundred and seventy-seventh! Well, old Bildad, you are determined that I, for one, shall not *lay* up many *lays* here below, where moth and rust do corrupt. It was an exceedingly *long lay* that, indeed; and though from the magnitude of the figure it might at first deceive a landsman, yet the slightest consideration will show that though seven hundred and seventy-seven is a pretty large number, yet, when you come to make a *teenth* of it, you will then see, I say, that the seven hundred and seventy-seventh part of a farthing is a good deal less than seven hundred and seventy-seven gold doubloons; and so I thought at the time.

"Why, blast your eyes, Bildad," cried Peleg, "thou dost not want to swindle this young man! he must have more than that."

"Seven hundred and seventy-seventh," again said Bildad, without lifting his eyes; and then went on mumbling—"for where your treasure is, there will your heart be also."

"I am going to put him down for the three hundredth," said Peleg, "do ye hear that, Bildad! The three hundredth lay, I say."

Bildad laid down his book, and turning solemnly towards him said, "Captain Peleg, thou hast a generous heart; but thou must consider the duty thou owest to the other owners of this ship—widows and orphans, many of them—and that if we too abundantly reward the labors of this young man,· we may be taking the bread from those widows and those orphans. The seven hundred and seventy-seventh lay, Captain Peleg."

"Thou Bildad!" roared Peleg, starting up and clattering about the cabin. "Blast ye, Captain Bildad, if I had followed thy advice in these matters, I would afore now had a conscience to lug about that would be heavy enough to founder the largest ship that ever sailed round Cape Horn."

"Captain Peleg," said Bildad steadily, "thy conscience may be drawing ten inches of water, or ten fathoms, I can't tell; but as thou art still an impenitent man, Captain Peleg, I greatly fear lest thy conscience be but a leaky one; and will in the end sink thee foundering down to the fiery pit, Captain Peleg."

"Fiery pit! fiery pit! ye insult me, man; past all natural bearing, ye insult me. It's an all-fired outrage to tell any human creature that he's bound to hell. Flukes and flames! Bildad, say that again to me, and start my soul-bolts, but I'll—I'll—yes, I'll swallow a live goat with all his hair and horns on. Out of the cabin, ye canting, drab-colored son of a wooden gun—a straight wake with ye!"

As he thundered out this he made a rush at Bildad, but with a marvellous oblique, sliding celerity, Bildad for that time eluded him.

Alarmed at this terrible outburst between the two principal and responsible owners of the ship, and feeling half a mind to give up all idea of sailing in a vessel so questionably owned and temporarily commanded, I stepped aside from the door to give egress to Bildad, who, I made no doubt, was all eagerness to vanish from before the awakened wrath of Peleg. But to my astonishment, he sat down again on the transom very quietly, and seemed to have not the slightest intention of withdrawing. He seemed quite used to impenitent Peleg and his ways. As for Peleg, after letting off his rage as he had, there seemed no more left in him, and he, too, sat down like a lamb, though he twitched a little as if still nervously agitated. "Whew!" he whistled at last—"the squall's gone off to leeward, I think. Bildad, thou used to be good at sharpening a lance, mend that pen, will ye. My jack-knife here needs the grindstone. That's he; thank ye, Bildad. Now then, my young man, Ishmael's thy name, didn't ye say? Well then, down ye go here, Ishmael, for the three hundredth lay."

"Captain Peleg," said I, "I have a friend with me who wants to ship too— shall I bring him down to-morrow."

"To be sure," said Peleg. "Fetch him along, and we'll look at him."

"What lay does he want?" groaned Bildad, glancing up from the book in which he had again been burying himself.

"Oh! never thee mind about that, Bildad," said Peleg. "Has he ever whaled it any?" turning to me.

"Killed more whales than I can count, Captain Peleg."

"Well, bring him along then."

And, after signing the papers, off I went; nothing doubting but that I had done a good morning's work, and that the Pequod was the identical ship that Yojo had provided to carry Queequeg and me round the Cape.

But I had not proceeded far, when I began to bethink me that the Captain with whom I was to sail yet remained unseen by me; though, indeed, in many cases, a whale-ship will be completely fitted out, and receive all her crew on board, ere the captain makes himself visible by arriving to take command; for sometimes these voyages are so prolonged, and the shore intervals at home so exceedingly brief, that if the captain have a family, or any absorbing concernment of that sort, he does not trouble himself much about his ship in port, but leaves her to the owners till all is ready for sea. However, it is always as well to have a look at him before irrevocably committing yourself into his hands. Turning back I accosted Captain Peleg, inquiring where Captain Ahab was to be found.

"And what dost thou want of Captain Ahab? It's all right enough; thou art shipped."

"Yes, but I should like to see him."

"But I don't think thou wilt be able to at present. I don't know exactly what's the matter with him; but he keeps close inside the house; a sort of sick, and yet he don't look so. In fact, he ain't sick; but no, he isn't well either. Anyhow, young man, he won't always see me, so I don't suppose he will thee. He's a queer man, Captain Ahab—so some think—but a good one. Oh, thou'lt like him well enough; no fear, no fear. He's a grand, ungodly, god-like man, Captain Ahab; doesn't speak much; but, when he does speak, then you may well listen. Mark ye, be forewarned; Ahab's above the common; Ahab's been in colleges, as well as 'mong the cannibals; been used to deeper wonders than the waves; fixed his fiery lance in mightier, stranger foes than whales. His lance; aye, the keenest and surest that out of all our isle! Oh! he ain't Captain Bildad; no, and he ain't Captain Peleg; *he's Ahab*, boy; and Ahab of old, thou knowest, was a crowned king!"

"And a very vile one. When that wicked king was slain, the dogs, did they not lick his blood?"

"Come hither to me—hither, hither," said Peleg, with a significance in his eye that almost startled me. "Look ye, lad; never say that on board the Pequod. Never say it anywhere. Captain Ahab did not name himself. 'Twas a foolish, ignorant whim of his crazy, widowed mother, who died when he was only a twelvemonth old. And yet the old squaw Tistig, at Gayhead, said that the name would somehow prove prophetic. And, perhaps, other fools like her may tell thee the same. I wish to warn thee. It's a lie. I know Captain Ahab well; I've sailed with him as mate years ago; I know what he is—a good man—not a pious, good man, like Bildad, but a swearing good man—something like me —only there's a good deal more of him. Aye, aye, I know that he was never very jolly; and I know that on the passage home, he was a little out of his mind for a spell; but it was the sharp shooting pains in his bleeding stump that brought that about, as any one might see. I know, too, that ever since he lost his leg last voyage by that accursed whale, he's been a kind of moody—desperate moody, and savage sometimes; but that will all pass off. And once for all, let me tell thee and assure thee, young man, it's better to sail with a moody good captain than a laughing bad one. So good-bye to thee—and wrong not Captain Ahab, because he happens to have a wicked name. Besides, my boy, he has a wife—not three voyages wedded—a sweet, resigned girl. Think of that; by that sweet girl that old man had a child: hold ye then there can be any utter, hopeless harm in Ahab? No, no, my lad; stricken, blasted, if he be, Ahab has his humanities!"

As I walked away, I was full of thoughtfulness; what had been incidentally revealed to me of Captain Ahab, filled me with a certain wild vagueness of painfulness concerning him. And somehow, at the time, I felt a sympathy and a sorrow for him, but for I don't know what, unless it was the cruel loss of his leg. And yet I also felt a strange awe of him; but that sort of awe, which I cannot at all describe, was not exactly awe; I do not know what it was. But I felt it; and it did not disincline me towards him; though I felt impatience at what seemed like mystery in him, so imperfectly as he was known to me then. However, my thoughts were at length carried in other directions, so that for the present dark Ahab slipped my mind.

CHAPTER XVII

THE RAMADAN

As Queequeg's Ramadan, or Fasting and Humiliation, was to continue all day, I did not choose to disturb him till towards night-fall; for I cherish the greatest respect towards everybody's religious obligations, never mind how comical, and could not find it in my heart to undervalue even a congregation of ants worshipping a toad-stool; or those other creatures in certain parts of our earth, who with a degree of footmanism quite unprecedented in other planets, bow down before the torso of a deceased landed proprietor merely on account of the inordinate possessions yet owned and rented in his name.

I say, we good Presbyterian Christians should be charitable in these things, and not fancy ourselves so vastly superior to other mortals, pagans and what not, because of their half-crazy conceits on these subjects. There was Queequeg, now, certainly entertaining the most absurd notions about Yojo and his Ramadan;—but what of that? Queequeg thought he knew what he was about, I suppose; he seemed to be content; and there let him rest. All our arguing with him would not avail; let him be, I say: and Heaven have mercy on us all—Presbyterians and Pagans alike—for we are all somehow dreadfully cracked about the head, and sadly need mending.

Toward evening, when I felt assured that all his performances and rituals must be over, I went up to his room and knocked at the door; but no answer. I tried to open it, but it was fastened inside. "Queequeg," said I softly through the keyhole:—all silent. "I say, Queequeg! why don't you speak? It's I—Ishmael." But all remained still as before. I began to grow alarmed. I had allowed him such abundant time; I thought he might have had an apoplectic fit. I looked through the key-hole; but the door opening into an odd corner of the room, the key-hole prospect was but a crooked and sinister one. I could only see part of the foot-board of the bed and a line of the wall, but nothing more. I was surprised to behold resting against the wall the wooden shaft of Queequeg's harpoon, which the landlady the evening previous had taken from him, before our mounting to the chamber. That's strange, thought I; but at any rate, since the harpoon stands yonder, and he seldom or never goes abroad without it, therefore he must be inside here, and no possible mistake.

"Queequeg!—Queequeg!"—all still. Something must have happened.

Apoplexy! I tried to burst open the door; but it stubbornly resisted. Running down stairs, I quickly stated my suspicions to the first person I met—the chambermaid. "La! la!" she cried, "I thought something must be the matter. I went to make the bed after breakfast, and the door was locked; and not a mouse to be heard; and it's been just so silent ever since. But I thought, maybe, you had both gone off and locked your baggage in for safe keeping. La! La, ma'am!—Mistress! murder! Mrs. Hussey! apoplexy!"—and with these cries she ran towards the kitchen, I following.

Mrs. Hussey soon appeared, with a mustard-pot in one hand and a vinegar-cruet in the other, having just broken away from the occupation of attending to the castors, and scolding her little black boy meantime.

"Wood-house!" cried I, "which way to it? Run for God's sake, and fetch something to pry open the door—the axe!—the axe!—he's had a stroke; depend upon it!"—and so saying I was unmethodically rushing up stairs again empty-handed, when Mrs. Hussey interposed the mustard-pot and vinegar-cruet, and the entire castor of her countenance.

"What's the matter with you, young man?"

"Get the axe! For God's sake, run for the doctor, some one, while I pry it open!"

"Look here," said the landlady, quickly putting down the vinegar-cruet, so as to have one hand free; "look here; are you talking about prying open any of my doors?"—and with that she seized my arm. "What's the matter with you? What's the matter with you, shipmate?"

In as calm, but rapid a manner as possible, I gave her to understand the whole case. Unconsciously clapping the vinegar-cruet to one side of her nose, she ruminated for an instant; then exclaimed—"No! I haven't seen it since I put it there." Running to a little closet under the landing of the stairs, she glanced in, and returning, told me that Queequeg's harpoon was missing. "He's killed himself," she cried. "It's unfort'nate Stiggs done over again—there goes another counterpane—God pity his poor mother!—it will be the ruin of my house. Has the poor lad a sister? Where's that girl?—there, Betty, go to Snarles the Painter, and tell him to paint me a sign, with—"no suicides permitted here, and no smoking in the parlor;"—might as well kill both birds at once. Kill? The Lord be merciful to his ghost! What's that noise there? You, young man, avast there!"

And running after me, she caught me as I was again trying to force open the door.

"I won't allow it; I won't have my premises spoiled. Go for the locksmith, there's one about a mile from here. But avast!" putting her hand in her side pocket, "here's a key that'll fit, I guess; let's see." And with that, she turned it in the lock; but, alas! Queequeg's supplemental bolt remained unwithdrawn within.

"Have to burst it open," said I, and was running down the entry a little, for a good start, when the landlady caught at me, again vowing I should not break down her premises; but I tore from her, and with a sudden bodily rush dashed myself full against the mark.

With a prodigious noise the door flew open, and the knob slamming against the door, sent the plaster to the ceiling; and there, good heavens! there sat Queequeg, altogether cool and self-collected; right in the middle of the room; squatting on his hams, and holding Yojo on top of his head. He looked neither one way nor the other way, but sat like a carved image with scarce a sign of active life.

"Queequeg," said, I, going up to him, "Queequeg, what's the matter with you?"

"He hain't been a sittin' so all day, has he?" said the landlady.

But all we said, not a word could we drag out of him; I almost felt like pushing him over, so as to change his position, for it was almost intolerable, it seemed so painfully and unnaturally constrained; especially, as in all probability he had been sitting so for upwards of eight or ten hours, going too without his regular meals.

"Mrs. Hussey," said I, "he's *alive* at all events; so leave us, if you please, and I will see to this strange affair myself."

Closing the door upon the landlady, I endeavored to prevail upon Queequeg to take a chair; but in vain. There he sat; and all he could do—for all my polite arts and blandishments—he would not move a peg, nor say a single word, not even look at me, nor notice my presence in any the slightest way.

I wonder, thought I, if this can possibly be a part of his Ramadan; do they fast on their hams that way in his native island. It must be so; yes, it's a part of his creed, I suppose; well, then, let him rest; he'll get up sooner or later, no doubt. It can't last for ever, thank God, and his Ramadan only comes once a year; and I don't believe it's very punctual then.

I went down to supper. After sitting a long time listening to the long stories of some sailors who had just come from a plum-pudding voyage, as they called it (that is, a short whaling-voyage in a schooner or brig, confined to the north of the line, in the Atlantic Ocean only); after listening to these plum-puddingers till nearly eleven o'clock, I went up stairs to go to bed, feeling quite sure by this time Queequeg must certainly have brought his Ramadan to a termination. But no; there he was just where I had left him; he had not stirred an inch. I began to grow vexed with him; it seemed so downright senseless and insane to be sitting there all day and half the night on his hams in a cold room, holding a piece of wood on his head.

"For heaven's sake, Queequeg, get up and shake yourself; get up and have some supper. You'll starve; you'll kill yourself, Queequeg." But not a word did he reply.

Despairing of him, therefore, I determined to go to bed and to sleep; and no doubt, before a great while, he would follow me. But previous to turning in, I took my heavy bearskin jacket, and threw it over him, as it promised to be a very cold night; and he had nothing but his ordinary round jacket on. For some time, do all I would, I could not get into the faintest doze. I had blown out the candle; and the mere thought of Queequeg—not four feet off— sitting there in that uneasy position, stark alone in the cold and dark; this made me really wretched. Think of it; sleeping all night in the same room with a wide awake pagan on his hams in this dreary, unaccountable Ramadan!

But somehow I dropped off at last, and knew nothing more till break of day; when, looking over the bedside, there squatted Queequeg, as if he had been screwed down to the floor. But as soon as the first glimpse of sun entered the window, up he got, with stiff and grating joints, but with a cheerful look; limped towards me where I lay; pressed his forehead again against mine; and said his Ramadan was over.

Now, as I before hinted, I have no objection to any person's religion, be it what it may, so long as that person does not kill or insult any other person, because that other person don't believe it also. But when a man's religion becomes really frantic; when it is a positive torment to him; and, in fine, makes this earth of ours an uncomfortable inn to lodge in; then I think it high time to take that individual aside and argue the point with him.

And just so I now did with Queequeg. "Queequeg," said I, "get into bed now, and lie and listen to me." I then went on, beginning with the rise and progress of the primitive religions, and coming down to the various religions of the present time, during which time I labored to show Queequeg that all these Lents, Ramadans, and prolonged ham-squattings in cold, cheerless rooms were stark nonsense; bad for the health; useless for the soul; opposed, in short, to the obvious laws of Hygiene and common sense. I told him, too, that he being in other things such an extremely sensible and sagacious savage, it pained me, very badly pained me, to see him now so deplorably foolish about this ridiculous Ramadan of his. Besides, argued I, fasting makes the body cave in; hence the spirit caves in; and all thoughts born of a fast must necessarily be half-starved. This is the reason why most dyspeptic religionists cherish such melancholy notions about their hereafters. In one word, Queequeg, said I, rather digressively; hell is an idea first born on an undigested apple-dumpling; and since then perpetuated through the hereditary dyspepsias nurtured by Ramadans.

I then asked Queequeg whether he himself was ever troubled with dyspepsia; expressing the idea very plainly, so that he could take it in. He said no; only upon one memorable occasion. It was after a great feast given by his father the king, on the gaining of a great battle wherein fifty of the enemy had been killed by about two o'clock in the afternoon, and all cooked and eaten that very evening.

"No more, Queequeg," said I, shuddering; "that will do;" for I knew the inferences without his further hinting them. I had seen a sailor who had visited that very island, and he told me that it was the custom, when a great battle had been gained there, to barbecue all the slain in the yard or garden of the victor; and then, one by one, they were placed in great wooden trenchers, and garnished round like a pilau, with breadfruit and cocoanuts; and with some parsley in their mouths, were sent round with the victor's compliments to all his friends, just as though these presents were so many Christmas turkeys.

After all, I do not think that my remarks about religion made much impression upon Queequeg. Because, in the first place, he somehow seemed dull of hearing on that important subject, unless considered from his own point of view; and, in the second place, he did not more than one third understand me, couch my ideas simply as I would; and, finally, he no doubt thought he knew a good deal more about the true religion than I did. He looked at me with a sort of condescending concern and compassion, as though he thought it a great pity that such a sensible young man should be so hopelessly lost to evangelical pagan piety.

At last we rose and dressed; and Queequeg, taking a prodigious hearty breakfast of chowders of all sorts, so that the landlady should not make much profit by reason of his Ramadan, we sallied out to board the Pequod, sauntering along, and picking our teeth with halibut bones.

CHAPTER XVIII

HIS MARK

As we were walking down the end of the wharf towards the ship, Queequeg carrying his harpoon, Captain Peleg in his gruff voice loudly hailed us from his wigwam, saying he had not suspected my friend was a cannibal, and furthermore announcing that he let no cannibals on board that craft, unless they previously produced their papers.

"What do you mean by that, Captain Peleg?" said I, now jumping on the bulwarks, and leaving my comrade standing on the wharf.

"I mean," he replied, "he must show his papers."

"Yea," said Captain Bildad in his hollow voice, sticking his head from behind Peleg's, out of the wigwam. "He must show that he's converted. Son of darkness," he added, turning to Queequeg, "art thou at present in communion with any Christian church?"

"Why," said I, "he's a member of the first Congregational Church." Here be it said, that many tattooed savages sailing in Nantucket ships at last come to be converted into the churches.

"First Congregational Church," cried Bildad, "what! that worships in Deacon Deuteronomy Coleman's meeting-house?" and so saying, taking out his spectacles, he rubbed them with his great yellow bandana handkerchief, and putting them on very carefully, came out of the wigwam, and leaning stiffly over the bulwarks, took a good long look at Queequeg.

"How long hath he been a member?" he then said, turning to me; "not very long, I rather guess, young man."

"No," said Peleg, "and he hasn't been baptized right either, or it would have washed some of that devil's blue off his face."

"Do tell, now," cried Bildad, "is this Philistine a regular member of Deacon Deuteronomy's meeting? I never saw him going there, and I pass it every Lord's day."

"I don't know anything about Deacon Deuteronomy or his meeting," said I, "all I know is, that Queequeg here is a born member of the First Congregational Church. He is a deacon himself, Queequeg is."

"Young man," said Bildad sternly, "thou art skylarking with me—explain thyself, thou young Hittite. What church dost thee mean? answer me."

Finding myself thus hard pushed, I replied. "I mean, sir, the same ancient Catholic Church to which you and I, and Captain Peleg there, and Queequeg here, and all of us, and every mother's son and soul of us belong; the great and everlasting First Congregation of this whole worshipping world; we all belong to that; only some of us cherish some crotchets noways touching the grand belief; in *that* we all join hands."

"Splice, thou mean'st *splice* hands," cried Peleg, drawing nearer. "Young man, you'd better ship for a missionary, instead of a fore-mast hand; I never heard a better sermon. Deacon Deuteronomy—why Father Mapple himself couldn't beat it, and he's reckon something. Come aboard, come aboard; never mind about the papers. I say, tell Quohog there—what's that you call him? tell Quohog to step along. By the great anchor, what a harpoon he's got there! looks like good stuff that; and he handles it about right. I say, Quohog, or whatever your name is, did you ever stand in the head of a whale-boat? did you ever strike a fish?"

Without saying a word, Queequeg, in his wild sort of way, jumped upon the bulwarks, from thence into the bows of one of the whale-boats hanging to the side; and then bracing his left knee, and poising his harpoon, cried out in some such way as this:—

"Cap'ain, you see him small drop tar on water dere? You see him? well, spose him one whale eye, well, den!" and taking sharp aim at it, he darted the iron right over old Bildad's broad brim, clean across the ship's decks, and struck the glistening tar spot out of sight.

"Now," said Queequeg, quietly hauling in the line, "spos-ee him whale-e eye; why, dad whale dead."

"Quick, Bildad," said Peleg, his partner, who, aghast at the close vicinity of the flying harpoon, had retreated towards the cabin gangway. "Quick, I say, you Bildad, and get the ship's papers. We must have Hedgehog there, I mean Quohog, in one of our boats. Look ye, Quohog, we'll give ye the ninetieth lay, and that's more than ever was given a harpooneer yet out of Nantucket."

So down we went into the cabin, and to my great joy Queequeg was soon enrolled among the same ship's company to which I myself belonged.

When all preliminaries were over and Peleg had got everything ready for signing, he turned to me and said, "I guess, Quohog there don't know how to write, does he? I say, Quohog, blast ye! dost thou sign thy name or make thy mark?"

But at this question, Queequeg, who had twice or thrice before taken part in similar ceremonies, looked no ways abashed; but taking the offered pen, copied upon the paper, in the proper place, an exact counterpart of a queer round figure which was tattooed upon his arm; so that through Captain Peleg's obstinate mistake touching his appellative, it stood something like this:—

Quohog.

his ✠ mark.

Meanwhile Captain Bildad sat earnestly and steadfastly eyeing Queequeg, and at last rising solemnly and fumbling in the huge pockets of his broad-skirted drab coat, took out a bundle of tracts, and selecting one entitled "The Latter Day Coming; or No Time to Lose," placed it in Queequeg's hands, and then grasping them and the book with both his, looked earnestly into his eyes, and said, "Son of darkness, I must do my duty by thee; I am part owner of this ship, and feel concerned for the souls of all its crew; if thou still clingest to thy Pagan ways, which I sadly fear, I beseech thee, remain not for aye a Belial bondsman. Spurn the idol Bell, and the hideous dragon; turn from the wrath to come; mind thine eye, I say; oh! goodness gracious! steer clear of the fiery pit!"

Something of the salt sea yet lingered in old Bildad's language, hetero-geneously mixed with Scriptural and domestic phrases.

"Avast there, avast there, Bildad, avast now spoiling our harpooneer," cried Peleg. "Pious harpooneers never make good voyages—it takes the shark out of 'em; no harpooneer is worth a straw who ain't pretty sharkish. There was young Nat Swaine, once the bravest boat-header out of all Nantucket and the Vineyard; he joined the meeting, and never came to good. He got so fright-ened about his plaguy soul, that he shrinked and sheered away from whales, for fear of afterclaps, in case he got stove and went to Davy Jones'."

"Peleg! Peleg!" said Bildad, lifting his eyes and hands, "thou thyself, as I myself, hast seen many a perilous time; thou knowest, Peleg, what it is to have the fear of death; how, then, can'st thou prate in this ungodly guise?

Thou beliest thine own heart, Peleg. Tell me, when this same Pequod here had her three masts overboard in that typhoon on Japan, that same voyage when thou went mate with Captain Ahab, did'st thou not think of Death and the Judgment then?"

"Hear him, hear him now," cried Peleg, marching across the cabin, and thrusting his hands far down into his pockets,—"hear him, all of ye. Think of that! When every moment we thought the ship would sink! Death and the Judgment then? What? With all three masts making such an everlasting thundering against the side; and every sea breaking over us, fore and aft. Think of Death and the Judgment then? No! no time to think about Death then. Life was what Captain Ahab and I was thinking of; and how to save all hands— how to rig jury-masts—how to get into the nearest port; that was what I was thinking of."

Bildad said no more, but buttoning up his coat, stalked on deck, where we followed him. There he stood, very quietly overlooking some sail-makers who were mending a top-sail in the waist. Now and then he stooped to pick up a patch, or save an end of the tarred twine, which otherwise might have been wasted.

CHAPTER XIX

THE PROPHET

"Shipmates, have ye shipped in that ship?"

Queequeg and I had just left the Pequod, and were sauntering away from the water, for the moment each occupied with his own thoughts, when the above words were put to us by a stranger, who, pausing before us, levelled his massive forefinger at the vessel in question. He was but shabbily apparelled in faded jacket and patched trousers; a rag of a black handkerchief investing his neck. A confluent small-pox had in all directions flowed over his face, and left it like the complicated ribbed bed of a torrent, when the rushing waters have been dried up.

"Have ye shipped in her?" he repeated.

"You mean the ship Pequod, I suppose," said I, trying to gain a little more time for an uninterrupted look at him.

"Aye, the Pequod—that ship there," he said, drawing back his whole arm, and then rapidly shoving it straight out from him, with the fixed bayonet of his pointed finger darted full at the object.

"Yes," said I, "we have just signed the articles."

"Anything down there about your souls?"

"About what?"

"Oh, perhaps you hav'n't got any," he said quickly. "No matter though, I know many chaps that hav'n't got any,—good luck to 'em; and they are all the better off for it. A soul's a sort of a fifth wheel to a wagon."

"What are you jabbering about, shipmate?" said I.

"*He's* got enough, though, to make up for all deficiencies of that sort in other chaps," abruptly said the stranger, placing a nervous emphasis upon the word *he*.

"Queequeg," said I, "let's go; this fellow has broken loose from somewhere; he's talking about something and somebody we don't know."

"Stop!" cried the stranger. "Ye said true—ye hav'n't seen Old Thunder yet, have ye?"

"Who's Old Thunder?" said I, again riveted with the insane earnestness of his manner.

"Captain Ahab."

"What! the captain of our ship, the Pequod?"

"Aye, among some of us old sailor chaps, he goes by that name. Ye hav'n't seen him yet, have ye?"

"No, we hav'n't. He's sick they say, but is getting better, and will be all right again before long."

"All right again before long!" laughed the stranger, with a solemnly derisive sort of laugh. "Look ye; when Captain Ahab is all right, then this left arm of mine will be all right; not before."

"What do you know about him?"

"What did they *tell* you about him? Say that!"

"They didn't tell much of anything about him; only I've heard that he's a good whale-hunter, and a good captain to his crew."

"That's true, that's true—yes, both true enough. But you must jump when he gives an order. Step and growl; growl and go—that's the word with Captain Ahab. But nothing about that thing that happened to him off Cape Horn, long ago, when he lay like dead for three days and nights; nothing about that deadly skrimmage with the Spaniard afore the altar in Santa?— heard nothing about that, eh? Nothing about the silver calabash he spat into? And nothing about his losing his leg last voyage, according to the prophecy. Didn't ye hear a word about them matters and something more, eh? No, I don't think ye did; how could ye? Who knows it? Not all Nantucket, I guess. But hows'ever, mayhap, ye've heard tell about the leg, and how he lost it; aye, ye have heard of that, I dare say. Oh yes, *that* every one knows a'most— I mean they know he's only one leg; and that a parmacetti took the other off."

"My friend," said I, "what all this gibberish of yours is about, I don't know, and I don't much care; for it seems to me that you must be a little damaged in the head. But if you are speaking of Captain Ahab, of that ship there, the Pequod, then let me tell you, that I know all about the loss of his leg."

"*All* about it, eh—sure you do?—all?"

"Pretty sure."

With finger pointed and eye levelled at the Pequod, the beggar-like stranger stood a moment, as if in a troubled reverie; then starting a little, turned and said:—"Ye've shipped, have ye? Names down on the papers? Well, well, what's signed, is signed; and what's to be, will be; and then again, perhaps it won't be, after all. Anyhow, it's all fixed and arranged a'ready; and some sailors or other must go with him, I suppose; as well these as any other men, God pity 'em! Morning to ye, shipmates, morning; the ineffable heavens bless ye; I'm sorry I stopped ye."

"Look here, friend," said I, "if you have anything important to tell us, out with it; but if you are only trying to bamboozle us, you are mistaken in your game; that's all I have to say."

"And it's said very well, and I like to hear a chap talk up that way; you are just the man for him—the likes of ye. Morning to ye, shipmates, morning! Oh! when ye get there, tell 'em I've concluded not to make one of 'em."

"Ah, my dear fellow, you can't fool us that way—you can't fool us. It is the easiest thing in the world for a man to look as if he had a great secret in him."

"Morning to ye, shipmates, morning."

"Morning it is," said I. "Come along, Queequeg, let's leave this crazy man. But stop, tell me your name, will you?"

"Elijah."

Elijah! thought I, and we walked away, both commenting, after each other's fashion, upon this ragged old sailor; and agreed that he was nothing but a humbug, trying to be a bugbear. But we had not gone perhaps above a hundred yards, when chancing to turn a corner, and looking back as I did so, who should be seen but Elijah following us, though at a distance. Somehow, the sight of him struck me so, that I said nothing to Queequeg of his being behind, but passed on with my comrade, anxious to see whether the stranger would turn the same corner that we did. He did; and then it seemed to me that he was dogging us, but with what intent I could not for the life of me imagine. This circumstance, coupled with his ambiguous, half-hinting, half-revealing, shrouded sort of talk, now begat in me all kinds of vague wonderments and half-apprehensions, and all connected with the Pequod; and Captain Ahab; and the leg he had lost; and the Cape Horn fit; and the silver calabash; and what Captain Peleg had said of him, when I left the ship the day previous; and the prediction of the squaw Tistig; and the voyage we had bound ourselves to sail; and a hundred other shadowy things.

I was resolved to satisfy myself whether this ragged Elijah was really dogging us or not, and with that intent crossed the way with Queequeg, and on that side of it retraced our steps. But Elijah passed on, without seeming to notice us. This relieved me; and once more, and finally as it seemed to me, I pronounced him in my heart, a humbug.

CHAPTER XX

ALL ASTIR

A DAY or two passed, and there was great activity aboard the Pequod. Not only were the old sails being mended, but new sails were coming on board, and bolts of canvas, and coils of rigging; in short, everything betokened that the ship's preparations were hurrying to a close. Captain Peleg seldom or never went ashore, but sat in his wigwam keeping a sharp look-out upon the hands: Bildad did all the purchasing and providing at the stores; and the men employed in the hold and on the rigging were working till long after night-fall.

On the day following Queequeg's signing articles, word was given at all the inns where the ship's company were stopping, that their chests must be on board before night, for there was no telling how soon the vessel might be sailing. So Queequeg and I got down our traps, resolving, however, to sleep ashore till the last. But it seems they always give very long notice in these cases, and the ship did not sail for several days. But no wonder; there was a good deal to be done, and there is no telling how many things to be thought of, before the Pequod was fully equipped.

Every one knows what a multitude of things—beds, saucepans, knives and

forks, shovels and tongs, napkins, nut-crackers, and what not, are indispensable
to the business of housekeeping. Just so with whaling, which necessitates a
three-years' housekeeping upon the wide ocean, far from all grocers, coster-
mongers, doctors, bakers, and bankers. And though this also holds true of
merchant vessels, yet not by any means to the same extent as with whalemen.
For besides the great length of the whaling voyage, the numerous articles
peculiar to the prosecution of the fishery, and the impossibility of replacing
them at the remote harbors usually frequented, it must be remembered, that
of all ships, whaling vessels are the most exposed to accidents of all kinds,
and especially to the destruction and loss of the very things upon which the
success of the voyage most depends. Hence, the spare boats, spare spars, and
spare lines and harpoons, and spare everythings, almost, but a spare Captain
and duplicate ship.

At the period of our arrival at the Island, the heaviest storage of the Pequod
had been almost completed; comprising her beef, bread, water, fuel, and iron
hoops and staves. But, as before hinted, for some time there was a continual fetching and carrying on board of divers odds and ends of things, both
large and small.

Chief among those who did this fetching and carrying was Captain Bildad's
sister, a lean old lady of a most determined and indefatigable spirit, but withal
very kindhearted, who seemed resolved that, if *she* could help it, nothing should
be found wanting in the Pequod, after once fairly getting to sea. At one time
she would come on board with a jar of pickles for the steward's pantry; another
time with a bunch of quills for the chief mate's desk, where he kept his log;
a third time with a roll of flannel for the small of some one's rheumatic back.
Never did any woman better deserve her name, which was Charity—Aunt Charity, as everybody called her. And like a sister of charity did this charitable
Aunt Charity bustle about hither and thither, ready to turn her hand and heart
to anything that promised to yield safety, comfort, and consolation to all on
board a ship in which her beloved brother Bildad was concerned, and in which
she herself owned a score or two of well-saved dollars.

But it was startling to see this excellent hearted Quakeress coming on board,
as she did the last day, with a long oil-ladle in one hand, and a still longer
whaling lance in the other. Nor was Bildad himself nor Captain Peleg at all
backward. As for Bildad, he carried about with him a long list of the articles
needed, and at every fresh arrival, down went his mark opposite that article
upon the paper. Every once and a while Peleg came hobbling out of his whalebone den, roaring at the men down the hatchways, roaring up to the riggers
at the mast-head, and then concluded by roaring back into his wigwam.

During these days of preparation, Queequeg and I often visited the craft,
and as often I asked about Captain Ahab, and how he was, and when he was
going to come on board his ship. To these questions they would answer, that
he was getting better and better, and was expected aboard every day; meantime, the two Captains, Peleg and Bildad, could attend to everything necessary
to fit the vessel for the voyage. If I had been downright honest with myself,
I would have seen very plainly in my heart that I did but half fancy being
committed this way to so long a voyage, without once laying my eyes on
the man who was to be the absolute dictator of it, so soon as the ship sailed
out upon the open sea. But when a man suspects any wrong, it sometimes
happens that if he be already involved in the matter, he insensibly strives to
cover up his suspicions even from himself. And much this way it was with me.
I said nothing, and tried to think nothing.

At last it was given out that some time next day the ship would certainly sail. So next morning, Queequeg and I took a very early start.

CHAPTER XXI

GOING ABOARD

It was nearly six o'clock, but only grey imperfect misty dawn, when we drew nigh the wharf.

"There are some sailors running ahead there, if I see right," said I to Queequeg, "it can't be shadow; she's off by sunrise, I guess; come on!"

"Avast!" cried a voice, whose owner at the same time coming close behind us, laid a hand upon both our shoulders, and then insinuating himself between us, stood stooping forward a little, in the uncertain twilight, strangely peering from Queequeg to me. It was Elijah.

"Going aboard?"

"Hands off, will you," said I.

"Lookee here," said Queequeg, shaking himself, "go 'way!"

"Ain't going aboard, then?"

"Yes, we are," said I, "but what business is that of yours? Do you know, Mr. Elijah, that I consider you a little impertinent?"

"No, no, no; I wasn't aware of that," said Elijah, slowly and wonderingly looking from me to Queequeg, with the most unaccountable glances.

"Elijah," said I, "you will oblige my friend and me by withdrawing. We are going to the Indian and Pacific Oceans, and would prefer not to be detained."

"Ye be, be ye? Coming back afore breakfast?"

"He's cracked, Queequeg," said I, "come on."

"Holloa!" cried stationary Elijah, hailing us when we had removed a few paces.

"Never mind him," said I, "Queequeg, come on."

But he stole up to us again, and suddenly clapping his hand on my shoulder, said—"Did ye see anything looking like men going towards that ship a while ago?"

Struck by this plain matter-of-fact question, I answered, saying "Yes, I thought I did see four or five men; but it was too dim to be sure."

"Very dim, very dim," said Elijah. "Morning to ye."

Once more we quitted him; but once more he came softly after us; and touching my shoulder again, said, "See if you can find 'em now, will ye?"

"Find who?"

"Morning to ye! morning to ye!" he rejoined, again moving off. "Oh! I was going to warn ye against—but never mind, never mind—it's all one, all in the family too;—sharp frost this morning, ain't it? Good-bye to ye. Shan't see ye again very soon, I guess; unless it's before the Grand Jury." And with these cracked words he finally departed, leaving me, for the moment, in no small wonderment at his frantic impudence.

At last, stepping on board the Pequod, we found everything in profound quiet, not a soul moving. The cabin entrance was locked within; the hatches

were all on, and lumbered with coils of rigging. Going forward to the forecastle, we found the slide of the scuttle open. Seeing a light, we went down,
and found only an old rigger there, wrapped in a tattered pea-jacket. He
was thrown at whole length upon two chests, his face downwards and inclosed
in his folded arms. The profoundest slumber slept upon him.

"Those sailors we saw, Queequeg, where can they have gone to?" said I,
looking dubiously at the sleeper. But it seemed that, when on the wharf,
Queequeg had not at all noticed what I now alluded to; hence I would have
thought myself to have been optically deceived in that matter, were it not
for Elijah's otherwise inexplicable question. But I beat the thing down; and
again marking the sleeper, jocularly hinted to Queequeg that perhaps we had
best sit up with the body; telling him to establish himself accordingly. He
put his hand upon the sleeper's rear, as though feeling if it was soft enough;
and then, without more ado, sat quietly down there.

"Gracious! Queequeg, don't sit there," said I.

"Oh! perry dood seat," said Queequeg, "my country way; won't hurt him
face."

"Face!" said I, "call that his face? very benevolent countenance then; but
how hard he breathes, he's heaving himself; get off, Queequeg, you are heavy,
it's grinding the face of the poor. Get off, Queequeg! Look, he'll twitch you
off soon. I wonder he don't wake."

Queequeg removed himself to just beyond the head of the sleeper, and
lighted his tomahawk pipe. I sat at the feet. We kept the pipe passing over
the sleeper, from one to the other. Meanwhile, upon questioning him in his
broken fashion, Queequeg gave me to understand that, in his land, owing to
the absence of settees and sofas of all sorts, the king, chiefs, and great people
generally, were in the custom of fattening some of the lower orders for otto-
mans; and to furnish a house comfortably in that respect, you had only to buy
up eight or ten lazy fellows, and lay them round in the piers and alcoves. Besides, it was very convenient on an excursion; much better than those garden-
chairs which are convertible into walking-sticks; upon occasion, a chief calling
his attendant, and desiring him to make a settee of himself under a spreading
tree, perhaps in some damp marshy place.

While narrating these things, every time Queequeg received the tomahawk
from me, he flourished the hatchet-side of it over the sleeper's head.

"What's that for, Queequeg?"

"Perry easy, kill-e; oh! perry easy!"

He was going on with some wild reminiscences about his tomahawk-pipe,
which, it seemed, had in its two uses both brained his foes and soothed his
soul, when we were directly attracted to the sleeping rigger. The strong vapor
now completely filling the contracted hole, it began to tell upon him. He
breathed with a sort of muffledness; then seemed troubled in the nose; then
revolved over once or twice; then sat up and rubbed his eyes.

"Holloa!" he breathed at last, "who be ye smokers?"

"Shipped men," answered I, "when does she sail?"

"Aye, aye, ye are going in her, be ye? She sails to-day. The Captain
came aboard last night."

"What Captain?—Ahab?"

"Who but him indeed?"

I was going to ask him some further questions concerning Ahab, when
we heard a noise on deck.

"Holloa! Starbuck's astir," said the rigger. "He's a lively chief·mate, that; good man, and a pious; but all alive now, I must turn to." And so saying he went on deck, and we followed.

It was now clear sunrise. Soon the crew came on board in twos and threes; the riggers bestirred themselves; the mates were actively engaged; and several of the shore people were busy in bringing various last things on board. Meanwhile Captain Ahab remained invisibly enshrined within his cabin.

CHAPTER XXII

MERRY CHRISTMAS

AT length, towards noon, upon the final dismissal of the ship's riggers, and after the Pequod had been hauled out from the wharf, and after the ever-thoughtful Charity had come off in a whale-boat, with her last gift—a night-cap for Stubb, the second mate, her brother-in-law, and a spare Bible for the steward—after all this, the two Captains, Peleg and Bildad, issued from the cabin, and turning to the chief mate, Peleg said:

"Now, Mr. Starbuck, are you sure everything is right? Captain Ahab is all ready—just spoke to him—nothing more to be got from shore, eh? Well, call all hands, then. Muster 'em aft here—blast 'em!"

"No need of profane words, however great the hurry, Peleg," said Bildad, "but away with thee, friend Starbuck, and do our bidding."

How now! Here upon the very point of starting for the voyage, Captain Peleg and Captain Bildad were going it with a high hand on the quarter-deck, just as if they were to be joint-commanders at sea, as well as to all appearances in port. And, as for Captain Ahab, no sign of him was yet to be seen; only, they said he was in the cabin. But then, the idea was, that his presence was by no means necessary in getting the ship under weigh, and steering her well out to sea. Indeed, as that was not at all his proper business, but the pilot's; and as he was not yet completely recovered—so they said—therefore, Captain Ahab stayed below. And all this seemed natural enough; especially as in the merchant service many captains never show themselves on deck for a considerable time after heaving up the anchor, but remain over the cabin table, having a farewell merry-making with their shore friends, before they quit the ship for good with the pilot.

But there was not much chance to think over the matter, for Captain Peleg was now all alive. He seemed to do most of the talking and commanding, and not Bildad.

"Aft here, ye sons of bachelors," he cried, as the sailors lingered at the main-mast. "Mr. Starbuck, drive 'em aft."

"Strike the tent there!"—was the next order. As I hinted before, this whalebone marquee was never pitched except in port; and on board the Pequod, for thirty years, the order to strike the tent was well known to be the next thing to heaving up the anchor.

"Man the capstan! Blood and thunder!—jump"—was the next command, and the crew sprang for the handspikes.

Now, in getting under weigh, the station generally occupied by the pilot is the forward part of the ship. And here Bildad, who, with Peleg, be it known, in addition to his other offices, was one of the licensed pilots of the port—he being suspected to have got himself made a pilot in order to save the Nantucket pilot-fee to all the ships he was concerned in, for he never piloted any other craft—Bildad, I say, might now be seen actively engaged in looking over the bows for the approaching anchor, and at intervals singing what seemed a dismal stave of psalmody, to cheer the hands at the windlass, who roared forth some sort of a chorus about the girls in Booble Alley, with hearty good will. Nevertheless, not three days previous, Bildad had told them that no profane songs would be allowed on board the Pequod, particularly in getting under weigh; and Charity, his sister, had placed a small choice copy of Watts in each seaman's berth.

Meantime, overseeing the other part of the ship, Captain Peleg ripped and swore astern in the most frightful manner. I almost thought he would sink the ship before the anchor could be got up; involuntarily I paused on my handspike, and told Queequeg to do the same, thinking of the perils we both ran, in starting on the voyage with such a devil for a pilot. I was comforting myself, however, with the thought that in pious Bildad might be found some salvation, spite of his seven hundred and seventy-seventh lay; when I felt a sudden sharp poke in my rear, and turning round, was horrified at the apparition of Captain Peleg in the act of withdrawing his leg from my immediate vicinity. That was my first kick.

"Is that the way they heave in the marchant service?" he roared. "Spring, thou sheep-head; spring, and break thy backbone! Why don't ye spring, I say, all of ye—spring! Quohag! spring, thou chap with the red whiskers; spring there, Scotch-cap; spring, thou green pants. Spring, I say, all of ye, and spring your eyes out!" And so saying, he moved along the windlass, here and there using his leg very freely, while imperturbable Bildad kept leading off with his psalmody. Thinks I, Captain Peleg must have been drinking something to-day.

At last the anchor was up, the sails were set, and off we glided. It was a short, cold Christmas; and as the short northern day merged into night, we found ourselves almost broad upon the wintry ocean, whose freezing spray cased us in ice, as in polished armor. The long rows of teeth on the bulwarks glistened in the moonlight; and like the white ivory tusks of some huge elephant, vast curving icicles depended from the bows.

Lank Bildad, as pilot, headed the first watch, and ever and anon, as the old craft deep dived into the green seas, and sent the shivering frost all over her, and the winds howled, and the cordage rang, his steady notes were heard,—

> "Sweet fields beyond the swelling flood,
>   Stand dressed in living green.
> So to the Jews old Canaan stood,
>   While Jordan rolled between."

Never did those sweet words sound more sweetly to me than then. They were full of hope and fruition. Spite of this frigid winter night in the boisterous Atlantic, spite of my wet feet and wetter jacket, there was yet, it then seemed to me, many a pleasant haven in store; and meads and glades so eternally vernal, that the grass shot up by the spring, untrodden, unwilted, remains at midsummer.

At last we gained such an offing, that the two pilots were needed no longer. The stout sail-boat that had accompanied us began ranging alongside.

It was curious and not unpleasing, how Peleg and Bildad were affected at this juncture, especially Captain Bildad. For loath to depart, yet; very loath to leave, for good, a ship bound on so long and perilous a voyage—beyond both stormy Capes; a ship in which some thousands of his hard earned dollars were invested; a ship, in which an old shipmate sailed as captain; a man almost as old as he, once more starting to encounter all the terrors of the pitiless jaw; loath to say good-bye to a thing so every way brimful of every interest to him,—poor old Bildad lingered long; paced the deck with anxious strides; ran down into the cabin to speak another farewell word there; again came on deck, and looked to windward; looked towards the wide and endless waters, only bounded by the far-off unseen Eastern Continents; looked towards the land; looked aloft; looked right and left; looked everywhere and nowhere; and at last, mechanically coiling a rope upon its pin, convulsively grasped stout Peleg by the hand, and holding up a lantern, for a moment stood gazing heroically in his face, as much as to say, "Nevertheless, friend Peleg, I can stand it; yes, I can."

As for Peleg himself, he took it more like a philosopher; but for all his philosophy, there was a tear twinkling in his eye, when the lantern came too near. And he, too, did not a little run from cabin to deck—now a word below, and now a word with Starbuck, the chief mate.

But, at last, he turned to his comrade, with a final sort of look about him, —"Captain Bildad—come, old shipmate, we must go. Back the mainyard there! Boat ahoy! Stand by to come close alongside, now! Careful, careful!—come, Bildad, boy—say your last. Luck to ye, Starbuck—luck to ye, Mr. Stubb—luck to ye, Mr. Flask—good-bye, and good luck to ye all—and this day three years I'll have a hot supper smoking for ye in old Nantucket. Hurrah and away!"

"God bless ye, and have ye in His holy keeping, men," murmured old Bildad, almost incoherently. "I hope ye'll have fine weather now, so that Captain Ahab may soon be moving among ye—a pleasant sun is all he needs, and ye'll have plenty of them in the tropic voyage ye go. Be careful in the hunt, ye mates. Don't stave the boats needlessly, ye harpooneers; good white cedar plank is raised full three per cent. within the year. Don't forget your prayers, either. Mr. Starbuck, mind that cooper don't waste the spare staves. Oh! the sail-needles are in the green locker! Don't whale it too much a' Lord's day, men; but don't miss a fair chance either, that's rejecting Heaven's good gifts. Have an eye to the molasses tierce, Mr. Stubb; it was a little leaky, I thought. If ye touch at the islands, Mr. Flask, beware of fornication. Good-bye, good-bye! Don't keep that cheese too long down in the hold, Mr. Starbuck; it'll spoil. Be careful with the butter—twenty cents the pound it was, and mind ye, if——"

"Come, come, Captain Bildad; stop palavering,—away!" and with that, Peleg hurried him over the side, and both dropt into the boat.

Ship and boat diverged; the cold, damp night breeze blew between; a screaming gull flew overhead; the two hulls wildly rolled; we gave three heavy-hearted cheers, and blindly plunged like fate into the lone Atlantic.

CHAPTER XXIII

THE LEE SHORE

SOME chapters back, one Bulkington was spoken of, a tall, new-landed mariner, encountered in New Bedford at the inn.

When on that shivering winter's night, the Pequod thrust her vindictive bows into the cold malicious waves, who should I see standing at her helm but Bulkington! I looked with sympathetic awe and fearfulness upon the man, who in mid-winter just landed from a four years' dangerous voyage, could so unrestingly push off again for still another tempestuous term. The land seemed scorching to his feet. Wonderfullest things are ever the unmentionable; deep memories yield no epitaphs; this six-inch chapter is the stoneless grave of Bulkington. Let me only say that it fared with him as with the storm-tossed ship, that miserably drives along the leeward land. The port would fain give succor; the port is pitiful; in the port is safety, comfort, hearthstone, supper, warm blankets, friends, all that's kind to our mortalities. But in that gale, the port, the land, is that ship's direst jeopardy; she must fly all hospitality; one touch of land, though it but graze the keel, would make her shudder through and through. With all her might she crowds all sail off shore; in so doing, fights 'gainst the very winds that fain would blow her homeward; seeks all the lashed sea's landlessness again; for refuge's sake forlornly rushing into peril; her only friend her bitterest foe!

Know ye now, Bulkington? Glimpses do ye seem to see of that mortally intolerable truth; that all deep, earnest thinking is but the intrepid effort of the soul to keep the open independence of her sea; while the wildest winds of heaven and earth conspire to cast her on the treacherous, slavish shore?

But as in landlessness alone resides the highest truth, shoreless, indefinite, as God—so, better is it to perish in that howling infinite, than be ingloriously dashed upon the lee, even if that were safety! For worm-like, then, oh! who would craven crawl to land! Terrors of the terrible! is all this agony so vain? Take heart, take heart, O Bulkington! Bear thee grimly, demigod! Up from the spray of thy ocean-perishing—straight up, leaps thy apotheosis!

CHAPTER XXIV

THE ADVOCATE

As Queequeg and I are now fairly embarked in this business of whaling; and as this business of whaling has somehow come to be regarded among landsmen as a rather unpoetical and disreputable pursuit; therefore, I am all anxiety to convince ye, ye landsmen, of the injustice hereby done to us hunters of whales.

In the first place, it may be deemed almost superfluous to establish the fact, that among people at large, the business of whaling is not accounted on a level with what are called the liberal professions. If a stranger were intro-duced into any miscellaneous metropolitan society, it would but slightly advance the general opinion of his merits, were he presented to the company as a harpooneer, say; and if in emulation of the naval officers he should append the initials S. W. F. (Sperm Whale Fishery) to his visiting card, such a procedure would be deemed pre-eminently presuming and ridiculous.

Doubtless one leading reason why the world declines honoring us whalemen, is this: they think that, at best, our vocation amounts to a butchering sort of business; and that when actively engaged therein, we are surrounded by all manner of defilements. Butchers we are, that is true. But butchers, also, and butchers of the bloodiest badge have been all Martial Commanders whom the world invariably delights to honor. And as for the matter of the alleged uncleanliness of our business, ye shall soon be initiated into certain facts hitherto pretty generally unknown, and which, upon the whole, will triumphantly plant the sperm whale-ship at least among the cleanliest things of this tidy earth. But even granting the charge in question to be true; what disordered slippery decks of a whale-ship are comparable to the unspeakable carrion of those battle-fields from which so many soldiers return to drink in all ladies' plaudits? And if the idea of peril so much enhances the popular conceit of the soldier's profession; let me assure ye that many a veteran who has freely marched up to a battery, would quickly recoil at the apparition of the sperm whale's vast tail, fanning into eddies the air over his head. For what are the comprehensible terrors of man compared with the interlinked terrors and wonders of God!

But, though the world scouts at us whale hunters, yet does it unwittingly pay us the profoundest homage; yea, an all-abounding adoration! for almost all the tapers, lamps, and candles that burn round the globe, burn, as before so many shrines, to our glory!

But look at this matter in other lights; weigh it in all sorts of scales; see what we whalemen are, and have been.

Why did the Dutch in De Witt's time have admirals of their whaling fleets? Why did Louis XVI. of France, at his own personal expense, fit out whaling ships from Dunkirk, and politely invite to that town some score or two of families from our own island of Nantucket? Why did Britain between the years 1750 and 1788 pay to her whalemen in bounties upwards of £1,000,000? And lastly, how comes it that we whalemen of America now outnumber all the rest of the banded whalemen in the world; sail a navy of upwards of seven hundred vessels; manned by eighteen thousand men; yearly consuming 4,000,000 of dollars; the ships worth, at the time of sailing, $20,000,000; and every year importing into our harbors a well reaped harvest of $7,000,000. How comes all this, if there be not something puissant in whaling?

But this is not the half; look again.

I freely assert, that the cosmopolite philosopher cannot, for his life, point out one single peaceful influence, which within the last sixty years has operated more potentially upon the whole broad world, taken in one aggregate, than the high and mighty business of whaling. One way and another, it has begotten events so remarkable in themselves, and so continuously momentous in their sequential issues, that whaling may well be regarded as that Egyptian mother, who bore offspring themselves pregnant from her womb. It would be a hopeless, endless task to catalogue all these things. Let a handful suffice. For many years past the whale-ship has been the pioneer in ferreting out the remotest and least known parts of the earth. She has explored seas and archipelagoes which had no chart, where no Cook or Vancouver had ever sailed. If American and European men-of-war now peacefully ride in once savage harbors, let them fire salutes to the honor and the glory of the whale-ship, which originally showed them the way, and first interpreted between them and the savages. They may celebrate as they will the heroes of Exploring Expeditions, your Cookes, your Krusensterns; but I say that scores of anonymous Captains have sailed out of Nantucket, that were as great, and greater than your Cooke and your Krusenstern. For in their succorless empty-handedness, they, in the heathenish sharked waters, and by the beaches of unrecorded, javelin islands, battled with virgin wonders and terrors that Cooke with all his marines and muskets would not have willingly dared. All that is made such a flourish of in the old South Sea Voyages, those things were but the lifetime commonplaces of our heroic Nantucketers. Often, adventures which Vancouver dedicates three chapters to, these men accounted unworthy of being set down in the ship's common log. Ah, the world! Oh, the world!

Until the whale fishery rounded Cape Horn, no commerce but colonial, scarcely any intercourse but colonial, was carried on between Europe and the long line of the opulent Spanish provinces on the Pacific coast. It was the whaleman who first broke through the jealous policy of the Spanish crown, touching those colonies; and, if space permitted, it might be distinctly shown how from those whalemen at last eventuated the liberation of Peru, Chili, and Bolivia from the yoke of Old Spain, and the establishment of the eternal democracy in those parts.

That great America on the other side of the sphere, Australia, was given to the enlightened world by the whaleman. After its first blunder-born discovery by a Dutchman, all other ships long shunned those shores as pestiferously barbarous; but the whale-ship touched there. The whale-ship is the true mother of that now mighty colony. Moreover, in the infancy of the first Australian settlement, the emigrants were several times saved from starvation by the benevolent biscuit of the whale-ship luckily dropping an anchor in their waters. The uncounted isles of all Polynesia confess the same truth, and do commercial homage to the whale-ship, that cleared the way for the missionary and the merchant, and in many cases carried the primitive missionaries to their first destinations. If that double-bolted land, Japan, is ever to become hospitable, it is the whale-ship alone to whom the credit will be due; for already she is on the threshold.

But if, in the face of all this, you still declare that whaling has no æsthetically noble associations connected with it, then am I ready to shiver fifty lances with you there, and unhorse you with a split helmet every time.

The whale has no famous author, and whaling no famous chronicler, you will say.

The whale no famous author, and whaling no famous chronicler? Who wrote the first account of our Leviathan? Who but mighty Job! And who composed the first narrative of a whaling-voyage? Who, but no less a prince than Alfred the Great, who, with his own royal pen, took down the words from Other, the Norwegian whale-hunter of those times! And who pronounced our glowing eulogy in Parliament? Who, but Edmund Burke!

True enough, but then whalemen themselves are poor devils; they have no good blood in their veins.

No good blood in their veins? They have something better than royal blood there. The grandmother of Benjamin Franklin was Mary Morrel; afterwards, by marriage, Mary Folger, one of the old settlers of Nantucket, and the ancestress to a long line of Folgers and harpooneers—all kith and kin to noble

Benjamin—this day darting the barbed iron from one side of the world to the other.

Good again; but then all confess that somehow whaling is not respectable.

Whaling not respectable? Whaling is imperial! By old English statutory law, the whale is declared "a royal fish."

Oh, that's only nominal! The whale himself has never figured in any grand imposing way.

The whale never figured in any grand imposing way? In one of the mighty triumphs given to a Roman general upon his entering the world's capital, the bones of a whale, brought all the way from the Syrian coast, were the most conspicuous object in the cymballed procession.

Grant it, since you cite it; but, say what you will, there is no real dignity in whaling.

No dignity in whaling? The dignity of our calling the very heavens attest. Cetus is a constellation in the South! No more! Drive down your hat in presence of the Czar, and take it off to Queequeg! No more! I know a man that, in his lifetime, has taken three hundred and fifty whales. I account that man more honorable than that great captain of antiquity who boasted of taking as many walled towns.

And, as for me, if, by any possibility, there be any as yet undiscovered prime thing in me; if I shall ever deserve any real repute in that small but high hushed world which I might not be unreasonably ambitious of; if hereafter I shall do anything that, upon the whole, a man might rather have done than to have left undone; if, at my death, my executors, or more properly my creditors, find any precious MSS. in my desk, then here I prospectively ascribe all the honor and the glory to whaling; for a whale-ship was my Yale College and my Harvard.

CHAPTER XXV

POSTSCRIPT

In behalf of the dignity of whaling, I would fain advance naught but substantiated facts. But after embattling his facts, an advocate who should wholly suppress a not unreasonable surmise, which might tell eloquently upon 'his cause —such an advocate, would he not be blameworthy?

It is well known that at the coronation of kings and queens, even modern ones, a certain curious process of seasoning them for their functions is gone through. There is a saltcellar of state, so called, and there may be a caster of state. How they use the salt, precisely—who knows? Certain I am, however, that a king's head is solemnly oiled at his coronation, even as a head of salad. Can it be, though, that they anoint it with a view of making its interior run well, as they anoint machinery? Much might be ruminated here, concerning the essential dignity of this regal process, because in common life we esteem but meanly and contemptibly a fellow who anoints his hair, and palpably smells of that anointing. In truth, a mature man who uses hair-oil, unless medicinally, that man has probably got a quoggy spot in him somewhere. As a general rule. he can't amount to much in his totality.

But the only thing to be considered here, is this—what kind of oil is used at coronations? Certainly it cannot be olive oil, nor macassar oil, nor castor oil, nor bear's oil, nor train oil, nor cod-liver oil. What then can it possibly be, but the sperm oil in its unmanufactured, unpolluted state, the sweetest of all oils?

Think of that, ye loyal Britons! we whalemen supply your kings and queens with coronation stuff!

CHAPTER XXVI

KNIGHTS AND SQUIRES

THE chief mate of the Pequod was Starbuck, a native of Nantucket, and a Quaker by descent. He was a long, earnest man, and though born on an icy coast, seemed well adapted to endure hot latitudes, his flesh being hard as twice-baked biscuit. Transported to the Indies, his live blood would not spoil like bottled ale. He must have been born in some time of general drought and famine, or upon one of those fast days for which his state is famous. Only some thirty arid summers had he seen; those summers had dried up all his physical superfluousness. But this, his thinness, so to speak, seemed no more the token of wasting anxieties and cares, than it seemed the indication of any bodily blight. It was merely the condensation of the man. He was by no means ill-looking; quite the contrary. His pure tight skin was an excellent fit; and closely wrapped up in it, and embalmed with inner health and strength, like a revivified Egyptian, this Starbuck seemed prepared to endure for long ages to come, and to endure always, as now; for be it Polar snow or torrid sun, like a patent chronometer, his interior vitality was warranted to do well in all climates. Looking into his eyes, you seemed to see there the yet lingering images of those thousand-fold perils he had calmly confronted through life. A staid, steadfast man, whose life for the most part was a telling pantomime of action, and not a tame chapter of sounds. Yet, for all his hardy sobriety and fortitude, there were certain qualities in him which at times affected, and in some cases seemed well nigh to overbalance all the rest. Uncommonly conscientious for a seaman, and endued with a deep natural reverence, the wild watery loneliness of his life did therefore strongly incline him to superstition; but to that sort of superstition, which in some organizations seems rather to spring, somehow, from intelligence than from ignorance. Outward portents and inward presentiments were his. And if at times these things bent the welded iron of his soul, much more did his far-away domestic memories of his young Cape wife and child, tend to bend him still more from the original ruggedness of his nature, and open him still further to those latent influences which, in some honest-hearted men, restrain the gush of dare-devil daring, so often evinced by others in the more perilous vicissitudes of the fishery. "I will have no man in my boat," said Starbuck, "who is not afraid of a whale." By this, he seemed to mean, not only that the most reliable and useful courage was that which arises from the fair estimation of the encountered peril, but that an utterly fearless man is a far more dangerous comrade than a coward.

"Aye, aye," said Stubb, the second mate, "Starbuck, there, is as careful a man as you'll find anywhere in this fishery." But we shall ere long see what that word "careful" precisely means when used by a man like Stubb, or almost any other whale hunter.

Starbuck was no crusader after perils; in him courage was not a sentiment;

but a thing simply useful to him, and always at hand upon all mortally practical occasions. Besides, he thought, perhaps, that in this business of whaling, courage was one of the great staple outfits of the ship, like her beef and her bread, and not to be foolishly wasted. Wherefore he had no fancy for lowering for whales after sun-down; nor for persisting in fighting a fish that too much persisted in fighting him. For, thought Starbuck, I am here in this critical ocean to kill whales for my living, and not to be killed by them for theirs; and that hundreds of men had been so killed Starbuck well knew. What doom was his own father's? Where, in the bottomless deeps, could he find the torn limbs of his brother?

With memories like these in him, and, moreover, given to a certain superstitiousness, as has been said; the courage of this Starbuck, which could, nevertheless, still flourish, must indeed have been extreme. But it was not in reasonable nature that a man so organized, and with such terrible experiences and remembrances as he had; it was not in nature that these things should fail in latently engendering an element in him, which, under suitable circumstances, would break out from its confinement, and burn all his courage up. And brave as he might be, it was that sort of bravery chiefly, visible in some intrepid men, which, while generally abiding firm in the conflict with seas, or winds, or whales, or any of the ordinary irrational horrors of the world, yet cannot withstand those more terrific, because more spiritual terrors, which sometimes menace you from the concentrating brow of an enraged and mighty man.

But were the coming narrative to reveal, in any instance, the complete abasement of poor Starbuck's fortitude, scarce might I have the heart to write it; for it is a thing most sorrowful, nay shocking, to expose the fall of valor in the soul. Men may seem detestable as joint stock-companies and nations; knaves, fools, and murderers there may be; men may have mean and meagre faces; but man, in the ideal, is so noble and so sparkling, such a grand and glowing creature, that over any ignominious blemish in him all his fellows should run to throw their costliest robes. That immaculate manliness we feel within ourselves, so far within us, that it remains intact though all the outer character seem gone; bleeds with keenest anguish at the undraped spectacle of a valor-ruined man. Nor can piety itself, at such a shameful sight, completely stifle her upbraidings against the permitting stars. But this august dignity I treat of, is not the dignity of kings and robes, but that abounding dignity which has no robed investiture. Thou shalt see it shining in the arm that wields a pick or drives a spike; that democratic dignity which, on all hands, radiates without end from God; Himself! The great God absolute! The centre and circumference of all democracy! His omnipresence, our divine equality!

If, then, to meanest mariners, and renegades and castaways, I shall hereafter ascribe high qualities, though dark; weave round them tragic graces; if even the most mournful, perchance the most abased, among them all, shall at times lift himself to the exalted mounts; if I shall touch that workman's arm with some ethereal light; if I shall spread a rainbow over his disastrous set of sun; then against all mortal critics bear me out in it, thou just Spirit of Equality, which hast spread one royal mantle of humanity over all my kind! Bear me out in it, thou great democratic God! who didst not refuse to the swart convict, Bunyan, the pale, poetic pearl; Thou who didst clothe with doubly hammered leaves of finest gold, the stumped and paupered arm of old Cervantes; Thou who didst pick up Andrew Jackson from the pebbles; who didst hurl him upon a war-horse; who didst thunder him higher than a throne!

Thou who, in all Thy mighty, earthly marchings, ever cullest Thy selectest champions from the kingly commons; bear me out in it, O God!

CHAPTER XXVII

KNIGHTS AND SQUIRES—*Continued*

STUBB was the second mate. He was a native of Cape Cod; and hence, according to local usage, was called a Cape-Cod-man. A happy-go-lucky; neither craven nor valiant; taking perils as they came with an indifferent air; and while engaged in the most imminent crisis of the chase, toiling away, calm and collected as a journeyman joiner engaged for the year. Good-humored, easy, and careless, he presided over his whale-boat as if the most deadly encounter were but a dinner, and his crew all invited guests. He was as particular about the comfortable arrangements of his part of the boat, as an old stage-driver is about the snugness of his box. When close to the whale, in the very death-lock of the fight, he handled his unpitying lance coolly and off-handedly, as a whistling tinker his hammer. He would hum over his old rigadig tunes while flank and flank with the most exasperated monster. Long usage had, for this Stubb, converted the jaws of death into an easy chair. What he thought of death itself, there is no telling. Whether he ever thought of it at all, might be a question; but, if he ever did chance to cast his mind that way after a comfortable dinner, no doubt, like a good sailor, he took it to be a sort of call of the watch to tumble aloft, and bestir themselves there, about something which he would find out when he obeyed the order, and not sooner.

What, perhaps, with other things, made Stubb such an easy-going, unfearing man, so cheerily trudging off with the burden of life in a world full of grave peddlers, all bowed to the ground with their packs; what helped to bring about that almost impious good-humor of his; that thing must have been his pipe. For, like his nose, his short, black little pipe was one of the regular features of his face. You would almost as soon have expected him to turn out of his bunk without his nose as without his pipe. He kept a whole row of pipes there ready loaded, stuck in a rack, within easy reach of his hand; and, whenever he turned in, he smoked them all out in succession, lighting one from the other to the end of the chapter; then loading them again to be in readiness anew. For, when Stubb dressed, instead of first putting his legs into his trowsers, he put his pipe into his mouth.

I say this continual smoking must have been one cause, at least, of his peculiar disposition; for every one knows that this earthly air, whether ashore or afloat, is terribly infected with the nameless miseries of the numberless mortals who have died exhaling it; and as in time of the cholera, some people go about with a camphorated handkerchief to their mouths; so, likewise, against all mortal tribulations, Stubb's tobacco smoke might have operated as a sort of disinfecting agent.

The third mate was Flask, a native of Tisbury, in Martha's Vineyard. A short, stout, ruddy young fellow, very pugnacious concerning whales, who somehow seemed to think that the great Leviathans had personally and hereditarily affronted him; and therefore it was a sort of point of honor with him, to destroy them whenever encountered. So utterly lost was he to all sense of reverence for the many marvels of their majestic bulk and mystic ways; and so dead to anything like an apprehension of any possible danger from encountering them; that in his poor opinion, the wondrous whale was but a species of magnified mouse, or at least water-rat, requiring only a little circumvention and some small application of time and trouble in order to kill and boil. This ignorant, unconscious fearlessness of his made him a little waggish in the matter of whales; he followed these fish for the fun of it; and a three years' voyage round Cape Horn was only a jolly joke that lasted that length of time. As a carpenter's nails are divided into wrought nails and cut nails; so mankind may be similarly divided. Little Flask was one of the wrought ones; made to clinch tight and last long. They called him King-Post on board of the Pequod; because, in form, he could be well likened to the short, square timber known by that name in Arctic whalers; and which by the means of many radiating side timbers inserted into it, serves to brace the ship against the icy concussions of those battering seas.

Now these three mates—Starbuck, Stubb, and Flask, were momentous men. They it was who by universal prescription commanded three of the Pequod's boats as headsmen. In that grand order of battle in which Captain Ahab would probably marshal his forces to descend on the whales, these three headsmen were as captains of companies. Or, being armed with their long keen whaling spears, they were as a picked trio of lancers; even as the harpooneers were flingers of javelins.

And since in this famous fishery, each mate or headsman, like a Gothic Knight of old, is always accompanied by his boat-steerer or harpooneer, who in certain conjunctures provides him with a fresh lance, when the former one has been badly twisted, or elbowed in the assault; and moreover, as there generally subsists between the two, a close intimacy and friendliness; it is therefore but meet, that in this place we set down who the Pequod's harpooneers were, and to what headsmen each of them belonged.

First of all was Queequeg, whom Starbuck, the chief mate, had selected for his squire. But Queequeg is already known.

Next was Tashtego, an unmixed Indian from Gay Head, the most westerly promontory of Martha's Vineyard, where there still exists the last remnant of a village of red men, which has long supplied the neighbouring island of Nantucket with many of her most daring harpooneers. In the fishery, they usually go by the generic name of Gay-Headers. Tashtego's long, lean, sable hair, his high cheek bones, and black rounding eyes—for an Indian, Oriental in their largeness, but Antarctic in their glittering expression—all this sufficiently proclaimed him an inheritor of the unvitiated blood of those proud warrior hunters, who, in quest of the great New England moose, had scoured, bow in hand, the aboriginal forests of the main. But no longer snuffing in the trail of the wild beasts of the woodland, Tashtego now hunted in the wake of the great whales of the sea; the unerring harpoon of the son fitly replacing the infallible arrow of the sires. To look at the tawny brawn of his lithe snaky limbs, you would almost have credited the superstitions of some of the earlier Puritans, and half-believed this wild Indian to be a son of the Prince of the Powers of the Air. Tashtego was Stubb the second mate's squire.

Third among the harpooneers was Daggoo, a gigantic, coal-black negro-savage, with a lion-like tread—an Ahasuerus to behold. Suspended from his ears were two golden hoops, so large that the sailors called them ring-bolts, and would talk of securing the top-sail halyards to them. In his youth Daggoo had voluntarily shipped on board of a whaler, lying in a lonely bay on his native coast.   And never having been anywhere in the world but in Africa, Nantucket, and the pagan harbors most frequented by whalemen; and having now led for many years the bold life of the fishery in the ships of owners uncommonly heedful of what manner of men they shipped; Daggoo retained all his barbaric virtues, and erect as a giraffe, moved about the decks in all the pomp of six feet five in his socks.   There was a corporeal humility in looking up at him; and a white man standing before him seemed a white flag come to beg truce of a fortress.   Curious to tell, this imperial negro, Ahasuerus Daggoo, was the Squire of little Flask, who looked like a chess-man beside him.   As for the residue of the Pequod's company, be it said, that at the present day not one in two of the many thousand men before the mast employed in the American whale fishery, are Americans born, though pretty nearly all the officers are. Herein it is the same with the American whale fishery as with the American army and military and merchant navies, and the engineering forces employed in the construction of the American Canals and Railroads.   The same, I say, because in all these cases the native American liberally provides the brains, the rest of the world as generously supplying the muscles.   No small number of these whaling seamen belong to the Azores, where the outward bound Nantucket whalers frequently touch to augment their crews from the hardy peasants of those rocky shores.   In like manner, the Greenland whalers sailing out of Hull or London, put in at the Shetland Islands, to receive the full complement of their crew.   Upon the passage homewards, they drop them there again.   How it is, there is no telling, but Islanders seem to make the best whalemen.   They were nearly all Islanders in the Pequod, *Isolatoes* too, I call such, not acknowledging the common continent of men, but each *Isolato* living on a separate continent of his own.   Yet now, federated along one keel, what a set these Isolatoes were!   An Anacharsis Clootz deputation from all the isles of the sea, and all the ends of the earth, accompanying Old Ahab in the Pequod to lay the world's grievances before that bar from which not very many of them ever come back.   Black Little Pip—he never did—oh, no! he went before.   Poor Alabama boy!   On the grim Pequod's forecastle, ye shall ere long see him, beating his tambourine; prelusive of the eternal time, when sent for, to the great quarter-deck on high, he was bid strike in with angels, and beat his tambourine in glory; called a coward here, hailed a hero there!

CHAPTER XXVIII

AHAB

FOR several days after leaving Nantucket, nothing above hatches was seen of Captain Ahab.   The mates regularly relieved each other at the watches, and for aught that could be seen to the contrary, they seemed to be the only commanders of the ship; only they sometimes issued from the cabin with orders so sudden and peremptory, that after all it was plain they but commanded vicariously.   Yes, their supreme lord and dictator was there, though hitherto unseen by any eyes not permitted to penetrate into the now sacred retreat of the cabin.

Every time I ascended to the deck from my watches below, I instantly gazed aft to mark if any strange face were visible; for my first vague disquietude touching the unknown captain, now in the seclusion of the sea, became almost a perturbation. This was strangely heightened at times by the ragged Elijah's diabolical incoherences uninvitingly recurring to me, with a subtle energy I could not have before conceived of. But poorly could I withstand them, much as in other moods I was almost ready to smile at the solemn whimsicalities of that outlandish prophet of the wharves. But whatever it was of apprehensiveness or uneasiness—to call it so—which I felt, yet whenever I came to look about me in the ship, it seemed against all warrantry to cherish such emotions. For though the harpooneers, with the great body of the crew, were a far more barbaric, heathenish, and motley set than any of the tame merchant-ship companies which my previous experiences had made me acquainted with, still I ascribed this—and rightly ascribed it—to the fierce uniqueness of the very nature of that wild Scandinavian vocation in which I had so abandonedly embarked. But it was especially the aspect of the three chief officers of the ship, the mates, which was most forcibly calculated to allay these colorless misgivings, and induce confidence and cheerfulness in every presentment of the voyage. Three better, more likely sea-officers and men, each in his own different way, could not readily be found, and they were every one of them Americans; a Nantucketer, a Vineyarder, a Cape man. Now, it being Christmas when the ship shot from out her harbor, for a space we had biting Polar weather, though all the time running away from it to the southward; and by every degree and minute of latitude which we sailed, gradually leaving that merciless winter, and all its intolerable weather behind us. It was one of those less lowering, but still grey and gloomy enough mornings of the transition, when with a fair wind the ship was rushing through the water with a vindictive sort of leaping and melancholy rapidity, that as I mounted to the deck at the call of the forenoon watch, so soon as I levelled my glance towards the taffrail, foreboding shivers ran over me. Reality outran apprehension; Captain Ahab stood upon his quarter-deck.

There seemed no sign of common bodily illness about him, nor of the recovery from any. He looked like a man cut away from the stake, when the fire has overrunningly wasted all the limbs without consuming them, or taking away one particle from their compacted aged robustness. His whole high, broad form, seemed made of solid bronze, and shaped in an unalterable mould, like Cellini's cast Perseus. Threading its way out from among his grey hairs, and continuing right down one side of his tawny scorched face and neck, till it disappeared in his clothing, you saw a slender rod-like mark, lividly whitish. It resembled that perpendicular seam sometimes made in the straight, lofty trunk of a great tree, when the upper lightning tearingly darts down it, and without wrenching a single twig, peels and grooves out the bark from top to bottom, ere running off into the soil, leaving the tree still greenly alive, but branded. Whether that mark was born with him, or whether it was the scar left by some desperate wound, no one could certainly say. By some tacit consent, throughout the voyage little or no allusion was made to it, especially by the mates. But once Tashtego's senior, an old Gay-Head Indian among the crew, superstitiously asserted that not till he was full forty years old did Ahab become that way branded, and then it came upon him, not in the fury of any mortal fray, but in an elemental strife at sea. Yet, this wild hint seemed inferentially negatived, by what a grey Manxman insinuated, an old sepulchral man, who, having never before sailed out of Nantucket, had never ere this laid eye upon wild Ahab. Nevertheless, the old sea-traditions, the immemorial credulities, popularly invested this old Manxman with preternatural powers of discernment. So that no white sailor seriously contradicted him when he said that if ever Captain Ahab should be tranquilly laid out—which might hardly come to pass, so he muttered—then, whoever should do that last office for the dead, would find a birth-mark on him from crown to sole.

So powerfully did the whole grim aspect of Ahab affect me, and the livid brand which streaked it, that for the first few moments I hardly noted that not a little of this overbearing grimness was owing to the barbaric white leg upon which he partly stood. It had previously come to me that this ivory leg had at sea been fashioned from the polished bone of the sperm whale's jaw. "Aye, he was dismasted off Japan," said the old Gay-Head Indian once; "but like his dismasted craft, he shipped another mast without coming home for it. He has a quiver of 'em."

I was struck with the singular posture he maintained. Upon each side of the Pequod's quarter deck, and pretty close to the mizzen shrouds, there was an auger hole, bored about half an inch or so, into the plank. His bone leg steadied in that hole; one arm elevated, and holding by a shroud; Captain Ahab stood erect, looking straight out beyond the ship's ever-pitching prow. There was an infinity of firmest fortitude, a determinate, unsurrenderable wilfulness, in the fixed and fearless, forward dedication of that glance. Not a word he spoke; nor did his officers say aught to him; though by all their minutest gestures and expressions, they plainly showed the uneasy, if not painful, consciousness of being under a troubled master-eye. And not only that, but moody stricken Ahab stood before them with a crucifixion in his face; in all the nameless regal overbearing dignity of some mighty woe.

Ere long, from his first visit in the air, he withdrew into his cabin. But after that morning, he was every day visible to the crew; either standing in his pivot-hole, or seated upon an ivory stool he had; or heavily walking the deck. As the sky grew less gloomy; indeed, began to grow a little genial, he became still less and less a recluse; as if, when the ship had sailed from home, nothing but the dead wintry bleakness of the sea had then kept him so secluded. And, by and by, it came to pass, that he was almost continually in the air; but, as yet, for all that he said, or perceptibly did, on the at last sunny deck, he seemed as unnecessary there as another mast. But the Pequod was only making a passage now; not regularly cruising; nearly all whaling preparatives needing supervision the mates were fully competent to, so that there was little or nothing, out of himself, to employ or excite Ahab, now; and thus chase away, for that one interval, the clouds that layer upon layer were piled upon his brow, as ever all clouds choose the loftiest peaks to pile themselves upon.

Nevertheless, ere long, the warm, warbling persuasiveness of the pleasant, holiday weather we came to, seemed gradually to charm him from his mood. For, as when the red-cheeked, dancing girls, April and May, trip home to the wintry, misanthropic woods; even the barest, ruggedest, most thunder-cloven old oak will at least send forth some few green sprouts, to welcome such glad-hearted visitants; so Ahab did, in the end, a little respond to the playful allurings of that girlish air. More than once did he put forth the faint blossom of a look, which, in any other man, would have soon flowered out in a smile.

CHAPTER XXIX

ENTER AHAB; TO HIM, STUBB

SOME days elapsed, and ice and icebergs all astern, the Pequod now went rolling through the bright Quito spring, which, at sea, almost perpetually reigns on the threshold of the eternal August of the Tropic. The warmly cool, clear, ringing, perfumed, overflowing, redundant days, were as crystal goblets of Persian sherbet, heaped up—flaked up, with rose-water snow. The starred and stately nights seemed haughty dames in jewelled velvets, nursing at home in lonely pride, the memory of their absent conquering Earls, the golden helmeted suns! For sleeping man, 'twas hard to choose between such winsome days and such seducing nights. But all the witcheries of that unwaning weather did not merely lend new spells and potencies to the outward world. Inward they turned upon the soul, especially when the still mild hours of eve came on; then, memory shot her crystals as the clear ice most forms of noiseless twilights. And all these subtle agencies, more and more they wrought on Ahab's texture.

Old age is always wakeful; as if, the longer linked with life, the less man has to do with aught that looks like death. Among sea-commanders, the old greybeards will oftenest leave their berths to visit the night-cloaked deck. It was so with Ahab; only that now, of late, he seemed so much to live in the open air, that truly speaking, his visits were more to the cabin, than from the cabin to the planks. "It feels like going down into one's tomb,"—he would mutter to himself,—"for an old captain like me to be descending this narrow scuttle, to go to my grave-dug berth."

So, almost every twenty-four hours, when the watches of the night were set, and the band on deck sentinelled the slumbers of the band below; and when if a rope was to be hauled upon the forecastle, the sailors flung it not rudely down, as by day, but with some cautiousness dropt it to its place, for fear of disturbing their slumbering shipmates; when this sort of steady quietude would begin to prevail, habitually, the silent steersman would watch the cabin-scuttle; and ere long the old man would emerge, griping at the iron banister, to help his crippled way. Some considering touch of humanity was in him; for at times like these, he usually abstained from patrolling the quarter-deck; because to his wearied mates, seeking repose within six inches of his ivory heel, such would have been the reverberating crack and din of that bony step, that their dreams would have been of the crunching teeth of sharks. But once, the mood was on him too deep for common regardings; and as with heavy, lumber-like pace he was measuring the ship from taffrail to mainmast, Stubb, the old second mate, came up from below, with a certain unassured, deprecating humorousness, hinted that if Captain Ahab was pleased to walk the planks, then, no one could say nay; but there might be some way of muffling the noise; hinting something indistinctly and hesitatingly about a globe of tow, and the insertion into it, of the ivory heel. Ah! Stubb, thou did'st not know Ahab then.

"Am I a cannon-ball, Stubb," said Ahab, "that thou wouldst wad me that fashion? But go thy ways; I had forgot. Below to thy nightly grave; where such as ye sleep between shrouds, to use ye to the filling one at last.—Down, dog, and kennel!"

Starting at the unforeseen concluding exclamation of the so suddenly scornful old man, Stubb was speechless a moment; then said excitedly, "I am not used to be spoken to that way, sir; I do but less than half like it, sir."

"Avast!" gritted Ahab between his set teeth, and violently moving away, as if to avoid some passionate temptation.

"No, sir; not yet," said Stubb, emboldened, "I will not tamely be called a dog, sir."

"Then be called ten times a donkey, and a mule, and an ass, and begone, or I'll clear the world of thee!"

As he said this, Ahab advanced upon him with such overbearing terrors in his aspect, that Stubb involuntarily retreated.

"I was never served so before without giving a hard blow for it," muttered Stubb, as he found himself descending the cabin-scuttle. "It's very queer. Stop, Stubb; somehow, now, I don't well know whether to go back and strike him, or—what's that?—down here on my knees and pray for him? Yes, that was the thought coming up in me; but it would be the first time I ever *did* pray. It's queer; very queer; and he's queer too; aye, take him fore and aft, he's about the queerest old man Stubb ever sailed with. How he flashed at me!— his eyes like powder-pans! is he mad? Anyway there's something on his mind, as sure as there must be something on a deck when it cracks. He ain't in his bed now, either, more than three hours out of the twenty-four; and he don't sleep then. Didn't that Dough-Boy, the steward, tell me that of a morning he always finds the old man's hammock clothes all rumpled and tumbled, and the sheets down at the foot, and the coverlid almost tied into knots, and the pillow a sort of frightful hot, as though a baked brick had been on it? A hot old man! I guess he's got what some folks ashore call a conscience; it's a kind of Tic-Dolly-row they say—worse nor a toothache. Well, well; I don't know what it is, but the Lord keep me from catching it. He's full of riddles; I wonder what he goes into the after hold for, every night, as Dough-Boy tells me he suspects; what's that for, I should like to know? Who's made appointments with him in the hold? Ain't that queer, now? But there's no telling, it's the old game— Here goes for a snooze. Damn me, it's worth a fellow's while to be born into the world, if only to fall right asleep. And now that I think of it, that's about the first thing babies do, and that's a sort of queer, too. Damn me, but all things are queer, come to think of 'em. But that's against my principles. Think not, is my eleventh commandment; and sleep when you can, is my twelfth— So here goes again. But how's that? didn't he call me a dog? blazes! he called me ten times a donkey, and piled a lot of jackasses on top of *that!* He might as well have kicked me, and done with it. Maybe he *did* kick me, and I didn't observe it, I was so taken all aback with his brow, somehow. It flashed like a bleached bone. What the devil's the matter with me? I don't stand right on my legs. Coming afoul of that old man has a sort of turned me wrong side out. By the Lord, I must have been dreaming, though—How? how? how?—but the only way's to stash it; so here goes to hammock again; and in the morning, I'll see how this plaguey juggling thinks over by daylight."

CHAPTER XXX

THE PIPE

WHEN Stubb had departed, Ahab stood for a while leaning over the bulwarks; and then, as had been usual with him of late, calling a sailor of the watch, he sent him below for his ivory stool, and also his pipe. Lighting the pipe at the binnacle lamp and planting the stool on the weather side of the deck, he sat and smoked.

In old Norse times, the thrones of the sea-loving Danish kings were fabricated, saith tradition, of the tusks of the narwhale. How could one look at Ahab then, seated on that tripod of bones, without bethinking him of the royalty it symbolized? For a Khan of the plank, and a king of the sea, and a great lord of Leviathans was Ahab.

Some moments passed, during which the thick vapor came from his mouth in quick and constant puffs, which blew back again into his face. "How now," he soliloquized at last, withdrawing the tube, "this smoking no longer soothes. Oh, my pipe! hard must it go with me if thy charm be gone! Here have I been unconsciously toiling, not pleasuring,—aye, and ignorantly smoking to windward all the while; to windward, and with such nervous whiffs, as if, like the dying whale, my final jets were the strongest and fullest of trouble. What business have I with this pipe? This thing that is meant for sereneness, to send up mild white vapors among mild white hairs, not among torn iron-grey locks like mine. I'll smoke no more——"

He tossed the still lighted pipe into the sea. The fire hissed in the waves; the same instant the ship shot by the bubble the sinking pipe made. With slouched hat, Ahab lurchingly paced the planks.

CHAPTER XXXI

QUEEN MAB

NEXT morning Stubb accosted Flask.

"Such a queer dream, King-Post, I never had. You know the old man's ivory leg, well I dreamed he kicked me with it; and when I tried to kick back, upon my soul, my little man, I kicked my leg right off! and then, presto! Ahab seemed a pyramid, and I, like a blazing fool, kept kicking at it. But what was still more curious, Flask—you know how curious all dreams are—through all this rage that I was in, I somehow seemed to be thinking to myself, that after all, it was not much of an insult, that kick from Ahab. "Why," thinks I, "what's the row? It's not a real leg, only a false one." And there's a mighty difference between a living thump and a dead thump. That's what makes a blow from the hand, Flask, fifty times more savage to bear than a blow from a cane. The living member—that makes the living insult, my little man. And thinks I to myself all the while, mind, while I was stubbing my silly toes against that cursed pyramid—so confoundedly contradictory was it all, all the while, I say, I was thinking to myself, "what's his leg now, but a cane—a whalebone cane. Yes," thinks I, "it was only a playful cudgelling—in fact, only a whaleboning that he gave me—not a base kick. Besides," thinks I, "look at it once; why, the end of it—the foot part—what a small-sort of end it is; whereas, if a broad footed, farmer kicked me, *there's* a devilish broad insult. But this insult is whittled down to a point only." But now comes the greatest joke of the dream, Flask. While I was battering away at the pyramid, a sort of badger-haired old merman, with a hump on his back, takes me by the shoulders, and slews me round. "What are you 'bout?" says he. Slid! man, but I was frightened. Such a phiz! But, somehow, next moment I was over the fright. "What am I about?" says I at last. "And what business is that of yours, I should like to know, Mr. Humpback? Do *you* want a kick?" By the lord, Flask, I had no sooner said that, than he turned round his stern to me, bent over, and a dragging up a lot of seaweed he had for a clout—what do you think, I saw?—why thunder alive, man, his stern was stuck full of marlinspikes, with the points out. Says I, on second thoughts, "I guess I won't kick you, old fellow." "Wise Stubb," said he, "wise Stubb;" and kept muttering it all the time, a sort of eating of his own gums like a chimney hag. Seeing he wasn't going to stop saying over his "wise Stubb, wise Stubb," I thought I might as well fall to kicking the pyramid again. But I had only just lifted my foot for it, when he roared out, "Stop that kicking!" "Halloa," says I, "what's the matter now, old fellow?" "Look ye here," says he; "let's argue the insult. Captain Ahab kicked ye, didn't he?" "Yes, he did," says I—"right *here* it was." "Very good," says he—"he used his ivory leg, didn't he?" "Yes, he did," says I. "Well then," says he, "wise Stubb, what have you to complain of? Didn't he kick with right good will? it wasn't a common pitch pine leg he kicked with, was it? No, you were kicked by a great man, and with a beautiful ivory leg, Stubb. It's an honor; I consider it an honor. Listen, wise Stubb. In old England the greatest lords think it great glory to be slapped by a queen, and made garter-knights of; but, be *your* boast, Stubb, that ye were kicked by old Ahab, and made a wise man of. Remember what I say; *be* kicked by him; account his kicks honors; and on no account kick back; for you can't help yourself, wise Stubb. Don't you see that pyramid?" With that, he all of a sudden seemed somehow, in some queer fashion, to swim off into the air. I snored; rolled over; and there I was in my hammock! Now, what do you think of that dream, Flask?"

"I don't know; it seems a sort of foolish to me, tho'."

"May be; may be. But it's made a wise man of me, Flask. D'ye see Ahab standing there, sideways looking over the stern? Well, the best thing you can do, Flask, is to let that old man alone; never speak to him, whatever he says. Halloa! What's that he shouts? Hark!"

"Mast-head, there! Look sharp, all of ye! There are whales hereabouts! If ye see a white one, split your lungs for him!"

"What do you think of that now, Flask? ain't there a small drop of something queer about that, eh? A white whale—did ye mark that, man? Look ye —there's something special in the wind. Stand by for it, Flask. Ahab has that that's bloody on his mind. But, mum; he comes this way."

CHAPTER XXXII

CETOLOGY

ALREADY we are boldly launched upon the deep; but soon we shall be lost in its unshored, harborless immensities. Ere that come to pass; ere the Pequod's weedy hull rolls side by side with the barnacled hulls of the leviathan; at the outset it is but well to attend to a matter almost indispensable to a thorough appreciative·understanding of the more special leviathanic revelations and allusions of all sorts which are to follow.

It is some systematized exhibition of the whale in his broad genera, that I would now fain put before you. Yet is it no easy task. The classification of the constituents of a chaos, nothing less is here essayed. Listen to what the best and latest authorities have laid down.

"No branch of Zoology is so much involved as that which is entitled Cetology," says Captain Scoresby, A.D. 1820.

"It is not my intention, were it in my power, to enter into the inquiry as to the true method of dividing the cetacea into groups and families. * * * Utter confusion exists among the historians of this animal" (sperm whale), says Surgeon Beale, A.D. 1839.

"Unfitness to pursue our research in the unfathomable waters." "Impenetrable veil covering our knowledge of the cetacea." "A field strewn with thorns." "All these incomplete indications but serve to torture us naturalists."

Thus speak of the whale, the great Cuvier, and John Hunter, and Lesson, those lights of zoology and anatomy. Nevertheless, though of real knowledge there be little, yet of books there are a plenty; and so in some small degree, with cetology, or the science of whales. Many are the men, small and great, old and new, landsmen and seamen, who have at large or in little, written of the whale. Run over a few:—The Authors of the Bible; Aristotle; Pliny; Aldrovandi; Sir Thomas Browne; Gesner; Ray; Linnæus; Rondeletius; Willoughby; Green; Artedi; Sibbald; Brisson; Marten; Lacépède; Bonneterre; Desmarest; Baron Cuvier; Frederick Cuvier; John Hunter; Owen; Scoresby; Beale; Bennett; J. Ross Browne; the Author of Miriam Coffin; Olmstead; and the Rev. T. Cheever. But to what ultimate generalizing purpose all these have written, the above cited extracts will show.

Of the names in the list of whale authors, only those following Owen ever saw living whales; and but one of them was a real professional harpooneer and whaleman. I mean Captain Scoresby. On the separate subject of the Greenland or right-whale, he is the best existing authority. But Scoresby knew nothing and says nothing of the great sperm whale, compared with which the Greenland whale is almost unworthy mentioning. And here be it said, that the Greenland whale is an usurper upon the throne of the seas. He is not even by any means the largest of the whales. Yet, owing to the long priority of his claims, and the profound ignorance which, till some seventy years back, invested the then fabulous or utterly unknown sperm-whale, and which ignorance to this present day still reigns in all but some few scientific retreats and whale-ports; this usurpation has been every way complete. Reference to nearly all the leviathanic allusions in the great poets of past days, will satisfy you that the Greenland whale, without one rival, was to them the monarch of the seas. But the time has at last come for a new proclamation. This is Charing Cross; hear ye! good people all,—the Greenland whale is deposed,—the great sperm whale now reigneth!

There are only two books in being which at all pretend to put the living sperm whale before you, and at the same time, in the remotest degree succeed in the attempt. Those books are Beale's and Bennett's; both in their time surgeons to the English South-Sea whale-ships, and both exact and reliable men. The original matter touching the sperm whale to be found in their volumes is necessarily small; but so far as it goes, it is of excellent quality, though mostly confined to scientific description. As yet, however, the sperm whale, scientific or poetic, lives not complete in any literature. Far above all other hunted whales, his is an unwritten life.

Now the various species of whales need some sort of popular comprehensive classification, if only an easy outline one for the present, hereafter to be filled in all its departments by subsequent laborers. As no better man advances to take this matter in hand, I hereupon offer my own poor endeavors. I promise nothing complete; because any human thing supposed to be complete, must for that very reason infallibly be faulty. I shall not pretend to a minute anatomical description of the various species, or—in this place at least—to much of any description. My object here is simply to project the draught of a systematization of cetology. I am the architect, not the builder.

But it is a ponderous task; no ordinary letter-sorter in the Post-office is equal to it. To grope down into the bottom of the sea after them; to have one's hands among the unspeakable foundations, ribs, and very pelvis of the world; this is a fearful thing. What am I that I should essay to hook the nose of this leviathan! The awful tauntings in Job might well appal me. "Will he (the leviathan) make a covenant with thee? Behold the hope of him is vain!" But I have swam through libraries and sailed through oceans; I have had to do with whales with these visible hands; I am in earnest; and I will try. There are some preliminaries to settle.

First: The uncertain, unsettled condition of this science of Cetology is in the very vestibule attested by the fact, that in some quarters it still remains a moot point whether a whale be a fish. In his System of Nature, A.D. 1776, Linnæus declares, "I hereby separate the whales from the fish." But of my own knowledge, I know that down to the year 1850, sharks and shad, alewives and herring, against Linnæus's express edict, were still found dividing the possession of the same seas with the Leviathan.

The grounds upon which Linnæus would fain have banished the whales from the waters, he states as follows: "On account of their warm bilocular heart, their lungs, their moveable eyelids, their hollow ears, penem intrantem feminam mammis lactantem," and finally, "ex lege naturæ jure meritoque." I submitted all this to my friends Simeon Macey and Charley Coffin, of Nantucket, both messmates of mine in a certain voyage, and they united in the opinion that the reasons set forth were altogether insufficient. Charley profanely hinted they were humbug.

Be it known that, waiving all argument, I take the good old fashioned ground that the whale is a fish, and call upon holy Jonah to back me. This fundamental thing settled, the next point is, in what internal respect does the whale differ from other fish. Above, Linnæus has given you those items. But in brief, they are these: lungs and warm blood; whereas, all other fish are lungless and cold blooded.

Next: how shall we define the whale, by his obvious externals, so as conspicuously to label him for all time to come? To be short, then, a whale is *a spouting fish with a horizontal tail.* There you have him. However contracted, that definition is the result of expanded meditation. A walrus spouts much like a whale, but the walrus is not a fish, because he is amphibious. But the last term of the definition is still more cogent, as coupled with the first. Almost any one must have noticed that all the fish familiar to landsmen have not a flat, but a vertical, or up-and-down tail. Whereas, among spouting fish the tail, though it may be similarly shaped, invariably assumes a horizontal position.

By the above definition of what a whale is, I do by no means exclude from the leviathanic brotherhood any sea creature hitherto identified with the whale by the best informed Nantucketers; nor, on the other hand, link with it any fish hitherto authoritatively regarded as alien. Hence, all the smaller, spouting, and horizontal tailed fish must be included in this ground-plan of Cetology. Now, then, come the grand divisions of the entire whale host.

First: According to magnitude I divide the whales into three primary BOOKS (subdivisible into CHAPTERS), and these shall comprehend them all, both small and large.

I. The FOLIO WHALE; II. the OCTAVO WHALE; III. the DUODECIMO WHALE.

As the type of the FOLIO I present the *Sperm Whale;* of the OCTAVO, the *Grampus;* of the DUODECIMO, the *Porpoise.*

FOLIOS. Among these I here include the following chapters:—I. The *Sperm Whale;* II. the *Right Whale;* III. the *Fin Back Whale;* IV. the *Humpbacked Whale;* V. the *Razor Back Whale;* VI. the *Sulphur Bottom Whale.*

BOOK I. (*Folio*), CHAPTER I. (*Sperm Whale*).—This whale, among the English of old vaguely known as the Trumpa whale, and the Physeter whale, and the Anvil Headed whale, is the present Cachalot of the French, and the Pottsfich of the Germans, and the Macrocephalus of the Long Words. He is, without doubt, the largest inhabitant of the globe; the most formidable of all whales to encounter; the most majestic in aspect; and lastly, by far the most valuable in commerce; he being the only creature from which that valuable substance, spermaceti, is obtained. All his peculiarities will, in many other places, be enlarged upon. It is chiefly with his name that I now have to do. Philologically considered, it is absurd. Some centuries ago, when the sperm whale was almost wholly unknown in his own proper individuality, and when his oil was only accidentally obtained from the stranded fish; in those days spermaceti, it would seem, was popularly supposed to be derived from a creature identical with the one then known in England as the Greenland or Right Whale. It was the idea also, that this same spermaceti was that quickening humor of the Greenland Whale which the first syllable of the word literally expresses. In those times, also, spermaceti was exceedingly scarce, not being used for light, but only as an ointment and medicament. It was only to be had from the druggists as you nowadays buy an ounce of rhubarb. When, as I opine, in the course of time, the true nature of spermaceti became known, its original name was still retained by the dealers; no doubt to enhance its value by a notion so strangely significant of its scarcity. And so the appellation must at last have come to be bestowed upon the whale from which this spermaceti was really derived.

BOOK I. (*Folio*), CHAPTER II. (*Right Whale*).—In one respect this is the most venerable of the leviathans, being the one first regularly hunted by man. It yields the article commonly known as whalebone or baleen; and the oil specially known as "whale oil," an inferior article in commerce. Among the fishermen, he is indiscriminately designated by all the following titles: The Whale; the Greenland Whale; the Black Whale; the Great Whale; the True

Whale; the Right Whale. There is a deal of obscurity concerning the identity of the species thus multitudinously baptized. What then is the whale, which I include in the second species of my Folios? It is the Great Mysticetus of the English naturalists; the Greenland Whale of the English whalemen; the Baliene Ordinaire of the French whalemen; the Growlands Walfish of the Swedes. It is the whale which for more than two centuries past has been hunted by the Dutch and English in the Arctic seas; it is the whale which the American fishermen have long pursued in the Indian ocean, on the Brazil Banks, on the Nor' West Coast, and various other parts of the world, designated by them Right Whale Cruising Grounds.

Some pretend to see a difference between the Greenland whale of the English and the right whale of the Americans. But they precisely agree in all their grand features; nor has there yet been presented a single determinate fact upon which to ground a radical distinction. It is by endless subdivisions based upon the most inconclusive differences, that some departments of natural history become so repellingly intricate. The right whale will be elsewhere treated of at some length, with reference to elucidating the sperm whale.

BOOK I. (*Folio*), CHAPTER III. (*Fin-back*).—Under this head I reckon a monster which, by the various names of Fin-Back, Tall-Spout, and Long-John, has been seen almost in every sea and is commonly the whale whose distant jet is so often descried by passengers crossing the Atlantic, in the New York packet-tracks. In the length he attains, and in his baleen, the Fin-back resembles the right whale, but is of a less portly girth, and a lighter color, approaching to olive. His great lips present a cable-like aspect, formed by the intertwisting, slanting folds of large wrinkles. His grand distinguishing feature, the fin, from which he derives his name, is often a conspicuous object. This fin is some three or four feet long, growing vertically from the hinder part of the back, of an angular shape, and with a very sharp pointed end. Even if not the slightest other part of the creature be visible, this isolated fin will, at times, be seen plainly projecting from the surface. When the sea is moderately calm, and slightly marked with spherical ripples, and this gnomon-like fin stands up and casts shadows upon the wrinkled surface, it may well be supposed that the watery circle surrounding it somewhat resembles a dial, with its style and wavy hour-lines graved on it. On that Ahaz-dial the shadow often goes back. The Fin-Back is not gregarious. He seems a whale-hater, as some men are man-haters. Very shy; always going solitary; unexpectedly rising to the surface in the remotest and most sullen waters; his straight and single lofty jet rising like a tall misanthropic spear upon a barren plain; gifted with such wondrous power and velocity in swimming, as to defy all present pursuit from man; this leviathan seems the banished and unconquerable Cain of his race, bearing for his mark that style upon his back. From having the baleen in his mouth, the Fin-Back is sometimes included with the right whale, among a theoretic species denominated *Whalebone whales*, that is, whales with baleen. Of these so-called Whalebone whales, there would seem to be several varieties, most of which, however, are little known. Broad-nosed whales and beaked whales; pike-headed whales; bunched whales; under-jawed whales and rostrated whales, are the fishermen's names for a few sorts.

In connexion with this appellative of "Whalebone whales," it is of great importance to mention, that however such a nomenclature may be convenient in facilitating allusions to some kind of whales, yet it is in vain to attempt a clear classification of the Leviathan, founded upon either his baleen, or hump, or fin, or teeth; notwithstanding that those marked parts or features very obviously seem better adapted to afford the basis for a regular system of Cetology than any other detached bodily distinctions, which the whale, in his kinds, presents. How then? The baleen, hump, back-fin, and teeth; these are things whose peculiarities are indiscriminately dispersed among all sorts of whales, without any regard to what may be the nature of their structure in other and more essential particulars. Thus, the sperm whale and the humpbacked whale, each has a hump; but there the similitude ceases. Then, this same humpbacked whale and the Greenland whale, each of these has baleen; but there again the similitude ceases. And it is just the same with the other parts above mentioned. In various sorts of whales, they form such irregular combinations; or, in the case of any one of them detached, such an irregular isolation; as utterly to defy all general methodization formed upon such a basis. On this rock every one of the whale-naturalists has split.

But it may possibly be conceived that, in the internal parts of the whale, in his anatomy—there, at least, we shall be able to hit the right classification. Nay; what thing, for example, is there in the Greenland whale's anatomy more striking than his baleen? Yet we have seen that by his baleen it is impossible correctly to classify the Greenland whale. And if you descend into the bowels of the various leviathans, why there you will not find distinctions a fiftieth part as available to the systematizer as those external ones already enumerated. What then remains? nothing but to take hold of the whales bodily, in their entire liberal volume, and boldly sort them that way. And this is the Bibliographical system here adopted; and it is the only one that can possibly succeed, for it alone is practicable. To proceed.

BOOK I. (*Folio*), CHAPTER IV. (*Hump Back*).—This whale is often seen on the northern American coast. He has been frequently captured there, and towed into harbor. He has a great pack on him like a peddler; or you might call him the Elephant and Castle whale. At any rate, the popular name for him does not sufficiently distinguish him, since the sperm whale also has a hump, though a smaller one. His oil is not very valuable. He has baleen. He is the most gamesome and light-hearted of all the whales, making more gay foam and white water generally than any other of them.

BOOK I. (*Folio*), CHAPTER V. (*Razor Back*).—Of this whale little is known but his name. I have seen him at a distance off Cape Horn. Of a retiring nature, he eludes both hunters and philosophers. Though no coward, he has never yet shown any part of him but his back, which rises in a long sharp ridge. Let him go. I know little more of him, nor does anybody else.

BOOK I. (*Folio*), CHAPTER VI. (*Sulphur Bottom*).—Another retiring gentleman, with a brimstone belly, doubtless got by scraping along the Tartarian tiles in some of his profounder divings. He is seldom seen; at least I have never seen him except in the remoter southern seas, and then always at too great a distance to study his countenance. He is never chased; he would run away with rope-walks of line. Prodigies are told of him. Adieu, Sulphur Bottom! I can say nothing more that is true of ye, nor can the oldest Nantucketer.

Thus ends BOOK I. (*Folio*), and now begins BOOK II. (*Octavo*).

OCTAVOES. These embrace the whales of middling magnitude, among which at present may be numbered:—I., the *Grampus;* II., the *Black Fish;* III., the *Narwhale;* IV., the *Thrasher;* V., the *Killer.*

BOOK II. (*Octavo*), CHAPTER I. (*Grampus*).—Though this fish, whose loud sonorous breathing, or rather blowing, has furnished a proverb to landsmen, is so well known a denizen of the deep, yet is he not popularly classed among whales. But possessing all the grand distinctive features of the leviathan, most naturalists have recognised him for one. He is of moderate octavo size, varying from fifteen to twenty-five feet in length, and of corresponding dimensions round the waist. He swims in herds; he is never regularly hunted, though his oil is considerable in quantity, and pretty good for light. By some fishermen his approach is regarded as premonitory of the advance of the great sperm whale.

BOOK II. (*Octavo*), CHAPTER II. (*Black Fish*).—I give the popular fisher-men's names for all these fish, for generally they are the best. Where any name happens to be vague or inexpressive, I shall say so, and suggest another. I do so now, touching the Black Fish, so called, because blackness is the rule among almost all whales. So, call him the Hyena Whale, if you please. His voracity is well known, and from the circumstance that the inner angles of his lips are curved upwards, he carries an everlasting Mephistophelean grin on his face. This whale averages some sixteen or eighteen feet in length. He is found in almost all latitudes. He has a peculiar way of showing his dorsal hooked fin in swimming, which looks something like a Roman nose. When not more profit-ably employed, the sperm whale hunters sometimes capture the Hyena whale, to keep up the supply of cheap oil for domestic employment—as some frugal housekeepers, in the absence of company, and quite alone by themselves, burn unsavory tallow instead of odorous wax. Though their blubber is very thin, some of these whales will yield you upwards of thirty gallons of oil.

BOOK II. (*Octavo*), CHAPTER III. (*Narwhale*), that is, *Nostril whale*.—Another instance of a curiously named whale, so named I suppose from his peculiar horn being originally mistaken for a peaked nose. The creature is some sixteen feet in length, while its horn averages five feet, though some exceed ten, and even attain to fifteen feet. Strictly speaking, this horn is but a length-ened tusk, growing out from the jaw in a line a little depressed from the horizon-tal. But it is only found on the sinister side, which has an ill effect, giving its owner something analogous to the aspect of a clumsy left-handed man. What precise purpose this ivory horn or lance answers, it would be hard to say. It does not seem to be used like the blade of the sword-fish and bill-fish; though some sailors tell me that the Narwhale employs it for a rake in turning over the bottom of the sea for food. Charley Coffin said it was used for an ice-piercer; for the Narwhale, rising to the surface of the Polar Sea, and finding it sheeted with ice, thrusts his horn up, and so breaks through. But you cannot prove either of these surmises to be correct. My own opinion is, that however this one-sided horn may really be used by the Narwhale—however that may be—it would certainly be very convenient to him for a folder in reading pamphlets. The Narwhale I have heard called the Tusked whale, the Horned whale, and the Unicorn whale. He is certainly a curious example of the Unicornism to be found in almost every kingdom of animated nature. From certain cloistered old authors I have gathered that this same sea-unicorn's horn was in ancient days regarded as the great antidote against poison, and as such, preparations of it brought immense prices. It was also distilled to a volatile salts for fainting ladies, the same way that the horns of the male deer are manufactured into hartshorn. Originally it was in itself accounted an object of great curiosity. Black Letter tells me that Sir Martin Frobisher on his return from that voyage, when Queen Bess did gallantly wave her jewelled hand to him from a window of Greenwich Palace, as his bold ship sailed down the Thames; "when Sir Martin returned from that voyage," saith Black Letter, "on bended knees he presented to her highness a prodigious long horn of the Narwhale, which for a long period after hung in the castle at Windsor." An Irish author avers that the Earl of

Leicester, on bended knees, did likewise present to her highness another horn, pertaining to a land beast of the unicorn nature.

The Narwhale has a very picturesque, leopard-like look, being of a milk-white ground color, dotted with round and oblong spots of black. His oil is very superior, clear and fine; but there is little of it, and he is seldom hunted. He is mostly found in the circumpolar seas.

BOOK II. (*Octavo*), CHAPTER IV. (*Killer*).—Of this whale little is precisely known to the Nantucketer, and nothing at all to the professed naturalists. From what I have seen of him at a distance, I should say that he was about the bigness of a grampus. He is very savage—a sort of Feegee fish. He sometimes takes the great Folio whales by the lip, and hangs there like a leech, till the mighty brute is worried to death. The Killer is never hunted. I never heard what sort of oil he has. Exception might be taken to the name bestowed upon this whale, on the ground of its indistinctness. For we are all killers, on land and on sea; Bonapartes and Sharks included.

BOOK II. (*Octavo*), CHAPTER V. (*Thrasher*).—This gentleman is famous for his tail, which he uses for a ferule in thrashing his foes. He mounts the Folio whale's back, and as he swims, he works his passage by flogging him; as some schoolmasters get along in the world by a similar process. Still less is known of the Thrasher than of the Killer. Both are outlaws, even in the lawless seas.

Thus ends BOOK II. (*Octavo*), and begins BOOK III. (*Duodecimo.*)

DUODECIMOES.—These include the smaller whales. I. The Huzza Porpoise. II. The Algerine Porpoise. III. The Mealy-mouthed Porpoise.

To those who have not chanced specially to study the subject, it may possibly seem strange, that fishes not commonly exceeding four or five feet should be marshalled among WHALES—a word, which, in the popular sense, always conveys an idea of hugeness. But the creatures set down above as Duodecimoes are infallibly whales, by the terms of my definition of what a whale is—i.e. a spouting fish, with a horizontal tail.

BOOK II. (*Duodecimo*), CHAPTER I. (*Huzza Porpoise*).—This is the common porpoise found almost all over the globe. The name is of my own bestowal; for there are more than one sort of porpoises, and something must be done to distinguish them. I call him thus, because he always swims in hilarious shoals, which upon the broad sea keep tossing themselves to heaven like caps in a Fourth-of-July crowd. Their appearance is generally hailed with delight by the mariner. Full of fine spirits, they invariably come from the breezy billows to windward. They are the lads that always live before the wind. They are accounted a lucky omen. If you yourself can withstand three cheers at beholding these vivacious fish, then heaven help ye; the spirit of godly gamesomeness is not in ye. A well-fed, plump Huzza Porpoise will yield you one good gallon of good oil. But the fine and delicate fluid extracted from his jaws is exceedingly valuable. It is in request among jewellers and watchmakers. Sailors put it on their hones. Porpoise meat is good eating, you know. It may never have occurred to you that a porpoise spouts. Indeed, his spout is so small that it is not very readily discernible. But the next time you have a chance, watch him; and you will then see the great Sperm whale himself in miniature.

BOOK III. (*Duodecimo*), CHAPTER II. (*Algerine Porpoise*).—A pirate. Very savage. He is only found, I think, in the Pacific. He is somewhat larger than the Huzza Porpoise, but much of the same general make. Provoke him, and he will buckle to a shark. I have lowered for him many times, but never yet saw him captured.

BOOK III. (*Duodecimo*), CHAPTER III. (*Mealy-mouthed Porpoise*).—The largest kind of Porpoise; and only found in the Pacific, so far as it is known. The only English name, by which he has hitherto been designated, is that of the fishers—Right-Whale Porpoise, from the circumstance that he is chiefly found in the vicinity of that Folio. In shape, he differs in some degree from the Huzza Porpoise, being of a less rotund and jolly girth; indeed, he is of quite a neat and gentleman-like figure. He has no fins on his back (most other porpoises have), he has a lovely tail, and sentimental Indian eyes of a hazel hue. But his mealy-mouth spoils him. Though his entire back down to his side fins is of a deep sable, yet a boundary line, distinct as the mark in a ship's hull, called the "bright waist," that line streaks him from stem to stern, with two separate colors, black above and white below. The white comprises part of his head, and the whole of his mouth, which makes him look as if he had just escaped from a felonious visit to a meal-bag. A most mean and mealy aspect! His oil is much like that of the common porpoise.

*   *   *   *   *

Beyond the DUODECIMO, this system does not proceed, inasmuch as the Porpoise is the smallest of the whales. Above, you have all the Leviathans of note. But there are a rabble of uncertain, fugitive, half-fabulous whales, which, as an American whaleman, I know by reputation, but not personally. I shall enumerate them by their forecastle appellations; for possibly such a list may be valuable to future investigators, who may complete what I have here but begun. If any of the following whales, shall hereafter be caught and marked, then he can readily be incorporated into this System, according to his Folio, Octavo, or Duodecimo magnitude:—The Bottle-Nose Whale; the Junk Whale; the Pudding-Headed Whale; the Cape Whale; the Leading Whale; the Cannon Whale; the Scragg Whale; the Coppered Whale; the Elephant Whale; the Iceberg Whale; the Quog Whale; the Blue Whale; &c. From Icelandic, Dutch, and old English authorities, there might be quoted other lists of uncertain whales, blessed with all manner of uncouth names. But I omit them as altogether obsolete; and can hardly help suspecting them for mere sounds, full of Leviathanism, but signifying nothing.

Finally: It was stated at the outset, that this system would not be here, and at once, perfected. You cannot but plainly see that I have kept my word. But I now leave my cetological System standing thus unfinished, even as the great Cathedral of Cologne was left, with the crane still standing upon the top of the uncompleted tower. For small erections may be finished by their first architects; grand ones, true ones, ever leave the copestone to posterity. God keep me from ever completing anything. This whole book is but a draught—nay, but the draught of a draught. Oh, Time, Strength, Cash, and Patience!

CHAPTER XXXIII

THE SPECKSYNDER

CONCERNING the officers of the whale-craft, this seems as good a place as any to set down a little domestic peculiarity on ship-board, arising from the existence of the harpooneer class of officers, a class unknown of course in any other marine than the whale-fleet.

The large importance attached to the harpooneer's vocation is evinced by the fact, that originally in the old Dutch Fishery, two centuries and more ago, the command of a whale ship was not wholly lodged in the person now called the captain, but was divided between him and an officer called the Specksynder. Literally this word means Fat-Cutter; usage, however, in time made it equivalent to Chief Harpooneer. In those days, the captain's authority was restricted to the navigation and general management of the vessel: while over the whale-hunting department and all its concerns, the Specksynder or Chief Harpooneer reigned supreme. In the British Greenland Fishery, under the corrupted title of Specksioneer, this old Dutch official is still retained, but his former dignity is sadly abridged. At present he ranks simply as senior Harpooneer; and as such, is but one of the captain's more inferior subalterns. Nevertheless, as upon the good conduct of the harpooneers the success of a whaling voyage largely depends, and since in the American Fishery he is not only an important officer in the boat, but under certain circumstances (night watches on a whaling ground) the command of the ship's deck is also his; therefore the grand political maxim of the sea demands, that he should nominally live apart from the men before the mast, and be in some way distinguished as their professional superior; though always, by them, familiarly regarded as their social equal.

Now, the grand distinction drawn between officer and man at sea, is this— the first lives aft, the last forward. Hence, in whale-ships and merchantmen alike, the mates have their quarters with the captain; and so, too, in most of the American whalers the harpooneers are lodged in the after part of the ship. That is to say, they take their meals in the captain's cabin, and sleep in a place indirectly communicating with it.

Though the long period of a Southern whaling voyage (by far the longest of all voyages now or ever made by man), the peculiar perils of it, and the community of interest prevailing among a company, all of whom, high or low, depend for their profits, not upon fixed wages, but upon their common luck, together with their common vigilance, intrepidity, and hard work; though all these things do in some cases tend to beget a less rigorous discipline than in merchantmen generally; yet, never mind how much like an old Mesopotamian family these whalemen may, in some primitive instances, live together; for all that, the punctilious externals, at least, of the quarter-deck are seldom materially relaxed, and in no instance done away. Indeed, many are the Nantucket ships in which you will see the skipper parading his quarter-deck with an elated grandeur not surpassed in any military navy; nay, extorting almost as much outward homage as if he wore the imperial purple, and not the shabbiest of pilot-cloth.

And though of all men the moody captain of the Pequod was the least given to that sort of shallowest assumption; and though the only homage he ever exacted, was implicit, instantaneous obedience; though he required no man to remove the shoes from his feet ere stepping upon the quarter-deck; and though there were times when, owing to peculiar circumstances connected with events hereafter to be detailed, he addressed them in unusual terms, whether of condescension or *in terrorem,* or otherwise; yet even Captain Ahab was by no means unobservant of the paramount forms and usages of the sea.

Nor, perhaps, will it fail to be eventually perceived, that behind those forms and usages, as it were, he sometimes masked himself; incidentally making use of them for other and more private ends than they were legitimately intended to subserve. That certain sultanism of his brain, which had otherwise in a good degree remained unmanifested; through those forms that same sultanism became incarnate in an irresistible dictatorship. For be a man's intellectual superiority what it will, it can never assume the practical, available supremacy over other men, without the aid of some sort of external arts and entrenchments, always, in themselves, more or less paltry and base. This it is, that for ever keep God's true princes of the Empire from the world's hustings; and leaves the highest honors that this air can give, to those men who become famous more through their infinite inferiority to the choice hidden handful of the Divine Inert, than through their undoubted superiority over the dead level of the mass. Such large virtue lurks in these small things when extreme political superstitions invest them, that in some royal instances even to idiot imbecility they have imparted potency. But when, as in the case of Nicholas the Czar, the ringed crown of geographical empire encircles an imperial brain; then, the plebeian herds crouch abased before the tremendous centralization. Nor, will the tragic dramatist who would depict mortal indomitableness in its fullest sweep and direct swing, ever forget a hint, incidentally so important in his art, as the one now alluded to.

But Ahab, my Captain, still moves before me in all his Nantucket grimness and shagginess; and in this episode touching Emperors and Kings, I must not conceal that I have only to do with a poor old whale-hunter like him; and, therefore, all outward majestical trappings and housings are denied me. Oh, Ahab! what shall be grand in thee, it must needs be plucked at from the skies, and dived for in the deep, and featured in the unbodied air!

CHAPTER XXXIV

THE CABIN-TABLE

It is noon; and Dough-Boy, the steward, thrusting his pale loaf-of-bread face from the cabin-scuttle, announces dinner to his lord and master who, sitting in the lee quarter-boat, has just been taking an observation of the sun; and is now mutely reckoning the latitude on the smooth, medallion-shaped tablet, reserved for that daily purpose on the upper part of his ivory leg. From his complete inattention to the tidings, you would think that moody Ahab had not heard his menial. But presently, catching hold of the mizen shrouds, he swings himself to the deck, and in an even, unexhilarated voice, saying, "Dinner, Mr. Starbuck," disappears into the cabin.

When the last echo of his sultan's step has died away, and Starbuck, the first Emir, has every reason to suppose that he is seated, then Starbuck rouses from his quietude, takes a few turns along the planks, and, after a grave peep into the binnacle, says, with some touch of pleasantness, "Dinner, Mr. Stubb," and descends the scuttle. The second Emir lounges about the rigging awhile, and then slightly shaking the main brace, to see whether it will be all right with that important rope, he likewise takes up the old burden, and with a rapid "Dinner, Mr. Flask," follows after his predecessors.

But the third Emir, now seeing himself all alone on the quarter-deck, seems to feel relieved from some curious restraint; for, tipping all sorts of knowing winks in all sorts of directions, and kicking off his shoes, he strikes into a sharp but noiseless squall of a hornpipe right over the Grand Turk's head; and then, by a dexterous sleight, pitching his cap up into the mizentop for a shelf, he goes down rollicking, so far at least as he remains visible from the deck, reversing all other processions, by bringing up the rear with music. But ere stepping into the cabin doorway below, he pauses, ships a new face altogether, and, then, independent, hilarious little Flask enters King Ahab's presence, in the character of Abjectus, or the Slave.

It is not the least among the strange things bred by the intense artificialness of sea-usages, that while in the open air of the deck some officers will, upon provocation, bear themselves boldly and defyingly enough towards their commander; yet, ten to one, let those very officers the next moment go down to their customary dinner in that same commander's cabin, and straightway their inoffensive, not to say deprecatory and humble air towards him, as he sits at the head of the table; this is marvellous, sometimes most comical. Wherefore this difference? A problem? Perhaps not. To have been Belshazzar, King of Babylon; and to have been Belshazzar, not haughtily but courteously, therein certainly must have been some touch of mundane grandeur. But he who in the rightly regal and intelligent spirit presides over his own private dinner-table of invited guests, that man's unchallenged power and dominion of individual influence for the time; that man's royalty of state transcends Belshazzar's, for Belshazzar was not the greatest. Who has but once dined his friends, has tasted what it is to be Cæsar. It is a witchery of social czarship which there is no withstanding. Now, if to this consideration you superadd the official supremacy of a ship-master, then, by inference, you will derive the cause of that peculiarity of sea-life just mentioned.

Over his ivory-inlaid table, Ahab presided like a mute, maned sea-lion on the white coral beach, surrounded by his warlike but still deferential cubs. In his own proper turn, each officer waited to be served. They were as little children before Ahab; and yet, in Ahab, there seemed not to lurk the smallest social arrogance. With one mind, their intent eyes all fastened upon the old man's knife, as he carved the chief dish before him. I do not suppose that for the world they would have profaned that moment with the slightest observation. even upon so neutral a topic as the weather. No! And when reaching out his knife and fork, between which the slice of beef was locked, Ahab thereby motioned Starbuck's plate towards him, the mate received his meat as though receiving alms; and cut it tenderly; and a little started if, perchance, the knife grazed against the plate; and chewed it noiselessly; and swallowed it, not without circumspection. For, like the Coronation banquet at Frankfort, where the German Emperor profoundly dines with the seven Imperial Electors, so these cabin meals were somehow solemn meals, eaten in awful silence; and yet at table old Ahab forbade not conversation; only he himself was dumb. What a relief it was to choking Stubb, when a rat made a sudden racket in the hold below. And poor little Flask, he was the youngest son, and little boy of this weary family party. His were the shin-bones of the saline beef; his would have been the drumsticks. For Flask to have presumed to help himself, this must have seemed to him tantamount to larceny in the first degree. Had he helped himself at the table, doubtless, never more would he have been able to hold his head up in this honest world; nevertheless, strange to say, Ahab never forbade him. And had Flask helped himself, the chances were Ahab had never so much as noticed it. Least of all, did Flask presume to help himself to butter. Whether he thought the owners of the ship denied it to him, on account of its clotting his clear, sunny complexion; or whether he deemed that, on so long a voyage in such marketless waters, butter was at a premium, and therefore was not for him, a subaltern; however it was, Flask, alas! was a butterless man!

Another thing. Flask was the last person down at the dinner, and Flask is the first man up. Consider! For hereby Flask's dinner was badly jammed in point of time. Starbuck and Stubb both had the start of him; and yet they also have the privilege of lounging in the rear. If Stubb even, who is but a peg higher than Flask, happens to have but a small appetite, and soon shows symptoms of concluding his repast, then Flask must bestir himself, he will not get more than three mouthfuls that day; for it is against holy usage for Stubb to precede Flask to the deck. Therefore it was that Flask once admitted in private, that ever since he had arisen to the dignity of an officer, from that moment he had never known what it was to be otherwise than hungry, more or less. For what he ate did not so much relieve his hunger, as keep it immortal in him. Peace and satisfaction, thought Flask, have for ever departed from my stomach. I am an officer; but, how I wish I could fist a bit of old-fashioned beef in the forecastle, as I used to when I was before the mast. There's the fruits of promotion now; there's the vanity of glory: there's the insanity of life! Besides, if it were so that any mere sailor of the Pequod had a grudge against Flask in Flask's official capacity, all that sailor had to do, in order to obtain ample vengeance, was to go aft at dinner-time, and get a peep at Flask through the cabin sky-light, sitting silly and dumfoundered before awful Ahab.

· Now, Ahab and his three mates formed what may be called the first table in the Pequod's cabin. After their departure, taking place in inverted order to their arrival, the canvas cloth was cleared, or rather was restored to some hurried order by the pallid steward. And then the three harpooneers were bidden to the feast, they being its residuary legatees. They made a sort of temporary servants' hall of the high and mighty cabin.

In strange contrast to the hardly tolerable constraint and nameless invisible domineerings of the captain's table, was the entire care-free license and ease, the almost frantic democracy of those inferior fellows the harpooneers. While their masters, the mates, seemed afraid of the sound of the hinges of their own jaws, the harpooneers chewed their food with such a relish that there was a report to it. They dined like lords; they filled their bellies like Indian ships all day loading with spices. Such portentous appetites had Queequeg and Tashtego, that to fill out the vacancies made by the previous repast, often the pale Dough-Boy was fain to bring on a great baron of salt-junk, seemingly quarried out of the solid ox. And if he were not lively about it, if he did not go with a nimble hop-skip-and-jump, then Tashtego had an ungentlemanly way of accelerating him by darting a fork at his back, harpoonwise. And once Daggoo, seized with a sudden humor, assisted Dough-Boy's memory by snatching him up bodily, and thrusting his head into a great empty wooden trencher, while Tashtego, knife in hand, began laying out the circle preliminary to scalping him. He was naturally a very nervous, shuddering sort of little fellow, this bread-faced steward; the progeny of a bankrupt baker and a hospital nurse. And what with the standing spectacle of the black terrific Ahab, and the periodical tumultuous visitations of these three savages, Dough-Boy's whole life was one continual lip-quiver. Commonly, after seeing the harpooneers furnished with all things they demanded, he would escape from their clutches into his little pantry adjoining, and fearfully peep out at them through the blinds of its door, till all was over.

It was a sight to see Queequeg seated over against Tashtego, opposing his filed teeth to the Indian's; crosswise to them, Daggoo seated on the floor, for a bench would have brought his hearse-plumed head to the low carlines; at every motion of his colossal limbs, making the low cabin framework to shake, as when an African elephant goes passenger in a ship. But for all this, the great negro was wonderfully abstemious, not to say dainty. It seemed hardly possible that by such comparatively small mouthfuls he could keep up the vitality diffused through so broad, baronial, and superb a person. But, doubtless, this noble savage fed strong and drank deep of the abounding element of air; and through his dilated nostrils snuffed in the sublime life of the worlds. Not by beef or by bread, are giants made or nourished. But Queequeg, he had a mortal, barbaric smack of the lip in eating—an ugly sound enough—so much so, that the trembling Dough-Boy almost looked to see whether any marks of teeth lurked in his own lean arms. And when he would hear Tashtego singing out for him to produce himself, that his bones might be picked, the simple-witted Steward all but shattered the crockery hanging round him in the pantry, by his sudden fits of the palsy. Nor did the whetstone which the harpooneers carried in their pockets, for their lances and other weapons; and with which whetstones, at dinner, they would ostentatiously sharpen their knives; that grating sound did not at all tend to tranquillize poor Dough-Boy. How could he forget that in his Island days, Queequeg, for one, must certainly have been guilty of some murderous, convivial indiscretions. Alas! Dough-Boy! hard fares the white waiter who waits upon cannibals. Not a napkin should he carry on his arm, but a buckler. In good time, though, to his great delight, the three salt-sea warriors would rise and depart; to his credulous, fable-mongering ears, all their martial bones jingling in them at every step, like Moorish scimetars in scabbards.

But, though these barbarians dined in the cabin, and nominally lived there; still, being anything but sedentary in their habits, they were scarcely ever in it except at meal-times, and just before sleeping-time, when they passed through it to their own peculiar quarters.

In this one matter, Ahab seemed no exception to most American whale captains, who, as a set, rather incline to the opinion that by rights the ship's cabin belongs to them; and that it is by courtesy alone that anybody else is, at any time, permitted there. So that, in real truth, the mates and harpooneers of the Pequod might more properly be said to have lived out of the cabin than in it. For when they did enter it, it was something as a street-door enters a house; turning inwards for a moment, only to be turned out the next; and, as a permanent thing, residing in the open air. Nor did they lose much hereby; in the cabin was no companionship; socially, Ahab was inaccessible. Though nominally included in the census of Christendom, he was still an alien to it. He lived in the world, as the last of the Grisly Bears lived in settled Missouri. And as when Spring and Summer had departed, that wild Logan of the woods, burying himself in the hollow of a tree, lived out the winter there, sucking his own paws; so, in his inclement, howling old age, Ahab's soul, shut up in the caved trunk of his body, there fed upon the sullen paws of its gloom!

CHAPTER XXXV

THE MAST-HEAD

IT was during the more pleasant weather, that in due rotation with the other seamen my first mast-head came round.

In most American whalemen the mast-heads are manned almost simultaneously with the vessel's leaving her port; even though she may have fifteen thousand miles, and more, to sail ere reaching her proper cruising ground. And if, after a three, four, or five years' voyage she is drawing nigh home with anything empty in her—say, an empty vial even—then, her mast-heads are kept manned to the last; and not till her skysail-poles sail in among the spires of the port, does she altogether relinquish the hope of capturing one whale more.

Now, as the business of standing mast-heads, ashore or afloat, is a very ancient and interesting one, let us in some measure expatiate here. I take it, that the earliest standers of mast-heads were the old Egyptians; because, in all my researches, I find none prior to them. For though their progenitors, the builders of Babel, must, doubtless, by their tower, have intended to rear the loftiest mast-head in all Asia, or Africa either; yet (ere the final truck was put to it) as that great stone mast of theirs may be said to have gone by the board, in the dread gale of God's wrath; therefore, we cannot give these Babel builders priority over the Egyptians. And that the Egyptians were a nation of mast-head standers, is an assertion based upon the general belief among archæologists, that the first pyramids were founded for astronomical purposes: a theory singularly supported by the peculiar stair-like formation of all four sides of those edifices; whereby, with prodigious long upliftings of their legs, those old astronomers were wont to mount to the apex, and sing out for new stars; even as the look-outs of a modern ship sing out for a sail, or a whale just bearing in sight. In Saint Stylites, the famous Christian hermit of old times, who built him a lofty stone pillar in the desert and spent the whole latter portion of his life on its summit, hoisting his food from the ground with a tackle; in him we have a remarkable instance of a dauntless stander-of-mast-heads; who was not to be driven from his place by fogs or frosts, rain, hail, or sleet; but valiantly facing everything out to the last, literally died at his post. Of modern standers-of-mast-heads we have but a lifeless set; mere stone, iron, and bronze men; who, though well capable of facing out a stiff gale, are still entirely incompetent to the business of singing out upon discovering any strange sight. There is Napoleon; who, upon the top of the column of Vendôme, stands with arms folded, some one hundred and fifty feet in the air; careless, now, who rules the decks below; whether Louis Philippe, Louis Blanc, or Louis the Devil. Great Washington, too, stands high aloft on his towering main-mast in Baltimore, and like one of Hercules' pillars, his column marks that point of human grandeur beyond which few mortals will go. Admiral Nelson, also, on a capstan of gun-metal, stands his mast-head in Trafalgar Square; and ever when most obscured by that London smoke, token is yet given that a hidden hero is there; for where there is smoke, must be fire. But neither great Washington, nor Napoleon, nor Nelson, will answer a single hail from below, however madly invoked to befriend by their counsels the distracted decks upon which they gaze; however it may be surmised, that their spirits penetrate through the thick haze of the future, and descry what shoals and what rocks must be shunned.

It may seem unwarrantable to couple in any respect the mast-head standers of the land with those of the sea; but that in truth it is not so, is plainly evinced by an item for which Obed Macy, the sole historian of Nantucket, stands accountable. The worthy Obed tells us, that in the early times of the whale fishery, ere ships were regularly launched in pursuit of the game, the people of that island erected lofty spars along the sea-coast, to which the look-outs ascended by means of nailed cleats, something as fowls go upstairs in a hen-house. A few years ago this same plan was adopted by the Bay whalemen of

New Zealand, who, upon descrying the game, gave notice to the ready-manned boats nigh the beach. But this custom has now become obsolete; turn we then to the one proper mast-head, that of a whale-ship at sea. The three mast-heads are kept manned from sun-rise to sun-set; the seamen taking their regular turns (as at the helm), and relieving each other every two hours. In the serene weather of the tropics it is exceedingly pleasant the mast-head; nay, to a dreamy meditative man it is delightful. There you stand, a hundred feet above the silent decks, striding along the deep, as if the masts were gigantic stilts, while beneath you and between your legs, as it were, swim the hugest monsters of the sea, even as ships once sailed between the boots of the famous Colossus at old Rhodes. There you stand, lost in the infinite series of the sea, with nothing ruffled but the waves. The tranced ship indolently rolls; the drowsy trade winds blow; everything resolves you into languor. For the most part, in this tropic whaling life, a sublime uneventfulness invests you; you hear no news; read no gazettes; extras with startling accounts of common-places never delude you into unnecessary excitements; you hear of no domestic afflictions; bankrupt securities; fall of stocks; are never troubled with the thought of what you shall have for dinner—for all your meals for three years and more are snugly stowed in casks, and your bill of fare is immutable.

In one of those southern whalemen, on a long three or four years' voyage, as often happens, the sum of the various hours you spend at the mast-head would amount to several entire months. And it is much to be deplored that the place to which you devote so considerable a portion of the whole term of your natural life, should be so sadly destitute of anything approaching to a cosy inhabitive-ness, or adapted to breed a comfortable localness of feeling, such as pertains to a bed, a hammock, a hearse, a sentry box, a pulpit, a coach, or any other of those small and snug contrivances in which men temporarily isolate themselves. Your most usual point of perch is the head of the t' gallant-mast, where you stand upon two thin parallel sticks (almost peculiar to whalemen) called the t' gallant cross-trees. Here, tossed about by the sea, the beginner feels about as cosy as he would standing on a bull's horns. To be sure, in cold weather you may carry your house aloft with you, in the shape of a watch-coat; but prop-erly speaking the thickest watch-coat is no more of a house than the unclad body; for as the soul is glued inside of its fleshy tabernacle, and cannot freely move about in it, nor even move out of it, without running great risk of perish-ing (like an ignorant pilgrim crossing the snowy Alps in winter); so a watch-coat is not so much of a house as it is a mere envelope, or additional skin en-casing you. You cannot put a shelf or chest of drawers in your body, and no more can you make a convenient closet of your watch-coat.

Concerning all this, it is much to be deplored that the mast-heads of a southern whale ship are unprovided with those enviable little tents or pulpits, called *crow's-nests*, in which the look-outs of a Greenland whaler are protected from the inclement weather of the frozen seas. In the fireside narrative of Captain Sleet, entitled "A Voyage among the Icebergs, in quest of the Greenland Whale, and incidentally for the re-discovery of the Lost Icelandic Colonies of Old Greenland;" in this admirable volume, all standers of mast-heads are furnished with a charmingly circumstantial account of the then recently in-vented *crow's-nest* of the Glacier, which was the name of Captain Sleet's good craft. He called it the *Sleet's crow's-nest*, in honor of himself; he being the original inventor and patentee, and free from all ridiculous false delicacy, and holding that if we call our own children after our own names (we fathers being the original inventors and patentees), so likewise should we denominate after ourselves any other apparatus we may beget. In shape, the Sleet's crow's-nest is something like a large tierce or pipe; it is open above, however, where it is furnished with a movable side-screen to keep to windward of your head in a hard gale. Being fixed on the summit of the mast, you ascend into it through a little trap-hatch in the bottom. On the after side, or side next the stern of the ship, is a comfortable seat, with a locker underneath for umbrellas, comforters, and coats. In front is a leather rack, in which to keep your speaking trumpet, pipe, telescope, and other nautical conveniences. When Captain Sleet in person stood his mast-head in this crow's nest of his, he tells us that he always had a rifle with him (also fixed in the rack), together with a powder flask and shot, for the purpose of popping off the stray narwhales, or vagrant sea unicorns infesting those waters; for you cannot successfully shoot at them from the deck owing to the resistance of the water, but to shoot down upon them is a very different thing. Now, it was plainly a labor of love for Captain Sleet to describe, as he does, all the little detailed conveniences of his crow's-nest; but though he so enlarges upon many of these, and though he treats us to a very scientific account of his experiments in this crow's-nest, with a small compass he kept there for the purpose of counteracting the errors resulting from what is called the "local attraction" of all binnacle magnets; an error ascribable to the horizontal vicinity of the iron in the ship's planks, and in the Glacier's case, perhaps, to there having been so many broken-down blacksmiths among her crew; I say, that 'though the Captain is very discreet and scientific here, yet, for all his learned "binnacle deviations," "azimuth compass observations," and "approximate errors," he knows very well, Captain Sleet, that he was not so much immersed in those profound magnetic meditations, as to fail being attracted occasionally towards that well replenished little case-bottle, so nicely tucked in on one side of his crow's-nest, within easy reach of his hand. Though, upon the whole, I greatly admire and even love the brave, the honest, and learned Captain; yet I take it very ill of him that he should so utterly ignore that case-bottle, seeing what a faithful friend and comforter it must have been, while with mittened fingers and hooded head he was studying the mathematics aloft there in that bird's nest within three or four perches of the pole.

But if we Southern whale-fishers are not so snugly housed aloft as Captain Sleet and his Greenlandmen were; yet that disadvantage is greatly counter-balanced by the widely contrasting serenity of those seductive seas in which we South fishers mostly float. For one, I used to lounge up the rigging very leisurely, resting in the top to have a chat with Queequeg, or any one else off duty whom I might find there; then ascending a little way farther, and throwing a lazy leg over the top-sail yard, take a preliminary view of the watery pastures, and so at last mount to my ultimate destination.

Let me make a clean breast of it here, and frankly admit that I kept but sorry guard. With the problem of the universe revolving in me, how could I—being left completely to myself at such a thought-engendering altitude,—how could I but lightly hold my obligations to observe all whale-ships' standing orders, "Keep your weather eye open, and sing out every time."

And let me in this place movingly admonish you, ye ship-owners of Nantucket! Beware of enlisting in your vigilant fisheries any lad with lean brow and hollow eye; given to unseasonable meditativeness; and who offers to ship with the Phædon instead of Bowditch in his head. Beware of such an one, I say: your whales must be seen before they can be killed; and this sunken-eyed young Platonist will tow you ten wakes round the world, and never make you one pint of sperm the richer. Nor are these monitions at all unneeded. For nowadays, the whale-fishery furnishes an asylum for many romantic, melancholy, and absent-minded young men, disgusted with the carking care of earth, and seeking sentiment in tar and blubber. Childe Harold not unfrequently perches himself upon the mast-head of some luckless disappointed whale-ship, and in moody phrase ejaculates:—

> "Roll on, thou deep and dark blue ocean, roll!
> Ten thousand blubber-hunters sweep over thee in vain."

Very often do the captains of such ships take those absent-minded young philosophers to task, upbraiding them with not feeling sufficient "interest" in the voyage; half-hinting that they are so hopelessly lost to all honorable ambition, as that in their secret souls they would rather not see whales than otherwise. But all in vain; those young Platonists have a notion that their vision is imperfect; they are short-sighted; what use, then, to strain the visual nerve? They have left their opera-glasses at home.

"Why, thou monkey," said a harpooneer to one of these lads, "we've been cruising now hard upon three years, and thou hast not raised a whale yet. Whales are scarce as hen's teeth whenever thou art up here." Perhaps they were; or perhaps there might have been shoals of them in the far horizon; but lulled into such an opium-like listnessness of vacant unconscious reverie is this absent-minded youth by the blending cadence of waves with thoughts, that at last he loses his identity; takes the mystic ocean at his feet for the visible image of that deep, blue, bottomless soul, pervading mankind and nature; and every strange, half-seen, gliding, beautiful thing that eludes him; every dimly-discovered, uprising fin of some undiscernible form, seems to him the embodiment of those elusive thoughts that only people the soul by continually flitting through it. In this enchanted mood, thy spirit ebbs away to whence it came; becomes diffused through time and space; like Cranmer's sprinkled Pantheistic ashes, forming at last a part of every shore the round globe over.

There is no life in thee, now, except that rocking life imparted by a gentle rolling ship; by her, borrowed from the sea; by the sea, from the inscrutable tides of God. But while this sleep, this dream is on ye, move your foot or hand an inch; slip your hold at all; and your identity comes back in horror. Over Descartian vortices you hover. And perhaps, at mid-day, in the fairest weather, with one half-throttled shriek you drop through that transparent air into the summer sea, no more to rise for ever. Heed it well, ye Pantheists!

CHAPTER XXXVI

THE QUARTER-DECK

(*Enter Ahab: Then, all*)

IT was not a great while after the affair of the pipe, that one morning shortly after breakfast, Ahab, as was his wont, ascended the cabin-gangway to the deck. There most sea-captains usually walk at that hour, as country gentlemen, after the same meal, take a few turns in the garden.

Soon his steady, ivory stride was heard, as to and fro he paced his old rounds, upon planks so familiar to his tread, that they were all over dented, like geological stones, with the peculiar mark of his walk. Did you fixedly gaze, too, upon that ribbed and dented brow; there also, you would see still stranger foot-prints—the foot-prints of his one unsleeping, ever-pacing thought.

But on the occasion in question, those dents looked deeper, even as his nervous step that morning left a deeper mark. And, so full of his thought was Ahab, that at every uniform turn that he made, now at the main-mast and now at the binnacle, you could almost see that thought turn in him as he turned, and pace in him as he paced; so completely possessing him, indeed, that it all but seemed the inward mould of every outer movement.

"D'ye mark him, Flask?" whispered Stubb; "the chick that's in him pecks the shell. 'Twill soon be out."

The hours wore on;—Ahab now shut up within his cabin; anon, pacing the deck, with the same intense bigotry of purpose in his aspect.

It drew near the close of day. Suddenly he came to a halt by the bulwarks, and inserting his bone leg into the auger-hole there, and with one hand grasping a shroud, he ordered Starbuck to send everybody aft.

"Sir!" said the mate, astonished at an order seldom or never given on shipboard except in some extraordinary case.

"Send everybody aft," repeated Ahab. "Mast-heads, there! come down!"

When the entire ship's company were assembled, and with curious and not wholly unapprehensive faces, were eyeing him, for he looked not unlike the weather horizon when a storm is coming up, Ahab, after rapidly glancing over the bulwarks, and then darting his eyes among the crew, started from his standpoint; and as though not a soul were nigh him resumed his heavy turns upon the deck. With bent head and half-slouched hat he continued to pace, unmindful of the wondering whispering among the men; till Stubb cautiously whispered to Flask, that Ahab must have summoned them there for the purpose of witnessing a pedestrian feat. But this did not last long. Vehemently pausing, he cried:—

"What do ye do when ye see a whale, men?"

"Sing out for him!" was the impulsive rejoinder from a score of clubbed voices.

"Good!" cried Ahab, with a wild approval in his tones; observing the hearty animation into which his unexpected question had so magnetically thrown them.

"And what do ye next, men?"

"Lower away, and after him!"

"And what tune is it ye pull to, men?"

"A dead whale or a stove boat!"

More and more strangely and fiercely glad and approving, grew the countenance of the old man at every shout; while the mariners began to gaze curiously at each other, as if marvelling how it was that they themselves became so excited at such seemingly purposeless questions.

But, they were all eagerness again, as Ahab, now half-revolving in his pivot-hole, with one hand reaching high up a shroud, and tightly, almost convulsively grasping it, addressed them thus:—

"All ye mast-headers have before now heard me give orders about a white whale. Look ye! d'ye see this Spanish ounce of gold?"—holding up a broad bright coin to the sun—"it is a sixteen dollar piece, men. D'ye see it? Mr. Starbuck, hand me yon top-maul."

While the mate was getting the hammer, Ahab, without speaking, was

slowly rubbing the gold piece against the skirts of his jacket, as if to heighten
its lustre, and without using any words was meanwhile lowly humming to himself, producing a sound so strangely muffled and inarticulate that it seemed the
mechanical humming of the wheels of his vitality in him.

Receiving the top-maul from Starbuck, he advanced towards the main-mast
with the hammer uplifted in one hand, exhibiting the gold with the other, and
with a high raised voice exclaiming: "Whosoever of ye raises me a white-
headed whale with a wrinkled brow and a crooked jaw; whosoever of ye raises
me that white-headed whale, with three holes punctured in his starboard fluke
—look ye, whosoever of ye raises me that same white whale, he shall have this
gold ounce, my boys!"

"Huzza! huzza!" cried the seamen, as with swinging tarpaulins they hailed
the act of nailing the gold to the mast.

"It's a white whale, I say," resumed Ahab, as he threw down the top-
maul: "a white whale. Skin your eyes for him, men; look sharp for white
water; if ye see but a bubble, sing out."

All this while Tashtego, Daggoo, and Queequeg had looked on with even
more intense interest and surprise than the rest, and at the mention of the
wrinkled brow and crooked jaw they had started as if each was separately
touched by some specific recollection.

"Captain Ahab," said Tashtego, "that white whale must be the same that
some call Moby-Dick."

"Moby-Dick?" shouted Ahab. "Do ye know the white whale then, Tash?"

"Does he fan-tail a little curious, sir, before he goes down?" said the Gay-
Header deliberately.

"And has he a curious spout, too," said Daggoo, "very bushy, even for a
parmacetty, and mighty quick, Captain Ahab?"

"And he have one, two, tree—oh! good many iron in him hide, too, Captain,"
cried Queequeg disjointedly, "all twiske-tee be-twisk, like him—him—" faltering hard for a word, and screwing his hand round and round as though un-
corking a bottle—"like him—him——"

"Corkscrew!" cried Ahab, "aye, Queequeg, the harpoons lie all twisted
and wrenched in him; aye, Daggoo, his spout is a big one, like a whole shock
of wheat, and white as a pile of our Nantucket wool after the great annual
sheep-shearing; aye, Tashtego, and he fan-tails like a split jib in a squall. Death
and devils! men, it is Moby-Dick ye have seen—Moby-Dick—Moby-Dick!"

"Captain Ahab," said Starbuck, who, with Stubb and Flask, had thus far
been eyeing his superior with increasing surprise, but at last seemed struck
with a thought which somewhat explained all the wonder. "Captain Ahab,
I have heard of Moby-Dick—but it was not Moby-Dick that took off thy leg?"

"Who told thee that?" cried Ahab; then pausing, "Aye, Starbuck; aye, my
hearties all round; it was Moby-Dick that dismasted me; Moby-Dick that
brought me to this dead stump I stand on now. Aye, aye," he shouted with
a terrific, loud, animal sob, like that of a heart-stricken moose; "Aye, aye! it
was that accursed white whale that razeed me; made a poor begging lubber of
me for ever and a day!" Then tossing both arms, with measureless imprecations he shouted out: "Aye, aye! and I'll chase him round Good Hope, and
round the Horn, and round the Norway Maelstrom, and round perdition's
flames before I give him up. And this is what ye have shipped for, men! to
chase that white whale on both sides of land, and over all sides of earth, till
he spouts black blood and rolls fin out. What say ye, men, will ye splice hands
on it, now? I think ye do look brave."

"Aye, aye!" shouted the harpooneers and seamen, running closer to the excited old man: "A sharp eye for the white whale; a sharp lance for Moby-Dick!"

"God bless ye," he seemed to half sob and half shout. "God bless ye, men. Steward! go draw the great measure of grog. But what's this long face about, Mr. Starbuck; wilt thou not chase the white whale? art not game for Moby-Dick?"

"I am game for his crooked jaw, and for the jaws of Death too, Captain Ahab, if it fairly comes in the way of the business we follow; but I came here to hunt whales, not my commander's vengeance. How many barrels will thy vengeance yield thee even if thou gettest it, Captain Ahab? it will not fetch thee much in our Nantucket market."

"Nantucket market! Hoot! But come closer, Starbuck; thou requirest a little lower layer. If money's to be the measurer, man, and the accountants have computed their great counting-house the globe, by girdling it with guineas, one to every three parts of an inch; then, let me tell thee, that my vengeance will fetch a great premium *here!*"

"He smites his chest," whispered Stubb, "what's that for? methinks it rings most vast, but hollow."

"Vengeance on a dumb brute!" cried Starbuck, "that simply smote thee from blindest instinct! Madness! To be enraged with a dumb thing, Captain Ahab, seems blasphemous."

"Hark ye yet again,—the little lower layer. All visible objects, man, are but as pasteboard masks. But in each event—in the living act, the undoubted deed—there, some unknown but still reasoning thing puts forth the mouldings of its features from behind the unreasoning mask. If man will strike, strike through the mask! How can the prisoner reach outside except by thrusting through the wall? To me, the white whale is that wall, shoved near to me. Sometimes I think there's naught beyond. But 'tis enough. He tasks me; he heaps me; I see in him outrageous strength, with an inscrutable malice sinewing it. That inscrutable thing is chiefly what I hate; and be the white whale agent, or be the white whale principal, I will wreak that hate upon him. Talk not to me of blasphemy, man; I'd strike the sun if it insulted me. For could the sun do that, then could I do the other; since there is ever a sort of fair play herein, jealousy presiding over all creations. But not my master, man, is even that fair play. Who's over me? Truth hath no confines. Take off thine eye! more intolerable than fiends' glarings is a doltish stare! So, so; thou reddenest and palest; my heat has melted thee to anger-glow. But look ye, Starbuck, what is said in heat, that thing unsays itself. There are men from whom warm words are small indignity. I meant not to incense thee. Let it go. Look! see yonder Turkish cheeks of spotted tawn—living, breathing pictures painted by the sun. The Pagan leopards—the unrecking and unworshipping things, that live; and seek, and give no reasons for the torrid life they feel! The crew, man, the crew! Are they not one and all with Ahab, in this matter of the whale? See Stubb! he laughs! See yonder Chilian! he snorts to think of it. Stand up amid the general hurricane, thy one tost sapling cannot, Starbuck! And what is it? Reckon it. 'Tis but to help strike a fin; no wondrous feat for Starbuck. What is it more? From this one poor hunt, then, the best lance out of all Nantucket, surely he will not hang back, when every foremast-hand has clutched a whetstone? Ah! constrainings seize thee; I see! the billow lifts thee! Speak, but speak!—Aye, aye! thy silence, then, *that* voices thee. (*Aside*) Something shot from my dilated nostrils, he has inhaled it in his lungs. Starbuck now is mine; cannot oppose me now, without rebellion."

"God keep me!—keep us all!" murmured Starbuck, lowly.

But in his joy at the enchanted, tacit acquiescence of the mate, Ahab did not hear his foreboding invocation; nor yet the low laugh from the hold; nor yet the presaging vibrations of the winds in the cordage; nor yet the hollow flap of the sails against the masts, as for a moment their hearts sank in. For again Starbuck's downcast eyes lighted up with the stubbornness of life; the subterranean laugh died away; the winds blew on; the sails filled out; the ship heaved and rolled as before. Ah, ye admonitions and warnings! why stay ye not when ye come? But rather are ye predictions than warnings, ye shadows! Yet not so much predictions from without, as verifications of the foregoing things within. For with little external to constrain us, the innermost necessities in our being, these still drive us on.

"The measure! the measure!" cried Ahab.

Receiving the brimming pewter, and turning to the harpooneers, he ordered them to produce their weapons. Then ranging them before him near the capstan, with their harpoons in their hands, while his three mates stood at his side with their lances, and the rest of the ship's company formed a circle round the group; he stood for an instant searchingly eyeing every man of his crew. But those wild eyes met his, as the bloodshot eyes of the prairie wolves meet the eye of their leader, ere he rushes on at their head in the trail of the bison; but, alas! only to fall into the hidden snare of the Indian.

"Drink and pass!" he cried, handing the heavy charged flagon to the nearest seamen. "The crew alone now drink. Round with it, round! Short draughts—long swallows, men; 'tis hot as Satan's hoof. So, so; it goes round excellently. It spiralizes in ye; forks out at the serpent-snapping eye. Well done; almost drained. That way it went, this way it comes. Hand it me—here's a hollow! Men, ye seem the years; so brimming life is gulped and gone. Steward, refill!

"Attend now, my braves. I have mustered ye all round this capstan; and ye mates, flank me with your lances; and ye harpooneers, stand there with your irons; and ye, stout mariners, ring me in, that I may in some sort revive a noble custom of my fishermen fathers before me. O men, you will yet see that—— Ha! boy, come back? bad pennies come not sooner. Hand it me. Why, now, this pewter had run brimming again, wer't not thou St. Vitus' imp—away, thou ague!

"Advance, ye mates! Cross your lances full before me. Well done! Let me touch the axis." So saying, with extended arm, he grasped the three level, radiating lances at their crossed centre; while so doing, suddenly and nervously twitched them; meanwhile, glancing intently from Starbuck to Stubb; from Stubb to Flask. It seemed as though, by some nameless, interior volition, he would fain have shocked into them the same fiery emotion accumulated within the Leyden jar of his own magnetic life. The three mates quailed before his strong, sustained, and mystic aspect. Stubb and Flask looked sideways from him; the honest eye of Starbuck fell downright.

"In vain!" cried Ahab; "but, maybe, 'tis well. For did ye three but once take the full-forced shock, then mine own electric thing, *that* had perhaps expired from out me. Perchance, too, it would have dropped ye dead. Perchance ye need it not. Down lances! And now, ye mates, I do appoint ye three cupbearers to my three pagan kinsmen there—yon three most honorable gentlemen and noblemen, my valiant harpooneers. Disdain the task? What, when the great Pope washes the feet of beggars, using his tiara for ewer? Oh, my sweet cardinals! your own condescension, *that* shall bend ye to it. I do not order ye; ye will it. Cut your seizings and draw the poles, ye harpooneers!"

Silently obeying the order, the three harpooneers now stood with the detached iron part of their harpoons, some three feet long, held, barbs up, before him.

"Stab me not with that keen steel! Cant them; cant them over! know ye not the goblet end? Turn up the socket! So, so; now, ye cupbearers, advance. The irons! take them; hold them while I fill!" Forthwith, slowly going from one officer to the other, he brimmed the harpoon sockets with the fiery waters from the pewter.

"Now, three to three, ye stand. Commend the murderous chalices! Bestow them, ye who are now made parties to this indissoluble league. Ha! Starbuck! but the deed is done! Yon ratifying sun now waits to sit upon it. Drink, ye harpooneers! drink and swear, ye men that man the deathful whaleboat's bow —Death to Moby-Dick! God hunt us all, if we do not hunt Moby-Dick to his death!" The long, barbed steel goblets were lifted; and to cries and maledictions against the White Whale, the spirits were simultaneously quaffed down with a hiss. Starbuck paled, and turned, and shivered. Once more, and finally, the replenished pewter went the rounds among the frantic crew; when, waving his free hand to them, they all dispersed; and Ahab retired within his cabin.

CHAPTER XXXVII

SUNSET

The cabin; by the stern windows; Ahab sitting alone, and gazing out.

I LEAVE a white and turbid wake; pale waters, paler cheeks, where'er I sail. The envious billows sidelong swell to whelm my track; let them; but first I pass.

Yonder, by the ever-brimming goblet's rim, the warm waves blush like wine. The gold brow plumbs the blue. The diver sun—slow dived from noon, —goes down; my soul mounts up! she wearies with her endless hill. Is, then, the crown too heavy that I wear? this Iron Crown of Lombardy. Yet is it bright with many a gem; I, the wearer, see not its far flashings; but darkly feel that I wear that, that dazzlingly confounds. 'Tis iron—that I know— not gold. 'Tis split, too—that I feel; the jagged edge galls me so, my brain seems to beat against the solid metal; aye, steel skull, mine; the sort that needs no helmet in the most brain-battering fight!

Dry heat upon my brow? Oh! time was, when as the sunrise nobly spurred me, so the sunset soothed. No more. This lovely light, it lights not me; all loveliness is anguish to me, since I can ne'er enjoy. Gifted with the high perception, I lack the low, enjoying power; damned, most subtly and most malignantly! damned in the midst of Paradise! Good night—good night! (*waving his hand, he moves from the window.*)

'Twas not so hard a task. I thought to find one stubborn, at the least; but my one cogged circle fits into all their various wheels, and they revolve. Or, if you will, like so many ant-hills of powder, they all stand before me; and I their match. Oh, hard! that to fire others, the match itself must needs be wasting! . What I've dared, I've willed; and what I've willed, I'll do! They think me mad—Starbuck does; but I'm demoniac, I am madness maddened! That wild madness that's only calm to comprehend itself! The prophecy was that I should be dismembered; and—aye! I lost this leg. I now prophesy that I will dismember my dismemberer. Now, then, be the prophet and the fulfiller one. That's more than ye, ye great gods, ever were. I laugh and hoot at ye, ye cricket-players, ye pugilists, ye deaf Burkes and blinded Bendigoes! I will not say as schoolboys do to bullies,—Take some one of your own size; don't pommel *me!* No, ye've knocked me down, and I am up again; but *ye* have run and hidden. Come forth from behind your cotton bags! I have no long gun to reach ye. Come, Ahab's compliments to ye; come and see if ye can swerve me. Swerve me? ye cannot swerve me, else ye swerve yourselves! man has ye there. Swerve me? The path to my fixed purpose is laid with iron rails, whereon my soul is grooved to run. Over unsounded gorges, through the rifled hearts of mountains, under torrents' beds, unerringly I rush! Naught's an obstacle, naught's an angle to the iron way!

CHAPTER XXXVIII

DUSK

By the Mainmast; Starbuck leaning against it.

My soul is more than matched; she's overmanned; and by a madman! Insufferable sting, that sanity should ground arms on such a field! But he drilled deep down, and blasted all my reason out of me! I think I see his impious end; but feel that I must help him to it. Will I, nill I, the ineffable thing has tied me to him; tows me with a cable I have no knife to cut. Horrible old man! Who's over him, he cries;—aye, he would be a democrat to all above; look, how he lords it over all below! Oh! I plainly see my miserable office, —to obey, rebelling; and worse yet, to hate with touch of pity! For in his eyes I read some lurid woe would shrivel me up, had I it. Yet is there hope. Time and tide flow wide. The hated whale has the round watery world to swim in, as the small gold-fish has its glassy globe. His heaven-insulting purpose, God may wedge aside. I would up heart, were it not like lead. But my whole clock's run down; my heart the all-controlling weight, I have no key to lift again.

[*A burst of revelry from the forecastle.*

Oh, God! to sail with such a heathen crew that have small touch of human mothers in them! Whelped somewhere by the sharkish sea. The White Whale is their demigorgon. Hark! the infernal orgies! that revelry is forward! mark the unfaltering silence aft! Methinks it pictures life. Foremost through the sparkling sea shoots on the gay, embattled, bantering bow, but only to drag dark Ahab after it, where he broods within his sternward cabin, builded over the dead water of the wake, and farther on, hunted by its wolfish gurglings. The long howl thrills me through! Peace! ye revellers, and set the·watch! Oh, life! 'tis in an hour like this, with soul beat down and held to knowledge,—as wild, untutored things are forced to feed—Oh, life! 'tis now that I do feel the latent horror in thee! but 'tis not me! that horror's out of me, and with the soft feeling of the human in me, yet will I try to fight ye, ye grim, phantom futures! Stand by me, hold me, bind me, O ye blessed influences!

CHAPTER XXXIX

FIRST NIGHT-WATCH

FORE-TOP

(Stubb solus, and mending a brace)

HA! ha! ha! ha! hem! clear my throat!—I've been thinking over it ever since, and that ha, ha's the final consequence. Why so? Because a laugh's the wisest, easiest answer to all that's queer; and come what will, one comfort's always left—that unfailing comfort is, it's all predestinated. I heard not all his talk with Starbuck; but to my poor eye Starbuck then looked something as I the other evening felt. Be sure the old Mogul has fixed him, too. I twigged it, knew it; had had the gift, might readily have prophesied it—for when I clapped my eye upon his skull I saw it. Well, Stubb, *wise* Stubb—that's my title—well, Stubb, what of it, Stubb? Here's a carcase. I know not all that may be coming, but be it what it will, I'll go to it laughing. Such a waggish leering as lurks in all your horribles! I feel funny. Fa, la! lirra, skirra! What's my juicy little pear at home doing now? Crying its eyes out?—Giving a party to the last arrived harpooneers, I dare say, gay as a frigate's pennant, and so am I—fa, la! lirra, skirra! Oh—

> We'll drink to-night with hearts as light,
> To love, as gay and fleeting
> As bubbles that swim, on the beaker's brim,
> And break on the lips while meeting.

A brave stave that—who calls? Mr. Starbuck? Aye, aye, sir—*(Aside)* he's my superior, he has his too, if I'm not mistaken.—Aye, aye, sir, just through with this job—coming.

CHAPTER XL

MIDNIGHT, FORECASTLE

HARPOONEERS AND SAILORS

(Foresail rises and discovers the watch standing, lounging, leaning, and lying in various attitudes, all singing in chorus.)

> Farewell and adieu to you, Spanish ladies!
> Farewell and adieu to you, ladies of Spain!
> Our captain's commanded.—

1ST NANTUCKET SAILOR

Oh, boys, don't be sentimental; it's bad for the digestion!   Take a tonic,
follow me!

(Sings, and all follow)

> Our captain stood upon the deck,   12
>   A spy-glass in his hand
> A viewing of those gallant whales
>   That blew at every strand.
> Oh, your tubs in your boats, my boys,
>   And by your braces stand,
> And we'll have one of those fine whales,
>   Hand, boys, over hand!
> So, be cheery, my lads! may your hearts never fail!
> While the bold harpooneer is striking the whale!

MATE'S VOICE FROM THE QUARTER-DECK

Eight bells there, forward!

2D NANTUCKET SAILOR

Avast the chorus!   Eight bells there! d'ye hear, bell-boy?   Strike the bell
eight, thou Pip! thou blackling! and let me call the watch.   I've the sort of
mouth for that—the hogshead mouth.   So, so, *(thrusts his head down the
scuttle,)* Star—bo-l-e-e-n-s, a-h-o-y!   Eight bells there below!   Tumble up!

DUTCH SAILOR

Grand snoozing to-night, maty; fat night for that.   I mark this in our old
Mogul's wine; it's quite as deadening to some as filliping to others.   We sing;
they sleep—aye, lie down there, like ground-tier butts.   At 'em again!   There,
take this copper-pump, and hail 'em through it.   Tell 'em to avast dreaming
of their lasses.   Tell 'em it's the resurrection; they must kiss their last, and
come to judgment.   That's the way—*that's* it; thy throat ain't spoiled with
eating Amsterdam butter.

FRENCH SAILOR

Hist, boys! let's have a jig or two before we ride to anchor in Blanket
Bay.   What say ye?   There comes the other watch.   Stand by all legs!   Pip!
little Pip! hurrah with your tambourine!

PIP
(Sulky and sleepy)

Don't know where it is.

FRENCH SAILOR

Beat thy belly, then, and wag thy ears.   Jig it, men, I say; merry's the
word; hurrah!   Damn me, won't you dance?   Form, now, Indian-file, and gallop
into the double-shuffle!   Throw yourselves!   Legs! legs!

ICELAND SAILOR

I don't like your floor, maty; it's too springy to my taste. I'm used to ice-floors. I'm sorry to throw cold water on the subject; but excuse me.

MALTESE SAILOR

Me too; where's your girls? Who but a fool would take his left hand by his right, and say to himself, how d'ye do? Partners! I must have partners!

SICILIAN SAILOR

Aye; girls and a green!—then I'll hop with ye; yea, turn grasshopper!

LONG-ISLAND SAILOR

Well, well, ye sulkies, there's plenty more of us. Hoe corn when you may, say I. All legs go to harvest soon. Ah! here comes the music; now for it!

AZORE SAILOR

(*Ascending, and pitching the tambourine up the scuttle.*)
Here you are, Pip; and there's the windlass-bits; up you mount! Now, boys!

(*The half of them dance to the tambourine; some go below; some sleep or lie among the coils of rigging. Oaths a-plenty.*)

AZORE SAILOR
(*Dancing*)

Go it, Pip! Bang it, bell-boy! Rig it, dig it, stig it, quig it, bell-boy! Make fire-flies; break the jinglers!

PIP

Jinglers, you say?—there goes another, dropped off; I pound it so.

CHINA SAILOR

Rattle thy teeth, then, and pound away; make a pagoda of thyself.

FRENCH SAILOR

Merry-mad! Hold up thy hoop, Pip, till I jump through it! Split jibs! tear yourselves!

TASHTEGO
(*Quietly smoking*)

That's a white man; he calls that fun: humph! I save my sweat.

OLD MANX SAILOR

I wonder whether those jolly lads bethink them of what they are dancing over. I'll dance over your grave, I will—that's the bitterest threat of your

night-women, that beat head-winds round corners. O Christ! to think of
the green navies and the green-skulled crews! Well, well; belike the whole
world's a ball, as you scholars have it; and so 'tis right to make one ball-room
of it. Dance on, lads, you're young; I was once.

3D NANTUCKET SAILOR

Spell oh! whew! this is worse than pulling after whales in a calm—give
us a whiff, Tash.

(*They cease dancing, and gather in clusters. Meantime the sky darkens—
the wind rises.*)

LASCAR SAILOR

By Brahma! boys, it'll be douse sail soon. The sky-born, high-tide Ganges
turned to wind! Thou showest thy black brow, Seeva!

MALTESE SAILOR
(*Reclining and shaking his cap*)

It's the waves—the snow's caps turn to jig it now. They'll shake their
tassels soon. Now would all the waves were women, then I'd go drown, and
chassee with them evermore! There's naught so sweet on earth—heaven may
not match it!—as those swift glances of warm, wild bosoms in the dance, when
the over-arboring arms hide such ripe, bursting grapes.

SICILIAN SAILOR
(*Reclining*)

Tell me not of it! Hark ye, lad—fleet interlacings of the limbs—lithe
swayings—coyings—flutterings! lip! heart! hip! all graze: unceasing touch and
go! not taste, observe ye, else come satiety. Eh, Pagan? (*Nudging.*)

TAHITIAN SAILOR
(*Reclining on a mat*)

Hail, holy nakedness of our dancing girls!—the Heeva-Heeva! Ah! low
veiled, high palmed Tahiti! I still rest me on thy mat, but the soft soil has
slid! I saw thee woven in the wood, my mat! green the first day I brought
ye thence; now worn and wilted quite. Ah me!—not thou nor I can bear
the change! How then, if so be transplanted to yon sky? Hear I the roaring
streams from Pirohitee's peak of spears, when they leap down the crags and
drown the villages?—The blast! the blast! Up, spine, and meet it! (*Leaps
to his feet.*)

PORTUGUESE SAILOR

How the sea rolls swashing 'gainst the side! Stand by for reefing, hearties!
the winds are just crossing swords, pell-mell they'll go lunging presently.

DANISH SAILOR

Crack, crack, old ship! so long as thou crackest, thou holdest! Well done!
The mate there holds ye to it stiffly. He's no more afraid than the isle fort at

Cattegat, put there to fight the Baltic with storm-lashed guns, on which the sea-salt cakes!

4TH NANTUCKET SAILOR

He has his orders, mind ye that. I heard old Ahab tell him he must always kill a squall, something as they burst a waterspout with a pistol—fire your ship right into it!

ENGLISH SAILOR

Blood! but that old man's a grand old cove! We are the lads to hunt him up his whale!

ALL

Aye! aye!

OLD MANX SAILOR

How the three pines shake! Pines are the hardest sort of tree to live when shifted to any other soil, and here there's none but the crew's cursed clay. Steady, helmsmen! steady. This is the sort of weather when brave hearts snap ashore, and keeled hulls split at sea. Our captain has his birthmark; look yonder, boys, there's another in the sky—lurid-like, ye see, all else pitch black.

DAGGOO

What of that? Who's afraid of black's afraid of me! I'm quarried out of it!

SPANISH SAILOR

(*Aside.*) He wants to bully, ah!—the old grudge makes me touchy. (*Advancing.*) Aye, harpooneer, thy race is the undeniable dark side of mankind—devilish dark at that. No offence.

DAGGOO (*grimly*)

None.

ST. JAGO'S SAILOR

That Spaniard's mad or drunk. But that can't be, or else in his one case our old Mogul's fire-waters are somewhat long in working.

5TH NANTUCKET SAILOR

What's that I saw—lightning? Yes.

SPANISH SAILOR

No; Daggoo showing his teeth.

DAGGOO (*springing*)

Swallow thine, mannikin! White skin, white liver!

SPANISH SAILOR (*meeting him*)

Knife thee heartily! big frame, small spirit!

ALL

A row! a row! a row!

TASHTEGO (*with a whiff*)

A row a'low, and a row aloft—Gods and men—both brawlers! Humph!

BELFAST SAILOR

A row! arrah a row! The Virgin be blessed, a row! Plunge in with ye!

ENGLISH SAILOR

Fair play! Snatch the Spaniard's knife! A ring, a ring!

OLD MANX SAILOR

Ready formed. There! the ringed horizon. In that ring Cain struck Abel. Sweet work, right work! No? Why then, God, mad'st thou the ring?

MATE'S VOICE FROM THE QUARTER DECK

Hands by the halyards! in top-gallant sails! Stand by to reef topsails!

ALL

The squall! the squall! jump, my jollies! (*They scatter.*)

PIP (*shrinking under the windlass*)

Jollies? Lord help such jollies! Crish, crash! there goes the jib-stay! Blang-whang! God! Duck lower, Pip, here comes the royal yard! It's worse than being in the whirled woods, the last day of the year! Who'd go climbing after chestnuts now? But there they go, all cursing, and here I don't. Fine prospects to 'em; they're on the road to heaven. Hold on hard! Jimmini, what a squall! But those chaps there are worse yet—they are your white squalls, they. White squalls? White Whale, shirr! shirr! Here have I heard all their chat just now, and the White Whale—shirr! shirr!—but spoken of once! and only this evening—it makes me jingle all over like my tambourine— that anaconda of an old man swore 'em in to hunt him! Oh, thou big white God aloft there somewhere in yon darkness, have mercy on this small black boy down here; preserve him from all men that have no bowels to feel fear!

*   *   *   *   *

CHAPTER XLI

MOBY-DICK

I, ISHMAEL, was one of that crew; my shouts had gone up with the rest; my oath had been welded with theirs; and stronger I shouted, and more did I hammer and clinch my oath, because of the dread in my soul. A wild, mystical, sympathetical feeling was in me; Ahab's quenchless feud seemed mine. With greedy ears I learned the history of that murderous monster against whom I and all the others had taken our oaths of violence and revenge.

For some time past, though at intervals only, the unaccompanied, secluded White Whale had haunted those uncivilized seas mostly frequented by the Sperm Whale fishermen. But not all of them knew of his existence; only a few of them, comparatively, had knowingly seen him; while the number who as yet had actually and knowingly given battle to him, was small indeed. For, owing to the large number of whale-cruisers; the disorderly way they were sprinkled over the entire watery circumference, many of them adventurously pushing their quest along solitary latitudes, so as seldom or never for a whole twelvemonth or more on a stretch, to encounter a single newstelling sail of any sort; the inordinate length of each separate voyage; the irregularity of the times of sailing from home; all these, with other circumstances, direct and indirect, long obstructed the spread through the whole world-wide whaling-fleet of the special individualizing tidings concerning Moby-Dick. It was hardly to be doubted, that several vessels reported to have encountered, at such or such a time, or on such or such a meridian, a Sperm Whale of uncommon magnitude and malignity, which whale, after doing great mischief to his assailants, had completely escaped them; to some minds it was not an unfair presumption, I say, that the whale in question must have been no other than Moby-Dick. Yet as of late the Sperm Whale fishery had been marked by various and not unfrequent instances of great ferocity, cunning, and malice in the monster attacked; therefore it was, that those who by accident ignorantly gave battle to Moby-Dick; such hunters, perhaps, for the most part, were content to ascribe the peculiar terror he bred, more, as it were, to the perils of the Sperm Whale fishery at large, than to the individual cause. In that way, mostly, the disastrous encounter between Ahab and the whale had hitherto been popularly regarded.

And as for those who, previously hearing of the White Whale, by chance caught sight of him; in the beginning of the thing they had every one of them, almost, as boldly and fearlessly lowered for him, as for any other whale of that species. But at length, such calamities did ensue in these assaults—not restricted to sprained wrists and ankles, broken limbs, or devouring amputations—but fatal to the last degree of fatality; those repeated disastrous repulses, all accumulating and piling their terrors upon Moby-Dick; those things had gone far to shake the fortitude of many brave hunters, to whom the story of the White Whale had eventually come.

Nor did wild rumors of all sorts fail to exaggerate, and still the more horrify the true histories of these deadly encounters. For not only do fabulous rumors naturally grow out of the very body of all surprising terrible events,—as the smitten tree gives birth to its fungi; but, in maritime life, far more than in that of terra firma, wild rumors abound, wherever there is any adequate reality for them to cling to. And as the sea surpasses the land in this matter, so the whale fishery surpasses every other sort of maritime life, in the wonderfulness and fearfulness of the rumors which sometimes circulate there. For not only are whalemen as a body unexempt from that ignorance and superstitiousness hereditary to all sailors; but of all sailors, they are by all odds the most directly brought into contact with whatever is appallingly astonishing in the sea; face to face they not only eye its greatest marvels, but, hand to jaw, give battle to them. Alone, in such remotest waters, that though you sailed a thousand miles, and passed a thousand shores, you would not come to any chiselled hearth stone, or aught hospitable beneath that part of the sun; in such latitudes and longitudes, pursuing too such a calling as he does, the whaleman is wrapped by influences all tending to make his fancy pregnant with many a mighty birth.

No wonder, then, that ever gathering volume from the mere transit over the wildest watery spaces, the outblown rumors of the White Whale did in the end incorporate with themselves all manner of morbid hints, and half-formed fœtal suggestions of supernatural agencies, which eventually invested Moby-Dick with new terrors unborrowed from anything that visibly appears. So that in many cases such a panic did he finally strike, that few who by those rumors, at least, had heard of the White Whale, few of those hunters were willing to encounter the perils of his jaw.

But there were still other and more vital practical influences at work. Not even at the present day has the original prestige of the Sperm Whale, as fearfully distinguished from all other species of the leviathan, died out of the minds of the whalemen as a body. There are those this day among them, who, though intelligent and courageous enough in offering battle to the Greenland or Right Whale, would perhaps—either from professional inexperience, or incompetency, or timidity, decline a contest with the Sperm Whale; at any rate, there are plenty of whalemen, especially among those whaling nations not sailing under the American flag, who have never hostilely encountered the Sperm Whale, but whose sole knowledge of the leviathan is restricted to the ignoble monster primitively pursued in the North; seated on their hatches, these men will hearken with a childish fire-side interest and awe, to the wild, strange tales of Southern whaling. Nor is the pre-eminent tremendousness of the great Sperm Whale anywhere more feelingly comprehended, than on board of those prows which stem him.

And as if the now tested reality of his might had in former legendary times thrown its shadow before it; we find some book naturalists—Olassen and Povelson—declaring the Sperm Whale not only to be a consternation to every other creature in the sea, but also to be so incredibly ferocious as continually to be athirst for human blood. Nor even down to so late a time as Cuvier's, were these or almost similar impressions effaced. For in his Natural History, the Baron himself affirms that at sight of the Sperm Whale, all fish (sharks included) are "struck with the most lively terrors," and "often in the precipitancy of their flight dash themselves against the rocks with such violence as to cause instantaneous death." And however the general experiences in the fishery may amend such reports as these; yet in their full terribleness, even to the bloodthirsty item of Povelson, the superstitious belief in them is, in some vicissitudes of their vocation, revived in the minds of the hunters.

So that overawed by the rumors and portents concerning him, not a few of the fishermen recalled, in reference to Moby-Dick, the earlier days of the Sperm Whale fishery, when it was oftentimes hard to induce long practised Right whalemen to embark in the perils of this new and daring warfare; such men protesting that although other leviathans might be hopefully pursued, yet to chase and point lances at such an apparition as the Sperm Whale was not for mortal man. That to attempt it, would be inevitably to be torn into a quick eternity. On this head, there are some remarkable documents that may be consulted.

Nevertheless, some there were, who even in the face of these things were ready to give chase to Moby-Dick; and a still greater number who, chancing only to hear of him distantly and vaguely, without the specific details of any certain calamity, and without superstitious accompaniments, were sufficiently hardy not to flee from the battle it offered.

One of the wild suggestings referred to, as at last coming to be linked with the White Whale in the minds of the superstitiously inclined, was the unearthly conceit that Moby-Dick was ubiquitous; that he had actually been encountered in opposite latitudes at one and the same instant of time.

Nor, credulous as such minds must have been, was this conceit altogether without some faint show of superstitious probability. For as the secrets of the currents in the seas have never yet been divulged, even to the most erudite research; so the hidden ways of the Sperm Whale when beneath the surface remain, in great part, unaccountable to his pursuers; and from time to time have originated the most curious and contradictory speculations regarding them, especially concerning the mystic modes whereby, after sounding to a great depth, he transports himself with such vast swiftness to the most widely distant points.

It is a thing well known to both American and English whale-ships, and as well a thing placed upon authoritative record years ago by Scoresby, that some whales have been captured far north in the Pacific, in whose bodies have been found the barbs of harpoons darted in the Greenland seas. Nor is it to be gainsaid, that in some of these instances it has been declared that the interval of time between the two assaults could not have exceeded very many days. Hence, by inference, it has been believed by some whalemen, that the Nor' West Passage, so long a problem to man, was never a problem to the whale. So that here, in the real living experience of living men, the prodigies related in old times of the inland Strello mountain in Portugal (near whose top there was said to be a lake in which the wrecks of ships floated up to the surface); and that still more wonderful story of the Arethusa fountain near Syracuse (whose waters were believed to have come from the Holy Land by an underground passage); these fabulous narrations are almost fully equalled by the realities of the whaleman.

Forced into familiarity, then, with such prodigies as these; and knowing that after repeated, intrepid assaults, the White Whale had escaped alive; it cannot be much matter of surprise that some whalemen should go still further in their superstitions; declaring Moby-Dick not only ubiquitous, but immortal (for immortality is but ubiquity in time); that though groves of spears should be planted in his flanks, ne would still swim away unharmed; or if indeed he should ever be made to spout thick blood, such a sight would be but a ghastly deception; for again in unensanguined billows hundreds of leagues away, his unsullied jet would once more be seen.

But even stripped of these supernatural surmisings, there was enough in the earthly make and incontestable character of the monster to strike the imagination with unwonted power. For, it was not so much his uncommon bulk that so much distinguished him from other sperm whales, but, as was elsewhere thrown out—a peculiar snow-white wrinkled forehead, and a high, pyramidical white hump. These were his prominent features; the tokens whereby, even in the limitless, uncharted seas, he revealed his identity, at a long distance, to those who knew him.

The rest of his body was so streaked, and spotted, and marbled with the same shrouded hue, that, in the end, he had gained his distinctive appellation of the White Whale; a name, indeed, literally justified by his vivid aspect, when seen gliding at high noon through a dark blue sea, leaving a milky-way wake of creamy foam, all spangled with golden gleamings.

Nor was it his unwonted magnitude, nor his remarkable hue, nor yet his deformed lower jaw, that so much invested the whale with natural terror, as that unexampled, intelligent malignity which, according to specific accounts, he had over and over again evinced in his assaults. More than all, his treacherous retreats struck more of dismay than perhaps aught else. For, when swimming before his exulting pursuers, with every apparent symptom of alarm, he had several times been known to turn round suddenly, and, bearing down upon them, either stave their boats to splinters, or drive them back in consternation to their ship.

Already several fatalities had attended his chase. But though similar disasters, however little bruited ashore, were by no means unusual in the fishery; yet, in most instances, such seemed the White Whale's infernal aforethought of ferocity, that every dismembering or death that he caused, was not wholly regarded as having been inflicted by an unintelligent agent.

Judge, then, to what pitches of inflamed, distracted fury the minds of his more desperate hunters were impelled, when amid the chips of chewed boats, and the sinking limbs of torn comrades, they swam out of the white curds of the whale's direful wrath into the serene, exasperating sunlight, that smiled on, as if at a birth or a bridal.

His three boats stove around him, and oars and men both whirling in the eddies; one captain, seizing the line-knife from his broken prow, had dashed at the whale, as an Arkansas duellist at his foe, blindly seeking with a six-inch blade to reach the fathom-deep life of the whale. That captain was Ahab. And then it was, that suddenly sweeping his sickle-shaped lower jaw beneath him, Moby-Dick had reaped away Ahab's leg, as a mower a blade of grass in the field. No turbaned Turk, no hired Venetian or Malay, could have smote him with more seeming malice. Small reason was there to doubt, then, that ever since that almost fatal encounter, Ahab had cherished a wild vindictiveness against the whale, all the more fell for that in his frantic morbidness he at last came to identify with him, not only all his bodily woes, but all his intellectual and spiritual exasperations. The White Whale swam before him as the monomaniac incarnation of all those malicious agencies which some deep men feel eating in them, till they are left living on with half a heart and half a lung. That intangible malignity which has been from the beginning; to whose dominion even the modern Christians ascribe one-half of the worlds; which the ancient Ophites of the East reverenced in their statue devil;—Ahab did not fall down and worship it like them; but deliriously transferring its idea to the abhorred White Whale, he pitted himself, all mutilated, against it. All that most maddens and torments; all that stirs up the lees of things; all truth with malice in it; all that cracks the sinews and cakes the brain; all the subtle demonisms of life and thought; all evil, to crazy Ahab, were visibly personified, and made practically assailable in Moby-Dick. He piled upon the whale's white hump the sum of all the general rage and hate felt by his whole race from Adam down; and then, as if his chest had been a mortar, he burst his hot heart's shell upon it.

It is not probable that this monomania in him took its instant rise at the precise time of his bodily dismemberment. Then, in darting at the monster, knife in hand, he had but given loose to a sudden, passionate, corporal animosity; and when he received the stroke that tore him, he probably but felt the agonizing bodily laceration, but nothing more. Yet, when by this collision forced to turn towards home, and for long months of days and weeks, Ahab and anguish lay stretched together in one hammock, rounding in mid winter that dreary, howling Patagonian Cape; then it was, that his torn body and gashed soul bled into one another; and so interfusing, made him mad. That it was only then, on the homeward voyage, after the encounter, that the final monomania seized him, seems all but certain from the fact that, at intervals during the passage, he was a raving lunatic; and, though unlimbed of a leg, yet such vital strength yet lurked in his Egyptian chest, and was moreover intensified by his delirium, that his mates were forced to lace him fast, even there, as he sailed, raving in his hammock. In a strait-jacket, he swung to the mad rockings of the gales. And, when running into more sufferable latitudes, the ship, with mild stun'sails spread, floated across the tranquil tropics, and, to all appearances, the old man's delirium seemed left behind him with the Cape Horn swells, and he came forth from his dark den into the blessed light and air; even then, when he bore that firm, collected front, however pale, and issued his calm orders once again; and his mates thanked God the direful madness was now gone; even then, Ahab, in his hidden self, raved on. Human madness is oftentimes a cunning and most feline thing. When you think it fled, it may have but become transfigured into some still subtler form. Ahab's full lunacy subsided not, but deepeningly contracted; like the unabated Hudson, when that noble Northman flows narrowly, but unfathomably through the Highland gorge. But, as in his narrow-flowing monomania, not one jot of Ahab's broad madness had been left behind! so in that broad madness, not one jot of his great natural intellect had perished. That before living agent, now became the living instrument. If such a furious trope may stand, his special lunacy stormed his general sanity, and carried it, and turned all its concentred cannon upon its own mad mark; so that far from having lost his strength, Ahab, to that one end, did now possess a thousand fold more potency than ever he had sanely brought to bear upon any one reasonable object.

This is much; yet Ahab's larger, darker, deeper part remains unhinted. But vain to popularize profundities, and all truth is profound. Winding far down from within the very heart of this spiked Hotel de Cluny where we here stand—however grand and wonderful, now quit it;—and take your way, ye nobler, sadder souls, to those vast Roman halls of Thermes; where far beneath the fantastic towers of man's upper earth, his root of grandeur, his whole awful essence sits in bearded state; an antique buried beneath antiquities, and throned on torsoes! So with a broken throne, the great gods mock that captive king; so like a Caryatid, he patient sits, upholding on his frozen brow the piled entablatures of ages. Wind ye down there, ye prouder, sadder souls! question that proud, sad king! A family likeness! aye, he did beget ye, ye young exiled royalties; and from your grim sire only will the old State-secret come.

Now, in his heart, Ahab had some glimpse of this, namely: all my means are sane, my motive and my object mad. Yet without power to kill, or change, or shun the fact; he likewise knew that to mankind he did long dissemble; in some sort, did still. But that thing of his dissembling was only subject to his perceptibility, not to his will determinate. Nevertheless, so well did he succeed in that dissembling, that when with ivory leg he stepped ashore at last, no Nantucketer thought him otherwise than but naturally grieved, and that to the quick, with the terrible casualty which had overtaken him.

The report of his undeniable delirium at sea was likewise popularly ascribed to a kindred cause. And so too, all the added moodiness which always afterwards, to the very day of sailing in the Pequod on the present voyage, sat brooding on his brow. Nor is it so. very unlikely, that far from distrusting his fitness for another whaling voyage, on account of such dark symptoms, the calculating people of that prudent isle were inclined to harbor the conceit, that for those very reasons he was all the better qualified and set on edge, for a pursuit so full of rage and wildness as the bloody hunt of whales. Gnawed within and scorched without, with the infixed, unrelenting fangs of some incurable idea; such an one, could he be found, would seem the very man to dart his iron and lift his lance against the most appalling of all brutes. Or, if for any reason thought to be corporeally incapacitated for that, yet such an one would seem superlatively competent to cheer and howl on his underlings to the attack. But be all this as it may, certain it is, that with the mad secret of his unabated rage bolted up and keyed in him, Ahab had purposely sailed upon the present voyage with the one only and all-engrossing object of hunting the White Whale. Had any one of his old acquaintances on shore but half dreamed of what was lurking in him then, how soon would their aghast and righteous souls have wrenched the ship from such a fiendish man! They were bent on profitable cruises, the profit to be counted down in dollars from the mint. He was intent on an audacious, immitigable, and supernatural revenge.

Here, then, was this grey-headed, ungodly old man, chasing with curses a Job's whale round the world, at the head of a crew, too, chiefly made up of mongrel renegades, and castaways, and cannibals—morally enfeebled also, by the incompetence of mere unaided virtue or right-mindedness in Starbuck, the invulnerable jollity of indifference and recklessness in Stubb, and the pervading mediocrity in Flask. Such a crew, so officered, seemed specially picked and packed by some infernal fatality to help him to his monomaniac revenge. How it was that they so aboundingly responded to the old man's ire—by what evil magic their souls were possessed, that at times his hate seemed almost theirs; the White Whale as much their insufferable foe as his; how all this came to be—what the White Whale was to them, or how to their unconscious understandings, also, in some dim, unsuspected way, he might have seemed the gliding great demon of the seas of life,—all this to explain, would be to dive deeper than Ishmael can go. The subterranean miner that works in us all, how can one tell whither leads his shaft by the ever shifting, muffled sound of his pick? Who does not feel the irresistible arm drag? What skiff in tow of a seventy-four can stand still? For one, I gave myself up to the abandonment of the time and the place; but while yet all a-rush to encounter the whale, could see naught in that brute but the deadliest ill.

CHAPTER XLII

THE WHITENESS OF THE WHALE

WHAT the White Whale was to Ahab, has been hinted; what, at times, he was to me, as yet remains unsaid.

Aside from those mere obvious considerations touching Moby-Dick, which could not but occasionally awaken in any man's soul some alarm, there was another thought, or rather vague, nameless horror concerning him, which at times by its intensity completely overpowered all the rest; and yet so mystical and well nigh ineffable was it, that I almost despair of putting it in a comprehensible form. It was the whiteness of the whale that above all things appalled me. But how can I hope to explain myself here; and yet, in some dim, random way, explain myself I must, else all these chapters might be naught.

Though in many natural objects, whiteness refiningly enhances beauty, as if imparting some special virtue of its own, as in marbles, japonicas, and pearls; and though various nations have in some way recognised a certain royal pre-eminence in this hue; even the barbaric, grand old kings of Pegu placing the title "Lord of the White Elephants" above all their other magniloquent ascriptions of dominion; and the modern kings of Siam unfurling the same snow-white quadruped in the royal standard; and the Hanoverian flag bearing the one figure of a snow-white charger; and the great Austrian Empire, Cæsarian, heir to overlording Rome, having for the imperial color the same imperial hue; and though this pre-eminence in it applies to the human race itself, giving the white man ideal mastership over every dusky tribe; and though, besides all this, whiteness has been even made significant of gladness, for among the Romans a white stone marked a joyful day; and though in other mortal sympathies and symbolizings, this same hue is made the emblem of many touching, noble things—the innocence of brides, the benignity of age; though among the Red Men of America the giving of the white belt of wampum was the deepest pledge of honor; though in many climes, whiteness typifies the majesty of Justice in the ermine of the Judge, and contributes to the daily state of kings and queens drawn by milk-white steeds; though even in the higher mysteries of the most august religions it has been made the symbol of the divine spotlessness and power; by the Persian fire worshippers, the white forked flame being held the holiest on the altar; and in the Greek mythologies, Great Jove himself being made incarnate in a snow-white bull; and though to the noble Iroquois, the midwinter sacrifice of the sacred White Dog was by far the holiest festival of their theology, that spotless, faithful creature being held the purest envoy they could send to the Great Spirit with the annual tidings of their own fidelity; and though directly from the Latin word for white, all Christian priests derive the name of one part of their sacred vesture, the alb or tunic, worn beneath the cassock; and though among the holy pomps of the Romish faith, white is specially employed in the celebration of the Passion of our Lord; though in the Vision of St. John, white robes are given to the redeemed, and the four-and-twenty elders stand clothed in white before the great white throne, and the Holy One that sitteth there white like wool; yet for all these accumulated associations, with whatever is sweet, and honorable, and sublime, there yet lurks an elusive something in the innermost idea of this hue, which strikes more of panic to the soul than that redness which affrights in blood.

This elusive quality it is, which causes the thought of whiteness, when divorced from more kindly associations, and coupled with any object terrible in itself, to heighten that terror to the farthest bounds. Witness the white bear of the poles, and the white shark of the tropics; what but their smooth, flaky whiteness makes them the transcendent horrors they are? That ghastly whiteness it is which imparts such an abhorrent mildness, even more loathsome than terrific, to the dumb gloating of their aspect. So that not the fierce-fanged tiger in his heraldic coat can so stagger courage as the white-shrouded bear or shark.

Bethink thee of the albatross, whence come those clouds of spiritual wonderment and pale dread, in which that white phantom sails in all imaginations?

Not Coleridge first threw that spell; but God's great, unflattering laureate, Nature.

Most famous in our Western annals and Indian traditions is that of the White Steed of the Prairies; a magnificent milk-white charger, large-eyed, small-headed, bluff-chested, and with the dignity of a thousand monarchs in his lofty, overscorning carriage. He was the elected Xerxes of vast herds of wild horses, whose pastures in those days were only fenced by the Rocky Mountains and the Alleghanies. At their flaming head he westward trooped it like that chosen star which every evening leads on the hosts of light. The flashing cascade of his mane, the curving comet of his tail, invested him with housings more resplendent than gold and silver-beaters could have furnished him. A most imperial and archangelical apparition of that unfallen, western world, which to the eyes of the old trappers and hunters revived the glories of those primeval times when Adam walked majestic as a god, bluff-browed and fearless as this mighty steed. Whether marching amid his aides and marshals in the van of countless cohorts that endlessly streamed it over the plains, like an Ohio; or whether with his circumambient subjects browsing all around at the horizon, the White Steed gallopingly reviewed them with warm nostrils reddening through his cool milkiness; in whatever aspect he presented himself, always to the bravest Indians he was the object of trembling reverence and awe. Nor can it be questioned from what stands on legendary record of this noble horse, that it was his spiritual whiteness chiefly, which so clothed him with divineness; and that this divineness had that in it which, though commanding worship, at the same time enforced a certain nameless terror.

But there are other instances where this whiteness loses all that accessory and strange glory which invests it in the White Steed and Albatross.

What is it that in the Albino man so peculiarly repels and often shocks the eye, as that sometimes he is loathed by his own kith and kin! It is that whiteness which invests him, a thing expressed by the name he bears. The Albino is as well made as other men—has no substantive deformity—and yet this mere aspect of all-pervading whiteness makes him more strangely hideous than the ugliest abortion. Why should this be so?

Nor, in quite other aspects, does Nature in her least palpable but not the less malicious agencies, fail to enlist among her forces this crowning attribute of the terrible. From its snowy aspect, the gauntleted ghost of the Southern Seas has been denominated the White Squall. Nor, in some historic instances, has the art of human malice omitted so potent an auxiliary. How wildly it heightens the effect of that passage in Froissart, when, masked in the snowy symbol of their faction, the desperate White Hoods of Ghent murder their bailiff in the market-place!

Nor, in some things, does the common, hereditary experience of all mankind fail to bear witness to the supernaturalism of this hue. It cannot well be doubted, that the one visible quality in the aspect of the dead which most appals the gazer, is the marble pallor lingering there; as if indeed that pallor were as much like the badge of consternation in the other world, as of mortal trepidation here. And from that pallor of the dead, we borrow the expressive hue of the shroud in which we wrap them. Nor even in our superstitions do we fail to throw the same snowy mantle round our phantoms; all ghosts rising in a milk-white fog—Yea, while these terrors seize us, let us add, that even the king of terrors, when personified by the evangelist, rides on his pallid horse.

Therefore, in his other moods, symbolize whatever grand or gracious thing he will by whiteness, no man can deny that in its profoundest idealized significance it calls up a peculiar apparition to the soul.

But though without dissent this point be fixed, how is mortal man to account for it? To analyse it, would seem impossible. Can we, then, by the citation of some of those instances wherein this thing of whiteness—though for the time either wholly or in great part stripped of all direct associations calculated to impart to it aught fearful, but nevertheless, is found to exert over us the same sorcery, however modified;—can we thus hope to light upon some chance clue to conduct us to the hidden cause we seek?

Let us try. But in a matter like this, subtlety appeals to subtlety, and without imagination no man can follow another into these halls. And though, doubtless, some at least of the imaginative impressions about to be presented may have been shared by most men, yet few perhaps were entirely conscious of them at the time, and therefore may not be able to recall them now.

Why to the man of untutored ideality, who happens to be but loosely acquainted with the peculiar character of the day, does the bare mention of Whitsuntide marshal in the fancy such long, dreary, speechless processions of slow-pacing pilgrims, down-cast and hooded with new fallen snow? Or, to the unread, unsophisticated Protestant of the Middle American States, why does the passing mention of a White Friar or a White Nun, evoke such an eyeless statue in the soul?

Or what is there apart from the traditions of dungeoned warriors and kings (which will not wholly account for it) that makes the White Tower of London tell so much more strongly on the imagination of an untravelled American, than those other storied structures, its neighbors—the Byward Tower, or even the Bloody? And those sublimer towers, the White Mountains of New Hampshire, whence, in peculiar moods, comes that gigantic ghostliness over the soul at the bare mention of that name, while the thought of Virginia's Blue Ridge is full of a soft, dewy, distant dreaminess? Oh, why, irrespective of all latitudes and longitudes, does the name of the White Sea exert such a spectralness over the fancy, while that of the Yellow Sea lulls us with mortal thoughts of long lacquered mild afternoons on the waves, followed by the gaudiest and yet sleepiest of sunsets? Or, to choose a wholly unsubstantial instance, purely addressed to the fancy, why, in reading the old fairy tales of Central Europe, does the "the tall pale man" of the Hartz forests, whose changeless pallor unrustlingly glides through the green of the groves—why is this phantom more terrible than all the whooping imps of the Blocksburg?

Nor is it, altogether, the remembrance of her cathedral-toppling earthquakes; nor the stampedoes of her frantic seas: nor the tearlessness of arid skies that never rain; nor the sight of her wide field of leaning spires, wrenched copestones, and crosses all adroop (like canted yards of anchored fleets); and her suburban avenues of house-walls lying over upon each other, as a tossed pack of cards;—it is not these things alone which make tearless Lima, the strangest, saddest city thou can'st see. For Lima has taken the white veil; and there is a higher horror in this whiteness of her woe. Old as Pizarro, this whiteness keeps her ruins for ever new; admits not the cheerful greenness of complete decay; spreads over her broken ramparts the rigid pallor of an apoplexy that fixes its own distortions.

I know that, to the common apprehension, this phenomenon of whiteness is not confessed to be the prime agent in exaggerating the terror of objects otherwise terrible; nor to the unimaginative mind is there aught of terror in those appearances whose awfulness to another mind almost solely consists in this one phenomenon, especially when exhibited under any form at all approaching to muteness or universality. What I mean by these two statements may perhaps be respectively elucidated by the following examples.

First: The mariner, when drawing nigh the coasts of foreign lands, if by night he hear the roar of breakers, starts to vigilance, and feels just enough of trepidation to sharpen all his faculties; but under precisely similar circumstances, let him be called from his hammock to view his ship sailing through a midnight sea of milky whiteness—as if from encircling headlands shoals of combed white bears were swimming round him, then he feels a silent, superstitious dread; the shrouded phantom of the whitened waters is horrible to him as a real ghost; in vain the lead assures him he is still off soundings; heart and helm they both go down; he never rests till blue water is under him again.   Yet where is the mariner who will tell thee, "Sir, it was not so much the fear of striking hidden rocks, as the fear of that hideous whiteness that so stirred me?"

Second: To the native Indian of Peru, the continual sight of the snow-howdahed Andes conveys naught of dread, except, perhaps, in the mere fancying of the eternal frosted desolateness reigning at such vast altitudes, and the natural conceit of what a fearfulness it would be to lose oneself in such inhuman solitude.   Much the same is it with the backwoodsman of the West, who with comparative indifference views an unbounded prairie sheeted with driven snow, no shadow of tree or twig to break the fixed trance of whiteness.   Not so the sailor, beholding the scenery of the Antarctic seas; where at times, by some infernal trick of legerdemain in the powers of frost and air, he, shivering and half shipwrecked, instead of rainbows speaking hope and solace to his misery, views what seems a boundless church-yard grinning upon him with its lean ice monuments and splintered crosses.

But thou sayest, methinks this white-lead chapter about whiteness is but a white flag hung out from a craven soul; thou surrenderest to a hypo, Ishmael.

Tell me, why this strong young colt, foaled in some peaceful valley of Vermont, far removed from all beasts of prey—why is it that upon the sunniest day, if you but shake a fresh buffalo robe behind him, so that he cannot even see it, but only smells its wild animal muskiness—why will he start, snort, and with bursting eyes paw the ground in phrensies of affright?   There is no remembrance in him of any gorings of wild creatures in his green northern home, so that the strange muskiness he smells cannot recall to him anything associated with the experience of former perils; for what knows he, this New England colt, of the black bisons of distant Oregon?

No: but here thou beholdest even in a dumb brute, the instinct of the knowledge of the demonism in the world.   Though thousands of miles from Oregon, still when he smells that savage musk, the rending, goring bison herds are as present as to the deserted wild foal of the prairies, which this instant they may be trampling into dust.

Thus, then, the muffled rollings of a milky sea; the bleak rustlings of the festooned frosts of mountains; the desolate shiftings of the windrowed snows of prairies; all these, to Ishmael, are as the shaking of that buffalo robe to the frightened colt!

Though neither knows where lie the nameless things of which the mystic sign gives forth such hints; yet with me, as with the colt, somewhere those things must exist.   Though in many of its aspects this visible world seems formed in love, the invisible spheres were formed in fright.

But not yet have we solved the incantation of this whiteness, and learned why it appeals with such power to the soul; and more strange and far more portentous—why, as we have seen, it is at once the most meaning symbol of spiritual things, nay, the very veil of the Christian's Deity; and yet should be as it is, the intensifying agent in things the most appalling to mankind.

Is it that by its indefiniteness it shadows forth the heartless voids and immensities of the universe, and thus stabs us from behind with the thought of annihilation, when beholding the white depths of the milky way? Or is it, that as in essence whiteness is not so much a color as the visible absence of color, and at the same time the concrete of all colors; is it for these reasons that there is such a dumb blankness, full of meaning, in a wide landscape of snows—a colorless, all-color of atheism from which we shrink? And when we consider that other theory of the natural philosophers, that all other earthly hues—every stately or lovely emblazoning—the sweet tinges of sunset skies and woods; yea, and the gilded velvets of butterflies, and the butterfly cheeks of young girls; all these are but subtile deceits, not actually inherent in substances, but only laid on from without; so that all deified Nature absolutely paints like the harlot, whose allurements cover nothing but the charnel-house within; and when we proceed farther, and consider that the mystical cosmetic which produces every one of her hues, the great principle of light, for ever remains white or colorless in itself, and if operating without medium upon matter, would touch all objects, even tulips and roses, with its own blank tinge—pondering all this, the palsied universe lies before us a leper; and like wilful travellers in Lapland, who refuse to wear colored and coloring glasses upon their eyes, so the wretched infidel gazes himself blind at the monumental white shroud that wraps all the prospect around him. And of all these things the Albino whale was the symbol. Wonder ye then at the fiery hunt?

CHAPTER XLIII

HARK!

"HIST! Did you hear that noise, Cabaco?"

It was the middle-watch: a fair moonlight; the seamen were standing in a cordon, extending from one of the fresh-water butts in the waist, to the scuttle-butt near the taffrail. In this manner, they passed the buckets to fill the scuttle-butt. Standing, for the most part, on the hallowed precincts of the quarter-deck, they were careful not to speak or rustle their feet. From hand to hand, the buckets went in the deepest silence, only broken by the occasional flap of a sail, and the steady hum of the unceasingly advancing keel.

It was in the midst of this repose, that Archy, one of the cordon, whose post was near the after-hatches, whispered to his neighbor, a Cholo, the words above.

"Hist! did you hear that noise, Cabaco?"

"Take the bucket, will ye, Archy? what noise d'ye mean?"

"There it is again—under the hatches—don't you hear it—a cough—it sounded like a cough."

"Cough be damned! Pass along that return bucket."

"There again—there it is!—it sounds like two or three sleepers turning over, now!"

"Caramba! have done, shipmate, will ye? It's the three soaked biscuits ye eat for supper turning over inside of ye—nothing else. Look to the bucket!"

"Say what ye will, shipmate; I've sharp ears."

"Aye, you are the chap, ain't ye, that heard the hum of the old Quakeress's knitting-needles fifty miles at sea from Nantucket; you're the chap."

"Grin away; we'll see what turns up. Hark ye, Cabaco, there is somebody down in the after-hold that has not yet been seen on deck; and I suspect our old Mogul knows something of it too. I heard Stubb tell Flask, one morning watch, that there was something of that sort in the wind."

"Tish! the bucket!"

CHAPTER XLIV

THE CHART

HAD you followed Captain Ahab down into his cabin after the squall that took place on the night succeeding that wild ratification of his purpose with his crew, you would have seen him go to a locker in the transom, and bringing out a large wrinkled roll of yellowish sea charts, spread them before him on his screwed-down table. Then seating himself before it, you would have seen him intently study the various lines and shadings which there met his eye; and with slow but steady pencil trace additional courses over spaces that before were blank. At intervals, he would refer to piles of old log-books beside him, wherein were set down the seasons and places in which, on various former voyages of various ships, sperm whales had been captured or seen.

While thus employed, the heavy pewter lamp suspended in chains over his head, continually rocked with the motion of the ship, and for ever threw shifting gleams and shadows of lines upon his wrinkled brow, till it almost seemed that while he himself was marking out lines and courses on the wrinkled charts, some invisible pencil was also tracing lines and courses upon the deeply marked chart of his forehead.

But it was not this night in particular that, in the solitude of his cabin, Ahab thus pondered over his charts. Almost every night they were brought out; almost every night some pencil marks were effaced, and others were substituted. For with the charts of all four oceans before him, Ahab was threading a maze of currents and eddies, with a view to the more certain accomplishment of that monomaniac thought of his soul.

Now, to any one not fully acquainted with the ways of the leviathans, it might seem an absurdly hopeless task thus to seek out one solitary creature in the unhooped oceans of this planet. But not so did it seem to Ahab, who knew the sets of all tides and currents; and thereby calculating the driftings of the sperm whale's food; and, also, calling to mind the regular, ascertained seasons for hunting him in particular latitudes; could arrive at reasonable surmises, almost approaching to certainties, concerning the timeliest day to be upon this or that ground in search of his prey.

So assured, indeed, is the fact concerning the periodicalness of the sperm whale's resorting to given waters, that many hunters believe that, could he be closely observed and studied throughout the world; were the logs for one voyage of the entire whale fleet carefully collated, then the migrations of the sperm whale would be found to correspond in invariability to those of the herring-shoals or the flights of swallows. On this hint, attempts have been made to construct elaborate migratory charts of the sperm whale.

Besides, when making a passage from one feeding-ground to another, the

sperm whales, guided by some infallible instinct—say, rather, secret intelligence
from the Deity—mostly swim in *veins,* as they are called; continuing their way
along a given ocean-line with such undeviating exactitude, that no ship ever
sailed her course, by any chart, with one tithe of such marvellous precision.
Though, in these cases, the direction taken by any one whale be straight as a
surveyor's parallel, and though the line of advance be strictly confined to its
own unavoidable, straight wake, yet the arbitrary *vein* in which at these times
he is said to swim, generally embraces some few miles in width (more or less, as
the vein is presumed to expand or contract); but never exceeds the visual sweep
from the whale-ship's mast-heads, when circumspectly gliding along this magic
zone.   The sum is, that at particular seasons within that breadth and along
that path, migrating whales may with great confidence be looked for.

And hence not only at substantiated times, upon well known separate feeding-
grounds, could Ahab hope to encounter his prey; but in crossing the widest ex-
panses of water between those grounds he could, by his art, so place and time
himself on his way, as even then not to be wholly without prospect of a meeting.

There was a circumstance which at first sight seemed to entangle his delirious but still methodical scheme.   But not so in the reality, perhaps.   Though
the gregarious sperm whales have their regular seasons for particular grounds,
yet in general you cannot conclude that the herds which haunted such and such
a latitude or longitude this year, say, will turn out to be identically the same
with those that were found there the preceding season; though there are peculiar
and unquestionable instances where the contrary of this has proved true.   In
general, the same remark, only within a less wide limit, applies to the solitaries
and hermits among the matured, aged sperm whales.   So that though Moby-
Dick had in a former year been seen, for example, on what is called the Seychelle
ground in the Indian ocean, or Volcano Bay on the Japanese Coast; yet it did
not follow, that were the Pequod to visit either of those spots at any subsequent
corresponding season, she would infallibly encounter him there.   So, too, with
some other feeding grounds, where he had at times revealed himself.   But all
these seemed only his casual stopping-places and ocean-inns, so to speak, not
his places of prolonged abode.   And where Ahab's chances of accomplishing his
object have hitherto been spoken of, allusion has only been made to whatever
way-side, antecedent, extra prospects were his, ere a particular set time or place
were attained, when all possibilities would become probabilities, and, as Ahab
fondly thought, every possibility the next thing to a certainty.   That particular
set time and place were conjoined in the one technical phrase—the Season-on-
the-Line.   For there and then, for several consecutive years, Moby-Dick had
been periodically descried, lingering in those waters for awhile, as the sun, in
its annual round, loiters for a predicted interval in any one sign of the Zodiac.
There it was, too, that most of the deadly encounters with the White Whale had
taken place; there the waves were storied with his deeds; there also was that
tragic spot where the monomaniac old man had found the awful motive to his
vengeance.   But in the cautious comprehensiveness and unloitering vigilance
with which Ahab threw his brooding soul into this unfaltering hunt, he would
not permit himself to rest all his hopes upon the one crowning fact above
mentioned, however flattering it might be to those hopes; nor in the sleeplessness
of his vow could he so tranquillize his unquiet heart as to postpone all intervening quest.

Now, the Pequod had sailed from Nantucket at the very beginning of the
Season-on-the-Line.   No possible endeavor then could enable her commander
to make the great passage southwards, double Cape Horn, and then running

down sixty degrees of latitude arrive in the equatorial Pacific in time to cruise there. Therefore, he must wait for the next ensuing season. Yet the premature hour of the Pequod's sailing had, perhaps, been correctly selected by Ahab, with a view to this very complexion of things. Because, an interval of three hundred and sixty-five days and nights was before him; an interval which, instead of impatiently enduring ashore, he would spend in a miscellaneous hunt; if by chance the White Whale, spending his vacation in seas far remote from his periodical feeding-grounds, should turn up his wrinkled brow off the Persian Gulf, or in the Bengal Bay, or China Seas, or in any other waters haunted by his race. So that Monsoons, Pampas, Nor-Westers, Harmattans, Trades; any wind but the Levanter and Simoom, might blow Moby-Dick into the devious zig-zag world-circle of the Pequod's circumnavigating wake.

But granting all this; yet, regarded discreetly and coolly, seems it not but a mad idea, this; that in the broad boundless ocean, one solitary whale, even if encountered, should be thought capable of individual recognition from his hunter, even as a white-bearded Mufti in the thronged thoroughfares of Constantinople? Yes. For the peculiar snow-white brow of Moby-Dick, and his snow-white hump, could not but be unmistakable. And have I not tallied the whale, Ahab would mutter to himself, as after poring over his charts till long after midnight he would throw himself back in reveries—tallied him, and shall he escape? His broad fins are bored, and scalloped out like a lost sheep's ear! And here, his mad mind would run on in a breathless race; till a weariness and faintness of pondering came over him; and in the open air of the deck he would seek to recover his strength. Ah, God! what trances of torments does that man endure who is consumed with one unachieved revengeful desire! He sleeps with clenched hands; and wakes with his own bloody nails in his palms.

Often, when forced from his hammock by exhausting and intolerably vivid dreams of the night, which, resuming his own intense thoughts through the day, carried them on amid a clashing of phrensies, and whirled them round and round in his blazing brain, till the very throbbing of his life-spot became insufferable anguish; and when, as was sometimes the case, these spiritual throes in him heaved his being up from its base, and a chasm seemed opening in him, from which forked flames and lightnings shot up, and accursed fiends beckoned him to leap down among them; when this hell in himself yawned beneath him, a wild cry would be heard through the ship; and with glaring eyes Ahab would burst from his state room, as though escaping from a bed that was on fire. Yet these, perhaps, instead of being the unsuppressable symptoms of some latent weakness, or fright at his own resolve, were but the plainest tokens of its intensity. For, at such times, crazy Ahab, the scheming, unappeasedly steadfast hunter of the White Whale; this Ahab that had gone to his hammock, was not the agent that so caused him to burst from it in horror again. The latter was the eternal, living principle or soul in him; and in sleep, being for the time dissociated from the characterizing mind, which at other times employed it for its outer vehicle or agent, it spontaneously sought escape from the scorching contiguity of the frantic thing, of which, for the time, it was no longer an integral. But as the mind does not exist unless leagued with the soul, therefore it must have been that, in Ahab's case, yielding up all his thoughts and fancies to his one supreme purpose; that purpose, by its own sheer inveteracy of will, forced itself against gods and devils into a kind of self-assumed, independent being of its own. Nay, could grimly live and burn, while the common vitality to which it was conjoined, fled horror-stricken from the unbidden and unfathered birth. Therefore, the tormented spirit that glared out of bodily eyes, when what seemed Ahab rushed from his room, was for the time but a vacated thing, a formless somnambulistic being, a ray of living light, to be sure, but without an object to color, and therefore a blankness in itself. God help thee, old man, thy thoughts have created a creature in thee; and he whose intense thinking thus makes him a Prometheus; a vulture feeds upon that heart for ever; that vulture the very creature he creates.

CHAPTER XLV

THE AFFIDAVIT

So far as what there may be of a narrative in this book; and, indeed, as indirectly touching one or two very interesting and curious particulars in the habits of sperm whales, the foregoing chapter, in its earlier part, is as important a one as will be found in this volume; but the leading matter of it requires to be still further and more familiarly enlarged upon, in order to be adequately understood, and moreover to take away any incredulity which a profound ignorance of the entire subject may induce in some minds, as to the natural verity of the main points of this affair.

I care not to perform this part of my task methodically; but shall be content to produce the desired impression by separate citations of items, practically or reliably known to me as a whaleman; and from these citations, I take it—the conclusion aimed at will naturally follow of itself.

First: I have personally known three instances where a whale, after receiving a harpoon, has effected a complete escape; and, after an interval (in one instance of three years), has been again struck by the same hand, and slain; when the two irons, both marked by the same private cypher, have been taken from the body. In the instance where three years intervened between the flinging of the two harpoons; and I think it may have been something more than that; the man who darted them happening, in the interval, to go in a trading ship on a voyage to Africa, went ashore there, joined a discovery party, and penetrated far into the interior, where he travelled for a period of nearly two years, often endangered by serpents, savages, tigers, poisonous miasmas, with all the other common perils incident to wandering in the heart of unknown regions. Meanwhile, the whale he had struck must also have been on its travels; no doubt it had thrice circumnavigated the globe, brushing with its flanks all the coasts of Africa: but to no purpose. This man and this whale again came together, and the one vanquished the other. I say I, myself, have known three instances similar to this; that is in two of them I saw the whales struck; and, upon the second attack, saw the two irons with the respective marks cut in them, afterwards taken from the dead fish. In the three-year instance, it so fell out that I was in the boat both times, first and last, and the last time distinctly recognized a peculiar sort of huge mole under the whale's eye, which I had observed there three years previous. I say three years, but I am pretty sure it was more than that. Here are three instances, then, which I personally know the truth of; but I have heard of many other instances from persons whose veracity in the matter there is no good ground to impeach.

Secondly: It is well known in the Sperm Whale Fishery, however ignorant the world ashore may be of it, that there have been several memorable historical instances where a particular whale in the ocean has been at distant times and places popularly cognisable. Why such a whale became thus marked was not altogether and originally owing to his bodily peculiarities as distinguished from other whales; for however peculiar in that respect any chance whale may be, they soon put an end to his peculiarities by killing him, and boiling him down into a peculiarly valuable oil. No: the reason was this: that from the fatal experiences of the fishery there hung a terrible prestige of perilousness about such a whale as there did about Rinaldo Rinaldini, insomuch that most fishermen were content to recognize him by merely touching their tarpaulins when he would be discovered lounging by them on the sea, without seeking to cultivate a more intimate acquaintance. Like some poor devils ashore that happen to know an irascible great man, they make distant unobtrusive salutations to him in the street, lest if they pursued the acquaintance further, they might receive a summary thump for their presumption.

But not only did each of these famous whales enjoy great individual celebrity —nay, you may call it an ocean-wide renown; not only was he famous in life and now is immortal in forecastle stories after death, but he was admitted into all the rights, privileges, and distinctions of a name; had as much a name indeed as Cambyses or Cæsar. Was it not so, O Timor Tom! thou famed leviathan, scarred like an iceberg, who so long did'st lurk in the Oriental straits of that name, whose spout was oft seen from the palmy beach of Ombay? Was it not so, O New Zealand Jack; thou terror of all cruisers that crossed their wakes in the vicinity of the Tattoo Land? Was it not so, O Morquan! King of Japan, whose lofty jet they say at times assumed the semblance of a snow-white cross against the sky? Was it not so, O Don Miguel! thou Chilian whale, marked like an old tortoise with mystic hieroglyphics upon the back! In plain prose here are four whales as well known to the students of Cetacean History as Marius or Sylla to the classic scholar.

But this is not all. New Zealand Tom and Don Miguel, after at various times creating great havoc among the boats of different vessels, were finally gone in quest of, systematically hunted out, chased and killed by valiant whaling captains, who heaved up their anchors with that express object as much in view, as in setting out through the Narragansett Woods, Captain Butler of old had it in his mind to capture that notorious murderous savage Annawon, the headmost warrior of the Indian King Philip.

I do not know where I can find a better place that just here, to make mention of one or two other things, which to me seem important, as in printed form establishing in all respects the reasonableness of the whole story of the White Whale, more especially the catastrophe. For this is one of those disheartening instances where truth requires full as much bolstering as error. So ignorant are most landsmen of some of the plainest and most palpable wonders of the world, that without some hints touching the plain facts, historical and otherwise, of the fishery, they might scout at Moby-Dick as a monstrous fable, or still worse and more detestable, a hideous and intolerable allegory.

First: Though most men have some vague flitting ideas of the general perils of the grand fishery, yet they have nothing like a fixed, vivid conception of those perils, and the frequency with which they recur. One reason perhaps is, that not one in fifty of the actual disasters and deaths by casualties in the fishery, ever finds a public record at home, however transient and immediately forgotten that record. Do you suppose that that poor fellow there, who this moment perhaps caught by the whale-line off the coast of New Guinea, is being carried down to the bottom of the sea by the sounding leviathan—do you suppose that that poor fellow's name will appear in the newspaper obituary you will read to-morrow at your breakfast? No: because the mails are very irregular between here and New Guinea. In fact, did you ever hear what might be called regular news direct or indirect from New Guinea? Yet I will tell you that upon one particular voyage which I made to the Pacific, among many others we spoke thirty different ships, every one of which had had a death by a whale, some of them more than one, and three that had each lost a boat's crew. For God's sake, be economical with your lamps and candles! not a gallon you burn, but at least one drop of man's blood was spilled for it.

Secondly: People ashore have indeed some indefinite idea that a whale is an enormous creature of enormous power; but I have ever found that when narrating to them some specific example of this two-fold enormousness, they have significantly complimented me upon my facetiousness; when, I declare upon my soul, I had no more idea of being facetious than Moses, when he wrote the history of the plagues of Egypt.

But fortunately the special point I here seek can be established upon testimony entirely independent of my own. That point is this: The Sperm Whale is in some cases sufficiently powerful, knowing, and judiciously malicious, as with direct aforethought to stave in; utterly destroy, and sink a large ship; and what is more, the Sperm Whale *has* done it.

First: In the year 1820 the ship Essex, Captain Pollard, of Nantucket, was cruising in the Pacific Ocean. One day she saw spouts, lowered her boats, and gave chase to a shoal of sperm whales. Ere long, several of the whales were wounded; when, suddenly, a very large whale escaping from the boats, issued from the shoal, and bore directly down upon the ship. Dashing his forehead against her hull, he so stove her in, that in less than "ten minutes" she settled down and fell over. Not a surviving plank of her has been seen since. After the severest exposure, part of the crew reached the land in their boats. Being returned home at last, Captain Pollard once more sailed for the Pacific in command of another ship, but the gods shipwrecked him again upon unknown rocks and breakers; for the second time his ship was utterly lost, and forthwith forswearing the sea, he has never tempted it since. At this day Captain Pollard is a resident of Nantucket. I have seen Owen Chace, who was chief mate of the Essex at the time of the tragedy; I have read his plain and faithful narrative; I have conversed with his son; and all this within a few miles of the scene of the catastrophe.

The following are extracts from Chace's narrative: "Every fact seemed to warrant me in concluding that it was anything but chance which directed his operations; he made two several attacks upon the ship, at a short interval between them, both of which, according to their direction, were calculated to do us the most injury, by being made ahead, and thereby combining the speed of the two objects for the shock; to effect which, the exact manœuvres which he made were necessary. His aspect was most horrible, and such as indicated resentment and fury. He came directly from the shoal which we had just before entered, and in which we had struck three of his companions, as if fired with revenge for their sufferings." Again: "At all events, the whole circumstances taken .together, all happening before my own eyes, and producing, at the time, impressions in my mind of decided, calculating mischief, on the part of the whale (many of which impressions I cannot now recall), induce me to be satisfied that I am correct in my opinion."

Here are his reflections some time after quitting the ship, during a black night in an open boat, when almost despairing of reaching any hospitable shore. "The dark ocean and swelling waters were nothing; the fears of being swallowed up by some dreadful tempest, or dashed upon hidden rocks, with all the other ordinary subjects of fearful contemplation, seemed scarcely entitled to a moment's thought; the dismal looking wreck, and *the horrid aspect and revenge of the whale,* wholly engrossed my reflections, until day again made its appearance."

In another place, he speaks of *"the mysterious and mortal attack of the animal."*

*   *   *   *   *   *   *   *   *
*   *   *   *   *   *   *   *   *

Secondly: The ship Union, also of Nantucket, was in the year 1807 totally lost off the Azores by a similar onset, but the authentic particulars of this catastrophe I have never chanced to encounter, though from the whale hunters I have now and then heard casual allusions to it.

Thirdly: Some eighteen or twenty years ago Commodore J—— then commanding an American sloop-of-war of the first class, happened to be dining with a party of whaling captains, on board a Nantucket ship in the harbor of Oahu, Sandwich Islands.   Conversation turning upon whales, the Commodore was pleased to be sceptical touching the amazing strength ascribed to them by the professional gentlemen present.   He peremptorily denied for example, that any whale could so smite his stout sloop-of-war as to cause her to leak so much as a thimbleful.   Very good; but there is more coming.   Some weeks after, the commodore set sail in this impregnable craft for Valparaiso.   But he was stopped on the way by a portly sperm whale, that begged a few moments' confidential business with him.   That business consisted in fetching the Commodore's craft such a thwack, that with all his pumps going he made straight for the nearest port to heave down and repair.   I am not superstitious, but I consider the Commodore's interview with that whale as providential.   Was not Saul of Tarsus converted from unbelief by a similar fright?   I tell you, the sperm whale will stand no nonsense.

I will now refer you to Langsdorff's Voyages for a little circumstance in point, peculiarly interesting to the writer hereof.   Langsdorff, you must know by the way, was attached to the Russian Admiral Krusenstern's famous Discovery Expedition in the beginning of the present century.   Captain Langsdorff thus begins his seventeenth chapter.

"By the thirteenth of May our ship was ready to sail, and the next day we were out in the open sea, on our way to Ochotsh.   The weather was very clear and fine, but so intolerably cold that we were obliged to keep on our fur clothing.   For some days we had very little wind; it was not till the nineteenth that a brisk gale from the northwest sprang up.   An uncommonly large whale, the body of which was larger than the ship itself, lay almost at the surface of the water, but was not perceived by any one on board till the moment when the ship, which was in full sail, was almost upon him, so that it was impossible to prevent its striking against him.   We were thus placed in the most imminent danger, as this gigantic creature, setting up its back, raised the ship three feet at least out of the water.   The masts reeled, and the sails fell altogether, while we who were below all sprang instantly upon the deck, concluding that we had struck upon some rock; instead of this we saw the monster sailing off with the utmost gravity and solemnity.   Captain D'Wolf applied immediately to the pumps to examine whether or not the vessel had received any damage from the shock, but we found that very happily it had escaped entirely uninjured."

Now, the Captain D'Wolf here alluded to as commanding the ship in question, is a New Englander, who, after a long life of unusual adventures as a sea-captain, this day resides in the village of Dorchester near Boston.   I have the honor of being a nephew of his.   I have particularly questioned him concerning this passage in Langsdorff. He substantiates every word. The ship, however, was by no means a large one: a Russian craft built on the Siberian coast, and purchased by my uncle after bartering away the vessel in which he sailed from home.

In that up and down manly book of old-fashioned adventure, so full, too, of honest wonders—the voyage of Lionel Wafer, one of ancient Dampier's old chums—I found a little matter set down so like that just quoted from Langsdorff, that I cannot forbear inserting it here for a corroborative example, if such be needed.

Lionel, it seems, was on his way to "John Ferdinando," as he calls the modern Juan Fernandes. "In our way thither," he says, "about four o'clock in the morning, when we were about one hundred and fifty leagues from the Main of America, our ship felt a terrible shock, which put our men in such consternation that they could hardly tell where they were or what to think; but every one began to prepare for death. And, indeed, the shock was so sudden and violent, that we took it for granted the ship had struck against a rock; but when the amazement was a little over, we cast the lead, and sounded, but found no ground. * * * The suddenness of the shock made the guns leap in their carriages, and several of the men were shaken out of their hammocks. Captain Davis, who lay with his head on a gun, was thrown out of his cabin!" Lionel then goes on to impute the shock to an earthquake, and seems to substantiate the imputation by stating that a great earthquake, somewhere about that time, did actually do great mischief along the Spanish land. But I should not much wonder if, in the darkness of that early hour of the morning, the shock was after all caused by an unseen whale vertically bumping the hull from beneath.

I might proceed with several more examples, one way or another known to me, of the great power and malice at times of the sperm whale. In more than one instance. he has been known, not only to chase the assailing boats back to their ships, but to pursue the ship itself, and long withstand all the lances hurled at him from its decks. The English ship Pusie Hall can tell a story on that head; and, as for his strength, let me say, that there have been examples where the lines attached to a running sperm whale have, in a calm, been transferred to the ship, and secured there; the whale towing her great hull through the water, as a horse walks off with a cart. Again, it is very often observed that, if the sperm whale, once struck, is allowed time to rally, he then acts, not so often with blind rage, as with wilful, deliberate designs of destruction to his pursuers; nor is it without conveying some eloquent indication of his character, that upon being attacked he will frequently open his mouth, and retain it in that dread expansion for several consecutive minutes. But I must be content with only one more and a concluding illustration; a remarkable and most significant one, by which you will not fail to see, that not only is the most marvellous event in this book corroborated by plain facts of the present day, but that these marvels (like all marvels) are mere repetitions of the ages; so that for the millionth time we say amen with Solomon— Verily there is nothing new under the sun.

In the sixth Christian century lived Procopius, a Christian magistrate of Constantinople, in the days when Justinian was Emperor and Belisarius general. As many know, he wrote the history of his own times, a work every way of uncommon value. By the best authorities, he had always been considered a most trustworthy and unexaggerating historian, except in some one or two particulars, not at all affecting the matter presently to be mentioned.

Now, in this history of his, Procopius mentions that, during the term of his prefecture at Constantinople, a great sea-monster was captured in the neighboring Propontis, or Sea of Marmora, after having destroyed vessels at intervals in those waters for a period of more than fifty years. A fact thus set down in substantial history cannot easily be gainsaid. Nor is there any reason it should be. Of what precise species this sea-monster was, is not mentioned. But as he destroyed ships, as well as for other reasons, he must have been a whale; and I am strongly inclined to think a sperm whale. And I will tell you why. For a long time I fancied that the sperm whale had been always unknown in the Mediterranean and the deep waters connecting with it. Even now I am certain that those seas are not, and perhaps never can be, in the present constitution of things, a place for his habitual gregarious resort. But further investigations have recently proved to me, that in modern times there have been isolated instances of the presence of the sperm whale in the Mediterranean. I am told, on good authority, that on the Barbary coast, a Commodore Davis of the British navy found the skeleton of a sperm whale. Now, as a vessel of war readily passes through the Dardanelles, hence a sperm whale could, by the same route, pass out of the Mediterranean into the Propontis.

In the Propontis, as far as I can learn, none of that peculiar substance called *brit* is to be found, the aliment of the right whale. But I have every reason to believe that the food of the sperm whale—squid or cuttle-fish— lurks at the bottom of that sea, because large creatures, but by no means the largest of that sort, have been found at its surface. If, then, you properly put these statements together, and reason upon them a bit, you will clearly perceive that, according to all human reasoning, Procopius's sea-monster, that for half a century stove the ships of a Roman Emperor, must in all probability have been a sperm whale.

CHAPTER XLVI

SURMISES

THOUGH consumed with the hot fire of his purpose, Ahab in all his thoughts and actions ever had in view the ultimate capture of Moby-Dick; though he seemed ready to sacrifice all mortal interests to that one passion; nevertheless it may have been that he was by nature and long habituation far too wedded to a fiery whaleman's ways, altogether to abandon the collateral prosecution of the voyage. Or at least if this were otherwise, there were not wanting other motives much more influential with him. It would be refining too much, perhaps, even considering his monomania, to hint that his vindictiveness towards the White Whale might have possibly extended itself in some degree to all sperm whales, and that the more monsters he slew by so much the more he multiplied the chances that each subsequently encountered whale would prove to be the hated one he hunted. But if such an hypothesis be indeed exceptionable, there were still additional considerations which, though not so strictly according with the wildness of his ruling passion, yet were by no means incapable of swaying him.

To accomplish his object Ahab must use tools; and of all tools used in the shadow of the moon, men are most apt to get out of order. He knew, for example, that however magnetic his ascendence in some respects was over Starbuck, yet that ascendency did not cover the complete spiritual man any more than mere corporeal superiority involves intellectual mastership; for to the purely spiritual, the intellectual but stands in a sort of corporeal relation. Starbuck's body and Starbuck's coerced will were Ahab's, so long as Ahab kept his magnet at Starbuck's brain; still he knew that for all this the chief mate, in his soul, abhorred his captain's quest, and could he, would joyfully disintegrate himself from it, or even frustrate it. It might be that a long interval would elapse ere the White Whale was seen. During that long interval Starbuck would ever be apt to fall into open relapses of rebellion against his captain's leadership, unless some ordinary, prudential, circumstantial influences were brought to bear upon him. Not only that, but the subtle insanity of Ahab respecting Moby-Dick was noways more significantly manifested than in his superlative sense and shrewdness in foreseeing that, for the present, the hunt should in some way be stripped of that strange imaginative impiousness which naturally invested it; that the full terror of the voyage must be kept withdrawn into the obscure background (for few men's courage is proof against protracted meditation unrelieved by action); that when they stood their long night watches, his officers and men must have some nearer things to think of than Moby-Dick. For however eagerly and impetuously the savage crew had hailed the announcement of his quest; yet all sailors of all sorts are more or less capricious and unreliable—they live in the varying outer weather, and they inhale its fickleness—and when retained for any object remote and blank in the pursuit, however promissory of life and passion in the end, it is above all things requisite that temporary interests and employments should intervene and hold them healthily suspended for the final dash.

Nor was Ahab unmindful of another thing. In times of strong emotion mankind disdain all base considerations; but such times are evanescent. The permanent constitutional condition of the manufactured man, thought Ahab, is sordidness. Granting that the White Whale fully incites the hearts of this my savage crew, and playing round their savageness even breeds a certain generous knight-errantism in them, still, while for the love of it they give chase to Moby-Dick, they must also have food for their more common, daily appetites. For even the high lifted and chivalric Crusaders of old times were not content to traverse two thousand miles of land to fight for their holy sepulchre, without committing burglaries, picking pockets, and gaining other pious perquisites by the way. Had they been strictly held to their one final and romantic object—that final and romantic object, too many would have turned from in disgust. I will not strip these men, thought Ahab, of all hopes of cash—aye, cash. They may scorn cash now; but let some months go by, and no perspective promise of it to them, and then this same quiescent cash all at once mutinying in them, this same cash would soon cashier Ahab.

Nor was there wanting still another precautionary motive more related to Ahab personally. Having impulsively, it is probable, and perhaps somewhat prematurely revealed the prime but private purpose of the Pequod's voyage, Ahab was now entirely conscious that, in so doing, he had indirectly laid himself open to the unanswerable charge of usurpation; and with perfect impunity, both moral and legal, his crew if so disposed, and to that end competent, could refuse all further obedience to him, and even violently wrest from him the command.   From even the barely hinted imputation of usurpation, and the possible consequences of such a suppressed impression gaining ground, Ahab must of course have been most anxious to protect himself.   That protection could only consist in his own predominating brain and heart and hand, backed by a heedful, closely calculating attention to every minute atmospheric influence which it was possible for his crew to be subjected to.

For all these reasons then, and others perhaps too analytic to be verbally developed here, Ahab plainly saw that he must still in a good degree continue true to the natural, nominal purpose of the Pequod's voyage; observe all customary usages; and not only that, but force himself to evince all his well known passionate interest in the general pursuit of his profession.

Be all this as it may, his voice was now often heard hailing the three mastheads and admonishing them to keep a bright look-out, and not omit reporting even a porpoise.   This vigilance was not long without reward.

CHAPTER XLVII

THE MAT-MAKER

IT was a cloudy, sultry afternoon; the seamen were lazily lounging about the decks, or vacantly gazing over into the lead-colored waters. Queequeg and I were mildly employed weaving what is called a sword-mat, for an additional lashing to our boat. So still and subdued and yet somehow preluding was all the scene, and such an incantation of revelry lurked in the air, that each silent sailor seemed resolved into his own invisible self.

I was the attendant or page of Queequeg, while busy at the mat. As I kept passing and repassing the filling or woof of marline between the long yarns of the warp, using my own hand for the shuttle, and as Queequeg, standing sideways, ever and anon slid his heavy oaken sword between the threads, and idly looking off unto the water, carelessly and unthinkingly drove home every yarn: I say so strange a dreaminess did there then reign all over the ship and all over the sea, only broken by the intermitting dull sound of the sword, that it seemed as if this were the Loom of Time, and I myself were a shuttle mechanically weaving and weaving away at the Fates. There lay the fixed threads of the warp subject to but one single, ever returning, unchanging vibration, and that vibration merely enough to admit of the crosswise interblending of other threads with its own. This warp seemed necessity; and here, thought I, with my own hand I ply my own shuttle and weave my own destiny into these unalterable threads. Meantime, Queequeg's impulsive, indifferent sword, sometimes hitting the woof slantingly, or crookedly, or strongly, or weakly, as the case might be; and by this difference in the concluding blow producing a corresponding contrast in the final aspect of the completed fabric; this savage's sword, thought I, which thus finally shapes and fashions both warp and woof; this easy, indifferent sword must be chance —aye, chance, free will, and necessity—no wise incompatible—all interweavingly working together. The straight warp of necessity, not to be swerved from its ultimate course—its every alternating vibration, indeed, only tending to that; free will still free to ply her shuttle between given threads; and chance, though restrained in its play within the right lines of necessity, and sideways in its motions directed by free will, though thus prescribed to by both, chance by turns rules either, and has the last featuring blow at events.

*   *   *   *   *

Thus we were weaving and weaving away when I started at a sound so strange, long drawn, and musically wild and unearthly, that the ball of free will dropped from my hand, and I stood gazing up at the clouds whence that voice dropped like a wing. High aloft in the cross-trees was that mad Gay-Header, Tashtego. His body was reaching eagerly forward, his hand stretched out like a wand, and at brief sudden intervals he continued his cries. To be sure the same sound was that very moment perhaps being heard all over the seas, from hundreds of whalemen's look-outs perched as high in the air; but from few of those lungs could that accustomed old cry have derived such a marvellous cadence as from Tashtego the Indian's.

As he stood hovering over you half suspended in air, so wildly and eagerly peering towards the horizon, you would have thought him some prophet or seer beholding the shadows of Fate, and by those wild cries announcing their coming.

"There she blows! there! there! there! she blows! she blows!"

"Where-away?"

"On the lee-beam, about two miles off! a school of them!"

Instantly all was commotion.

The Sperm Whale blows as a clock ticks, with the same undeviating and reliable uniformity. And thereby whalemen distinguish this fish from other tribes of his genus.

"There go flukes!" was now the cry from Tashtego; and the whales disappeared.

"Quick, steward!" cried Ahab. "Time! time!"

Dough-Boy hurried below, glanced at the watch, and reported the exact minute to Ahab.

The ship was now kept away from the wind, and she went gently rolling before it. Tashtego reporting that the whales had gone down heading to leeward, we confidently looked to see them again directly in advance of our bows. For that singular craft at times evinced by the Sperm Whale when, sounding with his head in one direction, he nevertheless, while concealed beneath the surface, mills round, and swiftly swims off in the opposite quarter —this deceitfulness of his could not now be in action; for there was no reason to suppose that the fish seen by Tashtego had been in any way alarmed, or indeed knew at all of our vicinity. One of the men selected for shipkeepers—that is, those not appointed to the boats, by this time relieved the Indian at the main-mast head. The sailors at the fore and mizzen had come down; the line tubs were fixed in their places; the cranes were thrust out; the mainyard was backed, and the three boats swung over the sea like three samphire baskets over high cliffs. Outside of the bulwarks their eager crew with one hand clung to the rail, while one foot was expectantly poised on the gunwale. So look the line of man-of-war's men about to throw themselves on board an enemy's ship.

But at this critical instant a sudden exclamation was heard that took every eye from the whale. With a start all glared at dark Ahab, who was surrounded by five dusky phantoms that seemed fresh formed out of air.

CHAPTER XLVIII

THE FIRST LOWERING

THE phantoms, for so they then seemed, were flitting on the other side of the deck, and, with a noiseless celerity, were casting loose the tackles and bands of the boat which swung there. This boat had always been deemed one of the spare boats, though technically called the captain's, on account of its hanging from the starboard quarter. The figure that now stood by its bows was tall and swart, with one white tooth evilly protruding from its steel-like lips. A rumpled Chinese jacket of black cotton funereally invested him, with wide black trousers of the same dark stuff. But strangely crowning this ebonness was a glistening white plaited turban, the living hair braided and coiled round and round upon his head. Less swart in aspect, the companions of this figure were of that vivid, tiger-yellow complexion peculiar to some of the aboriginal natives of the Manillas;—a race notorious for a certain diabolism of subtilty, and by some honest white mariners supposed to be the paid spies and secret confidential agents on the water of the devil, their lord, whose counting-room they supposed to be elsewhere.

While yet the wondering ship's company were gazing upon these strangers, Ahab cried out to the white-turbaned old man at their head, "All ready there, Fedallah?"

"Ready," was the half-hissed reply.

"Lower away then; d'ye hear?" shouting across the deck. "Lower away there, I say."

Such was the thunder of his voice, that spite of their amazement the men sprang over the rail; the sheaves whirled round in the blocks; with a wallow, the three boats dropped into the sea; while, with a dexterous, off-handed daring, unknown in any other vocation, the sailors, goat-like, leaped down the rolling ship's side into the tossed boats below.

Hardly had they pulled out from under the ship's lee, when a fourth keel, coming from the windward side, pulled round under the stern, and showed the five strangers rowing Ahab, who, standing erect in the stern, loudly hailed Starbuck, Stubb, and Flask, to spread themselves widely, so as to cover a large expanse of water. But with all their eyes again riveted upon the swart Fedallah and his crew, the inmates of the other boats obeyed not the command.

"Captain Ahab?—" said Starbuck.

"Spread yourselves," cried Ahab; "give way, all four boats. Thou, Flask, pull out more to leeward!"

"Aye, aye, sir," cheerily cried little King-Post, sweeping round his great steering oar. "Lay back!" addressing his crew. "There!—there!—there again! There she blows right ahead, boys!—lay back!"

"Never heed yonder yellow boys, Archy."

"Oh, I don't mind 'em, sir," said Archy; "I knew it all before now. Didn't I hear 'em in the hold? And didn't I tell Cabaco here of it? What say ye, Cabaco? They are stowaways, Mr. Flask."

"Pull, pull, my fine hearts-alive; pull, my children; pull, my little ones," drawlingly and soothingly sighed Stubb to his crew, some of whom still showed signs of uneasiness. "Why don't you break your backbones, my boys? What is it you stare at? Those chaps in yonder boat? Tut! They are only five more hands come to help us—never mind from where—the more the merrier. Pull, then, do pull; never mind the brimstone—devils are good fellows enough. So, so; there you are now; that's the stroke for a thousand pounds; that's the stroke to sweep the stakes! Hurrah for the gold cup of sperm oil, my heroes! Three cheers, men—all hearts alive! Easy, easy; don't be in a hurry—don't be in a hurry. Why don't you snap your oars, you rascals? Bite something, you dogs! So, so, so, then;—softly, softly! That's it—that's it! long and strong. Give way there, give way! The devil fetch ye, ye ragamuffin rapscallions; ye are all asleep. Stop snoring, ye sleepers, and pull. Pull, will ye? pull, can't ye? pull, won't ye? Why in the name of gudgeons and ginger-cakes don't ye pull?—pull and break something! pull, and start your eyes out! Here!" whipping out the sharp knife from his girdle; "every mother's son of ye draw his knife, and pull with the blade between his teeth. That's it—that's it. Now ye do something; that looks like it, my steel-bits. Start her—start her, my silverspoons! Start her, marling-spikes!"

Stubb's exordium to his crew is given here at large, because he had rather a peculiar way of talking to them in general, and especially in inculcating the religion of rowing. But you must not suppose from this specimen of his sermonizings that he ever flew into downright passions with his congregation. Not at all; and therein consisted his chief peculiarity. He would say the most terrific things to his crew, in a tone so strangely compounded of fun and fury, and the fury seemed so calculated merely as a spice to the fun, that no oarsman could hear such queer invocations without pulling for dear life, and yet pulling for the mere joke of the thing. Besides he all the time looked so easy and indolent himself, so loungingly managed his steering-oar, and so broadly gaped—open-mouthed at times—that the mere sight of such a yawning commander, by sheer force of contrast, acted like a charm upon the crew. Then again, Stubb was one of those odd sort of humorists, whose jollity is sometimes so curiously ambiguous, as to put all inferiors on their guard in the matter of obeying them.

In obedience to a sign from Ahab, Starbuck was now pulling obliquely across Stubb's bow; and when for a minute or so the two boats were pretty near to each other, Stubb hailed the mate.

"Mr. Starbuck! larboard boat there, ahoy! a word with ye, sir, if ye please!"

"Halloa!" returned Starbuck, turning round not a single inch as he spoke; still earnestly but whisperingly urging his crew; his face set like a flint from Stubb's.

"What think ye of those yellow boys, sir!"

"Smuggled on board, somehow, before the ship sailed. (Strong, strong, boys!") in a whisper to his crew, then speaking out loud again: "A sad business, Mr. Stubb! (seethe her, seethe her, my lads!) but never mind, Mr. Stubb, all for the best. Let all your crew pull strong, come what will. (Spring, my men, spring!) There's hogsheads of sperm ahead, Mr. Stubb, and that's what ye came for. (Pull, my boys!) Sperm, sperm's the play! This at least is duty; duty and profit hand in hand."

"Aye, aye, I thought as much," soliloquized Stubb, when the boats diverged, "as soon as I clapt eye on 'em, I thought so. Aye, and that's what he went into the after hold for, so often, as Dough-Boy long suspected. They were hidden down there. The White Whale's at the bottom of it. Well, well, so

be it! Can't be helped! All right! Give way, men! It ain't the White
Whale to-day! Give way!"

Now the advent of these outlandish strangers at such a critical instant
as the lowering of the boats from the deck, this had not unreasonably awakened a sort of superstitious amazement in some of the ship's company; but
Archy's fancied discovery having some time previous got abroad among them,
though indeed not credited then, this had in some small measure prepared
them for the event. It took off the extreme edge of their wonder; and so
what with all this and Stubb's confident way of accounting for their appearance,
they were for the time freed from superstitious surmisings; though the affair
still left abundant room for all manner of wild conjectures as to dark Ahab's
precise agency in the matter from the beginning. For me, I silently recalled
the mysterious shadows I had seen creeping on board the Pequod during the
dim Nantucket dawn, as well as the enigmatical hintings of the unaccountable
Elijah.

Meantime, Ahab, out of hearing of his officers, having sided the farthest
to windward, was still ranging ahead of the other boats; a circumstance bespeaking how potent a crew was pulling him. Those tiger yellow creatures
of his seemed all steel and whalebone; like five trip-hammers they rose and
fell with regular strokes of strength, which periodically started the boat along
the water like a horizontal burst boiler out of a Mississippi steamer. As for
Fedallah, who was seen pulling the harpooneer oar, he had thrown aside his
black jacket, and displayed his naked chest with the whole part of his body
above the gunwale, clearly cut against the alternating depressions of the watery
horizon; while at the other end of the boat Ahab, with one arm, like a fencer's,
thrown half backward into the air, as if to counterbalance any tendency to
trip; Ahab was seen steadily managing his steering oar as in a thousand boat
lowerings ere the White Whale had torn him. All at once the outstretched
arm gave a peculiar motion and then remained fixed, while the boat's five oars
were seen simultaneously peaked. Boat and crew sat motionless on the sea.
Instantly the three spread boats in the rear paused on their way. The whales
had irregularly settled bodily down into the blue, thus giving no distantly
discernible token of the movement, though from his closer vicinity Ahab had
observed it.

"Every man look out along his oars!" cried Starbuck. "Thou, Queequeg,
stand up!"

Nimbly springing up on the triangular raised box in the bow, the savage
stood erect there, and with intensely eager eyes gazed off towards the spot
where the chase had last been descried. Likewise upon the extreme stern of
the boat where it was also triangularly platformed level with the gunwale,
Starbuck himself was seen coolly and adroitly balancing himself to the jerking tossings of his chip of a craft, and silently eyeing the vast blue eye of the
sea.

Not very far distant Flask's boat was also lying breathlessly still; its
commander recklessly standing upon the top of the loggerhead, a stout sort
of post rooted in the keel, and rising some two feet above the level of the
stern platform. It is used for catching turns with the whale line. Its top is
not more spacious than the palm of a man's hand, and standing upon such
a base as that, Flask seemed perched at the mast-head of some ship which
had sunk to all but her trucks. But little King-Post was small and short, and
at the same time little King-Post was full of a large and tall ambition, so
that this loggerhead stand-point of his did by no means satisfy King-Post.

"I can't see three seas off; tip us up an oar there, and let me on to that."

Upon this, Daggoo, with either hand upon the gunwale to steady his way, swiftly slid aft, and then erecting himself volunteered his lofty shoulders for a pedestal.

"Good a mast-head as any, sir.   Will you mount?"

"That I will, and thank ye very much, my fine fellow; only I wish you fifty feet taller."

Whereupon planting his feet firmly against two opposite planks of the boat, the gigantic negro, stooping a little, presented his flat palm to Flask's foot, and then putting Flask's hand on his hearse-plumed head and bidding him spring as he himself should toss, with one dexterous fling landed the little man high and dry on his shoulders.   And here was Flask now standing, Daggoo with one lifted arm furnishing him with a breastband to lean against and steady himself by.

At any time it is a strange sight to the tyro to see with what wondrous habitude of unconscious skill the whaleman will maintain an erect posture in his boat, even when pitched about by the most riotously perverse and cross-running seas.   Still more strange to see him giddily perched upon the logger-head itself, under such circumstances.   But the sight of little Flask mounted upon gigantic Daggoo was yet more curious; for sustaining himself with a cool, indifferent, easy, unthought of, barbaric majesty, the noble negro to every roll of the sea harmoniously rolled his fine form.   On his broad back, flaxen-haired Flask seemed a snow-flake.   The bearer looked nobler than the rider.   Though truly vivacious, tumultuous, ostentatious little Flask would now and then stamp with impatience; but not one added heave did he thereby give to the negro's lordly chest.   So have I seen Passion and Vanity stamping the living magnanimous earth, but the earth did not alter her tides and her seasons for that.

Meanwhile Stubb, the third mate, betrayed no such far-gazing solicitudes. The whales might have made one of their regular soundings, not a temporary dive from mere fright; and if that were the case, Stubb, as his wont in such cases, it seems, was resolved to solace the languishing interval with his pipe. He withdrew it from his hatband, where he always wore it aslant like a feather.   He loaded it, and rammed home the loading with his thumb-end; but hardly had he ignited his match across the rough sandpaper of his hand, when Tashtego, his harpooneer, whose eyes had been setting to windward like two fixed stars, suddenly dropped like light from his erect attitude to his seat, crying out in a quick phrensy of hurry, "Down, down all, and give way! —there they are!"

To a landsman, no whale, nor any sign of a herring, would have been visible at that moment; nothing but a troubled bit of greenish white water, and thin scattered puffs of vapor hovering over it, and suffusingly blowing off to leeward, like the confused scud from white rolling billows.   The air around suddenly vibrated and tingled, as it were, like the air over intensely heated plates of iron.   Beneath this atmospheric waving and curling, and partially beneath a thin layer of water, also, the whales were swimming.   Seen in advance of all the other indications, the puffs of vapor they spouted, seemed their forerunning couriers and detached flying outriders.

All four boats were now in keen pursuit of that one spot of troubled water and air.   But it bade far to outstrip them; it flew on and on, as a mass of interblending bubbles borne down a rapid stream from the hills.

"Pull, pull, my good boys," said Starbuck, in the lowest possible but intensest concentrated whisper to his men; while the sharp fixed glance from his eyes darted straight ahead of the bow, almost seemed as two visible needles in two unerring binnacle compasses. He did not say much to his crew, though, nor did his crew say anything to him. Only the silence of the boat was at intervals startlingly pierced by one of his peculiar whispers, now harsh with command, now soft with entreaty.

How different the loud little King-Post. "Sing out and say something, my hearties. Roar and pull, my thunderbolts! Beach me, beach me on their black backs, boy; only do that for me, and I'll sign over to you my Martha's Vineyard plantation, boys; including wife and children, boys. Lay me on—lay me on! O Lord, Lord! but I shall go stark, staring mad! See! see that white water!" And so shouting, he pulled his hat from his head, and stamped up and down on it; then picking it up, flirted it far off upon the sea; and finally fell to rearing and plunging in the boat's stern like a crazed colt from the prairie.

."Look at that chap now," philosophically drawled Stubb, who, with his unlighted short pipe, mechanically retained between his teeth, at a short distance, followed after—"He's got fits, that Flask has. Fits? yes, give him fits—that's the very word—pitch fits into 'em. Merrily, merrily, hearts-alive. Pudding for supper, you know;—merry's the word. Pull, babes—pull, sucklings—pull, all. But what the devil are you hurrying about? Softly, softly, and steadily, my men. Only pull, and keep pulling; nothing more. Crack all your backbones, and bite your knives in two—that's all. Take it easy—why don't ye take it easy, I say, and burst all your livers and lungs!"

But what it was that inscrutable Ahab said to that tiger-yellow crew of his—these were words best omitted here; for you live under the blessed light of the evangelical land. Only the infidel sharks in the audacious seas may give ear to such words, when, with tornado brow, and eyes of red murder, and foam-glued lips, Ahab leaped after his prey.

Meanwhile, all the boats tore on. The repeated specific allusions of Flask to "that whale," as he called the fictitious monster which he declared to be incessantly tantalizing his boat's bow with its tail—these allusions of his were at times so vivid and life-like, that they would cause some one or two of his men to snatch a fearful look over his shoulder. But this was against all rule; for the oarsmen must put out their eyes, and ram a skewer through their necks; usages announcing that they must have no organs but ears, and no limbs but arms, in these critical moments.

It was a sight full of quick wonder and awe! The vast swells of the omnipotent sea; the surging, hollow roar they made, as they rolled along the eight gunwales, like gigantic bowls in a boundless bowling-green; the brief suspended agony of the boat, as it would tip for an instant on the knife-like edge of the sharper waves, that almost seemed threatening to cut it in two; the sudden profound dip into the watery glens and hollows; the keen spurrings and goadings to gain the top of the opposite hill; the headlong, sled-like slide down its other side;—all these, with the cries of the headsmen and harpooneers; and the shuddering gasps of the oarsmen, with the wondrous sight of the ivory Pequod bearing down upon her boats with outstretched sails, like a wild hen after her screaming brood;—all this was thrilling. Not the raw recruit, marching from the bosom of his wife into the fever heat of his first battle; not the dead man's ghost encountering the first unknown phantom in the other world;—neither of these can feel stranger and stronger emotions than that man does, who for the first time finds himself pulling into the charmed, churned circle of the hunted sperm whale.

The dancing white water made by the chase was now becoming more and more visible, owing to the increasing darkness of the dun cloud-shadows flung upon the sea. The jets of vapor no longer blended, but tilted everywhere to right and left; the whales seemed separating their wakes. The boats were pulled more apart; Starbuck giving chase to three whales running dead to leeward. Our sail was now set, and, with the still rising wind, we rushed along; the boat going with such madness through the water, that the lee oars could scarcely be worked rapidly enough to escape being torn from the row-locks.

Soon we were running through a suffusing wide veil of mist; neither ship nor boat to be seen.

"Give way, men," whispered Starbuck, drawing still further aft the sheet of his sail; "there is time to kill a fish yet before the squall comes. There's white water again!—close to! Spring!"

Soon after, two cries in quick succession on each side of us denoted that the other boats had got fast; but hardly were they overheard, when with a lightning-like hurtling whisper Starbuck said: "Stand up!" and Queequeg, harpoon in hand, sprang to his feet.

Though not one of the oarsmen was then facing the life and death peril so close to them ahead, yet with their eyes on the intense countenance of the mate in the stern of the boat, they knew that the imminent instant had come; they heard, too, an enormous wallowing sound as of fifty elephants stirring in their litter. Meanwhile the boat was still booming through the mist, the waves curling and hissing around us like the erected crests of enraged serpents.

"That's his hump. *There, there,* give it to him!" whispered Starbuck.

A short rushing sound leaped out of the boat; it was the darted iron of Queequeg. Then all in one welded commotion came an invisible push from astern, while forward the boat seemed striking on a ledge; the sail collapsed and exploded; a gush of scalding vapor shot up near by; something rolled and tumbled like an earthquake beneath us. The whole crew were half suffocated as they were tossed helter-skelter into the white curdling cream of the squall. Squall, whale and harpoon had all blended together; and the whale, merely grazed by the iron, escaped.

Though completely swamped, the boat was nearly unharmed. Swimming round it we picked up the floating oars, and lashing them across the gunwale, tumbled back to our places. There we sat up to our knees in the sea, the water covering every rib and plank, so that to our downward gazing eyes the suspended craft seemed a coral boat grown up to us from the bottom of the ocean.

The wind increased to a howl; the waves dashed their bucklers together; the whole squall roared, forked, and crackled around us like a white fire upon the prairie, in which, unconsumed, we were burning; immortal in these jaws of death! In vain we hailed the other boats; as well roar to the live coals down the chimney of a flaming furnace as hail those boats in that storm. Meanwhile the driving scud, rack, and mist, grew darker with the shadows of night; no sign of the ship could be seen. The rising sea forbade all attempts to bale out the boat. The oars were useless as propellers, performing now the office of life-preservers. So, cutting the lashing of the waterproof match keg, after many failures Starbuck contrived to ignite the lamp in the lantern; then stretching it on a waif pole, handed it to Queequeg as the standard-bearer of this forlorn hope. There, then, he sat, holding up that imbecile candle in the heart of that almighty forlornness. There, then, he sat, the sign and symbol of a man without faith, hopelessly holding up hope in the midst of despair.

Wet, drenched through, and shivering cold, despairing of ship or boat, we lifted up our eyes as the dawn came on. The mist still spread over the sea, the empty lantern lay crushed in the bottom of the boat. Suddenly Quee-queg started to his feet, hollowing his hand to his ear. We all heard a faint creaking, as of ropes and yards hitherto muffled by the storm. The sound come nearer and nearer; the thick mists were dimly parted by a huge, vague form. Affrighted, we all sprang into the sea as the ship at last loomed into view, bearing right down upon us within a distance of not much more than its length.

Floating on the waves we saw the abandoned boat, as for one instant it tossed and gaped beneath the ship's bows like a chip at the base of a cataract; and then the vast hull rolled over it, and it was seen no more till it came up weltering astern. Again we swam for it, were dashed against it by the seas, and were at last taken up and safely landed on board. Ere the squall came close to, the other boats had cut loose from their fish and returned to the ship in good time. The ship had given us up, but was still cruising, if haply it might light upon some token of our perishing,—an oar or a lance pole.

CHAPTER XLIX

THE HYENA

THERE are certain queer times and occasions in this strange mixed affair we call life when a man takes this whole universe for a vast practical joke, though the wit thereof he but dimly discerns, and more than suspects that the joke is at nobody's expense but his own. However, nothing dispirits, and nothing seems worth while disputing. He bolts down all events, all creeds, and be-liefs, and persuasions, all hard things visible and invisible, never mind how knobby; as an ostrich of potent digestion gobbles down bullets and gun flints. And as for small difficulties and worryings, prospects of sudden disaster, peril of life and limb; all these, and death itself, seem to him only sly, good-natured hits, and jolly punches in the side bestowed by the unseen and unaccountable old joker. That odd sort of wayward mood I am speaking of, comes over a man only in some time of extreme tribulation; it comes in the very midst of his earnestness, so that what just before might have seemed to him a thing most momentous, now seems but a part of the general joke. There is nothing like the perils of whaling to breed this free and easy sort of genial, desperado philosophy; and with it I now regarded this whole voyage of the Pequod, and the great White Whale its object.

"Queequeg," said I, when they had dragged me, the last man, to the deck, and I was still shaking myself in my jacket to fling off the water; "Quee-queg, my fine friend, does this sort of thing often happen?" Without much emo-tion, though soaked through just like me, he gave me to understand that such things did often happen.

"Mr. Stubb," said I, turning to that worthy, who, buttoned up in his oil-jacket, was now calmly smoking his pipe in the rain; "Mr. Stubb, I think I have heard you say that of all whalemen you ever met, our chief mate, Mr. Starbuck, is by far the more careful and prudent. I suppose then, that going plump on a flying whale with your sail set in a foggy squall is the height of a whaleman's discretion?"

"Certain. I've lowered for whales from a leaking ship in a gale off Cape Horn."

"Mr. Flask," said I, turning to little King-Post, who was standing close by; "you are experienced in these things, and I am not. Will you tell me whether it is an unalterable law in this fishery, Mr. Flask, for an oarsman to break his own back pulling himself back-foremost into death's jaws?"

"Can't you twist that smaller?" said Flask. "Yes, that's the law. I should like to see a boat's crew backing water up to a whale face foremost. Ha, ha! the whale would give them squint for squint, mind that!"

Here, then, from three impartial witnesses, I had a deliberate statement of the entire case. Considering, therefore, that squalls and capsizings in the water and consequent bivouacks on the deep, were matters of common occurrence in this kind of life; considering that at the superlatively critical instant of going on to the whale I must resign my life into the hands of him who steered the boat—oftentimes a fellow who at that very moment is in his impetuousness upon the point of scuttling the craft with his own frantic stampings; considering that the particular disaster to our own particular boat was chiefly to be imputed to Starbuck's driving on to his whale almost in the teeth of a squall, and considering that Starbuck, notwithstanding, was famous for his great heedfulness in the fishery; considering that I belonged to this uncommonly prudent Starbuck's boat; and finally considering in what a devil's chase I was implicated, touching the White Whale; taking all things together, I say, I thought I might as well go below and make a rough draft of my will. "Queequeg," said I, "come along, you shall be my lawyer, executor, and legatee."

It may seem strange that of all men sailors should be tinkering at their last wills and testaments, but there are no people in the world more fond of that diversion. This was the fourth time in my nautical life that I had done the same thing. After the ceremony was concluded upon the present occasion, I felt all the easier; a stone was rolled away from my heart. Besides, all the days I should now live would be as good as the days that Lazarus lived after his resurrection; a supplementary clean gain of so many months or weeks as the case may be. I survived myself; my death and burial were locked up in my chest. I looked round me tranquilly and contentedly, like a quiet ghost with a clean conscience sitting inside the bars of a snug family vault.

Now then, thought I, unconsciously rolling up the sleeves of my frock, here goes for a cool, collected dive at death and destruction, and the devil fetch the hindmost.

CHAPTER L

AHAB'S BOAT AND CREW.   FEDALLAH

"Who would have thought it, Flask!" cried Stubb; "if I had but one leg you would not catch me in a boat, unless may be to stop the plug-hole with my timber toe.   Oh! he's a wonderful old man!"

"I don't think it so strange, after all, on that account," said Flask.   "If his leg were off at the hip, now, it would be a different thing.   That would disable him; but he has one knee, and good part of the other left, you know."

"I don't know that, my little man; I never yet saw him kneel."

*   *   *   *   *

Among whale-wise people it has often been argued whether, considering the paramount importance of his life to the success of the voyage, it is right for a whaling captain to jeopardize that life in the active perils of the chase.   So Tamerlane's soldiers often argued with tears in their eyes, whether that invaluable life of his ought to be carried into the thickest of the fight.

But with Ahab the question assumed a modified aspect.   Considering that with two legs man is but a hobbling wight in all times of danger; considering that the pursuit of whales is always under great and extraordinary difficulties; that every individual moment, indeed, then comprises a peril; under these circumstances is it wise for any maimed man to enter a whale-boat in the hunt?   As a general thing, the joint-owners of the Pequod must have plainly thought not.

Ahab well knew that although his friends at home would think little of his entering a boat in certain comparatively harmless vicissitudes of the chase, for the sake of being near the scene of action and giving his orders in person, yet for Captain Ahab to have a boat actually apportioned to him as a regular headsman in the hunt—above all for Captain Ahab to be supplied with five extra men, as that same boat's crew, he well knew that such generous conceits never entered the heads of the owners of the Pequod.   Therefore he had not solicited a boat's crew from them, nor had he in any way hinted his desires on that head.   Nevertheless he had taken private measures of his own touching all that matter.   Until Cabaco's published discovery, the sailors had little foreseen it, though to be sure when, after being a little while out of port, all hands had concluded the customary business of fitting the whaleboats for service; when some time after this Ahab was now and then found bestirring himself in the matter of making thole-pins with his own hands for what was thought to be one of the spare boats, and even solicitously cutting the small wooden skewers, which when the line is running out are pinned over the groove in the bow: when all this was observed in him, and particularly his solicitude in having an extra coat of sheathing in the bottom of the boat, as if to make it better withstand the pointed pressure of his ivory limb; and also the anxiety he evinced in exactly shaping the thigh board, or clumsy cleat, as it is sometimes called, the horizontal piece in the boat's bow for bracing the knee against in darting or stabbing at the whale; when it was observed how often he stood up in that boat with his solitary knee fixed in the semi-circular depression in the cleat, and with the carpenter's chisel gouged out a little here and straightened it a little there; all these things, I say, had awakened much interest and curiosity at the time. But almost everybody supposed that this particular preparative heedfulness in Ahab must only be with a view to the ultimate chase of Moby-Dick; for he had already revealed his intention to hunt that mortal monster in person. But such a supposition did by no means involve the remotest suspicion as to any boat's crew being assigned to that boat.

Now, with the subordinate phantoms, what wonder remained soon waned away; for in a whaler wonders soon wane. Besides, now and then such unaccountable odds and ends of strange nations come up from the unknown nooks and ash-holes of the earth to man these floating outlaws of whalers; and the ships themselves often pick up such queer castaway creatures found tossing about the open sea on planks, bits of wreck, oars, whale-boats, canoes, blown-off Japanese junks, and what not; that Beelzebub himself might climb up the side and step down into the cabin to chat with the captain, and it would not create any unsubduable excitement in the forecastle.

But be all this as it may, certain it is that while the subordinate phantoms soon found their place among the crew, though still as it were somehow distinct from them, yet that hair-turbaned Fedallah remained a muffled mystery to the last. Whence he came in a mannerly world like this, by what sort of unaccountable tie he soon evinced himself to be linked with Ahab's peculiar fortunes; nay, so far as to have some sort of a half-hinted influence; Heaven knows, but it might have been even authority over him; all this none knew, but one cannot sustain an indifferent air concerning Fedallah. He was such a creature as civilized, domestic people in the temperate zone only see in their dreams, and that but dimly; but the like of whom now and then glide among the unchanging Asiatic communities, especially the Oriental isles to the east of the continent—those insulated, immemorial, unalterable countries, which even in these modern days still preserve much of the ghostly aboriginalness of earth's primal generations, when the memory of the first man was a distinct recollection, and all men his descendants, unknowing whence he came, eyed each other as real phantoms, and asked of the sun and the moon why they were created and to what end; when though, according to Genesis, the angels indeed consorted with the daughters of men, the devils also, add the uncanonical Rabbins, indulged in mundane amours.

CHAPTER LI

THE SPIRIT-SPOUT

Days, weeks passed, and under easy sail, the ivory Pequod had slowly swept across four several cruising-grounds; that off the Azores; off the Cape de Verdes; on the Plate (so called), being off the mouth of the Rio de la Plata; and the Carrol Ground, an unstaked, watery locality, southerly from St. Helena.

It was while gliding through these latter waters that one serene and moonlight night, when all the waves rolled by like scrolls of silver; and, by their soft, suffusing seethings, made what seemed a silvery silence, not a solitude: on such a silent night a silvery jet was seen far in advance of the white bubbles at the bow. Lit up by the moon, it looked celestial; seemed some plumed and glittering god uprising from the sea. Fedallah first descried this jet. For of these moonlight nights, it was his wont to mount to the main-mast head, and stand a look-out there, with the same precision as if it had been day. And yet, though herds of whales were seen by night, not one whaleman in a hundred would venture a lowering for them. You may think with what emotions, then, the seamen beheld this old Oriental perched aloft at such unusual hours; his turban and the moon, companions in one sky. But when, after spending his uniform interval there for several successive nights without uttering a single sound; when, after all this silence, his unearthly voice was heard announcing that silvery, moon-lit jet, every reclining mariner started to his feet as if some winged spirit had lighted in the rigging, and hailed the mortal crew. "There she blows!" Had the trump of judgment blown, they could not have quivered more; yet still they felt no terror; rather pleasure. For though it was a most unwonted hour, yet so impressive was the cry, and so deliriously exciting that almost every soul on board instinctively desired a lowering.

Walking the deck with quick, side-lunging strides, Ahab commanded the t'gallant sails and royals to be set, and every stunsail spread. The best man in the ship must take the helm. Then, with every mast-head manned, the piled-up craft rolled down before the wind. The strange, upheaving, lifting tendency of the taffrail breeze filling the hollows of so many sails, made the buoyant, hovering deck to feel like air beneath the feet; while still she rushed along, as if two antagonistic influences were struggling in her—one to mount direct to heaven, the other to drive yawingly to some horizontal goal. And had you watched Ahab's face that night, you would have thought that in him also two different things were warring. While his one live leg made lively echoes along the deck, every stroke of his dead limb sounded like a coffin-tap. On life and death this old man walked. But though the ship so swiftly sped, and though from every eye, like arrows, the eager glances shot, yet the silvery jet was no more seen that night. Every sailor swore he saw it once, but not a second time.

This midnight-spout had almost grown a forgotten thing, when, some days after, lo! at the same silent hour, it was again announced: again it was descried by all; but upon making sail to overtake it, once more it disappeared as if it had never been. And so it served us night after night, till no one heeded it but to wonder at it. Mysteriously jetted into the clear moonlight, or starlight, as the case might be; disappearing again for one whole day, or two days, or three; and somehow seeming at every distinct repetition to be advancing still farther and farther in our van, this solitary jet seemed for ever alluring us on.

Nor with the immemorial superstition of their race, and in accordance with the preternaturalness, as it seemed, which in many things invested the Pequod, were there wanting some of the seamen who swore that whenever and wherever descried; at however remote times, or in however far apart latitudes and longitudes, that unnearable spout was cast by one self-same whale; and that whale, Moby-Dick. For a time, there reigned, too, a sense of peculiar dread at this flitting apparition, as if it were treacherously beckoning us on and on, in order that the monster might turn round upon us, and rend us at last in the remotest and most savage seas.

These temporary apprehensions, so vague but so awful, derived a wondrous potency from the contrasting serenity of the weather, in which, beneath all its blue blandness, some thought there lurked a devilish charm, as for days and days we voyaged along, through seas so wearily, lonesomely mild, that all space, in repugnance to our vengeful errand, seemed vacating itself of life before our urn-like prow.

But, at last, when turning to the eastward, the Cape winds began howling around us, and we rose and fell upon the long, troubled seas that are there; when the ivory-tusked Pequod sharply bowed to the blast, and gored the dark waves in her madness, till, like showers of silver chips, the foam-flakes flew over her bulwarks; then all this desolate vacuity of life went away, but gave place to sights more dismal than before.

Close to our bows, strange forms in the water darted hither and thither before us; while thick in our rear flew the inscrutable sea-ravens. And every morning, perched on our stays, rows of these birds were seen; and spite of our hootings, for a long time obstinately clung to the hemp, as though they deemed our ship some drifting, uninhabited craft; a thing appointed to desolation, and therefore fit roosting-place for their homeless selves. And heaved and heaved, still unrestingly heaved the black sea, as if its vast tides were a conscience; and the great mundane soul were in anguish and remorse for the long sin and suffering it had bred. Cape of Good Hope, do they call ye? Rather Cape Tormentoto, as called of yore; for long allured by the perfidious silences that before had attended us, we found ourselves launched into this tormented sea, where guilty beings transformed into those fowls and these fish, seemed condemned to swim on everlastingly without any haven in store, or beat that black air without any horizon. But calm, snow-white, and unvarying; still directing its fountain of feathers to the sky; still beckoning us on from before, the solitary jet would at times be descried.

During all this blackness of the elements, Ahab, though assuming for the time the almost continual command of the drenched and dangerous deck, manifested the gloomiest reserve; and more seldom than ever addressed his mates. In tempestuous times like these, after everything above and aloft has been secured, nothing more can be done but passively to await the issue of the gale. Then Captain and crew become practical fatalists. So, with his ivory leg inserted into its accustomed hole, and with one hand firmly grasping a shroud, Ahab for hours and hours would stand gazing dead to windward, while an occasional squall of sleet or snow would all but congeal his very eyelashes together. Meantime, the crew driven from the forward part of the ship by the perilous seas that burstingly broke over its bows, stood in a line along the bulwarks in the waist; and the better to guard against the leaping waves, each man had slipped himself into a sort of bow line secured to the rail, in which he swung as in a loosened belt. Few or no words were spoken; and the silent ship, as if manned by painted sailors in wax, day after day tore on through all the swift madness and gladness of the demoniac waves. By night the same muteness of humanity before the shrieks of the ocean prevailed; still in silence the men swung in the bowlines; still wordless Ahab stood up to the blast. Even when wearied nature seemed demanding repose he would not seek that repose in his hammock. Never could Starbuck forget the old man's aspect, when one night going down into the cabin to mark how the barometer stood, he saw him with closed eyes sitting straight in his floor-screwed chair; the rain and half-melted sleet of the storm from which he had some time before emerged, still slowly dripping from the unremoved hat and coat. On the table beside him lay unrolled one of those charts of tides and currents which have previously been spoken of. His lantern swung from his tightly clenched hand. Though the body was erect, the head was thrown back so that the closed eyes were pointed towards the needle of the tell-tale that swung from a beam in the ceiling.

Terrible old man! thought Starbuck with a shudder, sleeping in this gale, still thou steadfastly eyest thy purpose.

CHAPTER LII

THE ALBATROSS

SOUTH-EASTWARD from the Cape, off the distant Crozetts, a good cruising ground for Right Whalemen, a sail loomed ahead, the Goney (Albatross) by name. As she slowly drew nigh, from my lofty perch at the fore-mast-head, I had a good view of that sight so remarkable to a tyro in the far ocean fisheries—a whaler at sea, and long absent from home.

As if the waves had been fullers, this craft was bleached like the skeleton of a stranded walrus. All down her sides, this spectral appearance was traced with long channels of reddened rust, while all her spars and her rigging were like the thick branches of trees furred over with hoar-frost. Only her lower sails were set. A wild sight it was to see her long-bearded look-outs at those three mast-heads. They seemed clad in the skins of beasts, so torn and be-patched the raiment that had survived nearly four years of cruising. Stand-ing in iron hoops nailed to the mast, they swayed and swung over a fathomless sea; and though, when the ship slowly glided close under our stern, we six men in the air came so nigh to each other that we might almost have leaped from the mast-heads of one ship to those of the other; yet, those forlorn-looking fishermen, mildly eyeing us as they passed, said not one word to our own look-outs, while the quarter-deck hail was being heard from below.

"Ship ahoy! Have ye seen the White Whale?"

But as the strange captain, leaning over the pallid bulwarks, was in the act of putting his trumpet to his mouth, it somehow fell from his hand into the sea; and the wind now rising amain, he in vain strove to make himself heard without it. Meantime his ship was still increasing the distance between. While in various silent ways the seamen of the Pequod were evincing their observance of this ominous incident at the first mere mention of the White Whale's name to another ship, Ahab for a moment paused; it almost seemed as though he would have lowered a boat to board the stranger, had not the threatening wind forbade. But taking advantage of his windward position, he again seized his trumpet, and knowing by her aspect that the stranger vessel was a Nantucketer and shortly bound home, he loudly hailed—"Ahoy there! This is the Pequod, bound round the world! Tell them to address all future letters to the Pacific ocean! and this time three years, if I am not at home, tell them to address them to——"

At that moment the two wakes were fairly crossed, and instantly, then, in accordance with their singular ways, shoals of small harmless fish, that for some days before had been placidly swimming by our side, darted away with what seemed shuddering fins, and ranged themselves fore and aft with the stranger's flanks. Though in the course of his continual voyagings Ahab must often before have noticed a similar sight, yet, to any monomaniac man, the veriest trifles capriciously carry meanings.

"Swim away from me, do ye?" murmured Ahab, gazing over into the water. There seemed but little in the words, but the tone conveyed more of deep help-less sadness than the insane old man had ever before evinced. But turning to the steersman, who thus far had been holding the ship in the wind to diminish her headway, he cried out in his old lion voice,—"Up helm! Keep her off round the world!"

Round the world! There is much in that sound to inspire proud feelings; but whereto does all that circumnavigation conduct? Only through number-less perils to the very point whence we started, where those that we left behind secure, were all the time before us.

Were this world an endless plain, and by sailing eastward we could for ever reach new distances, and discover sights more sweet and strange than any Cyclades or Islands of King Solomon, then there were promise in the voyage. But in pursuit of those far mysteries we dream of, or in tormented chase of that demon phantom that, some time or other, swims before all human hearts; while chasing such over this round globe, they either lead us on in barren mazes or midway leave us whelmed.

CHAPTER LIII

THE GAM

THE ostensible reason why Ahab did not go on board of the whaler we had spoken was this: the wind and sea betokened storms. But even had this not been the case, he would not after all, perhaps, have boarded her—judging by his subsequent conduct on similar occasions—if so it had been that, by the process of hailing, he had obtained a negative answer to the question he put. For, as it eventually turned out, he cared not to consort, even for five minutes, with any stranger captain, except he could contribute some of that information he so absorbingly sought. But all this might remain inadequately estimated, were not something said here of the peculiar usages of whaling-vessels when meeting each other in foreign seas, and especially on a common cruising-ground.

If two strangers crossing the Pine Barrens in New York State, or the equally desolate Salisbury Plain in England; if casually encountering each other in such inhospitable wilds, these twain, for the life of them, cannot well avoid a mutual salutation; and stopping for a moment to interchange the news; and, perhaps, sitting down for a while and resting in concert; then, how much more natural that upon the illimitable Pine Barrens and Salisbury Plains of the sea, two whaling vessels descrying each other at the ends of the earth—off lone Fanning's Island, or the far away King's Mills; how much more natural, I say, that under such circumstances these ships should not only interchange hails, but come into still closer, more friendly and sociable contact? And especially would this seem to be a matter of course, in the case of vessels owned in one seaport, and whose captains, officers, and not a few of the men are personally known to each other; and consequently, have all sorts of dear domestic things to talk about.

For the long absent ship, the outward-bounder, perhaps, has letters on board; at any rate, she will be sure to let her have some papers of a date a year or two later than the last one on her blurred and thumb-worn files. And in return for that courtesy, the outward-bound ship would receive the latest whaling intelligence from the cruising-ground to which she may be destined, a thing of the utmost importance to her. And in degree, all this will hold true concerning whaling vessels crossing each other's track on the cruising-ground itself, even though they are equally long absent from home. For one of them may have received a transfer of letters from some third, and now far remote vessel; and some of those letters may be for the people of the ship she now meets. Besides, they would exchange the whaling news, and have an agreeable chat. For not only would they meet with all the sympathies of sailors, but likewise with all the peculiar congenialities arising from a common pursuit and mutually shared privations and perils.

Nor would difference of country make any very essential difference; that is, so long as both parties speak one language, as is the case with Americans and English. Though, to be sure, from the small number of English whalers, such meetings do not very often occur, and when they do occur there is too apt to be a sort of shyness between them; for your Englishman is rather reserved, and your Yankee, he does not fancy that sort of thing in anybody but himself. Besides, the English whalers sometimes affect a kind of metropolitan superiority over the American whalers; regarding the long, lean Nantucketer, with his non-descript provincialisms, as a sort of sea-peasant. But where this superiority in the English whaleman does really consist, it would be hard to say, seeing that the Yankees in one day, collectively, kill more whales than all the English, collectively, in ten years. But this is a harmless little foible in the English whale-hunters, which the Nantucketer does not take much to heart; probably, because he knows that he has a few foibles himself.

So, then, we see that of all ships separately sailing the sea, whalers have most reason to be sociable—and they are so. Whereas, some merchant ships crossing each other's wake in the mid-Atlantic, will oftentimes pass on without so much as a single word of recognition, mutually cutting each other on the high seas, like a brace of dandies in Broadway; and all the time indulging, perhaps, in finical criticism upon each other's rig. As for Men-of-War, when they chance to meet at sea, they first go through such a string of silly bowings and scrapings, such a ducking of ensigns, that there does not seem to be much right-down hearty good-will and brotherly love about it all. As touching Slave-ships meeting, why, they are in such a prodigious hurry, they run away from each other as soon as possible. And as for Pirates, when they chance to cross each other's cross-bones, the first hail is—"How many skulls?"—the same way that whalers hail—"How many barrels?" And that question once answered, pirates straightway steer apart, for they are infernal villains on both sides, and don't like to see overmuch of each other's villainous likenesses.

But look at the godly, honest, unostentatious, hospitable, sociable, free-and-easy whaler! What does the whaler do when she meets another whaler in any sort of decent weather? She has a *"Gam,"* a thing so utterly unknown to all other ships that they never heard of the name even; and if by chance they should hear of it, they only grin at it, and repeat gamesome stuff about "spouters" and "blubber-boilers," and such like pretty exclamations. Why it is that all Merchant-seamen, and also all Pirates and Man-of-War's men, and Slave-ship sailors, cherish such a scornful feeling towards Whale-ships; this is a question it would be hard to answer. Because, in the case of pirates, say, I should like to know whether that profession of theirs has any peculiar glory about it. It sometimes ends in uncommon elevation, indeed; but only at the gallows. And besides, when a man is elevated in that odd fashion, he has no proper foundation for his superior altitude. Hence, I conclude, that in boasting himself to be high lifted above a whaleman, in that assertion the pirate has no solid basis to stand on.

But what is a *Gam?* You might wear out your index-finger running up and down the columns of dictionaries, and never find the word. Dr. Johnson never attained to that erudition; Noah Webster's ark does not hold it. Nevertheless, this same expressive word has now for many years been in constant use among some fifteen thousand true born Yankees. Certainly, it needs a definition, and should be incorporated into the Lexicon. With that view, let me learnedly define it.

GAM. Noun—*A social meeting of two (or more) Whaleships, generally on a cruising-ground; when, after exchanging hails, they exchange visits by boats' crews: the two captains remaining, for the time, on board of one ship, and the two chief mates on the other.*

There is another little item about Gamming which must not be forgotten here. All professions have their own little peculiarities of detail; so has the whale fishery. In a pirate, man-of-war, or slave ship, when the captain is rowed anywhere in his boat, he always sits in the stern sheets on a comfortable, sometimes cushioned seat there, and often steers himself with a pretty little milliner's tiller decorated with gay cords and ribbons. But the whale-boat has no seat astern, no sofa of that sort whatever, and no tiller at all. High times indeed, if whaling captains were wheeled about the water on castors like gouty old aldermen in patent chairs. And as for a tiller, the whale-boat never admits of any such effeminacy; and therefore as in gamming a complete boat's crew must leave the ship, and hence as the boat steerer or harpooneer is of the number, that subordinate is the steersman upon the occasion, and the captain, having no place to sit in, is pulled off to his visit all standing like a pine tree. And often you will notice that being conscious of the eyes of the whole visible world resting on him from the sides of the two ships, this standing captain is all alive to the importance of sustaining his dignity by maintaining his legs. Nor is this any very easy matter; for in his rear is the immense projecting steering oar hitting him now and then in the small of his back, the after-oar reciprocating by rapping his knees in front. He is thus completely wedged before and behind, and can only expand himself sideways by settling down on his stretched legs; but a sudden, violent pitch of the boat will often go far to topple him, because length of foundation is nothing without corresponding breadth. Merely make a spread angle of two poles, and you cannot stand them up. Then, again, it would never do in plain sight of the world's riveted eyes, it would never do, I say, for this straddling captain to be seen steadying himself the slightest particle by catching hold of anything with his hands; indeed, as token of his entire, buoyant self-command, he generally carries his hands in his trousers' pockets; but perhaps being generally very large, heavy hands, he carries them there for ballast. Nevertheless there have occurred instances, well authenticated ones too, where the captain has been known for an uncommonly critical moment or two, in a sudden squall say—to seize hold of the nearest oarsman's hair, and hold on there like grim death.

CHAPTER LIV

THE TOWN-HO'S STORY

(As told at the Golden Inn)

THE Cape of Good Hope, and all the watery region round about there, is much like some noted four corners of a great highway, where you meet more travellers than in any other part.

It was not very long after speaking the Goney that another homeward-bound whaleman, the Town-Ho, was encountered. She was manned almost wholly by Polynesians. In the short gam that ensued she gave us strong news of Moby-Dick. To some the general interest in the White Whale was now wildly heightened by a circumstance of the Town-Ho's story, which seemed obscurely to involve with the whale a certain wondrous, inverted visitation of one of those so called judgments of God which at times are said to overtake some men. This latter circumstance, with its own particular accompaniments, forming what may be called the secret part of the tragedy about to be narrated, never reached the ears of Captain Ahab or his mates. For that secret part of the story was unknown to the captain of the Town-Ho himself. It was the private property of three confederate white seamen of that ship, one of whom, it seems, communicated it to Tashtego with Romish injunctions of secrecy, but the following night Tashtego rambled in his sleep, and revealed so much of it in that way, that when he was wakened he could not well withhold the rest. Nevertheless, so potent an influence did this thing have on those seamen in the Pequod who came to the full knowledge of it, and by such a strange delicacy, to call it so, were they governed in this matter, that they kept the secret among themselves so that it never transpired abaft the Pequod's main-mast. Interweaving in its proper place this darker thread with the story as publicly narrated on the ship, the whole of this strange affair I now proceed to put on lasting record.

For my humor's sake, I shall preserve the style in which I once narrated it at Lima, to a lounging circle of my Spanish friends, one saint's eve, smoking upon the thick-gilt tiled piazza of the Golden Inn. Of those fine cavaliers, the young Dons, Pedro and Sebastian, were on the closer terms with me; and hence the interluding questions they occasionally put, and which are duly answered at the time.

"Some two years prior to my first learning the events which I am about rehearsing to you, gentlemen, the Town-Ho, Sperm Whaler of Nantucket, was cruising in your Pacific here, not very many days' sail eastward from the eaves of this good Golden Inn. She was somewhere to the northward of the Line. One morning upon handling the pumps, according to daily usage, it was observed that she made more water in her hold than common. They supposed a sword-fish had stabbed her, gentlemen. But the captain, having some unusual reason for believing that rare good luck awaited him in those latitudes; and therefore being very averse to quit them, and the leak not being then considered at all dangerous, though, indeed, they could not find it after searching the hold as low down as was possible in rather heavy weather, the ship still continued her cruisings, the mariners working at the pumps at wide and easy intervals; but no good luck came; more days went by, and not only was the leak yet undiscovered, but it sensibly increased. So much so, that now taking some alarm, the captain, making all sail, stood away for the nearest harbor among the islands, there to have his hull hove out and repaired.

"Though no small passage was before her, yet, if the commonest chance favoured, he did not at all fear that his ship would founder by the way, because his pumps were of the best, and being periodically relieved at them, those six-and-thirty men of his could easily keep the ship free; never mind if the leak should double on her. In truth, well nigh the whole of this passage being attended by very prosperous breezes, the Town-Ho had all but certainly arrived in perfect safety at her port without the occurrence of the least fatality, had it not been for the brutal overbearing of Radney, the mate, a Vineyarder, and the bitterly provoked vengeance of Steelkilt, a Lakeman and desperado from Buffalo.

" 'Lakeman!—Buffalo! Pray, what is a Lakeman, and where is Buffalo?' said Don Sebastian, rising in his swinging mat of grass.

"On the eastern shore of our Lake Erie, Don; but—I crave your courtesy—may be, you shall soon hear further of all that. Now, gentlemen, in square-sail brigs and three-masted ships, well nigh as large and stout as any that ever sailed out of your old Callao to far Manilla; this Lakeman, in the land-locked heart of our America, had yet been nurtured by all those agrarian freebooting impressions popularly connected with the open ocean. For in their interflowing aggregate, those grand fresh-water seas of ours,—Erie, and Ontario, and Huron, and Superior, and Michigan,—possess an ocean-like expansiveness, with many of the ocean's noblest traits; with many of its rimmed varieties of races and of climes. They contain round archipelagoes of romantic isles, even as the Polynesian waters do; in large part, are shored by two great contrasting nations, as the Atlantic is; they furnish long maritime approaches to our numerous territorial colonies from the East, dotted all round their banks; here and there are frowned upon by batteries, and by the goat-like craggy guns of lofty Mackinaw; they have heard the fleet thunderings of naval victories; at intervals, they yield their beaches to wild barbarians, whose red painted faces flash from out their peltry wigwams; for leagues and leagues are flanked by ancient and unentered forests, where the gaunt pines stand like serried lines of kings in Gothic genealogies; those same woods harboring wild Afric beasts of prey, and silken creatures whose exported furs give robes to Tartar Emperors; they mirror the paved capitals of Buffalo and Cleveland, as well as Winnebago villages; they float alike the full-rigged merchant ship, the armed cruiser of the State, the steamer, and the beech canoe; they are swept by Borean and dismasting blasts as direful as any that lash the salted wave; they know what shipwrecks are, for out of sight of land, however inland, they have drowned full many a midnight ship with all its shrieking crew. Thus, gentlemen, though an inlander, Steelkilt was wild-ocean born, and wild-ocean nurtured; as much of an audacious mariner as any. And for Radney, though in his infancy he may have laid him down on the lone Nantucket beach, to nurse at his maternal sea; though in after life he had long followed our austere Atlantic and your contemplative Pacific; yet was he quite as vengeful and full of social quarrel as the backwoods seaman, fresh from the latitudes of buck-horn handled Bowie-knives. Yet was this Nantucketer a man with some good-hearted traits; and this Lakeman, a mariner, who though a sort of devil indeed. might yet by inflexible firmness, only tempered by that common decency of human recognition which is the meanest slave's right; thus treated, this Steel-kilt had long been retained harmless and docile. At all events, he had proved

so thus far; but Radney was doomed and made mad, and Steelkilt—but, gentlemen, you shall hear.

"It was not more than a day or two at the furthest after pointing her prow
for her island haven, that the Town-Ho's leak seemed again increasing, but
only so as to require an hour or more at the pumps every day. You must
know that in a settled and civilized ocean like our Atlantic, for example, some
skippers think little of pumping their whole way across it; though of a still,
sleepy night, should the officer of the deck happen to forget his duty in that
respect, the probability would be that he and his shipmates would never again
remember it, on account of all hands gently subsiding to the bottom. Nor in
the solitary and savage seas far from you to the westward, gentlemen, is it
altogether unusual for ships to keep clanging at their pump-handles in full
chorus even for a voyage of considerable length; that is, if it lie along a tolerably accessible coast, or if any other reasonable retreat is afforded them. It
is only when a leaky vessel is in some very out of the way part of those waters,
some really landless latitude, that her captain begins to feel a little anxious.

"Much this way had it been with the Town-Ho; so when her leak was
found gaining once more, there was in truth some small concern manifested
by several of her company; especially by Radney the mate. He commanded
the upper sails to be well hoisted, sheeted home anew, and every way expanded
to the breeze. Now this Radney, I suppose, was as little of a coward, and as
little inclined to any sort of nervous apprehensiveness touching his own person
as any fearless, unthinking creature on land or on sea that you can conveniently
imagine, gentlemen. Therefore when he betrayed this solicitude about the
safety of the ship, some of the seamen declared that it was only on account of his
being a part owner in her. So when they were working that evening at the
pumps, there was on this head no small gamesomeness slily going on among
them, as they stood with their feet continually overflowed by the rippling clear
water; clear as any mountain spring, gentlemen—that bubbling from the pumps
ran across the deck, and poured itself out in steady spouts at the lee scupper-
holes.

"Now, as you well know, it is not seldom the case in this conventional world
of ours—watery or otherwise; that when a person placed in command over his
fellow-men finds one of them to be very significantly his superior in general
pride of manhood, straightway against that man he conceives an unconquerable
dislike and bitterness; and if he have a chance he will pull down and pulverize
that subaltern's tower, and make a little heap of dust of it. Be this conceit
of mine as it may, gentlemen, at all events Steelkilt was a tall and noble animal
with a head like a Roman, and a flowing golden beard like the tasseled housings
of your last viceroy's snorting charger; and a brain, and a heart, and a soul
in him, gentlemen, which had made Steelkilt Charlemagne, had he been born
son to Charlemagne's father. But Radney, the mate, was ugly as a mule;
yet as hardy, as stubborn, as malicious. He did not love Steelkilt, and Steelkilt
knew it.

"Espying the mate drawing near as he was toiling at the pump with the
rest, the Lakeman affected not to notice him, but unawed, went on with his gay
banterings.

" 'Aye, aye, my merry lads, it's a lively leak this; hold a cannikin, one of
ye, and let's have a taste. By the Lord, it's worth bottling! I tell ye what,
men, old Rad's investment must go for it! he had best cut away his part of
the hull and tow it home. The fact is, boys, that sword-fish only began the
job; he's come back again with a gang of ship-carpenters, saw-fish, and file-fish,

and what not; and the whole posse of 'em are now hard at work cutting and slashing at the bottom; making improvements, I suppose. If old Rad were here now, I'd tell him to jump overboard and scatter 'em. They're playing the devil with his estate, I can tell him. But he's a simple old soul,— Rad, and a beauty too. Boys, they say the rest of his property is invested in looking-glasses. I wonder if he'd give a poor devil like me the model of his nose.'

" 'Damn your eyes! what's that pump stopping for?' roared Radney, pretending not to have heard the sailors' talk. 'Thunder away at it!'

" 'Aye, aye, sir,' said Steelkilt, merry as a cricket. 'Lively, boys, lively, now!' And with that the pump clanged like fifty fire-engines; the men tossed their hats off to it, and ere long that peculiar gasping of the lungs was heard which denotes the fullest tension of life's utmost energies.

"Quitting the pump at last, with the rest of his band, the Lakeman went forward all panting, and sat himself down on the windlass; his face fiery red, his eyes bloodshot, and wiping the profuse sweat from his brow. Now what cozening fiend it was, gentlemen, that possessed Radney to meddle with such a man in that corporeally exasperated state, I know not; but so it happened. Intolerably striding along the deck, the mate commanded him to get a broom and sweep down the planks, and also a shovel, and remove some offensive matters consequent upon allowing a pig to run at large.

"Now, gentlemen, sweeping a ship's deck at sea is a piece of household work which in all times but raging gales is regularly attended to every evening; it has been known to be done in the case of ships actually foundering at the time. Such, gentlemen, is the inflexibility of sea-usages and the instinctive love of neatness in seamen; some of whom would not willingly drown without first washing their faces. But in all vessels this broom business is the prescriptive province of the boys, if boys there be aboard. Besides, it was the stronger men in the Town-Ho that had been divided into gangs, taking turns at the pumps; and being the most athletic seaman of them all, Steelkilt had been regularly assigned captain of one of the gangs; consequently he should have been freed from any trivial business not connected with truly nautical duties, such being the case with his comrades. I mention all these particulars so that you may understand exactly how this affair stood between the two men.

"But there was more than this: the order about the shovel was almost as plainly meant to sting and insult Steelkilt, as though Radney had spat in his face. Any man who has gone sailor in a whaleship will understand this; and all this and doubtless much more, the Lakeman fully comprehended when the mate uttered his command. But as he sat still for a moment, and as he steadfastly looked into the mate's malignant eye and perceived the stacks of powder-casks heaped up in him and the slow-match silently burning along towards them; as he instinctively saw all this, that strange forbearance and unwillingness to stir up the deeper passionateness in any already ireful being—a repugnance most felt, when felt at all, by really valiant men even when aggrieved—this nameless phantom feeling, gentlemen, stole over Steelkilt.

"Therefore, in his ordinary tone, only a little broken by the bodily exhaustion he was temporarily in, he answered him saying that sweeping the deck was not his business, and he would not do it. And then, without at all alluding to the shovel, he pointed to three lads as the customary sweepers; who, not being billeted at the pumps, had done little or nothing all day. To this, Radney replied with an oath, in a most domineering and outrageous manner unconditionally reiterating his command; meanwhile advancing upon the still seated Lakeman, with an uplifted cooper's club hammer which he had snatched from a cask near by.

"Heated and irritated as he was by his spasmodic toil at the pumps, for all his first nameless feeling of forbearance the sweating Steelkilt could but ill brook this bearing in the mate; but somehow still smothering the conflagration within him, without speaking he remained doggedly rooted to his seat, till at last the incensed Radney shook the hammer within a few inches of his face, furiously commanding him to do his bidding.

"Steelkilt rose, and slowly retreating round the windlass, steadily followed by the mate with his menacing hammer, deliberately repeated his intention not to obey. Seeing, however, that his forbearance had not the slightest effect, by an awful and unspeakable intimation with his twisted hand he warned off the foolish and infatuated man; but it was to no purpose. And in this way the two went once slowly round the windlass; when, resolved at last no longer to retreat, bethinking him that he had now forborne as much as comported with his humor, the Lakeman paused on the hatches and thus spoke to the officer:

" 'Mr. Radney, I will not obey you. Take that hammer away, or look to yourself.' But the predestinated mate coming still closer to him, where the Lakeman stood fixed, now shook the heavy hammer within an inch of his teeth; meanwhile repeating a string of insufferable maledictions. Retreating not the thousandth part of an inch; stabbing him in the eye with the unflinching poniard of his glance, Steelkilt, clenching his right hand behind him and creepingly drawing it back, told his persecutor that if the hammer but grazed his cheek he (Steelkilt) would murder him. But, gentlemen, the fool had been branded for the slaughter by the gods. Immediately the hammer touched the cheek; the next instant the lower jaw of the mate was stove in his head; he fell on the hatch spouting blood like a whale.

"Ere the cry could go aft Steelkilt was shaking one of the backstays leading far aloft to where two of his comrades were standing their mast-heads. They were both Canallers.

" 'Canallers!' cried Don Pedro. 'We have seen many whaleships in our harbors, but never heard of your Canallers. Pardon: who and what are they?'

" 'Canallers, Don, are the boatmen belonging to our grand Erie Canal. You must have heard of it.'

" 'Nay, Senor; hereabouts in this dull, warm, most lazy, and hereditary land, we know but little of your vigorous North.'

" 'Aye? Well then, Don, refill my cup. Your chicha's very fine; and ere proceeding further I will tell ye what our Canallers are; for such information may throw side-light upon my story.'

" 'For three hundred and sixty miles, gentlemen, through the entire breadth of the state of New York; through numerous populous cities and most thriving villages; through long, dismal, uninhabited swamps, and affluent, cultivated fields, unrivalled for fertility; by billiard-room and bar-room; through the holy-of-holies of great forests; on Roman arches over Indian rivers; through sun and shade; by happy hearts or broken; through all the wide contrasting scenery of those noble Mohawk counties; and especially, by rows of snow-white chapels, whose spires stand almost like milestones, flows one continual stream of Venetianly corrupt and often lawless life. There's your true Ashantee, gentlemen; there howl your pagans; where you ever find them, next door to you; under the long-flung shadow, and the snug patronizing lee of churches. For by some curious fatality, as it is often noted of your metropolitan freebooters that they ever encamp around the halls of justice, so sinners, gentlemen, most abound in holiest vicinities.

" 'Is that a friar passing?' said Don Pedro, looking downwards into the crowded plazza, with humorous concern.

" 'Well for our northern friend, Dame Isabella's Inquisition wanes in Lima,' laughed Don Sebastian. 'Proceed, Senor.'

" 'A moment! Pardon!' cried another of the company. 'In the name of all us Limeese, I but desire to express to you, sir sailor, that we have by no means overlooked your delicacy in not substituting present Lima for distant Venice in your corrupt comparison. Oh! do not bow and look surprised; you know the proverb all along this coast—"Corrupt as Lima." It but bears out your saying, too; churches more plentiful than billiard-tables, and for ever open—and "Corrupt as Lima." So, too, Venice; I have been there; the holy city of the blessed evangelist, St. Mark—St. Dominic, purge it! Your cup! Thanks: here I refill; now, you pour out again.'

"Freely depicted in his own vocation, gentlemen, the Canaller would make a fine dramatic hero, so abundantly and picturesquely wicked is he. Like Mark Antony, for days and days along his green-turfed, flowery Nile, he indolently floats, openly toying with his red-cheeked Cleopatra, ripening his apricot thigh upon the sunny deck. But ashore, all this effeminacy is dashed. The brigandish guise which the Canaller so proudly sports; his slouched and gaily-ribboned hat betoken his grand features. A terror to the smiling innocence of the villages through which he floats; his swart visage and bold swagger are not unshunned in cities. Once a vagabond on his own canal, I have received good turns from one of these Canallers; I thank him heartily; would fain be not ungrateful; but it is often one of the prime redeeming qualities of your man of violence, that at times he has as stiff an arm to back a poor stranger in a strait, as to plunder a wealthy one. In sum, gentlemen, what the wildness of this canal life is, is emphatically evinced by this; that our wild whale-fishery contains so many of its most finished graduates, and that scarce any race of mankind, except Sydney men, are so much distrusted by our whaling captains. Nor does it at all diminish the curiousness of this matter, that to many thousands of our rural boys and young men born along its line, the probationary life of the Grand Canal furnishes the sole transition between quietly reaping in a Christian cornfield, and recklessly ploughing the waters of the most barbaric seas.

" 'I see! I see!' impetuously exclaimed Don Pedro, spilling his chicha upon his silvery ruffles. 'No need to travel! The world's one Lima. I had thought, now, that at your temperate North the generations were cold and holy as the hills.—But the story.'

"I left off, gentlemen, where the Lakeman shook the backstay. Hardly had he done so, when he was surrounded by the three junior mates and the four harpooneers, who all crowded him to the deck. But sliding down the ropes like baleful comets, the two Canallers rushed into the uproar, and sought to drag their man out of it towards the forecastle. Others of the sailors joined with them in this attempt, and a twisted turmoil ensued; while standing out of harm's way, the valiant captain danced up and down with a whale-pike, calling upon his officers to manhandle that atrocious scoundrel, and smoke him along to the quarter-deck. At intervals, he ran close up to the revolving border of the confusion, and prying into the heart of it with his pike, sought to prick out the object of his resentment. But Steelkilt and his desperadoes were too much for them all; they succeeded in gaining the forecastle deck, where, hastily slewing about three or four large casks in a line with the windlass, these sea-Parisians entrenched themselves behind the barricade.

" 'Come out of that, ye pirates!' roared the captain, now menacing them with a pistol in each hand, just brought to him by the steward. 'Come out of that, ye cut-throats!'

"Steelkilt leaped on the barricade, and striding up and down there, defied the worst the pistols could do; but gave the captain to understand distinctly, that his (Steelkilt's) death would be the signal for a murderous mutiny on the part of all hands. Fearing in his heart lest this might prove but too true, the captain a little desisted, but still commanded the insurgents instantly to return to their duty.

" 'Will you promise not to touch us, if we do?' demanded their ringleader.

" 'Turn to! turn to!—I make no promise;—to your duty! Do you want to sink the ship, by knocking off at a time like this? Turn to!' and he once more raised a pistol.

" 'Sink the ship?' cried Steelkilt. 'Aye, let her sink. Not a man of us turns to, unless you swear not to raise a rope-yarn against us. What say ye, men?' turning to his comrades. A fierce cheer was their response.

"The Lakeman now patrolled the barricade, all the while keeping his eye on the Captain, and jerking out such sentences as these:—'It's not our fault; we didn't want it; I told him to take his hammer away; it was boy's business; he might have known me before this; I told him not to prick the buffalo; I believe I have broken a finger here against his cursed jaw; ain't those mincing knives down in the forecastle there, men? look to those handspikes, my hearties. Captain, by God, look to yourself; say the word; don't be a fool; forget it all; we are ready to turn to; treat us decently, and we're your men; but we won't be flogged.'

" 'Turn to! I make no promises, turn to, I say!'

" 'Look ye, now,' cried the Lakeman, flinging out his arm towards him, 'there are a few of us here (and I am one of them) who have shipped for the cruise, d'ye see; now as you well know, sir, we can claim our discharge as soon as the anchor is down; so we don't want a row; it's not our interest; we want to be peaceable; we are ready to work, but we won't be flogged.'

" 'Turn to!' roared the Captain.

"Steelkilt glanced round him a moment, and then said:—'I tell you what it is now, Captain, rather than kill ye, and be hung for such a shabby rascal, we won't lift a hand against ye unless ye attack us; but till you say the word about not flogging us, we don't do a hand's turn.'

" 'Down into the forecastle then, down with ye, I'll keep ye there till ye're sick of it. Down ye go.'

" 'Shall we?' cried the ringleader to his men. Most of them were against it; but at length, in obedience to Steelkilt, they preceded him down into their dark den, growlingly disappearing, like bears into a cave.

"As the Lakeman's bare head was just level with the planks, the Captain and his posse leaped the barricade, and rapidly drawing over the slide of the scuttle, planted their group of hands upon it, and loudly called for the steward to bring the heavy brass padlock belonging to the companionway. Then opening the slide a little, the Captain whispered something down the crack, closed it, and turned the key upon them—ten in number—leaving on deck some twenty or more, who thus far had remained neutral.

"All night a wide-awake watch was kept by all the officers, forward and aft, especially about the forecastle scuttle and fore hatchway; at which last place it was feared the insurgents might emerge, after breaking through the bulkhead below. But the hours of darkness passed in peace; the men who still remained at their duty toiling hard at the pumps, whose clinking and clanking at intervals through the dreary night dismally resounded through the ship.

"At sunrise the Captain went forward, and knocking on the deck, summoned the prisoners to work; but with a yell they refused. Water was then lowered down to them, and a couple of handfuls of biscuit were tossed after it; when again turning the key upon them and pocketing it, the Captain returned to the quarter-deck. Twice every day for three days this was repeated; but on the fourth morning a confused wrangling, and then a scuffling was heard, as the customary summons was delivered; and suddenly four men burst up from the forecastle, saying they were ready to turn to. The fetid closeness of the air, and a famishing diet, united perhaps to some fears of ultimate retribution, had constrained them to surrender at discretion. Emboldened by this, the Captain reiterated his demand to the rest, but Steelkilt shouted up to him a terrific hint to stop his babbling and betake himself where he belonged. On the fifth morning three others of the mutineers bolted up into the air from the desperate arms below that sought to restrain them. Only three were left.

" 'Better turn to, now?' said the Captain with a heartless jeer.

" 'Shut us up again, will ye!' cried Steelkilt.

" 'Oh! certainly,' said the Captain, and the key clicked.

"It was at this point, gentlemen, that enraged by the defection of seven of his former associates, and stung by the mocking voice that had last hailed him, and maddened by his long entombment in a place as black as the bowels of despair; it was then that Steelkilt proposed to the two Canallers, thus far apparently of one mind with him, to burst out of their hole at the next summoning of the garrison; and armed with their keen mincing knives (long, crescentic, heavy implements with a handle at each end) run amuck from the bowsprit to the taffrail; and if by any devilishness of desperation possible, seize the ship. For himself, he would do this, he said, whether they joined him or not. That was the last night he should spend in that den. But the scheme met with no opposition on the part of the other two; they swore they were ready for that, or for any other mad thing, for anything in short but a surrender. And what was more, they each insisted upon being the first man on deck, when the time to make the rush should come. But to this their leader as fiercely objected, reserving that priority for himself; particularly as his two comrades would not yield, the one to the other, in the matter; and both of them could not be first, for the ladder would but admit one man at a time. And here, gentlemen, the foul play of these miscreants must come out.

"Upon hearing the frantic project of their leader, each in his own separate soul had suddenly lighted, it would seem, upon the same piece of treachery, namely: to be foremost in breaking out, in order to be the first of the three, though the last of the ten, to surrender; and thereby secure whatever small chance of pardon such conduct might merit. But when Steelkilt made known his determination still to lead them to the last, they in some way, by some subtle chemistry of villany, mixed their before secret treacheries together; and when their leader fell into a doze, verbally opened their souls to each other in three sentences; and bound the sleeper with cords, and gagged him with cords; and shrieked out for the Captain at midnight.

"Thinking murder at hand, and smelling in the dark for the blood, he and all his armed mates and harpooneers rushed for the forecastle. In a few minutes the scuttle was opened, and, bound hand and foot, the still struggling ringleader was shoved up into the air by his perfidious allies, who at once claimed the honor of securing a man who had been fully ripe for murder. But all these were collared, and dragged along the deck like dead cattle; and, side by side, were seized up into the mizzen rigging, like three quarters of meat, and there they hung till morning. 'Damn ye,' cried the Captain, pacing to and fro before them, 'the vultures would not touch ye, ye villains!'

"At sunrise he summoned all hands; and separating those who had rebelled from those who had taken no part in the mutiny, he told the former that he had a good mind to flog them all round—thought, upon the whole, he would do so—he ought to—justice demanded it; but for the present, considering their timely surrender, he would let them go with a reprimand, which he accordingly administered in the vernacular.

" 'But as for you, ye carrion rogues,' turning to the three men in the rigging —'for you, I mean to mince ye up for the try-pots;' and, seizing a rope, he applied it with all his might to the backs of the two traitors, till they yelled no more, but lifelessly hung their heads sideways, as the two crucified thieves are drawn.

" 'My wrist is sprained with ye!' he cried, at last; 'but there is still rope enough left for you, my fine bantam, that wouldn't give up. Take that gag from his mouth, and let us hear what he can say for himself.'

"For a moment the exhausted mutineer made a tremulous motion of his cramped jaws, and then painfully twisting round his head, said in a sort of hiss, 'What I say is this—and mind it well—if you flog me, I murder you!'

" 'Say ye so? then see how ye frighten me'—and the Captain drew off with the rope to strike.

" 'Best not,' hissed the Lakeman.

" 'But I must,'—and the rope was once more drawn back for the stroke.

"Steelkilt here hissed out something, inaudible to all but the Captain; who, to the amazement of all hands, started back, paced the deck rapidly two or three times, and then suddenly throwing down his rope, said, 'I won't do it— let him go—cut him down: d'ye hear?'

But as the junior mates were hurrying to execute the order, a pale man, with a bandaged head, arrested them—Radney the chief mate. Ever since the blow, he had lain in his berth; but that morning, hearing the tumult on the deck, he had crept out, and thus far had watched the whole scene. Such was the state of his mouth, that he could hardly speak; but mumbling something about *his* being willing and able to do what the captain dared not attempt, he snatched the rope and advanced to his pinioned foe.

" 'You are a coward!' hissed the Lakeman.

" 'So I am, but take that.' The mate was in the very act of striking, when another hiss stayed his uplifted arm. He paused: and then pausing no more, made good his word, spite of Steelkilt's threat, whatever that might have been. The three men were then cut down, all hands were turned to, and, sullenly worked by the moody seamen, the iron pumps clanged as before.

"Just after dark that day, when one watch had retired below, a clamor was heard in the forecastle; and the two trembling traitors running up, besieged the cabin door, saying they durst not consort with the crew. Entreaties, cuffs, and kicks could not drive them back, so at their own instance they were put down in the ship's run for salvation. Still, no sign of mutiny reappeared among the rest. On the contrary, it seemed, that mainly at Steelkilt's instigation, they had resolved to maintain the strictest peacefulness, obey all orders to the last, and, when the ship reached port, desert her in a body. But in order to insure the speediest end to the voyage, they all agreed to another thing—namely, not to sing out for whales, in case any should be discovered. For, spite of her leak, and spite of all her other perils, the Town-Ho still maintained her mast-heads, and her captain was just as willing to lower for a fish that moment, as on the day his craft first struck the cruising ground; and Radney the mate was quite as ready to change his berth for a boat, and with his bandaged mouth seek to gag in death the vital jaw of the whale.

"But though the Lakeman had induced the seamen to adopt this sort of passiveness in their conduct, he kept his own counsel (at least till all was over) concerning his own proper and private revenge upon the man who had stung him in the ventricles of his heart. He was in Radney the chief mate's watch; and as if the infatuated man sought to run more than half way to meet his doom, after the scene at the rigging, he insisted, against the express counsel of the captain, upon resuming the head of his watch at night. Upon this, and one or two other circumstances, Steelkilt systematically built the plan of his revenge.

"During the night, Radney had an unseamanlike way of sitting on the bulwarks of the quarterdeck, and leaning his arm upon the gunwale of the boat which was hoisted up there, a little above the ship's side. In this attitude, it was well known, he sometimes dozed. There was a considerable vacancy between the boat and the ship, and down between this was the sea. Steelkilt calculated his time, and found that his next trick at the helm would come round at two o'clock, in the morning of the third day from that in which he had been betrayed. At his leisure, he employed the interval in braiding something very carefully in his watches below.

" 'What are you making there?' said a shipmate.

" 'What do you think? what does it look like?'

" 'Like a lanyard for your bag; but it's an odd one, seems to me.'

" 'Yes, rather oddish,' said the Lakeman, holding it at arm's length before him; 'but I think it will answer. Shipmate, I haven't enough twine,—have you any?'

"But there was none in the forecastle.

" 'Then I must get some from old Rad;' and he rose to go aft.

" 'You don't mean to go a begging to *him!*' said a sailor.

" 'Why not? Do you think he won't do me a turn, when it's to help himself in the end, shipmate?' and going to the mate, he looked at him quietly, and asked him for some twine to mend his hammock. It was given him—neither twine nor lanyard were seen again; but the next night an iron ball, closely netted, partly rolled from the pocket of the Lakeman's monkey jacket, as he was tucking the coat into his hammock for a pillow. Twenty-four hours after, his trick at the silent helm—nigh to the man who was apt to doze over the grave always ready dug to the seaman's hand—that fatal hour was then to come; and in the fore-ordaining soul of Steelkilt, the mate was already stark and stretched as a corpse, with his forehead crushed in.

"But, gentlemen, a fool saved the would-be murderer from the bloody deed he had planned. Yet complete revenge he had, and without being the avenger. For by a mysterious fatality, Heaven itself seemed to step in to take out of his hands into its own the damning thing he would have done.

"It was just between daybreak and sunrise of the morning of the second day, when they were washing down the decks, that a stupid Teneriffe man, drawing water in the main-chains, all at once shouted out, 'There she rolls! there she rolls!' Jesu, what a whale! It was Moby-Dick.

" 'Moby-Dick!' cried Don Sebastian; "St. Dominic! Sir sailor, but do whales have christenings? Whom call you Moby-Dick?'

. " 'A very white, and famous, and most deadly immortal monster, Don;—but that would be too long a story.'

" 'How? how?' cried all the young Spaniards, crowding.

" 'Nay, Dons, Dons—nay, nay! I cannot rehearse that now. Let me get more into the air, Sirs.'

" 'The chicha! the chicha!' cried Don Pedro; 'our vigorous friend looks faint;—fill up his empty glass!'

"No need, gentlemen; one moment, and I proceed.—Now, gentlemen, so suddenly perceiving the snowy whale within fifty yards of the ship—forgetful of the compact among the crew—in the excitement of the moment, the Teneriffe man had instinctively and involuntarily lifted his voice for the monster, though for some little time past it had been plainly beheld from the three sullen mast-heads. All was now a phrensy. 'The White Whale—the White Whale!' was the cry from captain, mates, and harpooneers, who, undeterred by fearful rumours, were all anxious to capture so famous and precious a fish; while the dogged crew eyed askance, and with curses, the appalling beauty of the vast milky mass, that lit up by a horizontal spangling sun, shifted and glistened like a living opal in the blue morning sea. Gentlemen, a strange fatality pervades the whole career of these events, as if verily mapped out before the world itself was charted. The mutineer was the bowsman of the mate, and when fast to a fish, it was his duty to sit next him, while Radney stood up with his lance in the prow, and haul in or slacken the line, at the word of command. Moreover, when the four boats were lowered, the mate's got the start; and none howled more fiercely with delight than did Steelkilt, as he 'strained at his oar. After a stiff pull, their harpooneer got fast, and, spear in hand, Radney sprang to the bow. He was always a furious man, it seems, in a boat. And now his bandaged cry was, to beach him on the whale's topmost back. Nothing loath, his bowsman hauled him up and up, through a blinding foam that blent two whitenesses together; till of a sudden the boat struck as against a sunken ledge, and keeling over, spilled out the standing mate. That instant, as he fell on the whale's slippery back, the boat righted, and was dashed aside by the swell, while Radney was tossed over into the sea, on the other flank of the whale. He struck out through the spray, and, for an instant, was dimly seen through that veil, wildly seeking to remove himself from the eye of Moby-Dick. But the whale rushed round in a sudden maelstrom; seized the swimmer between his jaws; and rearing high up with him, plunged headlong again, and went down.

"Meantime, at the first tap of the boat's bottom, the Lakeman had slackened the line, so as to drop astern from the whirlpool; calmly looking on, he thought his own thoughts. But a sudden, terrific, downward jerking of the boat, quickly brought his knife to the line. He cut it; and the whale was free. But, at some distance, Moby-Dick rose again, with some tatters of Radney's red woollen shirt, caught in the teeth that had destroyed him. All four boats gave chase again; but the whale eluded them, and finally wholly disappeared.

"In good time, the Town-Ho reached her port—a savage, solitary place—where no civilized creature resided. There, headed by the Lakeman, all but five or six of the foremast-men deliberately deserted among the palms; eventually, as it turned out, seizing a large double war-canoe of the savages, and setting sail for some other harbor.

"The ship's company being reduced to but a handful, the captain called upon the Islanders to assist him in the laborious business of heaving down the ship to stop the leak. But to such unresting vigilance over their dangerous allies were this small band of whites necessitated, both by night and by day, and so extreme was the hard work they underwent, that upon the vessel being ready again for sea, they were in such a weakened condition that the captain durst not put off with them in so heavy a vessel. After taking counsel with his officers, he anchored the ship as far off shore as possible; loaded and ran out his two cannon from the bows; stacked his muskets on the poop; and warning the Islanders not to approach the ship at their peril, took one man with him, and setting the sail of his best whaleboat, steered straight before the wind for Tahiti, five hundred miles distant, to procure a reinforcement to his crew.

"On the fourth day of the sail, a large canoe was descried, which seemed to have touched at a low isle of corals. He steered away from it; but the savage craft bore down on him; and soon the voice of Steelkilt hailed him to heave to, or he would run him under water. The captain presented a pistol. With one foot on each prow of the yoked war-canoes, the Lakeman laughed him to scorn; assuring him that if the pistol so much as clicked in the lock, he would bury him in bubbles and foam.

" 'What do you want of me?' cried the captain.

" 'Where are you bound? and for what are you bound?' demanded Steelkilt; 'no lies.'

" 'I am bound to Tahiti for more men.'

" 'Very good. Let me board you a moment—I come in peace.' With that he leaped from the canoe, swam to the boat; and climbing the gunwale, stood face to face with the captain.

" 'Cross your arms, sir; throw back your head. Now, repeat after me. As soon as Steelkilt leaves me, I swear to beach this boat on yonder island, and remain there six days. If I do not, may lightnings strike me!'

" 'A pretty scholar,' laughed the Lakeman. 'Adios, Senor!' and leaping into the sea, he swam back to his comrades.

"Watching the boat till it was fairly beached, and drawn up to the roots of the cocoa-nut trees, Steelkilt made sail again, and in due time arrived at Tahiti, his own place of destination. There, luck befriended him; two ships were about to sail for France, and were providentially in want of precisely that number of men which the sailor headed. They embarked, and so for ever got the start of their former captain, had he been at all minded to work them legal retribution. Some ten days after the French ships sailed, the whale-boat arrived, and the captain was forced to enlist some of the more civilized Tahitians, who had been somewhat used to the sea. Chartering a small native schooner, he returned with them to his vessel; and finding all right there, again resumed his cruisings.

"Where Steelkilt now is, gentlemen, none know, but upon the island of Nantucket, the widow of Radney still turns to the sea which refuses to give up its dead; still in dreams sees the awful white whale that destroyed him. * * *

" 'Are you through?' said Don Sebastian, quietly.

" 'I am, Don.'

" 'Then I entreat you, tell me if to the best of your own convictions, this your story is in substance really true? It is so passing wonderful! Did you get it from an unquestionable source? Bear with me if I seem to press.'

" 'Also bear with all of us, sir sailor; for we all join in Don Sebastian's suit,' cried the company, with exceeding interest.

" 'Is there a copy of the Holy Evangelists in the Golden Inn, gentlemen?'

" 'Nay,' said Don Sebastian; 'but I know a worthy priest near by, who will quickly procure one for me. I go for it; but are you well advised? this may grow too serious.'

" 'Will you be so good as to bring the priest also, Don?'

" 'Though there are no Auto-da-Fés in Lima now,' said one of the company to another; 'I fear our sailor friend runs risk of the archiepiscopacy. Let us withdraw more out of the moonlight. I see no need of this.'

" 'Excuse me for running after you, Don Sebastian; but may I also beg that you will be particular in procuring the largest sized Evangelists you can.'

*   *   *   *   *

" 'This is the priest, he brings you the Evangelists,' said Don Sebastian, gravely, returning with a tall and solemn figure.

" 'Let me remove my hat. Now, venerable priest, further into the light, and hold the Holy Book before me that I may touch it.

" 'So help me Heaven, and on my honor the story I have told ye, gentlemen, is in substance and its great items, true. I know it to be true; it happened on this ball; I trod the ship; I knew the crew; I have seen and talked with Steelkilt since the death of Radney.' "

CHAPTER LV

OF THE MONSTROUS PICTURES OF WHALES

I SHALL ere long paint to you as well as one can without canvas, something like the true form of the whale as he actually appears to the eye of the whale-man when in his own absolute body the whale is moored alongside the whale-ship so that he can be fairly stepped upon there. It may be worth while, therefore, previously to advert to those curious imaginary portraits of him which even down to the present day confidently challenge the faith of the landsman. It is time to set the world right in this matter, by proving such pictures of the whale all wrong.

It may be that the primal source of all those pictorial delusions will be found among the oldest Hindoo, Egyptian, and Grecian sculptures. For ever since those inventive but unscrupulous times when on the marble panellings of temples, the pedestals of statues, and on shields, medallions, cups, and coins, the dolphin was drawn in scales of chain-armor like Saladin's, and a helmeted head like St. George's; ever since then has something of the same sort of license prevailed, not only in most popular pictures of the whale, but in many scientific presentations of him.

Now, by all odds, the most ancient extant portrait anyways purporting to be the whale's, is to be found in the famous cavern-pagoda of Elephanta, in India. The Brahmins maintain that in the almost endless sculptures of that immemorial pagoda, all the trades and pursuits, every conceivable avocation of man, were prefigured ages before any of them actually came into being. No wonder then, that in some sort our noble profession of whaling should have been there shadowed forth. The Hindoo whale referred to, occurs in a separate department of the wall, depicting the incarnation of Vishnu in the form of leviathan, learnedly known as the Matse Avatar. But though this sculpture is half man and half whale, so as only to give the tail of the latter, yet that small section of him is all wrong. It looks more like the tapering tail of an anaconda, than the broad palms of the true whale's majestic flukes.

But go to the old Galleries, and look now at a great Christian painter's portrait of this fish; for he succeeds no better than the antediluvian Hindoo. It is Guido's picture of Perseus rescuing Andromeda from the sea-monster or whale. Where did Guido get the model of such a strange creature as that? Nor does Hogarth, in painting the same scene in his own "Perseus Descending," make out one whit better. The huge corpulence of that Hogarthian monster undulates on the surface, scarcely drawing one inch of water. It has a sort of howdah on its back, and its distended tusked mouth into which the billows are rolling, might be taken for the Traitors' Gate leading from the Thames by water into the Tower. Then, there are the Prodromus whales of old Scotch Sibbald, and Jonah's whale, as depicted in the prints of old Bibles and the cuts of old primers. What shall be said of these? As for the book-binder's whale winding like a vine-stalk round the stock of a descending anchor—as stamped and gilded on the backs and title-pages of many books both old and new—that is a very picturesque but purely fabulous creature, imitated, I take it, from the like figures on antique vases. Though universally denominated a dolphin, I nevertheless call this book-binder's fish an attempt at a whale; because it was so intended when the device was first introduced. It was introduced by an old Italian publisher somewhere about the 15th century, during the Revival of Learning; and in those days, and even down to a comparatively late period, dolphins were popularly supposed to be a species of the Leviathan.

In the vignettes and other embellishments of some ancient books you will at times meet with very curious touches at the whale, where all manner of spouts, jets d'eau, hot springs and cold, Saratoga and Baden-Baden, come bubbling up from his unexhausted brain. In the title-page of the original edition of the "Advancement of Learning" you will find some curious whales.

But quitting all these unprofessional attempts, let us glance at those pictures of leviathan purporting to be sober, scientific delineations, by those who know. In old Harris's collection of voyages there are some plates of whales extracted from a Dutch book of voyages, A. D. 1671, entitled "A Whaling Voyage to Spitzbergen in the ship Jonas in the Whale, Peter Peterson of Friesland, master." In one of those plates the whales, like great rafts of logs, are represented lying among ice-isles, with white bears running over their living backs. In another plate, the prodigious blunder is made of representing the whale with perpendicular flukes.

Then again, there is an imposing quarto, written by one Captain Colnett, a Post Captain in the English navy, entitled "A Voyage round Cape Horn into the South Seas, for the purpose of extending the Spermaceti Whale Fisheries." In this book is an outline purporting to be a "Picture of a Physeter or Spermaceti whale, drawn by scale from one killed on the coast of Mexico, August, 1793, and hoisted on deck." I doubt not the captain had this veracious picture taken for the benefit of his marines. To mention but one thing about it, let me say that it has an eye which applied, according to the accompanying scale, to a full grown sperm whale, would make the eye of that whale a bow-window some five feet long. Ah, my gallant captain, why did ye not give us Jonah looking out of that eye!

Nor are the most conscientious compilations of Natural History for the benefit of the young and tender, free from the same heinousness of mistake. Look at that popular work "Goldsmith's Animated Nature." In the abridged London edition of 1807, there are plates of an alleged "whale" and a "narwhale." I do not wish to seem inelegant, but this unsightly whale looks much like an amputated sow; and, as for the narwhale, one glimpse at it is enough to amaze one, that in this nineteenth century such a hippogriff could be palmed for genuine upon any intelligent public of schoolboys.

Then, again, in 1825, Bernard Germain, Count de Lacépède, a great naturalist, published a scientific systemized whale book, wherein are several pictures of the different species of the Leviathan. All these are not only incorrect, but the picture of the Mysticetus or Greenland whale (that is to say, the Right whale), even Scoresby, a long experienced man as touching that species, declares not to have its counterpart in nature.

But the placing of the cap-sheaf to all this blundering business was reserved for the scientific Frederick Cuvier, brother to the famous Baron. In 1836, he published a Natural History of Whales, in which he gives what he calls a picture of the Sperm Whale. Before showing that picture to any Nantucketer, you had best provide for your summary retreat from Nantucket. In a word, Frederick Cuvier's Sperm Whale is not a Sperm Whale, but a squash. Of course, he never had the benefit of a whaling voyage (such men seldom have), but whence he derived that picture, who can tell? Perhaps he got it as his scientific predecessor in the same field, Desmarest, got one of his authentic abortions; that is, from a Chinese drawing. And what sort of lively lads with the pencil those Chinese are, many queer cups and saucers inform us.

As for the sign-painters' whales seen in the streets hanging over the shops of oil-dealers, what shall be said of them? They are generally Richard III. whales, with dromedary humps, and very savage; breakfasting on three or four sailor tarts, that is whaleboats full of mariners: their deformities floundering in seas of blood and blue paint.

But these manifold mistakes in depicting the whale are not so very surprising after all. Consider! Most of the scientific drawings have been taken from the stranded fish; and these are about as correct as a drawing of a wrecked ship, with broken back, would correctly represent the noble animal itself in all its undashed pride of hull and spars. Though elephants have stood for their full-lengths, the living Leviathan has never yet fairly floated himself for his portrait. The living whale, in his full majesty and significance, is only to be seen at sea in unfathomable waters; and afloat the vast bulk of him is out of sight, like a launched line-of-battle ship; and out of that element it is a thing eternally impossible for mortal man to hoist him bodily into the air, so as to preserve all his mighty swells and undulations. And, not to speak of the highly presumable difference of contour between a young sucking whale and a full-grown Platonian Leviathan; yet, even in the case of one of those young sucking whales hoisted to a ship's deck, such is then the outlandish, eel-like, limbered, varying shape of him, that his precise expression the devil himself could not catch.

But it may be fancied, that from the naked skeleton of the stranded whale, accurate hints may be derived touching his true form. Not at all. For it is one of the more curious things about this Leviathan, that his skeleton gives very little idea of his general shape. Though Jeremy Bentham's skeleton, which hangs for candelabra in the library of one of his executors, correctly conveys the idea of a burly-browed utilitarian old gentleman, with all Jeremy's other leading personal characteristics; yet nothing of this kind could be inferred from any leviathan's articulated bones. In fact, as the great Hunter says, the mere skeleton of the whale bears the same relation to the fully invested and padded animal as the insect does to the chrysalis that so roundingly envelopes it. This peculiarity is strikingly evinced in the head, as in some part of this book will be incidentally shown. It is also very curiously displayed in the side fin, the bones of which almost exactly answer to the bones of the human hand, minus only the thumb. This fin has four regular bone-fingers, the index, middle, ring, and little finger. But all these are permanently lodged in their fleshy covering, as the human fingers in an artificial covering. "However recklessly the whale may sometimes serve us," said humorous Stubb one day, "he can never be truly said to handle us without mittens."

For all these reasons, then, any way you may look at it, you must needs conclude that the great Leviathan is that one creature in the world which must remain unpainted to the last. True, one portrait may hit the mark much nearer than another, but none can hit it with any very considerable degree of exactness. So there is no earthly way of finding out precisely what the whale really looks like. And the only mode in which you can derive even a tolerable idea of his living contour, is by going a whaling yourself; but by so doing, you run no small risk of being eternally stove and sunk by him. Wherefore, it seems to me you had best not be too fastidious in your curiosity touching this Leviathan.

CHAPTER LVI

OF THE LESS ERRONEOUS PICTURES OF WHALES, AND THE TRUE PICTURES OF WHALING SCENES

IN connexion with the monstrous pictures of whales, I am strongly tempted here to enter upon those still more monstrous stories of them which are to be found in certain books, both ancient and modern, especially in Pliny, Purchas, Hackluyt, Harris, Cuvier, &c. But I pass that matter by.

I know of only four published outlines of the great Sperm Whale; Colnett's, Huggins's, Frederick Cuvier's, and Beale's. In the previous chapter Colnett and Cuvier have been referred to. Huggins's is far better than theirs; but, by great odds, Beale's is the best. All Beale's drawings of this whale are good, excepting the middle figure in the picture of three whales in various attitudes, capping his second chapter. His frontispiece, boats attacking Sperm Whales, though no doubt calculated to excite the civil scepticism of some parlor men, is admirably correct and lifelike in its general effect. Some of the Sperm Whale drawings in J. Ross Browne are pretty correct in contour; but they are wretchedly engraved. That is not his fault though.

Of the Right Whale, the best outline pictures are in Scoresby; but they are drawn on too small a scale to convey a desirable impression. He has but one picture of whaling scenes, and this is a sad deficiency, because it is by such pictures only, when at all well done, that you can derive anything like a truthful idea of the living whale as seen by his living hunters.

But, taken for all in all, by far the finest, though in some details not the most correct, presentations of whales and whaling scenes to be anywhere found,

are two large French engravings, well executed, and taken from paintings by
one Garnery. Respectively, they represent attacks on the Sperm and Right
Whale. In the first engraving a noble Sperm Whale is depicted in full majesty
of might, just risen beneath the boat from the profundities of the ocean, and
bearing high in the air upon his back the terrific wreck of the stoven planks.
The prow of the boat is partially unbroken, and is drawn just balancing upon
the monster's spine; and standing in that prow, for that one single incom-
putable flash of time, you behold an oarsman, half shrouded by the incensed
boiling spout of the whale, and in the act of leaping, as if from a precipice.
The action of the whole thing is wonderfully good and true. The half-emptied
line-tub floats on the whitened sea; the wooden poles of the spilled harpoons
obliquely bob in it; the heads of the swimming crew are scattered about the
whale in contrasting expressions of affright; while in the black stormy distance
the ship is bearing down upon the scene. Serious fault might be found with
the anatomical details of this whale, but let that pass; since, for the life of
me, I could not draw so good a one.

In the second engraving, the boat is in the act of drawing alongside the
barnacled flank of a large running Right Whale, that rolls his black weedy
bulk in the sea like some mossy rock-slide from the Patagonian cliffs. His
jets are erect, full, and black like soot; so that from so abounding a smoke
in the chimney, you would think there must be a brave supper cooking in the
great bowels below. Sea fowls are pecking at the small crabs, shell-fish, and
other sea candies and maccaroni, which the Right Whale sometimes carries
on his pestilent back. And all the while the thick-lipped leviathan is rushing
through the deep, leaving tons of tumultuous white curds in his wake, and
causing the slight boat to rock in the swells like a skiff caught nigh the paddle-
wheels of an ocean steamer. Thus, the fore-ground is all raging commotion;
but behind, in admirable artistic contrast, is the glassy level of a sea becalmed,
the drooping unstarched sails of the powerless ship, and the inert mass of a
dead whale, a conquered fortress, with the flag of capture lazily hanging from
the whale-pole inserted into his spout-hole.

Who Garnery the painter is, or was, I know not. But my life for it he
was either practically conversant with his subject, or else marvellously tutored
by some experienced whaleman. The French are the lads for painting action.
Go and gaze upon all the paintings of Europe, and where will you find such
a gallery of living and breathing commotion on canvas, as in that triumphal
hall at Versailles; where the beholder fights his way, pell-mell, through the
consecutive great battles of France; where every sword seems a flash of the
Northern Lights, and the successive armed kings and Emperors dash by, like a
charge of crowned centaurs? Not wholly unworthy of a place in that gallery,
are these sea battle-pieces of Garnery.

The natural aptitude of the French for seizing the picturesqueness of things
seems to be peculiarly evinced in what paintings and engravings they have of
their whaling scenes. With not one tenth of England's experience in the fishery,
and not the thousandth part of that of the Americans, they have nevertheless
furnished both nations with the only finished sketches at all capable of conveying
the real spirit of the whale hunt. For the most part, the English and American whale draughtsmen seem entirely content with presenting the mechanical
outline of things, such as the vacant profile of the whale; which, so far as picturesqueness of effect is concerned, is about tantamount to sketching the profile of a pyramid. Even Scoresby, the justly renowned Right whaleman, after
giving us a stiff full length of the Greenland whale, and three or four delicate

miniatures of narwhales and porpoises, treats us to a series of classical engravings of boat hooks, chopping knives, and grapnels; and with the microscopic diligence of a Leuwenhoeck submits to the inspection of a shivering world ninety-six fac-similes of magnified Arctic snow crystals. I mean no disparagement to the excellent voyager (I honor him for a veteran), but in so important a matter it was certainly an oversight not to have procured for every crystal a sworn affidavit taken before a Greenland Justice of the Peace.

In addition to those fine engravings from Garnery, there are two other French engravings worthy of note, by some one who subscribes himself "H. Durand." One of them, though not precisely adapted to our present purpose, nevertheless deserves mention on other accounts. It is a quiet noon-scene among the isles of the Pacific; a French whaler anchored, inshore, in a calm, and lazily taking water on board; the loosened sails of the ship, and the long leaves of the palms in the background, both drooping together in the breezeless air. The effect is very fine, when considered with reference to its presenting the hardy fishermen under one of their few aspects of oriental repose. The other engraving is quite a different affair: the ship hove-to upon the open sea, and in the very heart of the Leviathanic life, with a Right Whale alongside; the vessel (in the act of cutting-in) hove over to the monster as if to a quay; and a boat, hurriedly pushing off from this scene of activity, is about giving chase to whales in the distance. The harpoons and lances lie levelled for use; three oarsmen are just setting the mast in its hole; while from a sudden roll of the sea, the little craft stands half-erect out of the water, like a rearing horse. From that ship, the smoke of the torments of the boiling whale is going up like the smoke over a village of smithies; and to windward, a black cloud, rising up with earnest of squalls and rains, seems to quicken the activity of the excited seamen.

CHAPTER LVII

OF WHALES IN PAINT; IN TEETH; IN WOOD; IN SHEET-IRON; IN STONE; IN MOUNTAINS; IN STARS

ON Tower-hill, as you go down to the London docks, you may have seen a crippled beggar (or kedger, as the sailors say) holding a painted board before him, representing the tragic scene in which he lost his leg. There are three whales and three boats; and one of the boats (presumed to contain the missing leg in all its original integrity) is being crunched by the jaws of the foremost whale. Any time these ten years, they tell me, has that man held up that picture, and exhibited that stump to an incredulous world. But the time of his justification has now come. His three whales are as good whales as were ever published in Wapping, at any rate; and his stump as unquestionable a stump as any you will find in the western clearings. But, though for ever mounted on that stump, never a stump-speech does the poor whaleman make; but, with downcast eyes, stands ruefully contemplating his own amputation.

Throughout the Pacific, and also in Nantucket, and New Bedford, and Sag Harbor, you will come across lively sketches of whales and whaling-scenes, graven by the fishermen themselves on Sperm Whale-teeth, or ladies' busks wrought out of the Right Whale-bone, and other like skrimshander articles, as the whalemen call the numerous little ingenious contrivances they elaborately carve out of the rough material, in their hours of ocean leisure. Some of them have little boxes of dentistical-looking implements, specially intended for the skrimshandering business. But, in general, they toil with their jack-knives alone; and, with that almost omnipotent tool of the sailor, they will turn you out anything you please, in the way of a mariner's fancy.

Long exile from Christendom and civilization inevitably restores a man to that condition in which God placed him, *i. e.* what is called savagery. Your true whale-hunter is as much a savage as an Iroquois. I myself am a savage, owning no allegiance but to the King of the Cannibals; and ready at any moment to rebel against him. Now, one of the peculiar characteristics of the savage in his domestic hours, is his wonderful patience of industry. An ancient Hawaiian war-club or spear-paddle, in its full multiplicity and elaboration of carving, is as great a trophy of human perseverance as a Latin lexicon. For, with but a bit of broken sea-shell or a shark's tooth, that miraculous intricacy of wooden network has been achieved; and it has cost steady years of steady application.

As with the Hawaiian savage, so with the white sailor-savage. With the same marvellous patience, and with the same single shark's tooth, of his one poor jack-knife, he will carve you a bit of bone sculpture, not quite as workmanlike, but as close packed in its maziness of design, as the Greek savage, Achilles's shield; and full of barbaric spirit and suggestiveness, as the prints of that fine old Dutch savage, Albert Durer.

Wooden whales, or whales cut in profile out of the small dark slabs of the noble South Sea warwood, are frequently met with in the forecastles of American whalers. Some of them are done with much accuracy.

At some old gable-roofed country houses you will see brass whales hung by the tail for knockers to the road-side door. When the porter is sleepy, the anvil-headed whale would be best. But these knocking whales are seldom remarkable as faithful essays. On the spires of some old-fashioned churches you will see sheet-iron whales placed there for weather-cocks; but they are so elevated, and besides that are to all intents and purposes so labelled with *"Hands off!"* you cannot examine them closely enough to decide upon their merit.

In bony, ribby regions of the earth, where at the base of high broken cliffs masses of rock lie strewn in fantastic groupings upon the plain, you will often discover images as of the petrified forms of the Leviathan partly merged in grass, which of a windy day breaks against them in a surf of green surges.

Then, again, in mountainous countries where the traveller is continually girdled by amphitheatrical heights; here and there from some lucky point of view you will catch passing glimpses of the profiles of whales defined along the undulating ridges. But you must be a thorough whaleman, to see these sights; and not only that, but if you wish to return to such a sight again, you must be sure and take the exact intersecting latitude and longitude of your first stand-point, else so chance-like are such observations of the hills, that your precise, previous stand-point would require a laborious re-discovery; like the Soloma islands, which still remain incognita, though once high-ruffed Mendanna trod them and old Figuera chronicled them.

Nor when expandingly lifted by your subject, can you fail to trace out great whales in the starry heavens, and boats in pursuit of them; as when long filled with thoughts of war the Eastern nations saw armies locked in battle among the clouds. Thus at the North have I chased Leviathan round and round the Pole with the revolutions of the bright points that first defined him to me. And beneath the effulgent Antarctic skies I have boarded the Argo-

Navis, and joined the chase against the starry Cetus far beyond the utmost stretch of Hydrus and the Flying Fish.

With a frigate's anchors for my bridle-bitts and fasces of harpoons for spurs, would I could mount that whale and leap the topmost skies, to see whether the fabled heavens with all their countless tents really lie encamped beyond my mortal sight!

CHAPTER LVIII

BRIT

STEERING north-eastward from the Crozetts, we fell in with vast meadows of brit, the minute, yellow substance, upon which the Right Whale largely feeds. For leagues and leagues it undulated round us, so that we seemed to be sailing through boundless fields of ripe and golden wheat.

On the second day, numbers of Right Whales were seen, who, secure from the attack of a Sperm Whaler like the Pequod, with open jaws sluggishly swam through the brit, which, adhering to the fringing fibres of that wondrous Venetian blind in their mouths, was in that manner separated from the water that escaped at the lip.

As morning mowers, who side by side slowly and seethingly advance their scythes through the long wet grass of marshy meads; even so these monsters swam, making a strange, grassy, cutting sound; and leaving behind them endless swaths of blue upon the yellow sea.

But it was only the sound they made as they parted the brit which at all reminded one of mowers. Seen from the mast-heads, especially when they paused and were stationary for a while, their vast black forms looked more like lifeless masses of rock than anything else. And as in the great hunting countries of India, the stranger at a distance will sometimes pass on the plains recumbent elephants without knowing them to be such, taking them for bare, blackened elevations of the soil; even so, often, with him, who for the first time beholds this species of the leviathans of the sea. And even when recognised at last, their immense magnitude renders it very hard really to believe that such bulky masses of overgrowth can possibly be instinct, in all parts, with the same sort of life that lives in a dog or a horse.

Indeed, in other respects, you can hardly regard any creatures of the deep with the same feelings that you do those of the shore. For though some old naturalists have maintained that all creatures of the land are of their kind in the sea; and though taking a broad general view of the thing, this may very well be; yet coming to specialties, where, for example, does the ocean furnish any fish that in disposition answers to the sagacious kindness of the dog? The accursed shark alone can in any generic respect be said to bear comparative analogy to him.

But though, to landsmen in general, the native inhabitants of the seas have ever been regarded with emotions unspeakably unsocial and repelling; though we know the sea to be an everlasting terra incognita, so that Columbus sailed over numberless unknown worlds to discover his one superficial western one; though, by vast odds, the most terrific of all mortal disasters have immemorially and indiscriminately befallen tens and hundreds of thousands of those who have gone upon the waters; though but a moment's consideration will teach, that however baby man may brag of his science and skill, and however much, in a flattering future, that science and skill may augment; yet for ever and for ever, to the crack of doom, the sea will insult and murder him, and pulverize the stateliest, stiffest frigate he can make; nevertheless, by the continual repetition of these very impressions, man has lost that sense of the full awfulness of the sea which aboriginally belongs to it.

The first boat we read of, floated on an ocean, that with Portuguese vengeance had whelmed a whole world without leaving so much as a widow. That same ocean rolls now; that same ocean destroyed the wrecked ships of last year. Yea, foolish mortals, Noah's flood is not yet subsided; two thirds of the fair world it yet covers.

Wherein differ the sea and the land, that a miracle upon one is not a miracle upon the other? Preternatural terrors rested upon the Hebrews, when under the feet of Korah and his company the live ground opened and swallowed them up for ever; yet not a modern sun ever sets, but in precisely the same manner the live sea swallows up ships and crews.

But not only is the sea such a foe to man who is an alien to it, but it is also a fiend to its own offspring; worse than the Persian host who murdered his own guests; sparing not the creatures which itself hath spawned. Like a savage tigress that tossing in the jungle overlays her own cubs, so the sea dashes even the mightiest whales against the rocks, and leaves them there side by side with the split wrecks of ships. No mercy, no power but its own controls it. Panting and snorting like a mad battle steed that has lost its rider, the masterless ocean overruns the globe.

Consider the subtleness of the sea; how its most dreaded creatures glide under water, unapparent for the most part, and treacherously hidden beneath the loveliest tints of azure. Consider also the devilish brilliance and beauty of many of its most remorseless tribes, as the dainty embellished shape of many species of sharks. Consider, once more, the universal cannibalism of the sea; all whose creatures prey upon each other, carrying on eternal war since the world began.

Consider all this; and then turn to this green, gentle, and most docile earth; consider them both, the sea and the land; and do you not find a strange analogy to something in yourself? For as this appalling ocean surrounds the verdant land, so in the soul of man there lies one insular Tahiti, full of peace and joy, but encompassed by all the horrors of the half known life. God help thee! Push not off from that isle, thou canst never return!

CHAPTER LIX

SQUID

SLOWLY wading through the meadows of brit, the Pequod still held on her way north-eastward towards the island of Java; a gentle air impelling her keel, so that in the surrounding serenity her three tall tapering masts mildly waved to that languid breeze, as three mild palms on a plain. And still, at wide intervals in the silvery night, the lonely, alluring jet would be seen.

But one transparent blue morning, when a stillness almost preternatural spread over the sea, however unattended with any stagnant calm; when the long burnished sun-glade on the waters seemed a golden finger laid across them, enjoining some secrecy; when the slippered waves whispered together as they softly ran on; in this profound hush of the visible sphere a strange spectre was seen by Daggoo from the main-mast-head.

In the distance, a great white mass lazily rose, and rising higher and higher, and disentangling itself from the azure, at last gleamed before our prow like a snow-slide, new slid from the hills. Thus glistening for a moment, as slowly it subsided, and sank. Then once more arose, and silently gleamed. It seemed not a whale; and yet is this Moby-Dick? thought Daggoo. Again the phantom went down, but on re-appearing once more, with a stiletto-like cry that startled every man from his nod, the negro yelled out—"There! there again! there she breaches! right ahead! The White Whale, the White Whale!"

Upon this, the seamen rushed to the yard-arms, as in swarming-time the bees rush to the boughs. Bare-headed in the sultry sun, Ahab stood on the bowsprit, and with one hand pushed far behind in readiness to wave his orders to the helmsman, cast his eager glance in the direction indicated aloft by the outstretched motionless arm of Daggoo.

Whether the flitting attendance of the one still and solitary jet had gradually worked upon Ahab, so that he was now prepared to connect the ideas of mildness and repose with the first sight of the particular whale he pursued; however this was, or whether his eagerness betrayed him; whichever way it might have been, no sooner did he distinctly perceive the white mass, than with a quick intensity he instantly gave orders for lowering.

The four boats were soon on the water; Ahab's in advance, and all swiftly pulling towards their prey. Soon it went down, and while, with oars suspended, we were awaiting its reappearance, lo! in the same spot where it sank, once more it slowly rose. Almost forgetting for the moment all thoughts of Moby-Dick, we now gazed at the most wondrous phenomenon which the secret seas have hitherto revealed to mankind. A vast pulpy mass, furlongs in length and breadth, of a glancing cream-color, lay floating on the water, innumerable long arms radiating from its centre, and curling and twisting like a nest of anacondas, as if blindly to catch at any hapless object within reach. No perceptible face or front did it have; no conceivable token of either sensation or instinct; but undulated there on the billows, an unearthly, formless, chance-like apparition of life.

As with a low sucking sound it slowly disappeared again, Starbuck still gazing at the agitated waters where it had sunk, with a wild voice exclaimed—"Almost rather had I seen Moby-Dick and fought him, than to have seen thee, thou white ghost!"

"What was it, Sir?" said Flask.

"The great live squid, which, they say, few whale-ships ever beheld, and returned to their ports to tell of it."

But Ahab said nothing; turning his boat, he sailed back to the vessel; the rest as silently following.

Whatever superstitions the sperm whalemen in general have connected with the sight of this object, certain it is, that a glimpse of it being so very unusual, that circumstance has gone far to invest it with portentousness. So rarely is it beheld, that though one and all of them declare it to be the largest animated thing in the ocean, yet very few of them have any but the most vague ideas concerning its true nature and form; notwithstanding, they believe it to furnish to the sperm whale his only food. For though other species of whales find their food above water, and may be seen by man in the act of feeding, the spermaceti

whale obtains his whole food in unknown zones below the surface; and only by
inference is it that any one can tell of what, precisely, that food consists. At
times, when closely pursued, he will disgorge what are supposed to be the detached arms of the squid; some of them thus exhibited exceeding twenty and
thirty feet in length. They fancy that the monster to which these arms belonged ordinarily clings by them to the bed of the ocean; and that the sperm
whale, unlike other species, is supplied with teeth in order to attack and tear it.

There seems some ground to imagine that the great Kraken of Bishop
Pontoppodan may ultimately resolve itself into Squid. The manner in which
the Bishop describes it, as alternately rising and sinking, with some other particulars he narrates, in all this the two correspond. But much abatement is
necessary with respect to the incredible bulk he assigns it.

By some naturalists who have vaguely heard rumors of the mysterious creature, here spoken of, it is included among the class of cuttle-fish, to which, indeed, in certain external respects it would seem to belong, but only as the Anak
of the tribe

CHAPTER LX

THE LINE

WITH reference to the whaling scene shortly to be described, as well as for the
better understanding of all similar scenes elsewhere presented, I have here to
speak of the magical, sometimes horrible whale-line.

The line originally used in the fishery was of the best hemp, slightly vapored
with tar, not impregnated with it, as in the case of ordinary ropes; for while
tar, as ordinarily used, makes the hemp more pliable to the rope-maker, and
also renders the rope itself more convenient to the sailor for common ship use;
yet, not only would the ordinary quantity too much stiffen the whale-line for
the close coiling to which it must be subjected: but as most seamen are beginning to learn, tar in general by no means adds to the rope's durability or
strength, however much it may give it compactness and gloss.

Of late years the Manilla rope has in the American fishery almost entirely
superseded hemp as a material for whale-lines; for, though not so durable as
hemp, it is stronger, and far more soft and elastic; and I will add (since there
is an æsthetics in all things), is much more handsome and becoming to the boat,
than hemp. Hemp is a dusky, dark fellow, a sort of Indian; but Manilla is as
a golden-haired Circassian to behold.

The whale line is only two thirds of an inch in thickness. At first sight, you
would not think it so strong as it really is. By experiment its one and fifty
yarns will each suspend a weight of one hundred and twenty pounds; so that
the whole rope will bear a strain nearly equal to three tons. In length, the
common sperm whale-line measures something over two hundred fathoms.
Towards the stern of the boat it is spirally coiled away in the tub, not like the
worm-pipe of a still though, but so as to form one round, cheese-shaped mass of
densely bedded "sheaves," or layers of concentric spiralizations, without any
hollow but the "heart," or minute vertical tube formed at the axis of the cheese.
As the least tangle or kink in the coiling would, in running out, infallibly take
somebody's arm, leg, or entire body off, the utmost precaution is used in stowing
the line in its tub. Some harpooneers will consume almost an entire morning

in this business, carrying the line high aloft and then reeving it downwards through a block towards the tub, so as in the act of coiling to free it from all possible wrinkles and twists.

In the English boats two tubs are used instead of one; the same line being continuously coiled in both tubs. There is some advantage in this; because these twin-tubs being so small they fit more readily into the boat, and do not strain it so much; whereas, the American tub, nearly three feet in diameter and of proportionate depth, makes a rather bulky freight for a craft whose planks are but one half-inch in thickness; for the bottom of the whale-boat is like critical ice, which will bear up a considerable distributed weight, but not very much of a concentrated one. When the painted canvas cover is clapped on the American tub-line, the boat looks as if it were pulling off with a prodigious great wedding-cake to present to the whales.

Both ends of the line are exposed; the lower end terminating in an eye-splice or loop coming up from the bottom against the side of the tub, and hanging over its edge completely disengaged from everything. This arrangement of the lower end is necessary on two accounts. First: In order to facilitate the fastening to it of an additional line from a neighboring boat, in case the stricken whale should sound so deep as to threaten to carry off the entire line originally attached to the harpoon. In these instances, the whale of course is shifted like a mug of ale, as it were, from the one boat to the other; though the first boat always hovers at hand to assist its consort. Second: This arrangement is indispensable for common safety's sake; for were the lower end of the line in any way attached to the boat, and were the whale then to run the line out to the end almost in a single, smoking minute as he sometimes does, he would not stop there, for the doomed boat would infallibly be dragged down after him into the profundity of the sea; and in that case no town-crier would ever find her again.

Before lowering the boat for the chase, the upper end of the line is taken aft from the tub, and passing round the loggerhead there, is again carried forward the entire length of the boat, resting crosswise upon the loom or handle of every man's oar, so that it jogs against his wrist in rowing; and also passing between the men, as they alternately sit at the opposite gunwales, to the leaded chocks or grooves in the extreme pointed prow of the boat, where a wooden pin or skewer the size of a common quill, prevents it from slipping out. From the chocks it hangs in a slight festoon over the bows, and is then passed inside the boat again; and some ten or twenty fathoms (called box-line) being coiled upon the box in the bows, it continues its way to the gunwale still a little further aft, and is then attached to the short-warp—the rope which is immediately connected with the harpoon; but previous to that connexion, the short-warp goes through sundry mystifications too tedious to detail.

Thus the whale-line folds the whole boat in its complicated coils, twisting and writhing around it in almost every direction. All the oarsmen are involved in its perilous contortions; so that to the timid eye of the landsman, they seem as Indian jugglers, with the deadliest snakes sportively festooning their limbs. Nor can any son of mortal woman, for the first time, seat himself amid those hempen intricacies, and while straining his utmost at the oar, bethink him that at any unknown instant the harpoon may be darted, and all these horrible contortions be put in play like ringed lightnings; he cannot be thus circumstanced without a shudder that makes the very marrow in his bones to quiver in him like a shaken jelly. Yet habit—strange thing! what cannot habit accomplish? —Gayer sallies, more merry mirth, better jokes, and brighter repartees, you never heard over your mahogany, than you will hear over the half-inch white cedar of the whale-boat, when thus hung in hangman's nooses; and, like the six burghers of Calais before King Edward, the six men composing the crew pull into the jaws of death, with a halter around every neck, as you may say.

Perhaps a very little thought will now enable you to account for those repeated whaling disasters—some few of which are casually chronicled—of this man or that man being taken out of the boat by the line, and lost. For, when the line is darting out, to be seated then in the boat, is like being seated in the midst of the manifold whizzings of a steam-engine in full play, when every flying beam, and shaft, and wheel, is grazing you. It is worse; for you cannot sit motionless in the heart of these perils, because the boat is rocking like a cradle, and you are pitched one way and the other, without the slightest warning; and only by a certain self-adjusting buoyancy and simultaneousness of volition and action, can you escape being made a Mazeppa of, and run away with where the all-seeing sun himself could never pierce you out.

Again: as the profound calm which only apparently precedes and prophesies of the storm, is perhaps more awful than the storm itself; for, indeed, the calm is but the wrapper and envelope of the storm; and contains it in itself, as the seemingly harmless rifle holds the fatal powder, and the ball, and the explosion; so the graceful repose of the line, as it silently serpentines about the oarsmen before being brought into actual play—this is a thing which carries more of true terror than any other aspect of this dangerous affair. But why say more? All men live enveloped in whale-lines. All are born with halters round their necks; but it is only when caught in the swift, sudden turn of death, that mortals realize the silent, subtle, ever-present perils of life. And if you be a philosopher, though seated in the whale-boat, you would not at heart feel one whit more of terror, than though seated before your evening fire with a poker, and not a harpoon, by your side.

CHAPTER LXI

STUBB KILLS A WHALE

IF to Starbuck the apparition of the Squid was a thing of portents, to Queequeg it was quite a different object.

"When you see him 'quid," said the savage, honing his harpoon in the bow of his hoisted boat, "then you quick see him 'parm whale."

The next day was exceedingly still and sultry, and with nothing special to engage them, the Pequod's crew could hardly resist the spell of sleep induced by such a vacant sea. For this part of the Indian Ocean through which we then were voyaging is not what whalemen call a lively ground; that is, it affords fewer glimpses of porpoises, dolphins, flying-fish, and other vivacious denizens of more stirring waters, than those off the Rio de la Plata, or the in-shore ground off Peru.

. It was my turn to stand at the foremost-head; and with my shoulders leaning against the slackened royal shrouds, to and fro I idly swayed in what seemed an enchanted air. No resolution could withstand it; in that dreamy mood losing all consciousness, at last my soul went out of my body; though my body still continued to sway as a pendulum will, long after the power which first moved it is withdrawn.

Ere forgetfulness altogether came over me, I had noticed that the seamen at the main and mizzen mast-heads were already drowsy. So that at last all three of us lifelessly swung from the spars, and for every swing that we made there was a nod from below from the slumbering helmsman. The waves, too, nodded their indolent crests; and across the wide trance of the sea, east nodded to west, and the sun over all.

Suddenly bubbles seemed bursting beneath my closed eyes; like vices my hands grasped the shrouds; some invisible, gracious agency preserved me; with a shock I came back to life. And lo! close under our lee, not forty fathoms off, a gigantic Sperm Whale lay rolling in the water like the capsized hull of a frigate, his broad, glossy back, of an Ethiopian hue, glistening in the sun's rays like a mirror. But lazily undulating in the trough of the sea, and ever and anon tranquilly spouting his vapory jet, the whale looked like a portly burgher smoking his pipe of a warm afternoon. But that pipe, poor whale, was thy last. As if struck by some enchanter's wand, the sleepy ship and every sleeper in it all at once started into wakefulness; and more than a score of voices from all parts of the vessel, simultaneously with the three notes from aloft, shouted forth the accustomed cry, as the great fish slowly and regularly spouted the sparkling brine into the air.

"Clear away the boats! Luff!" cried Ahab. And obeying his own order, he dashed the helm down before the helmsman could handle the spokes.

The sudden exclamations of the crew must have alarmed the whale; and ere the boats were down, majestically turning, he swam away to the leeward, but with such a steady tranquillity, and making so few ripples as he swam, that thinking after all he might not as yet be alarmed, Ahab gave orders that not an oar should be used, and no man must speak but in whispers. So seated like Ontario Indians on the gunwales of the boats, we swiftly but silently paddled along; the calm not admitting of the noiseless sails being set. Presently, as we thus glided in chase, the monster perpendicularly flitted his tail forty feet into the air, and then sank out of sight like a tower swallowed up.

"There go flukes!" was the cry, an announcement immediately followed by Stubb's producing his match and igniting his pipe, for now a respite was granted. After the full interval of his sounding had elapsed, the whale rose again, and being now in advance of the smoker's boat, and much nearer to it than to any of the others, Stubb counted upon the honor of the capture. It was obvious, now, that the whale had at length become aware of his pursuers. All silence of cautiousness was therefore no longer of use. Paddles were dropped, and oars came loudly into play. And still puffing at his pipe, Stubb cheered on his crew to the assault.

Yes, a mighty change had come over the fish. All alive to his jeopardy, he was going "head out;" that part obliquely projecting from the mad yeast which he brewed.

"Start her, start her, my men! Don't hurry yourselves; take plenty of time —but start her; start her like thunder-claps, that's all," cried Stubb, spluttering out the smoke as he spoke. "Start her, now; give 'em the long and strong stroke, Tashtego. Start her, Tash, my boy—start her, all; but keep cool, keep cool— cucumbers is the word—easy, easy—only start her like grim death and grinning devils, and raise the buried dead perpendicular out of their graves, boys—that's all. Start her!"

"Woo-hoo! Wa-hee!" screamed the Gay-Header in reply, raising some old war-whoop to the skies; as every oarsman in the strained boat involuntarily bounced forward with the one tremendous leading stroke which the eager Indian gave.

But his wild screams were answered by others quite as wild. "Kee-hee! Kee-hee!" yelled Daggoo, straining forwards and backwards on his seat, like a pacing tiger in his cage.

"Ka-la! Koo-loo!" howled Queequeg, as if smacking his lips over a mouthful of Grenadier's steak. And thus with oars and yells the keels cut the sea. Meanwhile, Stubb retaining his place in the van, still encouraged his men to the onset, all the while puffing the smoke from his mouth. Like desperadoes they tugged and they strained, till the welcome cry was heard—"Stand up, Tashtego!—give it to him!" The harpoon was hurled. "Stern all!" The oarsmen backed water; the same moment something went hot and hissing along every one of their wrists. It was the magical line. An instant before, Stubb had swiftly caught two additional turns with it round the loggerhead, whence, by reason of its increased rapid circlings, a hempen blue smoke now jetted up and mingled with the steady fumes from his pipe. As the line passed round and round the loggerhead; so also, just before reaching that point, it blisteringly passed through and through both of Stubb's hands, from which the hand-cloths, or squares of quilted canvas sometimes worn at these times, had accidentally dropped. It was like holding an enemy's sharp two-edged sword by the blade, and that enemy all the time striving to wrest it out of your clutch.

"Wet the line! wet the line!" cried Stubb to the tub oarsman (him seated by the tub) who, snatching off his hat, dashed the sea-water into it. More turns were taken, so that the line began holding its place. The boat now flew through the boiling water like a shark all fins. Stubb and Tashtego here changed places —stem for stern—a staggering business truly in that rocking commotion.

From the vibrating line extending the entire length of the upper part of the boat, and from its now being more tight than a harpstring, you would have thought the craft had two keels—one cleaving the water, the other the air—as the boat churned on through both opposing elements at once. A continual cascade played at the bows; a ceaseless whirling eddy in her wake; and, at the slightest motion from within, even but of a little finger, the vibrating, cracking craft canted over her spasmodic gunwale into the sea. Thus they rushed; each man with might and main clinging to his seat, to prevent being tossed to the foam; and the tall form of Tashtego at the steering oar crouching almost double, in order to bring down his centre of gravity. Whole Atlantics and Pacifics seemed passed as they shot on their way, till at length the whale somewhat slackened his flight.

"Haul in—haul in!" cried Stubb to the bowsman! and, facing round towards the whale, all hands began pulling the boat up to him, while yet the boat was being towed on. Soon ranging up by his flank, Stubb, firmly planting his knee in the clumsy cleat, darted dart after dart into the flying fish; at the word of command, the boat alternately sterning out of the way of the whale's horrible wallow, and then ranging up for another fling.

The red tide now poured from all sides of the monster like brooks down a hill. His tormented body rolled not in brine but in blood, which bubbled and seethed for furlongs behind in their wake. The slanting sun playing upon this crimson pond in the sea, sent back its reflection into every face, so that they all glowed to each other like red men. And all the while, jet after jet of white smoke was agonizingly shot from the spiracle of the whale, and vehement puff after puff from the mouth of the excited headsman; as at every dart, hauling in upon his crooked lance (by the line attached to it), Stubb straightened it again and again, by a few rapid blows against the gunwale, then again and again sent it into the whale.

"Pull up—pull up!" he now cried to the bowsman, as the waning whale relaxed in his wrath. "Pull up!—close to!" and the boat ranged along the fish's flank. When reaching far over the bow, Stubb slowly churned his long sharp lance into the fish, and kept it there, carefully churning and churning, as if cautiously seeking to feel after some gold watch that the whale might have swallowed, and which he was fearful of breaking ere he could hook it out. But that gold watch he sought was the innermost life of the fish. And now it is struck; for, starting from his trance into that unspeakable thing called his "flurry," the monster horribly wallowed in his blood, overwrapped himself in impenetrable, mad, boiling spray, so that the imperilled craft, instantly dropping astern, had much ado blindly to struggle out from that phrensied twilight into the clear air of the day.

And now abating in his flurry, the whale once more rolled out into view; surging from side to side; spasmodically dilating and contracting his spout-hole, with sharp, cracking, agonized respirations. At last, gush after gush of clotted red gore, as if it had been the purple lees of red wine, shot into the frighted air; and falling back again, ran dripping down his motionless flanks into the sea. His heart had burst!

"He's dead, Mr. Stubb," said Daggoo.

"Yes; both pipes smoked out!" and withdrawing his own from his mouth, Stubb scattered the dead ashes over the water; and, for a moment, stood thoughtfully eyeing the vast corpse he had made.

CHAPTER LXII

THE DART

A WORD concerning an incident in the last chapter.

According to the invariable usage of the fishery, the whale-boat pushes off from the ship, with the headsman or whale-killer as temporary steersman, and the harpooneer or whale-fastener pulling the foremost oar, the one known as the harpooneer-oar. Now it needs a strong, nervous arm to strike the first iron into the fish; for often, in what is called a long dart, the heavy implement has to be flung to the distance of twenty or thirty feet. But however prolonged and exhausting the chase, the harpooneer is expected to pull his oar meanwhile to the uttermost; indeed, he is expected to set an example of superhuman activity to the rest, not only by incredible rowing, but by repeated loud and intrepid exclamations; and what it is to keep shouting at the top of one's compass, while all the other muscles are strained and half started—what that is none know but those who have tried it. For one, I cannot bawl very heartily and work very recklessly at one and the same time. In this straining, bawling state, then, with his back to the fish, all at once the exhausted harpooneer hears the exciting cry—"Stand up, and give it to him!" He now has to drop and secure his oar, turn round on his centre half way, seize his harpoon from the crotch, and with what little strength may remain, he essays to pitch it somehow into the whale. No wonder, taking the whole fleet of whalemen in a body, that out of fifty fair chances for a dart, not five are successful; no wonder that so many hapless harpooneers are madly cursed and disrated; no wonder that some of them actually burst their blood-vessels in the boat; no wonder that some sperm whalemen are absent four years with four barrels; no wonder that to many ship owners, whaling is but a losing concern; for it is the harpooneer that makes the voyage, and if you take the breath out of his body how can you expect to find it there when most wanted!

Again, if the dart be successful, then at the second critical instant, that is, when the whale starts to run, the boat-header and harpooneer likewise start to running fore and aft, to the imminent jeopardy of themselves and every one else. It is then they change places; and the headsman, the chief officer of the little craft, takes his proper station in the bows of the boat.

Now, I care not who maintains the contrary, but all this is both foolish and unnecessary. The headsman should stay in the bows from first to last; he should both dart the harpoon and the lance, and no rowing whatever should be expected of him, except under circumstances obvious to any fisherman. I know that this would sometimes involve a slight loss of speed in the chase; but long experience in various whalemen of more than one nation has convinced me that in the vast majority of failures in the fishery, it has not by any means been so much the speed of the whale as the before described exhaustion of the harpooneer that has caused them.

To insure the greatest efficiency in the dart, the harpooneers of this world must start to their feet from out of idleness, and not from out of toil.

CHAPTER LXIII

THE CROTCH

OUT of the trunk, the branches grow; out of them, the twigs. So, in productive subjects, grow the chapters.

The crotch alluded to on a previous page deserves independent mention. It is a notched stick of a peculiar form, some two feet in length, which is perpendicularly inserted into the starboard gunwale near the bow, for the purpose of furnishing a rest for the wooden extremity of the harpoon, whose other naked, barbed end slopingly projects from the prow. Thereby the weapon is instantly at hand to its hurler, who snatches it up as readily from its rest as a backwoodsman swings his rifle from the wall. It is customary to have two harpoons reposing in the crotch, respectively called the first and second irons.

But these two harpoons, each by its own cord, are both connected with the line; the object being this: to dart them both, if possible, one instantly after the other into the same whale; so that if, in the coming drag, one should draw out, the other may still retain a hold. It is a doubling of the chances. But it very often happens that owing to the instantaneous, violent, convulsive running of the whale upon receiving the first iron, it becomes impossible for the harpooneer, however lightning-like in his movements, to pitch the second iron into him. Nevertheless, as the second iron is already connected with the line, and the line is running, hence that weapon must, at all events, be anticipatingly tossed out of the boat, somehow and somewhere; else the most terrible jeopardy would involve all hands. Tumbled into the water, it accordingly is in such cases; the spare coils of box line (mentioned in a preceding chapter) making this feat, in most instances, prudently practicable. But this critical act is not always unattended with the saddest and most fatal casualties.

Furthermore: you must know that when the second iron is thrown overboard, it thenceforth becomes a dangling, sharp-edged terror, skittishly curvetting about both boat and whale, entangling the lines, or cutting them, and making a prodigious sensation in all directions. Nor, in general, is it possible to secure it again until the whale is fairly captured and a corpse.

Consider, now, how it must be in the case of four boats all engaging one unusually strong, active, and knowing whale; when owing to these qualities in him, as well as to the thousand concurring accidents of such an audacious enterprise, eight or ten loose second irons may be simultaneously dangling about him. For, of course, each boat is supplied with several harpoons to bend on to the line should the first one be ineffectually darted without recovery. All these particulars are faithfully narrated here, as they will not fail to elucidate several most important, however intricate passages, in scenes hereafter to be painted.

CHAPTER LXIV

STUBB'S SUPPER

STUBB's whale had been killed some distance from the ship. It was a calm; so, forming a tandem of three boats, we commenced the slow business of towing the trophy to the Pequod. And now, as we eighteen men with our thirty-six arms, and one hundred and eighty thumbs and fingers, slowly toiled hour after hour upon that inert, sluggish corpse in the sea; and it seemed hardly to budge at all, except at long intervals; good evidence was hereby furnished of the enormousness of the mass we moved. For, upon the great canal of Hang-Ho, or whatever they call it, in China, four or five laborers on the foot-path will draw a bulky freighted junk at the rate of a mile an hour; but this grand argosy we towed heavily forged along, as if laden with pig-lead in bulk.

Darkness came' on; but three lights up and down in the Pequod's main-rigging dimly guided our way; till drawing nearer we saw Ahab dropping one of several more lanterns over the bulwarks. Vacantly eyeing the heaving whale for a moment, he issued the usual orders for securing it for the night, and then handing his lantern to a seaman, went his way into the cabin, and did not come forward again until morning.

Though, in overseeing the pursuit of this whale, Captain Ahab had evinced his customary activity, to call it so; yet now that the creature was dead, some vague dissatisfaction, or impatience, or despair, seemed working in him; as if the sight of that dead body reminded him that Moby-Dick was yet to be slain; and though a thousand other whales were brought to his ship, all that would not one jot advance his grand, monomaniac object. Very soon you would have thought from the sound on the Pequod's decks, that all hands were preparing to cast anchor in the deep; for heavy chains are being dragged along the deck, and thrust rattling out of the port-holes. But by those clanking links, the vast corpse itself, not the ship, is to be moored. Tied by the head to the stern, and by the tail to the bows, the whale now lies with its black hull close to the vessel's, and seen through the darkness of the night, which obscured the spars and rigging aloft, the two—ship and whale, seemed yoked together like colossal bullocks, whereof one reclines while the other remains standing.

If moody Ahab was now all quiescence, at least so far as could be known on deck, Stubb, his second mate, flushed with conquest, betrayed an unusual but still good-natured excitement. Such an unwonted bustle was he in that the staid Starbuck, his official superior, quietly resigned to him for the time the sole management of affairs. One small, helping cause of all this liveliness in Stubb, was soon made strangely manifest. Stubb was a high liver; he was somewhat intemperately fond of the whale as a flavorish thing to his palate.

"A steak, a steak, ere I sleep! You, Daggoo! overboard you go, and cut me one from his small!"

Here be it known, that though these wild fishermen do not, as a general thing, and according to the great military maxim, make the enemy defray the current expenses of the war (at least before realizing the proceeds of the voyage), yet now and then you find some of these Nantucketers who have a genuine relish for that particular part of the Sperm Whale designated by Stubb; comprising the tapering extremity of the body.

About midnight that steak was cut and cooked; and lighted by two lanterns of sperm oil, Stubb stoutly stood up to his spermaceti supper at the capstan-head, as if that capstan were a sideboard. Nor was Stubb the only banqueter on whale's flesh that night. Mingling their mumblings with his own mastications, thousands on thousands of sharks, swarming round the dead leviathan, smackingly feasted on its fatness. The few sleepers below in their bunks were often startled by the sharp slapping of their tails against the hull, within a few inches of the sleepers' hearts. Peering over the side you could just see them (as before you heard them) wallowing in the sullen, black waters, and turning over on their backs as they scooped out huge globular pieces of the whale of the bigness of a human head. This particular feat of the shark seems all but miraculous. How, at such an apparently unassailable surface, they contrive to gouge out such symmetrical mouthfuls, remains a part of the universal problem of all things. The mark they thus leave on the whale, may best be likened to the hollow made by a carpenter in countersinking for a screw.

Though amid all the smoking horror and diabolism of a sea-fight, sharks will be seen longingly gazing up to the ship's decks, like hungry dogs round a table where red meat is being carved, ready to bolt down every killed man that is tossed to them; and though, while the valiant butchers over the deck-table are thus cannibally carving each others' live meat with carving-knives all gilded and tasselled, the sharks, also, with their jewel-hilted mouths, are quarrelsomely carving away under the table at the dead meat; and though, were you to turn the whole affair upside down, it would still be pretty much the same thing, that is to say, a shocking sharkish business enough for all parties; and though sharks also are the invariable outriders of all slave ships crossing the Atlantic, systematically trotting alongside, to be handy in case a parcel is to be carried anywhere, or a dead slave to be decently buried; and though one or two other like instances might be set down, touching the set terms, places, and occasions, when sharks do most socially congregate, and most hilariously feast; yet is there no conceivable time or occasion when you will find them in such countless numbers, and in gayer or more jovial spirits, than around a dead sperm whale, moored by night to a whale-ship at sea. If you have never seen that sight, then suspend your decision about the propriety of devil-worship, and the expediency of conciliating the devil.

But, as yet, Stubb heeded not the mumblings of the banquet that was going on so nigh him, no more than the sharks heeded the smacking of his own epicurean lips.

"Cook, cook!—where's that old Fleece?" he cried at length, widening his legs still further, as if to form a more secure base for his supper; and, at the same time darting his fork into the dish, as if stabbing with his lance; "cook, you cook!—sail this way, cook!"

The old black, not in any very high glee at having been previously roused from his warm hammock at a most unseasonable hour, came shambling along from his galley, for, like many old blacks, there was something the matter with his knee-pans, which he did not keep well scoured like his other pans; this old Fleece, as they called him, came shuffling and limping along, assisting his step with his tongs, which, after a clumsy fashion, were made of straightened iron hoops; this old Ebony floundered along, and in obedience to the word of command, came to a dead stop on the opposite side of Stubb's sideboard; when, with both hands folded before him, and resting on his two-legged cane, he bowed his arched back still further over, at the same time sideways inclining his head, so as to bring his best ear into play.

"Cook," said Stubb, rapidly lifting a rather reddish morsel to his mouth, "don't you think this steak is rather overdone? You've been beating this steak too much, cook; it's too tender. Don't I always say that to be good, a whale-steak must be tough? There are those sharks now over the side, don't you see they prefer it tough and rare? What a shindy they are kicking up! Cook, go and talk to 'em; tell 'em they are welcome to help themselves civilly, and in moderation, but they must keep quiet. Blast me, if I can hear my own voice. Away, cook, and deliver my message. Here, take this lantern," snatching one from his sideboard; "now then, go and preach to them!"

Sullenly taking the offered lantern, old Fleece limped across the deck to the bulwarks; and then, with one hand dropping his light low over the sea, so as to get a good view of his congregation, with the other hand he solemnly flourished his tongs, and leaning far over the side in a mumbling voice began addressing the sharks, while Stubb, softly crawling behind, overheard all that was said.

"Fellow-critters: I'se ordered here to say dat you must stop dat dam noise dare. You hear? Stop dat dam smackin' ob de lips! Massa Stubb say dat you can fill your dam bellies up to de hatchings, but by Gor! you must stop dat dam racket!"

"Cook," here interposed Stubb, accompanying the word with a sudden slap on the shoulder,—"Cook! why, damn your eyes, you mustn't swear that way when you're preaching. That's no way to convert sinners, Cook!"

"Who dat? Den preach to him yourself," sullenly turning to go.

"No, Cook; go on, go on."

"Well, den, Belubed fellow-critters:"—

"Right!" exclaimed Stubb, approvingly, "coax 'em to it; try that," and Fleece continued.

"Do you is all sharks, and by natur wery woracious, yet I zay to you, fellow-critters, dat dat woraciousness—'top dat dam slappin' ob de tail! How you tink to hear, 'spose you keep up such a dam slapping and bitin' dare?"

"Cook," cried Stubb, collaring him, "I won't have that swearing. Talk to 'em gentlemanly."

Once more the sermon proceeded.

"Your woraciousness, fellow-critters, I don't blame ye so much for; dat is natur, and can't be helped; but to gobern dat wicked natur, dat is de pint. You is sharks, sartin; but if you gobern de shark in you, why den you be angel; for all angel is not'ing more dan de shark well goberned. Now, look here, bred'ren, just try wonst to be cibil, a helping yoursebls from dat whale. Don't be tearin' de blubber out your neighbour's mout, I say. Is not one shark dood right as toder to dat whale? And, by Gor, none on you has de right to dat whale; dat whale belong to some one else. I know some o' you has berry brig mout, brigger dan oders; but then de brig mouts sometimes has de small bellies; so dat de brigness ob de mout is not to swaller wid, but to bite off de blubber for de small fry ob sharks, dat can't get into de scrouge to help dem-selves."

"Well done, old Fleece!" cried Stubb, "that's Christianity; go on."

"No use goin' on; de dam willains will keep a scrougin' and slappin' each oder, Massa Stubb; dey don't hear one word; no use a-preaching to such dam g'uttons as you call 'em, till dare bellies is full, and dare bellies is bot-tomless; and when dey do get em full, dey wont hear you den; for den dey sink in de sea, go fast to sleep on de coral, and can't hear not'ing at all, no more, for eber and eber."

"Upon my soul, I am about of the same opinion; so give the benediction, Fleece, and I'll away to my supper."

Upon this, Fleece, holding both hands over the fishy mob, raised his shrill voice, and cried—

"Cussed fellow-critters! Kick up de damndest row as ever you can; fill your dam bellies 'till dey bust—and den die."

"Now, cook," said Stubb, resuming his supper at the capstan; "stand just where you stood before, there, over against me, and pay particular attention."

"All dention," said Fleece, again stooping over upon his tongs in the desired position.

"Well," said Stubb, helping himself freely meanwhile; "I shall now go back to the subject of this steak. In the first place, how old are you, cook?"

"What dat do wid de 'teak," said the old black, testily.

"Silence! How old are you, cook?"

" 'Bout ninety, dey say," he gloomily muttered.

"And have you lived in this world hard upon one hundred years, cook, and don't know yet how to cook a whale-steak?" rapidly bolting another mouth-ful at the last word, so that that morsel seemed a continuation of the question. "Where were you born, cook?"

" 'Hind de hatchway, in ferry-boat, goin' ober de Roanoke."

"Born in a ferry-boat! That's queer, too. But I want to know what country you were born in, cook?"

"Didn't I say de Roanoke country?" he cried, sharply.

"No, you didn't, cook; but I'll tell you what I'm coming to, cook. You must go home and be born over again; you don't know how to cook a whale-steak yet."

"Bress my soul, if I cook noder one," he growled, angrily, turning round to depart.

"Come back, cook;—here, hand me those tongs;—now take that bit of steak there, and tell me if you think that steak cooked as it should be? Take it, I say"—holding the tongs towards him—"take it, and taste it."

Faintly smacking his withered lips over it for a moment, the old negro muttered, "Best cooked 'teak I eber taste; joosy berry, joosy."

"Cook," said Stubb, squaring himself once more; "do you belong to the church?"

"Passed one once in Cape-Down," said the old man sullenly.

"And you have once in your life passed a holy church in Cape-Town, where you doubtless overheard a holy parson addressing his hearers as his beloved fellow-creatures, have you, cook! And yet you come here, and tell me such a dreadful lie as you did just now, eh?" said Stubb. "Where do you expect to go to, cook?"

"Go to bed berry soon," he mumbled, half-turning as he spoke.

"Avast! heave to! I mean when you die, cook. It's an awful question. Now what's your answer?"

"When dis old brack man dies," said the negro slowly, changing his whole air and demeanor, "he hisself won't go nowhere; but some bressed angel will come and fetch him."

"Fetch him? How? In a coach and four, as they fetched Elijah? And fetch him where?"

"Up dere," said Fleece, holding his tongs straight over his head, and keeping it there very solemnly.

"So, then, you expect to go up into our main-top, do you, cook, when you are dead? But don't you know the higher you climb, the colder it gets? Main-top, eh?"

"Didn't say dat t'all," said Fleece, again in the sulks.

"You said up there, didn't you? and now look yourself, and see where your tongs are pointing. But, perhaps you expect to get into heaven by crawling through the lubber's hole, cook; but, no, no, cook, you don't get there, except you go the regular way, round by the rigging. It's a ticklish business, but must be done, or else it's no go. But none of us are in heaven yet. Drop your tongs, cook, and hear my orders. Do ye hear? Hold your hat in one hand, and clap t'other a'top of your heart, when I'm giving my orders, cook. What! that your heart, there?—that's your gizzard! Aloft! aloft—that's it—now you have it. Hold it there now, and pay attention."

"All 'dention," said the old black, with both hands placed as desired, vainly wriggling his grizzled head, as if to get both ears in front at one and the same time.

"Well then, cook, you see this whale-steak of yours was so very bad, that I have put it out of sight as soon as possible; you see that, don't you? Well, for the future, when you cook another whale-steak for my private table here, the capstan, I'll tell you what to do so as not to spoil it by overdoing. Hold the steak in one hand, and show a live coal to it with the other; that done, dish it; d'ye hear? And now to-morrow, cook, when we are cutting in the fish, be sure you stand by to get the tips of his fins; have them put in pickle. As for the ends of the flukes, have them soused, cook. There, now ye may go."

But Fleece had hardly got three paces off, when he was recalled.

"Cook, give me cutlets for supper to-morrow night in the mid-watch. D'ye hear? away you sail, then.—Halloa! stop! make a bow before you go.—Avast heaving again! Whale-balls for breakfast—don't forget."

"Wish, by gor! whale eat him, 'stead of him eat whale. I'm bressed if he ain't more of shark dan Massa Shark hisself," muttered the old man, limping away; with which sage ejaculation he went to his hammock.

CHAPTER LXV

THE WHALE AS A DISH

THAT mortal man should feed upon the creature that feeds his lamp, and, like Stubb, eat him by his own light, as you may say; this seems so outlandish a thing that one must needs go a little into the history and philosophy of it.

It is upon record, that three centuries ago the tongue of the Right Whale was esteemed a great delicacy in France, and commanded large prices there. Also, that in Henry VIIIth's time, a certain cook of the court obtained a handsome reward for inventing an admirable sauce to be eaten with barbacued porpoises, which, you remember, are a species of whale. Porpoises, indeed, are to this day considered fine eating. The meat is made into balls about the size of billiard balls, and being well seasoned and spiced might be taken for turtle-balls or veal balls. The old monks of Dunfermline were very fond of them. They had a great porpoise grant from the crown.

The fact is, that among his hunters at least, the whale would by all hands be considered a noble dish, were there not so much of him; but when you come to sit down before a meat-pie nearly one hundred feet long, it takes away your appetite. Only the most unprejudiced of men like Stubb, nowadays partake of cooked whales; but the Esquimaux are not so fastidious. We all know how they live upon whales, and have rare old vintages of prime old train oil. Zogranda, one of their most famous doctors, recommends strips of blubber for infants, as being exceedingly juicy and nourishing. And this reminds me that certain Englishmen, who long ago were accidentally left in Greenland by a whaling vessel—that these men actually lived for several months on the mouldy scraps of whales which had been left ashore after trying out the blubber. Among the Dutch whalemen these scraps are called "fritters;" which, indeed, they greatly resemble, being brown and crisp, and smelling something like old Amsterdam housewives' dough-nuts or oly-cooks, when fresh. They have such an eatable look that the most self-denying stranger can hardly keep his hands off.

But what further depreciates the whale as a civilized dish, is his exceeding richness. He is the great prize ox of the sea, too fat to be delicately good. Look at his hump, which would be as fine eating as the buffalo's (which is esteemed a rare dish), were it not such a solid pyramid of fat. But the spermaceti itself, how bland and creamy that is; like the transparent, half jellied, white meat of a cocoanut in the third month of its growth, yet far too rich to supply a substitute for butter. Nevertheless, many whalemen have a method of absorbing it into some other substance, and then partaking of it. In the long try watches of the night it is a common thing for the seamen to dip their ship-biscuit into the huge oil-pots and let them fry there awhile. Many a good supper have I thus made.

In the case of a small Sperm Whale the brains are accounted a fine dish. The casket of the skull is broken into with an axe, and the two plump, whitish lobes being withdrawn (precisely resembling two large puddings), they are then mixed with flour, and cooked into a most delectable mess, in flavor somewhat resembling calves' head, which is quite a dish among some epicures; and every one knows that some young bucks among the epicures, by continually dining upon calves' brains, by and by get to have a little brains of their own, so as to be able to tell a calf's head from their own heads: which, indeed, requires uncommon discrimination. And that is the reason why a young buck with an intelligent looking calf's head before him, is somehow one of the saddest sights you can see. The head looks a sort of reproachfully at him, with an "Et tu Brute!" expression.

It is not, perhaps, entirely because the whale is so excessively unctuous that landsmen seem to regard the eating of him with abhorrence; that appears to result, in some way, from the consideration before mentioned: i. e. that a man should eat a newly murdered thing of the sea, and eat it too by its own light. But no doubt the first man that ever murdered an ox was regarded as a murderer; perhaps he was hung; and if he had been put on his trial by oxen, he certainly would have been; and he certainly deserved it if any murderer does. Go to the meat-market of a Saturday night and see the crowds of live bipeds staring up at the long rows of dead quadrupeds. Does not that sight take a tooth out of the cannibal's jaw? Cannibals? who is not a cannibal? I tell you it will be more tolerable for the Fejee that salted down a lean missionary in his cellar against a coming famine; it will be more tolerable for that provident Fejee, I say, in the day of judgment, than for thee, civilized and enlightened gourmand, who nailest geese to the ground and feastest on their bloated livers in thy paté-de-foie-gras.

But Stubb, he eats the whale by its own light, does he? and that is adding insult to injury, is it? Look at your knife-handle, there, my civilized and enlightened gourmand dining off that roast beef, what is that handle made of? —what but the bones of the brother of the very ox you are eating? And what do you pick your teeth with, after devouring that fat goose? With a feather of the same fowl. And with what quill did the Secretary of the Society for the Suppression of Cruelty to Ganders formally indite his circulars? It is only within the last month or two that that society passed a resolution to patronize nothing but steel pens.

CHAPTER LXVI

THE SHARK MASSACRE

WHEN in the Southern Fishery, a captured Sperm Whale, after long and weary toil, is brought alongside late at night, it is not, as a general thing at least, customary to proceed at once to the business of cutting him in. For that business is an exceedingly laborious one; is not very soon completed; and requires all hands to set about it. Therefore, the common usage is to take in all sail; lash the helm a'lee; and then send every one below to his hammock till daylight, with the reservation that, until that time, anchor-watches shall be kept; that is, two and two for an hour, each couple, the crew in rotation shall mount the deck to see that all goes well.

But sometimes, especially upon the Line in the Pacific, this plan will not answer at all; because such incalculable hosts of sharks gather round the moored carcase, that were he left so for six hours, say, on a stretch, little more than the skeleton would be visible by morning. In most other parts of the ocean, however, where these fish do not so largely abound, their wondrous voracity can be at times considerably diminished, by vigorously stirring them up with sharp whaling-spades, a procedure notwithstanding, which, in some instances, only seems to tickle them into still greater activity. But it was not thus in the present case with the Pequod's sharks; though, to be sure, any man unaccustomed to such sights, to have looked over her side that night, would have almost thought the whole round sea was one huge cheese, and those sharks the maggots in it.

Nevertheless, upon Stubb setting the anchor-watch after his supper was concluded; and when, accordingly, Queequeg and a forecastle seaman came on deck, no small excitement was created among the sharks; for immediately suspending the cutting stages over the side, and lowering three lanterns, so that they cast long gleams of light over the turbid sea, these two mariners, darting their long whaling-spades, kept up an incessant murdering of the sharks, by striking the keen steel deep into their skulls, seemingly their only vital part. But in the foamy confusion of their mixed and struggling hosts, the marksmen could not always hit their mark; and this brought about new revelations of the incredible ferocity of the foe. They viciously snapped, not only at each other's disembowelments, but like flexible bows, bent round, and bit their own; till those entrails seemed swallowed over and over again by the same mouth, to be oppositely voided by the gaping wound. Nor was this all. It was unsafe to meddle with the corpses and ghosts of these creatures. A sort of generic or Pantheistic vitality seemed to lurk in their very joints and bones, after what might be called the individual life had departed. Killed and hoisted on deck for the sake of his skin, one of these sharks almost took poor Queequeg's hand off, when he tried to shut down the dead lid of his murderous jaw.

"Queequeg no care what god made him shark," said the savage, agonizingly lifting his hand up and down; "wedder Fejee god or Nantucket god; but de god wat made shark must be one dam Ingin."

CHAPTER LXVII

CUTTING IN

IT was a Saturday night, and such a Sabbath as followed! Ex officio professors of Sabbath breaking are all whalemen. The ivory Pequod was turned into what seemed a shamble; every sailor a butcher. You would have thought we were offering up ten thousand red oxen to the sea gods.

In the first place, the enormous cutting tackles, among other ponderous things comprising a cluster of blocks generally painted green, and which no single man can possibly lift—this vast bunch of grapes was swayed up to the main-top and firmly lashed to the lower mast-head, the strongest point anywhere above a ship's deck. The end of the hawser-like rope winding through these intricacies, was then conducted to the windlass, and the huge lower block of the tackles was swung over the whale; to this block the great blubber hook, weighing some one hundred pounds, was attached. And now suspended in stages over the side, Starbuck and Stubb, the mates, armed with their long spades, began cutting a hole in the body for the insertion of the hook just above the nearest of the two side-fins. This done, a broad, semicircular line is cut round the hole, the hook is inserted, and the main body of the crew striking up a wild chorus, now commence heaving in one dense crowd at the windlass.   When instantly, the entire ship careens over on her side; every bolt in her starts like the nail-heads of an old house in frosty weather; she trembles, quivers, and nods her frighted mast-heads to the sky.   More and more she leans over to the whale, while every gasping heave of the windlass is answered by a helping heave from the billows; till at last, a swift, startling snap is heard; with a great swash the ship rolls upwards and backwards from the whale, and the triumphant tackle rises into sight dragging after it the disengaged semicircular end of the first strip of blubber.   Now as the blubber envelopes the whale precisely as the rind does an orange, so is it stripped off from the body precisely as an orange is sometimes stripped by spiralizing it. For the strain constantly kept up by the windlass continually keeps the whale rolling over and over in the water, and as the blubber in one strip uniformly peels off along the line called the "scarf," simultaneously cut by the spades of Starbuck and Stubb, the mates; and just as fast as it is thus peeled off, and indeed by that very act itself, it is all the time being hoisted higher and higher aloft till its upper end grazes the main-top; the men at the windlass then cease heaving, and for a moment or two the prodigious blood-dripping mass sways to and fro as if let down from the sky, and every one present must take good heed to dodge it when it swings, else it may box his ears and pitch him headlong overboard.

One of the attending harpooneers now advances with a long, keen weapon called a boarding-sword, and watching his chance he dexterously slices out a considerable hole in the lower part of the swaying mass.   Into this hole, the end of the second alternating great tackle is then hooked so as to retain a hold upon the blubber, in order to prepare for what follows.   Whereupon, this accomplished swordsman, warning all hands to stand off, once more makes a scientific dash at the mass, and with a few sidelong, desperate, lunging slicings, severs it completely in twain; so that while the short lower part is still fast, the long upper strip, called a blanket-piece, swings clear, and is all ready for lowering.   The heavers forward now resume their song, and while the one tackle is peeling and hoisting a second strip from the whale, the other is slowly slackened away, and down goes the first strip through the main hatchway right beneath, into an unfurnished parlor called the blubber-room.   Into this twilight apartment sundry nimble hands keep coiling away the long blanket-piece as if it were a great live mass of plaited serpents.   And thus the work proceeds; the two tackles hoisting and lowering simultaneously; both whale and windlass heaving, the heavers singing, the blubber-room gentlemen coiling, the mates scarfing, the ship straining, and all hands swearing occasionally, by way of assuaging the general friction.

CHAPTER LXVIII

THE BLANKET

I HAVE given no small attention to that not unvexed subject, the skin of the whale.   I have had controversies about it with experienced whalemen afloat, and learned naturalists ashore.   My original opinion remains unchanged; but it is only an opinion.

The question is, what and where is the skin of the whale?   Already you know what his blubber is. That blubber is something of the consistence of firm, close-grained beef, but tougher, more elastic and compact, and ranges from eight or ten to twelve and fifteen inches in thickness.

Now, however preposterous it may at first seem to talk of any creature's skin as being of that sort of consistence and thickness, yet in point of fact these are no arguments against such a presumption; because you cannot raise any other dense enveloping layer from the whale's body but that same blubber; and the outermost enveloping layer of any animal, if reasonably dense, what can that be but the skin? True, from the unmarred dead body of the whale, you may scrape off with your hand an infinitely thin, transparent substance, somewhat resembling the thinnest shreds of isinglass, only it is almost as flexible and soft as satin; that is, previous to being dried, when it not only contracts and thickens, but becomes rather hard and brittle. I have several such dried bits, which I use for marks in my whale-books. It is transparent, as I said before; and being laid upon the printed page, I have sometimes pleased myself with fancying it exerted a magnifying influence. At any rate, it is pleasant to read about whales through their own spectacles, as you may say. But what I am driving at here is this. That same infinitely thin, isinglass substance, which, I admit, invests the entire body of the whale, is not so much to be regarded as the skin of the creature, as the skin of the skin, so to speak; for it were simply ridiculous to say, that the proper skin of the tremendous whale is thinner and more tender than the skin of a new-born child. But no more of this.

Assuming the blubber to be the skin of the whale; then, when this skin, as in the case of a very large Sperm Whale, will yield the bulk of one hundred barrels of oil; and, when it is considered that, in quantity, or rather weight, that oil, in its expressed state, is only three fourths, and not the entire substance of the coat; some idea may hence be had of the enormousness of that animated mass, a mere part of whose mere integument yields such a lake of liquid as that. Reckoning ten barrels to the ton, you have ten tons for the net weight of only three quarters of the stuff of the whale's skin.

In life, the visible surface of the Sperm Whale is not the least among the many marvels he presents. Almost invariably it is all over obliquely crossed and re-crossed with numberless straight marks in thick array, something like those in the finest Italian line engravings. But these marks do not seem to be impressed upon the isinglass substance above mentioned, but seem to be seen through it, as if they were engraved upon the body itself. Nor is this all. In some instances, to the quick, observant eye, those linear marks, as in a veritable engraving, but afford the ground for far other delineations. These are hieroglyphical; that is, if you call those mysterious cyphers on the walls of pyramids hieroglyphics, then that is the proper word to use in the present connexion. By my retentive memory of the hieroglyphics upon one Sperm Whale in particular, I was much struck with a plate representing the old Indian characters chiselled on the famous hieroglyphic palisades on the banks of the Upper Mississippi. Like those mystic rocks, too, the mystic-marked whale remains undecipherable. This allusion to the Indian rocks reminds me of another thing. Besides all the other phenomena which the exterior of the Sperm Whale presents, he not seldom displays the back, and more especially his flanks, effaced in great part of the regular linear appearance, by reason of numerous rude scratches, altogether of an irregular, random aspect. I should say that those New England rocks on the sea-coast, which Agassiz imagines to bear the marks of violent scraping contact with vast floating icebergs—I should say, that those rocks must not a little resemble the Sperm Whale in this particular. It also seems to me that such scratches in the whale are probably made by hostile contact with other whales; for I have most remarked them in the large, full-grown bulls of the species.

A word or two more concerning this matter of the skin or blubber of the whale. It has already been said, that it is stript from him in long pieces, called blanket-pieces. Like most sea-terms, this one is very happy and significant. For the whale is indeed wrapt up in his blubber as in a real blanket or counterpane; or, still better, an Indian poncho slipt over his head, and skirting his extremity. It is by reason of this cosy blanketing of his body, that the whale is enabled to keep himself comfortable in all weathers, in all seas, times, and tides. What would become of a Greenland whale, say, in those shuddering, icy seas of the North, if unsupplied with his cosy surtout? True, other fish are found exceedingly brisk in those Hyperborean waters; but these, be it observed, are your cold-blooded, lungless fish, whose very bellies are refrigerators; creatures, that warm themselves under the lee of an iceberg, as a traveller in winter would bask before an inn fire; whereas, like man, the whale has lungs and warm blood. Freeze his blood, and he dies. How wonderful is it then—except after explanation—that this great monster, to whom corporeal warmth is as indispensable as it is to man; how wonderful that he should be found at home, immersed to his lips for life in those Arctic waters! where, when seamen fall overboard, they are sometimes found, months afterwards, perpendicularly frozen into the hearts of fields of ice, as a fly is found glued in amber. But more surprising is it to know, as has been proved by experiment, that the blood of a Polar whale is warmer than that of a Borneo negro in summer.

It does seem to me, that herein we see the rare virtue of a strong individual vitality, and the rare virtue of thick walls, and the rare virtue of interior spaciousness. Oh, man! admire and model thyself after the whale! Do thou, too, remain warm among ice. Do thou, too, live in this world without being of it. Be cool at the equator; keep thy blood fluid at the Pole. Like the great dome of St. Peter's, and like the great whale, retain, O man! in all seasons a temperature of thine own.

But how easy and how hopeless to teach these fine things! Of erections, how few are domed like St. Peter's! of creatures, how few vast as the whale!

CHAPTER LXIX

THE FUNERAL

"HAUL in the chains! Let the carcase go astern!"

The vast tackles have now done their duty. The peeled white body of the beheaded whale flashes like a marble sepulchre; though changed in hue, it has not perceptibly lost anything in bulk. It is still colossal. Slowly it floats more and more away, the water round it torn and splashed by the insatiate sharks, and the air above vexed with rapacious flights of screaming fowls, whose beaks are like so many insulting poniards in the whale. The vast white headless phantom floats further and further from the ship, and every rod that it so floats, what seem square roods of sharks and cubic roods of fowls, augment

the murderous din. For hours and hours from the almost stationary ship that
hideous sight is seen. Beneath the unclouded and mild azure sky, upon the
fair face of the pleasant sea, wafted by the joyous breezes, that great mass
of death floats on and on, till lost in infinite perspectives.

There's a most doleful and most mocking funeral! The sea-vultures all in
pious mourning, the air-sharks all punctiliously in black or speckled. In life
but few of them would have helped the whale, I ween, if peradventure he had
needed it; but upon the banquet of his funeral they most piously do pounce.
Oh, horrible vultureism of earth! from which not the mightiest whale is free.

Nor is this the end. Desecrated as the body is, a vengeful ghost survives
and hovers over it to scare. Espied by some timid man-of-war or blundering
discovery-vessel from afar, when the distance obscuring the swarming fowls,
nevertheless still shows the white mass floating in the sun, and the white spray
heaving high against it; straightway the whale's unharming corpse, with trembling fingers is set down in the log—*shoals, rocks, and breakers hereabouts:*
beware! And for years afterwards, perhaps, ships shun the place; leaping
over it as silly sheep leap over a vacuum, because their leader originally leaped
there when a stick was held. There's your law of precedents; there's your utility
of traditions; there's the story of your obstinate survival of old beliefs never
bottomed on the earth, and now not even hovering in the air! There's ortho-
doxy!

Thus, while in life the great whale's body may have been a real terror to
his foes, in his death his ghost becomes a powerless panic to a world.

Are you a believer in ghosts, my friend? There are other ghosts than
the Cock-Lane one, and far deeper men than Doctor Johnson who believe in
them.

CHAPTER LXX

THE SPHYNX

IT should not have been omitted that previous to completely stripping the
body of the leviathan, he was beheaded. Now, the beheading of the Sperm
Whale is a scientific anatomical feat, upon which experienced whale surgeons
very much pride themselves: and not without reason.

Consider that the whale has nothing that can properly be called a neck;
on the contrary, where his head and body seem to join, there, in that very
place, is the thickest part of him. Remember, also, that the surgeon must
operate from above, some eight or ten feet intervening between him and his
subject, and that subject almost hidden in a discolored, rolling, and oftentimes
tumultuous and bursting sea. Bear in mind, too, that under these untoward
circumstances he has to cut many feet deep in the flesh; and in that subterraneous manner, without so much as getting one single peep into the ever-
contracting gash thus made, he must skilfully steer clear of all adjacent, interdicted parts, and exactly divide the spine at a critical point hard by its insertion
into the skull. Do you not marvel, then, at Stubb's boast, that he demanded
but ten minutes to behead a sperm whale?

When first severed, the head is dropped astern and held there by a cable
till the body is stripped. That done, if it belong to a small whale it is hoisted
on deck to be deliberately disposed of. But, with a full grown leviathan this

is impossible; for the sperm whale's head embraces nearly one third of his entire bulk, and completely to suspend such a burden as that, even by the immense tackles of a whaler, this were as vain a thing as to attempt weighing a Dutch barn in jewellers' scales.

The Pequod's whale being decapitated and the body stripped, the head was hoisted against the ship's side—about half way out of the sea, so that it might yet in great part be buoyed up by its native element. And there with the strained craft steeply leaning over it, by reason of the enormous downward drag from the lower mast-head, and every yard-arm on that side projecting like a crane over the waves; there, that blood-dripping head hung to the Pequod's waist like the giant Holofernes's from the girdle of Judith.

When this last task was accomplished it was noon, and the seamen went below to their dinner. Silence reigned over the before tumultuous but now deserted deck. An intense copper calm, like a universal yellow lotus, was more and more unfolding its noiseless measureless leaves upon the sea.

A short space elapsed, and up into this noiselessness came Ahab alone from his cabin. Taking a few turns on the quarter-deck, he paused to gaze over the side, then slowly getting into the main-chains he took Stubb's long spade—still remaining there after the whale's decapitation—and striking it into the lower part of the half-suspended mass, placed its other end crutch-wise under one arm, and so stood leaning over with eyes attentively fixed on this head.

It was a black and hooded head; and hanging there in the midst of so intense a calm, it seemed the Sphynx's in the desert. "Speak, thou vast and venerable head," muttered Ahab, "which, though ungarnished with a beard, yet here and there lookest hoary with mosses; speak, mighty head, and tell us the secret thing that is in thee. Of all divers, thou hast dived the deepest. That head upon which the upper sun now gleams, has moved amid this world's foundations. Where unrecorded names and navies rust, and untold hopes and anchors rot; where in her murderous hold this frigate earth is ballasted with bones of millions of the drowned; there, in that awful water-land, there was thy most familiar home. Thou hast been where bell or diver never went; hast slept by many a sailor's side, where sleepless mothers would give their lives to lay them down. Thou saw'st the locked lovers when leaping from their flaming ship; heart to heart they sank beneath the exulting wave; true to each other, when heaven seemed false to them. Thou saw'st the murdered mate when tossed by pirates from the midnight deck; for hours he fell into the deeper midnight of the insatiate maw; and his murderers still sailed on unharmed—while swift lightnings shivered the neighboring ship that would have borne a righteous husband to outstretched, longing arms. O head! thou hast seen enough to split the planets and make an infidel of Abraham, and not one syllable is thine!"

"Sail ho!" cried a triumphant voice from the main-mast-head.

"Aye? Well, now, that's cheering," cried Ahab, suddenly erecting himself, while whole thunder-clouds swept aside from his brow. "That lively cry upon this deadly calm might almost convert a better man.—Where away?"

"Three points on the starboard bow, sir, and bringing down her breeze to us!"

"Better and better, man. Would now St. Paul would come along that way, and to my breezelessness bring his breeze! O Nature, and O soul of man! how far beyond all utterance are your linked analogies! not the smallest atom stirs or lives on matter, but has its cunning duplicate in mind."

CHAPTER LXXI

THE JEROBOAM'S STORY

HAND in hand, ship and breeze blew on; but the breeze came faster than the ship, and soon the Pequod began to rock.

By and by, through the glass the stranger's boats and manned mast-heads proved her a whale-ship. But as she was so far to windward, and shooting by, apparently making a passage to some other ground, the Pequod could not hope to reach her. So the signal was set to see what response would be made.

Here be it said, that like the vessels of military marines, the ships of the American Whale Fleet have each a private signal; all which signals being collected in a book with the names of the respective vessels attached, every captain is provided with it. Thereby, the whale commanders are enabled to recognise each other upon the ocean, even at considerable distances, and with no small facility.

The Pequod's signal was at last responded to by the stranger's setting her own; which proved the ship to be the Jeroboam of Nantucket. Squaring her yards, she bore down, ranged abeam under the Pequod's lee, and lowered a boat; it soon drew nigh; but, as the side-ladder was being rigged by Starbuck's order to accommodate the visiting captain, the stranger in question waved his hand from his boat's stern in token of that proceeding being entirely unnecessary. It turned out that the Jeroboam had a malignant epidemic on board, and that Mayhew, her captain, was fearful of infecting the Pequod's company. For, though himself and boat's crew remained untainted, and though his ship was half a rifle-shot off, and an incorruptible sea and air rolling and flowing between; yet conscientiously adhering to the timid quarantine of the land, he peremptorily refused to come into direct contact with the Pequod.

But this did by no means prevent all communication. Preserving an interval of some few yards between itself and the ship, the Jeroboam's boat by the occasional use of its oars contrived to keep parallel to the Pequod, as she heavily forged through the sea (for by this time it blew very fresh), with her main-topsail aback; though, indeed, at times by the sudden onset of a large rolling wave, the boat would be pushed some way ahead; but would be soon skilfully brought to her proper bearings again. Subject to this, and other the like interruptions now and then, a conversation was sustained between the two parties; but at intervals not without still another interruption of a very different sort.

Pulling an oar in the Jeroboam's boat, was a man of a singular appearance, even in that wild whaling life where individual notabilities make up all totalities. He was a small, short, youngish man, sprinkled all over his face with freckles, and wearing redundant yellow hair. A long-skirted cabalistically-cut coat of a faded walnut tinge enveloped him; the overlapping sleeves of which were rolled up on his wrists. A deep, settled, fanatic delirium was in his eyes.

So soon as this figure had been first descried, Stubb had exclaimed—"That's he! that's he!—the long-togged scaramouch the Town-Ho's company told us of!" Stubb here alluded to a strange story told of the Jeroboam, and a certain man among her crew, some time previous when the Pequod spoke the Town-Ho. According to this account and what was subsequently learned, it seemed that the scaramouch in question had gained a wonderful ascendency over almost everybody in the Jeroboam. His story was this:

He had been originally nurtured among the crazy society of Neskyeuna Shakers, where he had been a great prophet; in their cracked, secret meetings having several times descended from heaven by the way of a trap-door, announcing the speedy opening of the seventh vial, which he carried in his vest-pocket; but, which, instead of containing gunpowder, was supposed to be charged with laudanum. A strange, apostolic whim having seized him, he had left Neskyeuna for Nantucket, where, with that cunning peculiar to craziness, he assumed a steady, common sense exterior, and offered himself as a green-hand candidate for the Jeroboam's whaling voyage. They engaged him; but straightway upon the ship's getting out of sight of land, his insanity broke out in a freshet. He announced himself as the archangel Gabriel, and commanded the captain to jump overboard. He published his manifesto, whereby he set himself forth as the deliverer of the isles of the sea and vicar-general of all Oceanica. The unflinching earnestness with which he declared these things;—the dark, daring play of his sleepless, excited imagination, and all the preternatural terrors of real delirium, united to invest this Gabriel in the minds of the majority of the ignorant crew, with an atmosphere of sacredness. Moreover, they were afraid of him. As such a man, however, was not of much practical use in the ship, especially as he refused to work except when he pleased, the incredulous captain would fain have been rid of him; but apprised that that individual's intention was to land him in the first convenient port, the archangel forthwith opened all his seals and vials—devoting the ship and all hands to unconditional perdition, in case this intention was carried out. So strongly did he work upon his disciples among the crew, that at last in a body they went to the captain and told him if Gabriel was sent from the ship, not a man of them would remain. He was therefore forced to relinquish his plan. Nor would they permit Gabriel to be any way maltreated, say or do what he would; so that it came to pass that Gabriel had the complete freedom of the ship. The consequence of all this was, that the archangel cared little or nothing for the captain and mates; and since the epidemic had broken out, he carried a higher hand than ever; declaring that the plague, as he called it, was at his sole command; nor should it be stayed but according to his good pleasure. The sailors, mostly poor devils, cringed, and some of them fawned before him; in obedience to his instructions, sometimes rendering him personal homage, as to a god. Such things may seem incredible; but, however wondrous, they are true. Nor is the history of fanatics half so striking in respect to the measureless self-deception of the fanatic himself, as his measureless power of deceiving and bedevilling so many others. But it is time to return to the Pequod.

"I fear not thy epidemic, man," said Ahab from the bulwarks, to Captain Mayhew, who stood in the boat's stern; "come on board."

But now Gabriel started to his feet.

"Think, think of the fevers, yellow and bilious! Beware of the horrible plague!"

"Gabriel, Gabriel!" cried Captain Mayhew; "thou must either—" But that instant a headlong wave shot the boat far ahead, and its seethings drowned all speech.

"Hast thou seen the White Whale?" demanded Ahab, when the boat drifted back.

"Think, think of thy whale-boat, stoven and sunk! Beware of the horrible tail!"

"I tell thee again, Gabriel, that—" But again the boat tore ahead as if dragged by fiends. Nothing was said for some moments, while a succession of riotous waves rolled by, which by one of those occasional caprices of the seas were tumbling, not heaving it. Meantime, the hoisted sperm whale's head jogged about very violently, and Gabriel was seen eyeing it with rather more apprehensiveness than his archangel nature seemed to warrant.

When this interlude was over, Captain Mayhew began a dark story concerning Moby-Dick; not, however, without frequent interruptions from Gabriel, whenever his name was mentioned, and the crazy sea that seemed leagued with him.

It seemed that the Jeroboam had not long left home, when upon speaking a whale-ship, her people were reliably apprised of the existence of Moby-Dick, and the havoc he had made. Greedily sucking in this intelligence, Gabriel solemnly warned the captain against attacking the White Whale, in case the monster should be seen; in his gibbering insanity, pronouncing the White Whale to be no less a being than the Shaker God incarnated; the Shakers receiving the Bible. But when, some year or two afterwards, Moby-Dick was fairly sighted from the mast-heads, Macey, the chief mate, burned with ardor to encounter him; and the captain himself being not unwilling to let him have the opportunity, despite all the archangel's denunciations and forewarnings, Macey succeeded in persuading five men to man his boat. With them he pushed off; and, after much weary pulling, and many perilous, unsuccessful onsets, he at last succeeded in getting one iron fast. Meantime, Gabriel, ascending to the main-royal mast-head, was tossing one arm in frantic gestures, and hurling forth prophecies of speedy doom to the sacrilegious assailants of his divinity. Now, while Macey, the mate, was standing up in his boat's bow, and with all the reckless energy of his tribe was venting his wild exclamations upon the whale, and essaying to get a fair chance for his poised lance, lo! a broad white shadow rose from the sea; by its quick, fanning motion, temporarily taking the breath out of the bodies of the oarsmen. Next instant, the luckless mate, so full of furious life, was smitten bodily into the air, and making a long arc in his descent, fell into the sea at the distance of about fifty yards. Not a chip of the boat was harmed, nor a hair of any oarsman's head; but the mate for ever sank.

It is well to parenthesize here, that of the fatal accidents in the Sperm-Whale Fishery, this kind is perhaps almost as frequent as any. Sometimes, nothing is injured but the man who is thus annihilated; oftener the boat's bow is knocked off, or the thigh-board, in which the headsman stands, is torn from its place and accompanies the body. But strangest of all is the circumstance, that in more instances than one, when the body has been recovered, not a single mark of violence is discernible; the man being stark dead.

The whole calamity, with the falling form of Macey, was plainly descried from the ship. Raising a piercing shriek—"The vial! the vial!" Gabriel called off the terror-stricken crew from the further hunting of the whale. This terrible event clothed the archangel with added influence; because his credulous disciples believed that he had specifically foreannounced it, instead of only making a general prophecy, which any one might have done, and so have chanced to hit one of many marks in the wide margin allowed. He became a nameless terror to the ship.

Mayhew having concluded his narration, Ahab put such questions to him, that the stranger captain could not forbear inquiring whether he intended to hunt the White Whale, if opportunity should offer. To which Ahab answered—

"Aye." Straightway, then, Gabriel once more started to his feet, glaring upon the old man, and vehemently exclaimed, with downward pointed finger—"Think, think of the blasphemer—dead, and down there!—beware of the blasphemer's end!"

Ahab stolidly turned aside; then said to Mayhew, "Captain, I have just bethought me of my letter-bag; there is a letter for one of thy officers, if I mistake not. Starbuck, look over the bag."

Every whale-ship takes out a goodly number of letters for various ships, whose delivery to the persons to whom they may be addressed, depends upon the mere chance of encountering them in the four oceans. Thus, most letters never reach their mark; and many are only received after attaining an age of two or three years or more.

Soon Starbuck returned with a letter in his hand. It was sorely tumbled, damp, and covered with a dull, spotted, green mould, in consequence of being kept in a dark locker of the cabin. Of such a letter, Death himself might well have been the post-boy.

"Can'st not read it?" cried Ahab. "Give it me, man. Aye, aye, it's but a dim scrawl;—what's this?" As he was studying it out, Starbuck took a long cutting-spade pole, and with his knife slightly split the end, to insert the letter there, and in that way, hand it to the boat, without its coming any closer to the ship.

Meantime, Ahab holding the letter, muttered, "Mr. Har—yes, Mr. Harry— (a woman's pinny hand,—the man's wife, I'll wager)—Aye—Mr. Harry Macey, Ship Jeroboam;—why it's Macey, and he's dead!"

"Poor fellow! poor fellow! and from his wife," sighed Mayhew; "but let me have it."

"Nay, keep it thyself," cried Gabriel to Ahab; "thou art soon going that way."

"Curses throttle thee!" yelled Ahab. "Captain Mayhew, stand by now to receive it;" and taking the fatal missive from Starbuck's hands, he caught it in the slit of the pole, and reached it over towards the boat. But as he did so, the oarsmen expectantly desisted from rowing; the boat drifted a little towards the ship's stern; so that, as if by magic, the letter suddenly ranged along with Gabriel's eager hand. He clutched it in an instant, seized the boat-knife, and impaling the letter on it, sent it thus loaded back into the ship. It fell at Ahab's feet. Then Gabriel shrieked out to his comrades to give way with their oars, and in that manner the mutinous boat rapidly shot away from the Pequod.

As, after this interlude, the seamen resumed their work upon the jacket of the whale, many strange things were hinted in reference to this wild affair.

CHAPTER LXXII

THE MONKEY-ROPE

IN the tumultuous business of cutting-in and attending to a whale, there is much running backwards and forwards among the crew. Now hands are wanted here, and then again hands are wanted there. There is no staying in any one place; for at one and the same time everything has to be done everywhere. It is much the same with him who endeavors the description of the scene. We must now retrace our way a little. It was mentioned that upon first breaking ground in the whale's back, the blubber-hook was inserted into the original hole there cut by the spades of the mates. But how did so clumsy and weighty a mass as that same hook get fixed in that hole? It was inserted there by my particular friend Queequeg, whose duty it was, as harpooneer, to descend upon the monster's back for the special purpose referred to. But in very many cases, circumstances require that the harpooneer shall remain on the whale till the whole flensing or stripping operation is concluded. The whale, be it observed, lies almost entirely submerged, excepting the immediate parts operated upon. So down there, some ten feet below the level of the deck, the poor harpooneer flounders about, half on the whale and half in the water, as the vast mass revolves like a tread-mill beneath him. On the occasion in question, Queequeg figured in the Highland costume—a shirt and socks—in which to my eyes, at least, he appeared to uncommon advantage; and no one had a better chance to observe him, as will presently be seen.

Being the savage's bowsman, that is, the person who pulled the bow-oar in his boat (the second one from forward), it was my cheerful duty to attend upon him while taking that hard-scrabble scramble upon the dead whale's back. You have seen Italian organ-boys holding a dancing-ape by a long cord. Just so, from the ship's steep side, did I hold Queequeg down there in the sea, by what is technically called in the fishery a monkey-rope, attached to a strong strip of canvas belted round his waist.

It was a humorously perilous business for both of us. For, before we proceed further, it must be said that the monkey-rope was fast at both ends; fast to Queequeg's broad canvas belt, and fast to my narrow leather one. So that for better or for worse, we two, for the time, were wedded; and should poor Queequeg sink to rise no more, then both usage and honor demanded, that instead of cutting the cord, it should drag me down in his wake. So, then, an elongated Siamese ligature united us. Queequeg was my own inseparable twin brother; nor could I any way get rid of the dangerous liabilities which the hempen bond entailed.

So strongly and metaphysically did I conceive of my situation then, that while earnestly watching his motions, I seemed distinctly to perceive that my own individuality was now merged in a joint stock company of two: that my free will had received a mortal wound; and that another's mistake or misfortune might plunge innocent me into unmerited disaster and death. Therefore, I saw that here was a sort of interregnum in Providence; for its even-handed equity never could have sanctioned so gross an injustice. And yet still further pondering—while I jerked him now and then from between the whale and the ship, which would threaten to jam him—still further pondering, I say, I saw that this situation of mine was the precise situation of every mortal that breathes; only, in most cases, he, one way or other, has this Siamese connexion with a plurality of other mortals. If your banker breaks, you snap; if your apothecary by mistake sends you poison in your pills, you die. True, you may say that, by exceeding caution, you may possibly escape these and the multitudinous other evil chances of life. But handle Queequeg's monkey-rope heedfully as I would, sometimes he jerked it so, that I came very near sliding overboard. Nor could I possibly forget that, do what I would, I only had the management of one end of it.

I have hinted that I would often jerk poor Queequeg from between the whale and the ship—where he would occasionally fall, from the incessant rolling and swaying of both. But this was not the only jamming jeopardy he was exposed to. Unappalled by the massacre made upon them during the night, the sharks now freshly and more keenly allured by the before pent blood which began to flow from the carcase—the rabid creatures swarmed round it like bees in a beehive.

And right in among those sharks was Queequeg; who often pushed them aside with his floundering feet. A thing altogether incredible were it not that attracted by such prey as a dead whale, the otherwise miscellaneously carnivorous shark will seldom touch a man.

Nevertheless, it may well be believed that since they have such a ravenous finger in the pie, it is deemed but wise to look sharp to them. Accordingly, besides the monkey-rope, with which I now and then jerked the poor fellow from too close a vicinity to the maw of what seemed a peculiarly ferocious shark—he was provided with still another protection. Suspended over the side in one of the stages, Tashtego and Daggoo continually flourished over his head a couple of keen whale-spades, wherewith they slaughtered as many sharks as they could reach. This procedure of theirs, to be sure, was very disinterested and benevolent of them. They meant Queequeg's best happiness, I admit; but in their hasty zeal to befriend him, and from the circumstance that both he and the sharks were at times half hidden by the blood mudded water, those indiscreet spades of theirs would come nearer amputating a leg than a tail. But poor Queequeg, I suppose, straining and gasping there with that great iron hook— poor Queequeg, I suppose, only prayed to his Yojo, and gave up his life into the hands of his gods.

Well, well, my dear comrade and twin-brother, thought I, as I drew in and then slacked off the rope to every swell of the sea—what matters it, after all? Are you not the precious image of each and all of us men in this whaling world? That unsounded ocean you gasp in, is Life; those sharks, your foes; those spades, your friends; and what between sharks and spades you are in a sad pickle and peril, poor lad.

But courage! there is good cheer in store for you, Queequeg. For now, as with blue lips and bloodshot eyes the exhausted savage at last climbs up the chains and stands all dripping and involuntarily trembling over the side; the steward advances, and with a benevolent, consolatory glance hands him—what? Some hot Cogniac? No! hands him, ye gods; hands him a cup of tepid ginger and water!

"Ginger? Do I smell ginger?" suspiciously asked Stubb, coming near. "Yes, this must be ginger," peering into the as yet untasted cup. Then standing as if incredulous for a while, he calmly walked towards the astonished steward slowly saying, "Ginger? ginger? and will you have the goodness to tell me, Mr. Dough-Boy, where lies the virtue of ginger? Ginger! is ginger the sort of fuel you use, Dough-Boy, to kindle a fire in this shivering cannibal? Ginger!—what the devil is ginger?—sea-coal?—fire-wood?—lucifer matches?—tinder?—gunpowder?— what the devil is ginger, I say, that you offer this cup to our poor Queequeg here?"

"There is some sneaking Temperance Society movement about this business," he suddenly added, now approaching Starbuck, who had just come from forward. "Will you look at that kannakin, sir: smell of it, if you please." Then watching the mate's countenance, he add: "The steward, Mr. Starbuck, had the face to offer that calomel and jalap to Queequeg, there, this instant off the whale. Is the steward an apothecary, sir? and may I ask whether this is the sort of bitters by which he blows back the life into a half-drowned man?"

"I trust not," said Starbuck, "it is poor stuff enough."

"Aye, aye, steward," cried Stubb, "we'll teach you to drug a harpooneer; none of your apothecary's medicine here; you want to poison us, do ye? You have got out insurances on our lives and want to murder us all, and pocket the proceeds, do ye?"

"It was not me," cried Dough-Boy, "it was Aunt Charity that brought the ginger on board; and bade me never give the harpooneers any spirits, but only this ginger-jub—so she called it."

"Ginger-jub! you gingerly rascal! take that! and run along with ye to the lockers, and get something better. I hope I do no wrong, Mr. Starbuck. It is the captain's orders—grog for the harpooneer on a whale."

"Enough," replied Starbuck, "only don't hit him again, but——"

"Oh, I never hurt when I hit, except when I hit a whale or something of that sort; and this fellow's a weazel. What were you about saying, sir?"

"Only this: go down with him, and get what thou wantest thyself."

When Stubb reappeared, he came with a dark flask in one hand, and a sort of tea-caddy in the other. The first contained strong spirits, and was handed to Queequeg; the second was Aunt Charity's gift, and that was freely given to the waves.

CHAPTER LXXIII

STUBB AND FLASK KILL A RIGHT WHALE; AND THEN HAVE A TALK OVER HIM

It must be borne in borne in mind that all this time we have a Sperm Whale's prodigious head hanging to the Pequod's side. But we must let it continue hanging there a while till we can get a chance to attend to it. For the present other matters press, and the best we can do now for the head, is to pray heaven the tackles may hold.

Now, during the past night and forenoon, the Pequod had gradually drifted into a sea, which, by its occasional patches of yellow brit, gave unusual tokens of the vicinity of Right Whales, a species of the Leviathan that but few supposed to be at this particular time lurking anywhere near. And though all hands commonly disdained the capture of those inferior creatures; and though the Pequod was not commissioned to cruise for them at all, and though she had passed numbers of them near the Crozetts without lowering a boat; yet now that a Sperm Whale had been brought alongside and beheaded, to the surprise of all, the announcement was made that a Right Whale should be captured that day, if opportunity offered.

Nor was this long wanting. Tall spouts were seen to leeward; and two boats, Stubb's and Flask's, were detached in pursuit. Pulling further and further away, they at last became almost invisible to the men at the mast-head. But suddenly in the distance, they saw a great heap of tumultuous white water, and soon after news came from aloft that one or both the boats must be fast. An interval passed and the boats were in plain sight, in the act of being dragged right towards the ship by the towing whale. So close did the monster come to the hull, that at first it seemed as if he meant it malice; but suddenly going down in a maelstrom, within three rods of the planks, he wholly disappeared from view, as if diving under the keel. "Cut, cut!" was the cry from the ship to the boats, which, for one instant, seemed on the point of being brought with a deadly dash against the vessel's side. But having plenty of line yet in the tubs, and the whale not sounding very rapidly, they paid out abundance of rope, and at the same time pulled with all their might so as to get ahead of the ship. For a few minutes the struggle was intensely critical; for while they still slacked out the tightened line in one direction, and still plied their oars in another, the contending strain threatened to take them under. But it was only a few feet advance they sought to gain. And they stuck to it till they did gain it; when instantly, a swift tremor was felt running like lightning along the keel, as the strained line, scraping beneath the ship, suddenly rose to view under her bows, snapping and quivering; and so flinging off its drippings, that the drops fell like bits of broken glass on the water, while the whale beyond also rose to sight, and once more the boats were free to fly. But the fagged whale abated his speed, and blindly altering his course, went round the stern of the ship towing the two boats after him, so that they performed a complete circuit.

Meantime, they hauled more and more upon their lines, till close flanking him on both sides, Stubb answered Flask with lance for lance; and thus round and round the Pequod the battle went, while the multitudes of sharks that had before swum round the Sperm Whale's body, rushed to the fresh blood that was spilled, thirstily drinking at every new gash, as the eager Israelites did at the new bursting fountains that poured from the smitten rock.

At last his spout grew thick, and with a frightful roll and vomit, he turned upon his back a corpse.

While the two headsmen were engaged in making fast cords to his flukes, and in other ways getting the mass in readiness for towing, some conversation ensued between them.

"I wonder what the old man wants with this lump of foul lard," said Stubb, not without some disgust at the thought of having to do with so ignoble a leviathan.

"Wants with it?" said Flask, coiling some spare line in the boat's bow, "did you never hear that the ship which but once has a Sperm Whale's head hoisted on her starboard side, and at the same time a Right Whale's on the larboard; did you never hear, Stubb, that that ship can never afterwards capsize?"

"Why not?"

"I don't know, but I heard that gamboge ghost of a Fedallah saying so, and he seems to know all about ships' charms. But I sometimes think he'll charm the ship to no good at last. I don't half like that chap, Stubb. Did you ever notice how that tusk of his is a sort of carved into a snake's head, Stubb?"

"Sink him! I never look at him at all; but if ever I get a chance of a dark night, and he standing hard by the bulwarks, and no one by; look down there, Flask"—pointing into the sea with a peculiar motion of both hands—"Aye, will I! Flask, I take that Fedallah to be the devil in disguise. Do you believe that cock and bull story about his having been stowed away on board ship? He's the devil, I say. The reason why you don't see his tail, is because he tucks it up out of sight; he carries it coiled away in his pocket, I guess. Blast him! now that I think of it, he's always wanting oakum to stuff into the toes of his boots."

"He sleeps in his boots, don't he? He hasn't got any hammock; but I've seen him lay of nights in a coil of rigging."

"No doubt, and it's because of his cursed tail; he coils it down, do ye see, in the eye of the rigging."

"What's the old man have so much to do with him for?"

"Striking up a swap or a bargain, I suppose."

"Bargain?—about what?"

"Why, do ye see, the old man is hard bent after that White Whale, and the devil there is trying to come round him, and get him to swap away his silver watch, or his soul, or something of that sort, and then he'll surrender Moby-Dick."

"Pooh! Stubb, you are skylarking; how can Fedallah do that?"

"I don't know, Flask, but the devil is a curious chap, and a wicked one, I tell ye. Why, they say as how he went a sauntering into the old flag-ship once, switching his tail about devilish easy and gentlemanlike, and inquiring if the old governor was at home. Well, he was at home, and asked the devil what he wanted. The devil, switching his hoofs, up and says, "I want John." "What for?" says the old governor. "What business is that of yours?" says the devil, getting mad,—"I want to use him." "Take him," says the governor—and by the Lord, Flask, if the devil didn't give John the Asiatic cholera before he got through with him, I'll eat this whale in one mouthful. But look sharp—ain't you all ready there? Well, then, pull ahead, and let's get the whale alongside."

"I think I remember some such story as you were telling," said Flask, when at last the two boats were slowly advancing with their burden towards the ship, "but I can't remember where."

"Three Spaniards? Adventures of those three bloody-minded soldadoes? Did ye read it there, Flask? I guess ye did?"

"No: never saw such a book; heard of it, though. But now, tell me, Stubb, do you suppose that that devil you was speaking of just now, was the same you say is now on board the Pequod?"

"Am I the same man that helped kill this whale? Doesn't the devil live for ever; who ever heard that the devil was dead? Did you ever see any parson a wearing mourning for the devil? And if the devil has a latch-key to get into the admiral's cabin, don't you suppose he can crawl into a porthole? Tell me that, Mr. Flask?"

"How old do you suppose Fedallah is, Stubb?"

"Do you see that mainmast there?" pointing to the ship; "well, that's the figure one; now take all the hoops in the Pequod's hole, and string 'em along in a row with that mast, for oughts, do you see; well, that wouldn't begin to be Fedallah's age. Nor all the coopers in creation couldn't show hoops enough to make oughts enough."

"But see here, Stubb, I thought you a little boasted just now, that you meant to give Fedallah a sea-toss, if you got a good chance. Now, if he's so old as all those hoops of yours come to, and if he is going to live for ever, what good will it do to pitch him overboard—tell me that?"

"Give him a good ducking, anyhow."

"But he'd crawl back."

"Duck him again; and keep ducking him."

"Suppose he should take it into his head to duck you, though—yes, and drown you—what then?"

"I should like to see him try it; I'd give him such a pair of black eyes that he wouldn't dare to show his face in the admiral's cabin again for a long while, let alone down in the orlop there, where he lives, and hereabouts on the upper decks where he sneaks so much. Damn the devil, Flask; so you suppose I'm afraid of the devil? Who's afraid of him, except the old governor who daresn't catch him and put him in double-darbies, as he deserves, but lets him go about kidnapping people; aye, and signed a bond with him, that all the people the devil kidnapped, he'd roast for him? There's a governor!"

"Do you suppose Fedallah wants to kidnap Captain Ahab?"

"Do I suppose it? You'll know it before long, Flask. But I am going now to keep a sharp lookout on him; and if I see anything very suspicious going on, I'll just take him by the nape of his neck, and say—Look here, Beelzebub, you don't do it; and if he makes any fuss, by the Lord I'll make a grab into his pocket for his tail, take it to the capstan, and give him such a wrenching and heaving, that his tail will come short off at the stump—do you see; and then, I rather guess when he finds himself docked in that queer fashion, he'll sneak off without the poor satisfaction of feeling his tail between his legs."

"And what will you do with the tail, Stubb?"

"Do with it? Sell it for an ox whip when we get home;—what else?"

"Now, do you mean what you say, and have been saying all along, Stubb?"

"Mean or not mean, here we are at the ship."

The boats were here hailed, to tow the whale on the larboard side, where fluke chains and other necessaries were already prepared for securing him.

"Didn't I tell you so?" said Flask; "yes, you'll soon see this right whale's head hoisted up opposite that parmacetti's."

In good time, Flask's saying proved true. As before, the Pequod steeply leaned over towards the sperm whale's head, now, by the counterpoise of both heads, she regained her even keel; though sorely strained, you may well believe. So, when on one side you hoist in Locke's head, you go over that way; but now, on the other side, hoist in Kant's and you come back again; but in very poor plight. Thus, some minds for ever keep trimming boat. Oh, ye foolish! throw all these thunder-heads overboard, and then you will float light and right.

In disposing of the body of a right whale, when brought alongside the ship, the same preliminary proceedings commonly take place as in the case of a sperm whale; only, in the latter instance, the head is cut off whole, but in the former the lips and tongue are separately removed and hoisted on deck, with all the well known black bone attached to what is called the crown-piece. But nothing like this, in the present case, had been done. The carcases of both whales had dropped astern; and the head-laden ship not a little resembled a mule carrying a pair of overburdening panniers.

Meantime, Fedallah was calmly eyeing the right whale's head, and ever and anon glancing from the deep wrinkles there to the lines in his own hand. And Ahab chanced so to stand, that the Parsee occupied his shadow; while, if the Parsee's shadow was there at all it seemed only to blend with, and lengthen Ahab's. As the crew toiled on, Laplandish speculations were bandied among them, concerning all these passing things.

CHAPTER LXXIV

THE SPERM WHALE'S HEAD—CONTRASTED VIEW

HERE, now, are two great whales, laying their heads together; let us join them, and lay together our own.

Of the grand order of folio leviathans, the Sperm Whale and the Right Whale are by far the most noteworthy. They are the only whales regularly hunted by man. To the Nantucketer, they present the two extremes of all the known varieties of the whale. As the external difference between them is mainly observable in their heads; and as a head of each is this moment hanging from the Pequod's side; and as we may freely go from one to the other, by merely stepping across the deck:—where, I should like to know, will you obtain a better chance to study practical cetology than here?

In the first place, you are struck by the general contrast between these heads. Both are massive enough in all conscience; but there is a certain mathematical symmetry in the Sperm Whale's which the Right Whale's sadly lacks. There is more character in the Sperm Whale's head. As you behold it, you involuntarily yield the immense superiority to him, in point of pervading dignity. In the present instance, too, this dignity is heightened by the pepper and salt color of his head at the summit, giving token of advanced age and large experience. In short, he is what the fishermen technically call a "grey-headed whale."

Let us now note what is least dissimilar in these heads—namely, the two most important organs, the eye and the ear. Far back on the side of the head, and low down, near the angle of either whale's jaw, if you narrowly search, you will at last see a lashless eye, which you would fancy to be a young colt's eye; so out of all proportion is it to the magnitude of the head.

Now, from this peculiar sideway position of the whale's eyes, it is plain that he can never see an object which is exactly ahead, no more than he can one exactly astern. In a word, the position of the whale's eyes corresponds to that of a man's ears; and you may fancy, for yourself, how it would fare with you, did you sideways survey objects through your ears. You would find that you could only command some thirty degrees of vision in advance of the straight side-line of sight; and about thirty more behind it. If your bitterest foe were walking straight towards you, with dagger uplifted in broad day, you would not be able to see him, any more than if he were stealing upon you from behind. In a word, you would have two backs, so to speak; but, at the same time, also, two fronts (side fronts): for what is it that makes the front of a man—what, indeed, but his eyes?

Moreover, while in most other animals that I can now think of, the eyes are so planted as imperceptibly to blend their visual power, so as to produce one picture and not two to the brain; the peculiar position of the whale's eyes, effectually divided as they are by many cubic feet of solid head, which towers between them like a great mountain separating two lakes in valleys; this, of course, must wholly separate the impressions which each independent organ imparts. The whale, therefore, must see one distinct picture on this side, and another distinct picture on that side; while all between must be profound darkness and nothingness to him. Man may, in effect, be said to look out on the world from a sentry-box with two joined sashes for his window. But with the whale, these two sashes are separately inserted, making two distinct windows, but sadly impairing the view. This peculiarity of the whale's eyes is a thing always to be borne in mind in the fishery; and to be remembered by the reader in some subsequent scenes.

A curious and most puzzling question might be started concerning this visual matter as touching the Leviathan. But I must be content with a hint. So long as a man's eyes are open in the light, the act of seeing is involuntary; that is, he cannot then help mechanically seeing whatever objects are before him. Nevertheless, any one's experience will teach him, that though he can take in an undiscriminating sweep of things at one glance, it is quite impossible for him, attentively, and completely, to examine any two things—however large or however small—at one and the same instant of time; never mind if they lie side by side and touch each other. But if you now come to separate these two objects, and surround each by a circle of profound darkness; then, in order to see one of them, in such a manner as to bring your mind to bear on it, the other will be utterly excluded from your contemporary consciousness. How is it, then, with the whale? True, both his eyes, in themselves, must simultaneously act; but is his brain so much more comprehensive, combining, and subtle than man's, that he can at the same moment of time attentively examine two distinct prospects, one on one side of him, and the other in an exactly opposite direction? If he can, then is it as marvellous a thing in him, as if a man were able simultaneously to go through the demonstrations of two distinct problems in Euclid. Nor, strictly investigated, is there any incongruity in this comparison.

It may be but an idle whim, but it has always seemed to me, that the extraordinary vacillations of movement displayed by some whales when beset by three or four boats; the timidity and liability to queer frights, so common to such whales; I think that all this indirectly proceeds from the helpless perplexity of volition, in which their divided and diametrically opposite powers of vision must involve them.

But the ear of the whale is full as curious as the eye. If you are an entire stranger to their race, you might hunt over these two heads for hours, and never discover that organ. The ear has no external leaf whatever; and into the hole itself you can hardly insert a quill, so wondrously minute is it. It is lodged a little behind the eye. With respect to their ears, this important difference is to be observed between the sperm whale and the right. While the ear of the former has an external opening, that of the latter is entirely and evenly covered over with a membrane, so as to be quite imperceptible from without.

Is it not curious, that so vast a being as the whale should see the world through so small an eye, and hear the thunder through an ear which is smaller than a hare's? But if his eyes were broad as the lens of Herschel's great telescope; and his ears capacious as the porches of cathedrals; would that make him any longer of sight, or sharper of hearing? Not at all.—Why then do you try to "enlarge" your mind? Subtilize it.

Let us now with whatever levers and steam-engines we have at hand, cant over the sperm whale's head, so that it may lie bottom up; then, ascending by a ladder to the summit, have a peep down the mouth; and were it not that the body is now completely separated from it, with a lantern we might descend into the great Kentucky Mammoth Cave of his stomach. But let us hold on here by this tooth, and look about us where we are. What a really beautiful and chaste-looking mouth! from floor to ceiling, lined, or rather papered with a glistening white membrane, glossy as bridal satins.

But come out now, and look at this portentous lower jaw, which seems like the long narrow lid of an immense snuff-box, with the hinge at one end, instead of one side. If you pry it up, so as to get it overhead, and expose its rows of teeth, it seems a terrific portcullis; and such, alas! it proves to many a poor wight in the fishery, upon whom these spikes fall with impaling force. But far more terrible is it to behold, when fathoms down in the sea, you see some sulky whale, floating there suspended, with his prodigious jaw, some fifteen feet long, hanging straight down at right angles with his body, for all the world like a ship's jib-boom. This whale is not dead; he is only dispirited; out of sorts, perhaps; hypochondriac; and so supine, that the hinges of his jaw have relaxed, leaving him there in that ungainly sort of plight, a reproach to all his tribe, who must, no doubt, imprecate lock-jaws upon him.

In most cases this lower jaw—being easily unhinged by a practised artist—is disengaged and hoisted on deck for the purpose of extracting the ivory teeth, and furnishing a supply of that hard white whalebone with which the fishermen fashion all sorts of curious articles, including canes, umbrella-sticks, and handles to riding-whips.

With a long, weary hoist the jaw is dragged on board, as if it were an anchor; and when the proper time comes—some few days after the other work—Quee-queg, Daggoo, and Tashtego, being all accomplished dentists, are set to drawing teeth. With a keen cutting-spade, Queequeg lances the gums; then the jaw is lashed down to ringbolts, and a tackle being rigged from aloft, they drag out these teeth, as Michigan oxen drag stumps of old oaks out of wild wood-lands. There are generally forty-two teeth in all; in old whales, much worn down, but undecayed; nor filled after our artificial fashion. The jaw is afterwards sawn into slabs, and piled away like joists for building houses.

CHAPTER LXXV

THE RIGHT WHALE'S HEAD—CONTRASTED VIEW

CROSSING the deck, let us now have a good long look at the Right Whale's head.

As in general shape the noble Sperm Whale's head may be compared to a Roman war-chariot (especially in front, where it is so broadly rounded); so, at a broad view, the Right Whale's head bears a rather inelegant resemblance to a gigantic galliot-toed shoe. Two hundred years ago an old Dutch voyager likened its shape to that of a shoemaker's last. And in this same last or shoe, that old woman of the nursery tale with the swarming brood, might very comfortably be lodged, she and all her progeny.

But as you come nearer to this great head it begins to assume different aspects, according to your point of view. If you stand on its summit and look at these two f-shaped spout-holes, you would take the whole head for an enormous bass-viol, and these spiracles, the apertures in its sounding-board. Then, again, if you fix your eye upon this strange, crested, comb-like incrustation on the top of the mass—this green, barnacled thing, which the Greenlanders call the "crown," and the Southern fishers the "bonnet" of the Right Whale; fixing your eyes solely on this, you would take the head for the trunk of some huge oak, with a bird's nest in its crotch. At any rate, when you watch those live crabs that nestle here on this bonnet, such an idea will be almost sure to occur to you; unless, indeed, your fancy has been fixed by the technical term "crown" also bestowed upon it; in which case you will take great interest in thinking how this mighty monster is actually a diademed king of the sea, whose green crown has been put together for him in this marvellous manner. But if this whale be a king, he is a very sulky looking fellow to grace a diadem. Look at that hanging lower lip! what a huge sulk and pout is there! a sulk and pout, by carpenter's measurement, about twenty feet long and five feet deep; a sulk and pout that will yield you some 500 gallons of oil and more.

A great pity, now, that this unfortunate whale should be hare-lipped. The fissure is about a foot across. Probably the mother during an important in-

terval was sailing down the Peruvian coast, when earthquakes caused the beach
to gape. Over this lip, as over a slippery threshold, we now slide into the mouth.
Upon my word were I at Mackinaw, I should take this to be the inside of an
Indian wigwam.   Good Lord! is this the road that Jonah went?   The roof is
about twelve feet high, and runs to a pretty sharp angle, as if there were a
regular ridge-pole there; while these ribbed, arched, hairy sides, present us with
those wondrous, half vertical, scimetar-shaped slats of whalebone, say three
hundred on a side, which depending from the upper part of the head or crown
bone, form those Venetian blinds which have elsewhere been cursorily mentioned. The edges of these bones are fringed with hairy fibres, through which
the Right Whale strains the water, and in whose intricacies he retains the small
fish, when open-mouthed he goes through the seas of brit in feeding time.   In
the central blinds of bone, as they stand in their natural order, there are certain curious marks, curves, hollows, and ridges, whereby some whalemen calculate the creature's age, as the age of an oak by its circular rings.   Though the
certainty of this criterion is far from demonstrable, yet it has the savor of
analogical probability.   At any rate, if we yield to it, we must grant a far
greater age to the Right Whale than at first glance will seem reasonable.

In old times, there seem to have prevailed the most curious fancies concerning these blinds.   One voyager in Purchas calls them the wondrous "whiskers"
inside of the whale's mouth; another, "hogs' bristles;" a third old gentleman in
Hackluyt uses the following elegant language: "There are about two hundred
and fifty fins growing on each side of his upper *chop,* which arch over his tongue
on each side of his mouth."

As every one knows, these same "hogs' bristles," "fins," "whiskers," "blinds,"
or whatever you please, furnish to the ladies their busks and other stiffening
contrivances.   But in this particular, the demand has long been on the decline.
It was in Queen Anne's time that the bone was in its glory, the farthingale being
then all the fashion.   And as those ancient dames moved about gaily, though
in the jaws of the whale, as you may say; even so, in a shower, with the like
thoughtlessness, do we nowadays fly under the same jaws for protection; the
umbrella being a tent spread over the same bone.

But now forget all about blinds and whiskers for a moment, and, standing
in the Right Whale's mouth, look around you afresh.   Seeing all these colonnades
of bone so methodically ranged about, would you not think you were inside
of the great Haarlem organ, and gazing upon its thousand pipes?   For a carpet
to the organ we have a rug of the softest Turkey—the tongue, which is glued,
as it were, to the floor of the mouth.   It is very fat and tender, and apt to tear
in pieces in hoisting it on deck.   This particular tongue now before us; at a
passing glance I should say it was a six-barreler; that is, it will yield you about
that amount of oil.

Ere this, you must have plainly seen the truth of what I started with—
that the Sperm Whale and the Right Whale have almost entirely different heads.
To sum up, then: in the Right Whale's there is no great well of sperm; no ivory
teeth at all; no long, slender mandible of a lower jaw, like the Sperm Whale's.
Nor in the Sperm Whale are there any of those blinds of bone; no huge lower
lip; and scarcely anything of a tongue.   Again, the Right Whale has two external spout-holes, the Sperm Whale only one.

Look your last, now, on these venerable hooded heads, while they yet lie
together; for one will soon sink, unrecorded, in the sea; the other will not be
very long in following.

Can you catch the expression of the Sperm Whale's there?   It is the same he

died with, only some of the longer wrinkles in the forehead seem now faded
away.   I think his broad brow to be full of a prairie-like placidity, born of a
speculative indifference as to death.   But mark the other head's expression.   See
that amazing lower lip, pressed by accident against the vessel's side, so as firmly
to embrace the jaw.   Does not this whole head seem to speak of an enormous
practical resolution in facing death?   This Right Whale I take to have been a
Stoic; the Sperm Whale, a Platonian, who might have taken up Spinoza in his
latter years.

CHAPTER LXXVI

THE BATTERING-RAM

ERE quitting, for the nonce, the Sperm Whale's head, I would have you, as a
sensible physiologist, simply—particularly remark its front aspect, in all its compacted collectedness.   I would have you investigate it now with the sole view of
forming to yourself some unexaggerated, intelligent estimate of whatever battering-ram power may be lodged there.   Here is a vital point; for you must
either satisfactorily settle this matter with yourself, or for ever remain an infidel
as to one of the most appalling, but not the less true events, perhaps anywhere
to be found in all recorded history.

You observe that in the ordinary swimming position of the Sperm Whale,
the front of his head presents an almost wholly vertical plane to the water;
you observe that the lower part of that front slopes considerably backwards,
so as to furnish more of a retreat for the long socket which receives the boom-
like lower jaw; you observe that the mouth is entirely under the head, much
in the same way, indeed, as though your own mouth were entirely under your
chin.   Moreover you observe that the whale has no external nose; and that what
nose he has—his spout hole—is on the top of his head; you observe that his eyes
and ears are at the sides of his head; nearly one third of his entire length from
the front.   Wherefore, you must now have perceived that the front of the
Sperm Whale's head is a dead, blind wall, without a single organ or tender
prominence of any sort whatsoever.   Furthermore, you are now to consider that
only in the extreme, lower, backward sloping part of the front of the head, is
there the slightest vestige of bone; and not till you get near twenty feet from
the forehead do you come to the full cranial development.   So that this whole
enormous boneless mass is as one wad.   Finally, though, as will soon be revealed, its contents partly comprise the most delicate oil; yet, you are now
to be apprised of the nature of the substance which so impregnably invests all
that apparent effeminacy.   In some previous place I have described to you how
the blubber wraps the body of the whale, as the rind wraps an orange.   Just
so with the head; but with this difference: about the head this envelope, though
not so thick, is of a boneless toughness, inestimable by any man who has not
handled it.   The severest pointed harpoon, the sharpest lance darted by the
strongest human arm, impotently rebounds from it.   It is as though the forehead of the Sperm Whale were paved with horses' hoofs.   I do not think that
any sensation lurks in it.

Bethink yourself also of another thing.   When two large, loaded Indiamen
chance to crowd and crush towards each other in the docks, what do the sailors
do?   They do not suspend between them, at the point of coming contact, any

merely hard substance, like iron or wood. No, they hold there a large, round wad of tow and cork, enveloped in the thickest and toughest of ox-hide. That bravely and uninjured takes the jam which would have snapped all their oaken handspikes and iron crow-bars. By itself this sufficiently illustrates the obvious fact I drive at. But supplementary to this, it has hypothetically occurred to me, that as ordinary fish possess what is called a swimming bladder in them, capable, at will, of distension or contraction; and as the Sperm Whale, as far as I know, has no such provision in him; considering, too, the otherwise inexplicable manner in which he now depresses his head altogether beneath the surface, and anon swims with it high elevated out of the water; considering the. unobstructed elasticity of its envelop; considering the unique interior of his head; it has hypothetically occurred to me, I say, that those mystical lung-celled honeycombs there may possibly have some hitherto unknown and unsuspected connexion with the outer air, so as to be susceptible to atmospheric distension and contraction. If this be so, fancy the irresistibleness of that might, to which the most impalpable and destructive of all elements contributes.

Now, mark. Unerringly impelling this dead, impregnable, uninjurable wall, and this most buoyant thing within; there swims behind it all a mass of tremendous life, only to be adequately estimated as piled wood is—by the cord; and all obedient to one volition, as the smallest insect. So that when I shall hereafter detail to you all the specialties and concentrations of potency everywhere lurking in this expansive monster; when I shall show you some of his more inconsiderable braining feats; I trust you will have renounced all ignorant incredulity, and be ready to abide by this; that though the Sperm Whale stove a passage through the Isthmus of Darien, and mixed the Atlantic with the Pacific, you would not elevate one hair of your eye-brow. For unless you own the whale, you are but a provincial and sentimentalist in Truth. But clear Truth is a thing for salamander giants only to encounter; how small the chances for the provincials then? What befell the weakling youth lifting the dread goddess's veil at Lais?

CHAPTER LXXVII

THE GREAT HEIDELBURGH TUN

Now comes the Baling of the Case. But to comprehend it aright, you must know something of the curious internal structure of the thing operated upon.

Regarding the Sperm Whale's head as a solid oblong, you may, on an inclined plane, sideways divide it into two quoins; whereof the lower is the bony structure, forming the cranium and jaws, and the upper an unctuous mass wholly free from bones; its broad forward end forming the expanded vertical apparent forehead of the whale. At the middle of the forehead horizontally subdivide this upper quoin, and then you have two almost equal parts, which before were naturally divided by an internal wall of a thick tendinous substance.

The lower subdivided part, called the junk, is one immense honeycomb of oil, formed by the crossing and re-crossing, into ten thousand infiltrated cells, of tough elastic white fibres throughout its whole extent. The upper part, known as the Case, may be regarded as the great Heidelburgh Tun of the Sperm Whale. And as that famous great tierce is mystically carved in front, so the whale's vast plaited forehead forms innumerable strange devices for

emblematical adornment of his wondrous tun.   Moreover, as that of Heidelburgh was always replenished with the most excellent of the wines of the
Rhenish valleys, so the tun of the whale contains by far the most precious of
all his oily vintages; namely, the highly-prized spermaceti, in its absolutely
pure, limpid, and odoriferous state.   Nor is this precious substance found unalloyed in any other part of the creature.   Though in life it remains perfectly
fluid, yet, upon exposure to the air, after death, it soon begins to concrete;
sending forth beautiful crystalline shoots, as when the first thin delicate ice is
just forming in water.   A large whale's case generally yields about five hundred
gallons of sperm, though from unavoidable circumstances, considerable of it
is spilled, leaks, and dribbles away, or is otherwise irrevocably lost in the
ticklish business of securing what you can.

I know not with what fine and costly material the Heidelburgh Tun was
coated within, but in superlative richness that coating could not possibly have
compared with the silken pearl-colored membrane, like the lining of a fine
pelisse, forming the inner surface of the Sperm Whale's case.

It will have been seen that the Heidelburgh Tun of the Sperm Whale embraces the entire length of the entire top of the head; and since—as has been
elsewhere set forth—the head embraces one third of the whole length of the
creature, then setting that length down at eighty feet for a good sized whale,
you have more than twenty-six feet for the depth of the tun, when it is lengthwise hoisted up and down against a ship's side.

As in decapitating the whale, the operator's instrument is brought close
to the spot where an entrance is subsequently forced into the spermaceti magazine; he has, therefore, to be uncommonly heedful, lest a careless, untimely
stroke should invade the sanctuary and wastingly let out its invaluable contents.   It is this decapitated end of the head, also, which is at last elevated
out of the water, and retained in that position by the enormous cutting tackles,
whose hempen combinations, on one side, make quite a wilderness of ropes in
that quarter.

Thus much being said, attend now, I pray you, to that marvellous and—in
this particular instance—almost fatal operation whereby the Sperm Whale's
great Heidelburgh Tun is tapped.

CHAPTER LXXVIII

CISTERN AND BUCKETS

NIMBLE as a cat, Tashtego mounts aloft; and without altering his erect posture,
runs straight out upon the overhanging mainyard-arm, to the part where it
exactly projects over the hoisted Tun.   He has carried with him a light tackle
called a whip, consisting of only two parts, travelling through a single-sheaved
block.   Securing this block, so that it hangs down from the yard-arm, he swings
one end of the rope, till it is caught and firmly held by a hand on the deck.
Then, hand-over-hand, down the other part, the Indian drops through the air,
till dexterously he lands on the summit of the head.   There—still high elevated
above the rest of the company, to whom he vivaciously cries—he seems some
Turkish Muezzin calling the good people to prayers from the top of a tower.
A short-handled sharp spade being sent up to him, he diligently searches for

the proper place to begin breaking into the Tun. In this business he proceeds very heedfully, like a treasure-hunter in some old house, sounding the walls to find where the gold is masoned in. By the time this cautious search is over, a stout iron-bound bucket, precisely like a well-bucket, has been attached to one end of the whip; while the other end, being stretched across the deck, is there held by two or three alert hands. These last now hoist the bucket within grasp of the Indian, to whom another person has reached up a very long pole. Inserting this pole into the bucket, Tashtego downward guides the bucket into the Tun, till it entirely disappears; then giving the word to the seamen at the whip, up comes the bucket again, all bubbling like a dairy-maid's pail of new milk. Carefully lowered from its height, the full-freighted vessel is caught by an appointed hand, and quickly emptied into a large tub. Then re-mounting aloft, it again goes through the same round until the deep cistern will yield no more. Towards the end, Tashtego has to ram his long pole harder and harder, and deeper and deeper into the Tun, until some twenty feet of the pole have gone down.

Now, the people of the Pequod had been baling some time in this way; several tubs had been filled with the fragrant sperm; when all at once a queer accident happened. Whether it was that Tashtego, that wild Indian, was so heedless and reckless as to let go for a moment his one-handed hold on the great cabled tackles suspending the head; or whether the place where he stood was so treacherous and oozy; or whether the Evil One himself would have it to fall out so, without stating his particular reasons; how it was exactly, there is no telling now; but, on a sudden, as the eightieth or ninetieth bucket came suckingly up—my God! poor Tashtego—like the twin reciprocating bucket in a veritable well, dropped head-foremost down into this great Tun of Heidelburgh, and with a horrible oily gurgling, went clean out of sight!

"Man overboard!" cried Daggoo, who amid the general consternation first came to his senses. "Swing the bucket this way!" and putting one foot into it, so as the better to secure his slippery hand-hold on the whip itself, the hoisters ran him high up to the top of the head, almost before Tashtego could have reached its interior bottom. Meantime, there was a terrible tumult. Looking over the side, they saw the before lifeless head throbbing and heaving just below the surface of the sea, as if that moment seized with some momentous idea; whereas it was only the poor Indian unconsciously revealing by those struggles the perilous depth to which he had sunk.

At this instant, while Daggoo, on the summit of the head, was clearing the whip—which had somehow got foul of the great cutting tackles—a sharp cracking noise was heard; and to the unspeakable horror of all, one of the two enormous hooks suspending the head tore out, and with a vast vibration the enormous mass sideways swung, till the drunk ship reeled and shook as if smitten by an iceberg. The one remaining hook, upon which the entire strain now depended, seemed every instant to be on the point of giving way; an event still more likely from the violent motions of the head.

"Come down, come down!" yelled the seamen to Daggoo, but with one hand holding on to the heavy tackles, so that if the head should drop, he would still remain suspended; the negro having cleared the foul line, rammed down the bucket into the now collapsed well, meaning that the buried harpooneer should grasp it, and so be hoisted out.

"In heaven's name, man," cried Stubb, "are you ramming home a cartridge there?—Avast! How will that help him; jamming that iron-bound bucket on top of his head? Avast, will ye!"

"Stand clear of the tackle!" cried a voice like the bursting of a rocket.

Almost in the same instant, with a thunder-boom, the enormous mass dropped into the sea, like Niagara's Table-Rock into the whirlpool; the suddenly relieved hull rolled away from it, to far down her glittering copper; and all caught their breath, as half swinging—now over the sailors' heads, and now over the water—Daggoo, through a thick mist of spray, was dimly beheld clinging to the pendulous tackles, while poor, buried-alive Tashtego was sinking utterly down to the bottom of the sea! But hardly had the blinding vapor cleared away, when a naked figure with a boarding-sword in his hand, was for one swift moment seen hovering over the bulwarks. The next, a loud splash announced that my brave Queequeg had dived to the rescue. One packed rush was made to the side, and every eye counted every ripple, as moment followed moment, and no sign of either the sinker or the diver could be seen. Some hands now jumped into a boat alongside, and pushed a little off from the ship.

"Ha! ha!" cried Daggoo, all at once, from his now quiet, swinging perch overhead; and looking further off from the side, we saw an arm thrust upright from the blue waves; a sight strange to see, as an arm thrust forth from the grass over a grave.

"Both! both!—it is both!"— cried Daggoo again with a joyful shout; and soon after, Queequeg was seen boldly striking out with one hand, and with the other clutching the long hair of the Indian. Drawn into the waiting boat, they were quickly brought to the deck; but Tashtego was long in coming to, and Queequeg did not look very brisk.

Now, how had this noble rescue been accomplished? Why, diving after the slowly descending head, Queequeg with his keen sword had made side lunges near its bottom, so as to scuttle a large hole there; then dropping his sword, had thrust his long arm far inwards and upwards, and so hauled out our poor Tash by the head. He averred, that upon first thrusting in for him, a leg was presented; but well knowing that that was not as it ought to be, and might occasion great trouble;—he had thrust back the leg, and by a dexterous heave and toss, had wrought a somerset upon the Indian; so that with the next trial, he came forth in the good old way—head foremost. As for the great head itself, that was doing as well as could be expected.

And thus, through the courage and great skill in obstetrics of Queequeg, the deliverance, or rather, delivery of Tashtego, was successfully accomplished, in the teeth, too, of the most untoward and apparently hopeless impediments; which is a lesson by no means to be forgotten. Midwifery should be taught in the same course with fencing and boxing, riding and rowing.

I know that this queer adventure of the Gay-Header's will be sure to seem incredible to some landsmen, though they themselves may have either seen or heard of some one's falling into a cistern ashore; an accident which not seldom happens, and with much less reason too than the Indian's, considering the exceeding slipperiness of the curb of the Sperm Whale's well.

But, peradventure, it may be sagaciously urged, how is this? We thought the tissued, infiltrated head of the Sperm Whale, was the lightest and most corky part about him; and yet thou makest it sink in an element of a far greater specific gravity than itself. We have thee there. Not at all, but I have ye; for at the time poor Tash fell in, the case had been nearly emptied of its lighter contents, leaving little but the dense tendinous wall of the well—a double welded, hammered substance, as I have before said, much heavier than the sea water, and a lump of which sinks in it like lead almost. But the tendency to rapid sinking in this substance was in the present instance materially counteracted by the other parts of the head remaining undetached from it, so that it sank very slowly and deliberately indeed, affording Queequeg a fair chance for performing his agile obstetrics on the run, as you may say. Yes, it was a running delivery, so it was.

Now, had Tashtego perished in that head, it had been a very precious perishing; smothered in the very whitest and daintiest of fragrant spermaceti; coffined, hearsed, and tombed in the secret inner chamber and sanctum sanctorum of the whale. Only one sweeter end can readily be recalled—the delicious death of an Ohio honey-hunter, who seeking honey in the crotch of a hollow tree, found such exceeding store of it, that leaning too far over, it sucked him in, so that he died embalmed. How many, think ye, have likewise fallen into Plato's honey head, and sweetly perished there?

CHAPTER LXXIX

THE PRAIRIE

To scan the lines of his face, or feel the bumps on the head of this Leviathan; this is a thing which no Physiognomist or Phrenologist has as yet undertaken. Such an enterprise would seem almost as hopeful as for Lavater to have scrutinized the wrinkles on the Rock of Gibraltar, or for Gall to have mounted a ladder and manipulated the dome of the Pantheon. Still, in that famous work of his, Lavater not only treats of the various faces of men, but also attentively studies the faces of horses, birds, serpents, and fish; and dwells in detail upon the modifications of expression discernible therein. Nor have Gall and his disciple Spurzheim failed to throw out some hints touching the phrenological characteristics of other beings than man. Therefore, though I am but ill qualified for a pioneer, in the application of these two semi-sciences to the whale, I will do my endeavor. I try all things; I achieve what I can.

Physiognomically regarded, the Sperm Whale is an anomalous creature. He has no proper nose. And since the nose is the central and most conspicuous of the features; and since it perhaps most modifies and finally controls their combined expression; hence it would seem that its entire absence, as an external appendage, must very largely affect the countenance of the whale. For as in landscape gardening, a spire, cupola, monument, or tower of some sort, is deemed almost indispensable to the completion of the scene; so no face can be physiognomically in keeping without the elevated open-work belfry of the nose. Dash the nose from Phidias's marble Jove, and what a sorry remainder! Nevertheless, Leviathan is of so mighty a magnitude, all his proportions are so stately, that the same deficiency which in the sculptured Jove were hideous, in him is no blemish at all. Nay, it is an added grandeur. A nose to the whale would have been impertinent. As on your physiognomical voyage you sail round his vast head in your jolly-boat, your noble conceptions of him are never insulted by the reflection that he has a nose to be pulled. A pestilent conceit, which so often will insist upon obtruding even when beholding the mightiest royal beadle on his throne.

In some particulars, perhaps the most imposing physiognomical view to be had of the Sperm Whale, is that of the full front of his head. This aspect is sublime.

In thought, a fine human brow is like the East when troubled with the morning. In the repose of the pasture, the curled brow of the bull has a touch of the grand in it. Pushing heavy cannon up mountain defiles, the elephant's brow is majestic. Human or animal, the mystical brow is as that great golden seal affixed by the German Emperors to their decrees. It signifies—"God: done this day by my hand." But in most creatures, nay in man himself, very often the brow is but a mere strip of alpine land lying along the snow line. Few are the foreheads which like Shakespeare's or Melancthon's rise so high, and descend so low, that the eyes themselves seem clear, eternal, tideless mountain lakes; and all above them in the forehead's wrinkles, you seem to track the antlered thoughts descending there to drink, as the Highland hunters track the snow prints of the deer. But in the great Sperm Whale, this high and mighty god-like dignity inherent in the brow is so immensely amplified, that gazing on it, in that full front view, you feel the Deity and the dread powers more forcibly than in beholding any other object in living nature. For you see no one point precisely; not one distinct feature is revealed; no nose, eyes, ears, or mouth; no face; he has none, proper; nothing but that one broad firmament of a fore-head, pleated with riddles; dumbly lowering with the doom of boats, and ships, and men. Nor, in profile, does this wondrous brow diminish; though that way viewed, its grandeur does not domineer upon you so. In profile, you plainly perceive that horizontal, semi-crescentic depression in the forehead's middle, which, in man, is Lavater's mark of genius.

But how? Genius in the Sperm Whale? Has the Sperm Whale ever written a book, spoken a speech? No, his great genius is declared in his doing nothing particular to prove it. It is moreover declared in his pyramidical silence. And this reminds me that had the great Sperm Whale been known to the young Orient World, he would have been deified by their child-magian thoughts. They deified the crocodile of the Nile, because the crocodile is tongueless; and the Sperm Whale has no tongue, or at least it is so exceedingly small, as to be incapable of protrusion. If hereafter any highly cultured, poetical nation shall lure back to their birth-right, the merry May-day gods of old; and lovingly enthrone them again in the now egotistical sky; in the now unhaunted hill; then be sure, exalted to Jove's high seat, the great Sperm Whale shall lord it.

Champollion deciphered the wrinkled granite hieroglyphics. But there is no Champollion to decipher the Egypt of every man's and every being's face. Physiognomy, like every other human science, is but a passing fable. If then, Sir William Jones, who read in thirty languages, could not read the simplest peasant's face in its profounder and more subtle meanings, how may unlettered Ishmael hope to read the awful Chaldee of the Sperm Whale's brow? I but put that brow before you. Read it if you can.

CHAPTER LXXX

THE NUT

IF the Sperm Whale be physiognomically a Sphynx, to the phrenologist his brain seems that geometrical circle which it is impossible to square.

In the full-grown creature the skull will measure at least twenty feet in length. Unhinge the lower jaw, and the side view of this skull is as the side view of a moderately inclined plane resting throughout on a level base. But in life—as we have elsewhere seen—this inclined plane is angularly filled up, and almost squared by the enormous superincumbent mass of the junk and sperm. At the high end the skull forms a crater to bed that part of the mass; while under the long floor of this crater—in another cavity seldom exceeding ten inches in length and as many in depth—reposes the mere handful of this monster's brain. The brain is at least twenty feet from his apparent forehead in life; it is hidden away behind its vast outworks, like the innermost citadel within the amplified fortifications of Quebec. So like a choice casket is it secreted in him, that I have known some whalemen who peremptorily deny that the Sperm Whale has any other brain than that palpable semblance of one formed by the cubic-yards of his sperm magazine. Lying in strange folds, courses, and convolutions, to their apprehensions, it seems more in keeping with the idea of his general might to regard that mystic part of him as the seat of his intelligence.

It is plain, then, that phrenologically the head of this Leviathan, in the creature's living intact state, is an entire delusion. As for his true brain, you can then see no indications of it, nor feel any. The whale, like all things that are mighty, wears a false brow to the common world.

If you unload his skull of its spermy heaps and then take a rear view of its rear end, which is the high end, you will be struck by its resemblance to the human skull, beheld in the same situation, and from the same point of view. Indeed, place this reversed skull (scaled down to the human magnitude) among a plate of men's skulls, and you would involuntarily confound it with them; and remarking the depressions on one part of its summit, in phrenological phrase you would say—This man had no self-esteem, and no veneration. And by those negations, considered along with the affirmative fact of his prodigious bulk and power, you can best form to yourself the truest, though not the most exhilarating conception of what the most exalted potency is.

But if from the comparative dimensions of the whale's proper brain, you deem it incapable of being adequately charted, then I have another idea for you. If you attentively regard almost any quadruped's spine, you will be struck with the resemblance of its vertebræ to a strung necklace of dwarfed skulls, all bearing rudimental resemblance to the skull proper. It is a German conceit, that the vertebræ are absolutely undeveloped skulls. But the curious external resemblance, I take it the Germans were not the first men to perceive. A foreign friend once pointed it out to me, in the skeleton of a foe he had slain, and with the vertebræ of which he was inlaying, in a sort of basso-relievo, the beaked prow of his canoe. Now, I consider that the phrenologists have omitted an important thing in not pushing their investigations from the cerebellum through the spinal canal. For I believe that much of a man's character will be found betokened in his backbone. I would rather feel your spine than your skull, whoever you are. A thin joist of a spine never yet upheld a full and noble soul. I rejoice in my spine, as in the firm audacious staff of that flag which I fling half out to the world.

Apply this spinal branch of phrenology to the Sperm Whale. His cranial cavity is continuous with the first neck-vertebra; and in that vertebra the bottom of the spinal canal will measure ten inches across, being eight in height, and of a triangular figure with the base downwards. As it passes through the remaining vertebræ the canal tapers in size, but for a considerable distance remains of large capacity. Now, of course, this canal is filled with much the same strangely fibrous substance—the spinal cord—as the brain; and directly communicates with the brain. And what is still more, for many feet after emerging from the brain's cavity, the spinal cord remains of an undecreasing girth, almost equal to that of the brain. Under all these circumstances, would it be unreasonable to survey and map out the whale's spine phrenologically? For, viewed in this light, the wonderful comparative smallness of his brain proper is more than compensated by the wonderful comparative magnitude of his spinal cord.

But leaving this hint to operate as it may with the phrenologists, I would merely assume the spinal theory for a moment, in reference to the Sperm Whale's hump. This august hump, if I mistake not, rises over one of the larger vertebræ, and is, therefore, in some sort, the outer convex mould of it. From its relative situation then, I should call this high hump the organ of firmness or indomitableness in the Sperm Whale. And that the great monster is indomitable, you will yet have reason to know.

CHAPTER LXXXI

THE PEQUOD MEETS THE VIRGIN

THE predestinated day arrived, and we duly met the ship Jungfrau, Derick De Deer, master, of Bremen.

At one time the greatest whaling people in the world, the Dutch and Germans are now among the least; but here and there at very wide intervals of latitude and longitude, you still occasionally meet with their flag in the Pacific.

For some reason, the Jungfrau seemed quite eager to pay her respects. While yet some distance from the Pequod, she rounded to, and dropping a boat, her captain was impelled towards us, impatiently standing in the bows instead of the stern.

"What has he in his hand there?" cried Starbuck, pointing to something wavingly held by the German. "Impossible!—a lamp-feeder!"

"Not that," said Stubb, "no, no, it's a coffee-pot, Mr. Starbuck; he's coming off to make us our coffee, is the Yarman; don't you see that big tin can there alongside of him?—that's his boiling water. Oh! he's all right, is the Yarman."

"Go along with you," cried Flask, "it's a lamp-feeder and an oil-can. He's out of oil, and has come a-begging."

However curious it may seem for an oil-ship to be borrowing oil on the whale-ground, and however much it may invertedly contradict the old proverb about carrying coals to Newcastle, yet sometimes such a thing really happens; and in the present case Captain Derick De Deer did indubitably conduct a lamp-feeder as Flask did declare.

As he mounted the deck, Ahab abruptly accosted him, without at all heeding what he had in his hand; but in his broken lingo, the German soon evinced his complete ignorance of the White Whale; immediately turning the conversation to this lamp-feeder and oil-can, with some remarks touching his having to turn into his hammock at night in profound darkness—his last drop of Bremen oil being gone, and not a single flying-fish yet captured to supply the deficiency; concluding by hinting that his ship was indeed what in the Fishery is technically called a *clean* one (that is, an empty one), well deserving the name of Jungfrau or the Virgin.

His necessities supplied, Derick departed; but he had not gained his ship's side, when whales were almost simultaneously raised from the mast-heads of both vessels; and so eager for the chase was Derick, that without pausing to put his oil-can and lamp-feeder aboard, he slewed round his boat and made after the leviathan lamp-feeders.

Now, the game having risen to leeward, he and the other three German boats that soon followed him, had considerably the start of the Pequod's keels. There were eight whales, an average pod. Aware of their danger, they were going all abreast with great speed straight before the wind, rubbing their flanks as closely as so many spans of horses in harness. They left a great, wide wake, as though continually unrolling a great wide parchment upon the sea.

Full in this rapid wake, and many fathoms in the rear, swam a huge, humped old bull, which by his comparatively slow progress, as well as by the unusual yellowish incrustations overgrowing him, seemed afflicted with the jaundice, or some other infirmity. Whether this whale belonged to the pod in advance, seemed questionable; for it is not customary for such venerable leviathans to be at all social. Nevertheless, he stuck to their wake, though indeed their back water must have retarded him, because the white-bone or swell at his broad muzzle was a dashed one, like the swell formed when two hostile currents meet. His spout was short, slow, and laborious; coming forth with a choking sort of gush, and spending itself in torn shreds, followed by strange subterranean commotions in him, which seemed to have egress at his other buried extremity, causing the waters behind him to upbubble.

"Who's got some paregoric?" said Stubb, "he has the stomach-ache, I'm afraid. Lord, think of having half an acre of stomach-ache! Adverse winds are holding mad Christmas in him, boys. It's the first foul wind I ever knew to blow from astern; but look, did ever whale yaw so before? it must be, he's lost his tiller."

As an overladen Indiaman bearing down the Hindostan coast with a deck load of frightened horses, careens, buries, rolls, and wallows on her way; so did this old whale heave his aged bulk, and now and then partly turning over on his cumbrous rib-ends, expose the cause of his devious wake in the unnatural stump of his starboard fin. Whether he had lost that fin in battle, or had been born without it, it were hard to say.

"Only wait a bit, old chap, and I'll give ye a sling for that wounded arm," cried cruel Flask, pointing to the whale-line near him.

"Mind he don't sling thee with it," cried Starbuck. "Give way, or the German will have him."

With one intent all the combined rival boats were pointed for this one fish, because not only was he the largest, and therefore the most valuable whale, but he was nearest to them, and the other whales were going with such great velocity, moreover, as almost to defy pursuit for the time. At this juncture, the Pequod's keels had shot by the three German boats last lowered; but from the great start he had had, Derick's boat still led the chase, though every moment neared by his foreign rivals. The only thing they feared, was, that from being already so nigh to his mark, he would be enabled to dart his iron before they could completely overtake and pass him. As for Derick, he seemed quite confident that this would be the case, and occasionally with a deriding gesture shook his lamp-feeder at the other boats.

"The ungracious and ungrateful dog!" cried Starbuck; "he mocks and dares me with the very poor-box I filled for him not five minutes ago!"—then in his old intense whisper—"give way, greyhounds! Dog to it!"

"I tell ye what it is, men"—cried Stubb to his crew—"It's against my religion to get mad; but I'd like to eat that villainous Yarman—Pull—won't ye? Are ye going to let that rascal beat ye? Do ye love brandy? A hogshead of brandy, then, to the best man. Come, why don't some of ye burst a blood-vessel? Who's that been dropping an anchor overboard—we don't budge an inch—we're becalmed. Halloo, here's grass growing in the boat's bottom—and by the Lord, the mast there's budding. This won't do, boys. Look at that Yarman! The short and long of it is, men, will ye spit fire or not?"

"Oh! see the suds he makes!" cried Flask, dancing up and down—"What a hump—Oh, *do* pile on the beef—lays like a log!. Oh! my lads, *do* spring—slap-jacks and quohogs for supper, you know, my lads—baked clams and muffins—ho, *do, do,* spring,—he's a hundred barreler—don't lose him now—don't, oh, *don't!*—see that Yarman—Oh! won't ye pull for your duff, my lads—such a sog! such a sogger! Don't ye love sperm? There goes three thousand dollars, men!—a bank!—a whole bank! The bank of England!—Oh, *do, do, do!*—What's that Yarman about now?"

At this moment Derick was in the act of pitching his lamp-feeder at the advancing boats, and also his oil-can; perhaps with the double view of retarding his rivals' way, and at the same time economically accelerating his own by the momentary impetus of the backward toss.

"The unmannerly Dutch dogger!" cried Stubb. "Pull now, men, like fifty thousand line-of-battleship loads of red-haired devils. What d'ye say, Tashtego; are you the man to snap your spine in two-and-twenty pieces for the honor of old Gayhead? What d'ye say?"

"I say, pull like god-dam,"—cried the Indian.

Fiercely, but evenly incited by the taunts of the German, the Pequod's three boats now began ranging almost abreast; and, so disposed, momentarily neared him. In that fine, loose, chivalrous attitude of the headsmen when drawing near to his prey, the three mates stood up proudly, occasionally backing the after oarsman with an exhilarating cry of, "There she slides, now! ·Hurrah for the white-ash breeze! Down with the Yarman! Sail over him!"

But so decided an original start had Derick had, that spite of all their gallantry, he would have proved the victor in this race, had not a righteous judgment descended upon him in a crab which caught the blade of his midship oarsman. While this clumsy lubber was striving to free his white-ash, and while, in consequence, Derick's boat was nigh to capsizing, and he thundering away at his men in a mighty rage;—that was a good time for Starbuck, Stubb, and Flask. With a shout, they took a mortal start forwards, and slantingly ranged up on the German's quarter. An instant more, and all four boats were diagonally in the whale's immediate wake, while stretching from them, on both sides, was the foaming swell that he made.

It was a terrific, most pitiable, and maddening sight. The whale was now going head out, and sending his spout before him in a continual tormented jet; while his one poor fin beat his side in an agony of fright. Now to this hand, now to that, he yawed in his faltering flight, and still at every billow that he broke, he spasmodically sank in the sea, or sideways rolled towards the sky his one beating fin. So have I seen a bird with clipped wing, making affrighted broken circles in the air, vainly striving to escape the piratical hawks. But the bird has a voice, and with plaintive cries will make known her fear; but the fear of this vast dumb brute of the sea, was chained up and enchanted in him; he had no voice, save that choking respiration through his spiracle, and this made the sight of him unspeakably pitiable; while still, in his amazing bulk, portcullis jaw, and omnipotent tail, there was enough to appal the stoutest man who so pitied.

Seeing now that but a very few moments more would give the Pequod's boats the advantage, and rather than be thus foiled of his game, Derick chose to hazard what to him must have seemed a most unusually long dart, ere the last chance would for ever escape.

But no sooner did his harpooneer stand up for the stroke, than all three tigers—Queequeg, Tashtego, Daggoo—instinctively sprang to their feet, and standing in a diagonal row, simultaneously pointed their barbs; and darted over the head of the German harpooneer, their three Nantucket irons entered the whale. Blinding vapors of foam and white-fire! The three boats, in the first fury of the whale's headlong rush, bumped the German's aside with such force, that both Derick and his baffled harpooneer were spilled out, and sailed over by the three flying keels.

"Don't be afraid, my butter-boxes," cried Stubb, casting a passing glance upon them as he shot by; "ye'll be picked up presently—all right—I saw some sharks astern—St. Bernard's dogs, you know—relieve distressed travellers. Hurrah! this is the way to sail now. Every keel a sun-beam! Hurrah!— Here we go like three tin kettles at the tail of a mad cougar! This puts me in mind of fastening to an elephant in a tilbury on a plain—makes the wheel-spokes fly, boys, when you fasten to him that way; and there's danger of being pitched out too, when you strike a hill. Hurrah! this is the way a fellow feels when he's going to Davy Jones—all a rush down an endless inclined plane! Hurrah! this whale carries the everlasting mail!"

But the monster's run was a brief one. Giving a sudden gasp, he tumultuously sounded. With a grating rush, the three lines flew round the logger-heads with such a force as to gouge deep grooves in them; while so fearful were the harpooneers that this rapid sounding would soon exhaust the lines, that using all their dexterous might, they caught repeated smoking turns with the rope to hold on; till at last—owing to the perpendicular strain from the lead-lined chocks of the boats, whence the three ropes went straight down into the blue—the gunwales of the bows were almost even with the water, while the three sterns tilted high in the air. And the whale soon ceasing to sound, for some time they remained in that attitude, fearful of expending more line, though the position was a little ticklish. But though boats have been taken down and lost in this way, yet it is this "holding on," as it is called; this hooking up by the sharp barbs of his live flesh from the back; this it is that often torments the Leviathan into soon rising again to meet the sharp lance of his foes. Yet not to speak of the peril of the thing, it is to be doubted whether this course is always the best; for it is but reasonable to presume, that the longer the stricken whale stays under water, the more he is exhausted. Because, owing to the enormous surface of him—in a full grown sperm whale something less than 2000 square feet—the pressure of the water is immense. We all know what an astonishing atmospheric weight we ourselves stand up under; even here, above-ground, in the air; how vast, then, the burden of a whale, bearing on his back a column of two hundred fathoms of ocean! It must at least equal the weight of fifty atmospheres. One whaleman has estimated it at the weight of twenty line-of-battle ships, with all their guns, and stores, and men on board.

As the three boats lay there on that gently rolling sea, gazing down into its eternal blue noon; and as not a single groan or cry of any sort, nay, not so much as a ripple or a bubble came up from its depths; what landsman would have thought, that beneath all that silence and placidity, the utmost monster

of the seas was writhing and wrenching in agony! Not eight inches of perpendicular rope were visible at the bows. Seems it credible that by three such
thin threads the great Leviathan was suspended like the big weight to an
eight day clock. Suspended? and to what? To three bits of board. Is this
the creature of whom it was once so triumphantly said—"Canst thou fill his
skin with barbed irons? or his head with fish-spears? The sword of him that
layeth at him cannot hold, the spear, the dart, nor the habergeon: he esteemeth
iron as straw; the arrow cannot make him flee; darts are counted as stubble;
he laugheth at the shaking of a spear!" This the creature? this he? Oh!
that unfulfilments should follow the prophets. For with the strength of a thousand thighs in his tail, Leviathan had run his head under the mountains of
the sea, to hide him from the Pequod's fish-spears!

In that sloping afternoon sunlight, the shadows that the three boats sent
down beneath the surface, must have been long enough and broad enough to
shade half Xerxes' army. Who can tell how appalling to the wounded whale
must have been such huge phantoms flitting over his head!

"Stand by, men; he stirs," cried Starbuck, as the three lines suddenly
vibrated in the water, distinctly conducting upwards to them, as by magnetic
wires, the life and death throbs of the whale, so that every oarsman felt them
in his seat. The next moment, relieved in great part from the downward strain
at the bows, the boats gave a sudden bounce upwards, as a small icefield will,
when a dense herd of white bears are scared from it into the sea.

"Haul in! Haul in!" cried Starbuck again; "he's rising."

The lines, of which, hardly an instant before, not one hand's breadth could
have been gained, were now in long quick coils flung back all dripping into
the boats, and soon the whale broke water within two ship's lengths of the
hunters.

His motions plainly denoted his extreme exhaustion. In most land animals
there are certain valves or flood-gates in many of their veins, whereby when
wounded, the blood is in some degree at least instantly shut off in certain directions. Not so with the whale; one of whose peculiarities it is, to have an
entire non-valvular structure of the blood-vessels, so that when pierced even
by so small a point as a harpoon, a deadly drain is at once begun upon his
whole arterial system; and when this is heightened by the extraordinary pressure
of water at a great distance below the surface, his life may be said to pour
from him in incessant streams. Yet so vast is the quantity of blood in him,
and so distant and numerous its interior fountains, that he will keep thus bleeding and bleeding for a considerable period; even as in a drought a river will
flow, whose source is the well-springs of far-off and indiscernible hills. Even
now, when the boats pulled upon this whale, and perilously drew over his
swaying flukes, and the lances were darted into him, they were followed by
steady jets from the new made wound, which kept continually playing, while
the natural spouthole in his head was only at intervals, however rapid, sending
its affrighted moisture into the air. From this last vent no blood yet came,
because no vital part of him had thus far been struck. His life, as they significantly call it, was untouched.

As the boats now more closely surrounded him, the whole upper part of
his form, with much of it that is ordinarily submerged, was plainly revealed.
His eyes, or rather the places where his eyes had been, were beheld. As strange
misgrown masses gather in the knot-holes of the noblest oaks when prostrate,
so from the points which the whale's eyes had once occupied, now protruded
blind bulbs, horribly pitiable to see. But pity there was none. For all his

old age, and his one arm, and his blind eyes, he must die the death and be murdered, in order to light the gay bridals and other merry-makings of men, and also to illuminate the solemn churches that preach unconditional inoffensiveness by all to all. Still rolling in his blood, at last he partially disclosed a strangely discolored bunch or protuberance, the size of a bushel, low down on the flank.

"A nice spot," cried Flask; "just let me prick him there once."

"Avast!" cried Starbuck, "there's no need of that!"

But humane Starbuck was too late. At the instant of the dart an ulcerous jet shot from this cruel wound, and goaded by it into more than sufferable anguish, the whale now spouting thick blood, with swift fury blindly darted at the craft, bespattering them and their glorying crews all over with showers of gore, capsizing Flask's boat and marring the bows. It was his death stroke. For, by this time, so spent was he by loss of blood, that he helplessly rolled away from the wreck he had made; lay panting on his side, impotently flapped with his stumped fin, then over and over slowly revolved like a waning world; turned up the white secrets of his belly; lay like a log, and died. It was most piteous, that last expiring spout. As when by unseen hands the water is gradually drawn off from some mighty fountain, and with half-stifled melancholy gurglings the spray-column lowers and lowers to the ground—so the last long dying spout of the whale.

Soon, while the crews were awaiting the arrival of the ship, the body showed symptoms of sinking with all its treasures unrifled. Immediately, by Starbuck's orders, lines were secured to it at different points, so that ere long every boat was a buoy; the sunken whale being suspended a few inches beneath them by the cords. By very heedful management, when the ship drew nigh, the whale was transferred to her side, and was strongly secured there by the stiffest fluke-chains, for it was plain that unless artificially upheld, the body would at once sink to the bottom.

It so chanced that almost upon first cutting into him with the spade, the entire length of a corroded harpoon was found imbedded in his flesh, on the lower part of the bunch before described. But as the stumps of harpoons are frequently found in the dead bodies of captured whales, with the flesh perfectly healed around them, and no prominence of any kind to denote their place; therefore, there must needs have been some other unknown reason in the present case fully to account for the ulceration alluded to. But still more curious was the fact of a lance-head of stone being found in him, not far from the buried iron, the flesh perfectly firm about it. Who had darted that stone lance? And when? It might have been darted by some Nor' West Indian long before America was discovered.

What other marvels might have been rummaged out of this monstrous cabinet there is no telling. But a sudden stop was put to further discoveries, by the ship's being unprecedently dragged over sideways to the sea, owing to the body's immensely increasing tendency to sink. However, Starbuck, who had the ordering of affairs, hung on to it to the last; hung on to it so resolutely, indeed, that when at length the ship would have been capsized, if still persisting in locking arms with the body; then, when the command was given to break clear from it, such was the immovable strain upon the timber-heads to which the fluke-chains and cables were fastened, that it was impossible to cast them off. Meantime everything in the Pequod was aslant. To cross to the other side of the deck was like walking up the steep gabled roof of a house. The ship groaned and gasped. Many of the ivory inlayings of her bulwarks and cabins were started from their places, by the unnatural dislocation. In vain handspikes and crows were brought to bear upon the immovable fluke-chains, to pry them adrift from the timberheads; and so low had the whale now settled that the submerged ends could not be at all approached, while every moment whole tons of ponderosity seemed added to the sinking bulk, and the ship seemed on the point of going over.

"Hold on, hold on, won't ye?" cried Stubb to the body, "don't be in such a devil of a hurry to sink! By thunder, men, we must do something or go for it. No use prying there; avast, I say with your handspikes, and run one of ye for a prayer book and a pen-knife, and cut the big chains."

"Knife? Aye, aye," cried Queequeg, and seizing the carpenter's heavy hatchet, he leaned out of a porthole, and steel to iron, began slashing at the largest fluke-chains. But a few strokes, full of sparks, were given, when the exceeding strain effected the rest. With a terrific snap, every fastening went adrift; the ship righted, the carcase sank.

Now, this occasional inevitable sinking of the recently killed Sperm Whale is a very curious thing; nor has any fisherman yet adequately accounted for it. Usually the dead Sperm Whale floats with great buoyancy, with its side or belly considerably elevated above the surface. If the only whales that thus sank were old, meagre, and broken-hearted creatures, their pads of lard diminished and all their bones heavy and rheumatic; then you might with some reason assert that this sinking is caused by an uncommon specific gravity in the fish so sinking, consequent upon this absence of buoyant matter in him. But it is not so. For young whales, in the highest health, and swelling with noble aspirations, prematurely cut off in the warm flush and May of life, with all their panting lard about them; even these brawny, buoyant heroes do sometimes sink.

Be it said, however, that the Sperm Whale is far less liable to this accident than any other species. Where one of that sort go down, twenty Right Whales do. This difference in the species is no doubt imputable in no small degree to the greater quantity of bone in the Right Whale; his Venetian blinds alone sometimes weighing more than a ton; from this incumbrance the Sperm Whale is wholly free. But there are instances where, after the lapse of many hours or several days, the sunken whale again rises, more buoyant than in life. But the reason of this is obvious. Gases are generated in him; he swells to a prodigious magnitude; becomes a sort of animal balloon. A line-of-battle ship could hardly keep him under then. In the Shore Whaling, on soundings, among the Bays of New Zealand, when a Right Whale gives token of sinking, they fasten buoys to him, with plenty of rope; so that when the body has gone down, they know where to look for it when it shall have ascended again.

It was not long after the sinking of the body that a cry was heard from the Pequod's mast-heads, announcing that the Jungfrau was again lowering her boats; though the only spout in sight was that of a Fin-Back, belonging to the species of uncapturable whales, because of its incredible power of swimming. Nevertheless, the Fin-Back's spout is so similar to the Sperm Whale's, that by unskilful fishermen it is often mistaken for it. And consequently Derick and all his host were now in valiant chase of this unnearable brute. The Virgin crowding all sail, made after her four young keels, and thus they all disappeared far to leeward, still in bold, hopeful chase.

Oh! many are the Fin-Backs, and many are the Dericks, my friend.

CHAPTER LXXXII

THE HONOR AND GLORY OF WHALING

THERE are some enterprises in which a careful disorderliness is the true method.

The more I dive into this matter of whaling, and push my researches up to the very springhead of it, so much the more am I impressed with its great honorableness and antiquity; and especially when I find so many great demi-gods and heroes, prophets of all sorts, who one way or other have shed distinction upon it, I am transported with the reflection that I myself belong, though but subordinately, to so emblazoned a fraternity.

The gallant Perseus, a son of Jupiter, was the first whaleman; and to the eternal honor of our calling be it said, that the first whale attacked by our brotherhood was not killed with any sordid intent. Those were the knightly days of our profession, when we only bore arms to succor the distressed, and not to fill men's lamp-feeders. Every one knows the fine story of Perseus and Andromeda; how the lovely Andromeda, the daughter of a king, was tied to a rock on the seacoast, and as Leviathan was in the very act of carrying her off, Perseus, the prince of whalemen, intrepidly advancing, harpooned the monster, and delivered and married the maid. It was an admirable artistic exploit, rarely achieved by the best harpooneers of the present day; inasmuch as this Leviathan was slain at the very first dart. And let no man doubt this Arkite story; for in the ancient Joppa, now Jaffa, on the Syrian coast, in one of the Pagan temples, there stood for many ages the vast skeleton of a whale, which the city's legends and all the inhabitants asserted to be the identical bones of the monster that Perseus slew. When the Romans took Joppa, the same skeleton was carried to Italy in triumph. What seems most singular and suggestively important in this story, is this: it was from Joppa that Jonah set sail.

Akin to the adventure of Perseus and Andromeda—indeed, by some supposed to be indirectly derived from it—is that famous story of St. George and the Dragon; which dragon I maintain to have been a whale; for in many old chronicles whales and dragons are strangely jumbled together, and often stand for each other. "Thou art as a lion of the waters, and as a dragon of the sea," saith Ezekiel; hereby, plainly meaning a whale; in truth, some versions of the Bible use that word itself. Besides, it would much subtract from the glory of the exploit had St. George but encountered a crawling reptile of the land, instead of doing battle with the great monster of the deep. Any man may kill a snake, but only a Perseus, a St. George, a Coffin, have the heart in them to march boldly up to a whale.

Let not the modern paintings of this scene mislead us; for though the creature encountered by that valiant whaleman of old is vaguely represented of a griffin-like shape, and though the battle is depicted on land and the saint on horseback, yet considering the great ignorance of those times, when the true form of the whale was unknown to artists; and considering that as in Perseus' case, St. George's whale might have crawled up out of the sea on the beach; and considering that the animal ridden by St. George might have been only a large seal, or sea-horse; bearing all this in mind, it will not appear altogether incompatible with the sacred legend and the ancientest draughts of the scene, to hold this so-called dragon no other than the great Leviathan himself. In fact, placed before the strict and piercing truth, this whole story will fare like that fish, flesh, and fowl idol of the Philistines, Dagon by name; who being planted before the ark of Israel, his horse's head and both the palms of his hands fell off from him, and only the stump or fishy part of him remained. Thus, then, one of our own noble stamp, even a whaleman, is the tutelary guardian of England; and by good rights, we harpooneers of Nantucket should be enrolled in the most noble order of St. George. And therefore, let not the knights of that honorable company (none of whom, I venture to say, have ever had to do with a whale like their great patron), let them never eye a Nantucketer with disdain, since even in our woollen frocks and tarred trowsers we are much better entitled to St. George's decoration than they.

Whether to admit Hercules among us or not, concerning this I long remained dubious: for though according to the Greek mythologies, that antique Crockett and Kit Carson—that brawny doer of rejoicing good deeds, was swallowed down and thrown up by a whale; still, whether that strictly makes a whaleman of him, that might be mooted. It nowhere appears that he ever actually harpooned his fish, unless, indeed, from the inside. Nevertheless, he may be deemed a sort of involuntary whaleman! at any rate the whale caught him, if he did not the whale. I claim him for one of our clan.

But, by the best contradictory authorities, this Grecian story of Hercules and the whale is considered to be derived from the still more ancient Hebrew story of Jonah and the whale; and vice versa; certainly they are very similar. If I claim the demi-god then, why not the prophet?

Nor do heroes, saints, demigods, and prophets alone comprise the whole roll of our order. Our grand master is still to be named; for like royal kings of old times, we find the head-waters of our fraternity in nothing short of the great gods themselves. That wondrous oriental story is now to be rehearsed from the Shaster, which gives us the dread Vishnoo, one of the three persons in the godhead of the Hindoos; gives us this divine Vishnoo himself for our Lord; —Vishnoo, who, by the first of his ten earthly incarnations, has for ever set apart and sanctified the whale. When Brahma, or the God of Gods, saith the Shaster, resolved to recreate the world after one of its periodical dissolutions, he gave birth to Vishnoo, to preside over the work; but the Vedas, or mystical books, whose perusal would seem to have been indispensable to Vishnoo before beginning the creation, and which therefore must have contained something in the shape of practical hints to young architects, these Vedas were lying at the bottom of the waters; so Vishnoo became incarnate in a whale, and sounding down in him to the uttermost depths, rescued the sacred volumes. Was not this Vishnoo a whaleman, then? even as a man who rides a horse is called a horseman?

Perseus, St. George, Hercules, Jonah, and Vishnoo! there's a member-roll for you! What club but the whaleman's can head off like that?

CHAPTER LXXXIII

JONAH HISTORICALLY REGARDED

REFERENCE was made to the historical story of Jonah and the whale in the preceding chapter. Now some Nantucketers rather distrust this historical story of Jonah and the whale. But then there were some sceptical Greeks and

Romans, who, standing out from the orthodox pagans of their times, equally doubted the story of Hercules and the whale, and Arion and the dolphin; and yet their doubting those traditions did not make those traditions one whit the less facts, for all that.

One old Sag-Harbor whaleman's chief reason for questioning the Hebrew story was this:—He had one of those quaint old-fashioned Bibles, embellished with curious, unscientific plates; one of which represented Jonah's whale with two spouts in his head—a peculiarity only true with respect to a species of the Leviathan (the Right Whale, and the varieties of that order), concerning which the fishermen have this saying, "A penny roll would choke him;" his swallow is so very small. But, to this, Bishop Jebb's anticipative answer is ready. It is not necessary, hints the Bishop, that we consider Jonah as tombed in the whale's belly, but as temporarily lodged in some part of his mouth. And this seems reasonable enough in the good Bishop. For truly, the Right Whale's mouth would accommodate a couple of whist-tables, and comfortably seat all the players. Possibly, too, Jonah might have ensconced himself in a hollow tooth; but, on second thoughts, the Right Whale is toothless.

Another reason which Sag-Harbor (he went by that name) urged for his want of faith in this matter of the prophet, was something obscurely in reference to his incarcerated body and the whale's gastric juices. But this objection likewise falls to the ground, because a German exegetist supposes that Jonah must have taken refuge in the floating body of a *dead* whale—even as the French soldiers in the Russian campaign turned their dead horses into tents, and crawled into them. Besides, it has been divined by other continental commentators, that when Jonah was thrown overboard from the Joppa ship, he straightway effected his escape to another vessel near by, some vessel with a whale for a figure-head; and, I would add, possibly called "The Whale," as some craft are nowadays christened the "Shark," the "Gull," the "Eagle." Nor have there been wanting learned exegetists who have opined that the whale mentioned in the book of Jonah merely meant a life preserver—an inflated bag of wind—which the endangered prophet swam to, and so was saved from a watery doom. Poor Sag-Harbor, therefore, seems worsted all round. But he had still another reason for his want of faith. It was this, if I remember right: Jonah was swallowed by the whale in the Mediterranean Sea, and after three days he was vomited up somewhere within three days' journey of Nineveh, a city on the Tigris, very much more than three days' journey across from the nearest point of the Mediterranean coast. How is that?

But was there no other way for the whale to land the prophet within that short distance of Nineveh? Yes. He might have carried him round by the way of the Cape of Good Hope. But not to speak of the passage through the whole length of the Mediterranean, and another passage up the Persian Gulf and Red Sea, such a supposition would involve the complete circumnavigation of all Africa in three days, not to speak of the Tigris waters, near the site of Nineveh, being too shallow for any whale to swim in. Besides, this idea of Jonah's weathering the Cape of Good Hope at so early a day would wrest the honor of the discovery of that great headland from Bartholomew Diaz, its reputed discoverer, and so make modern history a liar.

But all these foolish arguments of old Sag-Harbor only evinced his foolish pride of reason—a thing still more reprehensible in him, seeing that he had but little learning except what he had picked up from the sun and the sea. I say it only shows his foolish, impious pride, and abominable, devilish rebellion against the reverend clergy. For by a Portuguese Catholic priest, this very idea of Jonah's going to Nineveh via the Cape of Good Hope was advanced as a signal magnification of the general miracle. And so it was. Besides, to this day, the highly enlightened Turks devoutly believe in the historical story of Jonah. And some three centuries ago, an English traveller in old Harris's Voyages, speaks of a Turkish Mosque built in honor of Jonah, in which Mosque was a miraculous lamp that burnt without any oil.

CHAPTER LXXXIV

PITCHPOLING

To make them run easily and swiftly, the axles of carriages are anointed; and for much the same purpose, some whalers perform an analogous operation upon their boat; they grease the bottom. Nor is it to be doubted that as such a procedure can do no harm, it may possibly be of no contemptible advantage; considering that oil and water are hostile; that oil is a sliding thing, and that the object in view is to make the boat slide bravely. Queequeg believed strongly in anointing his boat, and one morning not long after the German ship Jungfrau disappeared, took more than customary pains in that occupation; crawling under its bottom, where it hung over the side, and rubbing in the unctuousness as though diligently seeking to insure a crop of hair from the craft's bald keel. He seemed to be working in obedience to some particular presentiment. Nor did it remain unwarranted by the event.

Towards noon whales were raised; but so soon as the ship sailed down to them, they turned and fled with swift precipitancy; a disordered flight, as of Cleopatra's barges from Actium.

Nevertheless, the boats pursued, and Stubb's was foremost. By great exertion, Tashtego at last succeeded in planting one iron; but the stricken whale, without at all sounding, still continued his horizontal flight, with added fleetness. Such unintermitted strainings upon the planted iron must sooner or later inevitably extract it. It became imperative to lance the flying whale, or be content to lose him. But to haul the boat up to his flank was impossible, he swam so fast and furious. What then remained?

Of all the wondrous devices and dexterities, the sleights of hand and countless subtleties, to which the veteran whaleman is so often forced, none exceed that fine manœuvre with the lance called pitchpoling. Small sword, or broad sword, in all its exercises boasts nothing like it. It is only indispensable with an inveterate running whale; its grand fact and feature is the wonderful distance to which the long lance is accurately darted from a violently rocking, jerking boat, under extreme headway. Steel and wood included, the entire spear is some ten or twelve feet in length; the staff is much slighter than that of the harpoon, and also of a lighter material—pine. It is furnished with a small rope called a warp, of considerable length, by which it can be hauled back to the hand after darting.

But before going further, it is important to mention here, that though the harpoon may be pitchpoled in the same way with the lance, yet it is seldom done; and when done, is still less frequently successful, on account of the greater weight and inferior length of the harpoon as compared with the lance, which in effect become serious drawbacks. As a general thing, therefore, you must first get fast to a whale, before any pitchpoling comes into play.

Look now at Stubb; a man who from his humorous, deliberate coolness and equanimity in the direst emergencies, was specially qualified to excel in pitchpoling. Look at him; he stands upright in the tossed bow of the flying boat; wrapt in fleecy foam, the towing whale is forty feet ahead. Handling the long lance lightly, glancing twice or thrice along its length to see if it be exactly straight Stubb whistlingly gathers up the coil of the warp in one hand, so as to secure its free end in his grasp, leaving the rest unobstructed. Then holding the lance full before his waistband's middle, he levels it at the whale; when, covering him with it, he steadily depresses the butt-end in his hand, thereby elevating the point till the weapon stands fairly balanced upon his palm, fifteen feet in the air. He minds you somewhat of a juggler, balancing a long staff on his chin. Next moment with a rapid, nameless impulse, in a superb lofty arch the bright steel spans the foaming distance, and quivers in the life spot of the whale. Instead of sparkling water, he now spouts red blood.

"That drove the spigot out of him!" cries Stubb. " 'Tis July's immortal Fourth; all fountains must run wine to-day! Would now, it were old Orleans whiskey, or old Ohio, or unspeakable old Monongahela! Then, Tashtego, lad, I'd have ye hold a canakin to the jet, and we'd drink round it! Yea, verily, hearts alive, we'd brew choice punch in the spread of his spout-hole there, and from that live punch-bowl quaff the living stuff."

Again and again to such gamesome talk, the dexterous dart is repeated, the spear returning to its master like a greyhound held in skilful leash. The agonized whale goes into his flurry; the towline is slackened, and the pitchpoler dropping astern, folds his hands, and mutely watches the monster die.

CHAPTER LXXXV

THE FOUNTAIN

THAT for six thousand years—and no one knows how many millions of ages before—the great whales should have been spouting all over the sea, and sprinkling and mistifying the gardens of the deep, as with so many sprinkling or mistifying pots; and that for some centuries back, thousands of hunters should have been close by the fountain of the whale, watching these sprinklings and spoutings—that all this should be, and yet, that down to this blessed minute (fifteen and a quarter minutes past one o'clock P.M. of this sixteenth day of December, A.D. 1851), it should still remain a problem, whether these spoutings are, after all, really water, or nothing but vapor—this is surely a noteworthy thing.

Let us, then, look at this matter, along with some interesting items contingent. Every one knows that by the peculiar cunning of their gills, the finny tribes in general breathe the air which at all times is combined with the element in which they swim; hence, a herring or a cod might live a century, and never once raise its head above the surface. But owing to his marked internal structure which gives him regular lungs, like a human being's, the whale can only live by inhaling the disengaged air in the open atmosphere. Wherefore the necessity for his periodical visits to the upper world. But he cannot in any degree breathe through his mouth, for, in his ordinary attitude, the Sperm Whale's mouth is buried at least eight feet beneath the surface; and what is still more, his windpipe has no connexion with his mouth. No, he breathes through his spiracle alone; and this is on the top of his head.

If I say, that in any creature breathing is only a function indispensable to vitality, inasmuch as it withdraws from the air a certain element, which being subsequently brought into contact with the blood imparts to the blood its vivifying principle, I do not think I shall err; though I may possibly use some superfluous scientific words. Assume it, and it follows that if all the blood in a man could be aerated with one breath, he might then seal up his nostrils and not fetch another for a considerable time. That is to say, he would then live without breathing. Anomalous as it may seem, this is precisely the case with the whale, who systematically lives, by intervals, his full hour and more (when at the bottom) without drawing a single breath, or so much as in any way inhaling a particle of air; for, remember, he has no gills. How is this? Between his ribs and on each side of his spine he is supplied with a remarkable involved Cretan labyrinth of vermicelli-like vessels, which vessels, when he quits the surface, are completely distended with oxygenated blood. So that for an hour or more, a thousand fathoms in the sea, he carries a surplus stock of vitality in him, just as the camel crossing the waterless desert carries a surplus supply of drink for future use in its four supplementary stomachs. The anatomical fact of this labyrinth is indisputable; and that the supposition founded upon it is reasonable and true, seems the more cogent to me, when I consider the otherwise inexplicable obstinacy of that leviathan in *having his spoutings out,* as the fishermen phrase it. This is what I mean. If unmolested, upon rising to the surface, the Sperm Whale will continue there for a period of time exactly uniform with all his other unmolested risings. Say he stays eleven minutes, and jets seventy times, that is, respires seventy breaths; then whenever he rises again, he will be sure to have his seventy breaths over again, to a minute. Now, if after he fetches a few breaths you alarm him, so that he sounds, he will be always dodging up again to make good his regular allowance of air. And not till those seventy breaths are told, will he finally go down to stay out his full term below. Remark, however, that in different individuals these rates are different; but in any one they are alike. Now, why should the whale thus insist upon having his spoutings out, unless it be to replenish his reservoir of air, ere descending for good? How obvious is it, too, that this necessity for the whale's rising exposes him to all the fatal hazards of the chase. For not by hook or by net could this vast leviathan be caught, when sailing a thousand fathoms beneath the sunlight. Not so much thy skill, then, O hunter, as the great necessities that strike the victory to thee!

In man, breathing is incessantly going on—one breath only serving for two or three pulsations; so that whatever other business he has to attend to, waking or sleeping, breathe he must, or die he will. But the Sperm Whale only breathes about one seventh or Sunday of his time.

It has been said that the whale only breathes through his spout-hole; if it could truthfully be added that his spouts are mixed with water, then I opine we should be furnished with the reason why his sense of smell seems obliterated in him; for the only thing about him that at all answers to his nose is that identical spout-hole; and being so clogged with two elements, it could not be expected to have the power of smelling. But owing to the mystery of the spout—whether it be water or whether it be vapor—no absolute certainty can as yet be arrived at on this head. Sure it is, nevertheless, that the Sperm Whale has no proper olfactories. But what does he want of them? No roses, no violets, no Cologne-water in the sea.

Furthermore, as his windpipe solely opens into the tube of his spouting canal, and as that long canal—like the grand Erie Canal—is furnished with a sort of locks (that open and shut) for the downward retention of air or the upward exclusion of water, therefore the whale has no voice; unless you insult him by saying, that when he so strangely rumbles, he talks through his nose. But then again, what has the whale to say? Seldom have I known any profound being that had anything to say to this world, unless forced to stammer out something by way of getting a living. Oh! happy that the world is such an excellent listener!

Now, the spouting canal of the Sperm Whale, chiefly intended as it is for the conveyance of air, and for several feet laid along, horizontally, just beneath the upper surface of his head, and a little to one side; this curious canal is very much like a gas-pipe laid down in a city on one side of a street. But the question returns whether this gas-pipe is also a water-pipe; in other words, whether the spout of the Sperm Whale is the mere vapor of the exhaled breath, or whether that exhaled breath is mixed with water taken in at the mouth, and discharged through the spiracle. It is certain that the mouth indirectly communicates with the spouting canal; but it cannot be proved that this is for the purpose of discharging water through the spiracle. Because the greatest necessity for so doing would seem to be, when in feeding he accidentally takes in water. But the Sperm Whale's food is far beneath the surface, and there he cannot spout even if he would. Besides, if you regard him very closely, and time him with your watch, you will find that when unmolested, there is an undeviating rhyme between the periods of his jets and the ordinary periods of respiration.

But why pester one with all this reasoning on the subject? Speak out! You have seen him spout; then declare what the spout is; can you not tell water from air? My dear sir, in this world it is not so easy to settle these plain things. I have ever found your plain things the knottiest of all. And as for this whale spout, you might almost stand in it, and yet be undecided as to what it is precisely.

The central body of it is hidden in the snowy sparkling mist enveloping it; and how can you certainly tell whether any water falls from it when, always, when you are close enough to a whale to get a close view of his spout, he is in a prodigious commotion, the water cascading all around him. And if at such times you should think that you really perceived drops of moisture in the spout, how do you know that they are not merely condensed from its vapor; or how do you know that they are not those identical drops superficially lodged in the spout-hole fissure, which is countersunk into the summit of the whale's head? For even when tranquilly swimming through the mid-day sea in a calm, with his elevated hump sun-dried as a dromedary's in the desert; even then, the whale always carries a small basin of water on his head, as under a blazing sun you will sometimes see a cavity in a rock filled up with rain.

Nor is it at all prudent for the hunter to be over curious touching the precise nature of the whale spout. It will not do for him to be peering into it, and putting his face in it. You cannot go with your pitcher to this fountain and fill it, and bring it away. For even when coming into slight contact with the outer, vapory shreds of the jet, which will often happen, your skin will feverishly smart, from the acridness of the thing so touching it. And I know one, who coming into still closer contact with the spout, whether with some scientific object in view, or otherwise, I cannot say, the skin peeled off from his cheek and arm. Wherefore, among whalemen, the spout is deemed poisonous; they try to evade it. Another thing; I have heard it said, and I do not much doubt it, that if the jet is fairly spouted into your eyes, it will blind you. The wisest thing the investigator can do then, it seems to me, is to let this deadly spout alone.

Still, we can hypothesize, even if we cannot prove and establish. My hypothesis is this: that the spout is nothing but mist. And besides other reasons, to this conclusion I am impelled, by considerations touching the great inherent dignity and sublimity of the Sperm Whale; I account him no common, shallow being, inasmuch as it is an undisputed fact that he is never found on soundings, or near shores; all other whales sometimes are. He is both ponderous and profound. And I am convinced that from the heads of all ponderous profound beings, such as Plato, Pyrrho, the Devil, Jupiter, Dante, and so on, there always goes up a certain semi-visible steam, while in the act of thinking deep thoughts. While composing a little treatise on Eternity, I had the curiosity to place a mirror before me; and ere long saw reflected there, a curious involved worming and undulation in the atmosphere over my head. The invariable moisture of my hair, while plunged in deep thought, after six cups of hot tea in my thin shingled attic, of an August noon; this seems an additional argument for the above supposition.

And how nobly it raises our conceit of the mighty, misty monster, to behold him solemnly sailing through a calm tropical sea; his vast, mild head overhung by a canopy of vapor, engendered by his incommunicable contemplations, and that vapor—as you will sometimes see it—glorified by a rainbow, as if Heaven itself had put its seal upon his thoughts. For, d'ye see, rainbows do not visit the clear air; they only irradiate vapor. And so, through all the thick mists of the dim doubts in my mind, divine intuitions now and then shoot, enkindling my fog with a heavenly ray. And for this I thank God; for all have doubts; many deny; but doubts or denials, few along with them, have intuitions. Doubts of all things earthly, and intuitions of some things heavenly; this combination makes neither believer nor infidel, but makes a man who regards them both with equal eye.

CHAPTER LXXXVI

THE TAIL

OTHER poets have warbled the praises of the soft eye of the antelope, and the lovely plumage of the bird that never alights; less celestial, I celebrate a tail.

Reckoning the largest sized Sperm Whale's tail to begin at that point of the trunk where it tapers to about the girth of a man, it comprises upon its upper surface alone, an area of at least fifty square feet. The compact round body of its root expands into two broad, firm, flat palms or flukes, gradually shoaling away to less than an inch in thickness. At the crotch or junction, these flukes slightly overlap, then sideways recede from each other like wings, leaving a wide vacancy between. In no living thing are the lines of beauty more exquisitely defined than in the crescentic borders of these flukes. At its utmost expansion in the full grown whale, the tail will considerably exceed twenty feet across.

The entire member seems a dense webbed bed of welded sinews; but cut into it, and you find that three distinct strata compose it:—upper, middle, and lower. The fibres in the upper and lower layers, are long and horizontal; those of the middle one, very short, and running crosswise between the outside layers. This triune structure, as much as anything else, imparts power to the tail. To the student of old Roman walls, the middle layer will furnish a curious parallel to the thin course of tiles always alternating with the stone in those wonderful relics of the antique, and which undoubtedly contribute so much to the great strength of the masonry.

But as if this vast local power in the tendinous tail were not enough, the whole bulk of the leviathan is knit over with a warp and woof of muscular fibres and filaments, which passing on either side the loins and running down into the flukes, insensibly blend with them, and largely contribute to their might; so that in the tail the confluent measureless force of the whole whale seems concentrated to a point. Could annihilation occur to matter, this were the thing to do it.

Nor does this—its amazing strength at all tend to cripple the graceful flexion of its motions; where infantileness of ease undulates through a Titanism of power. On the contrary, those motions derive their most appalling beauty from it. Real strength never impairs beauty or harmony, but it oftens bestows it; and in everything imposingly beautiful, strength has much to do with the magic. Take away the tied tendons that all over seem bursting from the marble in the carved Hercules, and its charm would be gone. As devout Eckerman lifted the linen sheet from the naked corpse of Goethe, he was overwhelmed with the massive chest of the man, that seemed as a Roman triumphal arch. When Angelo paints even God the Father in human form, mark what robustness is there. And whatever they may reveal of the divine love in the Son, the soft, curled, hermaphroditical Italian pictures, in which his idea has been most successfully embodied; these pictures, so destitute as they are of all brawniness, hint nothing of any power, but the mere negative, feminine one of submission and endurance, which on all hands it is conceded, form the peculiar practical virtues of his teachings.

Such is the subtle elasticity of the organ I treat of, that whether wielded in sport, or in earnest, or in anger, whatever be the mood it be in, its flexions are invariably marked by exceeding grace. Therein no fairy's arm can transcend it.

Five great motions are peculiar to it. First, when used as a fin for progression; Second, when used as a mace in battle; Third, in sweeping; Fourth, in lobtailing; Fifth, in peaking flukes.

First: Being horizontal in its position, the Leviathan's tail acts in a different manner from the tails of all other sea creatures. It never wriggles. In man or fish, wriggling is a sign of inferiority. To the whale, his tail is the sole means of propulsion. Scroll-wise coiled forwards beneath the body, and then rapidly sprung backwards, it is this which gives that singular darting, leaping motion to the monster when furiously swimming. His side-fins only serve to steer by.

Second: It is a little significant, that while one sperm whale only fights another sperm whale with his head and jaw, nevertheless, in his conflicts with man, he chiefly and contemptuously uses his tail. In striking at a boat, he swiftly curves away his flukes from it, and the blow is only inflicted by the recoil. If it be made in the unobstructed air, especially if it descend to its mark, the stroke is then simply irresistible. No ribs of man or boat can withstand it. Your only salvation lies in eluding it; but if it comes sideways through the opposing water, then partly owing to the light buoyancy of the whale-boat, and the elasticity of its materials, a cracked rib or a dashed plank or two, a sort of stitch in the side, is generally the most serious result. These submerged side blows are so often received in the fishery, that they are accounted mere child's play. Some one strips off a frock, and the hole is stopped.

Third: I cannot demonstrate it, but it seems to me, that in the whale the sense of touch is concentrated in the tail; for in this respect there is a delicacy in it only equalled by the daintiness of the elephant's trunk. This delicacy is chiefly evinced in the action of sweeping, when in maidenly gentleness the whale with a certain soft slowness moves his immense flukes from side to side upon the surface of the sea; and if he feel but a sailor's whisker, woe to that sailor, whiskers and all. What tenderness there is in that preliminary touch! Had this tail any prehensile power, I should straightway bethink me of Darmonodes' elephant that so frequented the flower-market, and with low salutations presented nosegays to damsels, and then caressed their zones. On more accounts than one, a pity it is that the whale does not possess this prehensile virtue in his tail; for I have heard of yet another elephant, that when wounded in the fight, curved round his trunk and extracted the dart.

Fourth: Stealing unawares upon the whale in the fancied security of the middle of solitary seas, you find him unbent from the vast corpulence of his dignity, and kitten-like, he plays on the ocean as if it were a hearth. But still you see his power in his play. The broad palms of his tail are flirted high into the air; then smiting the surface, the thunderous concussion resounds for miles. You would almost think a great gun had been discharged; and if you noticed the light wreath of vapor from the spiracle at his other extremity, you would think that that was the smoke from the touch-hole.

Fifth: As in the ordinary floating posture of the leviathan the flukes lie considerably below the level of his back, they are then completely out of sight beneath the surface; but when he is about to plunge into the deeps, his entire flukes with at least thirty feet of his body are tossed erect in the air, and so remain vibrating a moment, till they downwards shoot out of view. Excepting the sublime *breach*—somewhere else to be described—this peaking of the whale's flukes is perhaps the grandest sight to be seen in all animated nature. Out of the bottomless profundities the gigantic tail seems spasmodically snatching at the highest heaven. So in dreams, have I seen majestic Satan thrusting forth his tormented colossal claw from the flame Baltic of Hell. But in gazing at such scenes, it is all in all what mood you are in; if in the Dantean, the devils will occur to you; if in that of Isaiah, the archangels. Standing at the mast-head of my ship during a sunrise that crimsoned sky and sea, I once saw a large herd of whales in the east, all heading towards the sun, and for a moment vibrating in concert with peaked flukes. As it seemed to me at the time, such a grand embodiment of adoration of the gods was never beheld, even in Persia, the home of the fire worshippers. As Ptolemy Philopater testified of the African elephant, I then testified of the whale, pronouncing him the most devout of all beings. For according to King Juba, the military elephants of antiquity often hailed the morning with their trunks uplifted in the profoundest silence.

The chance comparison in this chapter, between the whale and the elephant, so far as some aspects of the tail of the one and the trunk of the other are concerned, should not tend to place those two opposite organs on an equality, much less the creatures to which they respectively belong. For as the mightiest elephant is but a terrier to Leviathan, so, compared with Leviathan's tail, his trunk is but the stalk of a lily. The most direful blow from the elephant's trunk were as the playful tap of a fan, compared with the measureless crush and crash of the sperm whale's ponderous flukes, which in repeated instances have one after the other hurled entire boats with all their oars and crews into the air, very much as an Indian juggler tosses his balls.

The more I consider this mighty tail, the more do I deplore my inability to express it. At times there are gestures in it, which, though they would well grace the hand of man, remain wholly inexplicable. In an extensive herd, so remarkable, occasionally, are these mystic gestures, that I have heard hunters who have declared them akin to Free-Mason signs and symbols; that the whale, indeed, by these methods intelligently conversed with the world. Nor are there wanting other motions of the whale in his general body, full of strangeness, and unaccountable to his most experienced assailant. Dissect him how I may, then, I but go skin deep; I know him not, and never will. But if I know not even the tail of this whale, how understand his head? much more, how comprehend his face, when face he has none? Thou shalt see my back parts, my tail, he seems to say, but my face shall not be seen. But I cannot completely make out his back parts; and hint what he will about his face, I say again he has no face.

CHAPTER LXXXVII

THE GRAND ARMADA

THE long and narrow peninsula of Malacca, extending south-eastward from the territories of Burmah, forms the most southerly point of all Asia. In a continuous line from that peninsula stretch the long islands of Sumatra, Java, Bally, and Timor; which, with many others, form a vast mole, or rampart, lengthwise connecting Asia with Australia, and dividing the long unbroken Indian ocean from the thickly studded oriental archipelagoes. This rampart is pierced by several sally-ports for the convenience of ships and whales; conspicuous among which are the straits of Sunda and Malacca. By the straits of Sunda, chiefly, vessels bound to China from the west, emerge into the China seas.

Those narrow straits of Sunda divide Sumatra from Java; and standing midway in that vast rampart of islands, buttressed by that bold green promontory, known to seamen as Java Head; they not a little correspond to the central gateway opening into some vast walled empire: and considering the inexhaustible wealth of spices, and silks, and jewels, and gold, and ivory, with which the thousand islands of that oriental sea are enriched, it seems a significant provision of nature, that such treasures, by the very formation of the land, should at least bear the appearance, however ineffectual, of being guarded from the all-grasping western world. The shores of the Straits of Sunda are unsupplied with those domineering fortresses which guard the entrances to the Mediterranean, the Baltic, and the Propontis. Unlike the Danes, these Orientals do not demand the obsequious homage of lowered top-sails from the endless procession of ships before the wind, which for centuries past, by night and by day, have passed between the islands of Sumatra and Java, freighted with the costliest cargoes of the east. But while they freely waive a ceremonial like this, they do by no means renounce their claim to more solid tribute.

Time out of mind the piratical proas of the Malays, lurking among the low shaded coves and islets of Sumatra, have sallied out upon the vessels sailing through the straits, fiercely demanding tribute at the point of their spears. Though by the repeated bloody chastisements they have received at the hands of European cruisers, the audacity of these corsairs has of late been somewhat repressed; yet, even at the present day, we occasionally hear of English and American vessels, which, in those waters, have been remorselessly boarded and pillaged.

With a fair, fresh wind, the Pequod was now drawing nigh to these straits; Ahab purposing to pass through them into the Javan sea, and thence, cruising northwards, over waters known to be frequented here and there by the Sperm Whale, sweep inshore by the Philippine Islands, and gain the far coast of Japan, in time for the great whaling season there. By these means, the circumnavigating Pequod would sweep almost all the known Sperm Whale cruising grounds of the world, previous to descending upon the Line in the Pacific; where Ahab, though everywhere else foiled in his pursuit, firmly counted upon giving battle to Moby-Dick, in the sea he was most known to frequent; and at a season when he might most reasonably be presumed to be haunting it.

But how now? in this zoned quest, does Ahab touch no land? does his crew drink air? Surely, he will stop for water. Nay. For a long time, now, the circus-running sun has raced within his fiery ring, and needs no sustenance but what's in himself. So Ahab. Mark this, too, in the whaler. While other hulls are loaded down with alien stuff, to be transferred to foreign wharves; the world-wandering whale-ship carries no cargo but herself and crew, their weapons and their wants. She has a whole lake's contents bottled in her ample hold. She is ballasted with utilities; not altogether with unusable pig-lead and kentledge. She carries years' water in her. Clear old prime Nantucket water; which, when three years afloat, the Nantucketer, in the Pacific, prefers to drink before the brackish fluid, but yesterday rafted off in casks, from the Peruvian or Indian streams. Hence it is, that, while other ships may have gone to China from New York, and back again, touching at a score of ports, the whale-ship, in all that interval, may not have sighted one grain of soil; her crew having seen no man but floating seamen like themselves. So that did you carry them the news that another flood had come; they would only answer—"Well, boys, here's the ark!"

Now, as many Sperm Whales had been captured off the western coast of Java, in the near vicinity of the Straits of Sunda; indeed, as most of the ground, roundabout, was generally recognized by the fishermen as an excellent spot for cruising; therefore, as the Pequod gained more and more upon Java Head, the look-outs were repeatedly hailed, and admonished to keep wide awake. But though the green palmy cliffs of the land soon loomed on the starboard bow, and with delighted nostrils the fresh cinnamon was snuffed in the air, yet not a single jet was descried. Almost renouncing all thought of falling in with any game hereabouts, the ship had well nigh entered the straits, when the customary cheering cry was heard from aloft, and ere long a spectacle of singular magnificence saluted us.

But here be it premised, that owing to the unwearied activity with which of late they have been hunted over all four oceans, the Sperm Whales, instead of almost invariably sailing in small detached companies, as in former times, are now frequently met with in extensive herds, sometimes embracing so great a multitude, that it would almost seem as if numerous nations of them had sworn solemn league and covenant for mutual assistance and protection. To this aggregation of the Sperm Whale into such immense caravans, may be imputed the circumstance that even in the best cruising grounds, you may now sometimes sail for weeks and months together, without being greeted by a single spout; and then be suddenly saluted by what sometimes seems thousands on thousands.

Broad on both bows, at the distance of some two or three miles, and forming a great semicircle, embracing one half of the level horizon, a continuous chain of whale-jets were up-playing and sparkling in the noon-day air. Unlike the straight perpendicular twin-jets of the Right Whale, which, dividing at top, fall over in two branches, like the cleft drooping boughs of a willow, the single forward-slanting spout of the Sperm Whale presents a thick curled bush of white mist, continually rising and falling away to leeward.

Seen from the Pequod's decks, then, as she would rise on a high hill of the sea, this host of vapory spouts, individually curling up into the air, and beheld through a blending atmosphere of bluish haze, showed like the thousand cheerful chimneys of some dense metropolis, descried of a balmy autumnal morning, by some horseman on a height.

As marching armies approaching an unfriendly defile in the mountains, accelerate their march, all eagerness to place that perilous passage in their rear, and once more expand in comparative security upon the plain; even so did this vast fleet of whales now seem hurrying forward through the straits; gradually contracting the wings of their semicircle, and swimming on, in one solid, but still crescentic centre.

Crowding all sail the Pequod pressed after them; the harpooneers handling their weapons, and loudly cheering from the heads of their yet suspended boats. If the wind only held, little doubt had they, that chased through these Straits of Sunda, the vast host would only deploy into the Oriental seas to witness the capture of not a few of their number. And who could tell whether, in that congregated caravan, Moby-Dick himself might not temporarily be swimming, like the worshipped white-elephant in the coronation procession of the Siamese! So with stun-sail piled on stun-sail, we sailed along, driving these leviathans before us; when, of a sudden, the voice of Tashtego was heard, loudly directing attention to something in our wake.

Corresponding to the crescent in our van, we beheld another in our rear. It seemed formed of detached white vapors, rising and falling something like the spouts of the whales; only they did not so completely come and go; for they constantly hovered, without finally disappearing. Levelling his glass at this sight, Ahab quickly revolved in his pivot-hole, crying, "Aloft there, and rig whips and buckets to wet the sails;—Malays, sir, and after us!"

As if too long lurking behind the headlands, till the Pequod should fairly have entered the straits, these rascally Asiatics were now in hot pursuit, to make up for their over-cautious delay. But when the swift Pequod, with a fresh leading wind, was herself in hot chase; how very kind of these tawny philanthropists to assist in speeding her on to her own chosen pursuit—mere riding-whips and rowels to her, that they were. As with glass under arm, Ahab to-and-fro paced the deck; in his forward turn beholding the monsters he chased, and in the after one the bloodthirsty pirates chasing *him;* some such fancy as the above seemed his. And when he glanced upon the green walls of the watery defile in which the ship was then sailing, and bethought him that through that gate lay the route to his vengeance, and beheld, how that through that same gate he was now both chasing and being chased to his deadly end; and not only that, but a herd of remorseless wild pirates and inhuman atheistical devils were infernally cheering him on with their curses;—when all these conceits had passed through his brain, Ahab's brow was left gaunt and ribbed, like the black sand beach after some stormy tide has been gnawing it, without being able to drag the firm thing from its place.

But thoughts like these troubled very few of the reckless crew; and when, after steadily dropping and dropping the pirates astern, the Pequod at last shot by the vivid green Cockatoo Point on the Sumatra side, emerging at last upon the broad waters beyond; then, the harpooneers seemed more to grieve that the swift whales had been gaining upon the ship, than to rejoice that the ship had so victoriously gained upon the Malays. But still driving on in the wake of the whales, at length they seemed abating their speed; gradually the ship neared them; and the wind now dying away, word was passed to spring to the boats. But no sooner did the herd, by some presumed wonderful instinct of the Sperm Whale, become notified of the three keels that were after them, —though as yet a mile in their rear,—than they rallied again, and forming in close ranks and battalions, so that their spouts all looked like flashing lines of stacked bayonets, moved on with redoubled velocity.

Stripped to our shirts and drawers, we sprang to the white-ash, and after several hours' pulling were almost disposed to renounce the chase, when a general pausing commotion among the whales gave animating tokens that they were now at last under the influence of that strange perplexity of inert irresolu-tion, which, when the fishermen perceive it in the whale, they said he is gallied. The compact martial columns in which they had been hitherto rapidly and steadily swimming, were now broken up in one measureless rout; and like King Porus' elephants in the Indian battle with Alexander, they seemed going mad with consternation. In all directions expanding in vast irregular circles, and aimlessly swimming hither and thither, by their short thick spoutings, they plainly betrayed their distraction of panic. This was still more strangely evinced by those of their number, who, completely paralysed as it were, help-lessly floated like water-logged dismantled ships on the sea. Had these Levia-thans been but a flock of simple sheep, pursued over the pasture by three fierce wolves, they could not possibly have evinced such excessive dismay. But this occasional timidity is characteristic of almost all herding creatures. Though banding together in tens of thousands, the lion-maned buffaloes of the West have fled before a solitary horseman. Witness, too, all human beings, how when herded together in the sheepfold of a theatre's pit, they will, at the slight-est alarm of fire, rush helter-skelter for the outlets, crowding, trampling, jam-ming, and remorselessly dashing each other to death. Best, therefore, withhold any amazement at the strangely gallied whales before us, for there is no folly of the beast of the earth which is not infinitely outdone by the madness of men.

Though many of the whales, as has been said, were in violent motion, yet it is to be observed that as a whole the herd neither advanced nor retreated, but collectively remained in one place. As is customary in those cases, the boats at once separated, each making for some one lone whale on the outskirts of the shoal. In about three minutes' time, Queequeg's harpoon was flung; the stricken fish darted blinding spray in our faces, and then running away with us like light, steered straight for the heart of the herd. Though such a movement on the part of the whale struck under such circumstances, is in no wise un-precedented; and indeed is almost always more or less anticipated; yet does it present one of the more perilous vicissitudes of the fishery. For as the swift monster drags you deeper and deeper into the frantic shoal, you bid adieu to circumspect life and only exist in a delirious throb.

As, blind and deaf, the whale plunged forward, as if by sheer power of speed to rid himself of the iron leech that had fastened to him; as we thus tore a white gash in the sea, on all sides menaced as we flew, by the crazed creatures to and fro rushing about us; our beset boat was like a ship mobbed by ice-isles in a tempest, and striving to steer through their complicated channels and straits, knowing not at what moment it may be locked in and crushed.

But not a bit daunted, Queequeg steered us manfully; now sheering off from this monster directly across our route in advance; now edging away from that, whose colossal flukes were suspended overhead, while all the time, Starbuck stood up in the bows, lance in hand, pricking out of our way whatever whale he could reach by short darts, for there was no time to make long ones. Nor were the oarsmen quite idle, though their wonted duty was now altogether dispensed with. They chiefly attended to the shouting part of the business. "Out of the way, Commodore!" cried one, to a great dromedary that of a sudden rose bodily to the surface, and for an instant threatened to swamp us. "Hard down with your tail, there!" cried a second to another, which, close to our gunwale, seemed calmly cooling himself with his own fan-like extremity.

All whaleboats carry certain curious contrivances, originally invented by the Nantucket Indians, called druggs. Two thick squares of wood of equal size are stoutly clenched together, so that they cross each other's grain at right angles; a line of considerable length is then attached to the middle of this block, and the other end of the line being looped, it can in a moment be fastened to a harpoon. It is chiefly among gallied whales that this drugg is used. For then, more whales are close round you than you can possibly chase at one time. But sperm whales are not every day encountered; while you may, then, you must kill all you can. And if you cannot kill them all at once, you must wing them, so that they can be afterwards killed at your leisure. Hence it is, that at times like these the drugg comes into requisition. Our boat was furnished with three of them. The first and second were successfully darted, and we saw the whales staggeringly running off, fettered by the enormous sidelong resistance of the towing drugg. They were cramped like malefactors with the chain and ball. But upon flinging the third, in the act of tossing overboard the clumsy wooden block, it caught under one of the seats of the boat, and in an instant tore it out and carried it away, dropping the oarsman in the boat's bottom as the seat slid from under him. On both sides the sea came in at the wounded planks, but we stuffed two or three drawers and shirts in, and so stopped the leaks for the time.

It had been next to impossible to dart these drugged-harpoons, were it not that as we advanced into the herd, our whale's way greatly diminished; moreover, that as we went still further and further from the circumference of commotion, the direful disorders seemed waning. So that when at last the jerking harpoon drew out, and the towing whale sideways vanished; then, with the tapering force of his parting momentum, we glided between two whales into the innermost heart of the shoal, as if from some mountain torrent we had slid into a serene valley lake. Here the storms in the roaring glens between the outermost whales, were heard but not felt. In this central expanse the sea presented that smooth satin-like surface, called a sleek, produced by the subtle moisture thrown off by the whale in his more quiet moods. Yes, we

were now in that enchanted calm which they say lurks at the heart of every
commotion. And still in the distracted distance we beheld the tumults of
the outer concentric circles, and saw successive pods of whales, eight or ten in
each, swiftly going round and round, like multiplied spans of horses in a ring;
and so closely shoulder to shoulder, that a Titanic circus-rider might easily have
over-arched the middle ones, and so have gone round on their backs. Owing
to the density of the crowd of reposing whales, more immediately surrounding
the embayed axis of the herd, no possible chance of escape was at present afforded us. We must watch for a breach in the living wall that hemmed us
in; the wall that had only admitted us in order to shut us up. Keeping at
the centre of the lake, we were occasionally visited by small tame cows and
calves; the women and children of this routed host.

Now, inclusive of the occasional wide intervals between the revolving outer
circles, and inclusive of the spaces between the various pods in any one of those
circles, the entire area at this juncture, embraced by the whole multitude, must
have contained at least two or three square miles. At any rate—though indeed
such a test at such a time might be deceptive—spoutings might be discovered
from our low boat that seemed playing up almost from the rim of the horizon.
I mention this circumstance, because, as if the cows and calves had been purposely locked up in this innermost fold; and as if the wide extent of the herd
had hitherto prevented them from learning the precise cause of its stopping;
or, possibly, being so young, unsophisticated, and every way innocent and
inexperienced; however it may have been, these smaller whales—now and then
visiting our becalmed boat from the margin of the lake—evinced a wondrous
fearlessness and confidence, or else a still becharmed panic which it was impossible not to marvel at. Like household dogs they came snuffing round us,
right up to our gunwales, and touching them; till it almost seemed that some
spell had suddenly domesticated them. Queequeg patted their foreheads; Starbuck scratched their backs with his lance; but fearful of the consequences, for
the time refrained from darting it.

But far beneath this wondrous world upon the surface, another and still
stranger world met our eyes as we gazed over the side. For, suspended in
those watery vaults, floated the forms of the nursing mothers of the whales, and
those that by their enormous girth seemed shortly to become mothers. The
lake, as I have hinted, was to a considerable depth exceedingly transparent;
and as human infants while suckling will calmly and fixedly gaze away from
the breast, as if leading two different lives at the time; and while yet drawing
mortal nourishment, be still spiritually feasting upon some unearthly reminiscence;—even so did the young of these whales seem looking up towards us,
but not at us, as if we were but a bit of Gulf-weed in their new-born sight.
Floating on their sides, the mothers also seemed quietly eyeing us. One of
these little infants, that from certain queer tokens seemed hardly a day old,
might have measured some fourteen feet in length, and some six feet in girth.
He was a little frisky; though as yet his body seemed scarce yet recovered from
that irksome position it had so lately occupied in the maternal reticule; where,
tail to head, and all ready for the final spring, the unborn whale lies bent like
a Tartar's bow. The delicate side-fins, and the palms of his flukes, still
freshly retained the plaited crumpled appearance of a baby's ears newly arrived
from foreign parts.

"Line! line!" cried Queequeg, looking over the gunwale; "him fast! him
fast!—who line him! Who struck?—Two whale; one big, one little!"

"What ails ye, man?" cried Starbuck.

"Look-e here," said Queequeg, pointing down.

As when the stricken whale, that from the tub has reeled out hundreds of fathoms of rope; as, after deep sounding, he floats up again, and shows the slackened curling line buoyantly rising and spiralling towards the air; so now, Starbuck saw long coils of the umbilical cord of Madame Leviathan, by which the young cub seemed still tethered to its dam. Not seldom in the rapid vicissitudes of the chase, this natural line, with the maternal end loose, becomes entangled with the hempen one, so that the cub is thereby trapped. Some of the subtlest secrets of the seas seemed divulged to us in this enchanted pond. We saw young Leviathan amours in the deep.

And thus, though surrounded by circle upon circle of consternations and affrights, did these inscrutable creatures at the centre freely and fearlessly indulge in all peaceful concernments; yea, serenely revelled in dalliance and delight. But even so, amid the tornadoed Atlantic of my being, do I myself still for ever centrally disport in mute calm; and while ponderous planets of unwaning woe revolve round me, deep down and deep inland there I still bathe me in eternal mildness of joy.

Meanwhile, as we thus lay entranced, the occasional sudden frantic spectacles in the distance evinced the activity of the other boats, still engaged in drugging the whales on the frontier of the host; or possibly carrying on the war within the first circle, where abundance of room and some convenient retreats were afforded them. But the sight of the enraged drugged whales now and then blindly darting to and fro across the circles, was nothing to what at last met our eyes. It is sometimes the custom when fast to a whale more than commonly powerful and alert, to seek to hamstring him, as it were, by sundering or maiming his gigantic tail-tendon. It is done by darting a short-handled cutting-spade, to which is attached a rope for hauling it back again. A whale wounded (as we afterwards learned) in this part, but not effectually, as it seemed, had broken away from the boat, carrying along with him half of the harpoon line; and in the extraordinary agony of the wound, he was now dashing among the revolving circles like the lone mounted desperado Arnold, at the battle of Saratoga, carrying dismay wherever he went.

But agonizing as was the wound of this whale, and an appalling spectacle enough, any way; yet the peculiar horror with which he seemed to inspire the rest of the herd, was owing to a cause which at first the intervening distance obscured from us. But at length we perceived that by one of the unimaginable accidents of the fishery, this whale had become entangled in the harpoon-line that he towed; he had also run away with the cutting-spade in him; and while the free end of the rope attached to that weapon, had permanently caught in the coils of the harpoon-line round his tail, the cutting-spade itself had worked loose from his flesh. So that tormented to madness, he was now churning through the water, violently flailing with his flexible tail, and tossing the keen spade about him, wounding and murdering his own comrades.

This terrific object seemed to recall the whole herd from their stationary fright. First, the whales forming the margin of our lake began to crowd a little, and tumble against each other, as if lifted by half spent billows from afar; then the lake itself began faintly to heave and swell; the submarine bridal-chambers and nurseries vanished; in more and more contracting orbits the whales in the more central circles began to swim in thickening clusters. Yes, the long calm was departing. A low advancing hum was soon heard; and then like to the tumultuous masses of block-ice when the great river Hudson breaks up in Spring, the entire host of whales came tumbling upon their inner centre, as if to pile themselves up in one common mountain. Instantly Starbuck and Queequeg changed places; Starbuck taking the stern.

"Oars! Oars!" he intensely whispered, seizing the helm—"gripe your oars, and clutch your souls, now! My God, men, stand by! Shove him off, you Queequeg—the whale there!—prick him!—hit him! Stand up—stand up, and stay so! Spring, men—pull, men; never mind their backs—scrape them!—scrape away!"

The boat was now all but jammed between two vast black bulks, leaving a narrow Dardanelles between their long lengths. But by desperate endeavor we at last shot into a temporary opening; then giving way rapidly, and at the same time earnestly watching for another outlet. After many similar hairbreadth escapes, we at last swiftly glided into what had just been one of the outer circles, but now crossed by random whales, all violently making for one centre. This lucky salvation was cheaply purchased by the loss of Queequeg's hat, who, while standing in the bows to prick the fugitive whales, had his hat taken clean from his head by the air-eddy made by the sudden tossing of a pair of broad flukes close by.

Riotous and disordered as the universal commotion now was, it soon resolved itself into what seemed a systematic movement; for having clumped together at last in one dense body, they then renewed their onward flight with augmented fleetness. Further pursuit was useless; but the boats still lingered in their wake to pick up what drugged whales might be dropped astern, and likewise to secure one which Flask had killed and waifed. The waif is a pennoned pole, two or three of which are carried by every boat; and which, when additional game is at hand, are inserted upright into the floating body of a dead whale, both to mark its place on the sea, and also as token of prior possession, should the boats of any other ship draw near.

The result of this lowering was somewhat illustrative of that sagacious saying in the Fishery,—the more whales the less fish. Of all the drugged whales only one was captured. The rest contrived to escape for the time, but only to be taken, as will hereafter be seen, by some other craft than the Pequod.

CHAPTER LXXXVIII

SCHOOLS AND SCHOOLMASTERS

THE previous chapter gave account of an immense body or herd of Sperm Whales, and there was also then given the probable cause inducing those vast aggregations.

Now, though such great bodies are at times encountered, yet, as must have been seen, even at the present day, small detached bands are occasionally observed, embracing from twenty to fifty individuals each. Such bands are known as schools. They generally are of two sorts; those composed almost entirely of females, and those mustering none but young vigorous males, or bulls as they are familiarly designated.

In cavalier attendance upon the school of females, you invariably see a male of full grown magnitude, but not old; who, upon any alarm, evinces his gallantry by falling in the rear and covering the flight of his ladies. In truth, this gentleman is a luxurious Ottoman, swimming about over the watery world, surroundingly accompanied by all the solaces and endearments of the harem.

The contrast between this Ottoman and his concubines is striking; because, while he is always of the largest leviathanic proportions, the ladies, even at full growth, are not more than one-third of the bulk of an average-sized male. They are comparatively delicate, indeed; I dare say, not to exceed half a dozen yards round the waist. Nevertheless, it cannot be denied, that upon the whole they are hereditarily entitled to *em bon point*.

It is very curious to watch this harem and its lord in their indolent ramblings. Like fashionables, they are for ever on the move in leisurely search of variety. You meet them on the Line in time for the full flower of the Equatorial feeding season, having just returned, perhaps, from spending the summer in the Northern seas, and so cheating summer of all unpleasant weariness and warmth. By the time they have lounged up and down the promenade of the Equator awhile, they start for the Oriental waters in anticipation of the cool season there, and so evade the other excessive temperature of the year.

When serenely advancing on one of these journeys, if any strange suspicious sights are seen, my lord whale keeps a wary eye on his interesting family. Should any unwarrantably pert young Leviathan coming that way, presume to draw confidentially close to one of the ladies, with what prodigious fury the Bashaw assails him, and chases him away! High times, indeed, if unprincipled young rakes like him are to be permitted to invade the sanctity of domestic bliss; though do what the Bashaw will, he cannot keep the most notorious Lothario out of his bed; for, alas! all fish bed in common. As ashore, the ladies often cause the most terrible duels among their rival admirers; just so with the whales, who sometimes come to deadly battle, and all for love. They fence with their long lower jaws, sometimes locking them together, and so striving for the supremacy like elks that warringly interweave their antlers. Not a few are captured having the deep scars of these encounters—furrowed heads, broken teeth, scalloped fins; and in some instances, wrenched and dislocated mouths.

But supposing the invader of domestic bliss to betake himself away at the first rush of the harem's lord, then it is very diverting to watch that lord. Gently he insinuates his vast bulk among them again and revels there awhile, still in tantalizing vicinity to young Lothario, like pious Solomon devoutly worshipping among his thousand concubines. Granting other whales to be in sight, the fishermen will seldom give chase to one of these Grand Turks; for these Grand Turks are too lavish of their strength, and hence their unctuousness is small. As for the sons and the daughters they beget, why, those sons and daughters must take care of themselves; at least, with only the maternal help. For like certain other omnivorous roving lovers that might be named, my Lord Whale has no taste for the nursery, however much for the bower; and so, being a great traveller, he leaves his anonymous babies all over the world; every baby an exotic. In good time, nevertheless, as the ardor of youth declines; as years and dumps increase; as reflection lends her solemn pauses; in short, as a general lassitude overtakes the sated Turk; then a love of ease and virtue supplants the love for maidens; our Ottoman enters upon the impotent, repentant, admonitory stage of life, forswears, disbands the harem, and grown to an exemplary, sulky old soul, goes about all alone among the meridians and parallels saying his prayers, and warning each young Leviathan from his amorous errors.

Now, as the harem of whales is called by the fishermen a school, so is the lord and master of that school technically known as the schoolmaster. It is therefore not in strict character, however admirably satirical, that after going to school himself, he should then go abroad inculcating not what he learned there, but the folly of it. His title, schoolmaster, would very naturally seem derived from the name bestowed upon the harem itself, but some have surmised that the man who first thus entitled this sort of Ottoman whale, must have read the memoirs of Vidocq, and informed himself what sort of a country-schoolmaster that famous Frenchman was in his younger days, and what was the nature of those occult lessons he inculcated into some of his pupils.

The same secludedness and isolation to which the schoolmaster whale betakes himself in his advancing years, is true of all aged Sperm Whales. Almost universally, a lone whale—as a solitary Leviathan is called—proves an ancient one. Like venerable moss-bearded Daniel Boone, he will have no one near him but Nature herself; and her he takes to wife in the wilderness of waters, and the best of wives she is, though she keeps so many moody secrets.

The schools composing none but young and vigorous males, previously mentioned, offer a strong contrast to the harem schools. For while those female whales are characteristically timid, the young whales, or Forty-barrel-bulls, as they call them, are by far the most pugnacious of all Leviathans, and proverbially the most dangerous to encounter; excepting those wondrous grey-headed, grizzled whales, sometimes met, and these will fight you like grim fiends exasperated by a penal gout.

The Forty-barrel-bull schools are larger than the harem schools. Like a mob of young collegians, they are full of fight, fun, and wickedness, tumbling round the world at such a reckless, rollicking rate, that no prudent underwriter would insure them any more than he would a riotous lad at Yale or Harvard. They soon relinquish this turbulence though, and when about three fourths grown, break up, and separately go about in quest of settlements, that is, harems.

Another point of difference between the male and female schools is still more characteristic of the sexes. Say you strike a Forty-barrel-bull—poor devil! all his comrades quit him. But strike a member of the harem school, and her companions swim around her with every token of concern, sometimes lingering so near her and so long, as themselves to fall a prey.

CHAPTER LXXXIX

FAST-FISH AND LOOSE-FISH

THE allusion to the waifs and waif-poles in the last chapter but one, necessitates some account of the laws and regulations of the whale fishery, of which the waif may be deemed the grand symbol and badge.

It frequently happens that when several ships are cruising in company, a whale may be struck by one vessel, then escape, and be finally killed and captured by another vessel; and herein are indirectly comprised many minor contingencies, all partaking of this one grand feature. For example,—after a weary and perilous chase and capture of a whale, the body may get loose from the ship by reason of a violent storm; and drifting far away to leeward, be retaken by a second whaler, who, in a calm, snugly tows it alongside, without risk of life or line. Thus the most vexatious and violent disputes would often arise between the fishermen, were there not some written or unwritten, universal, undisputed law applicable to all cases.

Perhaps the only formal whaling code authorized by legislative enactment, was that of Holland. It was decreed by the States-General in A.D. 1695. But though no other nation has ever had any written whaling law, yet the American fishermen have been their own legislators and lawyers in this matter. They have provided a system which for terse comprehensiveness surpasses Justinian's Pandects and the By-laws of the Chinese Society for the Suppression of Meddling with other People's Business. Yes; these laws might be engraven on a Queen Anne's farthing, or the barb of a harpoon, and worn round the neck, so small are they.

I. A Fast-Fish belongs to the party fast to it.

II. A Loose-Fish is fair game for anybody who can soonest catch it.

But what plays the mischief with this masterly code is the admirable brevity of it, which necessitates a vast volume of commentaries to expound it.

First: What is a Fast-Fish? Alive or dead a fish is technically fast, when it is connected with an occupied ship or boat, by any medium at all controllable by the occupant or occupants,—a mast, an oar, a nine-inch cable, a telegraph wire, or a strand of cobweb, it is all the same. Likewise a fish is technically fast when it bears a waif, or any other recognised symbol of possession; so long as the party waifing it plainly evince their ability at any time to take it alongside, as well as their intention so to do.

These are scientific commentaries; but the commentaries of the whalemen themselves sometimes consist in hard words and harder knocks—the Coke-upon-Littleton of the fist. True, among the more upright and honourable whale-men allowances are always made for peculiar cases, where it would be an outrageous moral injustice for one party to claim possession of a whale previously chased or killed by another party. But others are by no means so scrupulous.

Some fifty years ago there was a curious case of whale-trover litigated in England, wherein the plaintiffs set forth that after a hard chase of a whale in the Northern seas; and when indeed they (the plaintiffs) had succeeded in harpooning the fish; they were at last, through peril of their lives, obliged to forsake not only their lines, but their boat itself. Ultimately the defendants (the crew of another ship) came up with the whale, struck, killed, seized, and finally appropriated it before the very eyes of the plaintiffs. And when those defendants were remonstrated with, their captain snapped his fingers in the plaintiffs' teeth, and assured them that by way of doxology to the deed he had done, he would now retain their line, harpoons, and boat, which had remained attached to the whale at the time of the seizure. Wherefore the plaintiffs now sued for the recovery of the value of their whale, line, harpoons, and boat.

Mr. Erskine was counsel for the defendants; Lord Ellenborough was the judge. In the course of the defence, the witty Erskine went on to illustrate his position, by alluding to a recent crim. con. case, wherein a gentleman, after in vain trying to bridle his wife's viciousness, had at last abandoned her upon the seas of life; but in the course of years, repenting of that step, he instituted an action to recover possession of her. Erskine was on the other side; and he then supported it by saying, that though the gentleman had originally harpooned the lady, and had once had her fast, and only by reason of the great stress of her plunging viciousness, had at last abandoned her; yet abandon her he did, so that she became a loose-fish; and therefore when a subsequent gentleman re-harpooned her, the lady then became that subsequent gentleman's property, along with whatever harpoon might have been found sticking in her.

Now in the present case Erskine contended that the examples of the whale and the lady were reciprocally illustrative of each other.

These pleadings, and the counter pleadings, being duly heard, the very learned judge in set terms decided, to wit,—That as for the boat, he awarded it to the plaintiffs, because they had merely abandoned it to save their lives; but that with regard to the controverted whale, harpoons, and line, they belonged to the defendants; the whale, because it was a Loose-Fish at the time of the final capture; and the harpoons and line because when the fish made off with them, it (the fish) acquired a property in those articles; and hence anybody who afterwards took the fish had a right to them. Now the plaintiffs afterwards took the fish; ergo, the aforesaid articles were theirs.

A common man looking at this decision of the very learned Judge, might possibly object to it. But ploughed up to the primary rock of the matter, the two great principles laid down in the twin whaling laws previously quoted, and applied and elucidated by Lord Ellenborough in the above cited case; these two laws touching Fast-Fish and Loose-Fish, I say, will, on reflection, be found the fundamentals of all human jurisprudence; for notwithstanding its complicated tracery of sculpture, the Temple of the Law, like the Temple of the Philistines, has but two props to stand on.

Is it not a saying in every one's mouth: Possession is half of the law: that is, regardless of how the thing came into possession? But often possession is the whole of the law. What are the sinews and souls of Russian serfs and Republican slaves but Fast-Fish, whereof possession is the whole of the law? What to the rapacious landlord is the widow's last mite but a Fast-Fish? What is yonder undetected villain's marble mansion with a door-plate for a waif; what is that but a Fast-Fish? What is the ruinous discount which Mordecai, the broker, gets from poor Woebegone, the bankrupt, on a loan to keep Woebegone's family from starvation; what is that ruinous discount but a Fast-Fish? What is the Archbishop of Savesoul's income of £100,0co seized from the scant bread and cheese of hundreds of thousands of broken-backed laborers (all sure of heaven without any of Savesoul's help) what is that globular 100,000 but a Fast-Fish? What are the Duke of Dunder's hereditary towns and hamlets but Fast-Fish? What to that redoubted harpooneer, John Bull, is poor Ireland, but a Fast-Fish? What to that apostolic lancer, Brother Jonathan, is Texas but a Fast-Fish? And concerning all these, is not Possession the whole of the law?

But if the doctrine of Fast-Fish be pretty generally applicable, the kindred doctrine of Loose-Fish is still more widely so. That is internationally and universally applicable.

What was America in 1492 but a Loose-Fish, in which Columbus struck the Spanish standard by way of waifing it for his royal master and mistress? What was Poland to the Czar? What Greece to the Turk? What India to England? What at last will Mexico be to the United States? All Loose-Fish.

What are the Rights of Man and the Liberties of the World but Loose-Fish? What all men's minds and opinions but Loose-Fish? What is the principle of religious belief in them but a Loose-Fish? What to the ostentatious smuggling verbalists are the thoughts of thinkers but Loose-Fish? What is the great globe itself but a Loose-Fish? And what are you, reader, but a Ioose-Fish and a Fast-Fish, too?

CHAPTER XC

HEADS OR TAILS

"De balena vero sufficit, si rex habeat caput, et regina caudam."

Bracton, l. 3, *c.* 3.

LATIN from the books of the Laws of England, which taken along with the context, means, that of all whales captured by anybody on the coast of that land, the King, as Honorary Grand Harpooneer, must have the head, and the Queen be respectfully presented with the tail. A division which, in the whale, is much like halving an apple; there is no intermediate remainder. Now as this law, under a modified form, is to this day in force in England; and as it offers in various respects a strange anomaly touching the general law of Fast and Loose-Fish, it is here treated of in a separate chapter, on the same courteous principle that prompts the English railways to be at the expense of a separate car, specially reserved for the accommodation of royalty. In the first place, in curious proof of the fact that the above-mentioned law is still in force, I proceed to lay before you a circumstance that happened within the last two years.

It seems that some honest mariners of Dover, or Sandwich, or some one of the Cinque Ports, had after a hard chase succeeded in killing and beaching a fine whale which they had originally descried afar off from the shore. Now the Cinque Ports are partially or somehow under the jurisdiction of a sort of policeman or beadle, called a Lord Warden. Holding the office directly from the crown, I believe, all the royal emoluments incident to the Cinque Port territories become by assignment his. By some writers this office is called a sinecure. But not so. Because the Lord Warden is busily employed at times in fobbing his perquisites; which are his chiefly by virtue of that same fobbing of them.

Now when these poor sun-burnt mariners, barefooted, and with their trowsers rolled high up on their eely legs, had wearily hauled their fat fish high and dry, promising themselves a good £150 from the precious oil and bone; and in fantasy sipping rare tea with their wives, and good ale with their cronies, upon the strength of their respective shares; up steps a very learned and most Christian and charitable gentleman, with a copy of Blackstone under his arm; and laying it upon the whale's head, he says—"Hands off! this fish, my masters, is a Fast-Fish. I seize it as the Lord Warden's." Upon this the poor mariners in their respectful consternation—so truly English—knowing not what to say, fall to vigorously scratching their heads all round; meanwhile ruefully glancing from the whale to the stranger. But that did in nowise mend the matter, or at all soften the hard heart of the learned gentleman with the copy of Blackstone. At length one of them, after long scratching about for his ideas, made bold to speak.

"Please, sir, who is the Lord Warden?"

"The Duke."

"But the Duke had nothing to do with taking this fish?"

"It is his."

"We have been at great trouble, and peril, and some expense, and is all that to go to the Duke's benefit; we getting nothing at all for our pains but our blisters?"

"It is his."

"Is the Duke so very poor as to be forced to this desperate mode of getting a livelihood?"

"It is his."

"I thought to relieve my old bed-ridden mother by part of my share of this whale."

"It is his."

"Won't the Duke be content with a quarter or a half?"

"It is his."

In a word, the whale was seized and sold, and his Grace the Duke of Wellington received the money. Thinking that viewed in some particular lights, the case might by a bare possibility in some small degree be deemed, under the circumstances, a rather hard one, an honest clergyman of the town respectfully addressed a note to his Grace, begging him to take the case of those unfortunate mariners into full consideration. To which my Lord Duke in substance replied (both letters were published) that he had already done so, and received the money, and would be obliged to the reverend gentleman if for the future he (the reverend gentleman) would decline meddling with other people's business. Is this the still militant old man, standing at the corners of the three kingdoms, on all hands coercing alms of beggars?

It will readily be seen that in this case the alleged right of the Duke to the whale was a delegated one from the Sovereign. We must needs inquire then on what principle the Sovereign is originally invested with that right. The law itself has already been set forth. But Plowdon gives us the reason for it. Says Plowdon, the whale so caught belongs to the King and Queen, "because of its superior excellence." And by the soundest commentators this has ever been held a cogent argument in such matters.

But why should the King have the head, and the Queen the tail? A reason for that, ye lawyers!

In his treatise on "Queen-Gold," or Queen-pin-money, an old King's Bench author, one William Prynne, thus discourseth: "Ye tail is ye Queen's, that ye Queen's wardrobe may be supplied with ye whalebone." Now this was written at a time when the black limber bone of the Greenland or Right whale was largely used in ladies' bodices. But this same bone is not in the tail; it is in the head, which is a sad mistake for a sagacious lawyer like Prynne. But is the Queen a mermaid, to be presented with a tail? An allegorical meaning may lurk here.

There are two royal fish so styled by the English law writers—the whale and the sturgeon; both royal property under certain limitations, and nominally supplying the tenth branch of the crown's ordinary revenue. I know not that any other author has hinted of the matter; but by inference it seems to me that the sturgeon must be divided in the same way as the whale, the King receiving the highly dense and elastic head peculiar to that fish, which, symbolically regarded, may possibly be humorously grounded upon some presumed congeniality. And thus there seems a reason in all things, even in law.

CHAPTER XCI

THE PEQUOD MEETS THE ROSEBUD

"In vain it was to rake for Ambergriese in the paunch of this Leviathan, insufferable fetor denying not inquiry."

Sir T. Browne, V. E."

IT was a week or two after the last whaling scene recounted, and when we were slowly sailing over a sleepy, vapory, mid-day sea, that the many noses on the Pequod's deck proved more vigilant discoverers than the three pairs of eyes aloft. A peculiar and not very pleasant smell was smelt in the sea.

"I will bet something now," said Stubb, "that somewhere hereabouts are some of those drugged whales we tickled the other day. I thought they would keel up before long."

Presently, the vapors in advance slid aside; and there in the distance lay a ship, whose furled sails betokened that some sort of whale must be alongside. As we glided nearer, the stranger showed French colors from his peak; and by the eddying cloud of vulture sea-fowl that circled, and hovered, and swooped around him, it was plain that the whale alongside must be what the fishermen call a blasted whale, that is, a whale that has died unmolested on the sea, and so floated an unappropriated corpse. It may well be conceived, what an unsavory odor such a mass must exhale; worse than an Assyrian city in the plague, when the living are incompetent to bury the departed. So intolerable indeed is it regarded by some, that no cupidity could persuade them to moor alongside of it. Yet are there those who will still do it; notwithstanding the fact that the oil obtained from such subjects is of a very inferior quality, and by no means of the nature of attar-of-rose.

Coming still nearer with the expiring breeze, we saw that the Frenchman had a second whale alongside; and this second whale seemed even more of a nosegay than the first. In truth, it turned out to be one of those problematical whales that seem to dry up and die with a sort of prodigious dyspepsia, or indigestion; leaving their defunct bodies almost entirely bankrupt of anything like oil. Nevertheless, in the proper place we shall see that no knowing fisherman will ever turn up his nose at such a whale as this, however much he may shun blasted whales in general.

The Pequod had now swept so nigh to the stranger, that Stubb vowed he recognised his cutting spade-pole entangled in the lines that were knotted round the tail of one of these whales.

"There's a pretty fellow, now," he banteringly laughed, standing in the ship's bows, "there's a jackal for ye! I well know that these Crappoes of Frenchmen are but poor devils in the fishery; sometimes lowering their boats for breakers, mistaking them for Sperm Whale spouts; yes, and sometimes sailing from their port with their hold full of boxes of tallow candles, and cases of snuffers, foreseeing that all the oil they will get won't be enough to dip the Captain's wick into; aye, we all know these things; but look ye, here's a Crappo that is content with our leavings, the drugged whale there, I mean; aye, and is content too with scraping the dry bones of that other precious fish he has there. Poor devil! I say, pass round a hat, some one, and let's make him a present of a little oil for dear charity's sake. For what oil he'll get from

that drugged whale there, wouldn't be fit to burn in a jail; no, not in a condemned cell.   And as for the other whale, why, I'll agree to get more oil by
chopping up and trying out these three masts of ours, than he'll get from that
bundle of bones; though, now that I think of it, it may contain something
worth a good deal more than oil; yes, ambergris.   I wonder now if our old
man has thought of that.   It's worth trying.   Yes, I'm in for it;" and so saying
he started for the quarter-deck.

By this time the faint air had become a complete calm; so that whether
or no, the Pequod was now fairly entrapped in the smell, with no hope of
escaping except by its breezing up again.   Issuing from the cabin, Stubb now
called his boat's crew, and pulled off for the stranger.   Drawing across her
bow, he perceived that in accordance with the fanciful French taste, the upper
part of her stem-piece was carved in the likeness of a huge drooping stalk,
was painted green, and for thorns had copper spikes projecting from it here
and there; the whole terminating in a symmetrical folded bulb of a bright red
color.   Upon her head boards, in large gilt letters, he read "Bouton de Rose,"
—Rose-button, or Rose-bud; and this was the romantic name of this aromatic
ship.

Though Stubb did not understand the *Bouton* part of the inscription, yet
the word *rose*, and the bulbous figure-head put together, sufficiently explained
the whole to him.

"A wooden rose-bud, eh?" he cried with his hand to his nose, "that will do
very well; but how like all creation it smells!"

Now in order to hold direct communication with the people on deck, he
had to pull round the bows to the starboard side, and thus come close to the
blasted whale; and so talk over it.

Arrived then at this spot, with one hand still to his nose, he bawled—
"Bouton-de-Rose, ahoy! are there any of you Bouton-de-Roses that speak
English?"

"Yes," rejoined a Guernsey-man from the bulwarks, who turned out to be
the chief-mate.

"Well, then, my Bouton-de-Rose-bud, have you seen the White Whale?"

"*What* whale?"

"The *White* Whale—a Sperm Whale—Moby-Dick, have ye seen him?"

"Never heard of such a whale.   Cachalot Blanche!   White Whale—no."

"Very good, then; good bye now, and I'll call again in a minute."

Then rapidly pulling back towards the Pequod, and seeing Ahab leaning
over the quarter-deck rail awaiting his report, he moulded his two hands into
a trumpet and shouted—"No, Sir!   No!'   Upon which Ahab retired, and Stubb
returned to the Frenchman.

He now perceived that the Guernsey-man, who had just got into the chains,
and was using a cutting-spade, had slung his nose in a sort of bag.

"What's the matter with your nose, there?" said Stubb.   "Broke it?"

"I wish it was broken, or that I didn't have any nose at all!" answered
the Guernsey-man, who did not seem to relish the job he was at very much.
"But what are you holding *yours* for?"

"Oh, nothing!   It's a wax nose; I have to hold it on.   Fine day, ain't it?
Air rather gardenny, I should say; throw us a bunch of posies, will ye, Bouton-
de-Rose?"

"What in the devil's name do you want here?" roared the Guernsey-man,
flying into a sudden passion.

"Oh! keep cool—cool? yes, that's the word; why don't you pack those whales in ice while you're working at 'em? But joking aside, though; do you know, Rose-bud, that it's all nonsense trying to get any oil out of such whales? As for that dried up one, there, he hasn't a gill in his whole carcase."

"I know that well enough; but, d'ye see, the Captain here won't believe it; this is his first voyage; he was a Cologne manufacturer before. But come aboard, and mayhap he'll believe you, if he won't me; and so I'll get out of this dirty scrape."

"Anything to oblige ye, my sweet and pleasant fellow," rejoined Stubb, and with that he soon mounted to the deck. There a queer scene presented itself. The sailors, in tasselled caps of red worsted, were getting the heavy tackles in readiness for the whales. But they worked rather slow and talked very fast, and seemed in anything but a good humor. All their noses upwardly projected from their faces like so many jib-booms. Now and then pairs of them would drop their work, and run up to the mast-head to get some fresh air. Some thinking they would catch the plague, dipped oakum in coaltar, and at intervals held it to their nostrils. Others having broken the stems of their pipes almost short off at the bowl, were vigorously puffing tobacco-smoke, so that it constantly filled their olfactories.

Stubb was struck by a shower of outcries and anathemas proceeding from the Captain's round-house abaft; and looking in that direction saw a fiery face thrust from behind the door, which was held ajar from within. This was the tormented surgeon, who, after in vain remonstrating against the proceedings of the day, had betaken himself to the Captain's round-house (*cabinet* he called it) to avoid the pest; but still, could not help yelling out his entreaties and indignations at times.

Marking all this, Stubb argued well for his scheme, and turning to the Guernsey-man had a little chat with him, during which the stranger mate expressed his detestation of his Captain as a conceited ignoramus, who had brought them all into so unsavory and unprofitable a pickle. Sounding him carefully, Stubb further perceived that the Guernsey-man had not the slightest suspicion concerning the ambergris. He therefore held his peace on that head, but otherwise was quite frank and confidential with him, so that the two quickly concocted a little plan for both circumventing and satirizing the Captain, without his at all dreaming of distrusting their sincerity. According to this little plan of theirs, the Guernsey-man, under cover of an interpreter's office, was to tell the Captain what he pleased, but as coming from Stubb; and as for Stubb, he was to utter any nonsense that should come uppermost in him during the interview.

By this time their destined victim appeared from his cabin. He was a small and dark, but rather delicate looking man for a sea-captain, with large whiskers and moustache, however; and wore a red cotton velvet vest with watch-seals at his side. To this gentleman, Stubb was now politely introduced by the Guernsey-man, who at once ostentatiously put on the aspect of interpreting between them.

"What shall I say to him first?" said he.

"Why," said Stubb, eyeing the velvet vest and the watch and seals, "you may as well begin by telling him that he looks a sort of babyish to me, though I don't pretend to be a judge."

"He says, Monsieur," said the Guernsey-man, in French, turning to his captain, "that only yesterday his ship spoke a vessel, whose captain and chief-mate, with six sailors, had all died of a fever caught from a blasted whale they had brought alongside."

Upon this the captain started, and eagerly desired to know more.

"What now?" said the Guernsey-man to Stubb.

"Why, since he takes it so easy, tell him that now I have eyed him carefully, I'm quite certain that he's no more fit to command a whale-ship than a St. Jago monkey. In fact, tell him from me he's a baboon."

"He vows and declares, Monsieur, that the other whale, the dried one, is far more deadly than the blasted one; in fine, Monsieur, he conjures us, as we value our lives, to cut loose from these fish."

Instantly the captain ran forward, and in a loud voice commanded his crew to desist from hoisting the cutting-tackles, and at once cast loose the cables and chains confining the whales to the ship.

"What now?" said the Guernsey-man, when the Captain had returned to them.

"Why, let me see; yes, you may as well tell him now that—that—in fact, tell him I've diddled him, and (aside to himself) perhaps somebody else."

"He says, Monsieur, that he's very happy to have been of any service to us."

Hearing this, the captain vowed that they were the grateful parties (meaning himself and mate) and concluded by inviting Stubb down into his cabin to drink a bottle of Bordeaux.

"He wants you to take a glass of wine with him," said the interpreter.

"Thank him heartily; but tell him it's against my principles to drink with the man I've diddled. In fact, tell him I must go."

"He says, Monsieur, that his principles won't admit of his drinking; but that if Monsieur wants to live another day to drink, then Monsieur had best drop all four boats, and pull the ship away from these whales, for it's so calm they won't drift."

By this time Stubb was over the side, and getting into his boat, hailed the Guernsey-man to this effect,—that having a long tow-line in his boat, he would do what he could to help them, by pulling out the lighter whale of the two from the ship's side. While the Frenchman's boats, then, were engaged in towing the ship one way, Stubb benevolently towed away at his whale the other way, ostentatiously slacking out a most unusually long tow-line.

Presently a breeze sprang up; Stubb feigned to cast off from the whale; hoisting his boats, the Frenchman soon increased his distance, while the Pequod slid in between him and Stubb's whale. Whereupon Stubb quickly pulled to the floating body, and hailing the Pequod to give notice of his intentions, at once proceeded to reap the fruit of his unrighteous cunning. Seizing his sharp boat-spade, he commenced an excavation in the body, a little behind the side fin. You would almost have thought he was digging a cellar there in the sea; and when at length his spade struck against the gaunt ribs, it was like turning up old Roman tiles and pottery buried in fat English loam. His boat's crew were all in high excitement, eagerly helping their chief, and looking as anxious as gold-hunters.

And all the time numberless fowls were diving, and ducking, and screaming, and yelling, and fighting around them. Stubb was beginning to look disappointed, especially as the horrible nosegay increased, when suddenly from out the very heart of this plague, there stole a faint stream of perfume, which flowed through the tide of bad smells without being absorbed by it, as one river will flow into and then along with another, without at all blending with it for a time.

"I have it, I have it," cried Stubb, with delight, striking something in the subterranean regions, "a purse! a purse!"

Dropping his spade, he thrust both hands in, and drew out handfuls of something that looked like ripe Windsor soap, or rich mottled old cheese; very unctuous and savory withal. You might easily dent it with your thumb; it is of a hue between yellow and ash color. And this, good friends, is ambergris, worth a gold guinea an ounce to any druggist. Some six handfuls were obtained; but more was unavoidably lost in the sea, and still more, perhaps, might have been secured were it not for impatient Ahab's loud command to Stubb to desist, and come on board, else the ship would bid them good-bye.

CHAPTER XCII

AMBERGRIS

Now this ambergris is a very curious substance, and so important as an article of commerce, that in 1791 a certain Nantucket-born Captain Coffin was examined at the bar of the English House of Commons on that subject. For at that time, and indeed until a comparatively late day, the precise origin of ambergris remained, like amber itself, a problem to the learned. Though the word ambergris is but the French compound for grey amber, yet the two substances are quite distinct. For amber, though at times found on the sea-coast, is also dug up in some far inland soils, whereas ambergris is never found except upon the sea. Besides, amber is a hard, transparent, brittle, odorless substance, used for mouth-pieces to pipes, for beads and ornaments; but ambergris is soft, waxy, and so highly fragrant and spicy, that it is largely used in perfumery, in pastiles, precious candles, hair-powders, and pomatum. The Turks use it in cooking, and also carry it to Mecca, for the same purpose that frankincense is carried to St. Peter's in Rome. Some wine merchants drop a few grains into claret, to flavor it.

Who would think, then, that such fine ladies and gentlemen should regale themselves with an essence found in the inglorious bowels of a sick whale! Yet so it is. By some, ambergris is supposed to be the cause, and by others the effect, of the dyspepsia in the whale. How to cure such a dyspepsia it were hard to say, unless by administering three or four boat loads of Brandreth's pills, and then running out of harm's way, as laborers do in blasting rocks.

I have forgotten to say that there were found in this ambergris, certain hard, round, bony plates, which at first Stubb thought might be sailors' trowsers buttons; but it afterwards turned out that they were nothing more than pieces of small squid bones embalmed in that manner.

Now that the incorruption of this most fragrant ambergris should be found in the heart of such decay; is this nothing? Bethink thee of that saying of St. Paul in Corinthians, about corruption and incorruption; how that we are sworn in dishonor, but raised in glory. And likewise call to mind that saying of Paracelsus about what it is that maketh the best musk. Also forget not the strange fact that of all things of ill-savor, Cologne-water, in its rudimental manufacturing stages, is the worst.

I should like to conclude the chapter with the above appeal, but cannot, owing to my anxiety to repel a charge often made against whalemen, and which, in the estimation of some already biased minds, might be considered as indirectly substantiated by what has been said of the Frenchman's two whales. Elsewhere in this volume the slanderous aspersion has been disproved, that the vocation of whaling is throughout a slatternly, untidy business. But there is another thing to rebut. They hint that all whales always smell bad. Now how did this odious stigma originate?

I opine, that it is plainly traceable to the first arrival of the Greenland whaling ships in London, more than two centuries ago. Because those whalemen did not then, and do not now, try out their oil at sea as the Southern ships have always done; but cutting up the fresh blubber in small bits, thrust it through the bung holes of large casks, and carry it home in that manner; the shortness of the season in those Icy Seas, and the sudden and violent storms to which they are exposed, forbidding any other course. The consequence is, that upon breaking into the hold, and unloading one of these whale ceme- teries, in the Greenland dock, a savor is given forth somewhat similar to that arising from excavating an old city graveyard, for the foundations of a Lying-in Hospital.

I partly surmise also, that this wicked charge against whalers may be like- wise imputed to the existence on the coast of Greenland, in former times, of a Dutch village called Schmerenburgh or Smeerenberg, which latter name is the one used by the learned Fogo Von Slack, in his great work on Smells, a text-book on that subject. As its name imports (smeer, fat; berg, to put up), this village was founded in order to afford a place for the blubber of the Dutch whale fleet to be tried out, without being taken home to Holland for that purpose. It was a collection of furnaces, fat-kettles, and oil sheds; and when the works were in full operation certainly gave forth no very pleasant savor. But all this is quite different with a South Sea Sperm Whaler; which in a voyage of four years perhaps, after completely filling her hold with oil, does not, perhaps, consume fifty days in the business of boiling out; and in the state that it is casked, the oil is nearly scentless. The truth is, that living or dead, if but decently treated, whales as a species are by no means creatures of ill odor; nor can whalemen be recognised, as the people of the middle ages affected to detect a Jew in the company, by the nose. Nor indeed can the whale possibly be otherwise than fragrant, when, as a general thing, he enjoys such high health; taking abundance of exercise; always out of doors; though, it is true, seldom in the open air. I say, that the motion of a Sperm Whale's flukes above water dispenses a perfume, as when a musk-scented lady rustles her dress in a warm parlor. What then shall I liken the Sperm Whale to for fragrance, considering his magnitude? Must it not be to that famous elephant, with jewelled tusks, and redolent with myrrh, which was led out of an Indian town to do honor to Alexander the Great?

CHAPTER XCIII

THE CASTAWAY

It was but some few days after encountering the Frenchman, that a most signifi- cant event befell the most insignificant of the Pequod's crew; an event most lamentable; and which ended in providing the sometimes madly merry and predestinated craft with a living and ever accompanying prophecy of whatever shattered sequel might prove her own.

Now, in the whale ship, it is not every one that goes in the boats. Some few hands are reserved called ship-keepers, whose province it is to work the vessel while the boats are pursuing the whale. As a general thing, these ship-keepers are as hardy fellows as the men comprising the boat's crews. But if there happen to be an unduly slender, clumsy, or timorous wight in the ship, that wight is certain to be made a ship-keeper. It was so in the Pequod with the little negro Pippin by nickname, Pip by abbreviation. Poor Pip! ye have heard of him before; ye must remember his tambourine on that dramatic midnight, so gloomy-jolly.

In outer aspect, Pip and Dough-Boy made a match, like a black pony and a white one, of equal developments, though of dissimilar color, driven in one eccentric span. But while hapless Dough-Boy was by nature dull and torpid in his intellects, Pip, though over tender-hearted, was at bottom very bright, with that pleasant, genial, jolly brightness peculiar to his tribe; a tribe, which ever enjoys all holidays and festivities with finer, freer relish than any other race. For blacks, the year's calendar should show naught but three hundred and sixty-five Fourth of Julys and New Year's Days. Nor smile so, while I write that this little black was brilliant, for even blackness has its brilliancy; behold you lustrous ebony, panelled in king's cabinets. But Pip loved life, and all life's peaceable securities; so that the panic-striking business in which he had somehow unaccountably become entrapped, had most sadly blurred his brightness; though, as ere long will be seen, what was thus temporarily subdued in him, in the end was destined to be luridly illumined by strange wild fires, that fictitiously showed him off to ten times the natural lustre with which in his native Tolland County in Connecticut, he had once enlivened many a fiddler's frolic on the green; and at melodious even-tide, with his gay ha-ha! had turned the round horizon into one star-belled tambourine. So, though in the clear air of day, suspended against a blue-veined neck, the pure-watered diamond drop will healthful glow; yet, when the cunning jeweller would show you the diamond in its most impressive lustre, he lays it against a gloomy ground, and then lights it up, not by the sun, but by some unnatural gases. Then come out those fiery effulgences, infernally superb; then the evil-blazing diamond, once the divinest symbol of the crystal skies, looks like some crown-jewel stolen from the King of Hell. But let us to the story.

It came to pass, that in the ambergris affair Stubb's after-oarsman chanced so to sprain his hand, as for a time to become quite maimed; and, temporarily, Pip was put into his place.

'The first time Stubb lowered with him, Pip evinced much nervousness; but happily, for that time, escaped close contact with the whale; and therefore came off not altogether discreditably; though Stubb observing him, took care, afterwards, to exhort him to cherish his courageousness to the utmost, for he might often find it needful.

Now upon the second lowering, the boat paddled upon the whale; and as the fish received the darted iron, it gave its customary rap, which happened, in this instance, to be right under Poor Pip's seat. The involuntary consternation of the moment caused him to leap, paddle in hand, out of the boat; and in such a way, that part of the slack whale line coming against his chest, he breasted it overboard with him, so as to become entangled in it, when at last plumping into the water. That instant the stricken whale started on a fierce run, the line swiftly straightened; and presto! poor Pip came all foaming up to the chocks of the boat, remorselessly dragged there by the line, which had taken several turns around his chest and neck.

Tashtego stood in the bows. He was full of the fire of the hunt. He hated Pip for a poltroon. Snatching the boatknife from its sheath, he suspended its sharp edge over the line, and turning towards Stubb, exclaimed interrogatively, "Cut?" Meantime Pip's blue, choked face plainly looked, Do for God's sake! All passed in a flash. In less than half a minute, this entire thing happened.

"Damn him, cut!" roared Stubb; and so the whale was lost and Pip was saved.

So soon as he recovered himself, the poor little negro was assailed by yells and execrations from the crew. Tranquilly permitting these irregular cursings to evaporate, Stubb then in a plain, business-like, but still half humorous manner, cursed Pip officially; and that done, unofficially gave him much wholesome advice. The substance was, Never jump from a boat, Pip, except—but all the rest was indefinite, as the soundest advice ever is. Now, in general, *Stick to the boat,* is your true motto in whaling; but cases will sometimes happen when *Leap from the boat,* is still better. Moreover, as if perceiving at last that if he should give undiluted conscientious advice to Pip, he would be leaving him too wide a margin to jump in for the future; Stubb suddenly dropped all advice, and concluded with a peremptory command, "Stick to the boat, Pip, or by the Lord, I won't pick you up if you jump; mind that. We can't afford to lose whales by the likes of you; a whale would sell for thirty times what you would, Pip, in Alabama. Bear that in mind, and don't jump any more." Hereby perhaps Stubb indirectly hinted, that though man loved his fellow, yet man is a money-making animal, which propensity too often interferes with his benevolence.

But we are all in the hands of the Gods; and Pip jumped again. It was under very similar circumstances to the first performance; but this time he did not breast out the line; and hence, when the whale started to run, Pip was left behind on the sea, like a hurried traveller's trunk. Alas! Stubb was but too true to his word. It was a beautiful, bounteous, blue day; the spangled sea calm and cool, and flatly stretching away, all round, to the horizon, like gold-beater's skin hammered out to the extremest. Bobbing up and down in that sea, Pip's ebon head showed like a head of cloves. No boat-knife was lifted when he fell so rapidly astern. Stubb's inexorable back was turned upon him; and the whale was winged. In three minutes, a whole mile of shoreless ocean was between Pip and Stubb. Out from the centre of the sea, poor Pip turned his crisp, curling, black head to the sun, another lonely castaway, though the loftiest and the brightest.

Now, in calm weather, to swim in the open ocean is as easy to the practised swimmer as to ride in a spring-carriage ashore. But the awful lonesomeness is intolerable. The intense concentration of self in the middle of such a heartless immensity, my God! who can tell it? Mark, how when sailors in a dead calm bathe in the open sea—mark how closely they hug their ship and only coast along her sides.

But had Stubb really abandoned the poor little negro to his fate? No; he did not mean to, at least. Because there were two boats in his wake, and he supposed, no doubt, that they would of course come up to Pip very quickly, and pick him up; though, indeed, such considerations towards oarsmen jeopardized through their own timidity, is not always manifested by the hunters in all similar instances; and such instances not unfrequently occur; almost invariably in the fishery, a coward, so called, is marked with the same ruthless detestation peculiar to military navies and armies.

But it so happened, that those boats, without seeing Pip, suddenly spying whales close to them on one side, turned, and gave chase; and Stubb's boat was now so far away, and he and all his crew so intent upon his fish, that Pip's ringed horizon began to expand around him miserably. By the merest chance the ship itself at last rescued him; but from that hour the little negro went about the deck an idiot; such, at least, they said he was. The sea had jeeringly kept his finite body up, but drowned the infinite of his soul. Not drowned entirely, though. Rather carried down alive to wondrous depths, where strange shapes of the unwarped primal world glided to and fro before his passive eyes; and the miser-merman, Wisdom, revealed his hoarded heaps; and among the joyous, heartless, ever-juvenile eternities, Pip saw the multitudinous, God-omnipresent, coral insects, that out of the firmament of waters heaved the colossal orbs. He saw God's foot upon the treadle of the loom, and spoke it; and therefore his shipmates called him mad. So man's insanity is heaven's sense; and wandering from all mortal reason, man comes at last to that celestial thought, which, to reason, is absurd and frantic; and weal or woe, feels then uncompromised, indifferent as his God.

For the rest, blame not Stubb too hardly. The thing is common in that fishery; and in the sequel of the narrative, it will then be seen what like abandonment befell myself.

CHAPTER XCIV

A SQUEEZE OF THE HAND

THAT whale of Stubb's, so dearly purchased, was duly brought to the Pequod's side, where all those cutting and hoisting operations previously detailed, were regularly gone through, even to the baling of the Heidelburgh Tun, or Case.

While some were occupied with this latter duty, others were employed in dragging away the larger tubs, so soon as filled with the sperm; and when the proper time arrived, this same sperm was carefully manipulated ere going to the try-works, of which anon.

It had cooled and crystallized to such a degree, that when, with several others, I sat down before a large Constantine's bath of it, I found it strangely concreted into lumps, here and there rolling about in the liquid part. It was our business to squeeze these lumps back into fluid. A sweet and unctuous duty! No wonder that in old times sperm was such a favourite cosmetic. Such a clearer! such a sweetener! such a softener! such a delicious mollifier! After having my hands in it for only a few minutes, my fingers felt like eels, and began, as it were to serpentine and spiralize.

As I sat there at my ease, cross-legged on the deck; after the bitter exertion at the windlass; under a blue tranquil sky; the ship under indolent sail, and gliding so serenely along; as I bathed my hands among those soft, gentle globules of infiltrated tissues, wove almost within the hour; as they richly broke to my fingers, and discharged all their opulence, like fully ripe grapes their wine; as I snuffled up that uncontaminated aroma,—literally and truly, like the smell of spring violets; I declare to you, that for the time I lived as in a musky meadow; I forgot all about our horrible oath; in that inexpressible

sperm, I washed my hands and my heart of it; I almost began to credit the
old Paracelsan superstition that sperm is of rare virtue in allaying the heat of
anger; while bathing in that bath, I felt divinely free from all ill-will, or petulance, or malice, of any sort whatsoever.

Squeeze! squeeze! squeeze! all the morning long; I squeezed that sperm
till I myself almost melted into it; I squeezed that sperm till a strange sort
of insanity came over me; and I found myself unwittingly squeezing my co-
laborers' hands in it, mistaking their hands for the gentle globules. Such an
abounding, affectionate, friendly, loving feeling did this avocation beget; that
at last I was continually squeezing their hands, and looking up into their eyes
sentimentally; as much as to say,—Oh! my dear fellow beings, why should
we longer cherish any social acerbities, or know the slightest ill-humor or envy!
Come; let us squeeze hands all round; nay, let us all squeeze ourselves into each
other; let us squeeze ourselves universally into the very milk and sperm of
kindness.

Would that I could keep squeezing that sperm for ever! For now, since
by many prolonged, repeated experiences, I have perceived that in all cases
man must eventually lower, or at least shift, his conceit of attainable felicity;
not placing it anywhere in the intellect or the fancy; but in the wife, the heart,
the bed, the table, the saddle, the fire-side, the country; now that I have perceived all this, I am ready to squeeze case eternally. In thoughts of the visions
of the night, I saw long rows of angels in paradise, each with his hands in a jar
of spermaceti.

*   *   *   *   *

Now, while discoursing of sperm, it behooves to speak of other things akin
to it, in the business of preparing the sperm whale for the try-works.

First comes white-horse, so called, which is obtained from the tapering part
of the fish, and also from the thicker portions of his flukes. It is tough with
congealed tendons—a wad of muscle—but still contains some oil. After being
severed from the whale, the white-horse is first cut into portable oblongs ere
going to the mincer. They look much like blocks of Berkshire marble.

Plum-pudding is the term bestowed upon certain fragmentary parts of the
whale's flesh, here and there adhering to the blanket of blubber, and often par-
ticipating to a considerable degree in its unctuousness. It is a most refreshing,
convivial, beautiful object to behold. As its name imports, it is of an exceedingly rich, mottled tint, with a bestreaked snowy and golden ground, dotted
with spots of the deepest crimson and purple. It is plums of rubies, in pictures
of citron. Spite of reason, it is hard to keep yourself from eating it. I confess,
that once I stole behind the foremast to try it. It tasted something as I should
conceive a royal cutlet from the thigh of Louis le Gros might have tasted, supposing him to have been killed the first day after the venison season, and that
particular venison season contemporary with an unusually fine vintage of the
vineyards of Champagne.

There is another substance, and a very singular one, which turns up in the
course of this business, but which I feel it to be very puzzling adequately to
describe. It is called slobgollion; an appellation original with the whalemen,
and even so is the nature of the substance. It is an ineffably oozy, stringy
affair, most frequently found in the tubs of sperm, after a prolonged squeezing,
and subsequent decanting. I hold it to be the wondrously thin, ruptured mem-
branes of the case, coalescing.

Gurry, so called, is a term properly belonging to right whalemen, but sometimes incidentally used by the sperm fishermen. It designates the dark, glutinous substance which is scraped off the back of the Greenland or right whale, and much of which covers the decks of those inferior souls who hunt that ignoble Leviathan.

Nippers.   Strictly this word is not indigenous to the whale's vocabulary. But as applied by whalemen, it becomes so. A whaleman's nipper is a short firm strip of tendinous stuff cut from the tapering part of Leviathan's tail: it averages an inch in thickness, and for the rest, is about the size of the iron part of a hoe.   Edgewise moved along the oily deck, it operates like a leathern squilgee; and by nameless blandishments, as of magic, allures along with it all impurities.

But to learn all about these recondite matters, your best way is at once to descend into the blubber-room, and have a long talk with its inmates. This place has previously been mentioned as the receptacle for the blanket-pieces, when stript and hoisted from the whale. When the proper time arrives for cutting up its contents, this apartment is a scene of terror to all tyros, especially by night. On one side, lit by a dull lantern, a space has been left clear for the workmen.   They generally go in pairs,—a pike-and-gaff-man and a spade-man. The whaling-pike is similar to a frigate's boarding-weapon of the same name. The gaff is something like a boat-hook. With his gaff, the gaffman hooks on to a sheet of blubber, and strives to hold it from slipping, as the ship pitches and lurches about.   Meanwhile, the spade-man stands on the sheet itself, perpendicularly chopping it into the portable horse-pieces. This spade is sharp as hone can make it; the spademan's feet are shoeless; the thing he stands on will sometimes irresistibly slide away from him, like a sledge. If he cuts off one of his own toes, or one of his assistants', would you be very much astonished? Toes are scarce among veteran blubber-room men.

CHAPTER XCV

THE CASSOCK

HAD you stepped on board the Pequod at a certain juncture of this post-mortemizing of the whale; and had you strolled forward nigh the windlass, pretty sure am I that you would have scanned with no small curiosity a very strange, enigmatical object, which you would have seen there, lying along lengthwise in the lee scuppers. Not the wondrous cistern in the whale's huge head; not the prodigy of his unhinged lower jaw; not the miracle of his symmetrical tail; none of these would so surprise you, as half a glimpse of that unaccountable cone,—longer than a Kentuckian is tall, nigh a foot in diameter at the base, and jet-black as Yojo, the ebony idol of Queequeg. And an idol, indeed, it is; or, rather, in old times, its likeness was. Such an idol as that found in the secret groves of Queen Maachah in Judea; and for worshipping which, king Asa, her son, did depose her, and destroyed the idol, and burnt it for an abomination at the brook Kedron, as darkly set forth in the 15th chapter of the first book of Kings.

Look at the sailor, called the mincer, who now comes along, and assisted by two allies, heavily backs the grandissimus, as the mariners call it, and with bowed shoulders, staggers off with it as if he were a grenadier carrying a dead comrade from the field. Extending it upon the forecastle deck, he now proceeds cylindrically to remove its dark pelt, as an African hunter the pelt of a boa. This done he turns the pelt inside out, like a pantaloon leg; gives it a good stretching, so as almost to double its diameter; and at last hangs it, well spread, in the rigging, to dry. Ere long, it is taken down; when removing some three feet of it, towards the pointed extremity, and then cutting two slits for arm-holes at the other end, he lengthwise slips himself bodily into it. The mincer now stands before you invested in the full canonicals of his calling. Immemorial to all his order, this investiture alone will adequately protect him, while employed in the peculiar functions of his office.

That office consists in mincing the horse-pieces of blubber for the pots; an operation which is conducted at a curious wooden horse, planted endwise against the bulwarks, and with a capacious tub beneath it, into which the minced pieces drop, fast as the sheets from a rapt orator's desk. Arrayed in decent black; occupying a conspicuous pulpit; intent on bible leaves; what a candidate for an archbishoprick, what a lad for a Pope were this mincer!

CHAPTER XCVI

THE TRY-WORKS

BESIDES her hoisted boats, an American whaler is outwardly distinguished by her try-works. She presents the curious anomaly of the most solid masonry joining with oak and hemp in constituting the completed ship. It is as if from the open field a brick-kiln were transported to her planks.

The try-works are planted between the foremast and mainmast, the most roomy part of the deck. The timbers beneath are of a peculiar strength, fitted to sustain the weight of an almost solid mass of brick and mortar, some ten feet by eight square, and five in height. The foundation does not penetrate the deck, but the masonry is firmly secured to the surface by ponderous knees of iron bracing it on all sides, and screwing it down to the timbers. On the flanks it is cased with wood, and at top completely covered by a large, sloping, battened hatchway. Removing this hatch we expose the great try-pots, two in number, and each of several barrels' capacity. When not in use, they are kept remarkably clean. Sometimes they are polished with soapstone and sand, till they shine within like silver punch-bowls. During the night-watches some cynical old sailors will crawl into them and coil themselves away there for a nap. While employed in polishing them—one man in each pot, side by side—many confidential communications are carried on, over the iron lips. It is a place also for profound mathematical meditation. It was in the left hand try-pot of the Pequod, with the soapstone diligently circling round me, that I was first indirectly struck by the remarkable fact, that in geometry all bodies gliding along the cycloid, my soapstone for example, will descend from any point in precisely the same time.

Removing the fire-board from the front of the try-works, the bare masonry of that side is exposed, penetrated by the two iron mouths of the furnaces, directly underneath the pots. These mouths are fitted with heavy doors of iron. The intense heat of the fire is prevented from communicating itself to the deck, by means of a shallow reservoir extending under the entire inclosed surface of the works. By a tunnel inserted at the rear, this reservoir is kept replenished with water as fast as it evaporates. There are no external chimneys; they open direct from the rear wall. And here let us go back for a moment.

It was about nine o'clock at night that the Pequod's try-works were first started on this present voyage. It belonged to Stubb to oversee the business.

"All ready there? Off hatch, then, and start her. You cook, fire the works." This was an easy thing, for the carpenter had been thrusting his shavings into the furnace throughout the passage. Here be it said that in a whaling voyage the first fire in the try-works has to be fed for a time with wood. After that no wood is used, except as a means of quick ignition to the staple fuel. In a word, after being tried out, the crisp, shrivelled blubber, now called scraps or fritters, still contains considerable of its unctuous properties. These fritters feed the flames. Like a plethoric burning martyr, or a self-consuming misanthrope, once ignited, the whale supplies his own fuel and burns by his own body. Would that he consumed his own smoke! for his smoke is horrible to inhale, and inhale it you must, and not only that, but you must live in it for the time. It has an unspeakable, wild, Hindoo odor about it, such as may lurk in the vicinity of funereal pyres. It smells like the left wing of the day of judgment; it is an argument for the pit.

By midnight the works were in full operation. We were clear from the carcase; sail had been made; the wind was freshening; the wild ocean darkness was intense. But that darkness was licked up by the fierce flames, which at intervals forked forth from the sooty flues, and illuminated every lofty rope in the rigging, as with the famed Greek fire. The burning ship drove on, as if remorselessly commissioned to some vengeful deed. So the pitch and sulphur-freighted brigs of the bold Hydriote, Canaris, issuing from their midnight harbors, with broad sheets of flame for sails, bore down upon the Turkish frigates, and folded them in conflagrations.

The hatch, removed from the top of the works, now afforded a wide hearth in front of them. Standing on this were the Tartarean shapes of the pagan harpooneers, always the whale-ship's stokers. With huge pronged poles they pitched hissing masses of blubber into the scalding pots, or stirred up the fires beneath, till the snaky flames darted, curling, out of the doors to catch them by the feet. The smoke rolled away in sullen heaps. To every pitch of the ship there was a pitch of the boiling oil, which seemed all eagerness to leap into their faces. Opposite the mouth of the works, on the farther side of the wide wooden hearth, was the windlass. This served for a sea-sofa. Here lounged the watch, when not otherwise employed, looking into the red heat of the fire, till their eyes felt scorched in their heads. Their tawny features, now all begrimed with smoke and sweat, their matted beards, and the contrasting barbaric brilliancy of their teeth, all these were strangely revealed in the capricious emblazonings of the works. As they narrated to each other their unholy adventures, their tales of terror told in words of mirth; as their uncivilized laughter forked upwards out of them, like the flames from the furnace; as to and fro, in their front, the harpooneers wildly gesticulated with their huge pronged forks and dippers; as the wind howled on, and the sea leaped, and the ship groaned and dived, and yet steadfastly shot her red hell farther and farther into the blackness of the sea and the night, and scornfully champed the white bone in her mouth, and viciously spat round her on all sides; then the rushing Pequod, freighted with savages, and laden with fire, and burning a corpse, and plunging into that blackness of darkness, seemed the material counterpart of her monomaniac commander's soul.

So seemed it to me, as I stood at her helm, and for long hours silently guided the way of this fire-ship on the sea. Wrapped, for that interval, in darkness myself, I but the better saw the redness, the madness, the ghastliness of others. The continual sight of the fiend shapes before me, capering half in smoke and half in fire, these at last begat kindred visions in my soul, so soon as I began to yield to that unaccountable drowsiness which ever would come over me at a midnight helm.

But that night, in particular, a strange (and ever since inexplicable) thing occurred to me. Starting from a brief standing sleep, I was horribly conscious of something fatally wrong. The jawbone tiller smote my side, which leaned against it; in my ears was the low hum of sails, just beginning to shake in the wind; I thought my eyes were open; I was half conscious of putting my fingers to the lids and mechanically stretching them still farther apart. But, spite of all this, I could see no compass before me to steer by; though it seemed but a minute since I had been watching the card, by the steady binnacle lamp illuminating it. Nothing seemed before me but a jet gloom, now and then made ghastly by flashes of redness. Uppermost was the impression, that whatever swift, rushing thing I stood on was not so much bound to any haven ahead as rushing from all havens astern. A stark, bewildered feeling, as of death, came over me. Convulsively my hands grasped the tiller, but with the crazy conceit that the tiller was, somehow, in some enchanted way, inverted. My God! what is the matter with me? thought I. Lo! in my brief sleep I had turned myself about, and was fronting the ship's stern, with my back to her prow and the compass. In an instant I faced back, just in time to prevent the vessel from flying up into the wind, and very probably capsizing her. How glad and how grateful the relief from this unnatural hallucination of the night, and the fatal contingency of being brought by the lee!

Look not too long in the face of the fire, O man! Never dream with thy hand on the helm! Turn not thy back to the compass; accept the first hint of the hitching tiller; believe not the artificial fire, when its redness makes all things look ghastly. To-morrow, in the natural sun, the skies will be bright; those who glared like devils in the forking flames, the morn will show in far other, at least gentler, relief; the glorious, golden, glad sun, the only true lamp —all others but liars!

Nevertheless the sun hides not Virginia's Dismal Swamp, nor Rome's accursed Campagna, nor wide Sahara, nor all the millions of miles of deserts and of griefs beneath the moon. The sun hides not the ocean, which is the dark side of this earth, and which is two thirds of this earth. So, therefore, that mortal man who hath more of joy than sorrow in him, that mortal man cannot be true—not true, or undeveloped. With books the same. The truest of all men was the Man of Sorrows, and the truest of all books is Solomon's, and Ecclesiastes is the fine hammered steel of woe. "All is vanity." ALL. This wilful world hath not got hold of unchristian Solomon's wisdom yet. But he who dodges hospitals and jails, and walks fast crossing grave-yards, and would rather talk of operas than hell; calls Cowper, Young, Pascal, Rousseau, poor devils all of sick men; and throughout a care-free lifetime swears by Rabelais as passing wise, and therefore jolly;—not that man is fitted to sit down on tomb-stones, and break the green damp mould with unfathomably wondrous Solomon.

But even Solomon, he says, "the man that wandereth out of the way of understanding shall remain" (i.e. even while living) "in the congregation of the dead." Give not thyself up, then, to fire, lest it invert thee, deaden thee; as for the time it did me. There is a wisdom that is woe; but there is a woe that is madness. And there is a Catskill eagle in some souls that can alike dive down into the blackest gorges, and soar out of them again and become invisible in the sunny spaces. And even if he for ever flies within the gorge, that gorge is in the mountains; so that even in his lowest swoop the mountain eagle is still higher than other birds upon the plain, even though they soar.

CHAPTER XCVII

THE LAMP

HAD you descended from the Pequod's try-works to the Pequod's forecastle, where the off duty watch were sleeping, for one single moment you would have almost thought you were standing in some illuminated shrine of canonized kings and counsellors. There they lay in their triangular oaken vaults, each mariner a chiselled muteness; a score of lamps flashing upon his hooded eyes.

In merchantmen, oil for the sailor is more scarce than the milk of queens. To dress in the dark, and eat in the dark, and stumble in darkness to his pallet, this is his usual lot. But the whaleman, as he seeks the food of light, so he lives in light. He makes his berth an Aladdin's lamp, and lays him down in it; so that in the pitchiest night the ship's black hull still houses an illumination.

See with what entire freedom the whaleman takes his handful of lamps— often but old bottles and vials, though—to the copper cooler at the try-works, and replenishes them there, as mugs of ale at a vat. He burns, too, the purest of oil, in its unmanufactured, and, therefore, unvitiated state; a fluid unknown to solar, lunar, or astral contrivances ashore. It is sweet as early grass butter in April. He goes and hunts for his oil, so as to be sure of its freshness and genuineness, even as the traveller on the prairie hunts up his own supper of game.

CHAPTER XCVIII

STOWING DOWN AND CLEARING UP

ALREADY has it been related how the great leviathan is afar off descried from the mast-head; how he is chased over the watery moors, and slaughtered in the valleys of the deep; how he is then towed alongside and beheaded; and how (on the principle which entitled the headsman of old to the garments in which the beheaded was killed) his great padded surtout becomes the property of his executioner; how, in due time, he is condemned to the pots, and, like Shadrach, Meshach, and Abednego, his spermaceti, oil, and bone pass un-scathed through the fire;—but now it remains to conclude the last chapter of this part of the description by rehearsing—singing, if I may—the romantic proceeding of decanting off his oil into the casks and striking them down into the hold, where once again leviathan returns to his native profundities, sliding along beneath the surface as before; but, alas! never more to rise and blow.

While still warm, the oil, like hot punch, is received into the six-barrel casks;

and while, perhaps, the ship is pitching and rolling this way and that in the midnight sea, the enormous casks are slewed round and headed over, end for end, and sometimes perilously scoot across the slippery deck, like so many land slides, till at last man-handled and stayed in their course; and all round the hoops, rap, rap, go as many hammers as can play upon them, for now, *ex officio,* every sailor is a cooper.

At length, when the last pint is casked, and all is cool, then the great hatchways are unsealed, the bowels of the ship are thrown open, and down go the casks to their final rest in the sea. This done, the hatches are replaced, and hermetically closed, like a closet walled up.

In the sperm fishery, this is perhaps one of the most remarkable incidents in all the business of whaling. One day the planks stream with freshets of blood and oil; on the sacred quarter-deck enormous masses of the whale's head are profanely piled; great rusty casks lie about, as in a brewery yard; the smoke from the try-works has besooted all the bulwarks; the mariners go about suffused with unctuousness; the entire ship seems great leviathan himself; while on all hands the din is deafening.

But a day or two after, you look about you, and prick your ears in this selfsame ship; and were it not for the tale-tell boats and try-works, you would all but swear you trod some silent merchant vessel, with a most scrupulously neat commander, The unmanufactured sperm oil possesses a singularly cleansing virtue. This is the reason why the decks never look so white as just after what they call an affair of oil. Besides, from the ashes of the burned scraps of the whale, a potent lye is readily made; and whenever any adhesiveness from the back of the whale remains clinging to the side, that lye quickly exterminates it. Hands go diligently along the bulwarks, and with buckets of water and rags restore them to their full tidiness. The soot is brushed from the lower rigging. All the numerous implements which have been in use are likewise faithfully cleansed and put away. The great hatch is scrubbed and placed upon the try-works, completely hiding the pots; every cask is out of sight; all tackles are coiled in unseen nooks; and when by the combined and simultaneous industry of almost the entire ship's company, the whole of this conscientious duty is at last concluded, then the crew themselves proceed to their own ablutions; shift themselves from top to toe; and finally issue to the immaculate deck, fresh and all aglow, as bridegrooms new-leaped from out the daintiest Holland.

Now, with elated step, they pace the planks in twos and threes, and humorously discourse of parlors, sofas, carpets, and fine cambrics; propose to mat the deck; think of having hangings to the top; object not to taking tea by moonlight on the piazza of the forecastle. To hint to such musked mariners of oil, and bone, and blubber, were little short of audacity. They know not the thing you distantly allude to. Away, and bring us napkins!

But mark: aloft there, at the three mast heads, stand three men intent on spying out more whales, which, if caught, infallibly will again soil the old oaken furniture, and drop at least one small grease-spot somewhere. Yes; and many is the time, when, after the severest uninterrupted labors, which know no night; continuing straight through for ninety-six hours; when from the boat, where they have swelled their wrists with all day rowing on the Line,—they only step to the deck to carry vast chains, and heave the heavy windlass, and cut and slash, yea, and in their very sweatings to be smoked and burned anew by the combined fires of the equatorial sun and the equatorial try-works; when, on the heel of all this, they have finally bestirred themselves to cleanse the ship, and make a spotless dairy room of it; many is the time the poor fellows, just buttoning the necks of their clean frocks, are startled by the cry of "There she blows!" and away they fly to fight another whale, and go through the whole weary thing again. Oh! my•friends, but this is man-killing! Yet this is life. For hardly have we mortals by long toilings extracted from this world's vast bulk its small but valuable sperm; and then, with weary patience, cleansed ourselves from its defilements, and learned to live here in clean tabernacles of the soul; hardly is this done, when—*There she blows!*—the ghost is spouted up, and away we sail to fight some other world, and go through young life's old routine again.

Oh! the metempsychosis! Oh! Pythagoras, that in bright Greece, two thousand years ago, did die, so good, so wise, so mild; I sailed with thee along the Peruvian coast last voyage—and, foolish as I am, taught thee, a green simple boy, how to splice a rope.

CHAPTER XCIX

THE DOUBLOON

ERE now it has been related how Ahab was wont to pace his quarter-deck, taking regular turns at either limit, the binnacle and mainmast; but in the multiplicity of other things requiring narration it has not been added how that sometimes in these walks, when most plunged in his mood, he was wont to pause in turn at each spot, and stand there strangely eyeing the particular object before him. When he halted before the binnacle, with his glance fastened on the pointed needle in the compass, that glance shot like a javelin with the pointed intensity of his purpose; and when resuming his walk he again paused before the mainmast, then, as the same riveted glance fastened upon the riveted gold coin there, he still wore the same aspect of nailed firmness, only dashed with a certain wild longing, if not hopefulness.

But one morning, turning to pass the doubloon, he seemed to be newly attracted by the strange figures and inscriptions stamped on it, as though now for the first time beginning to interpret for himself in some monomaniac way whatever significance might lurk in them. And some certain significance lurks in all things, else all things are little worth, and the round world itself but an empty cipher, except to sell by the cartload, as they do hills about Boston, to fill up some morass in the Milky Way.

Now this doubloon was of purest, virgin gold, raked somewhere out of the heart of gorgeous hills, whence, east and west, over golden sands, the headwaters of many a Pactolus flows. And though now nailed amidst all the rustiness of iron bolts and the verdigris of copper spikes, yet, untouchable and immaculate to any foulness, it still preserved its Quito glow. Nor, though placed amongst a ruthless crew and every hour passed by ruthless hands, and through the livelong nights shrouded with thick darkness which might cover any pilfering approach, nevertheless every sunrise found the doubloon where the sunset left it last. For it was set apart and sanctified to one awe-striking end; and however wanton in their sailor ways, one and all, the mariners revered it as the white whale's talisman. Sometimes they talked it over in the weary watch by night, wondering whose it was to be at last, and whether he would ever live to spend it.

Now those noble golden coins of South America are as medals of the sun and tropic token-pieces. Here palms, alpacas, and volcanoes; sun's disks and stars; ecliptics, horns-of-plenty, and rich banners waving, are in luxuriant profusion stamped; so that the precious gold seems almost to derive an added preciousness and enhancing glories, by passing through those fancy mints, so Spanishly poetic.

It so chanced that the doubloon of the Pequod was a most wealthy example of these things. On its round border it bore the letters, REPUBLICA DEL ECUADOR: QUITO. So this bright coin came from a country planted in the middle of the world, and beneath the great equator, and named after it; and it had been cast midway up the Andes, in the unwaning clime that knows no autumn. Zoned by those letters you saw the likeness of three Andes' summits; from one a flame; a tower on another; on the third a crowing cock; while arching over all was a segment of the partitioned zodiac, the signs all marked with their usual cabalistics, and the keystone sun entering the equinoctial point at Libra.

Before this equatorial coin, Ahab, not unobserved by others, was now pausing.

"There's something ever egotistical in mountain-tops and towers, and all other grand and lofty things; look here,—three peaks as proud as Lucifer. The firm tower, that is Ahab; the volcano, that is Ahab; the courageous, the undaunted, and victorious fowl, that, too, is Ahab; all are Ahab; and this round gold is but the image of the rounder globe, which, like a magician's glass, to each and every man in turn but mirrors back his own mysterious self. Great pains, small gains for those who ask the world to solve them; it cannot solve itself. Methinks now this coined sun wears a ruddy face; but see! aye, he enters the sign of storms, the equinox! and but six months before he wheeled out of a former equinox at Aries! From storm to storm! So be it, then. Born in throes, 't is fit that man should live in pains and die in pangs! So be it, then! Here's stout stuff for woe to work on. So be it, then."

"No fairy fingers can have pressed the gold, but devil's claws must have left their mouldings there since yesterday," murmured Starbuck to himself, leaning against the bulwarks. "The old man seems to read Belshazzar's awful writing. I have never marked the coin inspectingly. He goes below; let me read. A dark valley between three mighty, heaven-abiding peaks, that almost seem the Trinity, in some faint earthly symbol. So in this vale of Death, God girds us round; and over all our gloom, the sun of Righteousness still shines a beacon and a hope. If we bend down our eyes, the dark vale shows her mouldy soil; but if we lift them, the bright sun meets our glance half way, to cheer. Yet, oh, the great sun is no fixture; and if, at midnight, we would fain snatch some sweet solace from him, we gaze for him in vain! This coin speaks wisely, mildly, truly, but still sadly to me. I will quit it, lest Truth shake me falsely."

"There now's the old Mogul," soliloquized Stubb by the try-works, "he's been twigging it; and there goes Starbuck from the same, and both with faces which I should say might be somewhere within nine fathoms long. And all from looking at a piece of gold, which did I have it now on Negro Hill or in Corlaer's Hook, I'd not look at it very long ere spending it. Humph! in my poor, insignificant opinion, I regard this as queer. I have seen doubloons before now in my voyagings; your doubloons of old Spain, your doubloons of Peru, your doubloons of Chili, your doubloons of Bolivia, your doubloons of Popayan; with plenty of gold moidores and pistoles, and joes, and half joes, and quarter joes. What then should there be in this doubloon of the Equator that is so killing wonderful? By Golconda! let me read it once. Halloa! here's signs and wonders truly! That, now, is what old Bowditch in his Epitome calls the zodiac, and what my almanack below calls ditto. I'll get the almanack; and as I have heard devils can be raised with Daboll's arithmetic, I'll try my hand at raising a meaning out of these queer curvicues here with the Massachusetts calendar. Here's the book. Let's see now. Signs and wonders; and the sun, he's always among 'em. Hem͵, hem, hem; here they are—here they go—all alive:—Aries, or the Ram; Taurus, or the Bull and Jimimi! here's Gemini himself, or the Twins. Well; the sun he wheels among 'em. Aye, here on the coin he's just crossing the threshold between two of twelve sitting-rooms all in a ring. Book! you lie there; the fact is, you books must know your places. You'll do to give us the bare words and facts, but we come in to supply the thoughts. That's my small experience, so far as the Massachusetts calendar, and Bowditch's navigator, and Daboll's arithmetic go. Signs and wonders, eh? Pity if there is nothing wonderful in signs, and significant in wonders! There's a clue somewhere; wait a bit; hist—hark! By Jove, I have it! Look you, Doubloon, your zodiac here is the life of man in one round chapter; and now I'll read it off, straight out of the book. Come, Almanack! To begin: there's Aries, or the Ram—lecherous dog, he begets us; then, Taurus, or the Bull— he bumps us the first thing; then Gemini, or the Twins—that is, Virtue and Vice; we try to reach Virtue, when lo! comes Cancer the Crab, and drags us back; and here, going from Virtue, Leo, a roaring Lion, lies in the path—he gives a few fierce bites and surly dabs with his paw; we escape, and hail Virgo, the Virgin! that's our first love; we marry and think to be happy for aye, when pop comes Libra, or the Scales—happiness weighed and found wanting; and while we are very sad about that, Lord! how we suddenly jump, as Scorpio, or the Scorpion, stings us in the rear; we are curing the wound, when whang come the arrows all round; Sagittarius, or the Archer, is amusing himself. As we pluck out the shafts, stand aside! here's the battering-ram, Capricornus, or the Goat; full tilt, he comes rushing, and headlong we are tossed; when Aquarius, or the Water-bearer, pours out his whole deluge and drowns us; and to wind up with Pisces, or the Fishes, we sleep. There's a sermon now, writ in high heaven, and the sun goes through it every year, and yet comes out of it all alive and hearty. Jollily he, aloft there, wheels through toil and trouble; and so, alow here, does jolly Stubb. Oh, jolly's the word for aye! Adieu, Doubloon! But stop; here comes little King-Post; dodge round the try-works, now, and let's hear what he'll have to say. There; he's before it; he'll out with something presently. So, so; he's beginning."

"I see nothing here, but a round thing made of gold, and whoever raises a certain whale, this round thing belongs to him. So, what's all this staring been about? It is worth sixteen dollars, that's true; and at two cents the cigar, that's nine hundred and sixty cigars. I won't smoke dirty pipes like Stubb, but I like cigars, and here's nine hundred and sixty of them; so here goes Flask aloft to spy 'em out."

"Shall I call that wise or foolish, now; if it be really wise it has a foolish look to it; yet, if it be really foolish, then has it a sort of wiseish look to it. But, avast; here comes our old Manxman—the old hearse-driver, he must have been, that is, before he took to the sea. He luffs up before the doubloon; halloa, and goes round on the other side of the mast; why, there's a horse-shoe nailed on that side; and now he's back again; what does that mean? Hark! he's muttering—voice like an old worn-out coffee-mill. Prick ears, and listen!"

"If the White Whale be raised, it must be in a month and a day, when the sun stands in some one of these signs. I've studied signs, and know their marks; they were taught me two score years ago, by the old witch in Copenhagen. Now, in what sign will the sun then be? The horse-shoe sign; for there it is, right opposite the gold. And what's the horse-shoe sign? The lion is the horse-shoe sign—the roaring and devouring lion. Ship, old ship! my old head shakes to think of thee."

"There's another rendering now; but still one text. All sorts of men in one kind of world, you see. Dodge again! here comes Queequeg—all tattooing—looks like the signs of the Zodiac himself. What says the Cannibal? As I live he's comparing notes; looking at his thigh bone; thinks the sun is in the thigh, or in the calf, or in the bowels, I suppose, as the old women talk Surgeon's Astronomy in the back country. And by Jove, he's found something there in the vicinity of his thigh—I guess it's Sagittarius, or the Archer. No: he don't know what to make of the doubloon; he takes it for an old button off some king's trowsers. But, aside again! here comes that ghost-devil, Fedallah; tail coiled out of sight as usual, oakum in the toes of his pumps as usual. What does he say, with that look of his? Ah, only makes a sign to the sign and bows himself; there is a sun on the coin—fire worshipper, depend upon it. Ho! more and more. This way comes Pip—poor boy! would he had died, or I; he's half horrible to me. He too has been watching all of these interpreters—myself included—and look now, he comes to read, with that unearthly idiot face. Stand away again and hear him. Hark!"

"I look, you look, he looks; we look, ye look, they look."

"Upon my soul, he's been studying Murray's Grammar! Improving his mind, poor fellow! But what's that he says now—hist!"

"I look, you look, he looks; we look, ye look, they look."

"Why, he's getting it by heart—hist! again."

"I look, you look, he looks; we look, ye look, they look."

"Well, that's funny."

"And I, you, and he; and we, ye, and they, are all bats; and I'm a crow, especially when I stand a'top of this pine tree here. Caw! caw! caw! caw! caw! caw! Ain't I a crow? And where's the scare-crow? There he stands; two bones stuck into a pair of old trowsers, and two more poked into the sleeves of an old jacket."

"Wonder if he means me?—complimentary!—poor lad!—I could go hang myself. Anyway, for the present, I'll quit Pip's vicinity. I can stand the rest, for they have plain wits; but he's too crazy-witty for my sanity. So, so, I leave him muttering."

"Here's the ship's navel, this doubloon here, and they are all on fire to unscrew it. But, unscrew your navel, and what's the consequence? Then again, if it stays here, that is ugly, too, for when aught's nailed to the mast it's a sign that things grow desperate. Ha, ha! old Ahab! the White Whale; he'll nail ye! This is a pine tree. My father, in old Tolland county, cut down a pine tree once, and found a silver ring grown over in it; some old darkey's wedding ring. How did it get there? And so they'll say in the resurrection, when they come to fish up this old mast, and find a doubloon lodged in it, with bedded oysters for the shaggy bark. Oh, the gold! the precious, precious gold!—the green miser'll hoard ye soon! Hish! hish! God goes 'mong the worlds blackberrying. Cook! ho, cook! and cook us! Jenny! hey, hey, hey, hey, hey, Jenny, Jenny! and get your hoe-cake done!"

CHAPTER C

LEG AND ARM

THE PEQUOD, OF NANTUCKET, MEETS THE SAMUEL ENDERBY, OF LONDON

"SHIP, ahoy! Hast seen the White Whale?"

So cried Ahab, once more hailing a ship showing English colors, bearing down under the stern. Trumpet to mouth, the old man was standing in his hoisted quarter-boat, his ivory leg plainly revealed to the stranger captain, who was carelessly reclining in his own boat's bow. He was a darkly-tanned, burly, good-natured, fine-looking man, of sixty or thereabouts, dressed in a spacious roundabout, that hung round him in festoons of blue pilot-cloth; and one empty arm of this jacket streamed behind him like the broidered arm of a huzzar's surcoat.

"Hast seen the White Whale?"

"See you this?" and withdrawing it from the folds that had hidden it, he held up a white arm of sperm whale bone, terminating in a wooden head like a mallet.

"Man my boat!" cried Ahab, impetuously, and tossing about the oars near him—"Stand by to lower!"

In less than a minute, without quitting his little craft, he and his crew were dropped to the water, and were soon alongside of the stranger. But here a curious difficulty presented itself. In the excitement of the moment Ahab had forgotten that since the loss of his leg he had never once stepped on board of any vessel at sea but his own, and then it was always by an ingenious and very handy mechanical contrivance peculiar to the Pequod, and a thing not to be rigged and shipped in any other vessel at a moment's warning. Now, it is no very easy matter for anybody—except those who are almost hourly used to it, like whalemen—to clamber up a ship's side from a boat on the open sea; for the great swells now lift the boat high up towards the bulwarks, and then instantaneously drop it half way down to the kelson. So, deprived of one leg, and the strange ship of course being altogether unsupplied with the kindly invention, Ahab now found himself abjectly reduced to a clumsy landsman again; hopelessly eyeing the uncertain changeful height he could hardly hope to attain.

It has before been hinted, perhaps, that every little untoward circumstance that befel him, and which indirectly sprang from his luckless mishap, almost invariably irritated or exasperated Ahab. And in the present instance, all this was heightened by the sight of the two officers of the strange ship, leaning over the side, by the perpendicular ladder of nailed cleets there, and swinging towards him a pair of tastefully-ornamented man-ropes; for at first they did not seem to bethink them that a one-legged man must be too much of a cripple to use their sea bannisters. But this awkwardness only lasted a minute, because the strange captain, observing at a glance how affairs stood, cried out, "I see, I see! —avast heaving there! Jump, boys, and swing over the cutting-tackle."

As good luck would have it, they had had a whale alongside a day or two previous, and the great tackles were still aloft, and the massive curved blubber-hook now clean and dry, was still attached to the end. This was quickly lowered to Ahab, who at once comprehending it all, slid his solitary thigh into the curve of the hook (it was like sitting in the fluke of an anchor, or the crotch of an apple tree), and then giving the word, held himself fast, and at the same time also helped to hoist his own weight, by pulling hand-over-hand upon one of the running parts of the tackle. Soon he was carefully swung inside the high bulwarks, and gently landed upon the capstan head. With his ivory arm frankly thrust forth in welcome, the other captain advanced, and Ahab, putting out his ivory leg, and crossing the ivory arm (like two sword-fish blades) cried out in his walrus way, "Aye, aye, hearty! let us shake bones together!—an arm and a leg!—an arm that never can shrink, d'ye see; and a leg that never can run. Where did'st thou see the White Whale?—how long ago?"

"The White Whale," said the Englishman, pointing his ivory arm towards the East, and taking a rueful sight along it, as if it had been a telescope; "There I saw him, on the Line, last season."

"And he took that arm off, did he?" asked Ahab, now sliding down from the capstan, and resting on the Englishman's shoulder, as he did so.

"Aye, he was the cause of it, at least; and that leg, too?"

"Spin me the yarn," said Ahab; "how was it?"

"It was the first time in my life that I ever cruised on the Line," began the Englishman. "I was ignorant of the White Whale at that time. Well, one day we lowered for a pod of four or five whales, and my boat fastened to one of them; a regular circus horse he was, too, that went milling and milling round so, that my boat's crew could only trim dish, by sitting all their sterns on the outer gunwale. Presently up breaches from the bottom of the sea a bouncing great whale, with a milky-white head and hump, all crows' feet and wrinkles."

"It was he, it was he!" cried Ahab, suddenly letting out his suspended breath.

"And harpoons sticking in near his starboard. fin."

"Aye, aye—they were mine—my irons," cried Ahab, exultingly—"but on!"

"Give me a chance, then," said the Englishman, good-humoredly. "Well, this old great-grandfather, with the white head and hump, runs all afoam into the pod, and goes to snapping furiously at my fast-line."

"Aye, I see!—wanted to part it; free the fast-fish—an old trick—I know him."

"How it was exactly," continued the one-armed commander, "I do not know; but in biting the line, it got foul of his teeth, caught there somehow; but we didn't know it then; so that when we afterwards pulled on the line, bounce we came plump on to his hump! instead of the other whale's that went off to windward, all fluking. Seeing how matters stood, and what a noble great whale it was—the noblest and biggest I ever saw, sir, in my life—I resolved to capture him, spite of the boiling rage he seemed to be in. And thinking the hap-hazard line would get loose, or the tooth it was tangled to might draw (for I have a devil of a boat's crew for a pull on a whale-line); seeing all this, I say, I jumped into my first mate's boat—Mr. Mounttop's here (by the way, Captain—Mounttop; Mounttop—the captain);—as I was saying, I jumped into Mounttop's boat, which, d'ye see, was gunwale and gunwale with mine, then; and snatching the first harpoon, let this old great-grandfather have it. But, Lord, look you, sir—hearts and souls alive, man—the next instant, in a jiff, I was blind as a bat—both eyes out—all befogged and be-deadened with black foam—the whale's tail looming straight up out of it, perpendicular in the air, like a marble steeple. No use sterning all, then; but as I was groping at midday, with a blinding sun, all crown-jewels; as I was groping, I say, after the second iron, to toss it overboard—down comes the tail like a Lima tower, cutting my boat in two, leaving each half in splinters; and, flukes first, the white hump backed through the wreck, as though it was all chips. We all struck out. To escape his terrible flailings, I seized hold of my harpoon-pole sticking in him, and for a moment clung to that like a sucking fish. But a combing sea dashed me off, and at the same instant, the fish, taking one good dart forwards, went down like a flash; and the barb of that cursed second iron towing along near me caught me here" (clapping his hand just below his shoulder); "yes, caught me just here, I say, and bore me down to Hell's flames, I was thinking; when, when, all of a sudden, thank the good God, the barb ript its way along the flesh—clear along the whole length of my arm—came out nigh my wrist, and up I floated;—and that gentleman there will tell you the rest (by the way, captain—Dr. Bunger, ship's surgeon: Bunger, my lad,—the captain). Now, Bunger boy, spin your part of the yarn."

The professional gentleman thus familiarly pointed out, had been all the time standing near them, with nothing specific visible, to denote his gentlemanly rank on board. His face was an exceedingly round but sober one; he was dressed in a faded blue woollen frock or shirt, and patched trowsers; and had thus far been dividing his attention between a marlingspike he held in one hand, and a pill-box held in the other, occasionally casting a critical glance at the ivory limbs of the two crippled captains. But, at his superior's introduction of him to Ahab, he politely bowed, and straightway went on to do his captain's bidding.

"It was a shocking bad wound," began the whale-surgeon; "and, taking my advice, Captain Boomer here, stood our old Sammy—"

"Samuel Enderby is the name of my ship," interrupted the one-armed captain, addressing Ahab; "go on, boy."

"Stood our old Sammy off to the northward, to get out of the blazing hot weather there on the Line. But it was no use—I did all I could; sat up with him nights; was very severe with him in the matter of diet—"

"Oh, very severe!" chimed in the patient himself; then suddenly altering his voice, "Drinking hot rum toddies with me every night, till he couldn't see to put on the bandages; and sending me to bed, half seas over, about three o'clock in the morning. Oh, ye stars! he sat up with me indeed, and was very severe in my diet. Oh! a great watcher, and very dietetically severe, is Dr. Bunger. (Bunger, you dog, laugh out! why don't ye? You know you're a precious jolly rascal.) But, heave ahead, boy, I'd rather be killed by you than kept alive by any other man."

"My captain, you must have ere this perceived, respected sir"—said the imperturbable godly-looking Bunger, slightly bowing to Ahab—"is apt to be facetious at times; he spins us many clever things of that sort. But I may as well say—en passant, as the French remark—that I myself—that is to say, Jack Bunger, late of the reverend clergy—am a strict total abstinence man; I never drink—"

"Water!" cried the captain; "he never drinks it; it's a sort of fits to him; fresh water throws him into the hydrophobia; but go on—go on with the arm story."

"Yes, I may as well," said the surgeon, coolly. "I was about observing, sir, before Captain Boomer's facetious interruption, that spite of my best and severest endeavors, the wound kept getting worse and worse; the truth was, sir, it was as ugly gaping wound as surgeon ever saw; more than two feet and several inches long. I measured it with the lead line. In short, it grew black; I knew what was threatened, and off it came. But I had no hand in shipping that ivory arm there; that thing is against all rule"—pointing at it with the marlingspike—"that is the captain's work, not mine; he ordered the carpenter to make it; he had that club-hammer there put to the end, to knock some one's brains out with, I suppose, as he tried mine once. He flies into diabolical passions sometimes. Do ye see this dent, sir"—removing his hat, and brushing aside his hair, and exposing a bowl-like cavity in his skull, but which bore not the slightest scarry trace, or any token of ever having been a wound—"Well, the captain there will tell you how that came here; he knows."

"No, I don't," said the captain, "but his mother did; he was born with it. Oh, you solemn rogue, you—you Bunger! was there ever such another Bunger in the watery world? Bunger, when you die, you ought to die in pickle, you dog; you should be preserved to future ages, you rascal."

"What became of the White Whale?" now cried Ahab, who thus far had been impatiently listening to this bye-play between the two Englishmen.

"Oh!" cried the one-armed captain, "oh, yes! Well; after he sounded, we didn't see him again for some time; in fact, as I before hinted, I didn't then know what whale it was that had served me such a trick, till some time afterwards, when coming back to the Line, we heard about Moby-Dick—as some call him—and then I knew it was he."

"Did'st thou cross his wake again?"

"Twice."

"But could not fasten?"

"Didn't want to try to: ain't one limb enough? What should I do without this other arm? And I'm thinking Moby-Dick doesn't bite so much as he swallows."

"Well, then," interrupted Bunger, "give him your left arm for bait to get the right. Do you know, gentlemen"—very gravely and mathematically bowing to each Captain in succession—"Do you know, gentlemen, that the digestive organs of the whale are so inscrutably constructed by Divine Providence, that it is quite impossible for him to completely digest even a man's arm? And he knows it too. So that what you take for the White Whale's malice is only his awkwardness. For he never means to swallow a single limb; he only thinks to terrify by feints. But sometimes he is like the old juggling fellow, formerly a patient of mine in Ceylon, that making believe swallow jack-knives, once upon a time let one drop into him in good earnest, and there it stayed for a twelvemonth or more; when I gave him an emetic, and he heaved it up in small tacks, d'ye see. No possible way for him to digest that jack-knife, and fully incorporate it into his general bodily system. Yes, Captain Boomer, if you are quick enough about it, and have a mind to pawn one arm for the sake of the privilege of giving decent burial to the other, why in that case the arm is yours; only let the whale have another chance at you shortly, that's all."

"No, thank ye, Bunger," said the English Captain, "he's welcome to the arm he has, since I can't help it, and didn't know him then; but not to another one. No more White Whales for me; I've lowered for him once, and that has satisfied me. There would be great glory in killing him, I know that; and there is a ship-load of precious sperm in him, but, hark ye, he's best let alone; don't you think so, Captain?"—glancing at the ivory leg.

"He is. But he will still be hunted, for all that. What is best let alone, that accursed thing is not always what least allures. He's all a magnet! How long since thou saw'st him last? Which way heading?"

"Bless my soul, and curse the foul fiend's," cried Bunger, stoopingly walking round Ahab, and like a dog, strangely snuffing; "this man's blood—bring the thermometer!—it's at the boiling point!—his pulse makes these planks beat!—sir!"—taking a lancet from his pocket, and drawing near to Ahab's arm.

"Avast!" roared Ahab, dashing him against the bulwarks—"Man the boat! Which way heading?"

"Good God!" cried the English Captain, to whom the question was put. "What's the matter? He was heading east, I think.—Is your Captain crazy?" whispering Fedallah.

But Fedallah, putting a finger on his lip, slid over the bulwarks to take the boat's steering oar, and Ahab, swinging the cutting-tackle towards him, commanded the ship's sailors to stand by to lower.

In a moment he was standing in the boat's stern, and the Manilla men were springing to their oars. In vain the English Captain hailed him. With back to the stranger ship, and face set like a flint to his own, Ahab stood upright till alongside of the Pequod.

CHAPTER CI

THE DECANTER

Ere the English ship fades from sight, be it set down here, that she hailed from London, and was named after the late Samuel Enderby, merchant of that city, the original of the famous whaling house of Enderby & Sons; a house which in my poor whaleman's opinion, comes not far behind the united royal houses of the Tudors and Bourbons, in point of real historical interest. How long, prior to the year of our Lord 1775, this great whaling house was in existence, my numerous fish-documents do not make plain; but in that year (1775) it fitted out the first English ships that ever regularly hunted the Sperm Whale; though for some scores of years previous (ever since 1726) our valiant Coffins and Maceys of Nantucket and the Vineyard had in large fleets pursued that Leviathan, but only in the North and South Atlantic: not elsewhere. Be it distinctly recorded here, that the Nantucketers were the first among mankind to harpoon with civilized steel the great Sperm Whale; and that for half a century they were the only people of the whole globe who so harpooned him.

In 1778, a fine ship, the Amelia, fitted out for the express purpose, and at the sole charge of the vigorous Enderbys, boldly rounded Cape Horn, and was the first among the nations to lower a whale-boat of any sort in the great South Sea. The voyage was a skilful and lucky one; and returning to her berth with her hold full of the precious sperm, the Amelia's example was soon followed by other ships, English and American, and thus the vast Sperm Whale grounds of the Pacific were thrown open. But not content with this good deed, the indefatigable house again bestirred itself: Samuel and all his Sons—how many, their mother only knows—and under their immediate auspices, and partly, I think, at their expense, the British government was induced to send the sloop-of-war Rattler on a whaling voyage of discovery into the South Sea.

Commanded by a naval Post-Captain, the Rattler made a rattling voyage of it, and did some service; how much does not appear. But this is not all. In 1819, the same house fitted out a discovery whale ship of their own, to go on a testing cruise to the remote waters of Japan. That ship—well called the "Syren"—made a noble experimental cruise; and it was thus that the great Japanese Whaling Ground first became generally known. The Syren in this famous voyage was commanded by a Captain Coffin, a Nantucketer.

All honor to the Enderbies, therefore, whose house, I think, exists to the present day; though doubtless the original Samuel must long ago have slipped his cable for the great South Sea of the other world.

The ship named after him was worthy of the honor, being a very fast sailer and a noble craft every way. I boarded her once at midnight somewhere off the Patagonian coast, and drank good flip down in the forecastle. It was a fine gam we had, and they were all trumps—every soul on board. A short life to them, and a jolly death. And that fine gam I had—long, very long after old Ahab touched her planks with his ivory heel—it minds me of the noble, solid, Saxon hospitality of that ship; and may my parson forget me, and the devil remember me, if I ever lose sight of it. Flip? Did I say we had flip? Yes, and we flipped it at the rate of ten gallons the hour; and when the squall came (for it's squally off there by Patagonia), and all hands—visitors and all— were called to reef topsails, we were so top-heavy that we had to swing each other aloft in bowlines; and we ignorantly furled the skirts of our jackets into the sails, so that we hung there, reefed fast in the howling gale, a warning example to all drunken tars. However, the masts did not go overboard; and by and bye we scrambled down, so sober, that we had to pass the flip again, though the savage salt spray bursting down the forecastle scuttle, rather too much diluted and pickled it to my taste.

The beef was fine—tough, but with body in it. They said it was bull-beef; others, that it was dromedary beef; but I do not know, for certain, how that was. They had dumplings too; small, but substantial, symmetrically globular, and indestructible dumplings. I fancied that you could feel them, and roll them about in you after they were swallowed. If you stooped over too far forward, you risked their pitching out of you like billiard-balls. The bread— but that couldn't be helped; besides, it was an anti-scorbutic; in short, the bread contained the only fresh fare they had. But the forecastle was not very light, and it was very easy to step over into a dark corner when you ate it. But all in all, taking her from truck to helm, considering the dimensions of the cook's boilers, including his own live parchment boilers; fore and aft, I say, the Samuel Enderby was a jolly ship; of good fare and plenty; fine flip and strong; crack fellows all, and capital from boot heels to hat-band.

But why was it, think ye, that the Samuel Enderby, and some other English whalers I know of—not all though—were such famous, hospitable ships; that passed round the beef, and the bread, and the can, and the joke; and were not soon weary of eating, and drinking, and laughing? I will tell you. The abounding good cheer of these English whalers is matter for historical research. Nor have I been at all sparing of historical whale research, when it has seemed needed.

The English were preceded in the whale fishery by the Hollanders, Zeal- anders, and Danes; from whom they derived many terms still extant in the fishery; and what is yet more, their fat old fashions, touching plenty to eat and drink. For, as a general thing, the English merchant-ship scrimps her crew; but not so the English whaler. Hence, in the English, this thing of whaling good cheer is not normal and natural, but incidental and particular; and, therefore, must have some special origin, which is here pointed out, and will be still further elucidated.

During my researches in the Leviathanic histories, I stumbled upon an ancient Dutch volume, which, by the musty whaling smell of it, I knew must be about whalers. The title was, "Dan Coopman," wherefore I concluded that this must be the invaluable memoirs of some Amsterdam cooper in the fishery, as every whale ship must carry its cooper. I was reinforced in this opinion by seeing that it was the production of one "Fitz Swackhammer." But my friend Dr. Snodhead, a very learned man, professor of Low Dutch and High German in the college of Santa Claus and St. Pott's, to whom I handed the work for translation, giving him a box of sperm candles for his trouble—this same Dr. Snodhead, so soon as he spied the book, assured me that "Dan Coopman" did not mean "The Cooper," but "The Merchant." In short, this ancient and learned Low Dutch book treated of the commerce of Holland; and, among other subjects, contained a very interesting account of its whale fishery. And in this chapter it was, headed "Smeer," or "Fat," that I found a long detailed list of the outfits for the larders and cellars of 180 sail of Dutch whalemen; from which list, as translated by Dr. Snodhead, I transcribe the following:

400,000 lbs. of beef.
60,000 lbs. Friesland pork.
150,000 lbs. of stock fish.
550,000 lbs. of biscuit.
72,000 lbs. of soft bread.
2,800 firkins of butter.
20,000 lbs. Texel & Leyden cheese.
144,000 lbs. cheese (probably an inferior article).
550 ankers of Geneva.
10,800 barrels of beer.

Most statistical tables are parchingly dry in the reading; not so in the present case, however, where the reader is flooded with whole pipes, barrels, quarts, and gills of good gin and good cheer.

At the time, I devoted three days to the studious digesting of all this beer, beef, and bread, during which many profound thoughts were incidentally suggested to me, capable of a transcendental and Platonic application; and, furthermore, I compiled supplementary tables of my own, touching the probable quantity of stock-fish, &c., consumed by every Low Dutch harpooneer in that ancient Greenland and Spitzbergen whale fishery. In the first place, the amount of butter, and Texel and Leyden cheese consumed, seems amazing. I impute it, though, to their naturally unctuous natures, being rendered still more unctuous by the nature of their vocation, and especially by their pursuing their game in those frigid Polar Seas, on the very coasts of that Esquimaux country where the convivial natives pledge each other in bumpers of train oil.

The quantity of beer, too, is very large, 10,800 barrels. Now, as those polar fisheries could only be prosecuted in the short summer of that climate, so that the whole cruise of one of these Dutch whalemen, including the short voyage to and from the Spitzbergen sea, did not much exceed three months, say, and reckoning 30 men to each of their fleet of 180 sail, we have 5,400 Low Dutch seamen in all; therefore, I say, we have precisely two barrels of beer per man, for a twelve weeks' allowance, exclusive of his fair proportion of that 550 ankers of gin. Now, whether these gin and beer harpooneers, so fuddled as one might fancy them to have been, were the right sort of men to stand up in a boat's head, and take good aim at flying whales; this would seem somewhat improbable. Yet they did aim at them, and hit them too. But this was very far North, be it remembered, where beer agrees well with the constitution; upon the Equator, in our southern fishery, beer would be apt to make the harpooneer sleepy at the mast-head and boozy in his boat; and grievous loss might ensue to Nantucket and New Bedford.

But no more; enough has been said to show that the old Dutch whalers of two or three centuries ago were high livers; and that the English whalers have not neglected so excellent an example. For, say they, when cruising in an empty ship, if you can get nothing better out of the world, get a good dinner out of it, at least. And this empties the decanter.

CHAPTER CII

A BOWER IN THE ARSACIDES

HITHERTO, in descriptively treating of the Sperm Whale, I have chiefly dwelt upon the marvels of his outer aspect; or separately and in detail upon some few interior structural features. But to a large and thorough sweeping comprehension of him, it behoves me now to unbutton him still further, and untagging the points of his hose, unbuckling his garters, and casting loose the hooks and the eyes of the joints of his innermost bones, set him before you in his ultimatum; that is to say, in his unconditional skeleton.

But how now, Ishmael? How is it, that you, a mere oarsman in the fishery, pretend to know aught about the subterranean parts of the whale? Did erudite Stubb, mounted upon your capstan, deliver lectures on the anatomy of the Cetacea; and by help of the windlass, hold up a specimen rib for exhibition? Explain thyself, Ishmael. Can you land a full-grown whale on your deck for examination, as a cook dishes a roast-pig? Surely not. A veritable witness have you hitherto been, Ishmael; but have a care how you seize the privilege of Jonah alone; the privilege of discoursing upon the joists and beams; the rafters, ridge-pole, sleepers, and under-pinnings, making up the frame-work of leviathan; and belike of the tallow-vats, dairy-rooms, butteries, and cheeseries in his bowels.

I confess, that since Jonah, few whalemen have penetrated very far beneath the skin of the adult whale; nevertheless, I have been blessed with an opportunity to dissect him in miniature. In a ship I belonged to, a small cub Sperm Whale was once bodily hoisted to the deck for his poke or bag, to make sheaths for the barbs of the harpoons, and for the heads of the lances. Think you I let that chance go, without using my boat-hatchet and jack-knife, and breaking the seal and reading all the contents of that young cub?

And as for my exact knowledge of the bones of the leviathan in their gigantic, full grown development, for that rare knowledge I am indebted to my late royal friend Tranquo, king of Tranque, one of the Arsacides. For being at Tranque, years ago, when attached to the trading-ship Dey of Algiers, I was invited to spend part of the Arsacidean holidays with the lord of Tranque, at his retired palm villa at Pupella; a sea-side glen not very far distant from what our sailors called Bamboo-Town, his capital.

Among many other fine qualities, my royal friend Tranquo, being gifted with a devout love for all matters of barbaric vertù, had brought together in Pupella whatever rare things the more ingenious of his people could invent; chiefly carved woods of wonderful devices, chiselled shells, inlaid spears, costly paddles, aromatic canoes; and all these distributed among whatever natural wonders, the wonder-freighted, tribute-rendering waves had cast upon his shores.

Chief among these latter was a great Sperm Whale, which, after an unusually long raging gale, had been found dead and stranded, with his head against a cocoa-nut tree, whose plumage-like, tufted droopings seemed his verdant jet. When the vast body had at last been stripped of its fathom-deep enfoldings, and the bones become dust dry in the sun, then the skeleton was carefully transported up the Pupella glen, where a grand temple of lordly palms now sheltered it.

The ribs were hung with trophies; the vertebræ were carved with Arsacidean annals, in strange hieroglyphics; in the skull, the priests kept up an unextinguished aromatic flame, so that the mystic head again sent forth its vapory spout; while, suspended from a bough, the terrific lower jaw vibrated over all the devotees, like the hair-hung sword that so affrighted Damocles.

It was a wondrous sight. The wood was green as mosses of the Icy Glen; the trees stood high and haughty, feeling their living sap; the industrious earth beneath was as a weaver's loom, with a gorgeous carpet on it, whereof the ground-vine tendrils formed the warp and woof, and the living flowers the figures. All the trees, with all their laden branches; all the shrubs, and ferns, and grasses; the message-carrying air; all these unceasingly were active. Through the lacings of the leaves, the great sun seemed a flying shuttle weaving the unwearied verdure. Oh, busy weaver! unseen weaver!—pause!—one word! —whither flows the fabric? what palace may it deck? wherefore all these ceaseless toilings? Speak, weaver!—stay thy hand!—but one single word with thee! Nay—the shuttle flies—the figures float from forth the loom; the freshet-rushing carpet for ever slides away. The weaver-god, he weaves; and by that weaving is he deafened, that he hears no mortal voice; and by that humming, we, too, who look on the loom are deafened; and only when we escape it shall we hear the thousand voices that speak through it. For even so it is in all material factories. The spoken words that are inaudible among the flying spindles; those same words are plainly heard without the walls, bursting from the opened casements. Thereby have villainies been detected. Ah, mortal! then, be heedful; for so, in all this din of the great world's loom, thy subtlest thinkings may be overheard afar.

Now, amid the green, life-restless loom of that Arsacidean wood, the great, white, worshipped skeleton lay lounging—a gigantic idler! Yet, as the ever-woven verdant warp and woof intermixed and hummed around him, the mighty idler seemed the cunning weaver; himself all woven over with the vines; every month assuming greener, fresher verdure; but himself a skeleton. Life folded Death; Death trellised Life; the grim god wived with youthful Life, and begat him curly-headed glories.

Now, when with royal Tranquo I visited this wondrous whale, and saw the skull an altar, and the artificial smoke ascending from where the real jet had issued, I marvelled that the king should regard a chapel as an object of vertù. He laughed. But more I marvelled that the priests should swear that smoky jet of his was genuine. To and fro I paced before this skeleton— brushed the vines aside—broke through the ribs—and with a ball of Arsacidean twine, wandered, eddied long amid its many winding, shaded colonnades and arbors. But soon my line was out; and following it back, I emerged from the opening where I entered. I saw no living thing within; naught was there but bones.

Cutting me a green measuring-rod, I once more dived within the skeleton. From their arrow-slit in the skull, the priests perceived me taking the altitude of the final rib. "How now!" they shouted; "Dar'st thou measure this our god! That's for us." "Aye, priests—well, how long do ye make him, then?" But hereupon a fierce contest rose among them, concerning feet and inches; they cracked each other's sconces with their yard-sticks—the great skull echoed—and seizing that lucky chance, I quickly concluded my own admeasurements.

These admeasurements I now propose to set before you. But first, be it recorded, that, in this matter, I am not free to utter any fancied measurement I please. Because there are skeleton authorities you can refer to, to test my accuracy. There is a Leviathanic Museum, they tell me, in Hull, England, one of the whaling ports of that country, where they have some fine specimens of fin-backs and other whales. Likewise, I have heard that in the museum of Manchester, in New Hampshire, they have what the proprietors call "the only perfect specimen of a Greenland or River Whale in the United States." Moreover, at a place in Yorkshire, England, Burton Constable by name, a certain Sir Clifford Constable has in his possession the skeleton of a Sperm Whale, but of moderate size, by no means of the full-grown magnitude of my friend King Tranquo's.

In both cases, the stranded whales to which these two skeletons belonged, were originally claimed by their proprietors upon similar grounds. King Tranquo seizing his because he wanted it; and Sir Clifford, because he was lord of the seignories of those parts. Sir Clifford's whale has been articulated throughout; so that, like a great chest of drawers, you can open and shut him, in all his bony cavities—spread out his ribs like a gigantic fan—and swing all day upon his lower jaw. Locks are to be put upon some of his trapdoors and shutters; and a footman will show round future visitors with a bunch of keys at his side. Sir Clifford thinks of charging twopence for a peep at the whispering gallery in the spinal column; threepence to hear the echo in the hollow of his cerebellum; and sixpence for the unrivalled view from his forehead.

The skeleton dimensions I shall now proceed to set down are copied verbatim from my right arm, where I had them tatooed; as in my wild wanderings at that period, there was no other secure way of preserving such valuable statistics. But as I was crowded for space, and wished the other parts of my body to remain a blank page for a poem I was then composing—at least, what untattooed parts might remain—I did not trouble myself with the odd inches; nor, indeed, should inches at all enter into a congenial admeasurement of the whale.

CHAPTER CIII

MEASUREMENT OF THE WHALE'S SKELETON

IN the first place, I wish to lay before you a particular, plain statement, touching the living bulk of this leviathan, whose skeleton we are briefly to exhibit. Such a statement may prove useful here.

According to a careful calculation I have made, and which I partly base upon Captain Scoresby's estimate, of seventy tons for the largest sized Greenland whale of sixty feet in length; according to my careful calculation, I say, a Sperm Whale of the largest magnitude, between eighty-five and ninety feet in length, and something less than forty feet in its fullest circumference, such a whale will weigh at least ninety tons; so that, reckoning thirteen men to a ton, he would considerably outweigh the combined population of a whole village of one thousand one hundred inhabitants.

Think you not then that brains, like yoked cattle, should be put to this leviathan, to make him at all budge to any landsman's imagination?

Having already in various ways put before you his skull, spout-hole, jaw, teeth, tail, forehead, fins, and divers other parts, I shall now simply point out what is most interesting in the general bulk of his unobstructed bones. But as the colossal skull embraces so very large a proportion of the entire extent of the skeleton; as it is by far the most complicated part; and as nothing is to be repeated concerning it in this chapter, you must not fail to carry it in your mind, or under your arm, as we proceed, otherwise you will not gain a complete notion of the general structure we are about to view.

In length, the Sperm Whale's skeleton at Tranque measured seventy-two feet; so that when fully invested and extended in life, he must have been ninety feet long; for in the whale, the skeleton loses about one fifth in length compared with the living body. Of this seventy-two feet, his skull and jaw comprised some twenty feet, leaving some fifty feet of plain back-bone. Attached to this back-bone, for something less than a third of its length, was the mighty circular basket of ribs which once enclosed his vitals.

To me this vast ivory-ribbed chest, with the long, unrelieved spine, extending far away from it in a straight line, not a little resembled the hull of a great ship new-laid upon the stocks, when only some twenty of her naked bow-ribs are inserted, and the keel is otherwise, for the time, but a long, disconnected timber.

The ribs were ten on a side. The first, to begin from the neck, was nearly six feet long; the second, third, and fourth were each successively longer, till you came to the climax of the fifth, or one of the middle ribs, which measured eight feet and some inches. From that part, the remaining ribs diminished, till the tenth and last only spanned five feet and some inches. In general thickness, they all bore a seemly correspondence to their length. The middle ribs were the most arched. In some of the Arsacides they are used for beams whereon to lay footpath bridges over small streams.

In considering these ribs, I could not but be struck anew with the circumstance, so variously repeated in this book, that the skeleton of the whale is by no means the mould of his invested form. The largest of the Tranque ribs, one of the middle ones, occupied that part of the fish which, in life, is greatest in depth. Now, the greatest depth of the invested body of this particular whale must have been at least sixteen feet; whereas, the corresponding rib measured but little more than eight feet. So that this rib only conveyed half of the true notion of the living magnitude of that part. Besides, for some way, where I now saw but a naked spine, all that had been once wrapped round with tons of added bulk in flesh, muscle, blood, and bowels. Still more, for the ample fins, I here saw but a few disordered joints; and in place of the weighty and majestic, but boneless flukes, an utter blank!

How vain and foolish, then, thought I, for timid untravelled man to try to comprehend aright this wondrous whale, by merely poring over his dead at-

tenuated skeleton, stretched in this peaceful wood. No. Only in the heart
of quickest perils; only when within the eddyings of his angry flukes; only on
the profound unbounded sea, can the fully invested whale be truly and livingly
found out.

But the spine. For that, the best way we can consider it is, with a crane,
to pile its bones high up on end. No speedy enterprise. But now it's done, it
looks much like Pompey's Pillar.

There are forty and odd vertebræ in all, which in the skeleton are not
locked together. They mostly lie like the great knobbed blocks on a Gothic
spire, forming solid courses of heavy masonry. The largest, a middle one, is
in width something less than three feet, and in depth more than four. The
smallest, where the spine tapers away into the tail, is only two inches in
width, and looks something like a white billiard-ball. I was told that there
were still smaller ones, but they had been lost by some little cannibal urchins,
the priest's children, who had stolen them to play marbles with. Thus we
see how that the spine of even the hugest of living things tapers off at last
into simple child's play.

CHAPTER CIV

THE FOSSIL WHALE

From his mighty bulk the whale affords a most congenial theme whereon to
enlarge, amplify, and generally expatiate. Would you, you could not compress
him. By good rights he should only be treated of in imperial folio. Not to
tell over again his furlongs from spiracle to tail, and the yards he measures
about the waist; only think of the gigantic involutions of his intestines, where
they lie in him like great cables and hawsers coiled away in the subterranean
orlop-deck of a line-of-battle-ship.

Since I have undertaken to manhandle this Leviathan, it behoves me to
approve myself omnisciently exhaustive in the enterprise; not overlooking the
minutest seminal germs of his blood, and spinning him out to the uttermost
coil of his bowels. Having already described him in most of his present habita-
tory and anatomical peculiarities, it now remains to magnify him in an archæo-
logical, fossiliferous, and antediluvian point of view. Applied to any other
creature than the Leviathan—to an ant or a flea—such portly terms might
justly be deemed unwarrantably grandiloquent. But when Leviathan is the
text, the case is altered. Fain am I to stagger to this emprise under the
weightiest words of the dictionary. And here be it said, that whenever it has
been convenient to consult one in the course of these dissertations, I have invariably used a huge quarto edition of Johnson, expressly purchased for that
purpose; because that famous lexicographer's uncommon personal bulk more
fitted him to compile a lexicon to be used by a whale author like me.

One often hears of writers that rise and swell with their subject, though
it may seem but an ordinary one. How, then, with me, writing of this Leviathan? Unconsciously my chirography expands into placard capitals. Give
me a condor's quill! Give me Vesuvius' crater for an inkstand! Friends, hold
my arms! For in the mere act of penning my thoughts of this Leviathan, they
weary me, and make me faint with their outreaching comprehensiveness of
sweep, as if to include the whole circle of the sciences, and all the generations

of whales, and men, and mastodons, past, present, and to come, with all the revolving panoramas of empire on earth, and throughout the whole universe, not excluding its suburbs. Such, and so magnifying, is the virtue of a large and liberal theme! We expand to its bulk. To produce a mighty book, you must choose a mighty theme. No great and enduring volume can ever be written on the flea, though many there be who have tried it.

Ere entering upon the subject of Fossil Whales, I present my credentials as a geologist, by stating that in my miscellaneous time I have been a stone-mason, and also a great digger of ditches, canals and wells, wine-vaults, cellars, and cisterns of all sorts. Likewise, by way of preliminary, I desire to remind the reader, that while in the earlier geological strata there are found the fossils of monsters now almost completely extinct; the subsequent relics discovered in what are called the Tertiary formations seem the connecting, or at any rate intercepted links, between the antichronical creatures, and those whose remote posterity are said to have entered the Ark; all the Fossil Whales hitherto dis-covered belong to the Tertiary period, which is the last preceding the superficial formations. And though none of them precisely answer to any known species of the present time, they are yet sufficiently akin to them in general respects, to justify their taking rank as Cetacean fossils.

Detached broken fossils of pre-adamite whales, fragments of their bones and skeletons, have within thirty years past, at various intervals, been found at the base of the Alps, in Lombardy, in France, in England, in Scotland, and in the States of Louisiana, Mississippi, and Alabama. Among the more curious of such remains is part of a skull, which in the year 1779 was disinterred in the Rue Dauphiné in Paris, a short street opening almost directly upon the palace of the Tuileries; and bones disinterred in excavating the great docks of Antwerp, in Napoleon's time. Cuvier pronounced these fragments to have belonged to some utterly unknown Leviathanic species.

But by far the most wonderful of all cetacean relics was the almost complete vast skeleton of an extinct monster, found in the year 1842, on the plantation of Judge Creagh, in Alabama. The awe-stricken credulous slaves in the vicinity took it for the bones of one of the fallen angels. The Alabama doctors de-clared it a huge reptile, and bestowed upon it the name of Basilosaurus. But some specimen bones of it being taken across the sea to Owen, the English Anatomist, it turned out that this alleged reptile was a whale, though of a departed species. A significant illustration of the fact, again and again re-peated in this book, that the skeleton of the whale furnishes but little clue to the shape of his fully invested body. So Owen rechristened the monster Zeu-glodon; and in his paper read before the London Geological Society, pronounced it, in substance, one of the most extraordinary creatures which the mutations of the globe have blotted out of existence.

When I stand among these mighty Leviathan skeletons, skulls, tusks, jaws, ribs, and vertebræ, all characterized by partial resemblances to the existing breeds of sea-monsters; but at the same time bearing on the other hand similar affinities to the annihilated antichronical Leviathans, their incalculable seniors; I am, by a flood, borne back to that wondrous period, ere time itself can be said to have begun; for time began with man. Here Saturn's grey chaos rolls over me, and I obtain dim, shuddering glimpses into those Polar eternities; when wedged bastions of ice pressed hard upon what are now the Tropics; and in all the 25,000 miles of this world's circumference, not an inhabitable hand's breadth of land was visible. Then the whole world was the whale's; and, king of creation, he left his wake along the present lines of the Andes and the

Himmalehs. Who can show a pedigree like Leviathan? Ahab's harpoon had shed older blood than the Pharaoh's. Methuselah seems a schoolboy. I look round to shake hands with Shem. I am horror-struck at this antemosaic, unsourced existence of the unspeakable terrors of the whale, which, having been before all time, must needs exist after all humane ages are over.

But not alone has this Leviathan left his pre-adamite traces in the stereotype plates of nature, and in limestone and marl bequeathed his ancient bust; but upon Egyptian tablets, whose antiquity seems to claim for them an almost fossiliferous character, we find the unmistakable print of his fin. In an apartment of the great temple of Denderah, some fifty years ago, there was discovered upon the granite ceiling a sculptured and painted planisphere, abounding in centaurs, griffins, and dolphins, similar to the grotesque figures on the celestial globe of the moderns. Gliding among them, old Leviathan swam as of yore; was there swimming in that planisphere, centuries before Solomon was cradled.

Nor must there be omitted another strange attestation of the antiquity of the whale, in his own osseous post-diluvian reality, as set down by the venerable John Leo, the old Barbary traveller.

"Not far from the Sea-side, they have a Temple, the Rafters and Beams of which are made of Whale-Bones; for Whales of a monstrous size are oftentimes cast up dead upon that shore. The Common People imagine, that by a secret Power bestowed by God upon the Temple, no Whale can pass it without immediate death. But the truth of the matter is, that on either side of the Temple, there are Rocks that shoot two Miles into the Sea, and wound the Whales when they light upon 'em. They keep a Whale's Rib of an incredible length for a Miracle, which lying upon the Ground with its convex part uppermost, makes an Arch, the Head of which cannot be reached by a Man upon a Camel's Back. This Rib (says John Leo) is said to have layn there a hundred Years before I saw it. Their Historians affirm, that a Prophet who prophesy'd of Mahomet, came from this Temple, and some do not stand to assert, that the Prophet Jonas was cast forth by the Whale at the Base of the Temple."

In this Afric Temple of the Whale I leave you, reader, and if you be a Nantucketer, and a whaleman, you will silently worship there.

CHAPTER CV

DOES THE WHALE'S MAGNITUDE DIMINISH?—WILL HE PERISH?

INASMUCH, then, as this Leviathan comes floundering down upon us from the head-waters of the Eternities, it may be fitly inquired, whether, in the long course of his generations, he has not degenerated from the original bulk of his sires.

But upon investigation we find, that not only are the whales of the present day superior in magnitude to those whose fossil remains are found in the Tertiary system (embracing a distinct geological period prior to man), but of the whales found in that Tertiary system, those belonging to its latter formations exceed in size those of its earlier ones.

Of all the pre-adamite whales yet exhumed, by far the largest is the Alabama one mentioned in the last chapter, and that was less than seventy feet in length in the skeleton. Whereas, we have already seen, that the tape-measure gives seventy-two feet for the skeleton of a large sized modern whale. And I have heard, on whalemen's authority, that Sperm Whales have been captured near a hundred feet long at the time of capture.

But may it not be, that while the whales of the present hour are an advance in magnitude upon those of all previous geological periods; may it not be, that since Adam's time they have degenerated?

Assuredly, we must conclude so, if we are to credit the accounts of such gentlemen as Pliny, and the ancient naturalists generally. For Pliny tells us of Whales that embraced acres of living bulk, and Aldrovandus of others which measured eight hundred feet in length—Rope Walks and Thames Tunnels of Whales! And even in the days of Banks and Solander, Cooke's naturalists, we find a Danish member of the Academy of Sciences setting down certain Iceland Whales (reydan-siskur, or Wrinkled Bellies) at one hundred and twenty yards; that is, three hundred and sixty feet. And Lacépède, the French naturalist, in his elaborate history of whales, in the very beginning of his work (page 3), sets down the Right Whale at one hundred metres, three hundred and twenty-eight feet. And this work was published so late as A. D. 1825.

But will any whaleman believe these stories? No. The whale of to-day is as big as his ancestors in Pliny's time. And if ever I go where Pliny is, I, a whaleman (more than he was), will make bold to tell him so. Because I cannot understand how it is, that while the Egyptian mummies that were buried thousands of years before even Pliny was born, do not measure so much in their coffins as a modern Kentuckian in his socks; and while the cattle and other animals sculptured on the oldest Egyptian and Nineveh tablets, by the relative proportions in which they are drawn, just as plainly prove that the high-bred, stall-fed, prize cattle of Smithfield, not only equal, but far exceed in magnitude the fattest of Pharaoh's fat kine; in the face of all this, I will not admit that of all animals the whale alone should have degenerated.

But still another inquiry remains; one often agitated by the more recondite Nantucketers. Whether owing to the almost omniscient look-outs at the mast-heads of the whale-ships, now penetrating even through Behring's straits, and into the remotest secret drawers and lockers of the world; and the thousand harpoons and lances darted along all continental coasts; the moot point is, whether Leviathan can long endure so wide a chase, and so remorseless a havoc; whether he must not at last be exterminated from the waters, and the last whale, like the last man, smoke his last pipe, and then himself evaporate in the final puff.

Comparing the humped herds of whales with the humped herds of buffalo, which, not forty years ago, overspread by tens of thousands the prairies of Illinois and Missouri, and shook their iron manes and scowled with their thunder-clotted brows upon the sites of populous river-capitals, where now the polite broker sells you land at a dollar an inch; in such a comparison an irresistible argument would seem furnished, to show that the hunted whale cannot now escape speedy extinction.

But you must look at this matter in every light. Though so short a period ago—not a good lifetime—the census of the buffalo in Illinois exceeded the census of men now in London, and though at the present day not one horn or hoof of them remains in all that region; and though the cause of this wondrous extermination was the spear of man; yet the far different nature of the whale-hunt peremptorily forbids so inglorious an end to the Leviathan. Forty men in one ship hunting the Sperm Whale for forty-eight months think they have done extremely well, and thank God, if at last they carry home the oil of forty fish. Whereas, in the days of the old Canadian and Indian hunters and trappers of the West, when the far west (in whose sunset suns still rise) was a wilderness and a virgin, the same number of moccasined men, for the same number of months, mounted on horse instead of sailing in ships, would have slain not forty, but forty thousand and more buffaloes; a fact that, if need were, could be statistically stated.

Nor, considered aright, does it seem any argument in favor of the gradual extinction of the Sperm Whale, for example, that in former years (the latter part of the last century, say) these Leviathans, in small pods, were encountered much oftener than at present, and, in consequence, the voyages were not so prolonged, and were also much more remunerative. Because, as has been elsewhere noticed, those whales, influenced by some views to safety, now swim the seas in immense caravans, so that to a large degree the scattered solitaries, yokes, and pods, and schools of other days are now aggregated into vast but widely separated, unfrequent armies. That is all. And equally fallacious seems the conceit, that because the so-called whale-bone whales no longer haunt many grounds in former years abounding with them, hence that species also is declining. For they are only being driven from promontory to cape; and if one coast is no longer enlivened with their jets, then, be sure, some other and remoter strand has been very recently startled by the unfamiliar spectacle.

Furthermore: concerning these last mentioned Leviathans, they have two firm fortresses, which, in all human probability, will for ever remain impregnable. And as upon the invasion of their valleys, the frosty Swiss have retreated to their mountains; so, hunted from the savannas and glades of the middle seas, the whale-bone whales can at last resort to their Polar citadels, and diving under the ultimate glassy barriers and walls there, come up among icy fields and floes; and in a charmed circle of everlasting December, bid defiance to all pursuit from man.

But as perhaps fifty of these whale-bone whales are harpooned for one cachalot, some philosophers of the forecastle have concluded that this positive havoc has already very seriously diminished their battalions. But though for some time past a number of these whales, not less than 13,000, have been annually slain on the nor' west coast by the Americans alone; yet there are considerations which render even this circumstance of little or no account as an opposing argument in this matter.

Natural as it is to be somewhat incredulous concerning the populousness of the more enormous creatures of the globe, yet what shall we say to Harto, the historian of Goa, when he tells us that at one hunting the King of Siam took 4000 elephants; that in those regions elephants are numerous as droves of cattle in the temperate climes. And there seems no reason to doubt that if these elephants, which have now been hunted for thousands of years, by Semiramis, by Porus, by Hannibal, and by all the successive monarchs of the East—if they still survive there in great numbers, much more may the great whale outlast all hunting, since he has a pasture to expatiate in, which is precisely twice as large as all Asia, both Americas, Europe and Africa, New Holland, and all the Isles of the sea combined.

Moreover: we are to consider, that from the presumed great longevity of whales, their probably attaining the age of a century and more, therefore at any one period of time, several distinct adult generations must be contemporary. And what that is, we may soon gain some idea of, by imagining all the grave-yards, cemeteries, and family vaults of creation yielding up the live bodies of all the men, women, and children who were alive seventy-five years ago; and adding this countless host to the present human population of the globe.

Wherefore, for all these things, we account the whale immortal in his species, however perishable in his individuality. He swam the seas before the continents broke water; he once swam over the site of the Tuileries, and Windsor Castle, and the Kremlin. In Noah's flood he despised Noah's Ark; and if ever the world is to be again flooded, like the Netherlands, to kill off its rats, then the eternal whale will still survive, and rearing upon the topmost crest of the equatorial flood, spout his frothed defiance to the skies.

CHAPTER CVI

AHAB'S LEG

THE precipitating manner in which Captain Ahab had quitted the Samuel Enderby of London, had not been unattended with some small violence to his own person. He had lighted with such energy upon a thwart of his boat that his ivory leg had received a half-splintering shock. And when after gaining his own deck, and his own pivot-hole there, he so vehemently wheeled round with an urgent command to the steersman (it was, as ever, something about his not steering inflexibly enough); then, the already shaken ivory received such an additional twist and wrench, that though it still remained entire, and to all appearances lusty, yet Ahab did not deem it entirely trustworthy.

And, indeed, it seemed small matter for wonder, that for all his pervading, mad recklessness, Ahab did at times give careful heed to the condition of that dead bone upon which he partly stood. For it had not been very long prior to the Pequod's sailing from Nantucket, that he had been found one night lying prone upon the ground, and insensible; by some unknown, and seemingly inexplicable, unimaginable casualty, his ivory limb having been so violently displaced, that it had stake-wise smitten, and all but pierced his groin; nor was it without extreme difficulty that the agonizing wound was entirely cured.

Nor, at the time, had it failed to enter his monomaniac mind, that all the anguish of that then present suffering was but the direct issue of a former woe; and he too plainly seemed to see, that as the most poisonous· reptile of the marsh perpetuates his kind as inevitably as the sweetest songster of the grove; so, equally with every felicity, all miserable events do naturally beget their like. Yea, more than equally, thought Ahab; since both the ancestry and posterity of Grief go farther than the ancestry and posterity of Joy. For, not to hint of this: that it is an inference from certain canonic teachings, that while some natural enjoyments here shall have no children born to them for the other world, but, on the contrary, shall be followed by the joy-childlessness of all hell's despair; whereas, some guilty mortal miseries shall still fertilely beget to themselves an eternally progressive progeny of griefs beyond the grave; not at all to hint of this, there still seems an inequality in the deeper analysis of the thing. For, thought Ahab, while even the highest earthly felicities ever have a certain unsignifying pettiness lurking in them, but, at bottom, all heart-woes, a mystic significance, and, in some men, an archangelic grandeur; so do their diligent tracings-out not belie the obvious deduction. To trail the genealogies of these high mortal miseries, carries us at last among the sourceless primogenitures of the gods; so that, in the face of all the glad, hay-making suns, and soft-cymballing, round harvest-moons, we must needs give in to this: that the gods themselves are not for ever glad. The ineffaceable, sad birth-mark in the brow of man, is but the stamp of sorrow in the signers.

Unwittingly here a secret has been divulged, which perhaps might more properly, in set way, have been disclosed before. With many other particulars concerning Ahab, always had it remained a mystery to some, why it was, that for a certain period, both before and after the sailing of the Pequod, he had hidden himself away with such Grand-Lama-like exclusiveness; and, for that one interval, sought speechless refuge, as it were, among the marble senate of the dead. Captain Peleg's bruited reason for this thing appeared by no means adequate; though, indeed, as touching all Ahab's deeper part, every revelation partook more of significant darkness than of explanatory light. But, in the end, it all came out; this one matter did, at least. That direful mishap was at the bottom of his temporary recluseness. And not only this, but to that ever-contracting, dropping circle ashore, who, for any reason, possessed the privilege of a less banned approach to him; to that timid circle the above hinted casualty —remaining, as it did, moodily unaccounted for by Ahab—invested itself with terrors, not entirely underived from the land of spirits and of wails. So that, through their zeal for him, they had all conspired, so far as in them lay, to muffle up the knowledge of this thing from others; and hence it was, that not till a considerable interval had elapsed, did it transpire upon the Pequod's decks.

But be all this as it may; let the unseen, ambiguous synod in the air, or the vindictive princes and potentates of fire, have to do or not with earthly Ahab, yet, in this present matter of his leg, he took plain practical procedures;— he called the carpenter.

And when that functionary appeared before him, he bade him without delay set about making a new leg, and directed the mates to see him supplied with all the studs and joists of jaw-ivory (Sperm Whale) which had thus far been accumulated on the voyage, in order that a careful selection of the stoutest, clearest-grained stuff might be secured. This done, the carpenter received orders to have the leg completed that night; and to provide all the fittings for it, independent of those pertaining to the distrusted one in use. Moreover, the ship's forge was ordered to be hoisted out of its temporary idleness in the hold; and, to accelerate the affair, the blacksmith was commanded to proceed at once to the forging of whatever iron contrivances might be needed.

CHAPTER CVII

THE CARPENTER

SEAT thyself sultanically among the moons of Saturn, and take high abstracted man alone; and he seems a wonder, a grandeur, and a woe. But from the same point, take mankind in mass, and for the most part, they seem a mob of unnecessary duplicates, both contemporary and hereditary. But most humble though he was, and far from furnishing an example of the high, humane abstraction; the Pequod's carpenter was no duplicate; hence, he now comes in person on this stage.

Like all sea-going ship carpenters, and more especially those belonging to whaling vessels, he was, to a certain off-handed, practical extent, alike experienced in numerous trades and callings collateral to his own; the carpenter's pursuit being the ancient and outbranching trunk of all those numerous handicrafts which more or less have to do with wood as an auxiliary material. But, besides the application to him of the generic remark above, this carpenter of the Pequod was singularly efficient in those thousand nameless mechanical emergencies continually recurring in a large ship, upon a three or four years' voyage, in uncivilized and far-distant seas. For not to speak of his readiness in ordinary duties:—-repairing stove boats, sprung spars, reforming the shape of clumsy-bladed oars, inserting bull's eyes in the deck, or new tree-nails in the side planks, and other miscellaneous matters more directly pertaining to his special business; he was moreover unhesitatingly expert in all manner of conflicting aptitudes, both useful and capricious.

The one grand stage where he enacted all his various parts so manifold, was his vice-bench; a long rude ponderous table furnished with several vices, of different sizes, and both of iron and of wood. At all times except when whales were alongside, this bench was securely lashed athwartships against the rear of the Try-works.

A belaying pin is found too large to be easily inserted into its hole: the carpenter claps it into one of his ever-ready vices, and straightway files it smaller. A lost land-bird of strange plumage strays on board, and is made a captive: out of clean shaved rods of right-whale bone, and crossbeams of sperm whale ivory, the carpenter makes a pagoda-looking cage for it. An oarsman sprains his wrist: the carpenter concocts a soothing lotion. Stubb longed for vermilion stars to be painted upon the blade of his every oar; screwing each oar in his big vice of wood, the carpenter symmetrically supplies the constellation. A sailor takes a fancy to wear shark-bone ear-rings: the carpenter drills his ears. Another has the toothache: the carpenter out pincers, and clapping one hand upon his bench bids him be seated there; but the poor fellow unmanageably winces under the unconcluded operation; whirling round the handle of his wooden vice, the carpenter signs him to clap his jaw in that, if he would have him draw the tooth.

Thus, this carpenter was prepared at all points, and alike indifferent and without respect in all. Teeth he accounted bits of ivory; heads he deemed but top-blocks; men themselves he lightly held for capstans. But while now upon so wide a field thus variously accomplished, and with such liveliness of expertness in him, too; all this would seem to argue some uncommon vivacity of intelligence. But not precisely so. For nothing was this man more remarkable, than for a certain impersonal stolidity as it were; impersonal, I say; for it so shaded off into the surrounding infinite of things, that it seemed one with the general stolidity discernible in the whole visible world; which while pauselessly active in uncounted modes, still eternally holds its peace, and ignores you, though you dig foundations for cathedrals. Yet was this half-horrible stolidity in him, involving, too, as it appeared, an all-ramifying heartlessness;—yet was it oddly dashed at times, with an old, crutch-like, antediluvian, wheezing humorousness, not unstreaked now and then with a certain grizzled wittiness; such as might have served to pass the time during the midnight watch on the bearded forecastle of Noah's ark. Was it that this old carpenter had been a life-long wanderer, whose much rolling, to and fro, not only had gathered no moss; but what is more, had rubbed off whatever small outward clingings might have originally pertained to him? He was a stript abstract; an unfractioned integral; uncompromised as a new-born babe; living without premeditated reference to this world or the next. You might almost say, that this strange uncompromised-ness in him involved a sort of unintelligence; for in his numerous trades, he did not seem to work so much by reason or by instinct, or simply because he had been tutored to it, or by any intermixture of all these, even or uneven; but merely by a kind of deaf and dumb, spontaneous literal process. He was a pure manipulator; his brain, if he had ever had one, must have early oozed along into the muscles of his fingers. He was like one of those unreasoning but still highly useful, *multum in parvo,* Sheffield contrivances, assuming the exterior—though a little swelled—of a common pocket knife; but containing, not only blades of various sizes, but also screw-drivers, cork-screws, tweezers, awls, pens, rulers, nail-filers, countersinkers. So, if his superiors wanted to use the carpenter for a screw-driver, all they had to do was to open that part of him, and the screw was fast: or if for tweezers, take him up by the legs, and there they were.

Yet, as previously hinted, this omnitooled, open-and-shut carpenter, was, after all, no mere machine of an automaton. If he did not have a common soul in him, he had a subtle something that somehow anomalously did its duty. What that was, whether essence of quicksilver, or a few drops of hartshorn, there is no telling. But there it was; and there it had abided for now some sixty years or more. And this it was, this same unaccountable, cunning life-principle in him; this it was, that kept him a great part of the time soliloquizing; but only like an unreasoning wheel, which also hummingly soliloquizes; or rather, his body was a sentry-box and this soliloquizer on guard there, and talking all the time to keep himself awake.

CHAPTER CVIII

AHAB AND THE CARPENTER

THE DECK—FIRST NIGHT WATCH

(Carpenter standing before his vice-bench, and by the light of two lanterns busily filing the ivory joist for the leg, which joist is firmly fixed in the vice. Slabs of ivory, leather straps, pads, screws, and various tools of all sorts lying about the bench. Forward, the red flame of the forge is seen, where the blacksmith is at work.)

DRAT the file, and drat the bone! That is hard which should be soft, and that is soft which should be hard. So we go, who file old jaws and shin bones. Let's try another. Aye, now, this works better (*sneezes*). Halloa, this bone dust is (*sneezes*)—why it's (*sneezes*)—yes it's (*sneezes*)—bless my soul, it won't let me speak! This is what an old fellow gets now for working in dead lumber. Saw a live tree, and you don't get this dust; amputate a live bone, and you don't get it (*sneezes*). Come, come, you old Smut, there, bear a hand, and let's have that ferule and buckle-screw; I'll be ready for them presently. Lucky now (*sneezes*) there's no knee-joint to make; that might puzzle a little; but a mere shin-bone—why it's easy as making hop-poles; only I should like to put a good finish on. Time, time; if I but only had the time, I could turn him out as neat a leg now as ever (*sneezes*) scraped to a lady in a parlor. Those buckskin legs and calves of legs I've seen in shop windows wouldn't compare at all. They soak water, they do; and of course get rheumatic, and have to be doctored (*sneezes*) with washes and lotions, just like live legs. There; before I saw it off, now, I must call his old Mogulship, and see whether the length will be all right; too short, if anything, I guess. Ha! that's the heel; we are in luck; here he comes, or it's somebody else, that's certain.

AHAB (*advancing*)
(*During the ensuing scene, the carpenter continues sneezing at times.*)

Well, manmaker!

Just in time, sir. If the captain pleases, I will now mark the length. Let me measure, sir.

Measured for a leg! good. Well, it's not the first time. About it! There; keep thy finger on it. This is a cogent vice thou hast here, carpenter; let me feel its grip once. So, so; it does pinch some.

Oh, sir, it will break bones—beware, beware!

No fear; I like a good grip; I like to feel something in this slippery world that can hold, man. What's Prometheus about there?—the blacksmith, I mean —what's he about?

He must be forging the buckle-screw, sir, now.

Right. It's a partnership; he supplies the muscle part. He makes a fierce red flame there!

Aye, sir; he must have the white heat for his kind of fine work.

Um-m. So he must. I do deem it now a most meaning thing, that that old Greek, Prometheus, who made men, they say, should have been a black-smith, and animated them with fire; for what's made in fire must properly belong to fire; and so hell's probable. How the soot flies! This must be the remainder the Greek made the Africans of. Carpenter, when he's through with that buckle, tell him to forge a pair of steel shoulder-blades; there's a pedlar aboard with a crushing pack.

Sir?

Hold; while Prometheus is about it, I'll order a complete man after a desirable pattern. Imprimis, fifty feet high in his socks; then, chest modelled after the Thames Tunnel; then, legs with roots to 'em, to stay in one place; then, arms three feet through the wrist; no heart at all, brass forehead, and about a quarter of an acre of fine brains; and let me see—shall I order eyes to see outwards? No, but put a sky-light on top of his head to illuminate inwards. There, take the order, and away.

Now, what's he speaking about, and who's he speaking to, I should like to know? Shall I keep standing here? (*aside.*)

'Tis but indifferent architecture to make a blind dome; here's one. No, no, no; I must have a lantern.

Ho, ho! That's it, hey? Here are two, sir; one will serve my turn.

What art thou thrusting that thief-catcher into my face for, man? Thrusted light is worse than presented pistols.

I thought, sir, that you spoke to carpenter.

Carpenter? why that's—but no;—a very tidy, and, I may say, an extremely gentlemanlike sort of business thou art in here, carpenter;—or would'st thou rather work in clay?

Sir?—Clay? clay, sir? That's mud; we leave clay to ditchers, sir.

The fellow's impious! What art thou sneezing about?

Bone is rather dusty, sir.

Take the hint, then; and when thou art dead, never bury thyself under living people's noses.

Sir?—oh! ah!—I guess so;—yes—oh, dear!

Look ye, carpenter, I dare say thou callest thyself a right good workmanlike workman, eh? Well, then, will it speak thoroughly well for thy work, if, when I come to mount this leg thou makest, I shall nevertheless feel another leg in the same identical place with it; that is, carpenter, my old lost leg; the flesh and blood one, I mean. Canst thou not drive that old Adam away?

Truly, sir, I begin to understand somewhat now. Yes, I have heard something curious on that score, sir; how that a dismasted man never entirely loses the feeling of his old spar, but it will be still pricking him at times. May I humbly ask if it be really so, sir?

It is, man. Look, put thy live leg here in the place where mine was; so, now, here is only one distinct leg to the eye, yet two to the soul. Where thou feelest tingling life; there, exactly there, there to a hair, do I. Is't a riddle?

I should humbly call it a poser, sir.

Hist, then. How dost thou know that some entire, living, thinking thing may not be invisibly and uninterpenetratingly standing precisely where thou now standest; aye, and standing there in thy spite? In thy most solitary hours, then, dost thou not fear eavesdroppers? Hold, don't speak! And if I still feel the smart of my crushed leg, though it be now so long dissolved; then, why mayst not thou, carpenter, feel the fiery pains of hell for ever, and without a body? Hah!

Good Lord! Truly, sir, if it comes to that, I must calculate over again; I think I didn't carry a small figure, sir.

Look ye, pudding-heads should never grant premises.—How long before the leg is done?

Perhaps an hour, sir.

Bungle away at it then, and bring it to me (*turns to go*). Oh, Life! Here I am, proud as Greek god, and yet standing debtor to this blockhead for a bone to stand on! Cursed be that mortal inter-indebtedness which will not do away with ledgers. I would be free as air; and I'm down in the whole world's books. I am so rich, I could have given bid for bid with the wealthiest Prætorians at the auction of the Roman empire (which was the world's); and yet I owe for the flesh in the tongue I brag with. By heavens! I'll get a crucible, and into it, and dissolve myself down to one small, compendious vertebra. So.

CARPENTER (*resuming his work*)

Well, well, well! Stubb knows him best of all, and Stubb always says he's queer; says nothing but that one sufficient little word queer; he's queer, says Stubb; he's queer—queer, queer; and keeps dinning it into Mr. Starbuck all the time—queer, sir—queer, queer, very queer. And here's his leg! Yes, now that I think of it, here's his bed-fellow; has a stick of whale's jaw-bone for a wife! And this is the leg; he'll stand on this. What was that now about one leg standing in three places, and all three places standing in one hell—how was that? Oh! I don't wonder he looked so scornful at me! I'm a sort of strange-thoughted sometimes, they say; but that's only haphazard-like. Then, a short, little old body like me, should never undertake to wade out into deep waters with tall, heron-built captains; the water chucks you under the chin pretty quick, and there's a great cry for life-boats. And here's the heron's leg! long and slim, sure enough! Now, for most folks one pair of legs lasts a lifetime, and that must be because they use them mercifully, as a tender-hearted old lady uses her roly-poly old coach-horses. But Ahab; oh he's a hard driver. Look, driven one leg to death, and spavined the other for life, and now wears out bone legs by the cord. Halloa, there, you Smut! bear a hand there with those screws, and let's finish it before the resurrection fellow comes a-calling with his horn for all legs, true or false, as brewery men go round collecting old beer barrels, to fill 'em up again. What a leg this is! It looks like a real live leg, filed down to nothing but the core; he'll be standing on this to-morrow; he'll be taking altitudes on it. Halloa! I almost forgot the little oval slate, smoothed ivory, where he figures up the latitude. So, so; chisel, file, and sand-paper, now!

CHAPTER CIX

AHAB AND STARBUCK IN THE CABIN

ACCORDING to usage they were pumping the ship next morning; and lo! no inconsiderable oil came up with the water; the casks below must have sprung a bad leak. Much concern was shown; and Starbuck went down into the cabin to report this unfavorable affair.

Now, from the South and West the Pequod was drawing nigh to Formosa and the Bashee Isles, between which lies one of the tropical outlets from the China waters into the Pacific. And so Starbuck found Ahab with a general chart of the oriental archipelagoes spread before him; and another separate one representing the long eastern coasts of the Japanese islands—Niphon, Matsmai, and Sikoke. With his snow-white new ivory leg braced against the screwed leg of his table, and with a long pruning-hook of a jack-knife in his hand, the wondrous old man, with his back to the gangway door, was wrinkling his brow, and tracing his old courses again.

"Who's there?" hearing the footstep at the door, but not turning round to it. "On deck! Begone!"

"Captain Ahab mistakes; it is I. The oil in the hold is leaking, sir. We must up Burtons and break out."

"Up Burtons and break out? Now that we are nearing Japan; heave-to here for a week to tinker a parcel of old hoops?"

"Either do that, sir, or waste in one day more oil than we may make good in a year. What we come twenty thousand miles to get is worth saving, sir."

"So it is, so it is; if we get it."

"I was speaking of the oil in the hold, sir."

"And I was not speaking or thinking of that at all. Begone! Let it leak! I'm all aleak myself. Aye! leaks in leaks! not only full of leaky casks, but those leaky casks are in a leaky ship; and that's a far worse plight than the Pequod's, man. Yet I don't stop to plug my leak; for who can find it in the deep-loaded hull; or how hope to plug it, even if found, in this life's howling gale? Starbuck! I'll not have the Burtons hoisted."

"What will the owners say, sir?"

"Let the owners stand on Nantucket beach and outyell the Typhoons. What cares Ahab? Owners, owners? Thou art always prating to me, Starbuck, about those miserly owners, as if the owners were my conscience. But look ye, the only real owner of anything is its commander; and hark ye, my conscience is in this ship's keel.—On deck!"

"Captain Ahab," said the reddening mate, moving farther into the cabin, with a daring so strangely respectful and cautious that it almost seemed not only every way seeking to avoid the slightest outward manifestation of itself, but within also seemed more than half distrustful of itself; "A better man than I might well pass over in thee what he would quickly enough resent in a younger man; aye, and in a happier, Captain Ahab."

"Devils! Dost thou then so much as dare to critically think of me?—On deck!"

"Nay, sir, not yet; I do entreat. And I do dare, sir—to be forbearing! Shall we not understand each other better than hitherto, Captain Ahab?"

Ahab seized a loaded musket from the rack (forming part of most South-Sea-men's cabin furniture), and pointing it towards Starbuck, exclaimed: "There is one God that is Lord over the earth, and one Captain that is lord over the Pequod.—On deck!"

For an instant in the flashing eyes of the mate, and his fiery cheeks, you would have almost thought that he had really received the blaze of the levelled tube. But, mastering his emotion, he half calmly rose, and as he quitted the cabin, paused for an instant and said: "Thou hast outraged, not insulted me, sir; but for that I ask thee not to beware of Starbuck; thou wouldst but laugh; but let Ahab beware of Ahab; beware of thyself, old man."

"He waxes brave, but nevertheless obeys; most careful bravery that!" murmured Ahab, as Starbuck disappeared. "What's that he said—Ahab beware of Ahab—there's something there!" Then unconsciously using the musket for a staff, with an iron brow he paced to and fro in the little cabin; but presently the thick plaits of his forehead relaxed, and returning the gun to the rack, he went to the deck.

"Thou art but too good a fellow, Starbuck," he said lowly to the mate; then raising his voice to the crew: "Furl the t'gallant-sails, and close-reef the top-sails, fore and aft; back the main-yard; up Burtons, and break out in the main-hold."

It were perhaps vain to surmise exactly why it was, that as respecting Starbuck, Ahab thus acted. It may have been a flash of honesty in him; or mere prudential policy which, under the circumstance, imperiously forbade the slightest symptom of open disaffection, however transient, in the important chief officer of his ship. However it was, his orders were executed; and the Burtons were hoisted.

CHAPTER CX

QUEEQUEG IN HIS COFFIN

Upon searching, it was found that the casks last struck into the hold were perfectly sound, and that the leak must be farther off. So, it being calm weather, they broke out deeper and deeper, disturbing the slumbers of the huge ground-tier butts; and from that black midnight sending those gigantic moles into the daylight above. So deep did they go; and so ancient, and corroded, and weedy the aspect of the lowermost puncheons, that you almost looked next for some mouldy corner-stone cask containing coins of Captain Noah, with copies of the posted placards, vainly warning the infatuated old world from the flood. Tierce after tierce, too, of water, and bread, and beef, and shooks of staves, and iron bundles of hoops, were hoisted out, till at last the piled decks were hard to get about; and the hollow hull echoed under foot, as if you were treading over empty catacombs, and reeled and rolled in the sea like an air-freighted demijohn. Top-heavy was the ship as a dinnerless student with all Aristotle in his head. Well was it that the Typhoons did not visit them then.

Now, at this time it was that my poor pagan companion, and fast bosom-friend, Queequeg, was seized with a fever, which brought him nigh to his endless end.

Be it said, that in this vocation of whaling, sinecures are unknown; dignity and danger go hand in hand; till you get to be Captain, the higher you rise the harder you toil. So with poor Queequeg, who, as harpooneer, must not only face all the rage of the living whale, but—as we have elsewhere seen—mount his dead back in a rolling sea; and finally descend into the gloom of the hold, and bitterly sweating all day in that subterraneous confinement, resolutely manhandle the clumsiest casks and see to their stowage. To be short, among whalemen, the harpooneers are the holders, so called.

Poor Queequeg! when the ship was about half disembowelled, you should have stooped over the hatchway, and peered down upon him there; where, stripped to his woollen drawers, the tattooed savage was crawling about amid that dampness and slime, like a green spotted lizard at the bottom of a well. And a well, or an ice-house, it somehow proved to him, poor pagan; where, strange to say, for all the heat of his sweatings, he caught a terrible chill which lapsed into a fever; and at last, after some days' suffering, laid him in his hammock, close to the very sill of the door of death. How he wasted and wasted away in those few long-lingering days, till there seemed but little left of him but his frame and tattooing. But as all else in him thinned, and his cheekbones grew sharper, his eyes, nevertheless, seemed growing fuller and fuller; they became of a strange softness of lustre; and mildly but deeply looked out at you there from his sickness, a wondrous testimony to that immortal health in him which could not die, or be weakened. And like circles on the water, which, as they grow fainter, expand; so his eyes seemed rounding and rounding, like the rings of Eternity. An awe that cannot be named would steal over you as you sat by the side of this waning savage, and saw as strange things in his face, as any beheld who were bystanders when Zoroaster died. For whatever is truly wondrous and fearful in man, never yet was put into words or books. And the drawing near of Death, which alike levels all, alike impresses all with a last revelation, which only an author from the dead could adequately tell. So that—let us say it again—no dying Chaldee or Greek had higher and holier thoughts than those, whose mysterious shades you saw creeping over the face of poor Queequeg, as he quietly lay in his swaying hammock, and the rolling sea seemed gently rocking him to his final rest, and the ocean's invisible floodtide lifted him higher and higher towards his destined heaven.

Not a man of the crew but gave him up; and, as for Queequeg himself, what he thought of his case was forcibly shown by a curious favor he asked. He called one to him in the grey morning watch, when the day was just breaking, and taking his hand, said that while in Nantucket he had chanced to see certain little canoes of dark wood, like the rich war-wood of his native isle; and upon inquiry, he had learned that all whalemen who died in Nantucket, were laid in those same dark canoes, and that the fancy of being so laid had much pleased him; for it was not unlike the custom of his own race, who, after embalming a

dead warrior, stretched him out in his canoe, and so left him to be floated away
to the starry archipelagoes; for not only do they believe that the stars are isles,
but that far beyond all visible horizons, their own mild, uncontinented seas,
interflow with the blue heavens; and so form the white breakers of the milky
way. He added, that he shuddered at the thought of being buried in his hammock, according to the usual sea-custom, tossed like something vile to the death-
devouring sharks. No: he desired a canoe like those of Nantucket, all the more
congenial to him, being a whaleman, that like a whale-boat these coffin-canoes
were without a keel; though that involved but uncertain steering, and much lee-
way adown the dim ages.

Now, when this strange circumstance was made known aft, the carpenter
was at once commanded to do Queequeg's bidding, whatever it might include.
There was some heathenish, coffin-colored old lumber aboard, which, upon a
long previous voyage, had been cut from the aboriginal groves of the Lackaday
islands, and from these dark planks the coffin was recommended to be made.
No sooner was the carpenter apprised of the order, than taking his rule, he
forthwith with all the indifferent promptitude of his character, proceeded into
the forecastle and took Queequeg's measure with great accuracy, regularly chalk-
ing Queequeg's person as he shifted the rule.

"Ah! poor fellow! he'll have to die now," ejaculated the Long Island sailor.

Going to his vice-bench, the carpenter for convenience sake and general
reference, now transferringly measured on it the exact length of the coffin was to
be, and then made the transfer permanent by cutting two notches at its extremities. This done, he marshalled the planks and his tools, and to work.

When the last nail was driven, and the lid duly planed and fitted, he lightly
shouldered the coffin and went forward with it, inquiring whether they were ready
for it yet in that direction.

Overhearing the indignant but half-humorous cries with which the people
on deck began to drive the coffin away, Queequeg, to every one's consternation, commanded that the thing should be instantly brought to him, nor was
there any denying him; seeing that, of all mortals, some dying men are the
most tyrannical; and certainly, since they will shortly trouble us so little for
evermore, the poor fellows ought to be indulged.

Leaning over in his hammock, Queequeg long regarded the coffin with an
attentive eye. He then called for his harpoon, had the wooden stock drawn
from it, and then had the iron part placed in the coffin along with one of the
paddles of his boat. All by his own request, also, biscuits were then ranged
round the sides within: a flask of fresh water was placed at the head, and a
small bag of woody earth scraped up in the hold at the foot; and a piece of
sail-cloth being rolled up for a pillow, Queequeg now entreated to be lifted
into his final bed, that he might make trial of its comforts, if any it had. He
lay without moving a few minutes, then told one to go to his bag and bring
out his little god, Yojo. Then crossing his arms on his breast with Yojo between, he called for the coffin lid (hatch he called it) to be placed over him.
The head part turned over with a leather hinge, and there lay Queequeg in
his coffin with little but his composed countenance in view. "Rarmai" (it
will do; it is easy), he murmured at last, and signed to be placed in his hammock.

But ere this was done, Pip, who had been slily hovering near by all this
while, drew nigh to him where he lay, and with soft sobbings, took him by the
the land; in the other, holding his tambourine.

"Poor rover! will ye never have done with all this weary roving? where go ye now? But if the currents carry ye to those sweet Antilles where the beaches are only beat with water-lilies, will ye do one little errand for me? Seek out one Pip, who's now been missing long: I think he's in those far Antilles. If ye find him, then comfort him; for he must be very sad; for look! he's left his tambourine behind;—I found it. Rig-a-dig, dig, dig! Now, Queequeg, die; and I'll beat ye your dying march."

"I have heard," murmured Starbuck, gazing down the scuttle, "that in violent fevers, men, all ignorance, have talked in ancient tongues; and that when the mystery is probed, it turns out always that in their wholly forgotten childhood those ancient tongues had been really spoken in their hearing by some lofty scholars. So, to my fond faith, poor Pip, in this strange sweetness of his lunacy, brings heavenly vouchers of all our heavenly homes. Where learned he that, but there?—Hark! he speaks again: but more wildly now."

"Form two and two! Let's make a General of him! Ho, where's his harpoon? Lay it across here.—Rig-a-dig, dig, dig! huzza! Oh for a game cock now to sit upon his head and crow! Queequeg dies game!—mind ye that; Queequeg dies game!—take ye good heed of that; Queequeg dies game! I say; game, game, game! but base little Pip, he died a coward; died all a'shiver; —out upon Pip! Hark ye; if ye find Pip, tell all the Antilles he's a runaway; a coward, a coward, a coward! Tell them he jumped from a whale-boat! I'd never beat my tambourine over base Pip, and hail him General, if he were once more dying here. No, no! shame upon all cowards—shame upon them! Let 'em go drown like Pip, that jumped from a whale-boat. Shame! shame!"

During all this, Queequeg lay with closed eyes, as if in a dream. Pip was led away, and the sick man was replaced in his hammock.

But now that he had apparently made every preparation for death; now that his coffin was proved a good fit, Queequeg suddenly rallied; soon there seemed no need of the carpenter's box: and thereupon, when some expressed their delighted surprise, he, in substance, said, that the cause of his sudden convalescence was this;—at a critical moment, he had just recalled a little duty ashore, which he was leaving undone; and therefore had changed his mind about dying: he could not die yet, he averred. They asked him, then, whether to live or die was a matter of his own sovereign will and pleasure. He answered, certainly. In a word, it was Queequeg's conceit, that if a man made up his mind to live, mere sickness could not kill him: nothing but a whale, or a gale, or some violent, ungovernable, unintelligent destroyer of that sort.

Now, there is this noteworthy difference between savage and civilized; that while a sick, civilized man may be six months convalescing, generally speaking, a sick savage is almost half-well again in a day. So, in good time my Queequeg gained strength; and at length after sitting on the windlass for a few indolent days (but eating with a vigorous appetite) he suddenly leaped to his feet, threw out his arms and legs, gave himself a good stretching, yawned a little bit, and then springing into the head of his hoisted boat, and poising a harpoon, pronounced himself fit for a fight.

With a wild whimsiness, he now used his coffin for a sea-chest; and emptying into it his canvas bag of clothes, set them in order there. Many spare hours he spent, in carving the lid with all manner of grotesque figures and drawings; and it seemed that hereby he was striving, in his rude way, to copy parts of the twisted tattooing on his body. And this tattooing had been the work of a departed prophet and seer of his island, who, by those hieroglyphic marks, had written out on his body a complete theory of the heavens and the earth, and a mystical treatise on the art of attaining truth; so that Queequeg in his own proper person was a riddle to unfold; a wondrous work in one volume; but whose mysteries not even himself could read, though his own live heart beat against them; and these mysteries were therefore destined in the end to moulder away with the living parchment whereon they were inscribed, and so be unsolved to the last. And this thought it must have been which suggested to Ahab that wild exclamation of his, when one morning turning away from surveying poor Queequeg—"Oh, devilish tantalization of the gods!"

CHAPTER CXI

THE PACIFIC

WHEN gliding by the Bashee Isles we emerged at last upon the great South Sea; were it not for other things, I could have greeted my dear Pacific with uncounted thanks, for now the long supplication of my youth was answered; that serene ocean rolled eastwards from me a thousand leagues of blue.

There is, one knows not what sweet mystery about this sea, whose gently awful stirrings seem to speak of some hidden soul beneath; like those fabled undulations of the Ephesian sod over the buried Evangelist St. John. And meet it is, that over these sea-pastures, wide-rolling watery prairies and Potters' Fields of all four continents, the waves should rise and fall, and ebb and flow unceasingly; for here, millions of mixed shades and shadows, drowned dreams, somnambulisms, reveries; all that we call lives and souls, lie dreaming, dreaming, still; tossing like slumberers in their beds; the ever-rolling waves but made so by their restlessness.

To any meditative Magian rover, this serene Pacific, once beheld, must ever after be the sea of his adoption. It rolls the midmost waters of the world, the Indian ocean and Atlantic being but its arms. The same waves wash the moles of the new-built Californian towns, but yesterday planted by the recentest race of men, and lave the faded but still gorgeous skirts of Asiatic lands, older than Abraham; while all between float milky-ways of coral isles, and low-lying, endless, unknown Archipelagoes, and impenetrable Japans. Thus this mysterious, divine Pacific zones the world's whole bulk about; makes all coasts one bay to it; seems the tide-beating heart of earth. Lifted by those eternal swells, you needs must own the seductive god, bowing your head to Pan.

But few thoughts of Pan stirred Ahab's brain, as standing like an iron statue at his accustomed place beside the mizzen rigging, with one nostril he unthinkingly snuffed the sugary musk from the Bashee Isles (in whose sweet woods mild lovers must be walking), and with the other consciously inhaled the salt breath of the new found sea; that sea in which the hated White Whale must even then be swimming. Launched at length upon these almost final waters, and gliding towards the Japanese cruising-ground, the old man's purpose intensified itself. His firm lips met like the lips of a vice; the Delta of his forehead's veins swelled like overladen brooks; in his very sleep, his ringing cry ran through the vaulted hull, "Stern all! the White Whale spouts thick blood!"

CHAPTER CXII

THE BLACKSMITH

AVAILING himself of the mild, summer-cool weather that now reigned in these latitudes, and in preparation for the peculiarly active pursuits shortly to be anticipated, Perth, the begrimed, blistered old blacksmith had not removed his portable forge to the hold again, after concluding his contributory work for Ahab's leg, but still retained it on deck, fast lashed to ringbolts by the foremast; being now almost incessantly invoked by the headsmen, and harpooneers, and bowsmen to do some little job for them; altering, or repairing, or new shaping their various weapons and boat furniture. Often he would be surrounded by an eager circle, all waiting to be served; holding boat-spades, pike-heads, harpoons, and lances, and jealously watching his every sooty movement as he toiled. Nevertheless, this old man's was a patient hammer wielded by a patient arm. No murmur, no impatience, no petulance did come from him. Silent, slow, and solemn; bowing over still farther his chronically broken back, he toiled away, as if toil were life itself, and the heavy beating of his hammer the heavy beating of his heart. And so it was. —Most miserable!

A peculiar walk in this old man, a certain slight but painful appearing yawing in his gait, had at an early period of the voyage excited the curiosity of the mariners. And to the importunity of their persisted questionings he had finally given in; and so it came to pass that every one now knew the shameful story of his wretched fate.

Belated, and not innocently, one bitter winter's midnight, on the road running between two country towns, the blacksmith half-stupidly felt the deadly numbness stealing over him, and sought refuge in a leaning, dilapidated barn. The issue was, the loss of the extremities of both feet. Out of this revelation, part by part, at last came out the four acts of the gladness, and the one long, and as yet uncatastrophied fifth act of the grief of his life's drama.

He was an old man, who, at the age of nearly sixty, had postponedly encountered that thing in sorrow's technicals called ruin. He had been an artisan of famed excellence, and with plenty to do; owned a house and garden; embraced a youthful, daughter-like, loving wife, and three blithe, ruddy children; every Sunday went to a cheerful-looking church, planted in a grove. But one night, under cover of darkness, and further concealed in a most cunning disguisement, a desperate burglar slid into his happy home, and robbed them all of everything. And darker yet to tell, the blacksmith himself did ignorantly conduct this burglar into his family's heart. It was the Bottle Conjuror! Upon the opening of that fatal cork, forth flew the fiend, and shrivelled up his home. Now, for prudent, most wise, and economic reasons, the blacksmith's shop was in the basement of his dwelling, but with a separate entrance to it; so that always had the young and loving healthy wife listened with no unhappy nervousness, but with vigorous pleasure, to the stout ringing of her young-armed old husband's hammer; whose reverberations, muffled by passing through the floors and walls, came up to her, not unsweetly, in her nursery; and so, to stout Labor's iron lullaby, the blacksmith's infants were rocked to slumber.

Oh, woe on woe! Oh, Death, why canst thou not sometimes be timely?

Hadst thou taken this old blacksmith to thyself ere his full ruin came upon him, then had the young widow had a delicious grief, and her orphans a truly venerable, legendary sire to dream of in their after years; and all of them a care-killing competency. But Death plucked down some virtuous elder brother, on whose whistling daily toil solely hung the responsibilities of some other family, and left the worse than useless old man standing, till the hideous rot of life should make him easier to harvest.

Why tell the whole? The blows of the basement hammer every day grew more and more between; and each blow every day grew fainter than the last; the wife sat frozen at the window, with tearless eyes, glitteringly gazing into the weeping faces of her children; the bellows fell; the forge choked up with cinders; the house was sold; the mother dived down into the long church-yard grass; her children twice followed her thither; and the houseless, family-less old man staggered off a vagabond in crape; his every woe unreverenced; his grey head a scorn to flaxen curls!

Death seems the only desirable sequel for a career like this; but Death is only a launching into the region of the strange Untried; it is but the first salu-tation to the possibilities of the immense Remote, the Wild, the Watery, the Unshored; therefore, to the death-longing eyes of such men, who still have left in them some interior compunctions against suicide, does the all-con-tributed and all-receptive ocean alluringly spread forth his whole plain of unimaginable, taking terrors, and wonderful, new-life adventures; and from the hearts of infinite Pacifics, the thousand mermaids sing to them—"Come hither, broken-hearted; here is another life without the guilt of intermediate death; here are wonders supernatural, without dying for them. Come hither! bury thyself in a life which, to your now equally abhorred and abhorring, landed world, is more oblivious than death. Come hither; put up *thy* grave-stone, too, within the churchyard, and come hither, till we marry thee!"

Hearkening to these voices, East and West, by early sun-rise, and by fall of eve, the blacksmith's soul responded, Aye, I come! And so Perth went a-whaling.

CHAPTER CXIII

THE FORGE

WITH matted beard, and swathed in a bristling shark-skin apron, about mid-day, Perth was standing between his forge and anvil, the latter placed upon an iron-wood log, with one hand holding a pike-head in the coals, and with the other at his forge's lungs, when Captain Ahab came along, carrying in his hand a small rusty-looking leathern bag. While yet a little distance from the forge, moody Ahab paused; till at last, Perth, withdrawing his iron from the fire, began hammering it upon the anvil—the red mass sending off the sparks in thick hovering flights, some of which flew close to Ahab.

"Are these thy Mother Carey's chickens, Perth? they are always flying in thy wake; birds of good omen, too, but not to all;—look here, they burn; but thou—thou liv'st among them without a scorch."

"Because I am scorched all over, Captain Ahab," answered Perth, rest-ing for a moment on his hammer; "I am past scorching; not easily can'st thou scorch a scar."

"Well, well; no more. Thy shrunk voice sounds too calmly, sanely woful to me. · In no Paradise myself, I am impatient of all misery in others that is not mad. Thou should'st go mad, blacksmith; say, why dost thou not go mad? How can'st thou endure without being mad? Do the heavens yet hate thee, that thou can'st not go mad?—What wert thou making there?"

"Welding an old pike-head, sir; there were seams and dents in it."

"And can'st thou make it all smooth again, blacksmith, after such hard usage as it had?"

"I think so, sir."

"And I suppose thou can'st smoothe almost any seams and dents; never mind how hard the metal, blacksmith?"

"Aye, sir, I think I can; all seams and dents but one."

"Look ye here, then," cried Ahab, passionately advancing, and leaning with both hands on Perth's shoulders; "look ye here—*here*—can ye smoothe out a seam like this, blacksmith," sweeping one hand across his ribbed brow; "if thou could'st, blacksmith, glad enough would I lay my head upon thy anvil, and feel thy heaviest hammer between my eyes. Answer! Can'st thou smoothe this seam?"

"Oh! that is the one, sir! Said I not all seams and dents but one?"

"Aye, blacksmith, it is the one; aye, man, it is unsmoothable; for though thou only see'st it here in my flesh, it has worked down into the bone of my skull—*that* is all wrinkles! But, away with child's play; no more gaffs and pikes to-day. Look ye here!" jingling the leathern bag, as if it were full of gold coins. "I, too, want a harpoon made; one that a thousand yoke of fiends could not part, Perth; something that will stick in a whale like his own fin-bone. There's the stuff," flinging the pouch upon the anvil. "Look ye, blacksmith, these are the gathered nail-stubbs of the steel shoes of racing horses."

"Horse-shoe stubbs, sir? Why, Captain Ahab, thou has here, then, the best and stubbornest stuff we blacksmiths ever work."

"I know it, old man; these stubbs will weld together like glue from the melted bones of murderers. Quick! forge me the harpoon. And forge me first, twelve rods for its shank; then wind, and twist, and hammer these twelve together like the yarns and strands of a tow-line. Quick! I'll blow the fire."

When at last the twelve rods were made, Ahab tried them, one by one, by spiralling them, with his own hand, round a long, heavy iron bolt. "A flaw!" rejecting the last one. "Work that over again, Perth."

This done, Perth was about to begin welding the twelve into one, when Ahab stayed his hand, and said he would weld his own iron. As, then, with regular, gasping hems, he hammered on the anvil, Perth passing to him the glowing rods, one after the other, and the hard pressed forge shooting up its intense straight flame, the Parsee passed silently, and bowing over his head toward the fire, seemed invoking some curse or some blessing on the toil. But, as Ahab looked up, he slid aside.

"What's that bunch of lucifers dodging about there for?" muttered Stubb, looking on from the forecastle. "That Parsee smells fire like a fusee; and smells of it himself, like a hot musket's powder-pan."

At last the shank, in one complete rod, received its final heat; and as Perth, to temper it, plunged it all hissing into the cask of water near by, the scalding steam shot up into Ahab's bent face.

"Would'st thou brand me, Perth?" wincing for a moment with the pain; "have I been but forging my own branding-iron, then?"

"Pray God, not that; yet I fear something, Captain Ahab. Is not this harpoon for the White Whale?"

"For the white fiend! But now for the barbs; thou must make them thyself, man. Here are my razors—the best of steel; here, and make the barbs sharp as the needle-sleet of the Icy Sea."

For a moment, the old blacksmith eyed the razors as though he would fain not use them.

"Take them, man, I have no need for them; for I now neither shave, sup, nor pray till——but here—to work!"

Fashioned at last into an arrowy shape, and welded by Perth to the shank, the steel soon pointed the end of the iron; and as the blacksmith was about giving the barbs their final heat, prior to tempering them, he cried to Ahab to place the water-cask near.

"No, no—no water for that; I want it of the true death-temper. Ahoy, there! Tashtego, Queequeg, Daggoo! What say ye, pagans! Will ye give me as much blood as will cover this barb?" holding it high up. A cluster of dark nods replied, Yes. Three punctures were made in the heathen flesh, and the White Whale's barbs were then tempered.

"Ego non baptizo te in nomina patris, sed in nomine diaboli!" deliriously howled Ahab, as the malignant iron scorchingly devoured the baptismal blood.

Now, mustering the spare poles from below, and selecting one of hickory, with the bark still investing it, Ahab fitted the end to the socket of the iron. A coil of new tow-line was then unwound, and some fathoms of it taken to the windlass, and stretched to a great tension. Pressing his foot upon it, till the rope hummed like a harp-string, then eagerly bending over it, and seeing no strandings, Ahab exclaimed, "Good! and now for the seizings."

At one extremity the rope was unstranded, and the separate spread yarns were all braided and woven round the socket of the harpoon; the pole was then driven hard up into the socket; from the lower end the rope was traced half way along the pole's length, and firmly secured so, with intertwistings of twine. This done, pole, iron, and rope—like the Three Fates—remained inseparable, and Ahab moodily stalked away with the weapon; the sound of his ivory leg, and the sound of the hickory pole, both hollowly ringing along every plank. But ere he entered his cabin, a light, unnatural, half-bantering, yet most piteous sound was heard. Oh! Pip, thy wretched laugh, thy idle but unresting eye; all thy strange mummeries not unmeaningly blended with the black tragedy of the melancholy ship, and mocked it!

CHAPTER CXIV

THE GILDER

PENETRATING further and further into the heart of the Japanese cruising ground, the Pequod was soon all astir in the fishery. Often, in mild, pleasant weather, for twelve, fifteen, eighteen, and twenty hours on the stretch, they were engaged in the boats, steadily pulling, or sailing, or paddling after the whales, or for an interlude of sixty or seventy minutes calmly awaiting their uprising; though with but small success for their pains.

At such times, under an abated sun; afloat all day upon smooth, slow heaving swells; seated in his boat, light as a birch canoe; and so sociably mixing with the soft waves themselves, that like hearth-stone cats they purr against the gunwale; these are the times of dreamy quietude, when beholding the tranquil beauty and brilliancy of the ocean's skin, one forgets the tiger heart that pants beneath it; and would not willingly remember, that this velvet paw but conceals a remorseless fang.

These are the times, when in his whale-boat the rover softly feels a certain filial, confident, land-like feeling towards the sea; that he regards it as so much flowery earth; and the distant ship revealing only the tops of her masts, seems struggling forward, not through high rolling waves, but through the tall grass of a rolling prairie: as when the western emigrants' horses only show their erected ears, while their hidden bodies widely wade through the amazing verdure.

The long-drawn virgin vales; the mild blue hill-sides; as over these there steals the hush, the hum; you almost swear that play-wearied children lie sleeping in these solitudes, in some glad May-time, when the flowers of the woods are plucked. And all this mixes with your most mystic mood; so that fact and fancy, half-way meeting, interpenetrate, and form one seamless whole.

Nor did such soothing scenes, however temporary, fail of at least as temporary an effect on Ahab. But if these secret golden keys did seem to open in him his own secret golden treasuries, yet did his breath upon them prove but tarnishing.

Oh, grassy glades! oh, ever vernal endless landscapes in the soul; in ye, —though long parched by the dead drought of the earthy life,—in ye, men yet may roll, like young horses in new morning clover; and for some few fleeting moments, feel the cool dew of the life immortal on them. Would to God these blessed calms would last. But the mingled, mingling threads of life are woven by warp and woof: calms crossed by storms, a storm for every calm. There is no steady unretracing progress in this life; we do not advance through fixed gradations, and at the last one pause:—through infancy's unconscious spell, boyhood's thoughtless faith, adolescence' doubt (the common doom), then scepticism, then disbelief, resting at last in manhood's pondering repose of If. But once gone through, we trace the round again; and are infants, boys, and men, and Ifs eternally. Where lies the final harbor, whence we unmoor no more? In what rapt ether sails the world, of which the weariest will never weary? Where is the foundling's father hidden? Our souls are like those orphans whose unwedded mothers die in bearing them: the secret of our paternity lies in their grave, and we must there to learn it.

And that same day, too, gazing far down from his boat's side into that same golden sea, Starbuck lowly murmured:—

"Loveliness unfathomable, as ever lover saw in his young bride's eye!— Tell me not of thy teeth-tiered sharks, and thy kidnapping cannibal ways. Let faith oust fact; let fancy oust memory; I look deep down and do believe."

And Stubb, fish-like, with sparkling scales, leaped up in that same golden light:—

"I am Stubb, and Stubb has his history; but here Stubb takes oath that he has always been jolly!"

CHAPTER CXV

THE PEQUOD MEETS THE BACHELOR

AND jolly enough were the sights and the sounds that came bearing down before the wind, some few weeks after Ahab's harpoon had been welded.

It was a Nantucket ship, the Bachelor, which had just wedged in her last cask of oil, and bolted down her bursting hatches; and now, in glad holiday apparel, was joyously, though somewhat vain-gloriously, sailing round among the widely-separated ships on the ground, previous to pointing her prow for home.

The three men at her mast-head wore long streamers of narrow red bunting at their hats; from the stern, a whale-boat was suspended, bottom down; and hanging captive from the bowsprit was seen the long lower jaw of the last whale they had slain. Signals, ensigns, and jacks of all colors were flying from her rigging, on every side. Sideways lashed in each of her three basketed tops were two barrels of sperm; above which, in her top-mast cross-trees, you saw slender breakers of the same precious fluid, and nailed to her main truck was a brazen lamp.

As was afterwards learned, the Bachelor had met with the most surprising success; all the more wonderful, for that while cruising in the same seas numerous other vessels had gone entire months without securing a single fish. Not only had barrels of beef and bread been given away to make room for the far more valuable sperm, but additional supplemental casks had been bartered for, from the ships she had met; and these were stowed along the deck, and in the captain's and officers' state-rooms. Even the cabin table itself had been knocked into kindling-wood; and the cabin mess dined off the broad head of an oil-butt, lashed down to the floor for a centrepiece. In the forecastle, the sailors had actually caulked and pitched their chests, and filled them; it was humorously added, that the cook had clapped a head on his largest boiler, and filled it; that the steward had plugged his spare coffee-pot and filled it; that the harpooneers had headed the sockets of their irons and filled them; that indeed everything was filled with sperm, except the captain's pantaloons pockets, and those he reserved to thrust his hands into, in self-complacent testimony of his entire satisfaction.

As this glad ship of good luck bore down upon the moody Pequod, the barbarian sound of enormous drums came from her forecastle; and drawing still nearer, a crowd of her men were seen standing round her huge try-pots, which, covered with the parchment-like *poke* or stomach skin of the black fish, gave forth a loud roar to every stroke of the clenched hands of the crew. On the quarter-deck, the mates and harpooneers were dancing with the olive-hued girls who had eloped with them from the Polynesian Isles; while suspended in an ornamented boat, firmly secured aloft between the foremast and main-mast, three Long Island negroes, with glittering fiddle-bows of whale ivory, were presiding over the hilarious jig. Meanwhile, others of the ship's company were tumultuously busy at the masonry of the try-works, from which the huge pots had been removed. You would have almost thought they were pulling down the cursed Bastile, such wild cries they raised, as the now useless brick and mortar were being hurled into the sea.

Lord and master over all this scene, the captain stood erect on the ship's elevated quarter-deck, so that the whole rejoicing drama was full before him, and seemed merely contrived for his own individual diversion.

And Ahab, he too was standing on his quarter-deck, shaggy and black, with a stubborn gloom; and as the two ships crossed each other's wakes— one all jubilations for things past, the other all forebodings as to things to come—their two captains in themselves impersonated the whole striking contrast of the scene.

"Come aboard, come aboard!" cried the gay Bachelor's commander, lifting a glass and a bottle in the air.

"Hast seen the White Whale?" gritted Ahab in reply.

"No; only heard of him; but don't believe in him at all," said the other good-humoredly. "Come aboard!"

"Thou art too damned jolly. Sail on. Hast lost any men?"

"Not enough to speak of—two islanders, that's all;—but come aboard, old hearty, come along. I'll soon take that black from your brow. Come along, will ye (merry's the play); a full ship and homeward-bound."

"How wondrous familiar is a fool!" muttered Ahab; then aloud, "Thou art a full ship and homeward bound, thou sayst; well, then, call me an empty ship, and outward-bound. So go thy ways, and I will mine. Forward there! Set all sail, and keep her to the wind!"

And thus, while the one ship went cheerily before the breeze, the other stubbornly fought against it; and so the two vessels parted; the crew of the Pequod looking with grave, lingering glances towards the receding Bachelor; but the Bachelor's men never heeding their gaze for the lively revelry they were in. And as Ahab, leaning over the taffrail, eyed the homeward-bound craft, he took from his pocket a small vial of sand, and then looking from the ship to the vial, seemed thereby bringing two remote associations together, for that vial was filled with Nantucket soundings.

CHAPTER CXVI

THE DYING WHALE

NOT seldom in this life, when, on the right side, fortune's favorites sail close by us, we though all adroop before, catch somewhat of the rushing breeze, and joyfully feel our bagging sails fill out. So seemed it with the Pequod. For next day after encountering the gay Bachelor, whales were seen and four were slain; and one of them by Ahab.

It was far down the afternoon; and when all the spearings of the crimson fight were done: and floating in the lovely sunset sea and sky, sun and whale both stilly died together; then, such a sweetness and such plaintiveness, such inwreathing orisons curled up in that rosy air, that it almost seemed as if far over from the deep green convent valleys of the Manilla isles, the Spanish land-breeze, wantonly turned sailor, had gone to sea, freighted with these vesper hymns.

Soothed again, but only soothed to deeper gloom, Ahab, who had sterned off from the whale, sat intently watching his final wanings from the now tranquil boat. For that strange spectacle observable in all sperm whales dying —the turning sunwards of the head, and so expiring—that strange spectacle, beheld of such a placid evening, somehow to Ahab conveyed a wondrousness unknown before.

"He turns and turns him to it,—how slowly, but how steadfastly, his homage-rendering and invoking brow, with his last dying motions. He too worships fire; most faithful, broad, baronial vassal of the sun!—Oh that these too-favoring eyes should see these too-favoring sights. Look! here, far water-locked; beyond all hum of human weal or woe; in these most candid and im-partial seas; where to traditions no rocks furnish tablets; where for long Chinese ages, the billows have still rolled on speechless and unspoken to, as stars that shine upon the Niger's unknown source; here, too, life dies sunwards full of faith; but see! no sooner dead, than death whirls round the corpse, and it heads some other way.—

"Oh, thou dark Hindoo half of nature, who of drowned bones hast builded thy separate throne somewhere in the heart of these unverdured seas; thou art an infidel, thou queen, and too truly speakest to me in the wide-slaughtering Typhoon, and the hushed burial of its after calm. Nor has this thy whale sun-wards turned his dying head, and then gone round again, without a lesson to me.

"Oh, trebly hooped and welded hip of power! Oh, high aspiring, rain-bowed jet!—that one strivest, this one jettest all in vain! In vain, oh whale, dost thou seek intercedings with yon all-quickening sun, that only calls forth life, but gives it not again. Yet dost thou, darker half, rock me with a prouder, if a darker faith. All thy unnamable imminglings float beneath me here; I am buoyed by breaths of once living things, exhaled as air, but water now.

"Then hail, for ever hail, O sea, in whose eternal tossings the wild fowl finds his only rest. Born of earth, yet suckled by the sea; though hill and valley mothered me, ye billows are my foster-brothers!"

CHAPTER CXVII

THE WHALE WATCH

THE four whales slain that evening had died wide apart; one, far to windward; one, less distant, to leeward; one ahead; one astern. These last three were brought alongside ere nightfall; but the windward one could not be reached till morning; and the boat that had killed it lay by its side all night; and that boat was Ahab's.

The waif-pole was thrust upright into the dead whale's spout-hole; and the lantern hanging from its top, cast a troubled flickering glare upon the black, glossy back, and far out upon the midnight waves, which gently chafed the whale's broad flank, like soft surf upon a beach.

Ahab and all his boat's crew seemed asleep but the Parsee; who crouching in the bow, sat watching the sharks, that spectrally played round the whale, and tapped the light cedar planks with their tails. A sound like the moaning in squadrons over Asphaltites of unforgiven ghosts of Gomorrah, ran shuddering through the air.

Startled from his slumbers, Ahab, face to face, saw the Parsee; and hooped round by the gloom of the night they seemed the last men in a flooded world. "I have dreamed it again," said he.

"Of the hearses? Have I not said, old man, that neither hearse nor coffin can be thine?"

"And who are hearsed that die on the sea?"

"But I said, old man, that ere thou couldst die on this voyage, two hearses must verily be seen by thee on the sea; the first not made by mortal hands; and the visible wood of the last one must be grown in America."

"Aye, aye! a strange sight that, Parsee:—a hearse and its plumes floating over the ocean with the waves for the pall-bearers. Ha! Such a sight we shall not soon see."

"Believe it or not, thou canst not die till it be seen, old man."

"And what was that saying about thyself?"

"Though it come to the last, I shall still go before thee thy pilot."

"And when thou art so gone before—if that ever befall—then ere I can follow, thou must still appear to me, to pilot me still?—Was it not so? Well, then, did I believe all ye say, oh my pilot! I have here two pledges that I shall yet slay Moby-Dick and survive it."

"Take another pledge, old man," said the Parsee, as his eyes lighted up like fire-flies in the gloom—"Hemp only can kill thee."

"The gallows, ye mean.—I am immortal then, on land and on sea," cried Ahab, with a laugh of derision;—"Immortal on land and on sea!"

Both were silent again, as one man. The grey dawn came on, and the slumbering crew arose from the boat's bottom, and ere noon the dead whale was brought to the ship.

CHAPTER CXVIII

THE QUADRANT

THE season for the Line at length drew near; and every day when Ahab, coming from his cabin, cast his eyes aloft, the vigilant helmsman would ostentatiously handle his spokes, and the eager mariners quickly run to the braces, and would stand there with all their eyes centrally fixed on the nailed doubloon; impatient for the order to point the ship's prow for the equator. In good time the order came. It was hard upon high noon; and Ahab, seated in the bows of his high-hoisted boat, was about taking his wonted daily observation of the sun to determine his latitude.

Now, in that Japanese sea, the days in summer are as freshets of effulgences. That unblinkingly vivid Japanese sun seems the blazing focus of the glassy ocean's immeasurable burning-glass. The sky looks lacquered; clouds there are none; the horizon floats; and this nakedness of unrelieved radiance is as the insufferable splendors of God's throne. Well that Ahab's quadrant was furnished with colored glasses, through which to take site of that solar fire. So, swinging his seated form to the roll of the ship, and with his astrological-looking instrument placed to his eye, he remained in that posture for some moments to catch the precise instant when the sun should gain its precise meridian. Meantime while his whole attention was absorbed, the Parsee was kneeling beneath him on the ship's deck, and with face thrown up like Ahab's, was eyeing the same sun with him; only the lids of his eyes half hooded their orbs, and his wild face was subdued to an earthly passionlessness. At length the desired observation was taken; and with his pencil upon his ivory leg, Ahab

soon calculated what his latitude must be at that precise instant. Then falling
into a moment's revery, he again looked up towards the sun and murmured to
himself: "Thou sea-mark! thou high and mighty Pilot! thou tellest me truly
where I *am*—but canst thou cast the least hint where I *shall* be? Or canst
thou tell where some other thing besides me is this moment living? Where is
Moby-Dick? This instant thou must be eyeing him. These eyes of mine
look into the very eye that is even now beholding him; aye, and into the eye
that is even now equally beholding the objects on the unknown, thither side of
thee, thou sun!"

Then gazing at his quadrant, and handling, one after the other, its numerous cabalistical contrivances, he pondered again, and muttered: "Foolish
toy! babies' plaything of haughty Admirals, and Commodores, and Captains;
the world brags of thee, of thy cunning and might; but what after all canst
thou do, but tell the poor, pitiful point, where thou thyself happenest to be
on this wide planet, and the hand that holds thee: no! not one jot more! Thou
canst not tell where one drop of water or one grain of sand will be to-morrow
noon; and yet with thy impotence thou insultest the sun! Science! Curse
thee, thou vain toy; and cursed be all the things that cast man's eyes aloft
to that heaven, whose live vividness but scorches him, as these old eyes are
even now scorched with thy light, O sun! Level by nature to this earth's
horizon are the glances of man's eyes; not shot from the crown of his head, as
if God had meant him to gaze on his firmament. Curse thee, thou quadrant!"
dashing it to the deck, "no longer will I guide my earthly way by thee; the
level ship's compass, and the level dead-reckoning, by log and by line; *these*
shall conduct me, and show me my place on the sea. Aye," lighting from
the boat to the deck, "thus I trample on thee, thou paltry thing that feebly
pointest on high; thus I split and destroy thee!"

As the frantic old man thus spoke, and thus trampled with his live and
dead feet, a sneering triumph that seemed meant for Ahab, and a fatalistic
despair that seemed meant for himself—these passed over the mute, motionless Parsee's face. Unobserved he rose and glided away; while, awestruck
by the aspect of their commander, the seamen clustered together on the forecastle, till Ahab, troubledly pacing the deck, shouted out—"To the braces!
Up helm!—square in!"

In an instant the yards swung round; and as the ship half-wheeled upon
her heel, her three firm-seated graceful masts erectly poised upon her long,
ribbed hull seemed as the three Horatii pirouetting on one sufficient steed.

Standing between the knight-heads, Starbuck watched the Pequod's tumul--
tuous way, and Ahab's also, as he went lurching along the deck.

"I have sat before the dense coal fire and watched it all aglow, full of its
tormented flaming life; and I have seen it wane at last, down, down, to
dumbest dust. Old man of oceans! of all this fiery life of thine, what will at
length remain but one little heap of ashes!"

"Aye," cried Stubb, "but sea-coal ashes—mind ye that, Mr. Starbuck—
sea-coal, not your common charcoal. Well, well; I heard Ahab mutter, 'Here
some one thrusts these cards into these old hands of mine; swears that I must
play them, and no others.' And damn me, Ahab, but thou actest right; live
in the game, and die it!"

CHAPTER CXIX

THE CANDLES

WARMEST climes but nurse the cruellest fangs: the tiger of Bengal crouches in spiced groves of ceaseless verdure. Skies the most effulgent but basket the deadliest thunders: gorgeous Cuba knows tornadoes that never swept tame northern lands. So, too, it is, that in these resplendent Japanese seas the mariner encounters the direst of all storms, the Typhoon. It will sometimes burst from out that cloudless sky, like an exploding bomb upon a dazed and sleepy town.

Towards evening of that day, the Pequod was torn of her canvas, and bare-poled was left to fight a Typhoon which had struck her directly ahead. When darkness came on, sky and sea roared and split with the thunder, and blazed with the lightning, that showed the disabled masts fluttering here and there with the rags which the first fury of the tempest had left for its after sport.

Holding by a shroud, Starbuck was standing on the quarter-deck; at every flash of the lightning glancing aloft, to see what additional disaster might have befallen the intricate hamper there; while Stubb and Flask were directing the men in the higher hoisting and firmer lashing of the boats. But all their pains seemed naught. Though lifted to the very top of the cranes, the windward quarter boat (Ahab's) did not escape. A great rolling sea, dashing high up against the reeling ship's high tetering side, stove in the boat's bottom at the stern, and left it again, all dripping through like a sieve.

"Bad work, bad work! Mr. Starbuck," said Stubb, regarding the wreck, "but the sea will have its way. Stubb, for one, can't fight it. You see, Mr. Starbuck, a wave has such a great long start before it leaps, all around the world it runs, and then comes the spring! But as for me, all the start I have to meet it, is just across the deck here. But never mind; it's all in fun: so the old song says;"—(sings.)

> "Oh, jolly is the gale,
> And a joker is the whale,
> A' flourishin' his tail,—
> Such a funny, sporty, gamy, jesty, joky, hoky-poky lad, is the Ocean, oh!

> The scud all a flyin',
> That's his flip only foamin';
> When he stirs in the spicin',
> Such a funny, sporty, gamy, jesty, joky, hoky-poky lad, is the Ocean, oh!

> Thunder splits the ships,
> But he only smacks his lips,
> A tastin' of this flip,—
> Such a funny, sporty, gamy, jesty, joky, hoky-poky lad, is the Ocean, oh!

"Avast Stubb," cried Starbuck, "let the Typhoon sing, and strike his harp here in our rigging; but if thou art a brave man thou wilt hold thy peace."

"But I am not a brave man; never said I was a brave man; I am a coward; and I sing to keep up my spirits. And I tell you what it is, Mr. Starbuck,

there's no way to stop my singing in this world but to cut my throat.   And
when that's done, ten to one I sing ye the doxology for a wind-up."

"Madman! look through my eyes if thou hast none of thine own."

"What! how can you see better of a dark night than anybody else, never
mind how foolish?"

"Here!" cried Starbuck, seizing Stubb by the shoulder, and pointing his
hand towards the weather bow, "markest thou not that the gale comes from
the eastward, the very course Ahab is to run for Moby-Dick? the very course
he swung to this day noon? now mark his boat there; where is that stove?
In the stern-sheets, man; where he is wont to stand—his stand-point is stove,
man!   Now jump overboard, and sing away, if thou must!"

"I don't half understand ye: what's in the wind?"

"Yes, yes, round the Cape of Good Hope is the shortest way to Nantucket,"
soliloquized Starbuck suddenly, heedless of Stubb's question.   "The gale that
now hammers at us to stave us, we can turn it into a fair wind that will
drive us towards home.   Yonder, to windward, all is blackness of doom;
but to leeward, homeward—I see it lightens up there; but not with the
lightning."

At that moment in one of the intervals of profound darkness, following the
flashes, a voice was heard at his side; and almost at the same instant a volley
of thunder peals rolled overhead.

"Who's there?"

"Old Thunder!" said Ahab, groping his way along the bulwarks to his pivot-
hole; but suddenly finding his path made plain to him by elbowed lances of
fire.

Now, as the lightning rod to a spire on shore is intended to carry off the
perilous fluid into the soil; so the kindred rod which at sea some ships carry
to each mast, is intended to conduct it into the water.   But as this conductor
must descend to considerable depth, that its end may avoid all contact with
the hull; and as moreover, if kept constantly towing there, it would be liable
to many mishaps, besides interfering not a little with some of the rigging, and
more or less impeding the vessel's way in the water; because of all this, the
lower parts of a ship's lightning-rods are not always overboard; but are generally made in long slender links, so as to be the more readily hauled up into
the chains outside, or thrown down into the sea, as occasion may require.

"The rods! the rods!" cried Starbuck to the crew, suddenly admonished
to vigilance by the vivid lightning that had just been darting flambeaux, to light
Ahab to his post.   "Are they overboard? drop them over, fore and aft.   Quick!"

"Avast!" cried Ahab; "let's have fair play here, though we be the weaker
side.   Yet I'll contribute to raise rods on the Himmalehs and Andes, that
all the world may be secured; but out on privileges!   Let them be, sir."

"Look aloft!" cried Starbuck.   "The corpusants! the corpusants!"

All the yard-arms were tipped with a pallid fire; and touched at each tri-
pointed lightning-rod-end with three tapering white flames, each of the three tall
masts was silently burning in that sulphurous air, like three gigantic wax tapers
before an altar.

"Blast the boat! let it go!" cried Stubb at this instant, as a swashing sea
heaved up under his own little craft, so that its gunwale violently jammed
his hand, as he was passing a lashing.   "Blast it!"—but slipping backward on
the deck, his uplifted eyes caught the flames; and immediately shifting his
tone, he cried—"The corpusants have mercy on us all!"

To sailors, oaths are household words; they will swear in the trance of the calm, and in the teeth of the tempest; they will imprecate curses from the topsail-yard-arms, when most they teter over to a seething sea; but in all my voyagings, seldom have I heard a common oath when God's burning finger has been laid on the ship; when His "Mene, Mene, Tekel, Upharsin" has been woven into the shrouds and the cordage.

While this pallidness was burning aloft, few words were heard from the enchanted crew; who in one thick cluster stood on the forecastle, all their eyes gleaming in that pale phosphorescence, like a far away constellation of stars. Relieved against the ghostly light, the gigantic jet negro, Daggoo, loomed up to thrice his real stature, and seemed the black cloud from which the thunder had come. The parted mouth of Tashtego revealed his shark-white teeth, which strangely gleamed as if they too had been tipped by corpusants; while lit up by the preternatural light, Queequeg's tattooing burned like Satanic blue flames on his body.

The tableau all waned at last with the pallidness aloft; and once more the Pequod and every soul on her decks were wrapped in a pall. A moment or two passed, when Starbuck, going forward, pushed against some one. It was Stubb. "What thinkest thou now, man; I heard the cry; it was not the same in the song."

"No, no, it wasn't; I said the corpusants have mercy on us all; and I hope they will, still. But do they only have mercy on long faces?—have they no bowels for a laugh? And look ye, Mr. Starbuck—but it's too dark to look. Hear me, then: I take that mast-head flame we saw for a sign of good luck; for those masts are rooted in a hold that is going to be chock a' block with sperm-oil, d'ye see; and so, all that sperm will work up into the masts, like sap in a tree. Yes, our three masts will yet be as three spermaceti candles —that's the good promise we saw."

At that moment Starbuck caught sight of Stubb's face slowly beginning to glimmer into sight. Glancing upwards, he cried: "See! see!" and once more the high tapering flames were beheld with what seemed redoubled supernatural-ness in their pallor.

"The corpusants have mercy on us all," cried Stub, again.

At the base of the mainmast, full beneath the doubloon and the flame, the Parsee was kneeling in Ahab's front, but with his head bowed away from him; while near by, from the arched and overhanging rigging, where they had just been engaged securing a spar, a number of the seamen, arrested by the glare, now cohered together, and hung pendulous, like a knot of numbed wasps from a drooping, orchard twig. In various enchanted attitudes, like the stand-ing, or stepping, or running skeletons in Herculaneum, others remained rooted to the deck; but all their eyes upcast.

"Aye, aye, men!" cried Ahab. "Look up at it; mark it well; the white flame but lights the way to the White Whale! Hand me those main-mast links there; I would fain feel this pulse, and let mine beat against it; blood against fire! So."

Then turning—the last link held fast in his left hand, he put his foot upon the Parsee; and with fixed upward eye, and high-flung right arm, he stood erect before the lofty tri-pointed trinity of flames.

"Oh! thou clear spirit of clear fire, whom on these seas I as Persian once did worship, till in the sacramental act so burned by thee, that to this hour I bear the scar; I now know thee, thou clear spirit, and I now know that thy right worship is defiance. To neither love nor reverence wilt thou be kind; and e'en for hate thou canst but kill; and all are killed. No fearless fool now fronts thee. I own thy speechless, placeless power; but to the last gasp of my earthquake life will dispute its unconditional, unintegral mastery in me. In the midst of the personified impersonal, a personality stands here. Though but a point at best; whencesoe'er I came; wheresoe'er I go; yet while I earthly live, the queenly personality lives in me, and feels her royal rights. But war is pain, and hate is woe. Come in thy lowest form of love, and I will kneel and kiss thee; but at thy highest, come as mere supernal power; and though thou launchest navies of full-freighted worlds, there's that in here that still remains indifferent. Oh, thou clear spirit, of thy fire thou madest me, and like a true child of fire, I breathe it back to thee."

[*Sudden, repeated flashes of lightning; the nine flames leap lengthwise to thrice their previous height; Ahab, with the rest, closes his eyes, his right hand pressed hard upon them.*]

"I own thy speechless, placeless power; said I not so? Nor was it wrung from me; nor do I now drop these links. Thou canst blind; but I can then grope. Thou canst consume; but I can then be ashes. Take the homage of these poor eyes, and shutter-hands. I would not take it. The lightning flashes through my skull; mine eye-balls ache and ache; my whole beaten brain seems as beheaded, and rolling on some stunning ground. Oh, oh! Yet blindfold, yet will I talk to thee. Light though thou be, thou leapest out of darkness; but I am darkness leaping out of light, leaping out of thee! The javelins cease; open eyes; see, or not? There burn the flames! Oh, thou magnanimous! now I do glory in my genealogy. But thou art but my fiery father; my sweet mother, I know not. Oh, cruel! what hast thou done with her? There lies my puzzle; but thine is greater. Thou knowest not how came ye, hence callest thyself unbegotten; certainly knowest not thy beginning, hence callest thyself unbegun. I know that of me, which thou knowest not of thyself, oh, thou omnipotent. There is some unsuffusing thing beyond thee, thou clear spirit, to whom all thy eternity is but time, all thy creativeness mechanical. Through thee, thy flaming self, my scorched eyes do dimly see it. Oh, thou foundling fire, thou hermit immemorial, thou too hast thy incommunicable riddle, thy unparticipated grief. Here again with haughty agony, I read my sire. Leap! leap up, and lick the sky! I leap with thee; I burn with thee; would fain be welded with thee; defyingly I worship thee!"

"The boat! the boat!" cried Starbuck, "look at thy boat, old man!"

Ahab's harpoon, the one forged at Perth's fire, remained firmly lashed in its conspicuous crotch, so that it projected beyond his whale-boat's bow; but the sea that had stove its bottom had caused the loose leather sheath to drop off; and from the keen steel barb there now came a levelled flame of pale, forked fire. As the silent harpoon burned there like a serpent's tongue, Starbuck grasped Ahab by the arm—"God, God is against thee, old man; forbear! 't is an ill voyage! ill begun, ill continued; let me square the yards, while we may, old man, and make a fair wind of it homewards, to go on a better voyage than this."

Overhearing Starbuck, the panic-stricken crew instantly ran to the braces —though not a sail was left aloft. For the moment all the aghast mate's thoughts seemed theirs; they raised a half mutinous cry. But dashing the rattling lightning links to the deck, and snatching the burning harpoon, Ahab waved it like a torch among them; swearing to transfix with it the first sailor that but cast loose a rope's end. Petrified by his aspect, and still more shrinking from the fiery dart that he held, the men fell back in dismay, and Ahab again spoke:—

"All your oaths to hunt the White Whale are as binding as mine; and heart, soul, and body, lungs and life, old Ahab is bound. And that ye may know to what tune this heart beats: look ye here; thus I blow out the last fear!" And with one blast of his breath he extinguished the flame.

As in the hurricane that sweeps the plain, men fly the neighborhood of some lone, gigantic elm, whose very height and strength but render it so much the more unsafe, because so much the more a mark for thunderbolts; so at those last words of Ahab's many of the mariners did run from him in a terror of dismay.

CHAPTER CXX

THE DECK TOWARDS THE END OF THE FIRST NIGHT WATCH

Ahab standing by the helm. Starbuck approaching him.

"WE must send down the main-top-sail yard, sir. The band is working loose, and the lee lift is half-stranded. Shall I strike it, sir?"

"Strike nothing; lash it. If I had sky-sail poles, I'd sway them up now."

"Sir?—in God's name!—sir?"

"Well."

"The anchors are working, sir. Shall I get them inboard?"

"Strike nothing, and stir nothing, but lash everything. The wind rises, but it has not got up to my table-hands yet. Quick, and see to it.—By masts and keels! he takes me for the hunch-backed skipper of some coasting smack. Send down my main-top-sail yard! Ho, gluepots! Loftiest trucks were made for wildest winds, and this brain-truck of mine now sails amid the cloud-scud. Shall I strike that? Oh, none but cowards send down their brain-trucks in tempest time. What a hooroosh aloft there! I would e'en take it for sublime, did I not know that the colic is a noisy malady. Oh, take medicine, take medicine!"

CHAPTER CXXI

MIDNIGHT.—THE FORCASTLE BULWARKS

Stubb and Flask mounted on them, and passing additional lashings over the anchors there hanging.

"No, Stubb; you may pound that knot there as much as you please, but you will never pound into me what you were just now saying. And how long ago is it since you said the very contrary? Didn't you once say that whatever ship Ahab sails in, that ship should pay something extra on its insurance policy, just as though it were loaded with powder barrels aft and boxes of lucifers forward? Stop, now; didn't you say so?"

"Well, suppose I did? What then? I've part changed my flesh since that time, why not my mind? Besides, supposing we *are* loaded with powder barrels aft and lucifers forward; how the devil could the lucifers get afire in this drenching spray here? Why, my little man, you have pretty red hair, but you couldn't get afire now. Shake yourself; you're Aquarius, or the water-bearer, Flask; might fill pitchers at your coat collar. Don't you see, then, that for these extra risks the Marine Insurance companies have extra guarantees? Here are hydrants, Flask. But hark, again, and I'll answer ye the other thing. First take your leg off from the crown of the anchor here, though, so I can pass the rope; now listen. What's the mighty difference between holding a mast's lightning-rod in the storm, and standing close by a mast that hasn't got any lightning-rod at all in a storm? Don't you see, you timber-head, that no harm can home to the holder of the rod, unless the mast is first struck? What are you talking about, then? Not one ship in a hundred carries rods, and Ahab,—aye, man, and all of us,—were in no more danger then, in my poor opinion, than all the crews in ten thousand ships now sailing the seas. Why, you King-Post, you, I suppose you would have every man in the world go about with a small lightning-rod running up the corner of his hat, like a militia officer's skewered feather, and trailing behind like his sash. Why don't ye be sensible, Flask? it's easy to be sensible; why don't ye, then? any man with half an eye can be sensible."

"I don't know that, Stubb. You sometimes find it rather hard."

"Yes, when a fellow's soaked through, it's hard to be sensible, that's a fact. And I am about drenched with this spray. Never mind; catch the turn there, and pass it. Seems to me we are lashing down these anchors now as if they were never going to be used again. Tying these two anchors here, Flask, seems like tying a man's hands behind him. And what big generous hands they are, to be sure. These are your iron fists, hey? What a hold they have, too! I wonder, Flask, whether the world is anchored anywhere; if she is, she swings with an uncommon long cable, though. There, hammer that knot down, and we've done. So; next to touching land, lighting on deck is the most satisfactory. I say, just wring out my jacket skirts, will ye? Thank ye. They laugh at long-togs so, Flask; but seems to me, a long tailed coat ought always to be worn in all storms afloat. The tails tapering down that way, serve to carry off the water, d'ye see. Same with cocked hats; the cocks form gable-end eave-troughs, Flask. No more monkey-jackets and tarpaulins for me; I must mount a swallow-tail, and drive down a beaver; so. Halloa! whew! there goes my tarpaulin overboard; Lord, Lord, that the winds that come from heaven should be so unmannerly! This is a nasty night, lad."

CHAPTER CXXII

MIDNIGHT ALOFT.—THUNDER AND LIGHTNING

The Main-top-sail yard.—Tashtego passing new lashings around it.

"Um, um, um. Stop that thunder! Plenty too much thunder up here. What's the use of thunder? Um, um, um. We don't want thunder; we want rum; give us a glass of rum. Um, um, um!"

CHAPTER CXXIII

THE MUSKET

DURING the most violent shocks of the Typhoon, the man at the Pequod's jaw-bone tiller had several times been reelingly hurled to the deck by its spasmodic motions, even though preventer tackles had been attached to it—for they were slack—because some play to the tiller was indispensable.

In a severe gale like this, while the ship is but a tossed shuttlecock to the blast, it is by no means uncommon to see the needles in the compasses, at intervals, go round and round. It was thus with the Pequod's; at almost every shock the helmsman had not failed to notice the whirling velocity with which they revolved upon the cards; it is a sight that hardly anyone can behold without some sort of unwonted emotion.

Some hours after midnight, the Typhoon abated so much, that through the strenuous exertions of Starbuck and Stubb—one engaged forward and the other aft—the shivered remnants of the jib and fore and main-top-sails were cut adrift from the spars, and went eddying away to leeward, like the feathers of an albatross, which sometimes are cast to the winds when that storm-tossed bird is on the wing.

The three corresponding new sails were now bent and reefed, and a storm-trysail was set farther aft; so that the ship soon went through the water with some precision again; and the course—for the present, East-south-east—which he was to steer, if practicable, was once more given to the helmsman. For during the violence of the gale, he had only steered according to its vicissitudes. But as he was now bringing the ship as near her course as possible, watching the compass meanwhile, lo! a good sign! the wind seemed coming round astern; aye, the foul breeze became fair!

Instantly the yards were squared, to the lively song of *"Ho! the fair wind! oh-ye-ho, cheerly, men!"* the crew singing for joy, that so promising an event should so soon have falsified the evil portents preceding it.

In compliance with the standing order of his commander—to report immediately, and at any one of the twenty-four hours, any decided change in the affairs of the deck,—Starbuck had no sooner trimmed the yards to the breeze —however reluctantly and gloomily,—than he mechanically went below to apprise Captain Ahab of the circumstance.

Ere knocking at his state-room, he involuntarily paused before it a moment. The cabin lamp—taking long swings this way and that—was burning fitfully, and casting fitful shadows upon the old man's bolted door,—a thin one, with fixed blinds inserted, in place of upper panels. The isolated subterraneousness of the cabin made a certain humming silence to reign there, though it was hooped round by all the roar of the elements. The loaded muskets in the rack were shiningly revealed, as they stood upright against the forward bulkhead. Starbuck was an honest, upright man; but out of Starbuck's heart, at that instant when he saw the muskets, there strangely evolved an evil thought; but so blent with its neutral or good accompaniments that for the instant he hardly knew it for itself.

"He would have shot me once," he murmured, "yes, there's the very musket that he pointed at me;—that one with the studded stock; let me touch it— lift it. Strange, that I, who have handled so many deadly lances, strange, that

I should shake so now. Loaded? I must see. Aye, aye; and powder in the pan;—that's not good. Best spill it?—wait. I'll cure myself of this. I'll hold the musket boldly while I think.—I come to report a fair wind to him. But how fair? Fair for death and doom,—*that's* fair for Moby-Dick. It's a fair wind that's only fair for that accursed fish.—The very tube he pointed at me!— the very one; *this* one—I hold it here; he would have killed me with the very thing I handle now.—Aye and he would fain kill all his crew. Does he not say he will not strike his spars to any gale? Has he not dashed his heavenly quadrant? and in these same perilous seas, gropes he not his way by mere dead reckoning of the error-abounding log? and in this very Typhoon, did he not swear that he would have no lightning-rods? But shall this crazed old man be tamely suffered to drag a whole ship's company down to doom with him?—Yes, it would make him the wilful murderer of thirty men and more, if this ship come to any deadly harm; and come to deadly harm, my soul swears this ship will, if Ahab have his way. If, then, he were this instant—put aside, that crime would not be his. Ha! is he muttering in his sleep? Yes, just there,—in there, he's sleeping. Sleeping? aye, but still alive, and soon awake again. I can't withstand thee, then, old man. Not reasoning; not remonstrance; not entreaty wilt thou hearken to; all this thou scornest. Flat obedience to thy own flat commands, this is all thou breathest. Aye, and say'st the men have vow'd thy vow; say'st all of us are Ahabs. Great God forbid!— But is there no other way? no lawful way?—Make him a prisoner to be taken home? What! hope to wrest this old man's living power from his own living hands? Only a fool would try it. Say he were pinioned even; knotted all over with ropes and hawsers; chained down to ring-bolts on this cabin floor; he would be more hideous than a caged tiger, then. I could not endure the sight; could not possibly fly his howlings; all comfort, sleep itself, inestimable reason would leave me on the long intolerable voyage. What, then, remains? The land is hundreds of leagues away, and locked Japan the nearest. I stand alone here upon an open sea, with two oceans and a whole continent between me and law.—Aye, aye, 'tis so.—Is heaven a murderer when its lightning strikes a would-be murderer in his bed, tindering sheets and skin together?—And would I be a murderer, then, if"——and slowly, stealthily, and half sideways looking, he placed the loaded musket's end against the door.

"On this level, Ahab's hammock swings within; his head this way. A touch, and Starbuck may survive to hug his wife and child again.—Oh Mary! Mary! —boy! boy! boy!—But if I wake thee not to death, old man, who can tell to what unsounded deeps Starbuck's body this day week may sink, with all the crew! Great God, where art Thou? Shall I? shall I?—— The wind has gone down and shifted, sir; the fore and main topsails are reefed and set; she heads her course."

"Stern all! Oh Moby-Dick, I clutch thy heart at last!"

Such were the sounds that now came hurtling from out the old man's tormented sleep, as if Starbuck's voice had caused the long dumb dream to speak.

The yet levelled musket shook like a drunkard's arm against the panel; Starbuck seemed wrestling with an angel; but turning from the door, he placed the death-tube in its rack, and left the place.

"He's too sound asleep, Mr. Stubb; go thou down, and wake him and tell him. I must see to the deck here. Thou know'st what to say."

CHAPTER CXXIV

THE NEEDLE

NEXT morning the not-yet-subsided sea rolled in long slow billows of mighty bulk, and striving in the Pequod's gurgling track, pushed her on like giants' palms outspread. The strong, unstaggering breeze abounded so, that sky and air seemed vast outbellying sails; the whole world boomed before the wind. Muffled in the full morning light, the invisible sun was only known by the spread intensity of his place; where his bayonet rays moved on in stacks. Emblazonings, as of crowned Babylonian kings and queens, reigned over everything. The sea was as a crucible of molten gold, that bubblingly leaps with light and heat.

Long maintaining an enchanted silence, Ahab stood apart; and every time the tetering ship loweringly pitched down her bowsprit, he turned to eye the bright sun's rays produced ahead; and when she profoundly settled by the stern, he turned behind, and saw the sun's rearward place, and how the same yellow rays were blending with his undeviating wake.

"Ha, ha, my ship! thou mightest well be taken now for the sea-chariot of the sun. Ho, ho! all ye nations before my prow, I bring the sun to ye! Yoke on the farther billows; hallo! a tandem, I drive the sea!"

But suddenly reined back by some counter thought, he hurried towards the helm, huskily demanding how the ship was heading.

"East-sou-east, sir," said the frightened steersman.

"Thou liest!" smiting him with his clenched fist. "Heading East at this hour in the morning, and the sun astern?"

Upon this every soul was confounded; for the phenomenon just then observed by Ahab had unaccountably escaped every one else; but its very blinding palpableness must have been the cause.

Thrusting his head half way into the binnacle, Ahab caught one glimpse of the compasses; his uplifted arm slowly fell; for a moment he almost seemed to stagger. Standing behind him Starbuck looked, and lo! the two compasses pointed East, and the Pequod was as infallibly going West.

But ere the first wild alarm could get out abroad among the crew, the old man with a rigid laugh exclaimed, "I have it! It has happened before. Mr. Starbuck, last night's thunder turned our compasses—that's all. Thou hast before now heard of such a thing, I take it."

"Aye; but never before has it happened to me, sir," said the pale mate, gloomily.

Here, it must needs be said, that accidents like this have in more than one case occurred to ships in violent storms. The magnetic energy, as developed in the mariner's needle, is, as all know, essentially one with the electricity beheld in heaven; hence it is not to be much marvelled at, that such things should be. In instances where the lightning has actually struck the vessel, so as to smite down some of the spars and rigging, the effect upon the needle has at times been still more fatal; all its loadstone virtue being annihilated, so that the before magnetic steel was of no more use than an old wife's knitting needle. But in either case, the needle never again, of itself, recovers the original virtue thus marred or lost; and if the binnacle compasses be affected, the same fate reaches all the others that may be in the ship; even were the lowermost one inserted into the kelson.

Deliberately standing before the binnacle, and eyeing the transpointed compasses, the old man, with the sharp of his extended hand, now took the precise bearing of the sun, and satisfied that the needles were exactly inverted, shouted out his orders for the ship's course to be changed accordingly. The yards were hard up; and once more the Pequod thrust her undaunted bows into the opposing wind, for the supposed fair one had only been juggling her.

Meanwhile, whatever were his own secret thoughts, Starbuck said nothing, but quietly he issued all requisite orders; while Stubb and Flask—who in some small degree seemed then to be sharing his feelings—likewise unmurmuringly acquiesced. As for the men, though some of them lowly rumbled, their fear of Ahab was greater than their fear of Fate. But as ever before, the pagan harpooneers remained almost wholly unimpressed; or if impressed, it was only with a certain magnetism shot into their congenial hearts from inflexible Ahab's.

For a space the old man walked the deck in rolling reveries. But chancing to slip with his ivory heel, he saw the crushed copper sight-tubes of the quadrant he had the day before dashed to the deck.

"Thou poor, proud heaven-gazer and sun's pilot! yesterday I wrecked thee, and to-day the compasses would fain have wrecked me. So, so. But Ahab is lord over the level loadstone yet. Mr. Starbuck—a lance without the pole; a top-maul, and the smallest of the sail-maker's needles. Quick!"

Accessory, perhaps, to the impulse dictating the thing he was now about to do, were certain prudential motives, whose object might have been to revive the spirits of his crew by a stroke of his subtile skill, in a matter so wondrous as that of the inverted compasses. Besides, the old man well knew that to steer by transpointed needles, though clumsily practicable, was not a thing to be passed over by superstitious sailors, without some shudderings and evil portents.

"Men," said he, steadily turning upon the crew, as the mate handed him the things he had demanded, "my men, the thunder turned old Ahab's needles; but out of this bit of steel Ahab can make one of his own, that will point as true as any."

Abashed glances of servile wonder were exchanged by the sailors, as this was said; and with fascinated eyes they awaited whatever magic might follow. But Starbuck looked away.

With a blow from the top-maul Ahab knocked off the steel head of the lance, and then handing to the mate the long iron rod remaining, bade him hold it upright, without its touching the deck. Then, with the maul, after repeatedly smiting the upper end of this iron rod, he placed the blunted needle endwise on the top of it, and less strongly hammered that, several times, the mate still holding the rod as before. Then going through some small strange motions with it—whether indispensable to the magnetizing of the steel, or merely intended to augment the awe of the crew, is uncertain—he called for linen thread; and moving to the binnacle, slipped out the two reversed needles there, and horizontally suspended the sail-needle by its middle, over one of the compass cards. At first, the steel went round and round, quivering and vibrating at either end; but at last it settled to its place, when Ahab, who had been intently watching for this result, stepped frankly back from the binnacle, and pointing his stretched arm towards it, exclaimed,—"Look ye, for yourselves, if Ahab be not lord of the level loadstone! The sun is East, and that compass swears it!"

One after another they peered in, for nothing but their own eyes could persuade such ignorance as theirs, and one after another they slunk away.

In his fiery eyes of scorn and triumph, you then saw Ahab in all his fatal pride.

CHAPTER CXXV

THE LOG AND LINE

WHILE now the fated Pequod had been so long afloat this voyage, the log and line had but very seldom been in use. Owing to a confident reliance upon other means of determining the vessel's place, some merchantmen, and many whalemen, especially when cruising, wholly neglect to heave the log; though at the same time, and frequently more for form's sake than anything else, regularly putting down upon the customary slate the course steered by the ship, as well as the presumed average rate of progression every hour. It had been thus with the Pequod. The wooden reel and angular log attached hung, long untouched, just beneath the railing of the after bulwarks. Rains and spray had damped it; sun and wind had warped it; all the elements had combined to rot a thing that hung so idly. But heedless of all this, his mood seized Ahab, as he happened to glance upon the reel, not many hours after the magnet scene, and he remembered how his quadrant was no more, and recalled his frantic oath about the level log and line. The ship was sailing plungingly; astern the billows rolled in riots.

"Forward, there! Heave the log!"

Two seamen came. The golden-hued Tahitian and the grizzly Manxman. "Take the reel, one of ye, I'll heave."

They went towards the extreme stern, on the ship's lee side, where the deck, with the oblique energy of the wind, was now almost dipping into the creamy, sidelong-rushing sea.

The Manxman took the reel, and holding it high up, by the projecting handle-ends of the spindle, round which the spool of line revolved, so stood with the angular log hanging downwards, till Ahab advanced to him.

Ahab stood before him, and was lightly unwinding some thirty or forty turns to form a preliminary hand-coil to toss overboard, when the old Manxman, who was intently eyeing both him and the line, made bold to speak.

"Sir, I mistrust it; this line looks far gone, long heat and wet have spoiled it."

" 'Twill hold, old gentleman. Long heat and wet, have they spoiled thee? Thou seem'st to hold. Or, truer perhaps, life holds thee; not thou it."

"I hold the spool, sir. But just as my captain says. With these grey hairs of mine 'tis not worth while disputing, 'specially with a superior, who'll ne'er confess."

"What's that? There now's a patched professor in Queen Nature's granite-founded College; but methinks he's too subservient. Where wert thou born?"

"In the little rocky Isle of Man, sir."

"Excellent! Thou'st hit the world by that."

"I know not, sir, but I was born there."

"In the Isle of Man, hey? Well, the other way, it's good. Here's a man from Man; a man born in once independent Man, and now unmanned of Man; which is sucked in—by what? Up with the reel! The dead, blind wall butts all inquiring heads at last. Up with it! So."

The log was heaved. The loose coils rapidly straightened out in a long dragging line astern, and then, instantly, the reel began to whirl. In turn, jerkingly raised and lowered by the rolling billows, the towing resistance of the log caused the old reelman to stagger strangely.

"Hold hard!"

Snap; the overstrained line sagged down in one long festoon; the tugging log was gone.

"I crush the quadrant, the thunder turns the needles, and now the mad sea parts the log-line. But Ahab can mend all. Haul in here, Tahitian; reel up, Manxman. And look ye, let the carpenter make another log, and mend thou the line. See to it."

"There he goes now; to him nothing's happened; but to me, the skewer seems loosening out of the middle of the world. Haul in, haul in, Tahitian! These lines run whole, and whirling out: come in broken, and dragging slow. Ha, Pip? come to help; eh, Pip?"

"Pip? whom call ye Pip? Pip jumped from the whale-boat. Pip's missing. Let's see now if ye haven't fished him up here, fisherman. It drags hard; I guess he's holding on. Jerk him, Tahiti! Jerk him off; we haul in no cowards here. Ho! there's his arm just breaking water. A hatchet! a hatchet! cut it off—we haul in no cowards here. Captain Ahab! sir, sir! here's Pip, trying to get on board again."

"Peace, thou crazy loon," cried the Manxman, seizing him by the arm. "Away from the quarterdeck!"

"The greater idiot ever scolds the lesser," muttered Ahab, advancing. "Hands off from that holiness! Where sayest thou Pip was, boy?"

"Astern there, sir, astern! Lo! lo!"

"And who art thou, boy? I see not my reflection in the vacant pupils of thy eyes. Oh God! that man should be a thing for immortal souls to sieve through! Who art thou, boy?"

"Bell-boy, sir; ship's-crier; ding, dong, ding! Pip! Pip! Pip! One hundred pounds of clay reward for Pip; five feet high—looks cowardly —quickest known by that! Ding, dong, ding! Who's seen Pip the coward?"

"There can be no hearts above the snow-line. Oh, ye frozen heavens! look down here. Ye did beget this luckless child, and have abandoned him, ye creative libertines. Here, boy; Ahab's cabin shall be Pip's home henceforth, while Ahab lives. Thou touchest my inmost centre, boy; thou art tied to me by cords woven of my heart-strings. Come, let's down."

"What's this? here's velvet shark-skin," intently gazing at Ahab's hand, and feeling it. "Ah, now, had poor Pip but felt so kind a thing as this, perhaps he had ne'er been lost! This seems to me, sir, as a man-rope; something that weak souls may hold by. Oh, sir, let old Perth now come and rivet these two hands together; the black one with the white, for I will not let this go."

"Oh, boy, nor will I thee, unless I should thereby drag thee to worse horrors than are here. Come, then, to my cabin. Lo! ye believers in gods all goodness, and in man all ill, lo you! see the omniscient gods oblivious of suffering man; and man, though idiotic, and knowing not what he does, yet full of the sweet things of love and gratitude. Come! I feel prouder leading thee by thy black hand, than though I grasped an Emperor's!"

"There go two daft ones now," muttered the old Manxman. "One daft with strength, the other daft with weakness. But here's the end of the rotten line—all dripping, too. Mend it, eh? I think we had best have a new line altogether. I'll see Mr. Stubb about it."

CHAPTER CXXVI

THE LIFE-BUOY

STEERING now south-eastward by Ahab's levelled steel, and her progress solely determined by Ahab's level log and line; the Pequod held on her path towards the Equator. Making so long a passage through such unfrequented waters, descrying no ships, and ere long, sideways impelled by unvarying trade winds, over waves monotonously mild; all these seemed the strange calm things preluding some riotous and desperate scene.

At last, when the ship drew near to the outskirts, as it were, of the Equatorial fishing-ground, and in the deep darkness that goes before the dawn, was sailing by a cluster of rocky islets; the watch—then headed by Flask—was startled by a cry so plaintively wild and unearthly—like half-articulated wailings of the ghosts of all Herod's murdered Innocents—that one and all, they started from their reveries, and for the space of some moments stood, or sat, or leaned all transfixedly listening, like the carved Roman slave, while that wild cry remained within hearing. The Christian or civilized part of the crew said it was mermaids, and shuddered; but the pagan harpooneers remained unappalled. Yet the grey Manxman—the oldest mariner of all—declared that the wild thrilling sounds that were heard, were the voices of newly drowned men in the sea.

Below in his hammock, Ahab did not hear of this till grey dawn, when he came to the deck; it was then recounted to him by Flask, not unaccompanied with hinted dark meanings. He hollowly laughed, and thus explained the wonder.

Those rocky islands the ship had passed were the resort of great numbers of seals, and some young seals that had lost their dams, or some dams that had lost their cubs, must have risen nigh the ship and kept company with her, crying and sobbing with their human sort of wail. But this only the more affected some of them, because most mariners cherish a very superstitious feeling about seals, arising not only from their peculiar tones when in distress, but also from the human look of their round heads and semi-intelligent faces, seen peeringly uprising from the water alongside. In the sea, under certain circumstances, seals have more than once been mistaken for men.

But the bodings of the crew were destined to receive a most plausible confirmation in the fate of one of their number that morning. At sun-rise this man went from his hammock to his mast-head at the fore; and whether it was that he was not yet half waked from his sleep (for sailors sometimes go aloft in a transition state), whether it was thus with the man, there is now no telling; but, be that as it may, he had not been long at his perch, when a cry was heard—a cry and a rushing—and looking up, they saw a falling phantom in the air; and looking down, a little tossed heap of while bubbles in the blue of the sea.

The life-buoy—a long slender cask—was dropped from the stern, where it always hung obedient to a cunning spring; but no hand rose to seize it, and the sun having long beat upon this cask it had shrunken, so that it slowly filled, and the parched wood also filled at its every pore; and the studded iron-bound cask followed the sailor to the bottom, as if to yield him his pillow, though in sooth but a hard one.

And thus the first man of the Pequod that mounted the mast to look out for the White Whale, on the White Whale's own peculiar ground; that man was swallowed up in the deep. But few, perhaps, thought of that at the time. Indeed, in some sort, they were not grieved at this event, at least as a portent; for they regarded it, not as a foreshadowing of evil in the future, but as the fulfilment of an evil already presaged. They declared that now they knew the reason of those wild shrieks they had heard the night before. But again the old Manxman said nay.

The lost life-buoy was now to be replaced; Starbuck was directed to see to it; but as no cask of sufficient lightness could be found, and as in the feverish eagerness of what seemed the approaching crisis of the voyage, all hands were impatient of any toil but what was directly connected with its final end, whatever that might prove to be; therefore, they were going to leave the ship's stern unprovided with a buoy, when by certain strange signs and inuendoes Queequeg hinted a hint concerning his coffin.

"A life-buoy of a coffin!" cried Starbuck, starting.

"Rather queer, that, I should say," said Stubb.

"It will make a good enough one," said Flask, "the carpenter here can arrange it easily."

"Bring it up; there's nothing else for it," said Starbuck, after a melancholy pause. "Rig it, carpenter; do not look at me so—the coffin, I mean. Dost thou hear me? Rig it."

"And shall I nail down the lid, sir?" moving his hand as with a hammer.

"Aye."

"And shall I caulk the seams, sir?" moving his hand as with a caulking-iron.

"Aye."

"And shall I then pay over the same with pitch, sir?" moving his hand as with a pitch-pot.

"Away! what possesses thee to this? Make a life-buoy of the coffin, and no more.—Mr. Stubb, Mr. Flask, come forward with me."

"He goes off in a huff. The whole he can endure; at the parts he baulks. Now I don't like this. I make a leg for Captain Ahab, and he wears it like a gentleman; but I make a bandbox for Queequeg, and he won't put his head into it. Are all my pains to go for nothing with that coffin? And now I'm ordered to make a life-buoy of it. It's like turning an old coat; going to bring the flesh on the other side now. I don't like this cobbling sort of business—I don't like it at all; it's undignified; it's not my place. Let tinkers' brats do tinkerings; we are their betters. I like to take in hand none but clean, virgin, fair-and-square mathematical jobs, something that regularly begins at the beginning, and is at the middle when midway, and comes to an end at the conclusion; not a cobbler's job, that's at an end in the middle, and at the beginning at the end. It's the old woman's tricks to be giving cobbling jobs. Lord! what an affection all old women have for tinkers. I know an old woman of sixty-five who ran away with a bald-headed young tinker once. And that's the reason I never would work for lonely widow old women ashore, when I kept my job-shop in the Vineyard; they might have taken it into their lonely old heads to run off with me. But heigh-ho! there are no caps

at sea but snow-caps. Let me see. Nail down the lid; caulk the seams; pay
over the same with pitch; batten them down tight, and hang it with the snap-
spring over the ship's stern. Were ever such things done before with a coffin?
Some superstitious old carpenters, now, would be tied up in the rigging, ere
they would do the job. But I'm made of knotty Aroostook hemlock; I don't
budge. Cruppered with a coffin! Sailing about with a grave-yard tray! But
never mind. We workers in woods make bridal-bedsteads and card-tables, as
well as coffins and hearses. We work by the month, or by the job, or by
the profit; not for us to ask the why and wherefore of our work, unless it
be too confounded cobbling, and then we stash it if we can. Hem! I'll
do the job, now, tenderly. I'll have me—let's see—how many in the ship's
company, all told? But I've forgotten. Anyway, I'll have me thirty separate,
Turk's-headed life-lines, each three feet long hanging all round to the coffin.
Then, if the hull go down, there'll be thirty lively fellows all fighting for one
coffin, a sight not seen very often beneath the sun! Come hammer, caulking-
iron, pitch-pot, and marling-spike! Let's to it."

CHAPTER CXXVII

THE DECK

*The coffin laid upon two line-tubs, between the vice-bench and the open
hatchway; the Carpenter caulking its seams; the string of twisted oakum slowly
unwinding from a large roll of it placed in the bosom of his frock.—Ahab comes
slowly from the cabin-gangway, and hears Pip following him.*

"Back, lad; I will be with ye again presently. He goes! Not this hand com-
plies with my humor more genially than that boy.—Middle aisle of a church!
What's here?"

"Life-buoy, sir. Mr. Starbuck's orders. Oh, look, sir! Beware the hatchway!"

"Thank ye, man. Thy coffin lies handy to the vault."

"Sir? The hatchway? oh! So it does, sir, so it does."

"Art not thou the leg-maker? Look, did not this stump come from thy
shop?"

"I believe it did, sir; does the ferrule stand, sir?"

"Well enough. But art thou not also the undertaker?"

"Aye, sir; I patched up this thing here as a coffin for Queequeg; but they've
set me now to turning it into something else."

"Then tell me; art thou not an arrant, all-grasping, intermeddling, monopolizing, heathenish old scamp, to be one day making legs, and the next day
coffins to clap them in, and yet again life-buoys out of those same coffins? Thou
art as unprincipled as the gods, and as much of a jack-of-all-trades."

"But I do not mean anything, sir. I do as I do."

"The gods again. Hark ye, dost thou not ever sing working about a
coffin? The Titans, they say, hummed snatches when chipping out the craters
for volcanoes; and the grave-digger in the play sings, spade in hand. Dost
thou never?"

"Sing, sir? Do I sing? Oh, I'm indifferent enough, sir, for that; but the reason why the grave-digger made music must have been because there was none in his spade, sir. But the caulking mallet is full of it. Hark to it."

"Aye, and that's because the lid there's a sounding-board; and what in all things makes the sounding-board is this—there's naught beneath. And yet, a coffin with a body in it rings pretty much the same, Carpenter. Hast thou ever helped carry a bier, and heard the coffin knock against the churchyard gate, going in?"

"Faith, sir, I've——"

"Faith? What's that?"

"Why, faith, sir, it's only a sort of exclamation-like—that's all, sir."

"Um, um; go on."

"I was about to say, sir, that——"

"Art thou a silk-worm? Dost thou spin thy own shroud out of thyself? Look at thy bosom! Despatch! and get these traps out of sight."

"He goes aft. That was sudden, now; but squalls come sudden in hot latitudes. I've heard that the Isle of Albemarle, one of the Gallipagos, is cut by the Equator right in the middle. Seems to me some sort of Equator cuts yon old man, too, right in his middle. He's always under the Line—fiery hot, I tell ye! He's looking this way—come, oakum; quick. Here we go again.' This wooden mallet is the cork, and I'm the professor of musical glasses—tap, tap!"

(Ahab to himself.)

"There's a sight! There's a sound! The greyheaded wood-pecker tapping the hollow tree! Blind and dumb might well be envied now. See! that thing rests on two line-tubs, full of tow-lines. A most malicious wag, that fellow. Rat-tat! So man's seconds tick! Oh! how immaterial are all materials! What things real are there, but imponderable thoughts? Here now's the very dreaded symbol of grim death, by a mere hap, made the expressive sign of the help and hope of most endangered life. A life-buoy of a coffin! Does it go farther? Can it be that in some spiritual sense the coffin is, after all, but an immortality-preserver! I'll think of that. But no. So far gone am I in the dark side of earth, that its other side, the theoretic bright one, seems but uncertain twilight to me. Will ye never have done, Carpenter, with that accursed sound? I go below; let me not see that thing here when I return again. Now, then, Pip, we'll talk this over; I do suck most wondrous philosophies from thee! Some unknown conduits from the unknown worlds must empty into thee!"

CHAPTER CXXVIII

THE PEQUOD MEETS THE RACHEL

NEXT day, a large ship, the Rachel, was descried, bearing directly down upon the Pequod, all her spars thickly clustering with men. At the time the Pequod was making good speed through the water; but as the broad-winged windward stranger shot nigh to her, the boastful sails all fell together as blank bladders that are burst, and all life fled from the smitten hull.

"Bad news; she brings bad news," muttered the old Manxman. But ere her commander, who, with trumpet to mouth, stood up in his boat; ere he could hopefully hail, Ahab's voice was heard.

"Hast seen the White Whale?"

"Aye, yesterday. Have ye seen a whaleboat adrift?"

Throttling his joy, Ahab negatively answered this unexpected question; and would then have fain boarded the stranger, when the stranger captain himself, having stopped his vessel's way, was seen descending her side. A few keen pulls, and his boat-hook soon clinched the Pequod's main-chains, and he sprang to the deck. Immediately he was recognised by Ahab for a Nantucketer he knew. But no formal salutation was exchanged.

"Where was he?—not killed!—not killed!" cried Ahab, closely advancing. "How was it?"

It seemed that somewhat late on the afternoon of the day previous, while three of the stranger's boats were engaged with a shoal of whales, which had led them some four or five miles from the ship; and while they were yet in swift chase to windward, the white hump and head of Moby-Dick had suddenly loomed up out of the water, not very far to leeward; whereupon, the fourth rigged boat—a reserved one—had been instantly lowered in chase. After a keen sail before the wind, this fourth boat—the swiftest keeled of all—seemed to have succeeded in fastening—at least, as well as the man at the mast-head could tell anything about it. In the distance he saw the diminished dotted boat; and then a swift gleam of bubbling white water; and after that nothing more; whence it was concluded that the stricken whale must have indefinitely run away with his pursuers, as often happens. There was some apprehension, but no positive alarm, as yet. The recall signals were placed in the rigging; darkness came on; and forced to pick up her three far to windward boats—ere going in quest of the fourth one in the precisely opposite direction—the ship had not only been necessitated to leave that boat to its fate till near midnight, but, for the time, to increase her distance from it. But the rest of her crew being at last safe aboard, she crowded all sail—stunsail on stunsail—after the missing boat; kindling a fire in her try-pots for a beacon; and every other man aloft on the look-out. But though when she had thus sailed a sufficient distance to gain the presumed place of the absent ones when last seen; though she then paused to lower her spare boats to pull all around her; and not finding anything, had again dashed on; again paused, and lowered her boats; and though she had thus continued doing till daylight; yet not the least glimpse of the missing keel had been seen.

The story told, the stranger Captain immediately went on to reveal his object in boarding the Pequod. He desired that ship to unite with his own in the search; by sailing over the sea some four or five miles apart, on parallel lines, and so sweeping a double horizon, as it were.

"I will wager something now," whispered Stubb to Flask, "that some one in that missing boat wore off that Captain's best coat; mayhap, his watch—he's so cursed anxious to get it back. Who ever heard of two pious whaleships cruising after one missing whale-boat in the height of the whaling season? See, Flask, only see how pale he looks—pale in the very buttons of his eyes—look—it wasn't the coat—it must have have been the—"

"My boy, my own boy is among them. For God's sake—I beg, I conjure"—here exclaimed the stranger Captain to Ahab, who thus far had but icily received his petition. "For eight-and-forty hours let me charter your ship—I will gladly pay for it, and roundly pay for it—if there be no other way—

for eight-and-forty hours only—only that—you must, oh, you must, and you *shall* do this thing."

"His son!" cried Stubb, "oh, it's his son he's lost! I take back the coat and watch—what says Ahab? We must save that boy."

"He's drowned with the rest on 'em, last night," said the old Manx sailor standing behind them; "I heard; all of ye heard their spirits."

Now, as it shortly turned out, what made this incident of the Rachel's the more melancholy, was the circumstance, that not only was one of the Captain's sons among the number of the missing boat's crew; but among the number of the other boats' crews, at the same time, but on the other hand, separated from the ship during the dark vicissitudes of the chase, there had been still another son; as that for a time, the wretched father was plunged to the bottom of the cruellest perplexity; which was only solved for him by his chief mate's instinctively adopting the ordinary procedure of a whale-ship in such emergencies, that is, when placed between jeopardized but divided boats, always to pick up the majority first. But the captain, for some unknown constitutional reason, had refrained from mentioning all this, and not till forced to it by Ahab's iciness did he allude to his one yet missing boy; a little lad, but twelve years old, whose father with the earnest but unmisgiving hardihood of a Nantucketer's paternal love, had thus early sought to initiate him in the perils and wonders of a vocation almost immemorially the destiny of all his race. Nor does it unfrequently occur, that Nantucket captains will send a son of such tender age away from them, for a protracted three or four years' voyage in some other ship than their own; so that their first knowledge of a whaleman's career shall be unenervated by any chance display of a father's natural but untimely partiality, or undue apprehensiveness and concern.

Meantime, now the stranger was still beseeching his poor boon of Ahab; and Ahab still stood like an anvil, receiving every shock, but without the least quivering of his own.

"I will not go," said the stranger, "till you say *aye* to me. Do to me as you would have me do to you in the like case. For *you* too have a boy, Captain Ahab—though but a child, and nestling safely at home now—a child of your old age too—Yes, yes, you relent; I see it—run, run, men, now, and stand by to square in the yards."

"Avast," cried Ahab—"touch not a rope-yarn;" then in a voice that prolongingly moulded every word—"Captain Gardiner, I will not do it. Even now I lose time. Good-bye, good-bye. God bless ye, man, and may I forgive myself, but I must go. Mr. Starbuck, look at the binnacle watch, and in three minutes from this present instant warn off all strangers; then brace forward again, and let the ship sail as before."

Hurriedly turning, with averted face, he descended into his cabin, leaving the strange captain transfixed at this unconditional and utter rejection of his so earnest suit. But starting from his enchantment, Gardiner silently hurried to the side; more fell than stepped into his boat, and returned to his ship.

Soon the two ships diverged their wakes; and long as the strange vessel was in view, she was seen to yaw hither and thither at every dark spot, however small, on the sea. This way and that her yards were swung around; starboard and larboard, she continued to tack; now she beat against a head sea; and again it pushed her before it; while all the while, her masts and yards were thickly clustered with men, as three tall cherry trees, when the boys are cherrying among the boughs.

But by her still halting course and winding, woful way, you plainly saw that this ship that so wept with spray, still remained without comfort. She was Rachel, weeping for her children, because they were not.

CHAPTER CXXIX

THE CABIN

(Ahab moving to go on deck; Pip catches him by the hand to follow.)

"Lad, lad, I tell thee thou must not follow Ahab now. The hour is coming when Ahab would not scare thee from him, yet would not have thee by him. There is that in thee, poor lad, which I feel too curing to my malady. Like cures like; and for this hunt, my malady becomes my most desired health. Do thou abide below here, where they shall serve thee, as if thou wert the captain. Aye, lad, thou shalt sit here in my own screwed chair; another screw to it, thou must be."

"No, no, no! ye have not a whole body, sir; do ye but use poor me for your one lost leg; only tread upon me, sir; I ask no more, so I remain a part of ye."

"Oh! spite of million villains, this makes me a bigot in the fadeless fidelity of man!—and a black! and crazy!—but methinks like-cures-like applies to him too; he grows so sane again."

"They tell me, sir, that Stubb did once desert poor little Pip, whose drowned bones now show white, for all the blackness of his living skin. But I will never desert ye, sir, as Stubb did him. Sir, I must go with ye."

"If thou speakest thus to me much more, Ahab's purpose keels up in him. I tell thee no; it cannot be."

"Oh good master, master, master!"

"Weep so, and I will murder thee! have a care, for Ahab too is mad. Listen, and thou wilt often hear my ivory foot upon the deck, and still know that I am there. And now I quit thee. Thy hand!—Met! True art thou, lad, as the circumference to its centre. So: God for ever bless thee; and if it come to that,—God for ever save thee, let what will befall."

(Ahab goes; Pip steps one step forward.)

"Here he this instant stood; I stand in his air,—but I'm alone. Now were even poor Pip here I could endure it, but he's missing. Pip! Pip! Ding, dong, ding! Who's seen Pip? He must be up here; let's try the door. What? neither lock, nor bolt, nor bar; and yet there's no opening it. It must be the spell; he told me to stay here: Aye, and told me this screwed chair was mine. Here, then, I'll seat me, against the transom, in the ship's full middle, all her keel and her three masts before me. Here, our old sailors say, in their black seventy-fours great admirals sometimes sit at table, and lord it over rows of captains and lieutenants. Ha! what's this? epaulets! epaulets! the epaulets all come crowding. Pass round the decanters; glad to see ye; fill up, monsieurs! What an odd feeling, now, when a black boy's host to white men with gold lace upon their coats!—Monsieurs, have ye seen one Pip?—a little negro lad, five feet high, hang-dog look, and cowardly! Jumped from a whale-boat once;—seen him? No! Well then, fill up again, captains, and let's drink shame upon all cowards! I name no names. Shame upon them! Put one foot upon the table. Shame upon all cowards.—Hist! above there, I hear ivory— Oh, master! master! I am indeed down-hearted when you walk over me. But here I'll stay, though this stern strikes rocks; and they bulge through; and oysters come to join me."

CHAPTER CXXX

THE HAT

AND now that at the proper time and place, after so long and wide a preliminary cruise, Ahab,—all other whaling waters swept—seemed to have chased his foe into an ocean-fold, to slay him the more securely there; now, that he found himself hard by the very latitude and longitude where his tormenting wound had been inflicted; now that a vessel had been spoken which on the very day preceding had actually encountered Moby-Dick;—and now that all his successive meetings with various ships contrastingly concurred to show the demoniac indifference with which the White Whale tore his hunters, whether sinning or sinned against; now it was that there lurked a something in the old man's eyes, which it was hardly sufferable for feeble souls to see. As the unsetting polar star, which through the livelong, arctic, six months' night sustains its piercing, steady, central gaze; so Ahab's purpose now fixedly gleamed down upon the constant midnight of the gloomy crew. It domineered above them so, that all their bodings, doubts, misgivings, fears, were fain to hide beneath their souls, and not sprout forth a single spear or leaf.

In this foreshadowing interval too, all humor, forced or natural, vanished. Stubb no more strove to raise a smile; Starbuck no more strove to check one. Alike, joy and sorrow, hope and fear, seemed ground to finest dust, and powdered, for the time, in the clamped mortar of Ahab's iron soul. Like machines, they dumbly moved about the deck, ever conscious that the old man's despot eye was on them.

But did you deeply scan him in his more secret confidential hours; when he thought no glance but one was on him; then you would have seen that even as Ahab's eyes so awed the crew's, the inscrutable Parsee's glance awed his; or somehow, at least, in some wild way, at times affected it. Such an added, gliding strangeness began to invest the thin Fedallah now; such ceaseless shudderings shook him; that the men looked dubious at him; half uncertain, as it seemed, whether indeed he were a mortal substance, or else a tremulous shadow cast upon the deck by some unseen being's body. And that shadow was always hovering there. For not by night, even, had Fedallah ever certainly been known to slumber, or go below. He would stand still for hours: but never sat or leaned; his wan but wondrous eyes did plainly say—We two watchmen never rest.

Nor, at any time, by night or day could the mariners now step upon the deck, unless Ahab was before them; either standing in his pivot-hole, or exactly pacing the planks between two undeviating limits,—the main-mast and the mizen; or else they saw him standing in the cabin-scuttle,—his living foot advanced upon the deck, as if to step; his hat slouched heavily over his eyes; so that however motionless he stood, however the days and nights were added on, that he had not swung in his hammock; yet hidden beneath that slouching hat, they could never tell unerringly whether, for all this, his eyes were really closed at times: or whether he was still intently scanning them; no matter, though he stood so in the scuttle for a whole hour on the stretch, and the unheeded night-damp gathered in beads of dew upon that stone-carved coat and hat. The clothes that the night had wet, the next day's sunshine dried upon him; and so, day after day, and night after night; he went no more beneath the planks; whatever he wanted from the cabin that thing he sent for.

He ate in the same open air; that is, his two only meals,—breakfast and dinner: supper he never touched; nor reaped his beard; which darkly grew all gnarled, as unearthed roots of trees blown over, which still grow idly on at naked base, though perished in the upper verdure. But though his whole life was now become one watch on deck; and though the Parsee's mystic watch was without intermission as his own; yet these two never seemed to speak— one man to the other—unless at long intervals some passing unmomentous matter made it necessary. Though such a potent spell seemed secretly to join the twain; openly, and to the awe-struck crew, they seemed pole-like asunder. If by day they chanced to speak one word; by night, dumb men were both, so far as concerned the slightest verbal interchange. At times, for longest hours, without a single hail, they stood far parted in the starlight; Ahab in his scuttle, the Parsee by the mainmast; but still fixedly gazing upon each other; as if in the Parsee Ahab saw his forethrown shadow, in Ahab the Parsee his abandoned substance.

And yet, somehow, did Ahab—in his own proper self, as daily, hourly, and every instant, commandingly revealed to his subordinates,—Ahab seemed an independent lord; the Parsee but his slave. Still again both seemed yoked together, and an unseen tyrant driving them; the lean shade siding the solid rib. For be this Parsee what he may, all rib and keel was solid Ahab.

At the first faintest glimmering of the dawn, his iron voice was heard from aft—"Man the mast-heads!"—and all through the day, till after sunset and after twilight, the same voice every hour, at the striking of the helmsman's bell, was heard—"What d'ye see?—sharp! sharp!"

But when three or four days had slided by, after meeting the children-seeking Rachel; and no spout had yet been seen; the monomaniac old man seemed distrustful of his crew's fidelity; at least, of nearly all except the Pagan harpooneers; he seemed to doubt, even, whether Stubb and Flask might not willingly overlook the sight he sought. But if these suspicions were really his, he sagaciously refrained from verbally expressing them, however his actions might seem to hint them.

"I will have the first sight of the whale myself,"—he said. "Aye! Ahab must have the doubloon!" and with his own hands he rigged a nest of basketed bowlines; and sending a hand aloft, with a single sheaved block, to secure to the mainmast head, he received the two ends of the downward-reeved rope; and attaching one to his basket prepared a pin for the other end, in order to fasten it at the rail. This done, with that end yet in his hand and standing beside the pin, he looked round upon his crew, sweeping from one to the other; pausing his glance long upon Daggoo, Queequeg, Tashtego; but shunning Fedallah; and then settling his firm relying eye upon the chief mate, said,—"Take the rope, sir—I give it into thy hands, Starbuck." Then arranging his person in the basket, he gave the word for them to hoist him to his perch, Starbuck being the one who secured the rope at last; and afterwards stood near it. And thus, with one hand clinging round the royal mast, Ahab gazed abroad upon the sea for miles and miles,—ahead, astern, this side, and that,—within the wide expanded circle commanded at so great a height.

When in working with his hands at some lofty almost isolated place in the rigging, which chances to afford no foothold, the sailor at sea is hoisted up to that spot, and sustained there by the rope; under these circumstances, its fastened end on deck is always given in strict charge to some one man who has the special watch of it. Because in such a wilderness of running rigging, whose various different relations aloft cannot always be infallibly discerned by what is seen of them at the deck; and when the deck-ends of these ropes are being every few minutes cast down from the fastenings, it would be but a natural fatality, if, unprovided with a constant watchman, the hoisted sailor should by some carelessness of the crew be cast adrift and fall all swooping to the sea. So Ahab's proceedings in this matter were not unusual; the only strange thing about them seemed to be, that Starbuck, almost the one only man who had ever ventured to oppose him with anything in the slightest degree approaching to decision—one of those too, whose faithfulness on the look-out he had seemed to doubt somewhat; it was strange, that this was the very man he should select for his watchman; freely giving his whole life into such an otherwise distrusted person's hands.

Now, the first time Ahab was perched aloft; ere he had been there ten minutes; one of those red-billed savage sea-hawks which so often fly incommodiously close round the manned mast-heads of whalemen in these latitudes; one of these birds came wheeling and screaming round his head in a maze of untrackably swift circlings. Then it darted a thousand feet straight up into the air; then spiralized downwards, and went eddying again round his head.

But with his gaze fixed upon the dim and distant horizon, Ahab seemed not to mark this wild bird; nor, indeed, would any one else have marked it much, it being no uncommon circumstance; only now almost the least heedful eye seemed to see some sort of cunning meaning in almost every sight.

"Your hat, your hat, sir!" suddenly cried the Sicilian seaman, who being posted at the mizenmast-head, stood directly behind Ahab, though somewhat lower than his level, and with a deep gulf of air dividing them.

But already the sable wing was before the old man's eyes; the long hooked bill at his head; with a scream, the black hawk darted away with his prize.

An eagle flew thrice round Tarquin's head, removing his cap to replace it, and thereupon Tanaquil, his wife, declared that Tarquin would be king of Rome. But only by the replacing of the cap was that omen accounted good. Ahab's hat was never restored; the wild hawk flew on and on with it; far in advance of the prow: and at last disappeared; while from the point of that disappearance, a minute black spot was dimly discerned, falling from that vast height into the sea.

CHAPTER CXXXI

THE PEQUOD MEETS THE DELIGHT

THE intense Pequod sailed on; the rolling waves and days went by; the life-buoy-coffin still lightly swung; and another ship, most miserably misnamed the Delight, was descried. As she drew nigh, all eyes were fixed upon her broad beams, called shears, which, in some whaling-ships, cross the quarter-deck at the height of eight or nine feet; serving to carry the spare, unrigged, or disabled boats.

Upon the stranger's shears were beheld the shattered, white ribs, and some few splintered planks, of what had once been a whale-boat; but you now saw through this wreck, as plainly as you see through the peeled, half-unhinged, and bleaching skeleton of a horse.

"Hast seen the White Whale?"

"Look!" replied the hollow-cheeked captain from his taffrail; and with his trumpet he pointed to the wreck.

"Hast killed him?"

"The harpoon is not yet forged that ever will do that," answered the other, sadly glancing upon a rounded hammock on the deck, whose gathered sides some noiseless sailors were busy in sewing together.

"Not forged!" and snatching Perth's levelled iron from the crotch, Ahab held it out, exclaiming—"Look ye, Nantucketer; here in this hand I hold his death! Tempered in blood, and tempered by lightning are these barbs; and I swear to temper them triply in that hot place behind the fin, where the White Whale most feels his accursed life!"

"Then God keep thee, old man—see'st thou that"—pointing to the hammock—"I bury but one of five stout men, who were alive only yesterday; but were dead ere night. Only *that* one I bury; the rest were buried before they died; you sail upon their tomb." Then turning to his crew—"Are ye ready there? place the plank then on the rail, and lift the body; so, then—Oh! God"—advancing towards the hammock with uplifted hands—"may the resurrection and the life——"

"Brace forward! Up helm!" cried Ahab like lightning to his men.

But the suddenly started Pequod was not quick enough to escape the sound of the splash that the corpse soon made as it struck the sea; not so quick, indeed, but that some of the flying bubbles might have sprinkled her hull with their ghostly baptism.

As Ahab now glided from the dejected Delight, the strange life-buoy hanging at the Pequod's stern came into conspicuous relief.

"Ha! yonder! look yonder, men!" cried a foreboding voice in her wake. "In vain, oh, ye strangers, ye fly our sad burial; ye but turn us your taffrail to show us your coffin!"

CHAPTER CXXXII

THE SYMPHONY

It was a clear steel-blue day. The firmaments of air and sea were hardly separable in that all-pervading azure; only, the pensive air was transparently pure and soft, with a woman's look, and the robust and man-like sea heaved with long, strong, lingering swells, as Samson's chest in his sleep.

Hither, and thither, on high, glided the snow-white wings of small, unspeckled birds; these were the gentle thoughts of the feminine air; but to and fro in the deeps, far down in the bottomless blue, rushed mighty leviathans, sword-fish, and sharks; and these were the strong, troubled, murderous thinkings of the masculine sea.

But though thus contrasting within, the contrast was only in shades and shadows without; those two seemed one; it was only the sex, as it were, that distinguished them.

Aloft, like a royal czar and king, the sun seemed giving this gentle air to this bold and rolling sea; even as bride to groom. And at the girdling line of the horizon, a soft and tremulous motion—most seen here at the Equator— denoted the fond, throbbing trust, the loving alarms, with which the poor bride gave her bosom away.

Tied up and twisted; gnarled and knotted with wrinkles; haggardly firm and unyielding; his eyes glowing like coals, that still glow in the ashes of ruin; untottering Ahab stood forth in the clearness of the morn; lifting his splintered helmet of a brow to the fair girl's forehead of heaven.

Oh, immortal infancy, and innocency of the azure! Invisible winged creatures that frolic all round us! Sweet childhood of air and sky! how oblivious were ye of old Ahab's close-coiled woe! But so have I seen little Miriam and Martha, laughing-eyed elves, heedlessly gambol around their old sire; sporting with the circle of singed locks which grew on the marge of that burnt-out crater of his brain.

Slowly crossing the deck from the scuttle, Ahab leaned over the side, and watched how his shadow in the water sank and sank to his gaze, the more and the more that he strove to pierce the profundity. But the lovely aromas in that enchanted air did at last seem to dispel, for a moment, the cankerous thing in his soul. That glad, happy air, that winsome sky, did at last stroke and caress him; the step-mother world, so long cruel—forbidding—now threw affectionate arms round his stubborn neck, and did seem to joyously sob over him, as if over one, that however wilful and erring, she could yet find it in her heart to save and to bless. From beneath his slouched hat Ahab dropped a tear into the sea; nor did all the Pacific contain such wealth as that one wee drop.

Starbuck saw the old man; saw him, how he heavily leaned over the side; and he seemed to hear in his own true heart the measureless sobbing that stole out of the centre of the serenity around. Careful not to touch him, or be noticed by him, he yet drew near to him, and stood there.

Ahab turned.

"Starbuck!"

"Sir."

"Oh, Starbuck! it is a mild, mild wind, and a mild looking sky. On such a day—very much such a sweetness as this—I struck my first whale—a boy-harpooneer of eighteen! Forty—forty—forty years ago!—ago! Forty years of continual whaling! forty years of privation, and peril, and storm-time! forty years on the pitiless sea! for forty years has Ahab forsaken the peaceful land, for forty years to make war on the horrors of the deep! Aye and yes, Starbuck, out of those forty years I have not spent three ashore. When I think of this life I have led; the desolation of solitude it has been; the masoned, walled-town of a Captain's exclusiveness, which admits but small entrance to any sympathy from the green country without—oh, weariness! heaviness! Guinea-coast slavery of solitary command!—when I think of all this; only half-suspected, not so keenly known to me before—and how for forty years I have fed upon dry salted fare—fit emblem of the dry nourishment of my soul!—when the poorest landsman has had fresh fruit to his daily hand, and broken the world's fresh bread to my mouldy crusts—away, whole oceans away, from that young girl-wife I wedded past fifty, and sailed for Cape Horn the next day, leaving but one dent in my marriage pillow—wife? wife?—rather a widow with her husband alive! Aye, I widowed that poor girl when I married her, Starbuck; and then, the madness, the frenzy, the boiling blood and the smoking brow, with which, for a thousand lowerings old Ahab has furiously, foamingly chased his prey—more a demon than a man!—aye, aye! what a forty years' fool—fool—old fool, has old Ahab been! Why this strife of the chase? why weary, and palsy the arm at the oar, and the iron, and the lance? how the richer or better is Ahab now? Behold. Oh, Starbuck! is it not hard, that with this weary load I bear, one poor leg should have been snatched from under me? Here, brush this old hair aside; it blinds me, that I seem to weep. Locks so grey did never grow but from out some ashes! But do I look very old, so very, very old, Starbuck? I feel deadly faint, bowed, and humped, as though I were Adam, staggering beneath the piled centuries since Paradise. God! God! God!—crack my heart!—stave my brain!—mockery! mockery! bitter, biting mockery of grey hairs, have I lived enough joy to wear ye; and seem and feel thus intolerably old? Close! stand close to me, Starbuck; let me look into a human eye; it is better than to gaze into sea or sky; better than to gaze upon God. By the green land; by the bright hearth-stone! this is the magic glass, man; I see my wife and my child in thine eye. No, no; stay on board, on board!—lower not when I do; when branded Ahab gives chase to Moby-Dick. That hazard shall not be thine. No, no! not with the far away home I see in that eye!"

"Oh, my Captain! my Captain! noble soul! grand old heart, after all! why should any one give chase to that hated fish! Away with me! let us fly these deadly waters! let us home! Wife and child, too, are Starbuck's—wife and child of his brotherly, sisterly, play-fellow youth; even as thine, sir, are the wife and child of thy loving, longing, paternal old age! Away! let us away!—this instant let me alter the course! How cheerily, how hilariously, O my Captain, would we bowl on our way to see old Nantucket again! I think, sir, they have some such mild blue days, even as this, in Nantucket."

"They have, they have. I have seen them—some summer days in the morning. About this time—yes, it is his noon nap now—the boy vivaciously wakes; sits up in bed; and his mother tells him of me, of cannibal old me; how I am abroad upon the deep, but will yet come back to dance him again."

" 'Tis my Mary, my Mary herself! She promised that my boy, every morning, should be carried to the hill to catch the first glimpse of his father's sail! Yes, yes! no more! it is done! we head for Nantucket! Come, my Captain, study out the course, and let us away! See, see! the boy's face from the window! the boy's hand on the hill!"

But Ahab's glance was averted; like a blighted fruit tree he shook, and cast his last, cindered apple to the soil.

"What is it, what nameless, inscrutable, unearthly thing is it; what cozening, hidden lord and master, and cruel, remorseless emperor commands me; that against all natural lovings and longings, I so keep pushing, and crowding, and jamming myself on all the time; recklessly making me ready to do what in my own proper, natural heart, I durst not so much as dare? Is Ahab, Ahab? Is it I, God, or who, that lifts this arm? But if the great sun move not of himself; but is as an errand-boy in heaven; nor one single star can revolve, but by some invisible power; how then can this one small heart beat; this one small brain think thoughts; unless God does that beating, does that thinking, does that living, and not I? By heaven, man, we are turned round and round in this world, like yonder windlass, and Fate is the handspike. And all the time, lo! that smiling sky, and this unsounded sea! Look! see yon Albi-

core! who put it into him to chase and fang that flying-fish? Where do murderers go, man! Who's to doom, when the judge himself is dragged to the bar?
But it is a mild, mild wind, and a mild looking sky; and the air smells now,
as if it blew from a far-away meadow; they have been making hay somewhere
under the slopes of the Andes, Starbuck, and the mowers are sleeping among
the new-mown hay. Sleeping? Aye, toil we how we may, we all sleep at last
on the field. Sleep? Aye, and rust amid greenness; as last year's scythes flung
down, and left in the half-cut swaths—Starbuck!"

But blanched to a corpse's hue with despair, the Mate had stolen away.

Ahab crossed the deck to gaze over on the other side; but started at two
reflected, fixed eyes in the water there. Fedallah was motionlessly leaning over
the same rail.

CHAPTER CXXXIII

THE CHASE—FIRST DAY

THAT night, in the mid-watch, when the old man—as his wont at intervals—
stepped forth from the scuttle in which he leaned, and went to his pivot-hole,
he suddenly thrust out his face fiercely, snuffing up the sea air as a sagacious
ship's dog will, in drawing nigh to some barbarous isle. He declared that a
whale must be near. Soon that peculiar odor, sometimes to a great distance
given forth by the living sperm whale, was palpable to all the watch; nor
was any mariner surprised when, after inspecting the compass, and then the
dog-vane, and then ascertaining the precise bearing of the odor as nearly as
possible, Ahab rapidly ordered the ship's course to be slightly altered, and the
sail to be shortened.

The acute policy dictating these movements was sufficiently vindicated at
daybreak, by the sight of a long sleek on the sea directly and lengthwise ahead,
smooth as oil, and resembling in the pleated watery wrinkles bordering it,
the polished metallic-like marks of some swift tide-rip, at the mouth of a
deep, rapid stream.

"Man the mast-heads! Call all hands!"

Thundering with the butts of three clubbed handspikes on the forecastle
deck, Daggoo roused the sleepers with such judgment claps that they seemed
to exhale from the scuttle, so instantaneously did they appear with their clothes
in their hands.

"What d'ye see?" cried Ahab, flattening his face to the sky.

"Nothing, nothing, sir!" was the sound hailing down in reply.

"T'gallant sails!—stunsails! alow and aloft, and on both sides!"

All sail being set, he now cast loose the life-line, reserved for swaying him
to the main royal-mast head! and in a few moments they were hoisting him
thither, when, while but two thirds of the way aloft, and while peering ahead
through the horizontal vacancy between the main-top-sail and top-gallant-sail,
he raised a gull-like cry in the air, "There she blows!—there she blows! A
hump like a snow-hill! It is Moby-Dick!"

Fired by the cry which seemed simultaneously taken up by the three look-
outs, the men on deck rushed to the rigging to behold the famous whale they
had so long been pursuing. Ahab had now gained his final perch, some feet

above the other look-outs, Tashtego standing just beneath him on the cap of the top-gallant-mast, so that the Indian's head was almost on a level with Ahab's heel. From this height the whale was now seen some mile or so ahead, at every roll of the sea revealing his high sparkling hump, and regularly jetting his silent spout into the air. To the credulous mariners it seemed the same silent spout they had so long ago beheld in the moonlit Atlantic and Indian Oceans.

"And did none of ye see it before?" cried Ahab, hailing the perched men all around him.

"I saw him almost that same instant, sir, that Captain Ahab did, and I cried out," said Tashtego.

"Not the same instant; not the same—no, the doubloon is mine, Fate reserved the doubloon for me. *I* only; none of ye could have raised the White Whale first. There she blows! there she blows! there she blows! There again! —there again!" he cried, in long-drawn, lingering, methodic tones, attuned to the gradual prolongings of the whale's visible jets. "He's going to sound! In stunsails! Down top-gallant-sails! Stand by three boats. Mr. Starbuck, remember, stay on board, and keep the ship. Helm there! Luff, luff a point! So; steady, man, steady! There go flukes! No, no; only black water! All ready the boats there? Stand by, stand by! Lower me, Mr. Starbuck; lower, lower,—quick, quicker!" and he slid through the air to the deck.

"He is heading straight to leeward, sir," cried Stubb, "right away from us; cannot have seen the ship yet."

"Be dumb, man! Stand by the braces! Hard down the helm!—brace up! Shiver her!—shiver her!—So; well that! Boats, boats!"

Soon all the boats but Starbuck's were dropped; all the boat-sails set— all the paddles plying; with rippling swiftness, shooting to leeward; and Ahab heading the onset. A pale, death-glimmer lit up Fedallah's sunken eyes; a hideous motion gnawed his mouth.

Like noiseless nautilus shells, their light prows sped through the sea; but only slowly they neared the foe. As they neared him, the ocean grew still more smooth; seemed drawing a carpet over its waves; seemed a noon-meadow, so serenely it spread. At length the breathless hunter came so nigh his seemingly unsuspecting prey, that his entire dazzling hump was distinctly visible, sliding along the sea as if an isolated thing, and continually set in a revolving ring of finest, fleecy, greenish foam. He saw the vast, involved wrinkles of the slightly projecting head beyond. Before it, far out on the soft Turkish-rugged waters, went the glistening white shadow from his broad, milky forehead, a musical rippling playfully accompanying the shade; and behind, the blue waters interchangeably flowed over into the moving valley of his steady wake; and on either hand bright bubbles arose and danced by his side. But these were broken again by the light toes of hundreds of gay fowls softly feathering the sea, alternate with their fitful flight; and like to some flag-staff rising from the painted hull of an argosy, the tall but shattered pole of a recent lance projected from the White Whale's back; and at intervals one of the cloud of soft-toed fowls hovering, and to and fro skimming like a canopy over the fish, silently perched and rocked on this pole, the long tail feathers streaming like pennons.

A gentle joyousness—a mighty mildness of repose in swiftness, invested the gliding whale. Not the white bull Jupiter swimming away with ravished Europa clinging to his graceful horns; his lovely, leering eyes sideways intent upon the maid; with smooth bewitching fleetness, rippling straight for the nuptial bower in Crete; not Jove, not that great majesty Supreme! did surpass the glorified White Whale as he so divinely swam.

On each soft side—coincident with the parted swell, that but once leaving him, then flowed so wide away—on each bright side, the whale shed off enticings. No wonder there had been some among the hunters who namelessly transported and allured by all this serenity, had ventured to assail it; but had fatally found that quietude but the vesture of tornadoes. Yet calm, enticing calm, oh, whale! thou glidest on, to all who for the first time eye thee, no matter how many in that same way thou may'st have bejuggled and destroyed before.

And thus, through the serene tranquillities of the tropical sea, among waves whose handclappings were suspended by exceeding rapture, Moby-Dick moved on, still withholding from sight the full terrors of his submerged trunk, entirely hiding the wrenched hideousness of his jaw. But soon the fore part of him slowly rose from the water; for an instant his whole marbleized body formed a high arch, like Virginia's Natural Bridge, and warningly waving his bannered flukes in the air, the grand god revealed himself, sounded, and went out of sight. Hoveringly halting, and dipping on the wing, the white sea-fowls longingly lingered over the agitated pool that he left.

With oars apeak, and paddles down, the sheets of their sails adrift, the three boats now stilly floated, awaiting Moby-Dick's reappearance. .

"An hour," said Ahab, standing rooted in his boat's stern; and he gazed beyond the whale's place, towards the dim blue spaces and wide wooing vacancies to leeward. It was only an instant; for again his eyes seemed whirling round in his head as he swept the watery circle. The breeze now freshened; the sea began to swell.

"The birds!—the birds!" cried Tashtego.

In long Indian file, as when herons take wing, the white birds were now all flying towards Ahab's boat; and when within a few yards began fluttering over the water there, wheeling round and round, with joyous, expectant cries. Their vision was keener than man's; Ahab could discover no sign in the sea. But suddenly as he peered down and down into its depths, he profoundly saw a white living spot no bigger than a white weasel, with wonderful celerity uprising, and magnifying as it rose, till it turned, and there were plainly revealed two long crooked rows of white, glistening teeth, floating up from the undiscoverable bottom. It was Moby-Dick's open mouth and scrolled jaw; his vast, shadowed bulk still half blending with the blue of the sea. The glittering mouth yawned beneath the boat like an open-doored marble tomb; and giving one sidelong sweep with his steering oar, Ahab whirled the craft aside from this tremendous apparition. Then, calling upon Fedallah to change places with him, went forward to the bows, and seizing Perth's harpoon, commanded his crew to grasp their oars and stand by to stern.

Now, by reason of this timely spinning round the boat upon its axis, its bow, by anticipation, was made to face the whale's head while yet under water. But as if perceiving this stratagem, Moby-Dick, with that malicious intelligence ascribed to him, sidelingly transplanted himself, as it were, in an instant, shooting his pleated head lengthwise beneath the boat.

Through and through; through every plank and each rib, it thrilled for an instant, the whale obliquely lying on his back, in the manner of a biting shark, slowly and feelingly taking its bows full within his mouth, so that the long, narrow, scrolled lower jaw curled high up into the open air, and one of the teeth caught in a row-lock. The bluish pearl-white of the inside of the jaw was within six inches of Ahab's head, and reached higher than that. In this attitude the White Whale now shook the slight cedar as a mildly cruel cat her mouse. With unastonished eyes Fedallah gazed, and crossed his arms; but the tiger-yellow crew were tumbling over each other's heads to gain the uttermost stern.

And now, while both elastic gunwales were springing in and out, as the whale dallied with the doomed craft in this devilish way; and from his body being submerged beneath the boat, he could not be darted at from the bows, for the bows were almost inside of him, as it were; and while the other boats involuntarily paused, as before a quick crisis impossible to withstand, then it was that monomaniac Ahab, furious with this tantalizing vicinity of his foe, which placed him all alive and helpless in the very jaws he hated; frenzied with all this, he seized the long bone with his naked hands, and wildly strove to wrench it from its gripe. As now he thus vainly strove, the jaw slipped from him; the frail gunwales bent in, collapsed, and snapped, as both jaws, like an enormous shears, sliding farther aft, bit the craft completely in twain, and locked themselves fast again in the sea, midway between the two floating wrecks. These floated aside, the broken ends drooping, the crew at the stern-wreck clinging to the gunwales, and striving to hold fast to the oars to lash them across.

At that preluding moment, ere the boat was yet snapped, Ahab, the first to perceive the whale's intent, by the crafty uprising of his head, a movement that loosed his hold for the time; at that moment his hand had made one final effort to push the boat out of the bite. But only slipping farther into the whale's mouth, and tilting over sideways as it slipped, the boat had shaken off his hold on the jaw; spilled him out of it, as he leaned to the push; and so he fell flat-faced upon the sea.

Ripplingly withdrawing from his prey, Moby-Dick now lay at a little distance, vertically thrusting his oblong white head up and down in the billows; and at the same time slowly revolving his whole spindled body; so that when his vast wrinkled forehead rose—some twenty or more feet out of the water— the now rising swells, with all their confluent waves, dazzlingly broke against it; vindictively tossing their shivered spray still higher into the air. So, in a gale, the but half baffled Channel billows only recoil from the base of the Eddystone, triumphantly to overleap its summit with their scud.

But soon resuming his horizontal attitude, Moby-Dick swam swiftly round and round the wrecked crew; sideways churning the water in his vengeful wake, as if lashing himself up to still another and more deadly assault. The sight of the splintered boat seemed to madden him, as the blood of grapes and mulberries cast before Antiochus's elephants in the book of Maccabees. Meanwhile Ahab half smothered in the foam of the whale's insolent tail, and too much of a cripple to swim,—though he could still keep afloat, even in the heart of such a whirlpool as that; helpless Ahab's head was seen, like a tossed bubble which the least chance shock might burst. From the boat's fragmentary stern, Fedallah incuriously and mildly eyed him; the clinging crew, at the other drifting end, could not succor him; more than enough was it for them to look to themselves. For so revolvingly appalling was the White Whale's aspect, and so planetarily swift the ever-contracting circles he made, that he seemed horizontally swooping upon them. And though the other boats, unharmed, still hovered hard by; still they dared not pull into the eddy to strike, lest that should be the signal for the instant destruction of the jeopardized castaways, Ahab and all; nor in that case could they themselves hope to escape. With straining eyes, then, they remained on the outer edge of the direful zone, whose centre had now become the old man's head.

Meantime, from the beginning all this had been descried from the ship's mast-heads; and squaring her yards, she had borne down upon the scene; and was now so nigh, that Ahab in the water hailed her;—"Sail on the"—but that moment a breaking sea dashed on him from Moby-Dick, and whelmed him for the time. But struggling out of it again, and chancing to rise on a tower-ing crest, he shouted,—"Sail on the whale!—Drive him off!"

The Pequod's prows were pointed; and breaking up the charmed circle, she effectually parted the White Whale from his victim. As he sullenly swam off, the boats flew to the rescue.

Dragged into Stubb's boat with blood-shot, blinded eyes, the white brine caking in his wrinkles; the long tension of Ahab's bodily strength did crack, and helplessly he yielded to his body's doom for a time, lying all crushed in the bottom of Stubb's boat, like one trodden under foot of herds of elephants. Far inland, nameless wails came from him, as desolate sounds from out ravines.

But this intensity of his physical prostration did but so much the more abbreviate it. In an instant's compass, great hearts sometimes condense to one deep pang, the sum total of those shallow pains kindly diffused through feebler men's whole lives. And so, such hearts, though summary in each one suffering; still, if the gods decree it, in their life-time aggregate a whole age of woe, wholly made up of instantaneous intensities; for even in their pointless centres, those noble natures contain the entire circumferences of inferior souls.

"The harpoon," said Ahab, half way rising, and draggingly leaning on one bended arm—"is it safe?"

"Aye, sir, for it was not darted; this is it," said Stubb, showing it.

"Lay it before me;—any missing men?"

"One, two, three, four, five;—there were five oars, sir, and here are five men."

"That's good.—Help me, man; I wish to stand. So, so, I see him! there! there! going to leeward still; what a leaping spout!—Hands off from me! The eternal sap runs up in Ahab's bones again! Set the sail; out oars; the helm!"

It is often the case that when a boat is stove, its crew, being picked up by another boat, help to work that second boat; and the chase is thus continued with what is called double-banked oars. It was thus now. But the added power of the boat did not equal the added power of the whale, for he seemed to have treble-banked his every fin; swimming with a velocity which plainly showed, that if now, under these circumstances, pushed on, the chase would prove an indefinitely prolonged, if not a hopeless one; nor could any crew endure for so long a period, such an unintermitted, intense straining at the oar; a thing barely tolerable only in some one brief vicissitude. The ship itself, then, as it sometimes happens, offered the most promising intermediate means of overtaking the chase. Accordingly, the boats now made for her, and were soon swayed up to their cranes—the two parts of the wrecked boats having been previously secured by her—and then hoisting everything to her side, and stacking her canvas high up, and sideways outstretching it with stun-sails, like the double-jointed wings of an albatross; the Pequod bore down in the leeward wake of Moby-Dick. At the well known, methodic intervals, the whale's glittering spout was regularly announced from the manned mast-heads; and when he would be reported as just gone down, Ahab would take the time, and then pacing the deck, binnacle-watch in hand, so soon as the last second of the allotted hour expired, his voice was heard.—"Whose is the doubloon now? D'ye see him?" and if the reply was No, sir! straightway he commanded them to lift him to his perch. In this way the day wore on; Ahab, now aloft and motionless; anon, unrestingly pacing the planks.

As he was thus walking, uttering no sound, except to hail the men aloft, or to bid them hoist a sail still higher, or to spread one to a still greater breadth —thus to and fro pacing, beneath his slouched hat, at every turn he passed his own wrecked boat, which had been dropped upon the quarter-deck, and lay there reversed; broken bow to shattered stern. At last he paused before it; and as in an already over-clouded sky fresh troops of clouds will sometimes sail across, so over the old man's face there now stole some such added gloom as this.

Stubb saw him pause; and perhaps intending, not vainly, though, to evince his own unabated fortitude, and thus keep up a valiant place in his Captain's mind, he advanced, and eyeing the wreck exclaimed—"The thistle the ass refused; it pricked his mouth too keenly, sir, ha! ha!"

"What soulless thing is this that laughs before a wreck? Man, man! did I not know thee brave as fearless fire (and as mechanical) I could swear thou wert a poltroon. Groan nor laugh should be heard before a wreck."

"Aye, sir," said Starbuck drawing near, " 'tis a solemn sight; an omen, and an ill one."

"Omen? omen?—the dictionary! If the gods think to speak outright to man, they will honorably speak outright; not shake their heads, and give an old wives' darkling hint.—Begone! Ye two are the opposite poles of one thing; Starbuck is Stubb reversed, and Stubb is Starbuck; and ye two are all mankind; and Ahab stands alone among the millions of the peopled earth, nor gods nor men his neighbors! Cold, cold—I shiver!—How now? Aloft there! D'ye see him? Sing out for every spout, though he spout ten times a second!"

The day was nearly done; only the hem of his golden robe was rustling. Soon it was almost dark, but the look-out men still remained unset.

"Can't see the spout now, sir;—too dark"—cried a voice from the air.

"How heading when last seen?"

"As before, sir,—straight to leeward."

"Good! he will travel slower now 'tis night. Down royals and top-gallant stun-sails, Mr. Starbuck. We must not run over him before morning; he's making a passage now, and may heave-to a while. Helm there! keep her full before the wind!—Aloft! come down!—Mr. Stubb, send a fresh hand to the fore-mast-head, and see it manned till morning."—Then advancing towards the doubloon in the main-mast—"Men, this gold is mine, for I earned it; but I shall let it abide here till the White Whale is dead; and then, whosoever of ye first raises him, upon the day he shall be killed, this gold is that man's; and if on that day I shall again raise him, then, ten times its sum shall be divided among all of ye! Away now! the deck is thine, sir."

And so saying, he placed himself half way within the scuttle, and slouching his hat, stood there till dawn, except when at intervals rousing himself to see how the night wore on.

CHAPTER CXXXIV

THE CHASE—SECOND DAY

At day-break, the three mast-heads were punctually manned afresh.

"D'ye see him?" cried Ahab, after allowing a little space for the light to spread.

"See nothing, sir."

"Turn up all hands and make sail! he travels faster than I thought for;—the top-gallant sails!—aye, they should have been kept on her all night. But no matter—'tis but resting for the rush."

Here be it said, that this pertinacious pursuit of one particular whale, continued through day into night, and through night into day, is a thing by no means unprecedented in the South sea fishery. For such is the wonderful skill, prescience of experience, and invincible confidence acquired by some great natural geniuses among the Nantucket commanders; that from the simple observation of a whale when last descried, they will, under certain given circumstances, pretty accurately foretell both the direction in which he will continue to swim for a time, while out of sight, as well as his probable rate of progression during that period. And, in these cases, somewhat as a pilot, when about losing sight of a coast, whose general trending he well knows, and which he desires shortly to return to again, but at some farther point; like as this pilot stands by his compass, and takes the precise bearing of the cape at present visible, in order the more certainly to hit aright the remote, unseen headland, eventually to be visited; so does the fisherman, at his compass, with the whale; for after being chased, and diligently marked, through several hours of daylight, then, when night obscures the fish, the creature's future wake through the darkness is almost as established to the sagacious mind of the hunter, as the pilot's coast is to him. So that to this hunter's wondrous skill, the proverbial evanescence of a thing writ in water, a wake, is to all desired purposes well nigh as reliable as the steadfast land. And as the mighty iron Leviathan of the modern railway is so familiarly known in its every pace, that, with watches in their hands, men time his rate as doctors that of a baby's pulse; and lightly say of it, the up train or the down train will reach such or such a spot, at such or such an hour; even so, almost, there are occasions when these Nantucketers time that other Leviathan of the deep, according to the observed humor of his speed; and say to themselves, so many hours hence this whale will have gone two hundred miles, will have about reached this or that degree of latitude or longitude. But to render this acuteness at all successful in the end, the wind and the sea must be the whaleman's allies; for of what present avail to the becalmed or windbound mariner is the skill that assures him he is exactly ninety-three leagues and a quarter from his port? Inferable from these statements, are many collateral subtile matters touching the chase of whales.

The ship tore on; leaving such a furrow in the sea as when a cannon-ball, missent, becomes a plough-share and turns up the level field.

"By salt and hemp!" cried Stubb, "but this swift motion of the deck creeps up one's legs and tingles at the heart. This ship and I are two brave fellows!—Ha! ha! Some one take me up, and launch me, spine-wise, on the sea,—for by live-oaks! my spine's a keel. Ha, ha! we go the gait that leaves no dust behind!"

"There she blows—she blows!—she blows!—right ahead!" was now the mast-head cry.

"Aye, aye!" cried Stubb, "I knew it—ye can't escape—blow on and split your spout, O whale! the mad fiend himself is after ye! blow your trump—blister your lungs!—Ahab will dam off your blood, as a miller shuts his watergate upon the stream!"

And Stubb did but speak out for well nigh all that crew. The frenzies of the chase had by this time worked them bubblingly up, like old wine worked anew. Whatever pale fears and forebodings some of them might have felt before; these were not only now kept out of sight through the growing awe of Ahab, but they were broken up, and on all sides routed, as timid prairie hares that scatter before the bounding bison. The hand of Fate had snatched all their souls; and by the stirring perils of the previous day; the rack of the past night's suspense; the fixed, unfearing, blind, reckless way in which their wild craft went plunging towards its flying mark; by all these things, their hearts were bowled along. The wind that made great bellies of their sails, and rushed the vessel on by arms invisible as irresistible; this seemed the symbol of that unseen agency which so enslaved them to the race.

They were one man, not thirty. For as the one ship that held them all; though it was put together of all contrasting things—oak, and maple, and pine wood; iron, and pitch, and hemp—yet all these ran into each other in the one concrete hull, which shot on its way, both balanced and directed by the long central keel; even so, all the individualities of the crew, this man's valor, that man's fear; guilt and guiltiness, all varieties were welded into oneness, and were all directed to that fatal goal which Ahab their one lord and keel did point to.

The rigging lived. The mast-heads, like the tops of tall palms, were outspreadingly tufted with arms and legs. Clinging to a spar with one hand, some reached forth the other with impatient wavings; others, shading their eyes from the vivid sunlight, sat far out on the rocking yards; all the spars in full bearing of mortals, ready and ripe for their fate. Ah! how they still strove through that infinite blueness to seek out the thing that might destroy them!

"Why sing ye not out for him, if ye see him?" cried Ahab, when, after the lapse of some minutes since the first cry, no more had been heard. "Sway me up, men; ye have been deceived; not Moby-Dick casts one odd jet that way, and then disappears."

It was even so; in their headlong eagerness, the men had mistaken some other thing for the whale-spout, as the event itself soon proved; for hardly had Ahab reached his perch; hardly was the rope belayed to its pin on deck, when he struck the key-note to an orchestra, that made the air vibrate as with the combined discharges of rifles. The triumphant halloo of thirty buckskin lungs was heard, as—much nearer to the ship than the place of the imaginary jet, less than a mile ahead—Moby-Dick bodily burst into view! For not by any calm and indolent spoutings; not by the peaceable gush of that mystic fountain in his head, did the White Whale now reveal his vicinity; but by the far more wondrous phenomenon of breaching. Rising with his utmost velocity from the farthest depths, the Sperm Whale thus booms his entire bulk into the pure element of air, and piling up a mountain of dazzling foam, shows his place to the distance of seven miles and more. In those moments, the torn, enraged waves he shakes off, seem his mane; in some cases, this breaching is his act of defiance.

"There she breaches! there she breaches!" was the cry, as in his immeasurable bravadoes the White Whale tossed himself salmon-like to Heaven. So suddenly seen in the blue plain of the sea, and relieved against the still bluer margin of the sky, the spray that he raised, for the moment, intolerably glittered and glared like a glacier; and stood there gradually fading and fading away from its first sparkling intensity, to the dim mistiness of an advancing shower in a vale.

"Aye, breach your last to the sun, Moby-Dick!" cried Ahab, "thy hour and thy harpoon are at hand!—Down! down all of ye, but one man at the fore. The boats!—stand by!"

Unmindful of the tedious rope-ladders of the shrouds, the men, like shooting stars, slid to the deck, by the isolated backstays and halyards; while Ahab, less dartingly, but still rapidly was dropped from his perch.

"Lower away," he cried, so soon as he had reached his boat—a spare one, rigged the afternoon previous. "Mr. Starbuck, the ship is thine—keep away from the boats, but keep near them. Lower, all!"

As if to strike a quick terror into them, by this time being the first assailant himself, Moby-Dick had turned, and was now coming for the three crews. Ahab's boat was central; and cheering his men, he told them he would take the whale head-and-head,—that is, pull straight up to his forehead,—a not uncommon thing; for when within a certain limit, such a course excludes the coming onset from the whale's sidelong vision. But ere that close limit was gained, and while yet all three boats were plain as the ship's three masts to his eye; the White Whale churning himself into furious speed, almost in an instant as it were, rushing among the boats with open jaws, and a lashing tail, offered appalling battle on every side; and heedless of the irons darted at him from every boat, seemed only intent on annihilating each separate plank of which those boats were made. But skilfully manœuvred, incessantly wheeling like trained chargers in the field; the boats for a while eluded him; though, at times, but by a plank's breadth; while all the time, Ahab's unearthly slogan tore every other cry but his to shreds.

But at last in his untraceable evolutions, the White Whale so crossed and recrossed, and in a thousand ways entangled the slack of the three lines now fast to him, that they foreshortened, and, of themselves, warped the devoted boats towards the planted irons in him; though now for a moment the whale drew aside a little, as if to rally for a more tremendous charge. Seizing that opportunity, Ahab first paid out more line: and then was rapidly hauling and jerking in upon it again—hoping that way to disencumber it of some snarls—when lo!—a sight more savage than the embattled teeth of sharks!

Caught and twisted—corkscrewed in the mazes of the line, loose harpoons and lances, with all their bristling barbs and points, came flashing and dripping up to the chocks in the bows of Ahab's boat. Only one thing could be done. Seizing the boat-knife, he critically reached within—through—and then, without—the rays of steel; dragged in the line beyond, passed it, inboard, to the bowsman, and then, twice sundering the rope near the chocks—dropped the intercepted fagot of steel into the sea; and was all fast again. That instant, the White Whale made a sudden rush among the remaining tangles of the other lines; by so doing, irresistibly dragged the more involved boats of Stubb and Flask towards his flukes; dashed them together like two rolling husks on a surf-beaten beach, and then, diving down into the sea, disappeared in a boiling maelstrom, in which, for a space, the odorous cedar chips of the wrecks danced round and round, like the grated nutmeg in a swiftly stirred bowl of punch.

While the two crews were yet circling in the waters, reaching out after the revolving line-tubs, oars, and other floating furniture, while aslope little Flask bobbed up and down like an empty vial, twitching his legs upwards to escape the dreaded jaws of sharks; and Stubb was lustily singing out for some one to ladle him up; and while the old man's line—now parting—admitted of his pulling into the creamy pool to rescue whom he could;—in that wild simultaneousness of a thousand concreted perils,—Ahab's yet unstricken boat seemed drawn up towards Heaven by invisible wires,—as, arrow-like, shooting perpendicularly from the sea, the White Whale dashed his broad forehead against its bottom, and sent it, turning over and over, into the air; till it fell again—gunwale downwards—and Ahab and his men struggled out from under it, like seals from a sea-side cave.

The first uprising momentum of the whale—modifying its direction as he struck the surface—involuntarily launched him along it, to a little distance from the centre of the destruction he had made; and with his back to it, he now lay for a moment slowly feeling with his flukes from side to side; and whenever a stray oar, bit of plank, the least chip or crumb of the boats touched his skin, his tail swiftly drew back, and came sideways smiting the sea. But soon, as if satisfied that his work for that time was done, he pushed his pleated forehead through the ocean, and trailing after him the intertangled lines, continued his leeward way at a traveller's methodic pace.

As before, the attentive ship having descried the whole fight, again came bearing down to the rescue, and dropping a boat, picked up the floating mariners, tubs, oars, and whatever else could be caught at, and safely landed them on her decks. Some sprained shoulders, wrists, and ankles; livid contusions; wrenched harpoons and lances; inextricable intricacies of rope; shattered oars and planks; all these were there; but no fatal or even serious ill seemed to have befallen any one. As with Fedallah the day before, so Ahab was now found grimly clinging to his boat's broken half, which afforded a comparatively easy float; nor did it so exhaust him as the previous day's mishap.

But when he was helped to the deck, all eyes were fastened upon him; as instead of standing by himself he still half-hung upon the shoulder of Starbuck, who had thus far been the foremost to assist him. His ivory leg had been snapped off, leaving but one short sharp splinter.

"Aye aye, Starbuck, 'tis sweet to lean sometimes, be the leaner who he will; and would old Ahab had leaned oftener than he has."

"The ferrule has not stood, sir," said the carpenter, now coming up; "I put good work into that leg."

"But no bones broken, sir, I hope," said Stubb with true concern.

"Aye! and all splintered to pieces, Stubb!—d'ye see it.—But even with a broken bone, old Ahab is untouched; and I account no living bone of mine one jot more me, than this dead one that's lost. Nor White Whale, nor man, nor fiend, can so much as graze old Ahab in his own proper and inaccessible being. Can any lead touch yonder floor, any mast scrape yonder roof?—Aloft there! which way?"

"Dead to leeward, sir."

"Up helm, then; pile on the sail again, ship keepers! down the rest of the spare boats and rig them—Mr. Starbuck away, and muster the boat's crews."

"Let me first help thee towards the bulwarks, sir."

"Oh, oh, oh! how this splinter gores me now! Accursed fate! that the unconquerable captain in the soul should have such a craven mate!"

"Sir?"

"My body, man, not thee. Give me something for a cane—there, that shivered lance will do. Muster the men. Surely I have not seen him yet. By heaven it cannot be!—missing?—quick! call them all."

The old man's hinted thought was true. Upon mustering the company, the Parsee was not there.

"The Parsee!" cried Stubb—"he must have been caught in——"

"The black vomit wrench thee!—run all of ye above, alow, cabin, forecastle—find him—not gone—not gone!"

But quickly they returned to him with the tidings that the Parsee was nowhere to be found.

"Aye, sir," said Stubb—"caught among the tangles of your line—I thought I saw him dragging under."

"*My* line! *my* line? Gone?—gone? What means that little word?—What death-knell rings in it, that old Ahab shakes as if he were the belfry. The harpoon, too!—toss over the litter there,—d'ye see it?—the forged iron, men, the White Whale's—no, no, no,—blistered fool! this hand did dart it!—'tis in the fish!—Aloft there! Keep him nailed—Quick!—all hands to the rigging of the boats—collect the oars—harpooneers! the irons, the irons!—hoist the royals higher—a pull on all the sheets!—helm there! steady, steady for your life! I'll ten times girdle the unmeasured globe; yea and dive straight through it, but I'll slay him yet!"

"Great God! but for one single instant show thyself," cried Starbuck; "never, never wilt thou capture him, old man—In Jesus' name no more of this, that's worse than devil's madness. Two days chased; twice stove to splinters; thy very leg once more snatched from under thee; thy evil shadow gone—all good angels mobbing thee with warnings:—what more wouldst thou have?—Shall we keep chasing this murderous fish till he swamps the last man? Shall we be dragged by him to the bottom of the sea? Shall we be towed by him to the infernal world? Oh, oh,—Impiety and blasphemy·to hunt him more!"

"Starbuck, of late I've felt strangely moved to thee; ever since that hour we both saw—thou know'st what, in one another's eyes. But in this matter of the whale, be the front of thy face to me as the palm of this hand—a lipless, unfeatured blank. Ahab is for ever Ahab, man. This whole act's immutably decreed. 'Twas rehearsed by thee and me a billion years before this ocean rolled. Fool! I am the Fates' lieutenant; I act under orders. Look thou, underling! that thou obeyest mine.—Stand round me, men. Ye see an old man cut down to the stump; leaning on a shivered lance; propped up on a lonely foot. 'Tis Ahab—his body's part; but Ahab's soul's a centipede, that moves upon a hundred legs. I feel strained, half-stranded, as ropes that tow dismasted frigates in a gale; and I may look so. But ere I break, ye'll hear me crack; and till ye hear *that*, know that Ahab's hawser tows his purpose yet. Believe ye, men, in the things called omens? Then laugh aloud, and cry encore! For ere they drown, drowning things will twice rise to the surface; then rise again, to sink for evermore. So with Moby-Dick—two days he's floated—to-morrow will be the third. Aye, men, he'll rise once more,—but only to spout his last! D'ye feel brave men, brave?"

"As fearless fire," cried Stubb.

"And as mechanical," muttered Ahab. Then as the men went forward, he muttered on: "The things called omens! And yesterday I talked the same to Starbuck there, concerning my broken boat. Oh! how valiantly I seek to drive out of others' hearts what's clinched so fast in mine!—The Parsee—the Parsee!—gone, gone? and he was to go before:—but still was to be seen again ere I could perish—How's that?—There's a riddle now might baffle all the lawyers backed by the ghosts of the whole line of judges:—like a hawk's beak it pecks my brain. *I'll, I'll* solve it, though!"

When dusk descended, the whale was still in sight to leeward.

So once more the sail was shortened, and everything passed nearly as on the previous night; only, the sound of hammers, and the hum of the grindstone was heard till nearly daylight, as the men toiled by lanterns in the complete and careful rigging of the spare boats and sharpening their fresh weapons for the morrow. Meantime, of the broken keel of Ahab's wrecked craft the carpenter made him another leg; while still as on the night before, slouched Ahab stood fixed within his scuttle; his hid, heliotrope glance anticipatingly gone backward on its dial; set due eastward for the earliest sun.

CHAPTER CXXXV

THE CHASE.—THIRD DAY

THE morning of the third day dawned fair and fresh, and once more the solitary night-man at the fore-mast-head was relieved by crowds of the daylight look-outs, who dotted every mast and almost every spar.

"D'ye see him?" cried Ahab; but the whale was not yet in sight.

"In his infallible wake, though; but follow that wake, that's all. Helm there; steady, as thou goest, and hast been going. What a lovely day again! were it a new-made world, and made for a summer-house to the angels, and this morning the first of its throwing open to them, a fairer day could not dawn upon that world. Here's food for thought, had Ahab time to think; but Ahab never thinks; he only feels, feels, feels; *that's* tingling enough for mortal man! to think's audacity. God only has that right and privilege. Thinking is, or ought to be, a coolness and a calmness; and our poor hearts throb, and our poor brains beat too much for that. And yet, I've sometimes thought my brain was very calm—frozen calm, this old skull cracks so, like a glass in which the contents turned to ice, and shiver it. And still this hair is growing now; this moment growing, and heat must breed it; but no, it's like that sort of common grass that will grow anywhere, between the earthy clefts of Greenland ice or in Vesuvius lava. How the wild winds blow it; they whip it about me as the torn shreds of split sails lash the tossed ship they cling to. A vile wind that has no doubt blown ere this through prison corridors and cells, and wards of hospitals, and ventilated them, and now comes blowing hither as innocent as fleeces. Out upon it!—it's tainted. Were I the wind, I'd blow no more on such a wicked, miserable world. I'd crawl somewhere to a cave, and slink there. And yet, 'tis a noble and heroic thing, the wind! who ever conquered it? In every fight it has the last and bitterest blow. Run tilting at it, and you but run through it. Ha! a coward wind that strikes stark naked men, but will not stand to receive a single blow. Even Ahab is a braver thing—a nobler thing than *that*. Would now the wind but had a body; but all the things that most exasperate and outrage mortal man, all these things are bodiless, but only bodiless as objects, not as agents. There's a most special, a most cunning, oh, a most malicious difference! And yet, I say again, and swear it now, that there's something all glorious and gracious in the wind. These warm Trade

Winds, at least, that in the clear heavens blow straight on, in strong and steadfast, vigorous mildness; and veer not from their mark, however the baser currents of the sea may turn and tack, and mightiest Mississippies of the land shift and swerve about, uncertain where to go at last. And by the eternal Poles! these same Trades that so directly blow my good ship on; these Trades, or something like them—something so unchangeable, and full as strong, blow my keeled soul along! To it! Aloft there! What d'ye see?"

"Nothing, sir."

"Nothing! and noon at hand! The doubloon goes a-begging! See the sun! Aye, aye, it must be so. I've oversailed him. How, got the start? Aye, he's chasing *me* now; not I, *him*—that's bad; I might have known it, too. Fool! the lines—the harpoons he's towing. Aye, aye, I have run him by last night. About! about! Come down, all of ye, but the regular lookouts! Man the braces!"

Steering as she had done, the wind had been somewhat on the Pequod's quarter, so that now being pointed in the reverse direction, the braced ship sailed hard upon the breeze as she rechurned the cream in her own white wake.

"Against the wind he now steers for the open jaw," murmured Starbuck to himself, as he coiled the new-hauled main-brace upon the rail. "God keep us, but already my bones feel damp within me, and from the inside wet my flesh. I misdoubt me that I disobey my God in obeying him!"

"Stand by to sway me up!" cried Ahab, advancing to the hempen basket. "We should meet him soon."

"Aye, aye, sir," and straightway Starbuck did Ahab's bidding, and once more Ahab swung on high.

A whole hour now passed; gold-beaten out to ages. Time itself now held long breaths with keen suspense. But at last, some three points off the weather bow, Ahab descried the spout again, and instantly from the three mast-heads three shrieks went up as if the tongues of fire had voiced it.

"Forehead to forehead I meet thee, this third time, Moby-Dick! On deck there!—brace sharper up; crowd her into the wind's eye. He's too far off to lower yet, Mr. Starbuck. The sails shake! Stand over that helmsman with a top-maul! So, so; he travels fast, and I must down. But let me have one more good round look aloft here at the sea; there's time for that. An old, old sight, and yet somehow so young; aye, and not changed a wink since I first saw it, a boy, from the sand-hills of Nantucket! The same!—the same!—the same to Noah as to me. There's a soft shower to leeward. Such lovely leewardings! They must lead somewhere—to something else than common land, more palmy than the palms. Leeward! the White Whale goes that way; look to windward, then; the better if the bitterer quarter. But good-bye, good-bye, old mast-head! What's this?—green? aye, tiny mosses in these warped cracks. No such green weather stains on Ahab's head! There's the difference now between man's old age and matter's. But aye, old mast, we both grow old together; sound in our hulls, though, are we not, my ship? Aye, minus a leg, that's all. By heaven this dead wood has the better of my live flesh every way. I can't compare with it; and I've known some ships made of dead trees outlast the lives of men made of the most vital stuff of vital fathers. What's that he said? he should still go before me, my pilot; and yet to be seen again? But where? Will I have eyes at the bottom of the sea, supposing I descend those endless stairs? and all night I've been sailing from him, wherever he did sink to. Aye, aye, like many more thou told'st direful truth as touching thyself, O Parsee; but, Ahab, there thy shot feel short. Good-bye, mast-head—keep a good eye upon the whale, the while I'm gone. We'll talk to-morrow, nay, to-night, when the White Whale lies down there, tied by head and tail."

He gave the word; and still gazing round him, was steadily lowered through the cloven blue air to the deck.

In due time the boats were lowered; but as standing in his shallop's stern, Ahab just hovered upon the point of the descent, he waved to the mate,—who held one of the tackle-ropes on deck—and bade him pause.

"Starbuck!"

"Sir?"

"For the third time my soul's ship starts upon this voyage, Starbuck."

"Aye, sir, thou wilt have it so."

"Some ships sail from their ports, and ever afterwards are missing, Starbuck!"

"Truth, sir: saddest truth."

"Some men die at ebb tide; some at low water; some at the full of the flood;—and I feel now like a billow that's all one crested comb, Starbuck. I am old;—shake hands with me, man."

Their hands met; their eyes fastened; Starbuck's tears the glue.

"Oh, my captain, my captain!—noble heart—go not—go not!—see, it's a brave man that weeps; how great the agony of the persuasion then!"

"Lower away!"—cried Ahab, tossing the mate's arm from him. "Stand by the crew!"

In an instant the boat was pulling round close under the stern.

"The sharks! the sharks!" cried a voice from the low cabin-window there; "O master, my master, come back!"

But Ahab heard nothing; for his own voice was high-lifted then; and the boat leaped on.

Yet the voice spake true; for scarce had he pushed from the ship, when numbers of sharks, seemingly rising from out the dark waters beneath the hull, maliciously snapped at the blades of the oars, every time they dipped in the water; and in this way accompanied the boat with their bites. It is a thing not uncommonly happening to the whale-boats in those swarming seas; the sharks at times apparently following them in the same prescient way that vultures hover over the banners of marching regiments in the east. But these were the first sharks that had been observed by the Pequod since the White Whale had been first descried; and whether it was that Ahab's crew were all such tiger-yellow barbarians, and therefore their flesh more musky to the senses of the sharks—a matter sometimes well known to affect them,—however it was, they seemed to follow that one boat without molesting the others.

"Heart of wrought steel!" murmured Starbuck gazing over the side, and following with his eyes the receding boat—"canst thou yet ring boldly to that sight?—lowering thy keel among ravening sharks, and followed by them, open-mouthed to the chase; and this the critical third day?—For when three days flow together in one continuous intense pursuit; be sure the first is the morning, the second the noon, and the third the evening and the end of that thing—be that end what it may. Oh! my God! what is this that shoots through me, and leaves me so deadly calm, yet expectant,—fixed at the top of a shudder! Future things swim before me, as in empty outlines and skeletons; all the past is somehow grown dim. Mary, girl! thou fadest in pale glories behind me; boy! I seem to see but thy eyes grown wondrous blue. Strangest problems of life seem clearing; but clouds sweep between—Is my journey's end coming?

My legs feel faint; like his who has footed it all day.   Feel thy heart,—beats it yet?   Stir thyself, Starbuck!—stave it off—move, move! speak aloud!— Mast-head there!   See ye my boy's hand on the hill?—Crazed;—aloft there! —keep thy keenest eye upon the boats:—mark well the whale!—Ho! again!— drive off that hawk! see! he pecks—he tears the vane"—pointing to the red flag flying at the main-truck—"Ha! he soars away with it!—Where's the old man now? see'st thou that sight, oh Ahab!—shudder, shudder!"

The boats had not gone very far, when by a signal from the mast-heads—a downward pointed arm, Ahab knew that the whale had sounded; but intending to be near him at the next rising, he held on his way a little sideways from the vessel; the becharmed crew maintaining the profoundest silence, as the head-beat waves hammered and hammered against the opposing bow.

"Drive, drive in your nails, oh ye waves! to their uttermost heads drive them in! ye but strike a thing without a lid; and no coffin and no hearse can be mine:—and hemp only can kill me!   Ha! ha!"

Suddenly the waters around them slowly swelled in broad circles; then quickly upheaved, as if sideways sliding from a submerged berg of ice, swiftly rising to the surface.   A low rumbling sound was heard; a subterranean hum; and then all held their breaths; as bedraggled with trailing ropes, and harpoons, and lances, a vast form shot lengthwise, but obliquely from the sea.   Shrouded in a thin drooping veil of mist, it hovered for a moment in the rainbowed air; and then fell swamping back into the deep.   Crushed thirty feet upwards, the waters flashed for an instant like heaps of fountains, then brokenly sank in a shower of flakes, leaving the circling surface creamed like new milk round the marble trunk of the whale.

"Give way!" cried Ahab to the oarsmen, and the boats darted forward to the attack; but maddened by yesterday's fresh irons that corroded in him, Moby-Dick seemed combinedly possessed by all the angels that fell from heaven. The wide tiers of welded tendons overspreading his broad white forehead, beneath the transparent skin, looked knitted together; as head on, he came churning his tail among the boats; and once more flailed them apart; spilling out the irons and lances from the two mates' boats, and dashing in one side of the upper part of their bows, but leaving Ahab's almost without a scar.

While Daggoo and Queequeg were stopping the strained planks; and as the whale swimming out from them, turned, and showed one entire flank as he shot by them again; at that moment a quick cry went up.   Lashed round and round to the fish's back; pinioned in the turns upon turns in which, during the past night, the whale had reeled the involutions of the lines around him, the half torn body of the Parsee was seen; his sable raiment frayed to shreds; his distended eyes turned full upon old Ahab.

The harpoon dropped from his hand.

"Befooled, befooled!"—drawing in a long lean breath—"Aye, Parsee!   I see thee again.—Aye, and thou goest before; and this, *this* then is the hearse that thou didst promise.   But I hold thee to the last letter of thy word.   Where is the second hearse?   Away, mates, to the ship! those boats are useless now; repair them if ye can in time, and return to me; if not, Ahab is enough to die—Down, men! the first thing that but offers to jump from this boat I stand in, that thing I harpoon.   Ye are not other men, but my arms and my legs; and so obey me.—Where's the whale? gone down again?"

But he looked too nigh the boat; for as if bent upon escaping with the corpse he bore, and as if the particular place of the last encounter had been but a stage in his leeward voyage, Moby-Dick was now again steadily swimming forward; and had almost passed the ship,—which thus far had 'been sailing in the contrary direction to him, though for the present her headway had been stopped. He seemed swimming with his utmost velocity, and now only intent upon pursuing his own straight path in the sea.

"Oh! Ahab," cried Starbuck, "not too late is it, even now, the third day, to desise. See! Moby-Dick seeks thee not. It is thou, thou, that madly seekest him!"

Setting sail to the rising wind, the lonely boat was swiftly impelled to leeward, by both oars and canvas. And at last when Ahab was sliding by the vessel, so near as plainly to distinguish Starbuck's face as he leaned over the rail, he hailed him to turn the vessel about, and follow him, not too swiftly, at a judicious interval. Glancing upwards he saw Tashtego, Queequeg, and Daggoo, eagerly mounting to the three mast-heads; while the oarsmen were rocking in the two staved boats which had just been hoisted to the side, and were busily at work in repairing them. One after the other, through the port-holes, as he sped, he also caught flying glimpses of Stubb and Flask, busying themselves on deck among bundles of new irons and lances. As he saw all this; as he heard the hammers in the broken boats; far other hammers seemed driving a nail into his heart. But he rallied. And now marking that the vane or flag was gone from the main-mast-head, he shouted to Tashtego, who had just gained that perch, to descend again for another flag, and a hammer and nails, and so nail it to the mast.

Whether fagged by the three days' running chase, and the resistance to his swimming in the knotted hamper he bore; or whether it was some latent deceitfulness and malice in him: whichever was true, the White Whale's way now began to abate, as it seemed, from the boat so rapidly nearing him once more; though indeed the whale's last start had not been so long a one as before. And still as Ahab glided over the waves the unpitying sharks accompanied him; and so pertinaciously stuck to the boat; and so continually bit at the plying oars, that the blades became jagged and crunched, and left small splinters in the sea, at almost every dip.

"Heed them not! those teeth but give new rowlocks to your oars. Pull on! 'tis the better rest, the shark's jaw than the yielding water."

"But at every bite, sir, the thin blades grow smaller and smaller!"

"They will last long enough! pull on!—But who can tell"—he muttered— "whether these sharks swim to feast on the whale or on Ahab?—But pull on! Aye, all alive, now—we near him. The helm! take the helm! let me pass,"—and so saying, two of the oarsmen helped him forward to the bows of the still flying boat.

At length as the craft was cast to one side, and ran ranging along with the White Whale's flank, he seemed strangely oblivious of its advance—as the whale sometimes will—and Ahab was fairly within the smoky mountain mist, which, thrown off from the whale's spout, curled round his great Monadnock hump; he was even thus close to him; when, with body arched back, and both arms lengthwise high-lifted to the poise, he darted his fierce iron, and his far fiercer curse into the hated whale. As both steel and curse sank to the socket, as if sucked into a morass, Moby-Dick sideways writhed; spasmodically rolled his nigh flank against the bow, and, without staving a hole in it, so suddenly canted the boat over, that had it not been for the elevated part of the gunwale to which he then clung, Ahab would once more have been tossed into the sea. As it was, three of the oarsmen—who foreknew not the precise instant of the dart, and were therefore unprepared for its effects—these were flung out; but so fell, that, in an instant two of them clutched the gunwale again, and rising to its level on a combing wave, hurled themselves bodily inboard again; the third man helplessly dropping astern, but still afloat and swimming.

Almost simultaneously, with a mighty volition of ungraduated, instantaneous swiftness, the White Whale darted through the weltering sea. But when Ahab cried out to the steersman to take new turns with the line, and hold it so; and commanded the crew to turn round on their seats, and tow the boat up to the mark; the moment the treacherous line felt that double strain and tug, it snapped in the empty air!

"What breaks in me? Some sinew cracks!—'tis whole again; oars! oars! Burst in upon him!"

Hearing the tremendous rush of the sea-crashing boat, the whale wheeled round to present his blank forehead at bay; but in that evolution, catching sight of the nearing black hull of the ship; seemingly seeing in it the source of all his persecutions; bethinking it—it may be—a larger and nobler foe; of a sudden, he bore down upon its advancing prow, smiting his jaws amid fiery showers of foam.

Ahab staggered; his hand smote his forehead. "I grow blind; hands! stretch out before me that I may yet grope my way. It's night?"

"The whale! The ship!" cried the cringing oarsmen.

"Oars! oars! Slope downwards to thy depths, O sea, that ere it be for ever too late, Ahab may slide this last, last time upon his mark! I see: the ship! the ship! Dash on, my men! will ye not save my ship?"

But as the oarsmen violently forced their boat through the sledge-hammering seas, the before whale-smitten bow-ends of two planks burst through, and in an instant almost, the temporarily disabled boat lay nearly level with the waves; its half-wading, splashing crew, trying hard to stop the gap and bale out the pouring water.

Meantime, for that one beholding instant, Tashtego's mast-head hammer remained suspended in his hand; and the red flag, half-wrapping him as with a plaid, then streamed itself straight out from him, as his own forward-flowing heart; while Starbuck and Stubb, standing upon the bowsprit beneath, caught sight of the down-coming monster just as soon as he.

"The whale, the whale! Up helm, up helm! Oh, all ye sweet powers of air, now hug me close! Let not Starbuck die, if die he must, in a woman's fainting fit. Up helm, I say—ye fools, the jaw! the jaw! Is this the end of all my bursting prayers? all my life-long fidelities? Oh, Ahab, Ahab, lo, thy work. Steady! helmsman, steady. Nay, nay! Up helm again! He turns to meet us! Oh, his unappeasable brow drives on towards one, whose duty tells him he cannot depart. My God, stand by me now!"

"Stand not by me, but stand under me, whoever you are that will now help Stubb; for Stubb, too, sticks here. I grin at thee, thou grinning whale! Who ever helped Stubb, or kept Stubb awake, but Stubb's own unwinking eye? And now poor Stubb goes to bed upon a mattress that is all too soft; would it were stuffed with brushwood! I grin at thee, thou grinning whale! Look ye, sun, moon, and stars! I call ye assassins of as good a fellow as ever spouted up his ghost. For all that, I would yet ring glasses with thee, would ye but hand the cup! Oh, oh! oh, oh! thou grinning whale, but there'll be plenty of gulping soon! Why fly ye not, O Ahab! For me, off shoes and jacket to it; let Stubb die in his drawers! A most mouldy and over salted death, though;—cherries! cherries! cherries! Oh, Flask, for one red cherry ere we die!"

"Cherries? I only wish that we were where they grow. Oh, Stubb, I hope my poor mother's drawn my part-pay ere this; if not, few coppers will now come to her, for the voyage is up."

From the ship's bows, nearly all the seamen now hung inactive; hammers, bits of plank, lances, and harpoons, mechanically retained in their hands, just as they had darted from their various employments; all their enchanted eyes intent upon the whale, which from side to side strangely vibrating his pre-destinating head, sent a broad band of overspreading semicircular foam before him as he rushed. Retribution, swift vengeance, eternal malice were in his whole aspect, and spite of all that mortal man could do, the solid white buttress of his forehead smote the ship's starboard bow, till men and timbers reeled. Some fell flat upon their faces. Like dislodged trucks, the heads of the harpooneers aloft shook on their bull-like necks. Through the breach, they heard the waters pour, as mountain torrents down a flume.

"The ship! The hearse!—the second hearse!" cried Ahab from the boat; "its wood could only be American!"

Diving beneath the settling ship, the whale ran quivering along its keel; but turning under water, swiftly shot to the surface again, far off the other bow, but within a few yards of Ahab's boat, where, for a time, he lay quiescent.

"I turn my body from the sun. What ho, Tashtego! let me hear thy hammer. Oh! ye three unsurrendered spires of mine; thou uncracked keel; and only god-bullied hull; thou firm deck, and haughty helm, and Pole-pointed prow,—death-glorious ship! must ye then perish, and without me? Am I cut off from the last fond pride of meanest shipwrecked captains? Oh, lonely death on lonely life! Oh, now I feel my topmost greatness lies in my topmost grief. Ho ho! from all your farthest bonds, pour ye now in, ye bold billows of my whole foregone life, and top this one piled comber of my death! Towards thee I roll, thou all-destroying but unconquering whale; to the last I grapple with thee; from hell's heart I stab at thee; for hate's sake I spit my last breath at thee. Sink all coffins and all hearses to one common pool! and since neither can be mine, let me then tow to pieces, while still chasing thee, though tied to thee, thou damned whale! *Thus,* I give up the spear!"

The harpoon was darted; the stricken whale flew forward; with igniting velocity the line ran through the groove;—ran foul. Ahab stooped to clear it; he did clear it; but the flying turn caught him round the neck, and voicelessly as Turkish mutes bowstring their victim, he was shot out of the boat, ere the crew knew he was gone. Next instant, the heavy eye-splice in the rope's final end flew out of the stark-empty tub, knocked down an oarsman, and smiting the sea, disappeared in its depths.

For an instant, the tranced boat's crew stood still; then turned. "The ship? Great God, where is the ship?" Soon they through dim, bewildering mediums saw her sidelong fading phantom, as in the gaseous Fata Morgana; only the uppermost masts out of water; while fixed by infatuation, or fidelity, or fate, to their once lofty perches, the pagan harpooneers still maintained their sinking lookouts on the sea. And now, concentric circles seized the lone boat itself, and all its crew, and each floating oar, and every lance-pole, and spinning, animate and inanimate, all round and round in one vortex, carried the smallest chip of the Pequod out of sight.

But as the last whelmings intermixingly poured themselves over the sunken head of the Indian at the mainmast, leaving a few inches of the erect spar yet visible, together with long streaming yards of the flag, which calmly un-dulated, with ironical coincidings, over the destroying billows they almost touched;—at that instant, a red arm and a hammer hovered backwardly up-lifted in the open air, in the act of nailing the flag faster and yet faster to the subsiding spar. A sky-hawk that tauntingly had followed the main-truck down-wards from its natural home among the stars, pecking at the flag, and incom-moding Tashtego there; this bird now chanced to intercept its broad fluttering wing between the hammer and the wood; and simultaneously feeling that etherial thrill, the submerged savage beneath, in his death-gasp, kept his hammer frozen there; and so the bird of heaven, with archangelic shrieks, and his imperial beak thrust upwards, and his whole captive form folded in the flag of Ahab, went down with his ship, which, like Satan, would not sink to hell till she had dragged a living part of heaven along with her, and helmeted herself with it.

Now small fowls flew screaming over the yet yawning gulf; a sullen white surf beat against its steep sides; then all collapsed, and the great shroud of the sea rolled on as it rolled five thousand years ago.

EPILOGUE

"AND I ONLY AM ESCAPED ALONE TO TELL THEE"

JOB.

The drama's done. Why then here does any one step forth?—Because one did survive the wreck.

It so chanced, that after the Parsee's disappearance, I was he whom the Fates ordained to take the place of Ahab's bowsman, when that bowsman as-sumed the vacant post; the same, who, when on the last day the three men were tossed from out of the rocking boat, was dropped astern. So, floating on the margin of the ensuing scene, and in full sight of it, when the half-spent suction of the sunk ship reached me, I was then, but slowly, drawn towards the closing vortex. When I reached it, it had subsided to a creamy pool. Round and round, then, and ever contracting towards the button-like black bubble at the axis of that slowly wheeling circle, like another Ixion I did revolve. Till, gain-ing that vital centre; the black bubble upward burst; and now, liberated by reason of its cunning spring, and, owing to its great buoyancy, rising with great force, the coffin life-buoy shot lengthwise from the sea, fell over, and floated by my side. Buoyed up by that coffin, for almost one whole day and night, I floated on a soft and dirge-like main. The unharming sharks, they glided by as if with padlocks on their mouths; the savage sea-hawks sailed with sheathed beaks. On the second day, a sail drew near, nearer, and picked me up at last. It was the devious-cruising Rachel, that in her retracing search after her missing children, only found another orphan.

BOOK
TWO

OMOO: *A Narrative of Adventures in the South Seas*

AUTHOR'S PREFACE

NOWHERE, perhaps, are the proverbial characteristics of sailors shown under wilder aspects, than in the South Seas. For the most part, the vessels navigating those remote waters, are engaged in the Sperm Whale Fishery; a business, which is not only peculiarly fitted to attract the most reckless seamen of all nations, but in various ways, is calculated to foster in them a spirit of the utmost license. These voyages, also, are unusually long and perilous; the only harbours accessible are among the barbarous or semi-civilized islands of Polynesia, or along the lawless western coast of South America. Hence, scenes the most novel, and not directly connected with the business of whaling, frequently occur among the crews of ships in the Pacific.

Without pretending to give any account of the whale-fishery (for the scope of the narrative does not embrace the subject), it is, partly, the object of this work to convey some idea of the kind of life to which allusion is made, by means of a circumstantial history of adventures befalling the author.

Another object proposed, is to give a *familiar* account of the present condition of the converted Polynesians, as affected by their promiscuous intercourse with foreigners, and the teachings of the missionaries combined.

As a roving sailor, the author spent about three months in various parts of the islands of Tahiti and Imeeo, and under circumstances most favourable for correct observations on the social condition of the natives.

In every statement connected with missionary operations, a strict adherence to facts has, of course, been scrupulously observed; and in some instances, it has even been deemed advisable to quote previous voyagers, in corroboration of what is offered as the fruit of the author's own observations. Nothing but an earnest desire for truth and good has led him to touch upon this subject at all. And if he refrains from offering hints as to the best mode of remedying the evils which are pointed out, it is only because he thinks, that after being made acquainted with the facts, others are better qualified to do so.

Should a little jocoseness be shown upon some curious traits of the Tahitians, it proceeds from no intention to ridicule: things are merely described as, from their entire novelty, they first struck an unbiased observer.

The present narrative necessarily begins where *Typee* concludes, but has no further connexion with the latter work. All, therefore, necessary for the reader to understand, who has not read *Typee,* is given in a brief introduction.

No journal was kept by the author during his wanderings in the South Seas; so that, in preparing the ensuing chapters for the press, precision with respect to dates would have been impossible; and every occurrence has been put down from simple recollection. The frequency, however, with which these incidents have been verbally related, has tended to stamp them upon the memory.

Although it is believed that one or two imperfect Polynesian vocabularies have been published, none of the Tahitian dialect has yet appeared. At any rate, the author has had access to none whatever. In the use of the native words, therefore, he has been mostly governed by the bare recollection of sounds.

363

Upon several points connected with the history and ancient customs of Tahiti, collateral information has been obtained from the oldest books of South Sea voyages, and also from the *Polynesian Researches* of Ellis.

The title of the work—Omoo—is borrowed from the dialect of the Marquesas Islands, where, among other uses, the word signifies a rover, or rather, a person wandering from one island to another, like some of the natives, known among their countrymen as "Taboo kannakas."

In no respect does the author make pretensions to philosophic research. In a familiar way, he has merely described what he has seen; and if reflections are occasionally indulged in, they are spontaneous, and such as would, very probably, suggest themselves to the most casual observer.

CONTENTS

366

OMOO

INTRODUCTION

IN the summer of 1842, the author of this narrative, as a sailor before the mast, visited the Marquesas Islands in an American South Seaman. At the island of Nukuheva he left his vessel, which afterward sailed without him. Wandering in the interior, he came upon the valley of Typee, inhabited by a primitive tribe of savages, from which valley a fellow-sailor who accompanied him soon afterward effected his escape. The author, however, was detained in an indulgent captivity for about the space of four months; at the end of which period, he escaped in a boat which visited the bay.

This boat belonged to a vessel in need of men, which had recently touched at a neighbouring harbour of the same island, where the captain had been informed of the author's detention in Typee. Desirous of adding to his crew, he sailed round thither, and "hove to" off the mouth of the bay. As the Typees were considered hostile, the boat, manned by "Taboo" natives from the other harbour, was then sent in, with an interpreter at their head, to procure the author's release. This was finally accomplished, though not without peril to all concerned. At the time of his escape, the author was suffering severely from lameness.

The boat having gained the open sea, the ship appeared in the distance. Here the present narrative opens.

CHAPTER I

MY RECEPTION ABOARD

IT was in the middle of a bright tropical afternoon that we made good our escape from the bay. The vessel we sought lay with her main-topsail aback about a league from the land, and was the only object that broke the broad expanse of the ocean.

On approaching, she turned out to be a small, slatternly-looking craft, her hull and spars a dingy black, rigging all slack and bleached nearly white, and everything denoting an ill state of affairs aboard. The four boats hanging from her sides proclaimed her a whaler. Leaning carelessly over the bulwarks were the sailors, wild, haggard-looking fellows in Scotch caps and faded blue frocks; some of them with cheeks of a mottled bronze, to which sickness soon changes the rich berry-brown of a seaman's complexion in the tropics.

On the quarter-deck was one whom I took for the chief mate. He wore a broad-brimmed Panama hat, and his spy-glass was levelled as we advanced.

When we came alongside, a low cry ran fore and aft the deck, and everybody gazed at us with inquiring eyes. And well they might. To say nothing of the savage boat's crew, panting with excitement, all gesture and vociferation, my own appearance was calculated to excite curiosity. A robe of the native cloth was thrown over my shoulders, my hair and beard were uncut, and I betrayed other evidences of my recent adventure. Immediately on gaining the deck, they beset me on all sides with questions, the half of which I could not answer, so incessantly were they put.

As an instance of the curious coincidences which often befall the sailor, I must here mention, that two countenances before me were familiar. One was that of an old man-of-war's-man, whose acquaintance I had made in Rio de Janiero, at which place touched the ship in which I sailed from home. The other was a young man, whom, four years previous, I had frequently met in a sailor boarding-house in Liverpool. I remembered parting with him at Prince's Dock Gates, in the midst of a swarm of police-officers, truckmen, stevedores, beggars, and the like. And here we were again:—years had rolled by, many a league of ocean had been traversed, and we were thrown together under circumstances which almost made me doubt my own existence.

But a few moments passed ere I was sent for into the cabin by the captain.

He was quite a young man, pale and slender, more like a sickly counting-house clerk than a bluff sea-captain. Bidding me be seated, he ordered the steward to hand me a glass of Pisco. In the state I was, this stimulus almost made me delirious; so that of all I then went on to relate concerning my residence on the island I can scarcely remember a word. After this I was asked whether I desired to "ship"; of course I said yes; that is, if he would allow me to enter for one cruise, engaging to discharge me, if I so desired, at the next port. In this way men are frequently shipped on board whalemen in the South Seas. My stipulation was acceded to, and the ship's articles handed me to sign.

The mate was now called below, and charged to make a "well man" of me; not, let it be borne in mind, that the captain felt any great compassion for me, he only desired to have the benefit of my services as soon as possible.

Helping me on deck, the mate stretched me out on the windlass and commenced examining my limb; and then doctoring it after a fashion with something from the medicine-chest, rolled it up in a piece of an old sail, making so big a bundle, that with my feet resting on the windlass, I might have been taken for a sailor with the gout. While this was going on, someone removing my tappa cloak slipped on a blue frock in its place; and another, actuated by the same desire to make a civilized mortal of me, flourished about my head a great pair of sheep-shears, to the imminent jeopardy of both ears, and the certain destruction of hair and beard.

The day was now drawing to a close, and, as the land faded from my sight, I was alive to the change in my condition. But how far short of our expectations is oftentimes the fulfilment of the most ardent hopes. Safe aboard of a ship—so long my earnest prayer—with home and friends once more in prospect, I nevertheless felt weighed down by a melancholy that could not be shaken off. It was the thought of never more seeing those, who, notwithstanding their desire to retain me a captive, had, upon the whole, treated me so kindly. I was leaving them for ever.

So unforeseen and sudden had been my escape, so excited had I been through it all, and so great the contrast between the luxurious repose of the valley, and the wild noise and motion of a ship at sea, that at times my recent adventures had all the strangeness of a dream; and I could scarcely believe that the same sun now setting over a waste of waters, had that very morning risen above the mountains and peered in upon me as I lay on my mat in Typee.

Going below into the forecastle just after dark, I was inducted into a wretched "bunk" or sleeping-box built over another. The rickety bottoms of both were spread with several pieces of a blanket. A battered tin can was then handed me, containing about half a pint of "tea"—so called by courtesy, though whether the juice of such stalks as one finds floating therein deserves that title, is a matter all ship-owners must settle with their consciences. A cube of salt beef, on a hard round biscuit by way of platter, was also handed up; and without more ado, I made a meal, the salt flavour of which, after the Nebuchadnezzar fare of the valley, was positively delicious.

While thus engaged, an old sailor on a chest just under me was puffing out volumes of tobacco smoke. My supper finished, he brushed the stem of his sooty pipe against the sleeve of his frock, and politely waved it toward me. The attention was sailor-like; as for the nicety of the thing, no man who has lived in forecastles is at all fastidious; and so, after a few vigorous whiffs to induce repose, I turned over and tried my best to forget myself. But in vain. My crib, instead of extending fore and aft, as it should have done, was placed athwartships, that is, at right angles to the keel; and the vessel going before the wind, rolled to such a degree, that every time my heels went up and my head went down, I thought I was on the point of turning a somerset. Besides this, there were still more annoying causes of inquietude; and, every once in a while, a splash of water came down the open scuttle, and flung the spray in my face.

At last, after a sleepless night, broken twice by the merciless call of the watch, a peep of daylight struggled into view from above, and some one came below. It was my old friend with the pipe.

"Here, shipmate," said I, "help me out of this place, and let me go on deck."

"Halloa, who's that croaking?" was the rejoinder, as he peered into the obscurity where I lay. "Ay, Typee, my king of the cannibals, is it you! But I say, my lad, how's that spar of your'n? the mate says it's in a devil of a way; and last night set the steward to sharpening the handsaw: hope he won't have the carving of ye."

Long before daylight we arrived off the bay of Nukuheva, and making short tacks until morning, we then ran in, and sent a boat ashore with the natives who had brought me to the ship. Upon its return, we made sail again, and stood off from the land. There was a fine breeze; and, notwithstanding my bad night's rest, the cool, fresh air of a morning at sea was so bracing, that, as soon as I breathed it, my spirits rose at once.

Seated upon the windlass the greater portion of the day, and chatting freely with the men, I learned the history of the voyage thus far, and everything respecting the ship and its present condition.

These matters I will now throw together in the next chapter.

CHAPTER II

SOME ACCOUNT OF THE SHIP

First and foremost, I must give some account of the *Julia* herself; or *Little Jule*, as the sailors familiarly styled her.

She was a small barque of a beautiful model, something more than two hundred tons, Yankee-built and very old. Fitted for a privateer out of a New England port during the war of 1812, she had been captured at sea by a British cruiser, and, after seeing all sorts of service, was at last employed as a government packet in the Australian seas. Being condemned, however, about two years previous, she was purchased at auction by a house in Sydney, who, after some slight repairs, dispatched her on the present voyage.

Notwithstanding the repairs, she was still in a miserable plight. The lower masts were said to be unsound; the standing rigging was much worn; and, in some places, even the bulwarks were quite rotten. Still, she was tolerably tight, and but little more than the ordinary pumping of a morning served to keep her free.

But all this had nothing to do with her sailing; at that, brave *Little Jule*, plump *Little Jule* was a witch. Blow high, or blow low, she was always ready for the breeze; and when she dashed the waves from her prow, and pranced, and pawed the sea, you never thought of her patched sails and blistered hull. How the fleet creature would fly before the wind! rolling, now and then, to be sure, but in very playfulness. Sailing to windward, no gale could blow her over: with spars erect, she looked right up into the wind's eye, and so she went.

But after all, *Little Jule* was not to be confided in. Lively enough, and playful she was, but on that very account the more to be distrusted. Who knew, but that like some vivacious old mortal all at once sinking into a decline, she might, some dark night, spring a leak and carry us all to the bottom. However, she played us no such ugly trick, and therefore, I wrong *Little Jule* in supposing it.

She had a free, roving commission. According to her papers she might go whither she pleased—whaling, sealing, or anything else. Sperm whaling, however, was what she relied upon; though, as yet, only two fish had been brought alongside.

The day they sailed out of Sydney heads, the ship's company, all told, numbered some thirty-two souls; now, they mustered about twenty; the rest had deserted. Even the three junior mates who had headed the whale boats were gone; and of the four harpooneers, only one was left, a wild New Zealander or "*Mowree*," as his countrymen are more commonly called in the Pacific. But this was not all. More than half the seamen remaining were more or less unwell from a long sojourn in a dissipated port; some of them wholly unfit for duty, one or two dangerously ill, and the rest managing to stand their watch though they could do but little.

The captain was a young cockney, who, a few years before, had emigrated to Australia, and, by some favouritism or other, had procured the command of the vessel, though in no wise competent. He was essentially a landsman, and though a man of education, no more meant for the sea than a hair-dresser. Hence everybody made fun of him. They called him "The Cabin Boy," "Paper Jack," and half a dozen other undignified names. In truth, the men made no secret of the derision in which they held him; and as for the slender gentleman himself, he knew it all very well, and bore himself with becoming meekness. Holding as little intercourse with them as possible, he left everything to the chief mate, who, as the story went, had been given his captain in charge. Yet, despite his apparent unobtrusiveness, the silent captain had more to do with the men than they thought. In short, although one of your sheepish-looking fellows, he had a sort of still, timid cunning, which no one would have suspected, and which, for that very reason, was all the more active. So the bluff mate, who always thought he did what he pleased, was occasionally made a tool of; and some obnoxious measures which he carried out, in spite of all growlings, were little thought to originate with the dapper little fellow in nankeen jacket and white canvas pumps. But, to all appearance, at least, the mate had everything his own way; indeed, in most things this was actually the case; and it was quite plain that the captain stood in awe of him.

So far as courage, seamanship, and a natural aptitude for keeping riotous spirits in subjection were concerned, no man was better qualified for his vocation than John Jermin. He was the very beau-ideal of the efficient race of short, thick-set men. His hair curled in little rings of iron grey all over his round, bullet head. As for his countenance, it was strongly marked, deeply pitted with the small-pox. For the rest, there was a fierce little squint out of one eye; the nose had a rakish twist to one side; while his large mouth, and great white teeth, looked absolutely sharkish when he laughed. In a word, no one, after getting a fair look at him, would ever think of improving the shape of his nose, wanting in symmetry if it was. Notwithstanding his pugnacious looks, however, Jermin had a heart as big as a bullock's; that you saw at a glance.

Such was our mate; but he had one failing: he abhorred all weak infusions, and cleaved manfully to strong drink. At all times he was more or less under the influence of it. Taken in moderate quantities, I believe, in my soul, it did a man like him good; brightened his eyes, swept the cobwebs out of his brain, and regulated his pulse. But the worst of it was, that sometimes he drank too much, and a more obstreperous fellow than Jermin in his cups, you seldom came across. He was always for having a fight; but the very men he flogged loved him as a brother, for he had such an irresistibly good-natured way of knocking them down, that no one could find it in his heart to bear malice against him. So much for stout little Jermin.

All English whalemen are bound by law to carry a physician, who, of course, is rated a gentleman, and lives in the cabin, with nothing but his professional duties to attend to; but incidentally he drinks "flip" and plays cards with the captain. There was such a worthy aboard of the *Julia;* but, curious to tell, he lived in the forecastle with the men. And this was the way it happened.

In the early part of the voyage the doctor and the captain lived together as pleasantly as could be. To say nothing of many a can they drank over the cabin transom, both of them had read books, and one of them had travelled; so their stories never flagged. But once on a time they got into a dispute about politics, and the doctor, moreover, getting into a rage, drove home an argument with his fist, and left the captain on the floor literally silenced. This was carrying it with a high hand; so he was shut up in his state-room for ten days, and left to meditate on bread and water, and the impropriety of flying into a passion. Smarting under his disgrace, he undertook, a short time after his liberation, to leave the vessel clandestinely at one of the islands, but was brought back ignominiously, and again shut up. Being set at large for the second time, he vowed he would not live any longer with the captain, and went forward with his chests among the sailors, where he was received with open arms, as a good fellow and an injured man.

I must give some further account of him, for he figures largely in the narrative. His early history, like that of many other heroes, was enveloped in the profoundest obscurity; though he threw out hints of a patrimonial estate, a nabob uncle, and an unfortunate affair which sent him a-roving. All that was known, however, was this. He had gone out to Sydney as assistant-surgeon of an emigrant ship. On his arrival there, he went back into the country, and after a few months' wanderings, returned to Sydney penniless, and entered as doctor aboard of the *Julia*.

His personal appearance was remarkable. He was over six feet high—a tower of bones, with a complexion absolutely colourless, fair hair, and a light, unscrupulous grey eye, twinkling occasionally with the very devil of mischief. Among the crew, he went by the name of the Long Doctor, or, more frequently still, Doctor Long Ghost. And from whatever high estate Doctor Long Ghost might have fallen, he had certainly at some time or other spent money, drunk Burgundy, and associated with gentlemen.

As for his learning, he quoted Virgil, and talked of Hobbes of Malmsbury, besides repeating poetry by the canto, especially Hudibras. He was, moreover, a man who had seen the world. In the easiest way imaginable, he could refer to an amour he had in Palermo, his lion-hunting before breakfast among the Caffres, and the quality of the coffee to be drunk in Muscat; and about these places, and a hundred others, he had more anecdotes than I can tell of. Then such mellow old songs as he sang, in a voice so round and racy, the real juice of sound. How such notes came forth from his lank body was a constant marvel.

Upon the whole, Long Ghost was as entertaining a companion as one could wish; and to me in the *Julia*, an absolute godsend.

CHAPTER III

FURTHER ACCOUNT OF THE "JULIA"

Owing to the absence of anything like regular discipline, the vessel was in a state of the greatest uproar. The captain, having for some time past been more or less confined to the cabin from sickness, was seldom seen. The mate, however, was as hearty as a young lion, and ran about the decks making himself heard at all hours. Bembo, the New Zealand harpooneer, held little intercourse with anybody but the mate, who could talk to him freely in his own lingo. Part of his time he spent out on the bowsprit, fishing for albicores with a bone hook; and occasionally he waked all hands up of a dark night dancing some cannibal fandango all by himself on the forecastle. But, upon the whole, he was remarkably quiet, though something in his eye showed he was far from being harmless.

Doctor Long Ghost, having sent in a written resignation as the ship's doctor, gave himself out as a passenger for Sydney, and took the world quite easy. As for the crew, those who were sick seemed marvelously contented for men in their condition; and the rest, not displeased with the general license, gave themselves little thought of the morrow.

The *Julia's* provisions were very poor. When opened, the barrels of pork looked as if preserved in iron rust, and diffused an odour like a stale ragout. The beef was worse yet; a mahogany-coloured fibrous substance, so tough and tasteless, that I almost believed the cook's story of a horse's hoof with the shoe on having been fished up out of the pickle of one of the casks. Nor was the biscuit much better; nearly all of it was broken into hard little gunflints, honey-combed through and through, as if the worms usually infesting this article in long tropical voyages, had, in boring after nutriment, come out at the antipodes without finding anything.

Of what sailors call "small stores," we had but little. "Tea," however, we had in abundance; though, I dare say, the Hong merchants never had the shipping of it. Besides this, every other day we had what English seamen call "shot soup"—great round peas, polishing themselves like pebbles by rolling about in tepid water.

It was afterwards told me, that all our provisions had been purchased by the owners at an auction sale of condemned navy stores in Sydney.

But notwithstanding the wateriness of the first course of soup, and the saline flavour of the beef and pork, a sailor might have made a satisfactory meal aboard of the *Julia* had there been any side dishes—a potato or two, a yam, or a plantain. But there was nothing of the kind. Still, there was something else, which, in the estimation of the men, made up for all deficiencies; and that was the regular allowance of Pisco.

It may seem strange that in such a state of affairs the captain should be willing to keep the sea with his ship. But the truth was, that by lying in harbour, he ran the risk of losing the remainder of his men by desertion; and as it was, he still feared that, in some outlandish bay or other, he might one day find his anchor down, and no crew to weigh it.

With judicious officers the most unruly seamen can at sea be kept in some sort of subjection; but once get them within a cable's length of the land, and it is hard restraining them. It is for this reason, that many South Sea whalemen do not come to an anchor for eighteen or twenty months on a stretch. When fresh provisions are needed, they run for the nearest land—heave to eight or ten miles off, and send a boat ashore to trade. The crews manning vessels like these are for the most part villains of all nations and dyes; picked up in the lawless ports of the Spanish Main, and among the savages of the islands. Like galley-slaves, they are only to be governed by scourges and chains. Their officers go among them with dirk and pistol—concealed, but ready at a grasp.

Not a few of our own crew were men of this stamp; but, riotous at times as they were, the bluff, drunken energies of Jermin were just the thing to hold them in some sort of noisy subjection. Upon an emergency, he flew in among them, showering his kicks and cuffs right and left, and "creating a sensation" in every direction. And as hinted before, they bore his knockdown authority with great good-humour. A sober, discreet, dignified officer could have done nothing with them; such a set would have thrown him and his dignity overboard.

Matters being thus, there was nothing for the ship but to keep the sea. Nor was the captain without hope that the invalid portion of his crew, as well as himself, would soon recover; and then there was no telling what luck in the fishery might yet be in store for us. At any rate, at the time of my coming aboard, the report was, that Captain Guy was resolved upon retrieving the past, and filling the vessel with oil in the shortest space possible.

With this intention, we were now shaping our course for Hytyhoo, a village on the island of St. Christina—one of the Marquesas, and so named by Mendanna—for the purpose of obtaining eight seamen, who, some weeks before, had stepped ashore there from the *Julia*. It was supposed that, by this time, they must have recreated themselves sufficiently, and would be glad to return to their duty.

So to Hytyhoo, with all our canvas spread, and coquetting with the warm, breezy Trades we bowled along; gliding up and down the long, slow swells, the bonettas and albicores frolicking round us.

CHAPTER IV

A SCENE IN THE FORECASTLE

I HAD scarcely been aboard of the ship twenty-four hours, when a circumstance occurred, which, although noways picturesque, is so significant of the state of affairs, that I cannot forbear relating it.

In the first place, however, it must be known, that among the crew was a man so excessively ugly, that he went by the ironical appellation of "Beauty." He was the ship's carpenter; and for that reason was sometimes known by his nautical cognomen of "Chips." There was no absolute deformity about the man; he was symmetrically ugly. But ill favoured as he was in person, Beauty was none the less ugly in temper; but no one could blame him; his countenance had soured his heart. Now Jermin and Beauty were always at sword's points. The truth was, the latter was the only man in the ship whom the mate had never decidedly got the better of; and hence the grudge he bore him. As for Beauty, he prided himself upon talking up to the mate, as we shall soon see.

Toward evening there was something to be done on deck and the carpenter, who belonged to the watch was missing. "Where's that skulk, Chips?" shouted Jermin down the forecastle scuttle.

"Taking his ease, d'ye see, down here on a chest, if you want to know," replied that worthy himself, quietly withdrawing his pipe from his mouth. This insolence flung the fiery little mate into a mighty rage; but Beauty said nothing, puffing away with all the tranquillity imaginable. Here it must be remembered that, never mind what may be the provocation, no prudent officer ever dreams of entering a ship's forecastle on a hostile visit. If he wants to see anybody who happens to be there, and refuses to come up, why he must wait patiently until the sailor is willing. The reason is this. The place is very dark; and nothing is easier than to knock one descending on the head, before he knows where he is, and a very long while before he ever finds out who did it.

Nobody knew this better than Jermin, and so he contented himself with looking down the scuttle and storming. At last Beauty made some cool observation which set him half wild.

"Tumble on deck," he then bellowed—"come, up with you, or I'll jump down and make you." The carpenter begged him to go about it at once.

No sooner said than done: prudence forgotten, Jermin was there; and by a sort of instinct, had his man by the throat before he could well see him. One of the men now made a rush at him, but the rest dragged him off, protesting that they should have fair play.

"Now, come on deck," shouted the mate, struggling like a good fellow to hold the carpenter fast.

"Take me there," was the dogged answer, and Beauty wriggled about in the nervous grasp of the other like a couple of yards of boa-constrictor.

His assailant now undertook to make him up into a compact bundle, the more easily to transport him. While thus occupied, Beauty got his arms loose, and threw him over backward. But Jermin quickly recovered himself, when for a time they had it every way, dragging each other about, bumping their heads against the projecting beams, and returning each other's blows the first favourable opportunity that offered. Unfortunately, Jermin at last slipped and fell; his foe seating himself on his chest, and keeping him down. Now this was one of those situations in which the voice of counsel, or reproof, comes with peculiar unction. Nor did Beauty let the opportunity slip. But the mate said nothing in reply, only foaming at the mouth and struggling to rise.

Just then a thin tremor of a voice was heard from above. It was the captain; who, happening to ascend to the quarter-deck at the commencement of the scuffle, would gladly have returned to the cabin, but was prevented by the fear of ridicule. As the din increased, and it became evident that his officer was in serious trouble, he thought it would never do to stand leaning over the bulwarks, so he made his appearance on the forecastle, resolved, as his best policy, to treat the matter lightly.

"Why, why," he began, speaking pettishly, and very fast, "what's all this about?—Mr. Jermin, Mr. Jermin—carpenter, carpenter; what are you doing down there? Come on deck; come on deck."

Whereupon Doctor Long Ghost cries out in a squeak, "Ah! Miss Guy, is that you? Now, my dear, go right home, or you'll get hurt."

"Pooh, pooh! you, sir, whoever you are, I was not speaking to you; none of your nonsense. Mr. Jermin, I was talking to *you;* have the kindness to come on deck, sir; I want to see you."

"And how, in the devil's name, am I to get there?" cried the mate, furiously. "Jump down here, Captain Guy, and show yourself a man. Let me up, you Chips! unhand me, I say! Oh! I'll pay you for this, some day! Come on, Captain Guy"

At this appeal, the poor man was seized with a perfect spasm of fidgets. "Pooh, pooh, carpenter; have done with your nonsense! Let him up, sir; let him up! Do you hear? Let Mr. Jermin come on deck!"

"Go along with you, Paper Jack," replied Beauty; "this quarrel's between the mate and me; so go aft, where you belong!"

As the captain once more dipped his head down the scuttle to make answer, from an unseen hand he received, full in the face, the contents of a tin can of soaked biscuit and tea-leaves. The doctor was not far off just then. Without waiting for anything more, the discomfited gentleman, with both hands to his streaming face, retreated to the quarter-deck.

A few moments more, and Jermin, forced to a compromise, followed after, in his torn frock and scarred face, looking for all the world as if he had just disentangled himself from some intricate piece of machinery. For about half an hour both remained in the cabin, where the mate's rough tones were heard high above the low, smooth voice of the captain.

Of all his conflicts with the men, this was the first in which Jermin had been worsted; and he was proportionably enraged. Upon going below—as the steward afterward told us—he bluntly informed Guy that, for the future, he might look out for his ship himself; for *his* part, he was done with her, if that was the way he allowed his officers to be treated. After many high words, the captain finally assured him, that the first fitting opportunity the carpenter should be cordially flogged; though, as matters stood, the experiment would be a hazardous one. Upon this Jermin reluctantly consented to drop the matter for the present; and he soon drowned all thoughts of it in a can of flip, which Guy had previously instructed the steward to prepare, as a sop to allay his wrath.

Nothing more ever came of this.

CHAPTER V

WHAT HAPPENED AT HYTYHOO

LESS than forty-eight hours after leaving Nukuheva, the blue, looming island of St. Christina greeted us from afar. Drawing near the shore, the grim, black spars and waspish hull of a small man-of-war craft crept into view; the masts and yards lined distinctly against the sky. She was riding to her anchor in the bay, and proved to be a French corvette.

This pleased our captain exceedingly, and, coming on deck, he examined her from the mizzen rigging with his glass. His original intention was not to let go an anchor; but, counting upon the assistance of the corvette in case of any difficulty, he now changed his mind, and anchored alongside of her. As soon as a boat could be lowered, he then went off to pay his respects to the commander, and, moreover, as we supposed, to concert measures for the apprehension of the runaways.

Returning in the course of twenty minutes, he brought along with him two officers in undress and whiskers, and three or four drunken obstreperous old chiefs; one with his legs thrust into the armholes of a scarlet vest, another with a pair of spurs on his heels, and a third in a cocked hat and feather. In addition to these articles, they merely wore the ordinary costume of their race —a slip of native cloth about the loins. Indecorous as their behaviour was, these worthies turned out to be a deputation from the reverend the clergy of the island; and the object of their visit was to put our ship under a rigorous "Taboo," to prevent the disorderly scenes and facilities for desertion which would ensue, were the natives—men and women—allowed to come off to us freely.

There was little ceremony about the matter. The priests went aside for a moment, laid their shaven old crowns together, and went over a little mummery. Whereupon, their leader tore a long strip from his girdle of white tappa, and handed it to one of the French officers, who, after explaining what was to be done, gave it to Jermin. The mate at once went out to the end of the flying jib boom, and fastened there the mystic symbol of the ban. This put to flight a party of girls who had been observed swimming toward us. Tossing their arms about, and splashing the water like porpoises, with loud cries of "taboo! taboo!" they turned about and made for the shore.

The night of our arrival, the mate and the Mowree were to stand "watch and watch," relieving each other every four hours; the crew, as is sometimes customary when lying at an anchor, being allowed to remain all night below. A distrust of the men, however, was, in the present instance, the principal reason for this proceeding. Indeed, it was all but certain, that some kind of attempt would be made at desertion; and, therefore, when Jermin's first watch came on at eight bells (midnight)—by which time all was quiet—he mounted to the deck with a flask of spirits in one hand, and the other in readiness to assail the first countenance that showed itself above the forecastle scuttle.

Thus prepared, he doubtless meant to stay awake; but for all that, he before long fell asleep; and slept with such hearty good-will, too, that the men who left us that night might have been waked up by his snoring. Certain it was, the mate snored most strangely; and no wonder, with that crooked bugle of his. When he came to himself it was just dawn, but quite light enough to show two boats gone from the side. In an instant he knew what had happened.

Dragging the Mowree out of an old sail where he was napping, he ordered him to clear away another boat, and then darted into the cabin to tell the captain the news. Springing on deck again, he dove down into the forecastle for a couple of oarsmen, but hardly got there before there was a cry, and a loud splash heard over the side. It was the Mowree and the boat—into which he had just leaped to get ready for lowering—rolling over and over in the water.

The boat having at nightfall been hoisted up to its place over the starboard quarter, some one had so cut the tackles which held it there, that a moderate strain would at once part them. Bembo's weight had answered the purpose, showing that the deserters must have ascertained his specific gravity to a fibre of hemp. There was another boat remaining; but it was as well to examine it before attempting to lower. And it was well they did; for there was a hole in the bottom large enough to drop a barrel through: she had been scuttled most ruthlessly.

Jermin was frantic. Dashing his hat upon deck, he was about to plunge overboard and swim to the corvette for a cutter, when Captain Guy made his appearance and begged him to stay where he was. By this time the officer of the deck aboard the Frenchman had noticed our movements, and hailed to know what had happened. Guy informed him through his trumpet, and men to go in pursuit were instantly promised. There was a whistling of a boatswain's pipe, an order or two, and then a large cutter pulled out from the man-of-war's stern, and in half a dozen strokes was alongside. The mate leaped into her, and they pulled rapidly ashore.

Another cutter, carrying an armed crew, soon followed.

In an hour's time the first returned, towing the two whale boats, which had been found turned up like tortoises on the beach.

Noon came, and nothing more was heard from the deserters. Meanwhile Doctor Long Ghost and myself lounged about, cultivating an acquaintance, and gazing upon the shore scenery. The bay was as calm as death; the sun high and hot; and occasionally a still gliding canoe stole out from behind the headlands, and shot across the water.

And all the morning long our sick men limped about the deck, casting wistful glances inland, where the palm-trees waved and beckoned them into their reviving shades. Poor invalid rascals! How conducive to the restoration of their shattered health would have been those delicious groves! But hard-hearted Jermin assured them, with an oath, that foot of theirs should never touch the beach.

Toward sunset a crowd was seen coming down to the water. In advance of all were the fugitives—bareheaded—their frocks and trousers hanging in tatters, every face covered with blood and dust, and their arms pinioned behind them with green thongs. Following them up, was a shouting rabble of islanders, pricking them with the points of their long spears, the party from the corvette menacing them in flank with their naked cutlasses.

The bonus of a musket to the King of the Bay, and the promise of a tumbler full of powder for every man caught, had set the whole population on their track; and so successful was the hunt, that not only were that morning's deserters brought back, but five of those left behind on a former visit. The natives, however, were the mere hounds of the chase, raising the game in their coverts, but leaving the securing of it to the Frenchmen. Here, as elsewhere, the islanders have no idea of taking part in such a scuffle as ensues upon the capture of a party of desperate seamen.

The runaways were at once brought aboard, and, though they looked rather sulky, soon came round, and treated the whole affair as a frolicsome adventure.

CHAPTER VI

WE TOUCH AT LA DOMINICA

FEARFUL of spending another night in Hytyhoo, Captain Guy caused the ship to be got under way shortly after dark.

The next morning, when all supposed that we were fairly embarked for a long cruise, our course was suddenly altered for La Dominica, or Hivarhoo, an island just north of the one we had quitted. The object of this, as we learned, was to procure, if possible, several English sailors, who, according to the commander of the corvette, had recently gone ashore there from an American whaler and were desirous of shipping aboard of one of their own country's vessels.

We made the land in the afternoon, coming abreast of a shady glen opening from a deep bay, and winding by green defiles far out of sight. "Hands by the weather-main-brace!" roared the mate, jumping up on the bulwarks; and in a moment the prancing *Julia*, suddenly arrested in her course, bridled her head like a steed reined in, while the foam flaked under her bows.

This was the place where we expected to obtain the men; so a boat was at once got in readiness to go ashore. Now it was necessary to provide a picked crew—men the least likely to abscond. After considerable deliberation on the part of the captain and mate, four of the seamen were pitched upon as the most trustworthy; or rather they were selected from a choice assortment of suspicious characters as being of an inferior order of rascality.

Armed with cutlasses all round—the natives were said to be an ugly set— they were followed over the side by the invalid captain, who, on this occasion, it seems, was determined to signalize himself. Accordingly, in addition to his cutlass, he wore an old boarding belt, in which was thrust a brace of pistols. They at once shoved off.

My friend Long Ghost had, among other things which looked somewhat strange in a ship's forecastle, a capital spy-glass, and on the present occasion we had it in use.

When the boat neared the head of the inlet, though invisible to the naked eye, it was plainly revealed by the glass; looking no bigger than an egg-shell, and the men diminished to pigmies.

At last, borne on what seemed a long flake of foam, the tiny craft shot up the beach amid a shower of sparkles. Not a soul was there. Leaving one of their number by the water, the rest of the pigmies stepped ashore, looking about them very circumspectly, pausing now and then hand to ear, and peering under a dense grove which swept down within a few paces of the sea. No one came, and to all appearances everything was as still as the grave. Presently, he with the pistols, followed by the rest flourishing their bodkins, entered the wood and were soon lost to view. They did not stay long; probably anticipating some inhospitable ambush were they to stray any distance up the glen.

In a few moments they embarked again, and were soon riding pertly over the waves of the bay. All of a sudden the captain started to his feet—the boat spun round, and again made for the shore. Some twenty or thirty natives armed with spears which through the glass looked like reeds, had just come out of the grove, and were apparently shouting to the strangers not to be in such a hurry, but return and be sociable. But they were somewhat distrusted, for the boat paused about its length from the beach, when the captain standing up in its head delivered an address in pantomime, the object of which seemed to be, that the islanders should draw near. One of them stepped forward and made answer, seemingly again urging the strangers not to be diffident, but beach their boat. The captain declined, tossing his arms about in another panto-mime. In the end he said something which made them shake their spears; whereupon he fired a pistol among them, which set the whole party running; while one poor little fellow, dropping his spear and clapping his hand behind him, limped away in a manner which almost made me itch to get a shot at his assailant.

Wanton acts of cruelty like this are not unusual on the part of sea-captains landing at islands comparatively unknown. Even at the Pomotu group, but a day's sail from Tahiti, the islanders coming down to the shore have several times been fired at by trading schooners passing through their narrow channels; and this too as a mere amusement on the part of the ruffians.

Indeed, it is almost incredible, the light in which many sailors regard these naked heathens. They hardly consider them human. But it is a curious fact, that the more ignorant and degraded men are, the more contemptuously they look upon those whom they deem their inferiors.

All powers of persuasian being thus lost upon these foolish savages, and no hope left of holding further intercourse, the boat returned to the ship.

CHAPTER VII

WHAT HAPPENED AT HANNAMANOO

ON the other side of the island was the large and populous bay of Hannamanoo, where the men sought might yet be found. But as the sun was setting by the time the boat came alongside, we got our off-shore tacks aboard and stood away for an offing. About daybreak we wore, and ran in, and by the time the sun was well up, entered the long, narrow channel dividing the islands of La Dominica and St. Christina.

On one hand was a range of steep green bluffs hundreds of feet high, the white huts of the natives here and there nestling like birds' nests in deep clefts gushing with verdure. Across the water, the land rolled away in bright hill-sides, so warm and undulating, that they seemed almost to palpitate in the sun. On we swept, past bluff and grove, wooded glen and valley, and dark ravines lighted up far inland with wild falls of water. A fresh land-breeze filled our sails, the embayed waters were gentle as a lake, and every blue wave broke with a tinkle against our coppered prow.

On gaining the end of the channel we rounded a point, and came full upon the bay of Hannamanoo. This is the only harbour of any note about the island, though as far as a safe anchorage is concerned it hardly deserves the title.

Before we held any communication with the shore an incident occurred which may convey some further idea of the character of our crew.

Having approached as near the land as we could prudently, our headway was stopped, and we awaited the arrival of a canoe which was coming out of the bay. All at once we got into a strong current, which swept us rapidly toward a rocky promontory forming one side of the harbour. The wind had died away; so two boats were at once lowered for the purpose of pulling the ship's head round. Before this could be done, the eddies were whirling upon all sides, and the rock so near, that it seemed as if one might leap upon it from the mast-head. Notwithstanding the speechless fright of the captain, and the hoarse shouts of the unappalled Jermin, the men handled the ropes as deliberately as possible, some of them chuckling at the prospect of going ashore, and others so eager for the vessel to strike, that they could hardly contain themselves. Unexpectedly a countercurrent befriended us, and assisted by the boats we were soon out of danger.

What a disappointment for our crew! All their little plans for swimming ashore from the wreck, and having a fine time of it for the rest of their days, thus cruelly nipped in the bud.

Soon after, the canoe came alongside. In it were eight or ten natives, comely, vivacious-looking youths, all gesture and exclamation; the red feathers in their headbands perpetually nodding. With them also came a stranger, a renegado from Christendom and humanity—a white man, in the South Sea girdle, and tattooed in the face. A broad blue band stretched across his face from ear to ear, and on his forehead was the taper figure of a blue shark, nothing but fins from head to tail.

Some of us gazed upon this man with a feeling akin to horror, no ways abated when informed that he had voluntarily submitted to this embellishment of his countenance. What an impress! Far worse than Cain's—*his* was perhaps a wrinkle, or a freckle, which some of our modern cosmetics might have effaced; but the blue shark was a mark indelible, which all the waters of Abana and Pharpar, rivers of Damascus, could never wash out. He was an Englishman, Lem Hardy he called himself, who had deserted from a trading brig touching at the island for wood and water some ten years previous. He had gone ashore as a sovereign power, armed with a musket and a bag of ammunition, and ready, if need were, to prosecute war on his own account. The country was divided by the hostile kings of several large valleys. With one of them, from whom he first received overtures, he formed an alliance, and became what he now was, the military leader of the tribe, and war-god of the empire island.

His campaigns beat Napoleon's. In one night-attack, his invincible musket, backed by the light infantry of spears and javelins, vanquished two clans, and the next morning brought all the others at the feet of his royal ally.

Nor was the rise of his domestic fortunes at all behind the Corsican's: three days after landing, the exquisitely tattooed hand of a princess was his; receiving along with the damsel as her portion, one thousand fathoms of fine tappa, fifty double-braided mats of split grass, four hundred hogs, ten houses in different parts of her native valley, and the sacred protection of an express edict of the Taboo, declaring his person inviolable for ever.

Now, this man was settled for life, perfectly satisfied with his circumstances, and feeling no desire to return to his friends. "Friends," indeed, he had none. He told me his history. Thrown upon the world a foundling, his paternal origin was as much a mystery to him as the genealogy of Odin; and, scorned by everybody, he fled the parish workhouse when a boy, and launched upon the sea.

He had followed it for several years, a dog before the mast, and now he had thrown it up for ever.

And for the most part, it is just this sort of man—so many of whom are found among sailors—uncared for by a single soul, without ties, reckless, and impatient of the restraints of civilization, who are occasionally found quite at home upon the savage islands of the Pacific. And, glancing at their hard lot in their own country, what marvel at their choice?

According to the renegado, there was no other white man on the island; and as the captain could have no reason to suppose that Hardy intended to deceive us, he concluded that the Frenchmen were in some way or other mistaken in what they had told us. However, when our errand was made known to the rest of our visitors, one of them, a fine, stalwart fellow, his face all eyes and expression, volunteered for a cruise. All the wages he asked was a red shirt, a pair of trousers, and a hat, which were to be put on there and then; besides a plug of tobacco and a pipe. The bargain was struck directly; but Wymontoo afterward came in with a codicil, to the effect that a friend of his, who had come along with him, should be given ten whole sea-biscuits, without crack or flaw, twenty perfectly new and symmetrically straight nails, and one jack-knife. This being agreed to, the articles were at once handed over, the native receiving them with great avidity, and in the absence of clothing, using his mouth as a pocket to put the nails in. Two of them, however, were first made to take the place of a pair of ear-ornaments, curiously fashioned out of bits of whitened wood.

It now began breezing strongly from seaward, and no time was to be lost in getting away from the land; so after an affecting rubbing of noses between our new shipmate and his countrymen, we sailed away with him.

To our surprise, the farewell shouts from the canoe, as we dashed along under bellied royals, were heard unmoved by our islander; but it was not long thus. That very evening, when the dark blue of his native hills sank in the horizon, the poor savage leaned over the bulwarks, dropped his head upon his chest, and gave way to irrepressible emotions. The ship was plunging hard, and Wymontoo, sad to tell, in addition to his other pangs, was terribly sea-sick.

CHAPTER VIII

THE TATTOOERS OF LA DOMINICA

FOR awhile leaving *Little Jule* to sail away by herself, I will here put down some curious information obtained from Hardy.

The renegado had lived so long on the island that its customs were quite familiar; and I much lamented that, from the shortness of our stay, he could not tell us more than he did.

From the little intelligence gathered, however, I learned to my surprise that, in some things, the people of Hivarhoo, though of the same group of islands, differed considerably from my tropical friends in the valley of Typee.

As his tattooing attracted so much remark, Hardy had a good deal to say concerning the manner in which that art was practised upon the island.

Throughout the entire cluster the tattooers of Hivarhoo enjoyed no small reputation. They had carried their art to the highest perfection, and the profession was esteemed most honourable. No wonder, then, that like genteel tailors, they rated their services very high; so much so, that none but those belonging to the higher classes could afford to employ them. So true was this, that the elegance of one's tattooing was in most cases a sure indication of birth and riches.

Professors in large practice lived in spacious houses, divided by screens of tappa into numerous little apartments, where subjects were waited upon in private. The arrangement chiefly grew out of a singular ordinance of the Taboo, which enjoined the strictest privacy upon all men, high and low, while under the hands of a tattooer. For the time, the slightest intercourse with others is prohibited, and the small portion of food allowed, is pushed under the curtain by an unseen hand. The restriction with regard to food, is intended to reduce the blood, so as to diminish the inflammation consequent upon puncturing the skin. As it is, this comes on very soon, and takes some time to heal; so that the period of seclusion generally embraces many days, sometimes several weeks.

All traces of soreness vanished, the subject goes abroad; but only again to return; for, on account of the pain, only a small surface can be operated upon at once; and as the whole body is to be more or less embellished by a process so slow, the studios alluded to are constantly filled. Indeed, with a vanity elsewhere unheard of, many spend no small portion of their days thus sitting to an artist.

To begin the work, the period of adolescence is esteemed the most suitable. After casting about for some eminent tattooer, the friends of the youth take him to his house, to have the outlines of the general plan laid out. It behoves the professor to have a nice eye, for a suit to be worn for life should be well cut.

Some tattooers, yearning after perfection, employ, at large wages, one or two men of the commonest order—vile fellows, utterly regardless of appearances, upon whom they first try their patterns and practise generally. Their backs remorselessly scrawled over, and no more canvas remaining, they are dismissed, and ever after go about, the scorn of their countrymen.

Hapless wights! thus martyred in the cause of the Fine Arts.

Besides the regular practitioners, there are a parcel of shabby, itinerant tattooers, who, by virtue of their calling, stroll unmolested from one hostile bay to another, doing their work dog-cheap for the multitude. They always repair to the various religious festivals, which gather great crowds. When these are concluded, and the places where they are held vacated even by the tattooers, scores of little tents of coarse tappa are left standing, each with a solitary inmate, who, forbidden to talk to his unseen neighbours, is obliged to stay there till completely healed. The itinerants are a reproach to their profession, mere cobblers, dealing in nothing but jagged lines and clumsy patches, and utterly incapable of soaring to those heights of fancy attained by the gentlemen of the faculty.

All professors of the arts love to fraternize; and so, in Hannamanoo, the tattooers came together in the chapters of their worshipful order. In this society, duly organized, and conferring degrees, Hardy, from his influence as a white, was a sort of honorary Grand Master. The blue shark, and a sort of Urim and Thummim engraven upon his chest, were the seal of his initiation. All over Hivarhoo are established these orders of tattooers. The way in which the renegado's came to be founded is this. A year or two after his landing there happened to be a season of scarcity, owing to the partial failure of the bread-fruit harvest for several consecutive seasons. This brought about such a falling off in the number of subjects for tattooing, that the profession became quite needy. The royal ally of Hardy, however, hit upon a benevolent expedient to provide for their wants, at the same time conferring a boon upon many of his subjects.

By sound of conch-shell it was proclaimed before the palace, on the beach, and at the head of the valley, that Noomai, King of Hannamanoo, and friend of Hardee-Hardee, the white, kept open heart and table for all tattooers whatsoever; but to entitle themselves to this hospitality, they were commanded to practise without fee upon the meanest native soliciting their services.

Numbers at once flocked to the royal abode, both artists and sitters. It was a famous time; and the buildings of the palace being "taboo" to all but the tattooers and chiefs, the sitters bivouacked on the common, and formed an extensive encampment.

The "Lora Tattoo," or the Time of Tattooing, will be long remembered. An enthusiastic sitter celebrated the event in verse. Several lines were repeated to us by Hardy, some of which, in a sort of colloquial chant he translated nearly thus:

> "Where is that sound?
> In Hannamanoo.
> And wherefore that sound?
> The sound of a hundred hammers,
> Tapping, tapping, tapping
>   The shark teeth.

> "Where is that light?
> Round about the king's house.
> And the small laughter?
> The small, merry laughter it is
> Of the sons and daughters of the tattooed."

CHAPTER IX

WE STEER TO THE WESTWARD—STATE OF AFFAIRS

The night we left Hannamanoo was bright and starry, and so warm, that when the watches were relieved, most of the men, instead of going below, flung themselves around the foremast.

Toward morning, finding the heat of the forecastle unpleasant, I ascended to the deck where everything was noiseless. The Trades were blowing with a mild, steady strain upon the canvas, and the ship heading right out into the immense blank of the Western Pacific. The watch were asleep. With one foot resting on the rudder, even the man at the helm nodded, and the mate himself, with arms folded, was leaning against the capstan.

On such a night, and all alone, reverie was inevitable. I leaned over the side, and could not help thinking of the strange objects we might be sailing over.

But my meditations were soon interrupted by a grey, spectral shadow cast over the heaving billows. It was the dawn, soon followed by the first rays of the morning. They flashed into view at one end of the arched night, like—to compare great things with small—the gleamings of Guy Fawkes's lantern in the vaults of the Parliament House. Before long, what seemed a live ember rested for a moment on the rim of the ocean, and at last the blood-red sun stood full and round in the level East, and the long sea-day began.

Breakfast over, the first thing attended to was the formal baptism of Wymontoo, who, after thinking over his affairs during the night, looked dismal enough.

There were various opinions as to a suitable appellation. Some maintained that we ought to call him "Sunday," that being the day we caught him; others, "Eighteen Forty-two," the then year of our Lord; while Doctor Long Ghost remarked, that he ought, by all means, to retain his original name,—Wymontoo-Hee, meaning (as he maintained), in the figurative language of the island, something analogous to one who had got himself into a scrape. The mate put an end to the discussion by sousing the poor fellow with a bucket of salt water, and bestowing upon him the nautical appellation of "Luff."

Though a certain mirthfulness succeeded his first pangs at leaving home, Wymontoo—we will call him thus—gradually relapsed into his former mood, and became very melancholy. Often I noticed him crouching apart in the forecastle, his strange eyes gleaming restlessly, and watching the slightest movement of the men. Many a time he must have been thinking of his bamboo hut, when they were talking of Sydney and its dance-houses.

We were now fairly at sea, though to what particular cruising-ground we were going, no one knew; and, to all appearances, few cared. The men, after a fashion of their own, began to settle down into the routine of sea-life, as if everything was going on prosperously. Blown along over a smooth sea, there was nothing to do but steer the ship, and relieve the "look-outs" at the mast-heads. As for the sick, they had two or three more added to their number—the air of the island having disagreed with the constitutions of several of the runaways. To crown all, the captain again relapsed, and became quite ill.

The men fit for duty were divided into two small watches, headed respectively by the mate and the Mowree; the latter, by virtue of his being a harpooneer, succeeding to the place of the second mate, who had absconded.

In this state of things whaling was out of the question; but in the face of everything, Jermin maintained that the invalids would soon be well. However that might be, with the same pale blue sky overhead, we kept running steadily to the westward. For ever advancing, we seemed always in the same place, and every day was the former lived over again. We saw no ships, expected to see none. No sign of life was perceptible but the porpoises and other fish sporting under the bows like pups ashore. But, at intervals, the grey albatross, peculiar to these seas, came flapping his immense wings over us, and then skimmed away silently as if from a plague-ship. Or flights of the tropic bird, known among seamen as the "boatswain," wheeled round and round us, whistling shrilly as they flew.

The uncertainty hanging over our destination at this time, and the fact that we were abroad upon waters comparatively little traversed, lent an interest to this portion of the cruise which I shall never forget.

From obvious prudential considerations the Pacific has been principally sailed over in known tracts, and this is the reason why new islands are still occasionally discovered, by exploring ships and adventurous whalers, notwithstanding the great number of vessels of all kinds of late navigating this vast ocean. Indeed, considerable portions still remain wholly unexplored; and there is doubt as to the actual existence of certain shoals, and reefs, and small clusters of islands vaguely laid down in the charts. The mere circumstance, therefore, of a ship like ours penetrating into these regions, was sufficient to cause any reflecting mind to feel at least a little uneasy. For my own part, the many stories I had heard of ships striking at midnight upon unknown rocks, with all sail set, and a slumbering crew, often recurred to me, especially, as from the absence of discipline, and our being so short-handed, the watches at night were careless in the extreme.

But no thoughts like these were entertained by my reckless shipmates; and along we went, the sun every evening setting right ahead of our jib-boom.

For what reason the matè was so reserved with regard to our precise destination was never made known. The stories he told us, I, for one, did not believe; deeming them all a mere device to lull the crew.

He said we were bound to a fine cruising-ground, scarcely known to other whalemen, which he had himself discovered when commanding a small brig on a former voyage. Here, the sea was alive with large whales, so tame, that all you had to do was to go up and kill them: they were too frightened to resist. A little to leeward of this was a small cluster of islands, where we were going to refit, abounding with delicious fruits, and peopled by a race almost wholly unsophisticated by intercourse with strangers.

In order, perhaps, to guard against the possibility of any one finding out the precise latitude and longitude of the spot we were going to, Jermin never revealed to us the ship's place at noon, though such is the custom aboard of most vessels.

Meanwhile, he was very assiduous in his attention to the invalids. Doctor Long Ghost having given up the keys of the medicine-chest, they were handed over to him; and, as physician, he discharged his duties to the satisfaction of all. Pills and powders, in most cases, were thrown to the fish, and in place thereof, the contents of a mysterious little quarter cask were produced, diluted with water from the "butt." His draughts were mixed on the capstan, in coco-nut shells marked with the patients' names. Like shore doctors, he did not eschew his own medicines, for his professional calls in the forecastle were some-times made when he was comfortably tipsy; nor did he omit keeping his invalids in good-humour, spinning his yarns to them, by the hour, whenever he went to see them.

Owing to my lameness, from which I soon began to recover, I did no active duty, except standing an occasional "trick" at the helm. It was in the fore-castle chiefly that I spent my time, in company with the Long Doctor, who was at great pains to make himself agreeable. His books, though sadly torn and battered, were an invaluable resource. I read them through again and again, including a learned treatise on the yellow fever. In addition to these, he had an old file of Sydney papers, and I soon became intimately acquainted with the localities of all the advertising tradesmen there. In particular, the rhetorical flourishes of Stubbs, the real-estate auctioneer, diverted me exceed-ingly, and I set him down as no other than a pupil of Robins the Londoner.

Aside from the pleasure of his society, my intimacy with Long Ghost was of great service to me in other respects. His disgrace in the cabin only con-firmed the good-will of the democracy in the forecastle; and they not only treated him in the most friendly manner, but looked up to him with the utmost deference, besides laughing heartily at all his jokes. As his chosen associate, this feeling for him extended to me, and gradually we came to be regarded in the light of distinguished guests. At meal-times we were always first served, and otherwise were treated with much respect.

Among other devices to kill time, during the frequent calms, Long Ghost hit upon the game of chess. With a jack-knife, we carved the pieces quite tastefully out of bits of wood, and our board was the middle of a chest-lid, chalked into squares, which, in playing, we straddled at either end. Having no other suitable way of distinguishing the sets, I marked mine by tying round them little scarfs of black silk, torn from an old neckhandkerchief. Putting them in mourning this way, the doctor said, was quite appropriate, seeing that they had reason to feel sad three games out of four. Of chess, the men never could make head nor tail; indeed, their wonder rose to such a pitch, that they at last regarded the mysterious movements of the game with something more than perplexity; and after puzzling over them through several long engagements, they came to the conclusion that we must be a couple of necromancers.

CHAPTER X

A SEA-PARLOUR DESCRIBED, WITH SOME OF ITS TENANTS

I MAY as well give some idea of the place in which the doctor and I lived together so sociably.

Most persons know that a ship's forecastle embraces the forward part of the deck about the bowsprit: the same term, however, is generally bestowed upon the sailors' sleeping-quarters, which occupy a space immediately beneath, and are partitioned off by a bulkhead.

Planted right in the bows, or, as sailors say, in the very *eyes* of the ship, this delightful apartment is of a triangular shape, and is generally fitted with two tiers of rude bunks. Those of the *Julia* were in a most deplorable condition, mere wrecks, some having been torn down altogether to patch up others; and on one side there were but two standing. But with most of the men it made little difference whether they had a bunk or not, since, having no bedding, they had nothing to put in it but themselves.

Upon the boards of my own crib I spread all the old canvas and old clothes I could pick up. For a pillow, I wrapped an old jacket round a log. This helped a little the wear and tear of one's bones when the ship rolled.

Rude hammocks made out of old sails were in many cases used as substitutes for the demolished bunks; but the space they swung in was so confined, that they were far from being agreeable.

The general aspect of the forecastle was dungeon-like and dingy in the extreme. In the first place, it was not five feet from deck to deck, and even this space was encroached upon by two outlandish cross-timbers bracing the vessel, and by the sailors' chests, over which you must needs crawl in getting about. At meal-times, and especially when we indulged in after-dinner chat, we sat about the chests like a parcel of tailors.

In the middle of all, were two square, wooden columns, denominated in marine architecture "Bowsprit Bitts." They were about a foot apart, and between them, by a rusty chain, swung the forecastle lamp, burning day and night, and for ever casting two long black shadows. Lower down, between the bitts, was a locker, or sailors' pantry, kept in abominable disorder, and sometimes requiring a vigorous cleaning and fumigation.

All over, the ship was in a most dilapidated condition; but in the forecastle it looked like the hollow of an old tree going to decay. In every direction the wood was damp and discoloured, and here and there soft and porous. Moreover, it was hacked and hewed without mercy, the cook frequently helping himself to splinters for kindling-wood from the bitts and beams. Overhead, every carline was sooty, and here and there deep holes were burned in them, a freak of some drunken sailors on a voyage long previous.

From above, you entered by a plank, with two cleets, slanting down from the scuttle, which was a mere hole in the deck. There being no slide to draw over in case of emergency, the tarpaulin temporarily placed there was little protection from the spray heaved over the bows; so that in anything of a breeze the place was miserably wet. In a squall, the water fairly poured down in sheets like a cascade, swashing about, and afterward spurting up between the chests like the jets of a fountain.

Such were our accommodations aboard of the *Julia;* but bad as they were, we had not the undisputed possession of them. Myriads of cockroaches, and regiments of rats disputed the place with us. A greater calamity than this can scarcely befall a vessel in the South Seas.

So warm is the climate that it is almost impossible to get rid of them. You may seal up every hatchway, and fumigate the hull till the smoke forces itself out at the seams, and enough will survive to re-people the ship in an incredibly short period. In some vessels, the crews of which after a hard fight have given themselves up, as it were, for lost, the vermin seem to take actual possession, the sailors being mere tenants by sufferance. With Sperm Whalemen, hanging about the Line, as many of them do for a couple of years on a stretch, it is infinitely worse than with other vessels.

As for the *Julia,* these creatures never had such free and easy times as they did in her crazy old hull; every chink and cranny swarmed with them; they did not live among you, but you among them. So true was this, that the business of eating and drinking was better done in the dark than in the light of day.

Concerning the cockroaches, there was an extraordinary phenomenon, for which none of us could ever account.

Every night they had a jubilee. The first symptom was an unusual clustering and humming among the swarms lining the beams overhead, and the inside of the sleeping-places. This was succeeded by a prodigious coming and going on the part of those living out of sight. Presently they all came forth; the larger sort racing over the chests and planks; winged monsters darting to and fro in the air; and the small fry buzzing in heaps almost in a state of fusion.

On the first alarm, all who were able darted on deck; while some of the sick who were too feeble, lay perfectly quiet—the distracted vermin running over them at pleasure. The performance lasted some ten minutes, during which no hive ever hummed louder. Often it was lamented by us that the time of the visitation could never be predicted; it was liable to come upon us at any hour of the night, and what a relief it was when it happened to fall in the early part of the evening.

Nor must I forget the rats: they did not forget me. Tame as Trenck's mouse, they stood in their holes peering at you like old grandfathers in a doorway. Often they darted in upon us at meal-times, and nibbled our food. The first time they approached Wymontoo, he was actually frightened; but becoming accustomed to it, he soon got along with them much better than the rest. With curious dexterity he seized the animals by their legs, and flung them up the scuttle to find a watery grave.

But I have a story of my own to tell about these rats. One day the cabin steward made me a present of some molasses, which I was so choice of, that I kept it hid away in a tin can in the farthest corner of my bunk. Faring as we did, this molasses dropped upon a biscuit was a positive luxury, which I shared with none but the doctor, and then only in private. And sweet as the treacle was, how could bread thus prepared and eaten in secret be otherwise than pleasant?

One night our precious can ran low, and in canting it over in the dark, something besides the molasses slipped out. How long it had been there, kind Providence never revealed; nor were we over-anxious to know; for we hushed up the bare thought as quickly as possible. The creature certainly died a luscious death, quite equal to Clarence's in the butt of Malmsey.

CHAPTER XI

DOCTOR LONG GHOST A WAG—ONE OF HIS CAPERS

GRAVE though he was at times, Doctor Long Ghost was a decided wag.

Every one knows what lovers of fun sailors are ashore—afloat, they are absolutely mad after it. So his pranks were duly appreciated.

The poor old black cook! Unlashing his hammock for the night, and finding a wet log fast asleep in it; and then waking in the morning with his woolly head tarred. Opening his coppers, and finding an old boot boiling away as saucy as could be, and sometimes cakes of pitch candying in his oven.

Baltimore's tribulations were indeed sore; there was no peace for him day nor night. Poor fellow! he was altogether too good-natured. Say what they will about easy-tempered people, it is far better, on some accounts, to have the temper of a wolf. Whoever thought of taking liberties with gruff Black Dan!

The most curious of the doctor's jokes, was hoisting the men aloft by the foot or shoulder, when they fell asleep on deck during the night-watches.

Ascending from the forecastle on one occasion, he found every soul napping, and forthwith went about his capers. Fastening a rope's end to each sleeper, he rove the lines through a number of blocks, and conducted them all to the windlass; then, by heaving round cheerily, in spite of cries and struggles, he soon had them dangling aloft in all directions by arms and legs. Wakened by the uproar, we rushed up from below, and found the poor fellows swinging in the moonlight from the tops and lower yard-arms, like a parcel of pirates gibbeted at sea by a cruiser.

Connected with this sort of diversion, was another prank of his. During the night some of those on deck would come below to light a pipe, or take a mouthful of beef and biscuit. Sometimes they fell asleep; and being missed directly that anything was to be done, their shipmates often amused themselves by running them aloft with a pulley dropped down the scuttle from the fore-top.

One night, when all was perfectly still, I lay awake in the forecastle; the lamp was burning low and thick, and swinging from its blackened beam; and with the uniform motion of the ship, the men in the bunks rolled slowly from side to side; the hammocks swaying in unison.

Presently I heard a foot upon the ladder, and, looking up, saw a wide trousers leg. Immediately, Navy Bob, a stout, old Triton, stealthily descended, and at once went to groping in the locker after something to eat.

Supper ended, he proceeded to load his pipe. Now, for a good comfortable smoke at sea, there never was a better place than the *Julia's* forecastle at midnight. To enjoy the luxury, one wants to fall into a kind of dreamy reverie, only known to the children of the weed. And the very atmosphere of the place, laden as it was with the snores of the sleepers, was inducive of this. No wonder, then, that after a while Bob's head sank upon his breast; presently his hat fell off, the extinguished pipe dropped from his mouth, and the next moment he lay out on the chest as tranquil as an infant.

Suddenly an order was heard on deck, followed by the trampling of feet and the hauling of rigging. The yards were being braced, and soon after the sleeper was missed; for there was a whispered conference over the scuttle.

Directly a shadow glided across the forecastle and noiselessly approached the unsuspecting Bob. It was one of the watch with the end of a rope leading out of sight up the scuttle. Pausing an instant, the sailor pressed softly the chest of his victim, sounding his slumbers; and then hitching the cord to his ankle, returned to the deck.

Hardly was his back turned, when a long limb was thrust from a hammock opposite, and Doctor Long Ghost, leaping forth warily, whipped the rope from Bob's ankle, and fastened it like lightning to a great lumbering chest, the property of the man who had just disappeared.

Scarcely was the thing done, when lo! with a thundering bound, the clumsy box was torn from its fastenings, and banging from side to side, flew toward the scuttle. Here it jammed; and thinking that Bob, who was as strong as a windlass, was grappling a beam and trying to cut the line, the jokers on deck strained away furiously. On a sudden, the chest went aloft, and striking against the mast, flew open, raining down on the heads of the party a merciless shower of things too numerous to mention.

Of course the uproar roused all hands, and when we hurried on deck, there was the owner of the box, looking aghast at its scattered contents, and with one wandering hand taking the altitude of a bump on his head.

CHAPTER XII

DEATH AND BURIAL OF TWO OF THE CREW

The mirthfulness, which, at times, reigned among us, was in strange and shocking contrast with the situation of some of the invalids. Thus, at least, did it seem to me, though not to others.

But an event occurred about this period, which, in removing by far the most pitiable cases of suffering, tended to make less grating to my feelings the subsequent conduct of the crew.

We had been at sea about twenty days, when two of the sick who had rapidly grown worse, died one night within an hour of each other.

One occupied a bunk right next to mine, and for several days had not risen from it. During this period he was often delirious, starting up and glaring around him, and sometimes wildly tossing his arms.

On the night of his decease, I retired shortly after the middle watch began, and waking from a vague dream of horrors, felt something clammy resting on me. It was the sick man's hand. Two or three times during the evening previous, he had thrust it into my bunk, and I had quietly removed it; but now I started and flung it from me. The arm fell stark and stiff, and I knew that he was dead.

Waking the men, the corpse was immediately rolled up in the strips of blanketing upon which it lay, and carried on deck. The mate was then called, and preparations made for an instantaneous burial. Laying the body out on the forehatch, it was stitched up in one of the hammocks, some "kentlege" being placed at the feet instead of shot. This done, it was borne to the gangway, and placed on a plank laid across the bulwarks. Two men supported the inside end. By way of solemnity, the ship's headway was then stopped by hauling aback the main-top-sail.

The mate, who was far from being sober, then staggered up, and holding on to a shroud, gave the word. As the plank tipped, the body slid off slowly, and fell with a splash into the sea. A bubble or two, and nothing more was seen.

"Brace forward!" The main-yard swung round to its place, and the ship glided on, while the corpse, perhaps, was still sinking.

We had tossed a shipmate to the sharks, but no one would have thought it, to have gone among the crew immediately after. The dead man had been a churlish, unsocial fellow, while alive, and no favourite; and now that he was no more, little thought was bestowed upon him. All that was said, was concerning the disposal of his chest, which, having been always kept locked, was supposed to contain money. Some one volunteered to break it open, and distribute its contents, clothing and all, before the captain should demand it.

While myself and others were endeavouring to dissuade them from this, all started at a cry from the forecastle. There could be no one there but two of the sick, unable to crawl on deck. We went below, and found one of them dying on a chest. He had fallen out of his hammock in a fit, and was insensible. The eyes were open and fixed, and his breath coming and going convulsively. The men shrank from him; but the doctor, taking his hand, held it a few moments in his, and suddenly letting it fall, exclaimed, "He's gone!" The body was instantly borne up the ladder.

Another hammock was soon prepared, and the dead sailor stitched up as before. Some additional ceremony, however, was now insisted upon, and a Bible was called for. But none was to be had, not even a Prayer Book. When this was made known, Antone, a Portuguese, from the Cape-de-Verde Islands, stepped up, muttered something over the corpse of his countryman, and, with his finger, described upon the back of the hammock the figure of a large cross; whereupon it received the dead-launch.

These two men both perished from the proverbial indiscretions of seamen, heightened by circumstances apparent; but had either of them been ashore under proper treatment, he would, in all human probability, have recovered.

Behold here the fate of a sailor! They give him the last toss, and no one asks whose child he was.

For the rest of that night there was no more sleep. Many stayed on deck until broad morning, relating to each other those marvellous tales of the sea which the occasion was calculated to call forth. Little as I believed in such things, I could not listen to some of these stories unaffected. Above all was I struck by one of the carpenter's.

On a voyage to India, they had a fever aboard, which carried off nearly half the crew in the space of a few days. After this the men never went aloft in the night-time, except in couples. When top-sails were to be reefed, phantoms were seen at the yard-arm ends; and in tacking ship, voices called aloud from the tops. The carpenter himself, going with another man to furl the main-top-gallant-sail in a squall, was nearly pushed from the rigging by an unseen hand; and his shipmate swore that a wet hammock was flirted in his face.

Stories like these were related as gospel truths, by those who declared themselves eye-witnesses.

It is a circumstance not generally known, perhaps, that, among ignorant seamen, Finlanders, or Finns, as they are more commonly called, are regarded with peculiar superstition. For some reason or other, which I never could get at, they are supposed to possess the gift of second sight, and the power to wreak supernatural vengeance upon those who offend them. On this account they have great influence among sailors, and two or three with whom I have sailed at different times, were persons well calculated to produce this sort of impression, at least upon minds disposed to believe in such things.

Now, we had one of these sea-prophets aboard; an old, yellow-haired fellow, who always wore a rude seal-skin cap of his own make, and carried his tobacco in a large pouch made of the same stuff. Van, as we called him, was a quiet, inoffensive man to look at, and, among such a set, his occasional peculiarities had hitherto passed for nothing. At this time, however, he came out with a prediction, which was none the less remarkable from its absolute fulfilment, though not exactly in the spirit in which it was given out.

The night of the burial he laid his hand on the old horseshoe nailed as a charm to the foremast, and solemnly told us that, in less than three weeks, not one quarter of our number would remain aboard the ship—by that time they would have left her for ever.

Some laughed; Flash Jack called him an old fool; but among the men generally it produced a marked effect. For several days a degree of quiet reigned among us, and allusions of such a kind were made to recent events, as could be attributed to no other cause than the Finn's omen.

For my own part, what had lately come to pass was not without its influence. It forcibly brought to mind our really critical condition. Doctor Long Ghost, too, frequently revealed his apprehensions, and once assured me that he would give much to be safely landed upon any island around us.

Where we were, exactly, no one but the mate seemed to know, nor whither we were going. The captain—a mere cipher—was an invalid in his cabin; to say nothing more of so many of his men languishing in the forecastle.

Our keeping the sea under these circumstances, a matter strange enough at first, now seemed wholly unwarranted; and added to all was the thought that our fate was absolutely in the hand of the reckless Jermin. Were anything to happen to him, we would be left without a navigator, for, according to Jermin himself, he had, from the commencement of the voyage, always kept the ship's reckoning, the captain's nautical knowledge being insufficient.

But considerations like these, strange as it may seem, seldom or never occurred to the crew. They were alive only to superstitious fears; and when, in apparent contradiction to the Finn's prophecy, the sick men rallied a little, they began to recover their former spirits, and the recollection of what had occurred insensibly faded from their minds. In a week's time, the unworthiness of *Little Jule*, as a sea vessel, always a subject of jest, now became more so than ever. In the forecastle, Flash Jack, with his knife, often dug into the dank, rotten planks ribbed between us and death, and flung away the splinters with some sea joke.

As to the remaining invalids, they were hardly ill enough to occasion any serious apprehension, at least for the present, in the breasts of such thoughtless beings as themselves. And even those who suffered the most, studiously refrained from any expression of pain.

The truth is, that among sailors as a class, sickness at sea is so heartily detested, and the sick so little cared for, that the greatest invalid generally strives to mask his sufferings. He has given no sympathy to others, and he expects none in return. Their conduct, in this respect, so opposed to their generous-hearted behaviour ashore, painfully affects the landsman on his first intercourse with them as a sailor.

Sometimes, but seldom, our invalids inveighed· against their being kept at sea, where they could be of no service, when they ought to be ashore and in the way of recovery. But—"Oh! cheer up—cheer up, my hearties!"—the mate would say. And after this fashion he put a stop to their murmurings.

But there was one circumstance, to which heretofore I have but barely alluded, that tended more than anything else to reconcile many to their situation. This was the receiving regularly, twice every day, a certain portion of Pisco, which was served out at the capstan, by the steward, in little tin measures called "tots."

The lively affection seamen have for strong drink is well known; but in the South Seas, where it is so seldom to be had, a thorough-bred sailor deems scarcely any price too dear which will purchase his darling "tot." Nowadays, American whalemen in the Pacific never think of carrying spirits as a ration; and aboard of most of them, it is never served out even in times of the greatest hardships. All Sydney whalemen, however, still cling to the old custom, and carry it as a part of the regular supplies for the voyage.

In port, the allowance of Pisco was suspended; with a view, undoubtedly, of heightening the attractions of being out of sight of land.

Now, owing to the absence of proper discipline, our sick, in addition to what they took medicinally, often came in for their respective "tots" convivially; and, added to all this, the evening of the last day of the week was always celebrated by what is styled on board of English vessels, "The Saturday-night bottles." Two of these were sent down into the forecastle, just after dark; one for the starboard watch, and the other for the larboard.

By prescription, the oldest seamen in each claims the treat as his, and, accordingly, pours out the good cheer and passes it round like a lord doing the honours of his table. But the Saturday-night bottles were not all. The carpenter and cooper, in sea parlance, Chips and Bungs, who were the "Cods," or leaders of the forecastle, in some way or other, managed to obtain an extra supply, which perpetually kept them in fine after-dinner spirits, and, moreover, disposed them to look favorably upon a state of affairs like the present.

But where were the sperm whales all this time? In good sooth, it made little matter where they were, since we were in no condition to capture them. About this time, indeed, the men came down from the mastheads, where, until now, they had kept up the form of relieving each other every two hours. They swore they would go there no more. Upon this, the mate carelessly observed, that they would soon be where look-outs were entirely unnecessary, the whales he had in his eye (though Flash Jack said they were all in his) being so tame, that they made a practice of coming round ships, and scratching their backs against them.

Thus went the world of waters with us, some four weeks or more after leaving Hannamanoo.

CHAPTER XIII

OUR DESTINATION CHANGED

It was not long after the death of the two men, that Captain Guy was reported as fast declining, and in a day or two more, as dying. The doctor, who previously had refused to enter the cabin upon any consideration, now relented, and paid his old enemy a professional visit.

He prescribed a warm bath, which was thus prepared. The skylight being removed, a cask was lowered down into the cabin, and then filled with buckets of water from the ship's coppers. The cries of the patient, when dipped into this rude bath, were most painful to hear. They at last laid him on the transom, more dead than alive.

That evening, the mate was perfectly sober, and coming forward to the windlass, where we were lounging, summoned aft the doctor, myself, and two or three others of his favourites; when, in the presence of Bembo the Mowree, he spoke to us thus:

"I have something to say to ye, men. There's none but Bembo here as belongs aft, so I've picked ye out as the best men for'ard to take counsel with, d'ye see, consarning the ship. The captain's anchor is pretty nigh atrip; I shouldn't wonder if he croaked afore morning. So what's to be done? If we have to sew him up, some of those pirates there for'ard may take it into their heads to run off with the ship, because there's no one at the tiller. Now, I've detarmined what's best to be done; but I don't want to do it unless I've good men to back me, and make things all fair and square if ever we get home again."

We all asked what his plan was.

"I'll tell ye what it is, men. If the skipper dies, all agree to obey my orders, and in less than three weeks I'll engage to have five hundred barrels of sperm oil under hatches: enough to give every mother's son of ye a handful of dollars when we get to Sydney. If ye don't agree to this, ye won't have a farthing coming to ye."

Doctor Long Ghost at once broke in. He said that such a thing was not to be dreamt of; that if the captain died, the mate was in duty bound to navigate the ship to the nearest civilized port, and deliver her up into an English consul's hands; when, in all probability, after a run ashore, the crew would be sent home. Everything forbade the mate's plan. "Still," said he, assuming an air of indifference, "if the men say stick it out, stick it out say I; but in that case, the sooner we get to those islands of yours the better."

Something more he went on to say; and from the manner in which the rest regarded him, it was plain that our fate was in his hands. It was finally resolved upon, that if Captain Guy was no better in twenty-four hours, the ship's head should be pointed for the island of Tahiti.

This announcement produced a strong sensation—the sick rallied—and the rest speculated as to what was next to befall us; while the doctor, without alluding to Guy, congratulated me upon the prospect of soon beholding a place so famous as the island in question.

The night after the holding of the council, I happened to go on deck in the middle watch, and found the yards braced sharp up on the larboard tack, with the South-East Trades strong on our bow. The captain was no better; and we were off for Tahiti.

CHAPTER XIV

ROPE YARN

WHILE gliding along on our way, I cannot well omit some account of a poor devil we had among us, who went by the name of Rope Yarn, or Ropey.

He was a nondescript who had joined the ship as a landsman. Being so excessively timid and awkward, it was thought useless to try and make a sailor of him; so he was translated into the cabin as steward; the man previously filling that post, a good seaman, going among the crew and taking his place. But poor Ropey proved quite as clumsy among the crockery as in the rigging; and one day when the ship was pitching, having stumbled into the cabin with a wooden tureen of soup, he scalded the officers so that they didn't get over it in a week. Upon which, he was dismissed, and returned to the forecastle.

Now, nobody is so heartily despised as a pusillanimous, lazy, good-for-nothing land-lubber; a sailor has no bowels of compassion for him. Yet, useless as such a character may be in many respects, a ship's company is by no means disposed to let him reap any benefit from his deficiencies. Regarded in the light of a mechanical power, whenever there is any plain, hard work to be done, he is put to it like a lever; everyone giving him a pry.

Then, again, he is set about all the vilest work. Is there a heavy job at tarring to be done, he is pitched neck and shoulders into a tar-barrel, and set to work at it. Moreover, he is made to fetch and carry like a dog. Like as not, if the mate sends him after his quadrant, on the way he is met by the captain, who orders him to pick some oakum; and while he is hunting up a bit of rope, a sailor comes along and wants to know what the deuce he's after, and bids him be off to the forecastle.

"Obey the last order," is a precept inviolable at sea. So the land-lubber, afraid to refuse to do anything, rushes about distracted, and does nothing: in the end receiving a shower of kicks and cuffs from all quarters.

Added to his other hardships, he is seldom permitted to open his mouth unless spoken to; and then, he might better keep silent. Alas for him! if he should happen to be anything of a droll; for in an evil hour should he perpetrate a joke, he would never know the last of it.

The witticisms of others, however, upon himself, must be received in the greatest good-humour.

Woe be unto him, if at meal-times he so much as look sideways at the beef-kid before the rest are helped.

Then he is obliged to plead guilty to every piece of mischief which the real perpetrator refuses to acknowledge; thus taking the place of that sneaking rascal, nobody, ashore. In short there is no end to his tribulations.

The land-lubber's spirits often sink, and the first result of his being moody and miserable, is naturally enough an utter neglect of his toilet.

The sailors perhaps ought to make allowances; but heartless as they are, they do not. No sooner is his cleanliness questioned, than they rise upon him like a mob of the Middle Ages upon a Jew; drag him into the lee-scuppers, and strip him to the buff. In vain he bawls for mercy; in vain calls upon the captain to save him.

Alas! I say again, for the land-lubber at sea. He is the veriest wretch the watery world over. And such was Rope Yarn; of all land-lubbers, the most lubberly and the most miserable. A forlorn, stunted, hook-visaged mortal he was too; one of those, whom you know at a glance to have been tried hard and long in the furnace of affliction. His face was an absolute puzzle; though sharp and sallow, it had neither the wrinkles of age nor the smoothness of youth; so that for the soul of me, I could hardly tell whether he was twenty-five or fifty.

But to his history. In his better days, it seems he had been a journeyman baker in London, somewhere about Holborn; and on Sundays wore a blue coat and metal buttons, and spent his afternoons in a tavern, smoking his pipe and drinking his ale like a free and easy journeyman baker that he was. But this did not last long; for an intermeddling old fool was the ruin of him. He was told that London might do very well for elderly gentlemen and invalids; but for a lad of spirit, Australia was the Land of Promise. In a dark day Ropey wound up his affairs and embarked.

Arriving in Sydney with a small capital, and after a while waxing snug and comfortable by dint of hard kneading, he took unto himself a wife; and so far as *she* was concerned, might then have gone into the country and retired; for she effectually did his business. In short, the lady worked him woe in heart and pocket; and in the end, ran off with his till and his foreman. Ropey went to the sign of the Pipe and Tankard; got fuddled; and over his fifth pot meditated suicide—an intention carried out; for the next day he shipped as landsman aboard the *Julia*, South Seaman.

The ex-baker would have fared far better, had it not been for his heart, which was soft and underdone. A kind word made a fool of him; and hence most of the scrapes he got into. Two or three wags, aware of his infirmity, used to "draw him out" in conversation, whenever the most crabbed and choleric old seamen were present.

To give an instance. The watch below, just waked from their sleep, are all at breakfast; and Ropey, in one corner, is disconsolately partaking of its delicacies. Now, sailors newly waked are no cherubs; and therefore not a word is spoken, everybody munching his biscuit, grim and unshaven. At this juncture an affable-looking scamp—Flash Jack—crosses the forecastle, tin can in hand, and seats himself beside the land-lubber.

"Hard fare this, Ropey," he begins; "hard enough, too, for them that's known better and lived in Lunnun. I say now, Ropey, s'posing you were back to Holborn this morning, what would you have for breakfast, eh?"

"Have for breakfast!" cried Ropey, in a rapture. "Don't speak of it!"

"What ails that fellow?" here growled an old sea-bear, turning round savagely.

"Oh, nothing, nothing," said Jack; and then, leaning over to Rope Yarn, he bade him go on, but speak lower.

"Well, then," said he, in a smugged tone, his eyes lighting up like two lanterns, "well, then, I'd go to Mother Moll's that makes the great muffins: I'd go there, you know, and cock my foot on the 'ob, and call for a noggin o' somethink to begin with."

"And what then, Ropey?"

"Why then, Flashy," continued the poor victim, unconsciously warming with his theme: "why then, I'd draw my chair up and call for Betty, the gal wot tends to customers. Betty, my dear, says I, you looks charmin' this mornin'; give me a nice rasher of bacon and h'eggs, Betty my love; and I wants a pint of h'ale, and three nice hot muffins and butter—and a slice of Cheshire; and Betty, I wants——"

"A shark-steak, and be hanged to you!" roared Black Dan, with an oath. Whereupon, dragged over the chests, the ill-starred fellow is pummelled on deck.

I always made a point of befriending poor Ropey when I could; and, for this reason, was a great favourite of his.

CHAPTER XV

CHIPS AND BUNGS

BOUND into port, Chips and Bungs increased their devotion to the bottle; and, to the unspeakable envy of the rest, these jolly companions—or "the Partners," as the men called them—rolled about deck, day after day, in the merriest mood imaginable.

But jolly as they were in the main, two more discreet tipplers it would be hard to find. No one ever saw them take anything, except when the regular allowance was served out by the steward; and to make them quite sober and sensible, you had only to ask them how they contrived to keep otherwise. Some time after, however, their secret leaked out.

The casks of Pisco were kept down the after-hatchway, which, for this reason, was secured with bar and padlock. The cooper, nevertheless, from time to time, effected a burglarious entry, by descending into the fore-hold; and then, at the risk of being jammed to death, crawling along over a thousand obstructions, to where the casks were stowed.

On the first expedition, the only one to be got at lay among others, upon its bilge, with the bung-hole well over. With a bit of iron hoop, suitably bent, and a good deal of prying and punching, the bung was forced in; and then the cooper's neck-handkerchief, attached to the end of the hoop, was drawn in and out—the absorbed liquor being deliberately squeezed into a small bucket.

Bungs was a man after a bar-keeper's own heart. Drinking steadily, until just manageably tipsy, he contrived to continue so; getting neither more nor less inebriated, but, to use his own phrase, remaining "just about right." When in this interesting state he had a free lurch in his gait, a queer way of hitching up his waistbands, looked unnecessarily steady at you when speaking, and for the rest, was in very tolerable spirits. At these times, moreover, he was exceedingly patriotic; and in a most amusing way, frequently showed his patriotism whenever he happened to encounter Dunk, a good-natured, square-faced Dane, aboard.

It must be known here, by the bye, that the cooper had a true sailor admiration for Lord Nelson. But he entertained a very erroneous idea of the personal appearance of the hero. Not content with depriving him of an eye and an arm, he stoutly maintained that he had also lost a leg in one of his battles. Under this impression, he sometimes hopped up to Dunk, with one leg curiously locked behind him into his right arm, at the same time closing an eye.

In this attitude he would call upon him to look up, and behold the man who gave his countrymen such a thrashing at Copenhagen. "Look you, Dunk," says he, staggering about, and winking hard with one eye to keep the other shut, "Look you; one man—hang me, *half* a man—with one leg, one arm, one eye—hang me, with only a piece of a carcass, flogged your whole shabby nation. Do you deny it, you lubber?"

The Dane was a mule of a man, and understanding but little English, seldom made anything of a reply; so the cooper generally dropped his leg, and marched off, with the air of a man who despised saying anything further.

CHAPTER XVI

WE ENCOUNTER A GALE

THE mild blue weather we enjoyed after leaving the Marquesas, gradually changed as we ran farther south and approached Tahiti. In these generally tranquil seas, the wind sometimes blows with great violence; though, as every sailor knows, a spicy gale in the tropic latitudes of the Pacific, is far different from a tempest in the howling North Atlantic. We soon found ourselves battling with the waves, while the before mild Trades, like a woman roused, blew fiercely, but still warmly, in our face.

For all this, the mate carried sail without stint; and as for brave *Little Jule*, she stood up to it well; and though once in a while floored in the trough of a sea, sprang to her keel again and showed play. Every old timber groaned—every spar buckled—every chafed cord strained; and yet, spite of all, she plunged on her way like a racer. Jermin, sea-jockey that he was, sometimes stood in the fore-chains, with the spray every now and then dashing over him, and shouting out, "Well done, *Jule*—dive into it, sweetheart. Hurrah!"

One afternoon there was a mighty queer noise aloft, which set the men running in every direction. It was the main-top-gallant-mast. Crash! it broke off just above the cap, and held there by the rigging, dashed with every roll, from side to side, with all the hamper that belonged to it. The yard hung by a hair, and at every pitch, thumped against the cross-trees; while the sail streamed in ribbons, and the loose ropes coiled, and thrashed the air, like whip-lashes. "Stand from under!" and down came the rattling blocks, like so many shot. The yard, with a snap and a plunge, went hissing into the sea, disappeared, and shot its full length out again. The crest of a great wave then broke over it—the ship rushed by—and we saw the stick no more.

While this lively breeze continued, Baltimore, our old black cook, was in great tribulation.

Like most South Seamen, the *Julia's* "caboose," or cook-house, was planted on the larboard side of the forecastle. Under such a press of canvas, and with the heavy sea running, the barque, diving her bows under, now and then shipped green glassy waves, which, breaking over the head-rails, fairly deluged that part of the ship, and washed clean aft. The caboose-house—thought to be firmly lashed down to its place—served as a sort of breakwater to the inundation.

About these times, Baltimore always wore what he called his "gale-suit"; among other things, comprising a sou'-wester and a huge pair of well-anointed sea-boots, reaching almost to his knees. Thus equipped for a ducking or a drowning, as the case might be, our culinary high-priest drew to the slides of his temple, and performed his sooty rites in secret.

So afraid was the old man of being washed overboard, that he actually fastened one end of a small line to his waistbands, and coiling the rest about him, made use of it as occasion required. When engaged outside, he unwound the cord, and secured one end to a ring-bolt in the deck, so that if a chance sea washed him off his feet, it could do nothing more.

One evening, just as he was getting supper, the *Julia* reared up on her stern, like a vicious colt, and when she settled again forward, fairly *dished* a tremendous sea. Nothing could withstand it. One side of the rotten head-bulwarks came in with a crash; it smote the caboose, tore it from its moorings, and after boxing it about, dashed it against the windlass, where it stranded. The water then poured along the deck like a flood, rolling over and over pots, pans, and kettles, and even old Baltimore himself, who went breaching along like a porpoise.

Striking the taffrail, the wave subsided, and washing from side to side, left the drowning cook high and dry on the after-hatch; his extinguished pipe still between his teeth, and almost bitten in two.

The few men on deck having sprung into the main-rigging, sailor-like, did nothing but roar at his calamity.

The same night, our flying-jib-boom snapped off like a pipe-stem, and our spanker-gaff came down by the run.

By the following morning, the wind in a great measure had gone down; the sea with it; and by noon we had repaired our damages as well as we could, and were sailing along as pleasantly as ever.

But there was no help for the demolished bulwarks; we had nothing to replace them; and so, whenever it breezed again, our dauntless craft went along with her splintered prow dripping, but kicking up her fleet heels just as high as before.

CHAPTER XVII

THE CORAL ISLANDS

How far we sailed to the westward after leaving the Marquesas, or what might have been our latitude and longitude at any particular time, or how many leagues we voyaged on our passage to Tahiti, are matters about which, I am sorry to say, I cannot with any accuracy enlighten the reader. Jermin, as navigator, kept our reckoning; and, as hinted before, kept it all to himself. At noon, he brought out his quadrant, a rusty old thing, so odd-looking that it might have belonged to an astrologer.

Sometimes, when rather flustered from his potations, he went staggering about deck, instrument to eye, looking all over for the sun—a phenomenon which any sober observer might have seen right overhead. How upon earth he contrived, on some occasions, to settle his latitude, is more than I can tell. The longitude, he must either have obtained by the Rule of Three, or else by special revelation. Not that the chronometer in the cabin was seldom to be relied on, or was any ways fidgety; quite the contrary; it stood stockstill; and by that means, no doubt, the true Greenwich time—at the period of its stopping, at least—was preserved to a second.

The mate, however, in addition to his "Dead Reckoning," pretended to ascertain his meridian distance from Bow Bells by an occasional lunar observation. This, I believe, consists in obtaining with the proper instruments, the angular distance between the moon and some one of the stars. The operation generally requires two observers to take sights, at one and the same time.

Now, though the mate *alone* might have been thought well calculated for this, inasmuch as he generally saw things double, the doctor was usually called upon to play a sort of second quadrant to Jermin's first; and what with the capers of both, they used to furnish a good deal of diversion. The mate's tremulous attempts to level his instrument at the star he was after, were comical enough. For my own part, when he *did* catch sight of it, I hardly knew how he managed to separate it from the astral host revolving in his own brain.

However, by hook or by crook, he piloted us along; and before many days, a fellow sent aloft to darn a rent in the fore-top-sail, threw his hat into the air, and bawled out "Land ho!"

Land it was; but in what part of the South Seas, Jermin alone knew, and some doubted whether even *he* did. But no sooner was the announcement made, than he came running on deck, spy-glass in hand, and clapping it to his eye, turned round with the air of a man receiving indubitable assurance of something he was quite certain of before. The land was precisely that for which he had been steering; and, with a wind, in less than twenty-four hours we would sight Tahiti. What he said was verified.

The island turned out to be one of the Pomotu or Low Group—sometimes called the Coral Islands—perhaps the most remarkable and interesting in the Pacific. Lying to the east of Tahiti, the nearest are within a day's sail of that place.

They are very numerous; mostly small, low, and level; sometimes wooded, but always covered with verdure. Many are crescent-shaped; others resemble a horse-shoe in figure. These last are nothing more than narrow circles of land, surrounding a smooth lagoon, connected by a single opening with the sea. Some of the lagoons, said to have subterranean outlets, have no visible ones; the inclosing island, in such cases, being a complete zone of emerald. Other lagoons still, are girdled by numbers of small, green islets, very near to each other.

The origin of the entire group is generally ascribed to the coral insect.

According to some naturalists, this wonderful little creature, commencing its erections at the bottom of the sea, after the lapse of centuries, carries them up to the surface, where its labours cease. Here, the inequalities of the coral collect all floating bodies; forming, after a time, a soil, in which the seeds carried thither by birds, germinate, and cover the whole with vegetation. Here and there, all over this archipelago, numberless naked, detached coral formations are seen, just emerging, as it were, from the ocean. These would appear to be islands in the very process of creation—at any rate, one involuntarily concludes so, on beholding them.

As far as I know, there are but few bread-fruit trees in any part of the Pomotu group. In many places the coco-nut even does not grow; though, in others, it largely flourishes. Consequently, some of the islands are altogether uninhabited; others support but a single family; and in no place is the population very large. In some respects the natives resemble the Tahitians; their language, too, is very similar. The people of the south-easterly clusters—concerning whom, however, but little is known—have a bad name as cannibals; and for that reason their hospitality is seldom taxed by the mariner.

Within a few years past, missionaries from the Society group have settled among the leeward islands, where the natives have treated them kindly. Indeed, nominally, many of these people are now Christians; and, through the political influence of their instructors, no doubt, a short time since came under the allegiance of Pomaree, the Queen of Tahiti; with which island they always carried on considerable intercourse.

The Coral Islands are principally visited by the pearl-shell fishermen, who arrive in small schooners, carrying not more than five or six men.

For a long while the business was engrossed by Merenhout, the French Consul at Tahiti, but a Dutchman by birth, who, in one year, is said to have sent to France fifty thousand dollars' worth of shells. The oysters are found in the lagoons, and about the reefs; and, for half a dozen nails a day, or a compensation still less, the natives are hired to dive after them.

A great deal of coco-nut oil is also obtained in various places. Some of the uninhabited islands are covered with dense groves; and the ungathered nuts which have fallen year after year, lie upon the ground in incredible quantities. Two or three men, provided with the necessary apparatus for trying out the oil, will, in the course of a week or two, obtain enough to load one of the large sea-canoes.

Coco-nut oil is now manufactured in different parts of the South Seas, and forms no small part of the traffic carried on with trading vessels. A considerable quantity is annually exported from the Society Islands to Sydney. It is used in lamps and for machinery, being much cheaper than the sperm, and, for both purposes, better than the right-whale oil. They bottle it up in large bamboos, six or eight feet long; and these form part of the circulating medium of Tahiti.

To return to the ship. The wind dying away, evening came on before we drew near the island. But we had it in view during the whole afternoon.

It was small and round, presenting one enamelled level, free from trees, and did not seem four feet above the water. Beyond it was another and larger island, about which a tropical sunset was throwing its glories; flushing all that part of the heavens, and making it flame like a vast dyed oriel illuminated.

The Trades scarce filled our swooning sails; the air was languid with the aroma of a thousand strange, flowering shrubs. Upon inhaling it, one of the sick, who had recently shown symptoms of scurvy, cried out in pain, and was carried below. This is no unusual effect in such instances.

On we glided, within less than a cable's length of the shore, which was margined with foam that sparkled all round. Within, nestled the still, blue lagoon. No living thing was seen, and, for aught we knew, we might have been the first mortals who had ever beheld the spot. The thought was quickening to the fancy; nor could I help dreaming of the endless grottoes and galleries, far below the reach of the mariner's lead.

And what strange shapes were lurking there! Think of those arch creatures, the mermaids, chasing each other in and out of the coral cells, and catching their long hair in the coral twigs!

CHAPTER XVIII

TAHITI

At early dawn of the following morning we saw the Peaks of Tahiti. In clear weather they may be seen at the distance of ninety miles.

"Hivarhoo!" shouted Wymontoo, overjoyed, and running out upon the bow-sprit when the land was first faintly descried in the distance. But when the clouds floated away, and showed the three peaks standing like obelisks against the sky; and the bold shore undulating along the horizon, the tears gushed from his eyes. Poor fellow! It was not Hivarhoo. Green Hivarhoo was many a long league off.

Tahiti is by far the most famous island in the South Seas; indeed, a variety of causes has made it almost classic. Its natural features alone distinguish it from the surrounding groups. Two round and lofty promontories, whose mountains rise nine thousand feet above the level of the ocean, are connected by a low, narrow isthmus; the whole being some one hundred miles in circuit. From the great central peaks of the larger peninsula—Orohena, Aorai, and Pirohitee—the land radiates on all sides to the sea in sloping green ridges. Between these are broad and shadowy valleys—in aspect, each a Tempe—watered with fine streams, and thickly wooded. Unlike many of the other islands, there extends nearly all round Tahiti, a belt of low, alluvial soil, teeming with the richest vegetation. Here, chiefly, the natives dwell.

Seen from the sea, the prospect is magnificent. It is one mass of shaded tints of green, from beach to mountain top; endlessly diversified with valleys, ridges, glens, and cascades. Over the ridges, here and there, the loftier peaks fling their shadows, and far down the valleys. At the head of these, the water-falls flash out into the sunlight as if pouring through vertical bowers of verdure. Such enchantment, too, breathes over the whole, that it seems a fairy world, all fresh and blooming from the hand of the Creator.

Upon a near approach, the picture loses not its attractions. It is no exag-geration to say, that to a European of any sensibility, who, for the first time, wanders back into these valleys—away from the haunts of the natives—the ineffable repose and beauty of the landscape is such, that every object strikes him like something seen in a dream; and for a time he almost refuses to believe that scenes like these should have a commonplace existence. No wonder that the French bestowed upon the island the appellation of the New Cytherea. "Often," says De Bougainville, "I thought I was walking in the Garden of Eden."

Nor, when first discovered, did the inhabitants of this charming country at all diminish the wonder and admiration of the voyager. Their physical beauty and amiable dispositions harmonized completely with the softness of their clime. In truth, everything about them was calculated to awaken the liveliest interest. Glance at their civil and religious institutions. To their king, divine rights were paid; while for poetry, their mythology rivalled that of ancient Greece.

Of Tahiti, earlier and more full accounts were given than of any other island in Polynesia; and this is the reason why it still retains so strong a hold on the sympathies of all readers of South Sea voyages. The journals of its first visitors, containing, as they did, such romantic descriptions of a country and people before unheard of, produced a marked sensation throughout Europe; and when the first Tahitians were carried thither, Omai in London, and Aotooroo in Paris, were caressed by nobles, scholars, and ladies.

In addition to all this, several eventful occurrences, more or less connected with Tahiti, have tended to increase its celebrity. Over two centuries ago, Quiros, the Spaniard, is supposed to have touched at the island; and at intervals, Wallis, Byron, Cook, De Bougainville, Vancouver, Le Perouse, and other illus-trious navigators, refitted their vessels in its harbours. Here the famous Transit

of Venus was observed, in 1769. Here the memorable mutiny of the *Bounty*
afterward had its origin. It was to the pagans of Tahiti that the first regularly
constituted Protestant missionaries were sent; and from their shores also, have
sailed successive missions to the neighbouring islands.

These, with other events, which might be mentioned, have united in keeping
up the first interest which the place awakened; and the recent proceedings of
the French have more than ever called forth the sympathies of the public.

CHAPTER XIX

A SURPRISE—MORE ABOUT BEMBO

THE sight of the island was right welcome. Going into harbour after a cruise
is always joyous enough, and the sailor is apt to indulge in all sorts of pleasant
anticipations. But to us, the occasion was heightened by many things peculiar
to our situation.

Since steering for the land, our prospects had been much talked over. By
many it was supposed, that should the captain leave the ship, the crew were
no longer bound by her articles. This was the opinion of our forecastle Cokes;
though, probably, it would not have been sanctioned by the Marine Courts of
Law. At any rate, such was the state of both vessel and crew, that whatever
might be the event, a long stay, and many holidays in Tahiti, were confidently
predicted.

Everybody was in high spirits. The sick, who had been improving day by
day since the change in our destination, were on deck, and leaning over the
bulwarks; some all animation, and others silently admiring an object unrivalled
for its stately beauty—Tahiti from the sea.

The quarter-deck, however, furnished a marked contrast to what was going
on at the other end of the ship. The Mowree was there, as usual, scowling
by himself; and Jermin walked to and fro in deep thought, every now and then
looking to windward, or darting into the cabin and quickly returning.

With all our light sails wooingly spread, we held on our way, until, with the
doctor's glass, Papeetee, the village metropolis of Tahiti, came into view.
Several ships were descried lying in the harbour, and among them, one which
loomed up black and large; her two rows of teeth proclaiming a frigate. This
was the *Reine Blanche*, last from the Marquesas, and carrying at the fore,
the flag of Rear-Admiral Du Petit Thouars. Hardly had we made her out,
when the booming of her guns came over the water. She was firing a salute,
which afterward turned out to be in honour of a treaty; or rather—as far as
the natives were concerned—a forced cession of Tahiti to the French, that
morning concluded.

The cannonading had hardly died away, when Jermin's voice was heard
giving an order so unexpected that every one started. "Stand by to haul back
the main-yard!"

"What's that mean?" shouted the men, "are we not going into port?"

"Tumble after here, and no words!" cried the mate; and in a moment the
main-yard swung round, when, with her jib-boom pointing out to sea, the *Julia*
lay as quiet as a duck. We all looked blank—what was to come next?

Presently the steward made his appearance, carrying a mattress, which he spread out in the stern-sheets of the captain's boat; two or three chests, and other things belonging to his master, were similarly disposed of.

This was enough. A slight hint suffices for a sailor.

Still adhering to his resolution to keep the ship at sea in spite of everything, the captain, doubtless, intended to set himself ashore, leaving the vessel under the mate, to resume her voyage at once; but after a certain period agreed upon, to touch at the island, and take him off. All this, of course, could easily be done, without approaching any nearer the land with the *Julia* than we now were. Invalid whaling captains often adopt a plan like this; but, in the present instance, it was wholly unwarranted; and, everything considered, at war with the commonest principles of prudence and humanity. And, although, on Guy's part, this resolution showed more hardihood than he had ever been given credit for, it, at the same time, argued an unaccountable simplicity, in supposing that such a crew would, in any way, submit to the outrage.

It was soon made plain that we were right in our suspicions; and the men became furious. The cooper and carpenter volunteered to head a mutiny forthwith; and, while Jermin was below, four or five rushed aft to fasten down the cabin scuttle; others, throwing down the main-braces, called out to the rest to lend a hand, and fill away for the land. All this was done in an instant; and things were looking critical, when Doctor Long Ghost and myself prevailed upon them to wait a while, and do nothing hastily; there was plenty of time, and the ship was completely in our power.

While the preparations were still going on in the cabin, we mustered the men together, and went into counsel upon the forecastle.

It was with much difficulty that we could bring these rash spirits to a calm consideration of the case. But the doctor's influence at last began to tell; and, with a few exceptions, they agreed to be guided by him; assured that, if they did so, the ship would eventually be brought to her anchors, without any one getting into trouble. Still they told us, up and down, that if peaceable means failed, they would seize *Little Jule,* and carry her into Papeetee, if they all swung for it; but, for the present, the captain should have his own way.

By this time everything was ready; the boat was lowered and brought to the gangway; and the captain was helped on deck by the mate and steward. It was the first time we had seen him in more than two weeks, and he was greatly altered. As if anxious to elude every eye, a broad-brimmed Payta hat was pulled down over his brow; so that his face was only visible when the brim flapped aside. By a sling, rigged from the main-yard, the cook and Bembo now assisted in lowering him into the boat. As he went moaning over the side, he must have heard the whispered maledictions of his crew.

While the steward was busy adjusting matters in the boat, the mate, after a private interview with the Mowree, turned round abruptly, and told us that he was going ashore with the captain, to return as soon as possible. In his absence, Bembo, as next in rank, would command; there being nothing to do but keep the ship at a safe distance from the land. He then sprang into the boat, and, with only the cook and steward as oarsmen, steered for the shore.

Guy's thus leaving the ship in the men's hands, contrary to the mate's advice, was another evidence of his simplicity; for at this particular juncture, had neither the doctor nor myself been aboard, there is no telling what they might have done.

For the nonce, Bembo was captain; and, so far as mere seamanship was concerned, he was as competent to command as any one. In truth, a better seaman never swore. This accomplishment, by the bye, together with a surprising familiarity with most nautical names and phrases, comprised about all the English he knew.

Being a harpooneer, and, as such, having access to the cabin, this man, though not yet civilized, was, according to sea usages, which know no exceptions, held superior to the sailors; and therefore nothing was said against his being left in charge of the ship; nor did it occasion any surprise.

Some additional account must be given of Bembo. In the first place, he was far from being liked. A dark, moody savage, everybody but the mate more or less distrusted or feared him. Nor were these feelings unreciprocated. Unless duty called, he seldom went among the crew. Hard stories too were told about him; something, in particular, concerning an hereditary propensity to kill men and eat them. True, he came from a race of cannibals; but that was all that was known to a certainty.

Whatever unpleasant ideas were connected with the Mowree, his personal appearance no way lessened them. Unlike most of his countrymen, he was, if anything, below the ordinary height; but then, he was all compact, and under his swart, tattooed skin, the muscles worked like steel rods. Hair, crisp and coal-black, curled over shaggy brows, and ambushed small, intense eyes, always on the glare. In short, he was none of your effeminate barbarians.

Previous to this, he had been two or three voyages in Sydney whalemen; always, however, as in the present instance, shipping at the Bay of Islands, and receiving his discharge there on the homeward-bound passage. In this way, his countrymen frequently enter on board the colonial whaling vessels.

There was a man among us who had sailed with the Mowree on his first voyage, and he told me that he had not changed a particle since then.

Some queer things this fellow told me. The following is one of his stories. I give it for what it is worth; premising, however, that from what I know of Bembo, and the foolhardy, dare-devil feats sometimes performed in the sperm-whale fishery, I believe in its substantial truth.

As may be believed, Bembo was a wild one after a fish; indeed, all New Zealanders engaged in this business are; it seems to harmonize sweetly with their blood-thirsty propensities. At sea, the best English they speak is the South Seaman's slogan in lowering away, "A dead whale, or a stove boat!" Game to the marrow, these fellows are generally selected for harpooneers; a post in which a nervous, timid man would be rather out of his element.

In darting, the harpooneer, of course, stands erect in the head of the boat, one knee braced against a support. But Bembo disdained this; and was always pulled up to his fish, balancing himself right on the gunwale.

But to my story. One morning, at daybreak, they brought him up to a large, lone whale. He darted his harpoon, and missed; and the fish sounded. After a while, the monster rose again, about a mile off, and they made after him. But he was frightened, or "galled," as they call it; and noon came, and the boat was still chasing him. In whaling, as long as the fish is in sight, and no matter what may have been previously undergone, there is no giving up, except when night comes; and nowadays, when whales are so hard to be got, frequently not even then. At last, Bembo's whale was alongside for the second time. He darted both harpoons; but, as sometimes happens to the best men, by some unaccountable chance, once more missed. Though it is well known that such failures *will* happen at times, they, nevertheless, occasion the bitterest disappointment to a boat's crew, generally expressed in curses both loud and deep. And no wonder. Let any man pull with might and main for hours and hours together, under a burning sun; and if it does not make him a little peevish, he is no sailor.

The taunts of the seamen may have maddened the Mowree; however it was, no sooner was he brought up again, than, harpoon in hand, he bounded upon the whale's back, and for one dizzy second was seen there. The next, all was foam and fury, and both were out of sight. The men sheered off, flinging overboard the line as fast as they could; while ahead, nothing was seen but a red whirlpool of blood and brine.

Presently, a dark object swam out; the line began to straighten; then smoked round the loggerhead, and, quick as thought, the boat sped like an arrow through the water. They were "fast," and the whale was running.

Where was the Mowree? His brown hand was on the boat's gunwale; and he was hauled aboard in the very midst of the mad bubbles that burst under the bows.

Such a man, or devil, if you will, was Bembo.

CHAPTER XX

THE ROUND ROBIN—VISITORS FROM SHORE

AFTER the captain left, the land-breeze died away; and, as is usual about these islands, toward noon it fell a dead calm. There was nothing to do but haul up the courses, run down the jib, and lay and roll upon the swells. The repose of the elements seemed to communicate itself to the men; and for a time, there was a lull.

Early in the afternoon, the mate, having left the captain at Papeetee, returned to the ship. According to the steward, they were to go ashore again right after dinner with the remainder of Guy's effects.

On gaining the deck, Jermin purposely avoided us, and went below without saying a word. Meanwhile, Long Ghost and I laboured hard to diffuse the right spirit among the crew; impressing upon them that a little patience and management would, in the end, accomplish all that their violence could; and that, too, without making a serious matter of it.

For my own part, I felt that I was under a foreign flag; that an English consul was close at hand, and that sailors seldom obtain justice. It was best to be prudent. Still, so much did I sympathize with the men, so far, at least, as their real grievances were concerned; and so convinced was I of the cruelty and injustice of what Captain Guy seemed bent upon, that if need were, I stood ready to raise a hand.

In spite of all we could do, some of them again became most refractory, breathing nothing but downright mutiny. When we went below to dinner, these fellows stirred up such a prodigious tumult that the old hull fairly echoed. Many, and fierce too, were the speeches delivered, and uproarious the comments of the sailors. Among others, Long Jim, or—as the doctor afterward called him—Lacedæmonian Jim, rose in his place, and addressed the forecastle parliament in the following strain:

"Look ye, Britons! if, after what's happened, this here craft goes to sea with us, we are no men; and that's the way to say it. Speak the word, my livelies, and I'll pilot her in. I've been to Tahiti before, and I can do it."

Whereupon, he sat down amid a universal pounding of chest-lids, and cymballing of tin pans; the few invalids, who, as yet, had not been actively engaged with the rest, now taking part in the applause, creaking their bunk-boards and swinging their hammocks. Cries also were heard of "Handspikes and a shindy!" "Out stun-sails!" "Hurrah!"

Several now ran on deck, and, for the moment, I thought it was all over with us; but we finally succeeded in restoring some degree of quiet.

At last, by way of diverting their thoughts, I proposed that a "Round Robin" should be prepared and sent ashore to the consul, by Baltimore, the cook. The idea took mightily, and I was told to set about it at once. On turning to the doctor for the requisite materials, he told me he had none; there was not a fly-leaf, even, in any of his books. So, after great search, a damp, musty volume, entitled *A History of the most Atrocious and Bloody Piracies,* was produced, and its two remaining blank leaves being torn out, were, by help of a little pitch, lengthened into one sheet. For ink, some of the soot over the lamp was then mixed with water, by a fellow of a literary turn; and an immense quill, plucked from a distended albatross's wing, which, nailed against the bowsprit bitts, had long formed an ornament of the forecastle, supplied a pen.

Making use of the stationery thus provided, I indited, upon a chest-lid, a concise statement of our grievances; concluding with the earnest hope, that the consul would at once come off, and see how matters stood, for himself. Right beneath the note was described the circle about which the names were to be written; the great object of a Round Robin being to arrange the signatures in such a way, that, although they are all found in a ring, no man can be picked out as the leader of it.

Few among them had any regular names; many answering to some familiar title, expressive of a personal trait; or oftener still, to the name of the place from which they hailed; and in one or two cases were known by a handy syllable or two, significant of nothing in particular but the men who bore them. Some, to be sure, had, for the sake of formality, shipped under a feigned cognomen, or "Purser's name"; these, however, were almost forgotten by themselves; and so, to give the document an air of genuineness, it was decided that every man's name should be put down as it went among the crew. It is due to the doctor, to say, that the circumscribed device was his.

Folded, and sealed with a drop of tar, the round-robin was directed to "The English Consul, Tahiti"; and, handed to the cook, was by him delivered into that gentleman's hands as soon as the mate went ashore.

On the return of the boat, some time after dark, we learned a good deal from old Baltimore, who, having been allowed to run about as much as he pleased, had spent his time gossiping.

Owing to the proceedings of the French, everything in Tahiti was in an uproar. Pritchard, the missionary consul, was absent in England; but his place was temporarily filled by one Wilson, an educated white man, born on the island, and the son of an old missionary of that name, still living.

With natives and foreigners alike, Wilson the younger was exceedingly unpopular, being held an unprincipled and dissipated man, a character verified by his subsequent conduct. Pritchard's selecting a man like this to attend to the duties of his office, had occasioned general dissatisfaction ashore.

Though never in Europe or America, the acting consul had been several voyages to Sydney in a schooner belonging to the mission; and therefore our surprise was lessened, when Baltimore told us, that he and Captain Guy were as sociable as could be—old acquaintances, in fact; and that the latter had taken up his quarters at Wilson's house. For us, this boded ill.

The mate was now assailed by a hundred questions as to what was going to be done with us. His only reply was, that in the morning the consul would pay us a visit, and settle everything.

After holding our ground off the harbour during the night, in the morning a shore boat, manned by natives, was seen coming off. In it were Wilson and another white man, who proved to be a Doctor Johnson, an Englishman, and a resident physician of Papeetee.

Stopping our headway as they approached, Jermin advanced to the gangway to receive them. No sooner did the consul touch the deck, than he gave us a specimen of what he was.

"Mr. Jermin," he cried loftily, and not deigning to notice the respectful salutation of the person addressed, "Mr. Jermin, tack ship, and stand off from the land."

Upon this, the men looked hard at him, anxious to see what sort of a looking "cove" he was. Upon inspection, he turned out to be an exceedingly minute "cove," with a viciously pugged nose, and a decidedly thin pair of legs. There was nothing else noticeable about him. Jermin, with ill-assumed suavity, at once obeyed the order, and the ship's head soon pointed out to sea.

Now, contempt is as frequently produced at first sight as love; and thus was it with respect to Wilson. No one could look at him without conceiving a strong dislike, or a cordial desire to entertain such a feeling the first favourable opportunity. There was such an intolerable air of conceit about this man, that it was almost as much as one could do to refrain from running up and affronting him.

"So the *counsellor* is come," exclaimed Navy Bob, who, like all the rest, invariably styled him thus, much to mine and the doctor's diversion. "Ay," said another, "and for no good, I'll be bound."

Such were some of the observations made, as Wilson and the mate went below conversing.

But no one exceeded the cooper in the violence with which he inveighed against the ship and everything connected with her. Swearing like a trooper, he called the main-mast to witness, that if he (Bungs) ever again went out of sight of land in the *Julia*, he prayed Heaven that a fate might be his—altogether too remarkable to be here related.

Much had he to say also concerning the vileness of what we had to eat—not fit for a dog; besides enlarging upon the imprudence of entrusting the vessel longer to a man of the mate's intemperate habits. With so many sick, too, what could we expect to do in the fishery? It was no use talking; come what come might, the ship must let go her anchor.

Now, as Bungs, besides being an able seaman, a "Cod" in the forecastle, and about the oldest man in it, was, moreover, thus deeply imbued with feelings so warmly responded to by the rest, he was all at once selected to officiate as spokesman, as soon as the consul should see fit to address us. The selection was made contrary to mine and the doctor's advice; however, all assured us they would keep quiet, and hear everything Wilson had to say, before doing anything decisive.

We were not kept long in suspense; for very soon he was seen standing in the cabin gangway, with the tarnished tin case containing the ship's papers; and Jermin at once sung out for the ship's company to muster on the quarter-deck.

CHAPTER XXI

PROCEEDINGS OF THE CONSUL

THE order was instantly obeyed, and the sailors ranged themselves, facing the consul.

They were a wild company; men of many climes—not at all precise in their toilet arrangements, but picturesque in their very tatters. My friend, the Long Doctor, was there too; and with a view, perhaps, of enlisting the sympathies of the consul for a gentleman in distress, had taken more than ordinary pains with his appearance. But among the sailors, he looked like a land-crane blown off to sea, and consorting with petrels.

The forlorn Rope Yarn, however, was by far the most remarkable figure. Land-lubber that he was, his outfit of sea-clothing had long since been confiscated; and he was now fain to go about in whatever he could pick up. His upper garment—an unsailor-like article of dress which he persisted in wearing, though torn from his back twenty times in the day— was an old "claw-hammer-jacket," or swallow-tail coat, formerly belonging to Captain Guy, and which had formed one of his perquisites when steward.

By the side of Wilson was the mate, bareheaded, his grey locks lying in rings upon his bronzed brow, and his keen eye scanning the crowd as if he knew their every thought. His frock hung loosely, exposing his round throat, mossy chest, and short and nervous arm embossed with pugilistic bruises, and quaint with many a device in India ink.

In the midst of a portentous silence, the consul unrolled his papers, evidently intending to produce an effect by the exceeding bigness of his looks.

"Mr. Jermin, call off their names"; and he handed him a list of the ship's company.

All answered but the deserters and the two mariners at the bottom of the sea.

It was now supposed that the Round Robin would be produced, and something said about it. But not so. Among the consul's papers, that unique document was thought to be perceived; but, if there, it was too much despised to be made a subject of comment. Some present, very justly regarding it as an uncommon literary production, had been anticipating all sorts of miracles therefrom; and were, therefore, much touched at this neglect.

"Well, men," began Wilson again after a short pause, "although you all look hearty enough, I'm told there are some sick among you. Now then, Mr. Jermin, call off the names on that sick-list of yours, and let them go over to the other side of the deck—I should like to see who they are."

"So, then," said he, after we had all passed over, "*you* are the sick fellows, are you? Very good: I shall have you seen to. You will go down into the cabin, one by one, to Doctor Johnson, who will report your respective cases to me. Such as he pronounces in a dying state I shall have sent ashore; the rest will be provided with everything needful, and remain aboard."

At this announcement, we gazed strangely at each other, anxious to see who it was that looked like dying, and pretty nearly deciding to stay aboard and get well, rather than go ashore and be buried. There were some, nevertheless, who saw very plainly what Wilson was at, and they acted accordingly. For my own part, I resolved to assume as dying an expression as possible; hoping, that on the strength of it, I might be sent ashore, and so get rid of the ship without any further trouble.

With this intention, I determined to take no part in anything that might happen, until my case was decided upon. As for the doctor, he had all along pretended to be more or less unwell; and by a significant look now given me, it was plain that he was becoming decidedly worse.

The invalids disposed of for the present, and one of them having gone below to be examined, the consul turned round to the rest, and addressed them as follows:

"Men, I'm going to ask you two or three questions—let one of you answer yes or no, and the rest keep silent. Now then: Have you anything to say against your mate, Mr. Jermin?" And he looked sharply among the sailors, and, at last, right into the eye of the cooper, whom everybody was eyeing.

"Well, sir," faltered Bungs, "we can't say anything against Mr. Jermin's seamanship, but——"

"I want no *buts*," cried the consul, breaking in: "answer me *yes* or *no*— have you anything to say against Mr. Jermin?"

"I was going on to say, sir; Mr. Jermin's a very good man; but then——" Here the mate looked marlingspikes at Bungs; and Bungs, after stammering out something, looked straight down to a seam in the deck, and stopped short.

A rather assuming fellow heretofore, the cooper had sported many feathers in his cap; he was now showing the white one.

"So much then for that part of the business," exclaimed Wilson, smartly; "you have nothing to say against him, I see."

Upon this, several seemed to be on the point of saying a good deal; but disconcerted by the cooper's conduct, checked themselves, and the consul proceeded.

"Have you enough to eat, aboard? answer me, you man who spoke before."

"Well, I don't know as to that," said the cooper, looking excessively uneasy, and trying to edge back, but pushed forward again. "Some of that *salt horse* ain't as sweet as it might be."

"That's not what I asked you," shouted the consul, growing brave quite fast; "answer my questions as I put them, or I'll find a way to make you."

This was going a little too far. The ferment, into which the cooper's poltroonery had thrown the sailors, now brooked no restraint; and one of them— a young American who went by the name of Salem—dashed out from among the rest, and fetching the cooper a blow, that sent him humming over toward the consul, flourished a naked sheath-knife in the air, and burst forth with "I'm the little fellow that can answer your questions; just put them to me once, counsellor."

But the "counsellor" had no more questions to ask just then; for at the alarming apparition of Salem's knife, and the extraordinary effect produced upon Bungs, he had popped his head down the companionway, and was holding it there.

Upon the mate's assuring him, however, that it was all over, he looked up, quite flustered, if not frightened, but evidently determined to put as fierce a face on the matter as practicable. Speaking sharply, he warned all present to "look out"; and then repeated the question, whether there was enough to eat aboard. Every one now turned spokesman; and he was assailed by a perfect hurricane of yells, in which the oaths fell like hailstones.

"How's this! what d'ye mean?" he cried, upon the first lull; "who told you all to speak at once? Here, you man with the knife, you'll be putting someone's eyes out yet; d'ye hear, you sir? You seem to have a good deal to say, who are *you*, pray; where did *you* ship?"

"I'm nothing more nor a bloody *beach-comber*," retorted Salem, stepping forward piratically and eyeing him; "and if you want to know, I shipped at the Islands about four months ago."

"Only four months ago? And here you have more to say than men who have been aboard the whole voyage"; and the consul made a dash at looking furious, but failed. "Let me hear no more from *you*, sir. Where's that respectable, grey-headed man, the cooper? *he's* the one to answer my questions."

"There's no 'spectable, grey-headed men aboard," returned Salem; "we're all a parcel of mutineers and pirates!"

All this time, the mate was holding his peace; and Wilson, now completely abashed, and at a loss what to do, took him by the arm, and walked across the deck. Returning to the cabin-scuttle, after a close conversation, he abruptly addressed the sailors, without taking any further notice of what had just happened.

"For reasons you all know, men, this ship has been placed in my hands. As Captain Guy will remain ashore for the present, your mate, Mr. Jermin, will command until his recovery. According to my judgment, there is no reason why the voyage should not be at once resumed; especially, as I shall see that you have two more harpooneers, and enough good men to man three boats. As for the sick, neither you nor I have anything to do with them; they will be attended to by Doctor Johnson; but I've explained that matter before. As soon as things can be arranged—in a day or two, at farthest—you will go to sea for a three months' cruise, touching here, at the end of it, for your captain. Let me hear a good report of you, now, when you come back. At present, you will continue lying off and on the harbour. I will send you fresh provisions as soon as I can get them. There: I've nothing more to say; go forward to your stations."

And, without another word, he wheeled round to descend into the cabin. But hardly had he concluded, before the incensed men were dancing about him on every side, and calling upon him to lend an ear. Each one for himself denied the legality of what he proposed to do; insisted upon the necessity for taking the ship in; and finally gave him to understand, roughly and roundly, that go to sea in her they would not.

In the midst of this mutinous uproar, the alarmed consul stood fast by the scuttle. His tactics had been decided upon beforehand; indeed, they must have been concerted ashore, between him and the captain; for all he said, as he now hurried below, was, "Go forward, men; I'm through with you: you should have mentioned these matters before: my arrangements are concluded: go forward, I say; I've nothing more to say to you." And, drawing over the slide of the scuttle, he disappeared.

Upon the very point of following him down, the attention of the exasperated seamen was called off to a party who had just then taken the recreant Bungs in hand. Amid a shower of kicks and cuffs, the traitor was borne along to the forecastle, where—I forbear to relate what followed.

CHAPTER XXII

THE CONSUL'S DEPARTURE

DURING the scenes just described, Doctor Johnson was engaged in examining the sick; of whom, as it turned out, all but two were to remain in the ship. He had evidently received his cue from Wilson.

One of the last called below into the cabin, just as the quarter-deck gathering dispersed, I came on deck quite incensed. My lameness, which, to tell the truth, was now much better, was put down as, in a great measure, affected; and my name was on the list of those who would be fit for any duty in a day or two. This was enough. As for Doctor Long Ghost, the shore physician, instead of extending to him any professional sympathy, had treated him very cavalierly. To a certain extent, therefore, we were now both bent on making common cause with the sailors.

I must explain myself here. All we wanted was to have the ship snugly anchored in Papeetee Bay; entertaining no doubt that, could this be done, it would in some way or other peaceably lead to our emancipation. Without a downright mutiny, there was but one way to accomplish this: to induce the men to refuse all further duty, unless it were to work the vessel in. The only difficulty lay in restraining them within proper bounds. Nor was it without certain misgivings, that I found myself so situated, that I must necessarily link myself, however guardedly, with such a desperate company; and in an enterprise too, of which it was hard to conjecture what might be the result. But anything like neutrality was out of the question; and unconditional submission was equally so.

On going forward, we found them ten times more tumultuous than ever. After again restoring some degree of tranquillity, we once more urged our plan of quietly refusing duty, and awaiting the result. At first, few would hear of it; but in the end, a good number were convinced by our representations. Others held out. Nor were those who thought with us, in all things to be controlled.

Upon Wilson's coming on deck to enter his boat, he was beset on all sides; and, for a moment, I thought the ship would be seized before his very eyes.

"Nothing more to say to you, men; my arrangements are made. Go forward, where you belong. I'll take no insolence"; and, in a tremor, Wilson hurried over the side in the midst of a volley of execrations.

Shortly after his departure, the mate ordered the cook and steward into his boat; and saying that he was going to see how the captain did, left us, as before, under the charge of Bembo.

At this time we were lying becalmed, pretty close in with the land (having gone about again), our main-top-sail flapping against the mast with every roll.

The departure of the consul and Jermin was followed by a scene absolutely indescribable. The sailors ran about deck like madmen; Bembo, all the while, leaning against the taff-rail by himself, smoking his heathenish stone pipe, and never interfering.

The cooper, who that morning had got himself into a fluid of an exceedingly high temperature, now did his best to regain the favour of the crew. "Without distinction of party," he called upon all hands to step up, and partake of the contents of his bucket.

But it was quite plain that, before offering to intoxicate others, he had taken the wise precaution of getting well tipsy himself. He was now once more happy in the affection of his shipmates, who, one and all, pronounced him sound to the kelson.

The Pisco soon told; and, with great difficulty, we restrained a party in the very act of breaking into the after-hold in pursuit of more.

All manner of pranks were now played.

"Mast-head, there! what d'ye see?" bawled Beauty, hailing the main-truck through an enormous copper tunnel. "Stand by the stays," roared Flash Jack, hauling off with the cook's axe, at the fastenings of the main-stay. "Looky out for 'qualls!" shrieked the Portuguese, Antone, darting a handspike through the cabin skylight. And "Heave round cheerly, men," sang out Navy Bob, dancing a hornpipe on the forecastle.

CHAPTER XXIII

THE SECOND NIGHT OFF PAPEETEE

TOWARDS sunset, the mate came off, singing merrily, in the stern of his boat; and in attempting to climb up the side, succeeded in going plump into the water. He was rescued by the steward, and carried across the deck with many moving expressions of love for his bearer. Tumbled into the quarter-boat, he soon fell asleep, and waking about midnight, somewhat sobered, went forward among the men. Here, to prepare for what follows, we must leave him for a moment.

It was now plain enough, that Jermin was by no means unwilling to take the *Julia* to sea; indeed, there was nothing he so much desired; though what his reasons were, seeing our situation, we could only conjecture. Nevertheless, so it was; and having counted much upon his rough popularity with the men to reconcile them to a short cruise under him, he had consequently been disappointed in their behaviour. Still, thinking that they would take a different view of the matter, when they came to know what fine times he had in store for them, he resolved upon trying a little persuasion.

So on going forward, he put his head down the forecastle scuttle, and hailed us all quite cordially, inviting us down into the cabin; where, he said, he had something to make merry withal. Nothing loth, we went; and throwing ourselves along the transom, waited for the steward to serve us.

As the can circulated, Jermin, leaning on the table and occupying the captain's armchair secured to the deck, opened his mind as bluntly and freely as ever. He was by no means yet sober.

He told us we were acting very foolishly; that if we only stuck to the ship, he would lead us all a jovial life of it; enumerating the casks still remaining untapped in the *Julia's* wooden cellar. It was even hinted vaguely, that such a thing might happen as our not coming back for the captain; whom he spoke of but lightly; asserting, what he had often said before, that he was no sailor.

Moreover, and perhaps with special reference to Doctor Long Ghost and myself, he assured us generally, that if there were any among us studiously inclined, he would take great pleasure in teaching such the whole art and mystery of navigation, including the gratuitous use of his quadrant.

I should have mentioned that, previous to this, he had taken the doctor aside, and said something about reinstating him in the cabin with augmented dignity; beside throwing out a hint, that I myself was in some way or other to be promoted. But it was all to no purpose; bent the men were upon going ashore, and there was no moving them.

At last he flew into a rage—much increased by the frequency of his potations—and with many imprecations, concluded by driving everybody out of the cabin. We tumbled up the gangway in high good-humour.

Upon deck everything looked so quiet, that some of the most pugnacious spirits actually lamented that there was so little prospect of an exhilarating disturbance before morning. It was not five minutes, however, ere these fellows were gratified.

Sydney Ben—said to be a runaway Ticket-of-Leave-Man, and for reasons of his own, one of the few who still remained on duty—had, for the sake of the fun, gone down with the rest into the cabin; where Bembo, who meanwhile was left in charge of the deck, had frequently called out for him. At first, Ben pretended not to hear; but on being sung out for again and again, bluntly refused; at the same time, casting some illiberal reflections on the Mowree's maternal origin, which the latter had been long enough among sailors to understand as in the highest degree offensive. So just after the men came up from below, Bembo singled him out, and gave him such a cursing in his broken lingo, that it was enough to frighten one. The convict was the worse for liquor; indeed the Mowree had been tippling also, and before we knew it, a blow was struck by Ben, and the two men came together like magnets.

The Ticket-of-Leave-Man was a practised bruiser; but the savage knew nothing of the art pugilistic: and so they were even. It was clear hugging and wrenching till both came to the deck. Here they rolled over and over in the middle of a ring which seemed to form of itself. At last the white man's head fell back, and his face grew purple. Bembo's teeth were at his throat. Rushing in all round, they hauled the savage off, but not until repeatedly struck on the head would he let go.

His rage was now absolutely demoniac; he lay glaring, and writhing on the deck, without attempting to rise. Cowed, as they supposed he was, from his attitude, the men, rejoiced at seeing him thus humbled, left him; after rating him in sailor style, for a cannibal and a coward.

Ben was attended to, and led below.

Soon after this, the rest also, with but few exceptions, retired into the forecastle; and having been up nearly all the previous night, they quickly dropped about the chests and rolled into the hammocks. In an hour's time, not a sound could be heard in that part of the ship.

Before Bembo was dragged away, the mate had in vain endeavoured to separate the combatants, repeatedly striking the Mowree; but the seamen interposing, at last kept him off.

And intoxicated as he was, when they dispersed, he knew enough to charge the steward—a steady seaman be it remembered—with the present safety of the ship; and then went below, where he fell directly into another drunken sleep.

Having remained upon deck with the doctor some time after the rest had gone below, I was just on the point of following him down, when I saw the Mowree rise, draw a bucket of water, and holding it high above his head, pour its contents right over him. This he repeated several times. There was nothing very peculiar in the act, but something else about him struck me. However, I thought no more of it, but descended the scuttle.

After a restless nap, I found the atmosphere of the forecastle so close, from nearly all the men being down at the same time, that I hunted up an old pea-jacket and went on deck; intending to sleep it out there till morning. Here I found the cook and steward, Wymontoo, Rope Yarn, and the Dane; who, being all quiet, manageable fellows, and holding aloof from the rest since the captain's departure, had been ordered by the mate not to go below until sunrise. They were lying under the lee of the bulwarks; two or three fast asleep, and the others smoking their pipes, and conversing.

To my surprise, Bembo was at the helm; but there being so few to stand there now, they told me, he had offered to take his turn with the rest, at the same time heading the watch; and to this, of course, they made no objection.

It was a fine, bright night; all moon and stars, and white crests of waves. The breeze was light, but freshening; and close hauled, poor *Little Jule,* as if nothing had happened, was heading in for the land, which rose high and hazy in the distance.

After the day's uproar, the tranquillity of the scene was soothing, and I leaned over the side to enjoy it.

More than ever did I now lament my situation—but it was useless to repine, and I could not upbraid myself. So at last, becoming drowsy, I made a bed with my jacket under the windlass, and tried to forget myself.

How long I lay there, I cannot tell; but as I rose, the first object that met my eye, was Bembo at the helm; his dark figure slowly rising and falling with the ship's motion against the spangled heavens behind. He seemed all impatience and expectation; standing at arm's length from the spokes, with one foot advanced, and his bare head thrust forward. Where I was, the watch were out of sight; and no one else was stirring; the deserted decks and broad white sails were gleaming in the moonlight.

Presently, a swelling, dashing sound came upon my ear, and I had a sort of vague consciousness that I had been hearing it before. The next instant I was broad awake and on my feet. Right ahead, and so near that my heart stood still, was a long line of breakers, heaving and frothing. It was the coral reef, girdling the island. Behind it, and almost casting their shadows upon the deck, were the sleeping mountains, about whose hazy peaks the grey dawn was just breaking. The breeze had freshened, and with a steady, gliding motion, we were running straight for the reef.

All was taken in at a glance; the fell purpose of Bembo was obvious, and with a frenzied shout to wake the watch, I rushed aft. They sprang to their feet bewildered; and after a short, but desperate scuffle, we tore him· from the helm. In wrestling with him, the wheel—left for a moment unguarded—flew to leeward, thus fortunately, bringing the ship's head to the wind, and so retarding her progress. Previous to this, she had been kept three or four points free, so as to close with the breakers. Her headway now shortened, I steadied the helm, keeping the sails just lifting, while we glided obliquely toward the land. To have run off before the wind—an easy thing—would have been almost instant destruction, owing to a curve of the reef in that direction. At this time, the Dane and the steward were still struggling with the furious Mowree, and the others were running about irresolute and shouting.

But darting forward the instant I had the helm, the old cook thundered on the forecastle with a hand-spike, "Breakers! breakers close aboard!—'bout ship! 'bout ship!"

Up came the sailors, staring about them in stupid horror.

"Haul back the head-yards!" "Let go the lee fore-brace!" "Ready about! about!" were now shouted on all sides; while distracted by a thousand orders, they ran hither and thither, fairly panic-stricken.

It seemed all over with us; and I was just upon the point of throwing the ship full into the wind (a step, which, saving us for the instant, would have sealed our fate in the end), when a sharp cry shot by my ear like the flight of an arrow.

It was Salem: "All ready for'ard; hard down!"

Round and round went the spokes—the *Julia*, with her short keel, spinning to windward like a top. Soon, the jib-sheets lashed the stays, and the men, more self-possessed, flew to the braces.

"Main-sail haul!" was now heard, as the fresh breeze streamed fore and aft the deck; and directly the after-yards were whirled round.

In half-a-minute more, we were sailing away from the land on the other tack, with every sail distended.

Turning on our heel within little more than a biscuit's toss of the reef, no earthly power could have saved us, were it not that, up to the very brink of the coral rampart, there are no soundings.

CHAPTER XXIV

OUTBREAK OF THE CREW

THE purpose of Bembo had been made known to the men generally by the watch; and now that our salvation was certain, by an instinctive impulse they raised a cry, and rushed toward him.

Just before liberated by Dunk and the steward, he was standing doggedly by the mizzen-mast; and, as the infuriated sailors came on, his bloodshot eye rolled, and his sheath-knife glittered over his head.

"Down with him!" "Strike him down!" "Hang him at the main-yard!" such were the shouts now raised. But he stood unmoved, and, for a single instant, they absolutely faltered.

"Cowards!" cried Salem, and he flung himself upon him. The steel descended like a ray of light; but did no harm; for the sailor's heart was beating against the Mowree's before he was aware.

They both fell to the deck, when the knife was instantly seized, and Bembo secured.

"For'ard! for'ard with him!" was again the cry; "give him a sea-toss!" "Overboard with him!" and he was dragged along the deck, struggling and fighting with tooth and nail.

All this uproar immediately over the mate's head at last roused him from his drunken nap, and he came staggering on deck.

"What's this?" he shouted, running right in among them.

"It's the Mowree, zur; they are going to murder him, zur," here sobbed poor Rope Yarn, crawling close up to him.

"Avast! avast!" roared Jermin making a spring toward Bembo, and dashing two or three of the sailors aside. At this moment the wretch was partly flung over the bulwarks, which shook with his frantic struggles. In vain the doctor and others tried to save him: the men listened to nothing.

"Murder and mutiny, by the salt sea!" shouted the mate; and dashing his arms right and left, he planted his iron hand upon the Mowree's shoulder.

"There are two of us now; and as you serve him, you serve me," he cried, turning fiercely round.

"Over with them together, then," exclaimed the carpenter, springing forward; but the rest fell back before the courageous front of Jermin, and, with the speed of thought, Bembo, unharmed, stood upon deck.

"Aft with ye!" cried his deliverer; and he pushed him right among the men, taking care to follow him up close. Giving the sailors no time to recover, he pushed the Mowree before him, till they came to the cabin scuttle, when he drew the slide over him, and stood still. Throughout, Bembo never spoke one word.

"Now for'ard where ye belong!" cried the mate, addressing the seamen, who by this time, rallying again, had no idea of losing their victim.

"The Mowree! the Mowree!" they shouted.

Here the doctor, in answer to the mate's repeated questions, stepped forward, and related what Bembo had been doing; a matter which the mate but dimly understood from the violent threatenings he had been hearing.

For a moment he seemed to waver; but at last, turning the key in the padlock of the slide, he breathed through his set teeth—"Ye can't have him; I'll hand him over to the consul; so for'ard with ye, I say: when there's any drowning to be ‘done, I'll pass the word; so away with ye, ye blood-thirsty pirates!"

It was to no purpose that they begged or threatened: Jermin, although by no means sober, stood his ground manfully, and before long they dispersed, soon to forget everything that had happened.

Though we had no opportunity to hear him confess it, Bembo's intention to destroy us was beyond all question. His only motive could have been, a desire to revenge the contumely heaped upon him the night previous, operating upon a heart irreclaimably savage, and at no time fraternally disposed toward the crew.

During the whole of this scene the doctor did his best to save him. But well knowing that all I could do, would have been equally useless, I maintained my place at the wheel. Indeed, no one but Jermin could have prevented this murder.

CHAPTER XXV

JERMIN ENCOUNTERS AN OLD SHIPMATE

During the morning of the day which dawned upon the events just recounted, we remained a little to leeward of the harbour, waiting the appearance of the consul, who had promised the mate to come off in a shore boat for the purpose of seeing him.

By this time the men had forced his secret from the cooper; and the consequence was, that they kept him continually coming and going from the after-hold. The mate must have known this; but he said nothing, notwithstanding all the dancing, and singing, and occasional fighting which announced the flow of the Pisco.

The peaceable influence which the doctor and myself had heretofore been exerting, was now very nearly at an end.

Confident, from the aspect of matters, that the ship, after all, would be obliged to go in; and learning, moreover, that the mate had said so, the sailors, for the present, seemed in no hurry about it; especially as the bucket of Bungs gave such generous cheer.

As for Bembo, we were told that, after putting him in double irons, the mate had locked him up in the captain's state-room, taking the additional precaution of keeping the cabin scuttle secured. From this time forward we never saw the Mowree again, a circumstance which will explain itself as the narrative proceeds.

Noon came, and no consul; and as the afternoon advanced without any word even from the shore, the mate was justly incensed; more especially, as he had taken great pains to keep perfectly sober against Wilson's arrival.

Two or three hours before sundown, a small schooner came out of the harbour, and headed over for the adjoining island of Imeeo, or Moreea, in plain sight, about fifteen miles distant. The wind failing, the current swept her down under our bows, where we had a fair glimpse of the natives on her decks.

There were a score of them, perhaps, lounging upon spread mats, and smoking their pipes. On floating so near, and hearing the maudlin cries of our crew, and beholding their antics, they must have taken us for a pirate; at any rate, they got out their sweeps, and pulled away as fast as they could; the sight of our two six-pounders, which, by way of a joke, were now run out of the side-ports, giving a fresh impetus to their efforts. But they had not gone far, when a white man, with a red sash about his waist, made his appearance on deck, the natives immediately desisting.

Hailing us loudly, he said he was coming aboard; and after some confusion on the schooner's decks, a small canoe was launched overboard, and, in a minute or two, he was with us. He turned out to be an old shipmate of Jermin's, one Viner, long supposed dead, but now resident on the island.

The meeting of these men, under the circumstances, is one of a thousand occurrences appearing exaggerated in fiction; but, nevertheless, frequently realized in actual lives of adventure.

Some fifteen years previous, they had sailed together as officers of the bark *Jane*, of London, a South Seaman. Somewhere near the New Hebrides, they struck one night upon an unknown reef; and, in a few hours, the *Jane* went to pieces. The boats, however, were saved; some provisions also, a quadrant, and a few other articles. But several of the men were lost before they got clear of the wreck.

The three boats, commanded respectively by the captain, Jermin, and the third mate, then set sail for a small English settlement at the Bay of Islands in New Zealand. Of course they kept together as much as possible. After being at sea about a week, a Lascar in the captain's boat went crazy; and, it being dangerous to keep him, they tried to throw him overboard. In the confusion that ensued, the boat capsized from the sail's "jibing"; and a considerable sea running at the time, and the other boats being separated more than usual, only one man was picked up. The very next night it blew a heavy gale; and the remaining boats taking in all sail, made bundles of their oars, flung them overboard, and rode to them with plenty of line. When morning broke, Jermin and his men were alone upon the ocean; the third mate's boat, in all probability, having gone down.

After great hardships, the survivors caught sight of a brig, which took them on board, and eventually landed them in Sydney.

Ever since then our mate had sailed from that port, never once hearing of his lost shipmates, whom, by this time, of course, he had long given up. Judge then, his feelings, when Viner, the lost third mate, the instant he touched the deck, rushed up and wrung him by the hand.

During the gale his line had parted; so that the boat, drifting fast to leeward, was out of sight by morning. Reduced, after this, to great extremities, the boat touched, for fruit, at an island of which they knew nothing. The natives, at first, received them kindly; but one of the men getting into a quarrel on account of a woman, and the rest taking his part, they were all massacred but Viner, who, at the time, was in an adjoining village. After staying on the island more than two years, he finally escaped in the boat of an American whaler, which landed him at Valparaiso. From this period he had continued to follow the seas, as a man before the mast, until about eighteen months previous, when he went ashore at Tahiti, where he now owned the schooner we saw, in which he traded among the neighbouring islands.

The breeze springing up again just after nightfall, Viner left us, promising his old shipmate to see him again, three days hence, in Papeetee harbour.

CHAPTER XXVI

WE ENTER THE HARBOUR—JIM THE PILOT

Exhausted by the day's wassail, most of the men went below at an early hour, leaving the deck to the steward and two of the men remaining on duty; the mate, with Baltimore and the Dane, engaging to relieve them at midnight. At that hour, the ship—now standing off shore, under short sail—was to be tacked.

It was not long after midnight, when we were wakened in the forecastle by the lion roar of Jermin's voice, ordering a pull at the jib-halyards; and soon afterwards, a handspike struck the scuttle, and all hands were called to take the ship into port.

This was wholly unexpected; but we learned directly, that the mate, no longer relying upon the consul, and renouncing all thought of inducing the men to change their minds, had suddenly made up his own. He was going to beat up to the entrance of the harbour, so as to show a signal for a pilot before sunrise.

Notwithstanding this, the sailors absolutely refused to assist in working the ship under any circumstances whatever: to all mine and the doctor's entreaties lending a deaf ear. Sink or strike, they swore they would have nothing more to do with her. This perverseness was to be attributed, in a great measure, to the effects of their late debauch.

With a strong breeze, all sail set, and the ship in the hands of four or five men, exhausted by two nights' watching, our situation was bad enough; especially as the mate seemed more reckless than ever, and we were now to tack ship several times close under the land.

Well knowing that if anything untoward happened to the vessel before morning, it would be imputed to the conduct of the crew, and so lead to serious results, should they ever be brought to trial; I called together those on deck, to witness my declaration:—that now that the *Julia* was destined for the harbour (the only object for which *I*, at least, had been struggling), I was willing to do what I could, toward carrying her in safely. In this step I was followed by the doctor.

The hours passed anxiously until morning; when, being well to windward of the mouth of the harbour, we bore up for it, with the Union Jack at the fore. No sign, however, of boat or pilot was seen; and after running close in several times, the ensign was set at the mizzen-peak, Union down in distress. But it was of no avail.

Attributing to Wilson this unaccountable remissness on the part of those ashore, Jermin, quite enraged, now determined to stand boldly in upon his own responsibility; trusting solely to what he remembered of the harbour on a visit there many years previous.

This resolution was characteristic. Even with a competent pilot, Papeetee Bay is considered a ticklish one to enter. Formed by a bold sweep of the shore, it is protected seaward by the coral reef, upon which the rollers break with great violence. After stretching across the bay, the barrier extends on toward Point Venus, in the district of Matavai, eight or nine miles distant. Here there is an opening, by which ships enter, and glide down the smooth, deep canal, between the reef and the shore, to the harbour. But, by seamen generally, the leeward entrance is preferred, as the wind is extremely variable inside the reef. This latter entrance is a break in the barrier directly facing the bay and village of Papeetee. It is very narrow; and, from the baffling winds, currents, and sunken rocks, ships now and then grate their keels against the coral.

But the mate was not to be daunted; so, stationing what men he had at the braces, he sprang upon the bulwarks, and, bidding everybody keep wide awake, ordered the helm up. In a few moments, we were running in. Being toward noon, the wind was fast leaving us, and, by the time the breakers were roaring on either hand, little more than steerage-way was left. But on we glided—smoothly and deftly; avoiding the green, darkling objects here and there strewn in our path: Jermin occasionally looking down in the water, and then about him, with the utmost calmness, and not a word spoken. Just fanned along thus, it was not many minutes ere we were past all danger, and floated into the placid basin within. This was the cleverest specimen of his seamanship that he ever gave us.

As we held on toward the frigate and shipping, a canoe, coming out from among them, approached. In it were a boy and an old man—both islanders; the former nearly naked, and the latter dressed in an old naval frock-coat. Both were paddling with might and main; the old man, once in a while, tearing his paddle out of the water; and, after rapping his companion over the head, both fell to with fresh vigour. As they came within hail, the old fellow, springing to his feet and flourishing his paddle, cut some of the queerest of capers; all the while jabbering something which at first we could not understand.

Presently we made out the following:—"Ah! you *pemi*, ah!—you come!—What for you come?—You be fine for come no pilot.—I say, you *hear?*—I say, you *ita maitai* (no good).—You *hear?*—You no pilot.—Yes, you d——me, you no pilot 't all; I d—— you; you *hear?*"

This tirade, which showed plainly that, whatever the profane old rascal was at, he was in right good earnest, produced peals of laughter from the ship. Upon which, he seemed to get beside himself; and the boy, who, with suspended paddle, was staring about him, received a sound box over the head, which set him to work in a twinkling, and brought the canoe quite near. The orator now opening afresh, it turned out that his vehement rhetoric was all addressed to the mate, still standing conspicuously on the bulwarks.

But Jermin was in no humour for nonsense; so, with a sailor's blessing, he ordered him off. The old fellow then flew into a regular frenzy, cursing and swearing worse than any civilized being I ever heard.

"You *sabbe* me?" he shouted. "You know me, ah? Well: me *Jim,* me *pilot*—been pilot now long time."

"Ay," cried .Jermin, quite surprised, as indeed we all were, "you are the pilot, then, you old pagan. Why didn't you come off before this?"

"Ah! me *sabbee*,—me know—you *piratee* (pirate)—see you long time, but no me come—I *sabbee* you—you *ita maitai nuee* (superlatively bad)."

"Paddle away with ye," roared Jermin, in a rage; "be off! or I'll dart a harpoon at ye!"

But, instead of obeying the order, Jim, seizing his paddle, darted the canoe right up to the gangway, and, in two bounds, stood on deck. Pulling a greasy silk handkerchief still lower over his brow, and improving the sit of his frock-coat with a vigorous jerk, he then strode up to the mate; and, in a more flowery style than ever, gave him to understand that the redoubtable "Jim," himself, was before him; that the ship was *his* until the anchor was down; and he should like to hear what any one had to say to it.

As there now seemed little doubt that he was all he claimed to be, the *Julia* was at last surrendered.

Our gentleman now proceeded to bring us to an anchor, jumping up between the knight-heads, and bawling out "Luff! luff! *keepy off! keepy off!*" and insisting upon each time being respectfully responded to by the man at the helm. At this time our steerageway was almost gone; and yet, in giving his orders, the passionate old man made as much fuss as a white squall aboard the Flying Dutchman.

Jim turned out to be the regular pilot of the harbour; a post, be it known, of no small profit; and, in *his* eyes, at least, invested with immense importance. Our unceremonious entrance, therefore, was regarded as highly insulting, and tending to depreciate both the dignity and lucrativeness of his office.

The old man is something of a wizard. Having an understanding with the elements, certain phenomena of theirs are exhibited for his particular benefit. Unusually clear weather, with a fine steady breeze, is a certain sign that a merchantman is at hand; whale-spouts seen from the harbour, are tokens of a whaling vessel's approach; and thunder and lightning, happening so seldom as they do, are proof positive that a man-of-war is drawing near.

In short, Jim, the pilot, is quite a character in his way; and no one visits Tahiti without hearing some curious story about him.

CHAPTER XXVII

A GLANCE AT PAPEETEE—WE ARE SENT ABOARD THE FRIGATE

THE village of Papeetee struck us all very pleasantly. Lying in a semicircle round the bay, the tasteful mansions of the chiefs and foreign residents impart an air of tropical elegance, heightened by the palm-trees waving here and there, and the deep-green groves of the bread-fruit in the background. The squalid huts of the common people are out of sight, and there is nothing to mar the prospect.

All round the water, extends a wide, smooth beach of mixed pebbles and fragments of coral. This forms the thoroughfare of the village; the handsomest houses all facing it—the fluctuations of the tides being so inconsiderable, that they cause no inconvenience.

The Pritchard residence—a fine large building—occupies a site on one side of the bay: a green lawn slopes off to the sea; and in front waves the English flag. Across the water, the Tricolour also, and the Stars and Stripes, distinguish the residences of the other consuls.

What greatly added to the picturesqueness of the bay at this time, was the condemned hull of a large ship, which at the farther end of the harbour lay bilged upon the beach, its stern settled low in the water, and the other end high and dry. From where we lay, the trees behind seemed to lock their leafy boughs over its bowsprit; which, from its position, looked nearly upright.

She was an American whaler, a very old craft. Having sprung a leak at sea, she had made all sail for the island, to heave down for repairs. Found utterly unseaworthy, however, her oil was taken out and sent home in another vessel; the hull was then stripped and sold for a trifle.

Before leaving Tahiti, I had the curiosity to go over this poor old ship, thus stranded on a strange shore. What were my emotions, when I saw upon her stern the name of a small town on the river Hudson! She was from the noble stream on whose banks I was born; in whose waters I had a hundred times bathed. In an instant, palm-trees and elms—canoes and skiffs—church spires and bamboos—all mingled in one vision of the present and the past.

But we must not leave *Little Jule*.

At last the wishes of many were gratified; and like an aeronaut's grapnel, her rusty little anchor was caught in the coral groves at the bottom of Papeetee Bay. This must have been more than forty days after leaving the Marquesas.

The sails were yet unfurled, when a boat came alongside with our esteemed friend Wilson, the consul.

"How's this, how's this, Mr. Jermin?" he began, looking very savage as he touched the deck. "What brings you in without orders?"

"You did not come off to us, as you promised, sir; and there was no hanging on longer with nobody to work the ship," was the blunt reply.

"So the infernal scoundrels held out—did they? Very good; I'll make them *sweat* for it," and he eyed the scowling men with unwonted intrepidity. The truth was, he felt safer *now*, than when outside the reef.

"Muster the mutineers on the quarter-deck," he continued. "Drive them aft, sir, sick and well: I have a word to say to them."

"Now, men," said he, "you think it's all well with you, I suppose. You wished the ship in, and here she is. Captain Guy's ashore, and you think you must go too: but we'll see about that—I'll miserably disappoint you." (These last were his very words.) "Mr. Jermin, call off the names of those who did not refuse duty, and let them go over to the starboard side."

This done, a list was made out of the "mutineers," as he was pleased to call the rest. Among these, the doctor and myself were included; though the former stepped forward, and boldly pleaded the office held by him when the vessel left Sydney. The mate also—who had always been friendly—stated the service rendered by myself two nights previous, as well as my conduct when he announced his intention to enter the harbour. For myself, I stoutly maintained, that according to the tenor of the agreement made with Captain Guy, my time aboard the ship had expired—the cruise being virtually at an end, however it had been brought about—and I claimed my discharge.

But Wilson would hear nothing. Marking something in my manner, nevertheless, he asked my name and country; and then observed with a sneer, "Ah, you are the lad, I see, that wrote the Round Robin; I'll take good care of *you*, my fine fellow—step back, sir."

As for poor Long Ghost, he denounced him as a "Sydney Flash-Gorger"; though what under heaven he meant by that euphonious title, is more than I can tell. Upon this, the doctor gave him such a piece of his mind, that the consul furiously commanded him to hold his peace, or he would instantly have him seized into the rigging, and flogged. There was no help for either of us —we were judged by the company we kept.

All were now sent forward; not a word being said as to what he intended doing with us.

After a talk with the mate, the consul withdrew, going aboard the French frigate, which lay within a cable's length. We now suspected his object; and since matters had come to this pass, were rejoiced at it. In a day or two the Frenchman was to sail for Valparaiso, the usual place of rendezvous for the English squadron in the Pacific; and doubtless, Wilson meant to put us on board, and send us hither to be delivered up. Should our conjecture prove correct, all we had to expect, according to our most experienced shipmates, was the fag end of a cruise in one of her majesty's ships, and a discharge before long at Portsmouth.

We now proceeded to put on all the clothes we could—frock over frock, and trousers over trousers—so as to be in readiness for removal at a moment's warning. Armed ships allow nothing superfluous to litter up the deck; and therefore, should we go aboard the frigate, our chests and their contents would have to be left behind.

In an hour's time, the first cutter of the *Reine Blanche* came alongside, manned by eighteen or twenty sailors, armed with cutlasses and boarding-pistols—the officers, of course, wearing their side-arms, and the consul in an official cocked hat, borrowed for the occasion. The boat was painted a "pirate black," its crew were a dark, grim-looking set, and the officers uncommonly fierce-looking little Frenchmen. On the whole they were calculated to intimidate—the consul's object, doubtless, in bringing them.

Summoned aft again, every one's name was called separately; and being solemnly reminded that it was his last chance to escape punishment, was asked if he still refused duty. The response was instantaneous: "Ay, sir, I do." In some cases followed up by divers explanatory observations, cut short by Wilson's ordering the delinquent into the cutter. As a general thing, the order was promptly obeyed—some taking a sequence of hops, skips, and jumps, by way of showing, not only their unimpaired activity of body, but their alacrity in complying with all reasonable requests.

Having avowed their resolution not to pull another rope of the *Julia's*—even if at once restored to perfect health—all the invalids, with the exception of the two to be set ashore, accompanied us into the cutter. They were in high spirits; so much so, that something was insinuated about their not having been quite as ill as pretended.

The cooper's name was the last called; we did not hear what he answered, but he stayed behind. Nothing was done about the Mowree.

Shoving clear from the ship, three loud cheers were raised; Flash Jack and others receiving a sharp reprimand for it from the consul.

"Good-bye, *Little Jule*," cried Navy Bob, as we swept under the bows. "Don't fall overboard, Ropey," said another to the poor land-lubber, who, with Wymontoo, the Dane, and others left behind, was looking over at us from the forecastle.

"Give her three more!" cried Salem, springing to his feet and whirling his hat round. "You sacre dam raskeel," shouted the lieutenant of the party, bringing the flat of his sabre across his shoulders, "you now keepy steel."

The doctor and myself, more discreet, sat quietly in the bow of the cutter; and for my own part, though I did not repent what I had done, my reflections were far from being enviable.

CHAPTER XXVIII

RECEPTION FROM THE FRENCHMAN

IN a few moments, we were paraded in the frigate's gangway; the first lieutenant—an elderly, yellow-faced officer, in an ill-cut coat and tarnished gold lace—coming up, and frowning upon us.

This gentleman's head was a mere bald spot; his legs, sticks; in short, his whole physical vigour seemed exhausted in the production of one enormous moustache. Old Gamboge, as he was forthwith christened, now received a paper from the consul; and, opening it, proceeded to compare the goods delivered with the invoice.

After being thoroughly counted, a meek little midshipman was called, and we were soon after given in custody to half a dozen sailor-soldiers—fellows with tarpaulins and muskets. Preceded by a pompous functionary (whom we took for one of the ship's corporals, from his ratan and the gold lace on his sleeve), we were now escorted down the ladders to the berth deck.

Here we were politely handcuffed, all round; the man with the bamboo evincing the utmost solicitude in giving us a good fit from a large basket of the articles of assorted sizes.

Taken by surprise at such an uncivil reception, a few of the party demurred; but all coyness was, at last, overcome; and finally our feet were inserted into heavy anklets of iron, running along a great bar bolted down to the deck. After this, we considered ourselves permanently established in our new quarters.

"The deuce take their old iron!" exclaimed the doctor; "if I'd known this, I'd stayed behind."

"Ha, ha!" cried Flash Jack, "you're in for it, Doctor Long Ghost."

"My hands and feet are, anyway," was the reply.

They placed a sentry over us; a great lubber of a fellow, who marched up and down with a dilapidated old cutlass of most extraordinary dimensions. From its length, we had some idea that it was expressly intended to keep a crowd in order—reaching over the heads of half a dozen, say, so as to get a cut at somebody behind.

"Mercy!" ejaculated the doctor with a shudder, "what a sensation it must be to be killed by such a tool."

We fasted till night, when one of the boys came along with a couple of "kids" containing a thin, saffron-coloured fluid, with oily particles floating on top. The young wag told us this was soup: it turned out to be nothing more than oleaginous warm water. Such as it was, nevertheless, we were fain to make a meal of it, our sentry being attentive enough to undo our bracelets. The "kids" passed from mouth to mouth, and were soon emptied.

The next morning, when the sentry's back was turned, some one, whom we took for an English sailor, tossed over a few oranges, the rinds of which we afterwards used for cups.

On the second day nothing happened worthy of record. On the third, we were amused by the following scene.

A man, whom we supposed a boatswain's mate, from the silver whistle hanging from his neck, came below, driving before him a couple of blubbering boys, and followed by a whole troop of youngsters in tears. The pair, it seemed, were sent down to be punished by command of an officer; the rest had accompanied them out of sympathy.

The boatswain's mate went to work without delay, seizing the poor little culprits by their loose frocks, and using a ratan without mercy. The other boys wept, clasped their hands, and fell on their knees; but in vain; the boatswain's mate only hit out at them; once in a while making them yell ten times louder than ever.

In the midst of the tumult, down comes a midshipman, who, with a great air, orders the man on deck and running in among the boys, sets them to scampering in all directions.

The whole of this proceeding was regarded with infinite scorn by Navy Bob, who, years before, had been captain of the foretop on board a line-of-battle ship. In his estimation, it was a lubbery piece of business throughout: they did things differently in the English navy.

CHAPTER XXIX

THE "REINE BLANCHE"

I cannot forbear a brief reflection upon the scene ending the last chapter.

The ratanning of the young culprits, although significant of the imperfect discipline of a French man-of-war, may also be considered as in some measure characteristic of the nation.

In an American or English ship, a boy, when flogged, is either lashed to the breech of a gun, or brought right up to the gratings, the same way the men are. But as a general rule, he is never punished beyond his strength. You seldom or never draw a cry from the young rogue. He bites his tongue, and stands up to it like a hero. If practicable (which is not always the case), he makes a point of smiling under the operation. And so far from his companions taking any compassion on him, they always make merry over his misfortunes. Should he turn baby and cry, they are pretty sure to give him afterward a sly pounding in some dark corner.

This tough training produces its legitimate results. The boy becomes, in time, a thorough-bred tar, equally ready to strip and take a dozen on board his own ship, or, cutlass in hand, dash pell-mell on board the enemy's. Whereas the young Frenchman, as all the world knows, makes but an indifferent seaman; and though, for the most part, he fights well enough, somehow or other he seldom fights well enough to beat.

How few sea-battles have the French ever won! But more: how few ships have they ever carried *by the board*—that true criterion of naval courage! But not a word against French bravery—there is plenty of it; but not of the right sort. A Yankee's, or an Englishman's is the downright Waterloo "game." The French fight better on land; and not being essentially a maritime people, they ought to stay there. The best of shipwrights, they are no sailors.

And this carries me back to the *Reine Blanche,* as noble a specimen of what wood and iron can make, as ever floated.

She was a new ship: the present her maiden cruise. The greatest pains having been taken in her construction, she was accounted the "crack" craft in the French navy. She is one of the heavy sixty-gun frigates now in vogue all over the world, and which we Yankees were the first to introduce. In action these are the most murderous vessels ever launched.

The model of the *Reine Blanche* has all that warlike comeliness only to be seen in a fine fighting-ship. Still, there is a good deal of French flummery about her—brass-plates and other gewgaws, stuck on all over, like baubles on a handsome woman.

Among other things, she carries a stern gallery resting on the uplifted hands of two Caryatides, larger than life. You step out upon this from the commodore's cabin. To behold the rich hangings, and mirrors, and mahogany within, one is almost prepared to see a bevy of ladies trip forth on the balcony for an airing.

But come to tread the gun-deck, and all thoughts like these are put to flight. Such batteries of thunderbolt hurlers! with a sixty-eight pounder or two thrown in as make-weights. On the spar-deck, also, are carronades of enormous calibre.

Recently built, this vessel, of course, had the benefit of the latest improvements. I was quite amazed to see on what high principles of art some exceedingly simple things were done. But your Gaul is scientific about everything; what other people accomplish by a few hard knocks, he delights in achieving by a complex arrangement of the pulley, lever, and screw.

What demi-semi-quavers in a French air! In exchanging naval courtesies, I have known a French band play "Yankee Doodle" with such a string of variations, that no one but a "pretty 'cute" Yankee could tell what they were at.

In the French navy they have no marines; their men, taking turns at carrying the musket, are sailors one moment, and soldiers the next; a fellow running aloft in his line-frock to-day, to-morrow stands sentry at the admiral's cabin-door. This is fatal to anything like proper sailor pride. To make a man a seaman, he should be put to no other duty. Indeed, a thorough tar is unfit for anything else; and what is more, this fact is the best evidence of his being a true sailor.

On board the *Reine Blanche,* they did not have enough to eat; and what they *did* have, was not of the right sort. Instead of letting the sailors file their teeth against the rim of a hard sea-biscuit, they baked their bread daily in pitiful little rolls. Then they had no "grog"; as a substitute, they drugged the poor fellows with a thin, sour wine—the juice of a few grapes, perhaps, to a pint of the juice of water-facets. Moreover, the sailors asked for meat, and they gave them soup; a rascally substitute, as they well knew.

Ever since leaving home, they had been on "short allowance." At the present time, those belonging to the boats—and thus getting an occasional opportunity to run ashore—frequently sold their rations of bread to some less fortunate shipmate for sixfold its real value.

Another thing tending to promote dissatisfaction among the crew was, their having such a devil of a fellow for a captain. He was one of those horrid naval bores—a great disciplinarian. In port, he kept them constantly exercising yards and sails, and manœuvring with the boats; and at sea, they were for ever at quarters; running in and out the enormous guns, as if their arms were made for nothing else. Then there was the admiral aboard, also; and, no doubt, *he* too had a paternal eye over them.

In the ordinary routine of duty, we could not but be struck with the listless, slovenly behaviour of these men; there was nothing of the national vivacity in their movements; nothing of the quick precision perceptible on the deck of a thoroughly disciplined armed vessel.

All this, however, when we come to know the reason, was no matter of surprise; three-fourths of them were pressed men. Some old merchant sailors had been seized the very day they landed from distant voyages; while the landsmen, of whom there were many, had been driven down from the country in herds, and so sent to sea.

At the time, I was quite amazed to hear of press-gangs in a day of comparative peace; but the anomaly is accounted for by the fact, that, of late, the French have been building up a great military marine, to take the place of that which Nelson gave to the waves of the sea at Trafalgar. But it is to be hoped that they are not building their ships for the people across the channel to take. In case of a war, what a fluttering of French ensigns there would be!

Though I say the French are no sailors, I am fàr from seeking to underrate them as a people. They are an ingenious and right gallant nation. And, as an American, I take pride in asserting it.

CHAPTER XXX

THEY TAKE US ASHORE—WHAT HAPPENED THERE

FivE days and nights, if I remember right, we were aboard the frigate. On the afternoon of the fifth, we were told that the next morning she sailed for Valparaiso. Rejoiced at this, we prayed for a speedy passage. But, as it turned out, the consul had no idea of letting us off so easily. To our no small surprise, an officer came along toward night, and ordered us out of irons. Being then mustered in the gangway, we were escorted into a cutter alongside, and pulled ashore.

Accosted by Wilson as we struck the beach, he delivered us up to a numer ous guard of natives, who at once conducted us to a house near by. Here we were made to sit down under a shade without; and the consul and two elderly European residents passed by us, and entered.

After some delay, during which we were much diverted by the hilarious good-nature of our guard—one of our number was called out for, followed by an order for him to enter the house alone.

On returning a moment after, he told us we had little to encounter. It had simply been asked, whether he still continued of the same mind; on replying yes, something was put down upon a piece of paper, and he was waved outside. All being summoned in rotation, my own turn came at last.

Within, Wilson and his two friends were seated magisterially at a table— an inkstand, a pen, and a sheet of paper, lending quite a business-like air to the apartment. These three gentlemen, being arrayed in coats and pantaloons, looked respectable, at least in a country where complete suits of garments are so seldom met with. One present essayed a solemn aspect; but having a short neck and a full face, only made out to look stupid.

It was this individual who condescended to take a paternal interest in myself. After declaring my resolution with respect to the ship unalterable, I was proceeding to withdraw, in compliance with a sign from the consul, when the stranger turned round to him, saying, "Wait a minute, if you please, Mr. Wilson; let me talk to that youth. Come here, my young friend: I'm extremely sorry to see you associated with these bad men; do you know what it will end in?"

"Oh, that's the lad that wrote the Round Robin," interposed the consul. "He and that rascally doctor are at the bottom of the whole affair—go outside, sir."

I retired as from the presence of royalty; backing out with many bows.

The evident prejudice of Wilson against both the doctor and myself, was by no means inexplicable. A man of any education before the mast is always looked upon with dislike by his captain; and, never mind how peaceable he may be, should any disturbance arise, from his intellectual superiority, he is deemed to exert an underhand influence against the officers.

Little as I had seen of Captain Guy, the few glances cast upon me after being on board a week or so, were sufficient to reveal his enmity—a feeling quickened by my undisguised companionship with Long Ghost, whom he both feared and cordially hated. Guy's relations with the consul readily explain the latter's hostility.

The examination over, Wilson and his friends advanced to the doorway; when the former, assuming a severe expression, pronounced our perverseness, infatuation in the extreme. Nor was there any hope left: our last chance for pardon was gone. Even were we to become contrite, and crave permission to return to duty, it would not now be permitted.

"Oh! get along with your gammon, *counsellor*," exclaimed Black Dan, absolutely indignant that his understanding should be thus insulted.

Quite enraged, Wilson bade him hold his peace; and then, summoning a fat old native to his side, addressed him in Tahitian, giving directions for leading us away to a place of safe keeping.

Hereupon, being marshalled in order, with the old man at our head, we were put in motion, with loud shouts, along a fine pathway, running far on, through wide groves of the coco-nut and breadfruit.

The rest of our escort trotted on beside us in high good humour; jabbering broken English, and in a hundred ways giving us to understand that Wilson

was no favourite of theirs, and that we were prime, good fellows for holding
out as we did. They seemed to know our whole history.

The scenery around was delightful. The tropical day was fast drawing to
a close; and from where we were, the sun looked like a vast red fire burning in
the woodlands—its rays falling aslant through the endless ranks of trees, and
every leaf fringed with flame. Escaped from the confined decks of the frigate,
the air breathed spices to us; streams were heard flowing; green boughs were
rocking; and far inland, all sunset flushed, rose the still, steep peaks of the
island.

As we proceeded, I was more and more struck by the picturesqueness of
the wide, shaded road. In several places, durable bridges of wood were thrown
over large water-courses; others were spanned by a single arch of stone. In
any part of the road, three horsemen might have ridden abreast.

This beautiful avenue—by far the best thing which civilization has done
for the island—is called by foreigners "the Broom Road," though for what
reason I do not know. Originally planned for the convenience of the missionaries journeying from one station to another, it almost completely encompasses
the larger peninsula; skirting for a distance of at least sixty miles along the low,
fertile lands bordering the sea. But on the side next Taiarboo, or the lesser
peninsula, it sweeps through a narrow, secluded valley, and thus crosses the
island in that direction.

The uninhabited interior, being also impenetrable from the densely wooded
glens, frightful precipices, and sharp mountain ridges absolutely inaccessible,
is but little known, even to the natives themselves; and so, instead of striking
directly across from one village to another, they follow the Broom Road round
and round.

It is by no means, however, altogether travelled on foot; horses being now
quite plentiful. They were introduced from Chili; and possessing all the gaiety,
fleetness, and docility of the Spanish breed, are admirably adapted to the tastes
of the higher classes, who as equestrians have become very expert. The missionaries and chiefs never think of journeying except in the saddle; and at all
hours of the day, you see the latter galloping along at full speed. Like the
Sandwich Islanders, they ride like Pawnee-Loups.

For miles and miles I have travelled the Broom Road, and never wearied
of the continual change of scenery. But wherever it leads you—whether through
level woods, across grassy glens, or over hills waving with palms—the bright
blue sea on one side, and the green mountain pinnacles on the other, are always
in sight.

CHAPTER XXXI

THE CALABOOZA BERETANEE

ABOUT a mile from the village we came to a halt.

It was a beautiful spot. A mountain stream here flowed at the foot of a
verdant slope; on one hand, it murmured along until the waters, spreading
themselves upon a beach of small, sparkling shells, trickled into the sea; on the
other, was a long defile, where the eye pursued a gleaming, sinuous thread, lost
in shade and verdure.

The ground next the road was walled in by a low, rude parapet of stones;

and, upon the summit of the slope beyond, was a large, native house, the thatch dazzling white, and, in shape, an oval.

"Calabooza!   Calabooza Beretanee!" (the English Jail), cried our conductor, pointing to the building.

For a few months past, having been used by the consul as a house of confinement for his refractory sailors, it was thus styled to distinguish it from similar places in and about Papeetee.

Though extremely romantic in appearance, on a near approach it proved but ill adapted to domestic comfort. In short, it was a mere shell, recently built, and still unfinished. It was open all round, and tufts of grass were growing here and there under the very roof. The only piece of furniture was the "stocks," a clumsy machine for keeping people in one place, which, I believe, is pretty much out of date in most countries. It is still in use, however, among the Spaniards in South America; from whom, it seems, the Tahitians have borrowed the contrivance, as well as the name by which all places of confinement are known among them.

The stocks were nothing more than two stout timbers, about twenty feet in length, and precisely alike. One was placed edgeways on the ground, and the other resting on top, left, at regular intervals along the seam, several round holes, the object of which was evident at a glance.

By this time, our guide had informed us that he went by the name of *"Capin Bob"* (Captain Bob); and a hearty old Bob he proved. It was just the name for him. From the first, so pleased were we with the old man, that we cheerfully acquiesced in his authority.

Entering the building, he set us about fetching heaps of dry leaves to spread behind the stocks for a couch. A trunk of a small coco-nut tree was then placed for a bolster—rather a hard one, but the natives are used to it. For a pillow, they use a little billet of wood, scooped out, and standing on four short legs—a sort of head-stool.

These arrangements completed, Captain Bob proceeded to "hannapar," or secure us, for the night. The upper timber of the machine being lifted at one end, and our ankles placed in the semicircular spaces of the lower one, the other beam was then dropped; both being finally secured together by an old iron hoop at either extremity. This initiation was performed to the boisterous mirth of the natives, and diverted ourselves not a little.

Captain Bob now bustled about, like an old woman seeing the children to bed. A basket of baked "taro," or Indian turnip, was brought in, and we were given a piece all round. Then a great counterpane, of coarse, brown "tappa," was stretched over the whole party; and, after sundry injunctions to "moee-moee," and be "maitai"—in other words, to go to sleep, and be good boys— we were left to ourselves, fairly put to bed and tucked in.

Much talk was now had concerning our prospects in life; but the doctor and I, who lay side by side, thinking the occasion better adapted to meditation, kept pretty silent; and, before long, the rest ceased conversing, and, wearied with loss of rest on board the frigate, were soon sound asleep.

After sliding from one reverie into another, I started, and gave the doctor a pinch. He was dreaming, however; and, resolved to follow his example, I troubled him no more.

How the rest managed, I know not; but, for my own part, I found it very hard to get asleep. The consciousness of having one's foot *pinned;* and the impossibility of getting it anywhere else than just where it was, was most distressing.

But this was not all: there was no way of lying but straight on your back; unless, to be sure, one's limb went round and round in the ankle, like a swivel. Upon getting into a sort of doze, it was no wonder this uneasy posture gave me the nightmare. Under the delusion that I was about some gymnastics or other, I gave my unfortunate member such a twitch, that I started up with the idea that some one was dragging the stocks away.

Captain Bob and his friends lived in a little hamlet hard by; and when morning showed in the east, the old gentleman came forth from that direction likewise, emerging from a grove, and saluting us loudly as he approached.

Finding everybody awake, he set us at liberty; and, leading us down to the stream, ordered every man to strip and bathe.

"All han's, my boy, hanna-hanna, wash!" he cried. Bob was a linguist, and had been to sea in his day, as he many a time afterward told us.

At this moment, we were all alone with him; and it would have been the easiest thing in the world to have given him the slip; but he seemed to have no idea of such a thing; treating us so frankly and cordially, indeed, that even had we thought of running, we would have been ashamed of attempting it. He very well knew, nevertheless (as we ourselves were not slow in finding out), that, for various reasons, any attempt of the kind, without some previously arranged plan for leaving the island, would be certain to fail.

As Bob was a rare one every way, I must give some account of him. There was a good deal of "personal appearance" about him; in short, he was a corpulent giant; over six feet in height, and literally as big round as a hogshead. The enormous bulk of some of the Tahitians has been frequently spoken of by voyagers.

Beside being the English consul's gaoler, as it were, he carried on a little Tahitian farming; that is to say, he owned several groves of the breadfruit and palm, and never hindered their growing. Close by was a "taro" patch of his, which he occasionally visited.

Bob seldom disposed of the produce of his lands; it was all needed for domestic consumption. Indeed, for gormandizing, I would have matched him against any three common-council men at a civic feast.

A friend of Bob's told me that, owing to his voraciousness, his visits to other parts of the island were much dreaded; for, according to Tahitian customs, hospitality without charge is enjoined upon every one; and though it is reciprocal in most cases, in Bob's it was almost out of the question. The damage done to a native larder in one of his morning calls, was more than could be made good by his entertainer's spending the holidays with him.

The old man, as I have hinted, had, once upon a time, been a cruise or two in a whaling-vessel; and, therefore, he prided himself upon his English. Having acquired what he knew of it in the forecastle, he talked little else than sailor phrases, which sounded whimsically enough.

I asked him one day how old he was. "Olee?" he exclaimed, looking very profound in consequence of thoroughly understanding so subtle a question—"Oh! very olee—'tousand 'ear—more—big man when Capin Tootee (Captain Cook) heavey in sight." (In sea parlance, came into view.)

This was a thing impossible; but adapting my discourse to the man, I rejoined—"Ah! you see Capin Tootee—well, how you like him?"

"Oh! he maitai (good) friend of me, and know my wife."

On my assuring him strongly that he could not have been born at the time, he explained himself by saying that he was speaking of his father all the while. This, indeed, might very well have been.

It is a curious fact, that all these people, young and old, will tell you that they have enjoyed the honour of a personal acquaintance with the great navigator; and if you listen to them, they will go on and tell anecdotes without end. This springs from nothing but their great desire to please; well knowing that a more agreeable topic for a white man could not be selected. As for the anachronism of the thing, they seem to have no idea of it: days and years are all the same to them.

After our sunrise bath, Bob once more placed us in the stocks, almost moved to tears at subjecting us to so great a hardship; but he could not treat us otherwise, he said, on pain of the consul's displeasure. How long we were to be confined, he did not know; nor what was to be done with us in the end.

As noon advanced, and no signs of a meal were visible, some one inquired whether we were to be boarded, as well as lodged, at the Hotel de Calabooza?

"Vast heavey" (avast heaving, or wait a bit—) said Bob—"kow-kow" (food) "come ship by by."

And, sure enough, along comes Rope Yarn with a wooden bucket of the *Julia's* villainous biscuit. With a grin, he said it was a present from Wilson; it was all we were to get that day. A great cry was now raised; and well was it for the land-lubber that he had a pair of legs, and the men could not use theirs. One and all, we resolved not to touch the bread, come what come might; and so we told the natives.

Being extravagantly fond of ship-biscuit—the harder the better—they were quite overjoyed; and offered to give us every day, a small quantity of baked breadfruit and Indian turnip in exchange for the bread. This we agreed to; and every morning afterward, when the bucket came, its contents were at once handed over to Bob and his friends, who never ceased munching until nightfall.

Our exceedingly frugal meal of breadfruit over, Captain Bob waddled up to us with a couple of long poles hooked at one end, and several baskets of woven coco-nut branches.

Not far off was an extensive grove of orange-trees in full bearing; and myself and another were selected to go with him, and gather a supply for the party. When we went in among the trees, the sumptuousness of the orchard was unlike anything I had ever seen; while the fragrance shaken from the gently waving boughs, regaled our senses most delightfully.

In many places the trees formed a dense shade, spreading overhead a dark, rustling vault, groined with boughs, and studded here and there with the ripened spheres, like gilded balls. In several places, the overladen branches were borne to the earth, hiding the trunk in a tent of foliage. Once fairly in the grove, we could see nothing else; it was oranges all round.

To preserve the fruit from bruising, Bob, hooking the twigs with his pole, let them fall into his basket. But this would not do for us. Seizing hold of a bough, we brought such a shower to the ground, that our old friend was fain to run from under. Heedless of remonstrance, we then reclined in the shade, and feasted to our heart's content. Heaping up the baskets afterward, we returned to our comrades, by whom our arrival was hailed with loud plaudits; and in a marvellously short time, nothing was left of the oranges we brought but the rinds.

While inmates of the Calabooza, we had as much of the fruit as we wanted; and to this cause, and others that might be mentioned, may be ascribed the speedy restoration of our sick to comparative health.

The orange of Tahiti is delicious—small and sweet, with a thin, dry rind. Though now abounding, it was unknown before Cook's time, to whom the natives are indebted for so great a blessing. He likewise introduced several other kinds of fruit; among these were the fig, pine-apple, and lemon, now seldom met with. The lime still grows, and some of the poorer natives express the juice to sell to the shipping. It is highly valued as an anti-scorbutic. Nor was the variety of foreign fruits and vegetables which were introduced, the only benefit conferred by the first visitors to the Society group. Cattle and sheep were left at various places. More of them anon.

Thus, after all that of late years has been done for these islanders, Cook and Vancouver may, in one sense at least, be considered their greatest bene-factors.

CHAPTER XXXII

PROCEEDINGS OF THE FRENCH AT TAHITI

As I happened to arrive at the island at a very interesting period in its political affairs, it may be well to give some little account here of the proceedings of the French, by way of episode to the narrative. My information was obtained at the time from the general reports then rife among the natives, as well as from what I learned upon a subsequent visit, and reliable accounts which I have seen since reaching home.

It seems that for some time back the French had been making repeated ineffectual attempts to plant a Roman Catholic mission here. But, invariably treated with contumely, they sometimes met with open violence; and, in every case, those directly concerned in the enterprise were ultimately forced to depart. In one instance, two priests, Laval and Caset, after enduring a series of perse-cutions, were set upon by the natives, maltreated, and finally carried aboard a small trading schooner, which eventually put them ashore at Wallis' island— a savage place—some two thousand miles to the westward.

Now, that the resident English missionaries authorized the banishment of these priests, is a fact undenied by themselves. I was also repeatedly in-formed, that by their inflammatory harangues they instigated the riots which preceded the sailing of the schooner. At all events, it is certain that their unbounded influence with the natives would easily have enabled them to prevent everything that took place on this occasion, had they felt so inclined.

Melancholy as such an example of intolerance on the part of Protestant missionaries must appear, it is not the only one, and by no means the most flagrant, which might be presented. But I forbear to mention any others; since they have been more than hinted at by recent voyagers, and their repe-tition here would perhaps be attended with no good effect. Besides, the con-duct of the Sandwich Island missionaries in particular has latterly much amended in this respect.

The treatment of the two priests formed the principal ground (and the only justifiable one) upon which Du Petit Thouars demanded satisfaction; and which subsequently led to his seizure of the island. In addition to other things, he also charged, that the flag of Merenhout, the consul, had been repeatedly insulted, and the property of a certain French resident violently appropriated by the government. In the latter instance, the natives were perfectly in the right. At that time, the law against the traffic in ardent spirits (every now and then suspended and revived) happened to be in force; and finding a large quantity on the premises of Victor, a low, knavish adventurer from Marseilles, the Tahitians pronounced it forfeit.

For these, and similar alleged outrages, a large pecuniary restitution was demanded ($10,000), which there being no exchequer to supply, the island was forthwith seized, under cover of a mock treaty, dictated to the chiefs on the gun-deck of Du Petit Thouars' frigate. But, notwithstanding this formality, there now seems little doubt that the downfall of the Pomarees was decided upon at the Tuileries.

After establishing the Protectorate, so called, the rear-admiral sailed; leaving M. Bruat governor, assisted by Reine and Carpegne, civilians, named members of the Council of Government, and Merenhout, the consul, now made Commissioner Royal. No soldiers, however, were landed, until several months afterward. As men, Reine and Carpegne were not disliked by the natives; but Bruat and Merenhout they bitterly detested. In several interviews with the poor queen, the unfeeling governor sought to terrify her into compliance with his demands; clapping his hand upon his sword, shaking his fist in her face, and swearing violently. "Oh, king of a great nation," said Pomaree, in her letter to Louis Philippe, "fetch away this man; I and my people cannot endure his evil doings. He is a shameless man."

Although the excitement among the natives did not wholly subside upon the rear-admiral's departure, no overt act of violence immediately followed. The queen had fled to Imeeo; and the dissensions among the chiefs, together with the ill-advised conduct of the missionaries, prevented a union upon some common plan of resistance. But the great body of the people, as well as their queen, confidently relied upon the speedy interposition of England—a nation bound to them by many ties, and which, more than once, had solemnly guaranteed their independence.

As for the missionaries, they openly defied the French governor, childishly predicting fleets and armies from Britain. But what is the welfare of a spot like Tahiti, to the mighty interests of France and England! There was a remonstrance on one side, and a reply on the other; and there the matter rested. For once in their brawling lives, St. George and St. Denis were hand and glove; and they were not going to cross sabres about Tahiti.

During my stay upon the island, so far as I could see, there was little to denote that any change had taken place in the government. Such laws as they had were administered the same as ever; the missionaries went about unmolested, and comparative tranquillity everywhere prevailed. Nevertheless, I sometimes heard the natives inveighing against the French (no favourites, by the by, throughout Polynesia), and bitterly regretting that the queen had not, at the outset, made a stand.

In the house of the chief Adeea, frequent discussions toook place, concerning the ability of the island to cope with the French: the number of fighting men and muskets among the natives were talked of, as well as the propriety of fortifying several heights overlooking Papeetee. Imputing these symptoms to the mere resentment of a recent outrage, and not to any determined spirit of resistance, I little anticipated the gallant, though useless warfare, so soon to follow my departure.

At a period subsequent to my first visit, the island, which before was divided into nineteen districts, with a native chief over each, in capacity of governor and judge, was, by Bruat, divided into four. Over these he set as many recreant chiefs, Kitoti, Tati, Utamai, and Paraita; to whom he paid $1,000 each, to secure their assistance in carrying out his evil designs.

The first blood shed, in any regular conflict, was at Mahanar, upon the peninsula of Taraiboo. The fight originated in the seizure of a number of women from the shore, by men belonging to one of the French vessels of war. In this affair, the islanders fought desperately, killing about fifty of the enemy, and losing ninety of their own number. The French sailors and marines, who, at the time, were reported to be infuriated with liquor, gave no quarter; and the survivors only saved themselves by fleeing to the mountains. Subsequently, the battles of Hararparpi and Fararar were fought, in which the invaders met with indifferent success.

Shortly after the engagement at Hararparpi, three Frenchmen were waylaid in a pass of the valleys, and murdered by the incensed natives. One was Lefevre, a notorious scoundrel, and a spy, whom Bruat had sent to conduct a certain Major Fergus (said to be a Pole), to the hiding-place of four chiefs, whom the governor wished to seize and execute. This circumstance violently inflamed the hostility of both parties.

About this time, Kitoti, a depraved chief, and the pliant tool of Bruat, was induced by him to give a great feast in the Vale of Paree, to which all his countrymen were invited. The governor's object was to gain over all he could to his interests; he supplied an abundance of wine and brandy, and a scene of bestial intoxication was the natural consequence. Before it came to this, however, several speeches were made by the islanders. One of these, delivered by an aged warrior, who had formerly been at the head of the celebrated Aeorai Society, was characteristic. "This is a very good feast," said the reeling old man, "and the wine also is very good; but you evil-minded Wee-Wees (French), and you false-hearted men of Tahiti, are all very bad."

By the latest accounts, most of the islanders still refuse to submit to the French; and what turn events may hereafter take, it is hard to predict. At any rate, these disorders must accelerate the final extinction of their race.

Along with the few officers left by Du Petit Thouars, were several French priests, for whose unobstructed exertions in the dissemination of their faith the strongest guarantees were provided by an article of the treaty. But no one was bound to offer them facilities; much less a luncheon, the first day they went ashore. True, they had plenty of gold; but to the natives it was anathema—taboo—and, for several hours and some odd minutes, they would not touch it. Emissaries of the Pope and the devil, as the strangers were considered—the smell of sulphur hardly yet shaken out of their canonicals —what islander would venture to jeopardize his soul, and call down a blight on his breadfruit, by holding any intercourse with them! That morning the priests actually picnicked in a grove of coco-nut trees; but before night, Christian hospitality—in exchange for a commercial equivalent of hard dollars—was given them in an adjoining house.

Wanting in civility, as the conduct of the English missionaries may be thought, in withholding a decent reception to these persons, the latter were certainly to blame in needlessly placing themselves in so unpleasant a predicament. Under far better auspices, they might have settled upon some one of the thousand unconverted isles of the Pacific, rather than have forced themselves thus, upon a people already professedly Christians.

CHAPTER XXXIII

WE RECEIVE CALLS AT THE HOTEL DE CALABOOZA

OUR place of confinement being open all round, and so near the Broom Road, of course we were in plain sight of everybody passing; and, therefore, we had no lack of visitors among such an idle, inquisitive set as the Tahitians. For a few days they were coming and going continually; while thus ignobly fast by the foot, we were fain to give passive audience.

During this period, we were the lions of the neighbourhood; and, no doubt, strangers from the distant villages were taken to see the "Karhowrees" (white men), in the same way that countrymen, in a city, are gallanted to the Zoological Gardens.

All this gave us a fine opportunity of making observations. I was painfully struck by the considerable number of sickly or deformed persons; undoubtedly made so by a virulent complaint, which, under native treatment, almost invariably affects, in the end, the muscles and bones of the body. In particular, there is a distortion of the back, most unsightly to behold, originating in a horrible form of the malady.

Although this, and other bodily afflictions, were unknown before the discovery of the islands by the whites, there are several cases found of the Fa-Fa, or Elephantiasis—a native disease, which seems to have prevailed among them from the earliest antiquity. Affecting the legs and feet alone, it swells them, in some instances, to the girth of a man's body, covering the skin with scales. It might be supposed that one thus afflicted would be incapable of walking; but, to all appearance, they seem to be nearly as active as anybody; apparently suffering no pain, and bearing the calamity with a degree of cheerfulness truly marvellous.

The Fa-Fa is very gradual in its approaches, and years elapse before the limb is fully swollen. Its origin is ascribed by the natives to various causes, but the general impression seems to be that it arises, in most cases, from the eating of unripe breadfruit and Indian turnip. So far as I could find out, it is not hereditary. In no stage do they attempt a cure; the complaint being held incurable.

Speaking of the Fa-Fa, reminds me of a poor fellow, a sailor, whom I afterward saw at Roorootoo, a lone island, some two days' sail from Tahiti.

The island is very small, and its inhabitants nearly extinct. We sent a boat off to see whether any yams were to be had, as formerly the yams of Roorootoo were as famous among the islands round about, as Sicily oranges in the Mediterranean. Going ashore, to my surprise, I was accosted, near a little shanty of a church, by a white man, who limped forth from a wretched hut. His hair and beard were unshorn, his face deadly pale and haggard, and one limb swelled with the Fa-Fa to an incredible bigness. This was the first instance of a foreigner suffering from it that I had ever seen, or heard of; and the spectacle shocked me accordingly.

He had been there for years. From the first symptoms, he could not believe his complaint to be what it really was, and trusted it would soon disappear. But when it became plain that his only chance for recovery was a speedy change of climate, no ship would receive him as a sailor: to think of being taken as a passenger, was idle. This speaks little for the humanity of sea captains; but the truth is, that those in the Pacific have little enough of the virtue; and, nowadays, when so many charitable appeals are made to them, they have become callous.

I pitied the poor fellow from the bottom of my heart; but nothing could I do, as our captain was inexorable. "Why," said he, "here we are—started on a six months' cruise—I can't put back; and he is better off on the island than at sea. So on Roorootoo he must die." And probably he did.

I afterward heard of this melancholy object, from two seamen. His attempts to leave were still unavailing, and his hard fate was fast closing in.

Notwithstanding the physical degeneracy of the Tahitians as a people, among the chiefs, individuals of personable figures are still frequently met with; and, occasionally, majestic-looking men, and diminutive women as lovely as the nymphs who, nearly a century ago, swam round the ships of Wallis. In these instances, Tahitian beauty is quite as seducing as it proved to the crew of the *Bounty;* the young girls being just such creatures as a poet would picture in the tropics—soft, plump, and dreamy-eyed.

The natural complexion of both sexes is quite light; but the males appear much darker, from their exposure to the sun. A dark complexion, however, in a man is highly esteemed, as indicating 'strength of both body and soul. Hence there is a saying, of great antiquity among them,

> "If dark the cheek of the mother,
> The son will sound the war-conch;
> If strong her frame, he will give laws."

With this idea of manliness, no wonder the Tahitians regard all pale and tepid-looking Europeans as weak and feminine; whereas, a sailor, with a cheek like the breast of a roast turkey, is held a lad of brawn: to use their own phrase, a "taata tona," or man of bones.

Speaking of bones, recalls an ugly custom of theirs, now obsolete—that of making fish-hooks and gimblets out of those of their enemies. This beats the Scandinavians turning people's skulls into cups and saucers.

But to return to the Calabooza Beretanee. Immense was the interest we excited among the throngs that called there; they would stand talking about us by the hour, growing most unnecessarily excited too, and dancing up and down with all the vivacity of their race. They invariably sided with us; flying out against the consul, and denouncing him as "Ita maitai nuee," or very bad exceedingly. They must have borne him some grudge or other.

Nor were the women, sweet souls, at all backward in visiting. Indeed, they manifested even more interest than the men; gazing at us with eyes full of a thousand meanings; and conversing with marvellous rapidity. But, alas! inquisitive though they were, and, doubtless, taking some passing compassion on us, there was little real feeling in them after all, and still less sentimental sympathy. Many of them laughed outright at us, noting only what was ridiculous in our plight.

I think it was the second day of our confinement, that a wild, beautiful girl burst into the Calabooza, and, throwing herself into an arch attitude, stood afar off, and gazed at us. She was a heartless one:—tickled to death with Black Dan's nursing his chafed ankle, and indulging in certain moral reflections on the consul and Captain Guy. After laughing her fill at him, she condescended to notice the rest; glancing from one to another, in the most methodical and provoking manner imaginable. Whenever anything struck her comically, you saw it like a flash—her finger levelled instantaneously, and, flinging herself back, she gave loose to strange, hollow little notes of laughter, that sounded like the bass of a music-box, playing a lively air with the lid down.

Now, I knew not, that there was anything in my own appearance calculated to disarm ridicule; and, indeed, to have looked at all heroic, under the circumstances, would have been rather difficult. Still, I could not but feel exceedingly annoyed at the prospect of being screamed at in turn by this mischievous young witch, even though she were but an islander. And, to tell a secret, her beauty had something to do with this sort of feeling; and, pinioned as I was, to a log, and clad most unbecomingly, I began to grow sentimental.

Ere her glance fell upon me, I had, unconsciously, thrown myself into the most graceful attitude I could assume, leaned my head upon my hand, and summoned up as abstracted an expression as possible. Though my face was averted, I soon felt it flush, and knew that the glance was on me: deeper and deeper grew the flush, and not a sound of laughter.

Delicious thought! she was moved at the sight of me. I could stand it no longer, but started up. Lo! there she was; her great hazel eyes rounding and rounding in her head, like two stars, her whole frame in a merry quiver, and an expression about the mouth that was sudden and violent death to anything like sentiment.

The next moment she spun round, and, bursting from peal to peal of laughter, went racing out of the Calabooza; and, in mercy to me, never returned.

CHAPTER XXXIV

LIFE AT THE CALABOOZA

A few days passed; and, at last, our docility was rewarded by some indulgence on the part of Captain Bob.

He allowed the entire party to be at large during the day; only enjoining upon us always to keep within hail. This, to be sure, was in positive disobedience to Wilson's orders; and so, care had to be taken that he should not hear of it. There was little fear of the natives telling him; but strangers travelling the Broom Road might. By way of precaution, boys were stationed as scouts along the road. At sight of a white man, they sounded the alarm; when we all made for our respective holes (the stocks being purposely left open): the beam then descended, and we were prisoners. As soon as the traveller was out of sight, of course, we were liberated.

Notwithstanding the regular supply of food which we obtained from Captain Bob and his friends, it was so small, that we often felt most intolerably hungry. We could not blame them for not bringing us more, for we soon became aware that they had to pinch themselves, in order to give us what they did; beside, they received nothing for their kindness but the daily bucket of bread.

Among a people like the Tahitians, what we call "hard times" can only be experienced in a scarcity of edibles; yet, so destitute are many of the common people, that this most distressing consequence of civilization may be said, with them, to be ever present. To be sure, the natives about the Calabooza had abundance of limes and oranges; but what were *these* good for, except to impart a still keener edge to appetites which there was so little else to gratify? During the height of the breadfruit season, they fare better; but, at other times, the demands of the shipping exhaust the uncultivated resources of the island; and the lands being mostly owned by the chiefs, the inferior orders have to suffer for their cupidity. Deprived of their nets, many of them would starve.

As Captain Bob insensibly remitted his watchfulness, and we began to stroll farther and farther from the Calabooza, we managed, by a systematic foraging upon the country round about, to make up for some of our deficiencies. And fortunate it was, that the houses of the wealthier natives were just as open to us as those of the most destitute; we were treated as kindly in one as the other.

Once in a while, we came in at the death of a chief's pig; the noise of whose slaughtering was generally to be heard at a great distance. An occasion like this gathers the neighbours together, and they have a bit of a feast, where a stranger is always welcome. A good loud squeal, therefore, was music in our ears. It showed something going on in that direction.

Breaking in upon the party tumultuously, as we did, we always created a sensation. Sometimes, we found the animal still alive and struggling; in which case, it was generally dropped at our approach. To provide for these emergencies, Flash Jack generally repaired to the scene of operations with a sheath knife between his teeth, and a club in his hand. Others were exceedingly officious in singeing off the bristles, and disembowelling. Doctor Long Ghost and myself, however, never meddled with these preliminaries, but came to the feast itself, with unimpaired energies.

Like all lank men, my long friend had an appetite of his own. Others occasionally went about seeking what they might devour, but *he* was always on the alert.

He had an ingenious way of obviating an inconvenience which we all experienced at times. The islanders seldom use salt with their food; so he begged Rope Yarn to bring him some from the ship; also a little pepper, if he could; which, accordingly, was done. This he placed in a small leather wallet—a "'monkey bag" (so called by sailors)—usually worn as a purse about the neck.

"In my poor opinion," said Long Ghost, as he tucked the wallet out of sight, "it behooves a stranger in Tahiti to have his knife in readiness, and his caster slung."

CHAPTER XXXV

VISIT FROM AN OLD ACQUAINTANCE

WE had not been many days ashore, when Doctor Johnson was espied coming along the Broom Road.

We had heard that he meditated a visit, and suspected what he was after. Being upon the consul's hands, all our expenses were of course payable by him in his official capacity; and, therefore, as a friend of Wilson, and sure of good pay, the shore doctor had some idea of allowing us to run up a bill with him. True, it was rather awkward to ask us to take medicines, which, on board the ship, he told us were not needed. However, he resolved to put a bold face on the matter, and give us a call.

His approach was announced by one of the scouts, upon which some one suggested that we should let him enter, and then put him in the stocks. But Long Ghost proposed better sport. What it was, we shall presently see.

Very bland and amiable, Doctor Johnson advanced, and, resting his cane on the stocks, glanced to right and left, as we lay before him. "Well, my lads"—he began—"how do you find yourselves to-day?"

Looking very demure, the men made some rejoinder; and he went on.

"Those poor fellows I saw the other day—the sick, I mean—how are they?" and he scrutinized the company. At last, he singled out one who was assuming a most unearthly appearance, and remarked, that he looked as if he were extremely ill. "Yes," said the sailor dolefully, "I'm afeard, doctor, I'll soon be losing the number of my mess!" (a sea phrase, for departing this life) and he closed his eyes, and moaned.

"*What* does he say?" said Johnson, turning round eagerly.

"Why," exclaimed Flash Jack, who volunteered as interpreter, "he means he's going to *croak*" (die).

"*Croak!* and what does that mean, applied to a patient?"

"Oh! I understand," said he, when the word was explained; and he stepped over the stocks, and felt the man's pulse.

"What's his name?" he asked, turning this time to old Navy Bob.

"We calls him Jingling Joe," replied that worthy.

"Well then, men, you must take good care of poor Joseph; and I will send him a powder, which must be taken according to the directions. Some of you know how to read, I presume?"

"That ere young cove does," replied Bob, pointing toward the place where I lay, as if he were directing attention to a sail at sea.

After examining the rest—some of whom were really invalids, but convalescent, and others only pretending to be labouring under divers maladies, Johnson turned round, and addressed the party.

"Men," said he, "if any more of you are ailing, speak up, and let me know. By order of the consul, I'm to call every day; so if any of you are at all sick, it's my duty to prescribe for you. This sudden change from ship fare to shore living plays the deuce with you sailors, so be cautious about eating fruit. Good-day! I'll send you the medicines the first thing in the morning."

Now, I am inclined to suspect that with all his want of understanding, Johnson must have had some idea that we were quizzing him. Still, that was nothing, so long as it answered his purpose; and therefore, if he *did* see through us, he never showed it.

Sure enough, at the time appointed, along came a native lad with a small basket of coco-nut stalks, filled with powders, pill-boxes, and vials, each with names and directions written in a large, round hand. The sailors, one and all, made a snatch at the collection, under the strange impression that some of the vials were seasoned with spirits. But, asserting his privilege as physician to the first reading of the labels, Doctor Long Ghost was at last permitted to take possession of the basket.

The first thing lighted upon, was a large vial, labelled—"For William— rub well in."

This vial certainly had a spirituous smell; and upon handing it to the patient, he made a summary internal application of its contents. The doctor looked aghast.

There was now a mighty commotion. Powders and pills were voted mere drugs in the market, and the holders of vials were pronounced lucky dogs. Johnson must have known enough of sailors to make some of his medicines palatable—this, at least, Long Ghost suspected. Certain it was, every one took to the vials; if at all spicy, directions were unheeded, their contents all going one road.

The largest one of all, quite a bottle indeed, and having a sort of burnt brandy odour, was labelled—"For Daniel, drink freely, and until relieved." This, Black Dan proceeded to do; and would have made an end of it at once, had not the bottle, after a hard struggle, been snatched from his hands, and passed round, like a jovial decanter. The old tar had complained of the effects of an immoderate eating of fruit.

Upon calling the following morning, our physician found his precious row of patients reclining behind the stocks, and doing "as well as could be expected."

But the pills and powders were found to have been perfectly inactive: probably because none had been taken. To make them efficacious, it was suggested that, for the future, a bottle of Pisco should be sent along with them. According to Flash Jack's notions, unmitigated medical compounds were but dry stuff at the best, and needed something good to wash them down.

Thus far, our own M.D., Doctor Long Ghost, after starting the frolic, had taken no further part in it; but on the physician's third visit he took him to one side, and had a private confabulation. What it was, exactly, we could not tell; but from certain illustrative signs and gestures, I fancied that he was describing the symptoms of some mysterious disorganization of the vitals, which must have come on within the hour. Assisted by his familiarity with medical terms, he seemed to produce a marked impression. At last, Johnson went his way, promising aloud that he would send Long Ghost what he desired.

When the medicine boy came along the following morning, the doctor was the first to accost him, walking off with a small purple vial. This time, there was little else in the basket but a case bottle of the burnt brandy cordial, which, after much debate, was finally disposed of by some one pouring the contents, little by little, into the half of a coco-nut shell, and so giving all who desired, a glass. No further medicinal cheer remaining, the men dispersed.

An hour or two passed, when Flash Jack directed attention to my long friend, who, since the medicine boy left, had not been noticed till now. With eyes, closed, he was lying behind the stocks, and Jack was lifting his arm and letting it fall as if life were extinct. On running up with the rest, I at once connected the phenomenon with the mysterious vial. Searching his pocket, I found it, and holding it up, it proved to be laudanum. Flash Jack, snatching it from my hand in a rapture, quickly informed all present, what it was; and with much glee, proposed a nap for the company. Some of them not comprehending him exactly, the apparently defunct Long Ghost—who lay so still that I a little suspected the genuineness of his sleep—was rolled about as an illustration of the virtues of the vial's contents. The idea tickled everybody mightily; and throwing themselves down, the magic draught was passed from hand to hand. Thinking that, as a matter of course, they must at once become insensible, each man, upon taking his sip, fell back, and closed his eyes.

There was little fear of the result, since the narcotic was equally distributed.

But, curious to see how it would operate, I raised myself gently after a while, and looked around. It was about noon, and perfectly still; and as we all daily took the siesta, I was not much surprised to find every one quiet. Still, in one or two instances, I thought I detected a little peeping.

Presently, I heard a footstep, and saw Doctor Johnson approaching.

And perplexed enough did he look at the sight of his prostrate file of patients, plunged apparently in such unaccountable slumbers.

"Daniel," he cried, at last, punching in the side with his cane the individual thus designated—"Daniel, my good fellow, get up! do you hear?"

But Black Dan was immovable; and he poked the next sleeper.

"Joseph, Joseph! come, wake up! it's me, Doctor Johnson."

But Jingling Joe, with mouth open, and eyes shut, was not to be started.

"Bless my soul!" he exclaimed, with uplifted hands and cane, "what's got into 'em? I say, *men*"—he shouted, running up and down—"come to life, men! what under the sun's the matter with you?" and he struck the stocks, and bawled with increased vigour.

At last he paused, folded his hands over the head of his cane, and steadfastly gazed upon us. The notes of the nasal orchestra were rising and falling upon his ear, and a new idea suggested itself.

"Yes, yes; the rascals must have been getting boozy. Well, it's none of my business—I'll be off;" and off he went.

No sooner was he out of sight, than nearly all started to their feet; and a hearty laugh ensued.

Like myself, most of them had been watching the event from under a sly eyelid. By this time, too, Doctor Long Ghost was as wide awake as anybody. What were his reasons for taking laudanum,—if, indeed, he took any whatever,—is best known to himself; and, as it is neither mine nor the reader's business, we will say no more about it.

CHAPTER XXXVI

WE ARE CARRIED BEFORE THE CONSUL AND CAPTAIN

WE had been inmates of the Calabooza Beretanee about two weeks, when, one morning, Captain Bob, coming from the bath, in a state of utter nudity, brought into the building an armful of old tappa, and began to dress to go out.

The operation was quite simple. The tappa—of the coarsest kind—was in one long, heavy piece; and, fastening one end to a column of Hibiscus wood, supporting the Calabooza, he went off a few paces, and putting the other about his waist, wound himself right up to the post. This unique costume, in rotundity something like a farthingale, added immensely to his large bulk; so much so, that he fairly waddled in his gait. But he was only adhering to the fashion of his fathers; for, in the olden time, the "Kihee," or big girdle, was quite the mode for both sexes. Bob, despising recent innovations, still clung to it. He was a gentleman of the old school—one of the last of the Kihees.

He now told us, that he had orders to take us before the consul. Nothing loath, we formed in procession; and, with the old man at our head, sighing and labouring like an engine, and flanked by a guard of some twenty natives, we started for the village.

Arrived at the consular office, we found Wilson there, and four or five Europeans, seated in a row facing us; probably with the view of presenting as judicial an appearance as possible.

On one side was a couch, where Captain Guy reclined. He looked convalescent; and, as we found out, intended soon to go aboard his ship. He said nothing, but left everything to the consul.

The latter now rose, and, drawing forth a paper from a large roll, tied with red tape, commenced reading aloud.

It purported to be, "The affidavit of John Jermin, first officer of the British Colonial Barque *Julia;* Guy, Master;" and proved to be a long statement of matters, from the time of leaving Sydney, down to our arrival in the harbour. Though artfully drawn up, so as to bear hard against every one of us, it was pretty correct in the details; excepting, that it was wholly silent as to the manifold derelictions of the mate himself—a fact which imparted unusual significance to the concluding sentence, "And furthermore, this deponent sayeth not."

No comments were made, although we all looked round for the mate, to see whether it was possible that he could have authorized this use of his name. But he was not present.

The next document produced, was the deposition of the captain himself. As on all other occasions, however, he had very little to say for himself, and it was soon set aside.

The third affidavit, was that of the seamen remaining aboard the vessel, including the traitor Bungs, who, it seemed, had turned ship's evidence. It was an atrocious piece of exaggeration, from beginning to end; and those who signed it could not have known what they were about. Certainly Wymontoo did not, though his mark was there. In vain the consul commanded silence during the reading of this paper; comments were shouted out upon every paragraph.

The affidavits read, Wilson, who, all the while, looked as stiff as a poker, solemnly drew forth the ship's articles from their tin case. This document was a discoloured, musty, bilious-looking affair, and hard to read. When finished, the consul held it up; and, pointing to the marks of the ship's company, at the bottom, asked us, one by one, whether we acknowledged the same for our own.

"What's the use of asking that?" said Black Dan; "Captain Guy there knows as well as we they are."

"Silence, sir!" said Wilson, who, intending to produce a suitable impression by this ridiculous parade, was not a little mortified by the old sailor's bluntness.

A pause of a few moments now ensued; during which the bench of judges communed with Captain Guy, in a low tone, and the sailors canvassed the motives of the consul in having the affidavits taken.

The general idea seemed to be, that it was done with a view of "bouncing," or frightening us into submission. Such proved to be the case; for Wilson, rising to his feet again, addressed us as follows:—

"You see, men, that every preparation has been made to send you to Sydney for trial. The *Rosa* (a small Australian schooner, lying in the harbour) will sail for that place in the course of ten days, at farthest. The *Julia* sails on a cruise this day week. Do you still refuse duty?"

We did.

Hereupon the consul and captain exchanged glances; and the latter looked bitterly disappointed.

Presently I noticed Guy's eye upon me; and, for the first time, he spoke, and told me to come near. I stepped forward.

"Was it not you that was taken off the island?"

"It was."

"It is *you* then who owe your life to my humanity. Yet this is the gratitude of a sailor, Mr. Wilson!"

"Not so, sir." And I at once gave him to understand, that I was perfectly acquainted with his motives in sending a boat into the bay; his crew was reduced, and he merely wished to procure the sailor whom he expected to find there. The *ship* was the means of my deliverance, and no thanks to the benevolence of its captain.

Doctor Long Ghost also, had a word to say. In two masterly sentences he summed up Captain Guy's character, to the complete satisfaction of every seaman present.

Matters were now growing serious; especially as the sailors became riotous and talked about taking the consul and the captain back to the Calabooza with them.

The other judges fidgeted, and loudly commanded silence. It was at length restored; when Wilson, for the last time addressing us, said something more about the *Rosa* and Sydney, and concluded by reminding us, that a week would elapse ere the *Julia* sailed.

Leaving these hints to operate for themselves, he dismissed the party, ordering Captain Bob and his friends to escort us back whence we came.

CHAPTER XXXVII

THE FRENCH PRIESTS PAY THEIR RESPECTS

A DAY or two after the events just related, we were lounging in the Calabooza Beretanee, when we were honoured by a visit from three of the French priests; and as about the only notice ever taken of us by the English missionaries, was their leaving their cards for us in the shape of a package of tracts, we could not help thinking, that the Frenchmen, in making a personal call, were at least much better bred.

By this time they had settled themselves down quite near our habitation. A pleasant little stroll down the Broom Road, and a rustic cross peeped through the trees; and soon you came to as charming a place as one would wish to see: a soft knoll planted with old breadfruit trees; in front, a savannah, sloping to a grove of palms, and, between these, glimpses of blue, sunny waves.

On the summit of the knoll, was a rude chapel, of bamboos; quite small, and surmounted by the cross. Between the canes, at nightfall, the natives stole peeps at a small portable altar; a crucifix to correspond, and gilded candlesticks and censers. Their curiosity carried them no farther; nothing could induce them to worship there. Such queer ideas as they entertained of the hated strangers! Masses and chants were nothing more than evil spells. As for the priests themselves, they were no better than diabolical sorcerers; like those who, in old times, terrified their fathers.

Close by the chapel, was a range of native houses; rented from a chief, and handsomely furnished. Here lived the priests; and, very comfortably, too. They looked sanctimonious enough abroad; but that went for nothing: since, at home, in their retreat, they were a club of Friar Tucks; holding priestly wassail over many a good cup of red brandy, and rising late in the morning.

Pity it was, they couldn't marry—pity for the ladies of the island, I mean, and the cause of morality; for what business had the ecclesiastical old bachelors, with such a set of trim little native handmaidens? These damsels were their first converts; and devoted ones they were.

The priests, as I said before, were accounted necromancers: the appearance of two of our three visitors might have justified the conceit.

They were little, dried-up Frenchmen, in long, straight gowns of black cloth, and unsightly three-cornered hats—so preposterously big, that in putting them•on, the reverend fathers seemed extinguishing themselves.

Their companion was dressed differently. He wore a sort of yellow, flannel morning-gown, and a broad-brimmed Manilla hat. Large and portly, he was also hale and fifty; with a complexion like an autumnal leaf—handsome blue eyes—fine teeth, and a racy Milesian brogue. In short, he was an Irishman —Father Murphy, by name,—and, as such, pretty well known and very thoroughly disliked throughout all the Protestant missionary settlements in Polynesia. In early youth he had been sent to a religious seminary in France; and, taking orders there, had but once or twice afterward revisited his native land.

Father Murphy marched up to us briskly; and the first words he uttered were, to ask whether there were any of his countrymen among us. There were two of them: one, a lad of sixteen—a bright, curly-headed rascal—and, being a young Irishman, of course his name was Pat. The other was an ugly, and rather melancholy-looking scamp; one M'Gee, whose prospects in life had been blasted by a premature transportation to Sydney. This was the report, at least, though it might have been scandal.

In most of my shipmates were some redeeming qualities; but about M'Gee, there was nothing of the kind, and forced to consort with him, I could not help regretting, a thousand times, that the gallows had been so tardy. As if impelled, against her will, to send him into the world, Nature had done all she could to insure his being taken for what he was. About the eyes, there was no mistaking him; with a villainous cast in one, they seemed suspicious of each other.

Glancing away from him at once, the bluff priest rested his gaze on the good-humoured face of Pat, who, with a pleasant roguishness, was "twigging" the enormous hats (or "Hytee Belteezers," as land beavers are called by sailors), from under which, like a couple of snails, peeped the two little Frenchmen.

Pat and the priest were both from the same town in Meath; and, when this was found out, there was no end to the questions of the latter. To him, Pat seemed a letter from home, and·said a hundred times as much.

After a long talk between these two, and a little broken English from the Frenchman, our visitors took leave; but Father Murphy had hardly gone a dozen rods, when back he came, inquiring whether we were in want of anything.

"Yes," cried one, "something to eat." Upon this, he promised to send us some fresh wheat bread, of his own baking; a great luxury in Tahiti.

We all felicitated Pat upon picking up such a friend, and told him his fortune was made.

The next morning, a French servant of the priest's made his appearance, with a small bundle of clothing for our young Hibernian; and the promised bread for the party. Pat, being out at the knees and elbows, and, like the rest of us, not full inside, the present was acceptable all round.

In the afternoon, Father Murphy himself came along; and, in addition to his previous gifts, gave Pat a good deal of advice: said he was sorry to see him in limbo, and that he would have a talk with the consul about having him set free.

We saw nothing more of him for two or three days; at the end of which time he paid us another call, telling Pat that Wilson was inexorable, having refused to set him at liberty, unless to go aboard the ship. This, the priest now besought him to do forthwith; and so escape the punishment which, it seems, Wilson had been hinting at to his intercessor. Pat, however, was staunch against entreaties; and, with all the ardour of a sophomorean sailor, protested his intention to hold out to the last. With none of the meekness of a good little boy about him, the blunt youngster stormed away at such a rate, that it was hard to pacify him; and the priest said no more.

How it came to pass—whether from Murphy's speaking to the consul, or otherwise, we could not tell—but the next day, Pat was sent for by Wilson, and being escorted to the village by our good old keeper, three days elapsed before he returned.

Bent upon reclaiming him, they had taken him on board the ship; feasted him in the cabin; and, finding that of no avail, down they thrust him into the hold, in double irons, and on bread and water. All would not do; and so he was sent back to the Calabooza. Boy that he was, they must have counted upon his being more susceptible to discipline than the rest.

The interest felt in Pat's welfare, by his benevolent countryman, was very serviceable to the rest of us; especially as we all turned Catholics, and went to mass every morning, much to Captain Bob's consternation. Upon finding it out, he threatened to keep us in the stocks, if we did not desist. He went no farther than this, though; and so, every few days, we strolled down to the priest's residence, and had a mouthful to eat, and something generous to drink. In particular, Doctor Long Ghost and myself became huge favourites with Pat's friend; and many a time he regaled us from a quaint-looking travelling-case for spirits, stowed away in one corner of his dwelling. It held four square flasks, which, somehow or other, always contained just enough to need emptying. In truth, the fine old Irishman was a rosy fellow in canonicals. His countenance and his soul were always in a glow. It may be ungenerous to reveal his failings, but he often talked thick, and sometimes was perceptibly eccentric in his gait.

I never drink French brandy, but I pledge Father Murphy. His health again! And many jolly proselytes may he make in Polynesia!

CHAPTER XXXVIII

"LITTLE JULE" SAILS WITHOUT US

To make good the hint thrown out by the consul upon the conclusion of the Farce of the Affidavits, we were again brought before him within the time specified.

It was the same thing over again: he got nothing out of us, and we were remanded; our resolute behaviour annoying him prodigiously.

What we observed, led us to form the idea, that on first learning the state of affairs on board the *Julia*, Wilson must have addressed his invalid friend, the captain, something in the following style:

"Guy, my poor fellow, don't worry yourself now about those rascally sailors of yours. I'll dress them out for you—just leave it all to me, and set your mind at rest."

But handcuffs and stocks, big looks, threats, dark hints, and depositions, had all gone for nought.

Conscious that, as matters now stood, nothing serious could grow out of what had happened; and never dreaming that our being sent home for trial had ever been really thought of, we thoroughly understood Wilson, and laughed at him accordingly.

Since leaving the *Julia*, we had caught no glimpse of the mate; but we often heard of him.

It seemed that he remained on board, keeping house in the cabin for himself and Viner; who, going to see him according to promise, was induced to remain a guest. These two cronies now had fine times; tapping the captain's quarter-casks, playing cards on the transom, and giving balls of an evening to the ladies ashore. In short, they cut up so many queer capers, that the missionaries complained of them to the consul; and Jermin received a sharp reprimand.

This so affected him, that he drank still more freely than before; and one afternoon, when mellow as a grape, he took umbrage at a canoe full of natives, who, on being hailed from the deck to come aboard and show their papers, got frightened, and paddled for the shore. Lowering a boat instantly, he equipped Wymontoo and the Dane with a cutlass apiece, and seizing another himself, off they started in pursuit, the ship's ensign flying in the boat's stern. The alarmed islanders, beaching their canoe, with loud cries fled through the village, the mate after them, slashing his naked weapon to right and left. A crowd soon collected; and the "Karhowree toonee," or crazy stranger, was quickly taken before Wilson.

Now, it so chanced, that in a native house hard by, the consul and Captain Guy were having a quiet game at cribbage by themselves, a decanter on the table standing sentry. The obstreperous Jermin was brought in; and finding the two thus pleasantly occupied, it had a soothing effect upon him; and he insisted upon taking a hand at the cards, and a drink of the brandy. As the consul was nearly as tipsy as himself, and the captain dared not object for fear of giving offence, at it they went—all three of them—and made a night of it; the mate's delinquencies being summarily passed over, and his captors sent away.

An incident worth relating grew out of this freak.

There wandered about Papeetee, at this time, a shrivelled little fright of an Englishwoman, known among sailors as "Old Mother Tot." From New Zealand to the Sandwich Islands, she had been all over the South Seas; keeping a rude hut of entertainment for mariners, and supplying them with rum and dice. Upon the missionary islands, of course, such conduct was severely punishable; and at various places, Mother Tot's establishment had been shut up, and its proprietor made to quit in the first vessel that could be hired to land her elsewhere. But, with a perseverance invincible, wherever she went, she always started afresh; and so became notorious everywhere.

By some wicked spell of hers, a patient, one-eyed little cobbler followed her about, mending shoes for white men, doing the old woman's cooking, and bearing all her abuse without grumbling. Strange to relate, a battered Bible was seldom out of his sight; and whenever he had leisure, and his mistress' back was turned, he was for ever poring over it. This pious propensity used to enrage the old crone past belief; and oftentimes she boxed his ears with the book, and tried to burn it. Mother Tot and her man Josy were, indeed, a curious pair.

But to my story.

A week or so after our arrival in the harbour, the old lady had once again been hunted down, and forced for the time to abandon her nefarious calling. This was brought about chiefly by Wilson, who, for some reason unknown, had contracted the most violent hatred for her; which, on her part, was more than reciprocated.

Well: passing, in the evening, where the consul and his party were making merry, she peeped through the bamboos of the house; and straightway resolved to gratify her spite.

The night was very dark; and providing herself with a huge ship's lantern, which usually swung in her hut, she waited till they came forth. This happened about midnight; Wilson making his appearance, supported by two natives, holding him up by the arms. These three went first; and just as they got under a deep shade, a bright light was thrust within an inch of Wilson's nose. The old hag was kneeling before him, holding the lantern with uplifted hands.

"Ha, ha! my fine *counsellor*," she shrieked; "ye persecute a lone old body like me for selling rum—do ye? And here ye are, carried home drunk—Hoot! ye villain, I scorn ye!" And she spat upon him.

Terrified at the apparition, the poor natives—arrant believers in ghosts —dropped the trembling consul, and fled in all directions. After giving full vent to her rage, Mother Tot hobbled away, and left the three revellers to stagger home the best way they could.

The day following our last interview with Wilson, we learned that Captain Guy had gone on board his vessel, for the purpose of shipping a new crew. There was a round bounty offered; and a heavy bag of Spanish dollars, with the *Julia's* articles ready for signing, were laid on the capstanhead.

Now, there was no lack of idle sailors ashore, mostly "Beachcombers," who had formed themselves into an organized gang, headed by one Mack, a Scotchman, whom they styled the Commodore. By the laws of the fraternity, no member was allowed to ship on board a vessel, unless granted permission by the rest. In this way the gang controlled the port, all discharged seamen being forced to join them.

To Mack and his men our story was well known; indeed, they had several times called to see us; and of course, as sailors and congenial spirits, they were hard against Captain Guy.

Deeming the matter important, they came in a body to the Calabooza, and wished to know, whether, all things considered, we thought it best for any of them to join the *Julia*.

Anxious to pack the ship off as soon as possible, we answered, by all means. Some went so far as to laud the *Julia* to the skies, as the best and fastest of ships. Jermin too, as a good fellow, and a sailor every inch, came in for *his* share of praise; and as for the captain—quiet man, he would never trouble any one. In short, every inducement we could think of was presented; and Flash Jack ended by assuring the beachcombers solemnly, that now we were all well and hearty, nothing but a regard to principle prevented us from returning on board ourselves.

The result was, that a new crew was finally obtained, together with a steady New Englander for second mate, and three good whalemen for harpooneers. In part, what was wanting for the ship's larder was also supplied; and as far as could be done in a place like Tahiti, the damages the vessel had sustained were repaired. As for the Mowree, the authorities refusing to let him be put ashore, he was carried to sea in irons, down in the hold. What eventually became of him, we never heard.

Ropey, poor, poor Ropey, who a few days previous had fallen sick, was left ashore at the sailor hospital at Townor, a small place upon the beach between Papeetee and Matavai. Here, some time after, he breathed his last. No one knew his complaint; he must have died of hard times. Several of us saw him interred in the sand, and I planted a rude post to mark his resting-place.

The cooper, and the rest who had remained aboard from the first, of course, composed part of the *Julia's* new crew.

To account for the conduct, all along, of the consul and captain, in trying so hard to alter our purpose with respect to the ship, the following statement is all that is requisite. Beside an advance of from fifteen to twenty-five dollars demanded by every sailor shipping at Tahiti, an additional sum for each man so shipped, has to be paid into the hands of the government, as a charge of the port. Beside this, the men—with here and there an exception—will only ship for one cruise, thus becoming entitled to a discharge before the vessel reaches home; which, in time, creates the necessity of obtaining other men, at a similar cost. Now, the *Julia's* exchequer was at low-water mark, or, rather, it was quite empty; and, to meet these expenses, a good part of what little oil there was aboard had to be sold for a song to a merchant of Papeetee.

It was Sunday in Tahiti, and a glorious morning, when Captain Bob, waddling into the Calabooza, startled us by announcing, "Ah—my boy—shippy you, harree—maky sail!" In other words, the *Julia* was off.

The beach was quite near, and in this quarter altogether uninhabited; so down we ran, and, at a cable's length, saw *Little Jule* gliding past—topgallant-sails hoisting, and a boy aloft with one leg thrown over the yard, loosing the fore-royal. The decks were all life and commotion; the sailors on the forecastle singing "Ho, cheerly men!" as they catted the anchor; and the gallant Jermin, bareheaded as his wont, standing up on the bowsprit, and issuing his orders. By the man at the helm stood Captain Guy, very quiet and gentlemanly, and smoking a cigar. Soon the ship drew near the reef, and altering her course, glided out through the break, and went on her way.

Thus disappeared *Little Jule,* about three weeks after entering the harbour; and nothing more have I ever heard of her.

CHAPTER XXXIX

JERMIN SERVES US A GOOD TURN—FRIENDSHIPS IN POLYNESIA

THE ship out of the way, we were quite anxious to know what was going to be done with us. On this head, Captain Bob could tell us nothing; no further at least, than that he still considered himself responsible for our safe-keeping. However, he never put us to bed any more; and we had everything our own way.

The day after the *Julia* left, the old man came up to us in great tribulation, saying that the bucket of bread was no longer forthcoming, and that Wilson had refused to send anything in its place. One and all, we took this for a hint to disperse quietly, and go about our business. Nevertheless, we were not to be shaken off so easily; and taking a malicious pleasure in annoying our old enemy, we resolved, for the present, to stay where we were. For the part he had been acting, we learned that the consul was the laughing-stock of all the foreigners ashore, who frequently twitted him upon his hopeful protégés of the Calabooza Beretanee.

As we were wholly without resources, so long as we remained on the island no better place than Captain Bob's could be selected for an abiding-place. Beside, we heartily loved the old gentleman, and could not think of leaving him; so, telling him to give no thought as to wherewithal we should be clothed and fed, we resolved, by extending and systematizing our foraging operations, to provide for ourselves.

We were greatly assisted by a parting legacy of Jermin's. To him we were indebted for having all our chests sent ashore, and everything left therein. They were placed in the custody of a petty chief living near by, who was instructed by the consul not to allow them to be taken away; but we might call and make our toilets whenever we pleased.

We went to see Mahinee, the old chief; Captain Bob going along, and stoutly insisting upon having the chattels delivered up. At last this was done; and in solemn procession the chests were borne by the natives to the Calabooza. Here, we disposed them about quite tastefully; and made such a figure, that in the eyes of old Bob and his friends, the Calabooza Beretanee was by far the most sumptuously furnished saloon in Tahiti.

Indeed, so long as it remained thus furnished, the native courts of the district were held there; the judge, Mahinee, and his associates, sitting upon one of the chests, and the culprits and spectators thrown at full length upon the ground, both inside of the building, and under the shade of the trees without; while, leaning over the stocks as from a gallery, the worshipful crew of the *Julia* looked on, and canvassed the proceedings.

I should have mentioned before, that previous to the vessel's departure, the men had bartered away all the clothing they could possibly spare; but now, it was resolved to be more provident.

The contents of the chests were of the most miscellaneous description:— sewing utensils, marling-spikes, strips of calico, bits of rope, jack-knives;

nearly everything, in short, that a seaman could think of. But of wearing apparel, there was little but old frocks, remnants of jackets, and legs of trousers, with now and then the foot of a stocking. These, however, were far from being valueless; for, among the poorer Tahitians, everything European is highly esteemed. They come from "Beretanee, Fenooa Pararee" (Britain, Land of Wonders), and that is enough.

The chests themselves were deemed exceedingly precious, especially those with unfractured locks, which would absolutely click, and enable the owner to walk off with the key. Scars, however, and bruises, were considered great blemishes. One old fellow, smitten with the doctor's large mahogany chest (a well-filled one, by the by), and finding infinite satisfaction in merely sitting thereon, was detected in the act of applying a healing ointment to a shocking scratch which impaired the beauty of the lid.

There is no telling the love of a Tahitian for a sailor's trunk. So ornamental is it held as an article of furniture in his hut, that the women are incessantly tormenting their husbands to bestir themselves, and make them a present of one. When obtained, no pier-table just placed in a drawing-room, is regarded with half the delight. For these reasons, then, our coming into possession of our estate at this time, was an important event.

The islanders are much like the rest of the world; and the news of our good fortune brought us troops of "tayos" or friends, eager to form an alliance after the national custom, and do our slightest bidding.

The really curious way in which all the Polynesians are in the habit of making bosom friends at the shortest possible notice, is deserving of remark. Although, among a people like the Tahitians, vitiated as they are by sophisticating influences, this custom has in most cases degenerated into a mere mercenary relation, it nevertheless had its origin in a fine, and in some instances, heroic sentiment, formerly entertained by their fathers.

In the annals of the island are examples of extravagant friendships, unsurpassed by the story of Damon and Pythias: in truth, much more wonderful; for notwithstanding the devotion—even of life in some cases—to which they led, they were frequently entertained at first sight for some stranger from another island.

Filled with love and admiration for the first whites who came among them, the Polynesians could not testify the warmth of their emotions more strongly than by instantaneously making their abrupt proffer of friendship. Hence, in old voyages we read of chiefs coming off from the shore in their canoes, and going through with strange antics, expressive of this desire. In the same way, their inferiors accosted the seamen; and thus the practice has continued in some islands down to the present day.

There is a small place, not many days' sail from Tahiti, and seldom visited by shipping, where the vessel touched to which I then happened to belong.

Of course, among the simple-hearted natives, we had a friend all round. Mine was Poky, a handsome youth, who never could do enough for me. Every morning at sunrise, his canoe came alongside loaded with fruits of all kinds; upon being emptied, it was secured by a line to the bowsprit, under which it lay all day long, ready at any time to carry its owner ashore on an errand.

Seeing him so indefatigable, I told Poky one day, that I was a virtuoso in shells and curiosities of all kinds. That was enough; away he paddled for the head of the bay, and I never saw him again for twenty-four hours. The next morning, his canoe came gliding slowly along the shore, with the full-leaved bough of a tree for a sail. For the purpose of keeping the things dry, he had also built a sort of platform just behind the prow, railed in with green wicker-work; and here was a heap of yellow bananas and cowree shells; young coco-nuts and antlers of red coral; two or three pieces of carved wood; a little pocket-idol, black as jet, and rolls of printed tappa.

We were given a holiday; and upon going ashore, Poky, of course, was my companion and guide. For this, no mortal could be better qualified; his native country was not large, and he knew every inch of it. Gallanting me about, every one was stopped and ceremoniously introduced to Poky's "tayo karhowree nuee" or his particular white friend.

He showed me all the lions; but more than all, he took me to see a charming lioness—a young damsel—the daughter of a chief—the reputation of whose charms had spread to the neighbouring islands, and even brought suitors therefrom. Among these was Tooboi, the heir of Tamatoy, King of Raiatair, one of the Society Isles. The girl was certainly fair to look upon. Many heavens were in her sunny eyes; and the outline of that arm of hers, peeping forth from a capricious tappa robe, was the very curve of beauty.

Though there was no end to Poky's attentions, not a syllable did he ever breathe of reward; but sometimes he looked very knowing. At last the day came for sailing, and with it, also, his canoe, loaded down to the gunwale with a sea stock of fruits. Giving him all I could spare from my chest, I went on deck to take my place at the windlass; for the anchor was weighing. Poky followed, and heaved with me at the same handspike.

The anchor was soon up; and away we went out of the bay with more than twenty shallops towing astern. At last they left us; but long as I could see him at all, there was Poky, standing alone and motionless in the bow of his canoe.

CHAPTER XL

WE TAKE UNTO OURSELVES FRIENDS

THE arrival of the chests made my friend, the doctor, by far the wealthiest man of the party. So much the better for me, seeing that I had little or nothing myself; though from our intimacy, the natives courted my favour almost as much as his.

Among others, Kooloo was a candidate for my friendship; and being a comely youth, quite a buck in his way, I accepted his overtures. By this, I escaped the importunities of the rest; for be it known, that, though little inclined to jealousy in love matters, the Tahitian will hear of no rivals in his friendship.

Kooloo, running over his qualifications as a friend, first of all informed me, that he was a "Mickonaree," thus declaring his communion with the church.

The way this "tayo" of mine expressed his regard, was by assuring me over and over again, that the love he bore me was "nuee, nuee, nuee," or infinitesimally extensive. All over these seas, the word "nuee" is significant of quantity. Its repetition is like placing ciphers at the right hand of a numeral; the more places you carry it out to, the greater the sum. Judge, then, of Kooloo's esteem. Nor is the allusion to the ciphers at all inappropriate, seeing that, in themselves, Kooloo's professions turned out to be worthless. He was, alas! as sounding brass and a tinkling cymbal; one of those who make no music unless the clapper be silver.

In the course of a few days, the sailors, like the doctor and myself, were cajoled out of everything, and our "tayos," all round, began to cool off quite sensibly. So remiss did they become in their attentions, that we could no longer rely upon their bringing us the daily supply of food, which all of them had faithfully promised.

As for Kooloo, after sponging me well, he one morning played the part of a retrograde lover; informing me, that his affections had undergone a change; he had fallen in love at first sight with a smart sailor, who had just stepped ashore quite flush from a lucky whaling-cruise.

It was a touching interview, and with it, our connection dissolved. But the sadness which ensued would soon have been dissipated, had not my sensibilities been wounded by his indelicately sporting some of my gifts very soon after this transfer of his affections. Hardly a day passed, that I did not meet him on the Broom Road, airing himself in a Regatta shirt, which I had given him in happier hours.

He went by with such an easy saunter too, looking me pleasantly in the eye, and merely exchanging the cold salute of the road:—"Yar onor, boyoee," a mere side-walk how d'ye do. After several experiences like this, I began to entertain a sort of respect for Kooloo, as quite a man of the world. In good sooth, he turned out to be one; in one week's time giving me the cut direct, and lounging by without even nodding. He must have taken me for part of the landscape.

Before the chests were quite empty, we had a grand washing in the stream of our best raiment, for the purpose of looking tidy, and visiting the European chapel in the village. Every Sunday morning it is open for divine service, some member of the mission officiating. This was the first time we ever entered Papeetee unattended by an escort.

In the chapel there were about forty people present, including the officers of several ships in harbour. It was an energetic discourse, and the pulpit cushion was well pounded. Occupying a high seat in the synagogue, and stiff as a flagstaff, was our beloved guardian, Wilson. I shall never forget his look of wonder when his interesting wards filed in at the doorway, and took up a seat directly facing him.

Service over, we waited outside in hopes of seeing more of him; but sorely annoyed at the sight of us, he reconnoitred from the window, and never came forth until we had started for home.

CHAPTER XLI

WE LEVY CONTRIBUTIONS ON THE SHIPPING

SCARCELY a week went by after the *Julia's* sailing, when, with the proverbial restlessness of sailors, some of the men began to grow weary of the Calabooza Beretanee, and resolved to go boldly among the vessels in the bay, and offer to ship.

The thing was tried; but though strongly recommended by the commodore of the beachcombers, in the end they were invariably told by the captains to whom they applied, that they bore an equivocal character ashore, and would not answer. So often were they repulsed, that we pretty nearly gave up all thoughts of leaving the island in this way; and growing domestic again, settled down quietly at Captain Bob's.

It was about this time, that the whaling-ships, which have their regular seasons for cruising, began to arrive at Papeetee; and of course their crews frequently visited us. This is customary all over the Pacific. No sailor steps ashore, but he straightway goes to the "Calabooza," where he is almost sure to find some poor fellow or other in confinement for desertion, or alleged mutiny, or something of that sort. Sympathy is proffered, and if need be, tobacco. The latter, however, is most in request; as a solace to the captive, it is invaluable.

Having fairly carried the day against both consul and captain, we were objects of even more than ordinary interest to these philanthropists; and they always cordially applauded our conduct. Besides, they invariably brought along something in the way of refreshments; occasionally smuggling in a little Pisco. Upon one occasion, when there was quite a number present, a calabash was passed round, and a pecuniary collection taken up for our benefit.

One day a new-comer proposed that two or three of us should pay him a sly, nocturnal visit aboard his ship; engaging to send us away well freighted with provisions. This was not a bad idea; nor were we at all backward in acting upon it. Night after night every vessel in the harbour was visited in rotation, the foragers borrowing Captain Bob's canoe for the purpose. As we all took turns at this—two by two—in due course it came to Long Ghost and myself, for the sailors invariably linked us together. In such an enterprise, I somewhat distrusted the doctor, for he was no sailor, and very tall; and a canoe is the most ticklish of navigable things. However, it could not be helped; and so we went.

But a word about the canoes, before we go any farther. Among the Society Islands, the art of building them, like all native accomplishments, has greatly deteriorated; and they are now the most inelegant, as well as the most insecure of any in the South Seas. In Cook's time, according to his account, there was at Tahiti a royal fleet of seventeen hundred and twenty large war-canoes, handsomely carved, and otherwise adorned. At present, those used are quite small; nothing more than logs hollowed out, sharpened at one end, and then launched into the water.

To obviate a certain rolling propensity, the Tahitians, like all Polynesians, attach to them what sailors call an "outrigger." It consists of a pole floating alongside, parallel to the canoe, and connected with it by a couple of cross sticks, a yard or more in length. Thus equipped, the canoe cannot be overturned, unless you overcome the buoyancy of the pole, or lift it entirely out of the water.

Now, Captain Bob's "gig" was exceedingly small; so small, and of such a grotesque shape, that the sailors christened it the Pill Box; and by this appellation it always went. In fact, it was a sort of "sulky," meant for a solitary paddler, but on an emergency, capable of floating two or three. The outrigger was a mere switch, alternately rising in air, and then depressed in the water.

Assuming the command of the expedition, upon the strength of my being a sailor, I packed the Long Doctor with a paddle in the bow, and then shoving off, leaped into the stern; thus leaving him to do all the work, and reserving to myself the dignified sinecure of steering. All would have gone well, were it not that my paddler made such clumsy work, that the water spattered, and showered down upon us without ceasing. Continuing to ply his tool, however, quite energetically, I thought he would improve after a while, and so let him alone. But by and by, getting wet through with this little storm we were raising, and seeing no signs of its clearing off, I conjured him, in mercy's name, to stop short, and let me wring myself out. Upon this, he suddenly turned round, when the canoe gave a roll, the outrigger flew overhead, and the next moment came rap on the doctor's skull, and we were both in the water.

Fortunately, we were just over a ledge of coral, not half-a-fathom under the surface. Depressing one end of the filled canoe, and letting go of it quickly, it bounced up, and discharged a great part of its contents; so that we easily baled out the remainder, and again embarked. This time, my comrade coiled himself away in a very small space; and enjoining upon him not to draw a single unnecessary breath, I proceeded to urge the canoe along by myself. I was astonished at his docility, never speaking a word, and stirring neither hand nor foot; but the secret was, he was unable to swim, and in case we met with a second mishap, there were no more ledges beneath to stand upon. "Drowning's but a shabby way of going out of the world," he exclaimed, upon my rallying him; "and I'm not going to be guilty of it."

At last, the ship was at hand, and we approached with much caution, wishing to avoid being hailed by any one from the quarter-deck. Dropping silently under her bows, we heard a low whistle—the signal agreed upon—and presently a goodly sized bag was lowered over to us.

We cut the line, and then paddled away as fast as we could, and made the best of our way home. Here, we found the rest waiting impatiently.

The bag turned out to be well filled with sweet potatoes boiled, cubes of salt beef and pork, and a famous sailors' pudding, what they call "duff," made of flour and water, and of about the consistence of an underdone brick. With these delicacies, and keen appetites, we went out into the moonlight, and had a nocturnal picnic.

CHAPTER XLII

MOTOO-OTOO—A TAHITIAN CASUIST

THE Pill Box was sometimes employed for other purposes than that described in the last chapter. We sometimes went a-pleasuring in it.

Right in the middle of Papeetee harbour is a bright, green island, one circular grove of waving palms, and scarcely a hundred yards across. It is of coral formation; and all round, for many rods out, the bay is so shallow, that you might wade anywhere. Down in these waters, as transparent as air, you see coral plants of every hue and shape imaginable:—antlers, tufts of azure, waving reeds like stalks of grain, and pale green buds and mosses. In some places, you look through prickly branches down to a snow-white floor of sand, sprouting with flinty bulbs; and crawling among these are strange shapes:— some bristling with spikes, others clad in shining coats-of-mail, and here and there, round forms all spangled with eyes.

The island is called Motoo-Otoo; and around Motoo-Otoo have I often paddled of a white moonlight night, pausing now and then to admire the marine gardens beneath.

The place is the private property of the queen, who has a residence there—a melancholy-looking range of bamboo houses—neglected and falling to decay among the trees.

Commanding the harbour as it does, her majesty has done all she could to make a fortress of the island. The margin has been raised and levelled, and built up with a low parapet of hewn blocks of coral. Behind the parapet, are ranged at wide intervals, a number of rusty old cannon, of all fashions and calibres. They are mounted upon lame, decrepit-looking carriages, ready to sink under the useless burden of bearing them up. Indeed, two or three have given up the ghost altogether, and the pieces they sustained lie half-buried among their bleaching bones. Several of the cannon are spiked; probably with a view of making them more formidable; as they certainly must be to any one undertaking to fire them off.

Presented to Pomaree at various times by captains of British armed ships, these poor old "dogs of war," thus toothless and turned out to die, formerly bayed in full pack, as the battle hounds of Old England.

There was something about Motoo-Otoo that struck my fancy; and I registered a vow to plant my foot upon its soil, notwithstanding an old bareheaded sentry menaced me in the moonlight with an unsightly musket. As my canoe drew scarcely three inches of water, I could paddle close up to the parapet without grounding; but every time I came near, the old man ran toward me, pushing his piece forward, but never clapping it to his shoulder. Thinking he only meant to frighten me, I at last dashed the canoe right up to the wall, purposing a leap. It was the rashest act of my life; for never did coco-nut come nearer getting demolished, than mine did then. With the stock of his gun, the old warder fetched a tremendous blow, which I managed to dodge; and then falling back, succeeded in paddling out of harm's reach.

He must have been dumb; for never a word did he utter; but grinning from ear to ear, and with his white cotton robe streaming in the moonlight, he looked more like the spook of the island than anything mortal.

I tried to effect my object by attacking him in the rear—but he was all front; running about the place as I paddled, and presenting his confounded musket wherever I went. At last I was obliged to retreat; and to this day my vow remains unfulfilled.

It was a few days after my repulse from before the walls of Motoo-Otoo, that I heard a curious case of casuistry argued between one of the most clever and intelligent natives I ever saw in Tahiti, a man by the name of Arheetoo, and our learned Theban of a doctor.

It was this:—whether it was right and lawful for any one, being a native, to keep the European Sabbath, in preference to the day set apart as such by the missionaries, and so considered by the islanders in general.

It must be known, that the missionaries of the good ship *Duff*, who more than half-a-century ago established the Tahitian reckoning, came hither by the way of the Cape of Good Hope; and by thus sailing to the eastward, lost one precious day of their lives all round, getting about that much in advance of Greenwich time. For this reason, vessels coming round Cape Horn—as they most all do nowadays—find it Sunday in Tahiti, when, according to their own view of the matter, it ought to be Saturday. But as it won't do to alter the log, the sailors keep their Sabbath, and the islanders theirs.

This confusion perplexes the poor natives mightily; and it is to no purpose that you endeavour to explain so incomprehensible a phenomenon. I once saw a worthy old missionary essay to shed some light on the subject; and though

I understood but few of the words employed, I could easily get at the meaning of his illustrations. They were something like the following:

"Here," says he, "you see this circle" (describing a large one on the ground with a stick): "very good; now you see this spot" (marking a point in the perimeter): "well; this is Beretanee (England), and I'm going to sail round to Tahiti. Here I go, then;" (following the circle round), "and there goes the sun" (snatching up another stick, and commissioning a bandy-legged native to travel round with it in a contrary direction). "Now then, we are both off, and both going away from each other; and here you see I have arrived at Tahiti" (making a sudden stop); "and look now, where Bandy Legs is!"

But the crowd strenuously maintained, that Bandy Legs ought to be somewhere above them in the atmosphere; for it was a traditionary fact, that the people from the *Duff* came ashore when the sun was high overhead. And here the old gentleman, being a very good sort of man, doubtless, but no astronomer, was obliged to give up.

Arheetoo, the casuist alluded to, though a member of the church, and extremely conscientious about what Sabbath he kept, was more liberal in other matters. Learning that I was something of a "mickonaree" (in this sense, a man able to read, and cunning in the use of the pen), he desired the slight favour of my forging for him a set of papers; for which, he said, he would be much obliged, and give me a good dinner of roast pig and Indian turnip in the bargain.

Now, Arheetoo was one of those who board the shipping for their washing; and the competition being very great (the proudest chiefs not disdaining to solicit custom in person, though the work is done by their dependents), he had decided upon a course suggested by a knowing sailor, a friend of his. He wished to have manufactured a set of certificates, purporting to come from certain man-of-war and merchant captains, known to have visited the island; recommending him as one of the best getters-up of fine linen in all Polynesia.

At this time, Arheetoo had known me but two hours; and, as he made the proposition very coolly, I thought it rather presumptuous, and told him so. But as it was quite impossible to convey a hint, that there was a slight impropriety in the thing, I did not resent the insult, but simply declined.

CHAPTER XLIII

ONE IS JUDGED BY THE COMPANY HE KEEPS

ALTHOUGH, from its novelty, life at Captain Bob's was pleasant enough, for the time; there were some few annoyances connected with it, anything but agreeable to a "soul of sensibility."

Prejudiced against us by the malevolent representations of the consul and others, many worthy foreigners ashore regarded us as a set of lawless vagabonds; though, truth to speak, better behaved sailors never stepped on the island, nor any who gave less trouble to the natives. But, for all this, whenever we met a respectably dressed European, ten to one he shunned us, by going over to the other side of the road. This was very unpleasant, at least to myself; though, certes, it did not prey upon the minds of the others.

To give an instance.

Of a fine evening in Tahiti—but they are all fine evenings there—you may see a bevy of silk bonnets and parasols passing along the Broom Road: perhaps a band of pale, little white urchins—sickly exotics—and, oftener still, sedate, elderly gentlemen, with canes; at whose appearance the natives, here and there, slink into their huts. These are the missionaries, their wives, and children, taking a family airing. Sometimes, by the by, they take horse, and ride down to Point Venus and back; a distance of several miles. At this place is settled the only survivor of the first missionaries that landed—an old, white-headed, saint-like man, by the name of Wilson, the father of our friend, the consul.

The little parties on foot were frequently encountered; and, recalling, as they did, so many pleasant recollections of home and the ladies, I really longed for a dress coat and beaver, that I might step up and pay my respects. But, situated as I was, this was out of the question. On one occasion, however, I received a kind, inquisitive glance from a matron in gingham. Sweet lady! I have not forgotten her: her gown was a plaid.

But a glance, like hers, was not always bestowed.

One evening, passing the veranda of a missionary's dwelling, the dame, his wife, and a pretty, blonde young girl, with ringlets, were sitting there, enjoying the sea-breeze, then coming in, all cool and refreshing, from the spray of the reef. As I approached, the old lady peered hard at me; and her very cap seemed to convey a prim rebuke. The blue, English eyes, by her side, were also bent on me. But, oh Heavens! what a glance to receive, from such a beautiful creature! As for the mob cap, not a fig did I care for it; but, to be taken for anything but a cavalier, by the ringletted one, was absolutely unendurable.

I resolved on a courteous salute, to show my good-breeding, if nothing more. But, happening to wear a sort of turban—hereafter to be particularly alluded to—there was no taking it off and putting it on again, with anything like dignity. At any rate, then, here goes a bow. But, another difficulty presented itself: my loose frock was so voluminous, that I doubted whether any spinal curvature would be perceptible.

"Good-evening, ladies," exclaimed I, at last, advancing winningly; "a delightful air from the sea, ladies."

Hysterics and hartshorn! who would have thought it? The young lady screamed, and the old one came near fainting. As for myself, I retreated, in double quick time; and scarcely drew breath, until safely housed in the Calabooza.

CHAPTER XLIV

CATHEDRAL OF PAPOAR—THE CHURCH OF THE COCO-NUTS

On Sundays I always attended the principal native church on the outskirts of the village of Papeetee, and not far from the Calabooza Beretanee. It was esteemed the best specimen of architecture in Tahiti.

Of late, they have built their places of worship with more reference to durability than formerly. At one time, there were no less than thirty-six on the island—mere barns, tied together with thongs, which went to destruction in a very few years.

One, built many years ago in this style, was a most remarkable structure. It was erected by Pomaree II, who, on this occasion, showed all the zeal of a

royal proselyte.   The building was over seven hundred feet in length, and of a
proportionate width; the vast ridge-pole was at intervals supported by a row
of thirty-six cylindrical trunks of the breadfruit tree; and, all round, the wall-
plates rested on shafts of the palm.   The roof—steeply inclining to within a
man's height of the ground—was thatched with leaves, and the sides of the
edifice were open.   Thus spacious was the Royal Mission Chapel of Papoar.

At its dedication, three distinct sermons were, from different pulpits, preached
to an immense concourse gathered from all parts of the island.

As the chapel was built by the king's command, nearly as great a multitude
was employed in its construction as swarmed over the scaffolding of the great
temple of the Jews.   Much less time, however, was expended.   In less than three
weeks from planting the first post, the last tier of palmetto-leaves drooped from
the eaves, and the work was done.

Apportioned to the several chiefs and their dependents, the labour, though
immense, was greatly facilitated by every one's bringing his post, or his rafter,
or his pole strung with thatching, ready for instant use.   The materials thus
prepared being afterward secured together by thongs, there was literally
"neither hammer, nor axe, nor any tool of iron heard in the house while it was
building."

But the most singular circumstance connected with this South Sea cathedral,
remains to be related.   As well for the beauty, as the advantages of such a site,
the islanders love to dwell near the mountain streams; and so, a considerable
brook, after descending from the hills and watering the valley, was bridged over
in three places, and swept clean through the chapel.

Flowing waters! what an accompaniment to the songs of the sanctuary;
mingling with them, the praises and thanksgivings of the green solitudes inland.

But the chapel of the Polynesian Solomon has long since been deserted.   Its
thousand rafters of hibiscus have decayed, and fallen to the ground; and now,
the stream murmurs over them in its bed.

The present metropolitan church of Tahiti is very unlike the one just
described.   It is of moderate dimensions, boarded over, and painted white.   It
is furnished also with blinds, but no sashes; indeed, were it not for the rustic
thatch, it would remind one of a plain chapel at home.

The wood-work was all done by foreign carpenters, of whom there are always
several about Papeetee.

Within, its aspect is unique, and cannot fail to interest a stranger.   The
rafters overhead are bound round with fine matting of variegated dyes; and
all along the ridge-pole, these trappings hang pendent, in alternate bunches of
tassels and deep fringes of stained grass.   The floor is composed of rude planks.
Regular aisles run between ranges of native settees, bottomed with crossed
braids of the coco-nut fibre, and furnished with backs.

But the pulpit, made of a dark, lustrous wood, and standing at one end, is
by far the most striking object.   It is preposterously lofty; indeed, a capital
bird's-eye view of the congregation ought to be had from its summit.

Nor does the church lack a gallery, which runs round on three sides, and is
supported by columns of the coco-nut tree.

Its facings are here and there daubed over with a tawdry blue; and in other
places (without the slightest regard to uniformity), patches of the same colour
may be seen.   In their ardour to decorate the sanctuary, the converts must
have borrowed each a brush full of paint, and zealously daubed away at the
first surface that offered.

As hinted, the general impression is extremely curious.   Little light being admitted, and everything being of a dark colour, there is an indefinable Indian aspect of duskiness throughout. A strange, woody smell, also—more or less pervading every considerable edifice in Polynesia—is at once perceptible. It suggests the idea of worm-eaten idols packed away in some old lumber-room at hand.

For the most part, the congregation attending this church is composed of the better and wealthier orders—the chiefs and their retainers; in short, the rank and fashion of the island. This class is infinitely superior in personal beauty and general healthfulness to the "marenhoar," or common people; the latter having been more exposed to the worst and most debasing evils of foreign intercourse. On Sundays, the former are invariably arrayed in their finery; and thus appear to the best advantage. Nor are they driven to the chapel, as some of their inferiors are to other places of worship; on the contrary, capable of maintaining a handsome exterior, and possessing greater intelligence, they go voluntarily.

In respect of the woodland colonnade supporting its galleries, I called this chapel the Church of the Coco-nuts.

It was the first place for Christian worship in Polynesia that I had seen; and the impression upon entering during service was all the stronger. Majestic-looking chiefs, whose fathers had hurled the battle-club, and old men who had seen sacrifices smoking upon the altars of Oro, were there. And hark! hanging from the bough of a breadfruit tree without, a bell is being struck with a bar of iron by a native lad. In the same spot, the blast of the war-conch had often resounded. But to the proceedings within.

The place is well filled. Everywhere meets the eye the gay calico draperies worn on great occasions by the higher classes, and forming a strange contrast of patterns and colours. In some instances, these are so fashioned as to resemble as much as possible European garments. This is in excessively bad taste. Coats and pantaloons, too, are here and there seen; but they look awkwardly enough, and take away from the general effect.

But it is the array of countenances that most strikes you. Each is suffused with the peculiar animation of the Polynesians, when thus collected in large numbers. Every robe is rustling, every limb in motion, and an incessant buzzing going on throughout the assembly. The tumult is so great, that the voice of the placid old missionary, who now rises, is almost inaudible. Some degree of silence is at length obtained through the exertions of half-a-dozen strapping fellows, in white shirts and no pantaloons. Running in among the settees, they are at great pains to inculcate the impropriety of making a noise, by creating a most unnecessary racket themselves. This part of the service was quite comical.

There is a most interesting Sabbath School connected with the church; and the scholars, a vivacious, mischievous set, were in one part of the gallery. I was amused by a party in a corner. The teacher sat at one end of the bench, with a meek little fellow by his side. When the others were disorderly, this young martyr received a rap; intended, probably, as a sample of what the rest might expect, if they didn't amend.

Standing in the body of the church, and leaning against a pillar, was an old man, in appearance very different from others of his countrymen. He wore nothing but a coarse, scant mantle, of faded tappa; and from his staring, bewildered manner, I set him down as an aged bumpkin from the interior, unaccustomed to the strange sights and sounds of the metropolis. This old worthy was sharply reprimanded for standing up, and thus intercepting the view of those behind; but not comprehending exactly what was said to him, one of the white liveried gentry made no ceremony of grasping him by the shoulders and fairly crushing him down into a seat.

During all this, the old missionary in the pulpit—as well as his associates beneath, never ventured to interfere—leaving everything to native management. With South Sea islanders, assembled in any numbers, there is no other way of getting along.

CHAPTER XLV

A MISSIONARY'S SERMON; WITH SOME REFLECTIONS

SOME degree of order at length restored, the service was continued by singing. The choir was composed of twelve or fifteen ladies of the mission, occupying a long bench to the left of the pulpit. Almost the entire congregation joined in.

The first air fairly startled me; it was the brave tune of Old Hundred, adapted to a Tahitian psalm. After the graceless scenes I had recently passed through, this circumstance, with all its accessories, moved me forcibly.

Many voices around me were of great sweetness and compass. The singers, also, seemed to enjoy themselves mightily; some of them pausing, now and then, and looking round, as if to realize the scene more fully. In truth, they sang right joyously, despite the solemnity of the tune.

The Tahitians have much natural talent for singing; and, on all occasions, are exceedingly fond of it. I have often heard a stave or two of psalmody, hummed over by rakish young fellows, like a snatch from an opera.

With respect to singing, as in most other matters, the Tahitians widely differ from the people of the Sandwich Islands; where the parochial flocks may be said rather to *bleat* than *sing*.

The psalm concluded, a prayer followed. Very considerately, the good old missionary made it short; for the congregation became fidgety and inattentive as soon as it commenced.

A chapter of the Tahitian Bible was now read; a text selected; and the sermon began. It was listened to with more attention than I had anticipated.

Having been informed, from various sources, that the discourses of the missionaries, being calculated to engage the attention of their simple auditors, were, naturally enough, of a rather amusing description to strangers; in short, that they had much to say about steamboats, lord mayors' coaches, and the way fires are put out in London, I had taken care to provide myself with a good interpreter, in the person of an intelligent Hawaiian sailor, whose acquaintance I had made.

"Now, Jack," said I, before entering, "hear every word, and tell me what you can, as the missionary goes on."

Jack's was not, perhaps, a critical version of the discourse; and, at the time, I took no notes of what he said. Nevertheless, I will here venture to give what I remember of it; and, as far as possible, in Jack's phraseology, so as to lose nothing by a double translation.

"Good friends, I glad to see you; and I very well like to have some talk with you to-day. Good friends, very bad times in Tahiti; it make me weep. Pomaree is gone—the island no more yours, but the Wee-Wees' (French). Wicked priests here, too; and wicked idols in woman's clothes, and brass chains.

"Good friends, no you speak, or look at them—but I know you won't—they belong to a set of robbers—the wicked Wee-Wees. Soon these bad men be made to go very quick. Beretanee ships of thunder come, and away they go. But no more 'bout this now. I speak more by by.

"Good friends, many whale-ships here now; and many bad men come in 'em. No good sailors living—that you know very well. They come here, 'cause so bad they no keep 'em home.

"My good little girls, no run after sailors—no go where they go; they harm you. Where they come from, no good people talk to 'em—just like dogs. Here, they talk to Pomaree, and drink *arva* with great Poofai.

"Good friends, this very small island, but very wicked, and very poor; these two go together. Why Beretanee so great? Because that island good island, and send *mickonaree* to poor *kannaka*. In Beretanee, every man rich: plenty things to buy; and plenty things to sell. Houses bigger than Pomaree's, and more grand. Everybody, too, ride about in coaches, bigger than hers; and wear fine tappa every day. (Several luxurious appliances of civilization were here enumerated, and described.)

"Good friends, little to eat left at my house. Schooner from Sydney no bring bag of flour; and kannaka no bring pig and fruit enough. Mickonaree do great deal for kannaka; kannaka do little for mickonaree. So, good friends, weave plenty of coco-nut baskets, fill 'em, and bring 'em to-morrow."

Such was the substance of great part of this discourse; and, whatever may be thought of it, it was specially adapted to the minds of the islanders; who are susceptible to no impressions, except from things palpable, or novel and striking. To them, a dry sermon would be dry indeed.

The Tahitians can hardly ever be said to reflect: they are all impulse; and so, instead of expounding dogmas, the missionaries give them the large type, pleasing cuts, and short, and easy lessons of the primer. Hence, anything like a permanent religious impression, is seldom or never produced.

In fact, there is, perhaps, no race upon earth, less disposed, by nature, to the monitions of Christianity, than the people of the South Sea. And this assertion is made, with full knowledge of what is called the "Great Revival at the Sandwich Islands," about the year 1836; when several thousands were, in the course of a few weeks, admitted into the bosom of the Church. But this result was brought about by no sober moral convictions; as an almost instantaneous relapse into every kind of licentiousness soon afterward testified. It was the legitimate effect of a morbid feeling, engendered by the sense of severe physical wants, preying upon minds excessively prone to superstition; and, by fanatical preaching, inflamed into the belief, that the gods of the missionaries were taking vengeance upon the wickedness of the land.

It is a noteworthy fact, that those very traits in the Tahitians, which induced the London Missionary Society to regard them as the most promising subjects for conversion; and which led, moreover, to the selection of their island as the very first field for missionary labour, eventually proved the most serious obstruction. An air of softness in their manners, great apparent ingenuousness and docility, at first misled; but these were the mere accompaniments of an indolence, bodily and mental; a constitutional voluptuousness; and an aversion to the least restraint; which, however fitted for the luxurious state of nature, in the tropics, are the greatest possible hindrances to the strict moralities of Christianity.

Added to all this, is a quality inherent in Polynesians; and more akin to hypocrisy than anything else. It leads them to assume the most passionate interest in matters for which they really feel little or none whatever; but in which, those whose power they dread, or whose favour they court, they believe to be at all affected. Thus, in their heathen state, the Sandwich Islanders actually knocked out their teeth, tore their hair, and mangled their bodies with shells, to testify their inconsolable grief at the demise of a high chief, or member of the royal family. And yet, Vancouver relates, that, on such an occasion, upon which he happened to be present, those apparently the most abandoned to their feelings, immediately assumed the utmost light-heartedness, on receiving the present of a penny whistle, or a Dutch looking-glass. Similar instances, also, have come under my own observation.

The following is an illustration of the trait alluded to, as occasionally manifested among the converted Polynesians.

At one of the Society Islands—Raiatair, I believe—the natives, for special reasons, desired to commend themselves particularly to the favour of the missionaries. Accordingly, during divine service, many of them behaved in a manner, otherwise unaccountable, and precisely similar to their behaviour as heathens. They pretended to be wrought up to madness by the preaching which they heard. They rolled their eyes; foamed at the mouth; fell down in fits; and so, were carried home. Yet, strange to relate, all this was deemed the evidence of the power of the Most High; and, as such, was heralded abroad.

But, to return to the Church of the Coco-nuts. The blessing pronounced, the congregation disperse; enlivening the Broom Road with their waving mantles. On either hand, they disappear down the shaded pathways, which lead off from the main route, conducting to hamlets in the groves, or to the little marine villas upon the beach. There is considerable hilarity; and you would suppose them just from an old-fashioned "hevar," or jolly heathen dance. Those who carry Bibles, swing them carelessly from their arms, by cords of sinnate.

The Sabbath is no ordinary day with the Tahitians. So far as doing any work is concerned, it is scrupulously observed. The canoes are hauled up on the beach; the nets are spread to dry. Passing by the hen-coop huts, on the roadside, you find their occupants idle, as usual; but less disposed to gossip. After service, repose broods over the whole island; the valleys reaching inland look stiller than ever.

In short, it is Sunday—their "Taboo Day"; the very word, formerly expressing the sacredness of their pagan observances, now proclaiming the sanctity of the Christian Sabbath.

CHAPTER XLVI

SOMETHING ABOUT THE KANNAKIPPERS

A WORTHY young man, formerly a friend of mine (I speak of Kooloo with all possible courtesy, since after our intimacy there would be an impropriety in doing otherwise)—this worthy youth, having some genteel notions of retirement, dwelt in a "maroo boro," or breadfruit shade, a pretty nook in a wood, midway between the Calabooza Beretanee and the Church of Coco-nuts. Hence, at the latter place, he was one of the most regular worshippers.•

Kooloo was a blade. Standing up in the congregation in all the bravery of a striped calico shirt, with the skirts rakishly adjusted over a pair of white sailor trousers, and hair well anointed with coco-nut oil, he ogled the ladies with an air of supreme satisfaction. Nor were his glances unreturned.

But such looks as the Tahitian belles cast at each other: frequently turning up their noses at the advent of a new cotton mantle recently imported in the chest of some amorous sailor. Upon one occasion, I observed a group of young girls, in tunics of coarse, soiled sheeting, disdainfully pointing at a damsel in a flaming red one. "Oee tootai owree!" said they with ineffable scorn, "itai maitai!" (you are a good-for-nothing huzzy, no better than you should be).

Now, Kooloo communed with the church; so did all these censorious young ladies. Yet after eating breadfruit at the Eucharist, I knew several of them, the same night, to be guilty of some sad derelictions.

Puzzled by these things, I resolved to find out, if possible, what ideas, if any, they entertained of religion; but as one's spiritual concerns are rather delicate for a stranger to meddle with, I went to work as adroitly as I could.

Farnow, an old native who had recently retired from active pursuits, having thrown up the business of being a sort of running footman to the queen, had settled down in a snug little retreat, not fifty rods from Captain Bob's. His selecting our vicinity for his residence, may have been with some view to the advantages it afforded for introducing his three daughters into polite circles. At any rate, not averse to receiving the attentions of so devoted a gallant as the doctor, the sisters (communicants, be it remembered) kindly extended to him free permission to visit them sociably, whenever he pleased.

We dropped in one evening, and found the ladies at home. My long friend engaged his favourites, the two younger girls, at the game of "Now," or hunting a stone under three piles of tappa. For myself, I lounged on a mat with Ideea the eldest, dallying with her grass fan, and improving my knowledge of Tahitian.

The occasion was well adapted to my purpose, and I began.

"Ah, Ideea, mickonaree oee?" the same as drawling out—"By the by, Miss Ideea, do you belong to the church?"

"Yes, me mickonaree," was the reply.

But the assertion was at once qualified by certain reservations; so curious, that I cannot forbear their relation.

"Mickonaree ena," (church, member here), exclaimed she, laying her hand upon her mouth, and a strong emphasis on the adverb. In the same way, and with similar exclamations, she touched her eyes and hands. This done, her whole air changed in an instant; and she gave me to understand, by unmistakable gestures, that in certain other respects she was not exactly a "mickonaree." In short, Ideea was

> "A sad good Christian at the heart—
> A very heathen in the carnal part."

The explanation terminated in a burst of laughter, in which all three sisters joined; and for fear of looking silly, the doctor and myself. As soon as goodbreeding would permit, we took leave.

The hypocrisy in matters of religion, so apparent in all Polynesian converts, is most injudiciously nourished in Tahiti, by a zealous, and in many cases, a coercive superintendence over their spiritual well-being. But it is only manifested with respect to the common people, their superiors being exempted.

On Sunday mornings, when the prospect is rather small for a full house in the minor churches, a parcel of fellows are actually sent out with rattans into the highways and byways as whippers-in of the congregation. This is a sober fact.

These worthies constitute a religious police; and you always know them by the great white diapers they wear. On weekdays, they are quite as busy as on Sundays; to the great terror of the inhabitants, going all over the island, and spying out the wickedness thereof.

Moreover, they are the collectors of fines—levied generally in grass mats—for obstinate non-attendance upon divine worship, and other offences amenable to the ecclesiastical judicature of the missionaries.

Old Bob called these fellows "kannakippers," a corruption, I fancy, of our word constable.

He bore them a bitter grudge; and one day, drawing near home, and learning that two of them were just then making a domiciliary visit at his house, he ran behind a bush; and as they came forth, two green breadfruit from a hand unseen took them each between the shoulders. The sailors in the Calabooza were witnesses to this, as well as several natives; who, when the intruders were out of sight, applauded Captain Bob's spirit in no measured terms; the ladies present vehemently joining in. Indeed, the kannakippers have no greater enemies than the latter. And no wonder: the impertinent varlets, popping into their houses at all hours, are for ever prying into their peccadilloes.

Kooloo, who at times was patriotic and pensive, and mourned the evils under which his country was groaning, frequently inveighed against the statute, which thus authorized an utter stranger to interfere with domestic arrangements. He himself—quite a ladies' man—had often been annoyed thereby. He considered the kannakippers a bore.

Besides their confounded inquisitiveness, they add insult to injury, by making a point of dining out every day at some hut within the limits of their jurisdiction. As for the gentleman of the house, his meek endurance of these things is amazing. But "good easy man," there is nothing for him but to be as hospitable as possible.

These gentry are indefatigable. At the dead of night prowling round the houses, and in the daytime hunting amorous couples in the groves. Yet in one instance, the chase completely baffled them.

It was thus.

Several weeks previous to our arrival at the island, some one's husband and another person's wife, having taken a mutual fancy for each other, went out for a walk. The alarm was raised, and with hue and cry they were pursued; but nothing was seen of them again until the lapse of some ninety days; when we were called out from the Calabooza to behold a great mob inclosing the lovers, and escorting them for trial to the village.

Their appearance was most singular. The girdle excepted, they were quite naked; their hair was long, burned yellow at the ends, and entangled with burs; and their bodies scratched and scarred in all directions. It seems, that acting upon the "love in a cottage" principle, they had gone right into the interior; and throwing up a hut in an uninhabited valley, had lived there, until in an unlucky stroll, they were observed and captured.

They were subsequently condemned to make one hundred fathoms of Broom Road—a six months' work, if not more.

Often, when seated in a house, conversing quietly with its inmates, I have known them betray the greatest confusion at the sudden announcement of a kannakipper's being in sight. To be reported by one of these officials as a "Tootai Owree" (in general, signifying a bad person or disbeliever in Christianity), is as much dreaded as the forefinger of Titus Oates was, levelled at an alleged papist.

But the islanders take a sly revenge upon them. Upon entering a dwelling, the kannakippers oftentimes volunteer a pharisaical prayer-meeting: hence, they go in secret by the name of "Boora-Artuas," literally, "Pray-to-Gods."

CHAPTER XLVII

HOW THEY DRESS IN TAHITI

EXCEPT where the employment of making "tappa" is inflicted as a punishment, the echoes of the cloth-mallet have long since died away in the listless valleys of Tahiti. Formerly, the girls spent their mornings like ladies at their tambour frames; *now*, they are lounged away in almost utter indolence. True, most of them make their own garments; but this comprises but a stitch or two; the ladies of the mission, by the by, being entitled to the credit of teaching them to sew.

The "kihee whihenee," or petticoat, is a mere breadth of white cotton, or calico; loosely enveloping the person, from the waist to the feet. Fastened simply, by a single tuck, or by twisting the upper corners together, this garment frequently becomes disordered; thus affording an opportunity of being coquettishly adjusted. Over the "kihee," they wear a sort of gown, open in front, very loose, and as negligent as you please. The ladies here never dress for dinner.

But what shall be said of those horrid hats! Fancy a bunch of straw, plaited into the shape of a coal-scuttle, and stuck, bolt upright, on the crown; with a yard or two of red ribbon, flying about like kite-strings. Milliners of Paris, what would ye say to them! Though made by the natives, they are said to have been first contrived and recommended by the missionaries' wives; a report, which, I really trust, is nothing but scandal.

Curious to relate, these things for the head, are esteemed exceedingly becoming. The braiding of the straw is one of the few employments of the higher classes; all of which but minister to the silliest vanity. The young girls, however, wholly eschew the hats; leaving those dowdy old souls, their mothers, to make frights of themselves.

As for the men, those who aspire to European garments seem to have no perception of the relation subsisting between the various parts of a gentleman's costume. To the wearer of a coat, for instance, pantaloons are by no means indispensable; and, a bell-crowned hat and a girdle, are full dress. The young sailor, for whom Kooloo deserted me, presented him with a shaggy old pea-jacket; and, with this buttoned up to his chin, under a tropical sun, he promenaded the Broom Road, quite elated. Doctor Long Ghost, who saw him thus, ran away with the idea that he was under medical treatment at the time—in the act of taking, what the quacks call, a "sweat."

A bachelor friend of Captain Bob rejoiced in the possession of a full European suit; in which he often stormed the ladies' hearts. Having a military leaning, he ornamented the coat with a scarlet patch on the breast; and mounted it also, here and there, with several regimental buttons, slyly cut from the uniforms of a parcel of drunken marines, sent ashore on a holiday from a man-of-war. But, in spite of the ornaments, the dress was not exactly the thing. From the tightness of the cloth across the shoulders, his elbows projected from his sides, like an ungainly rider's; and his ponderous legs were jammed so hard into his slim, nether garments, that the threads of every seam showed; and, at every step, you looked for a catastrophe.

In general, there seems to be no settled style of dressing among the males: they wear anything they can get; in some cases, awkwardly modifying the fashions of their fathers, so as to accord with their own altered views of what is becoming.

But ridiculous as many of them now appear, in foreign habiliments, the Tahitians presented a far different appearance in the original national costume; which was graceful in the extreme, modest to all but the prudish, and peculiarly adapted to the climate. But the short kilts of dyed tappa, the tasselled maroes, and other articles formerly worn, are, at the present day, prohibited by law, as indecorous. For what reason necklaces and garlands of flowers, among the women, are also forbidden, I never could learn; but, it is said, that they were associated, in some way, with a forgotten heathen observance.

Many pleasant, and, seemingly, innocent sports and pastimes, are likewise interdicted. In old times, there were several athletic games practised; such as wrestling, foot-racing, throwing the javelin, and archery. In all these they greatly excelled; and, for some, splendid festivals were instituted. Among their everyday amusements, were dancing, tossing the football, kite-flying, flute-playing, and singing traditional ballads; *now*, all punishable offences; though most of them have been so long in disuse, that they are nearly forgotten.

In the same way, the "Opio," or festive harvest-home of the breadfruit, has been suppressed; though, as described to me, by Captain Bob, it seemed wholly free from any immoral tendency. Against tattooing, of any kind, there is a severe law.

That this abolition of their national amusements and customs was not willingly acquiesced in, is shown in the frequent violation of many of the statutes inhibiting them; and, especially, in the frequency with which their "hevars," or dances, are practised in secret.

Doubtless, in thus denationalizing the Tahitians, as it were, the missionaries were prompted by a sincere desire for good; but the effect has been lamentable. Supplied with no amusements, in place of those forbidden, the Tahitians, who require more recreation than other people, have sunk into a listlessness, or indulge in sensualities, a hundred times more pernicious than all the games ever celebrated in the Temple of Tanee.

CHAPTER XLVIII

TAHITI AS IT IS

As in the last few chapters, several matters connected with the general condition of the natives have been incidentally touched upon, it may be well not to leave so important a subject in a state calculated to convey erroneous impressions. Let us bestow upon it, therefore, something more than a mere cursory glance.

But in the first place, let it be distinctly understood, that in all I have to say upon this subject, both here and elsewhere, I mean no harm to the missionaries nor their cause; I merely desire to set forth things as they actually exist.

Of the results which have flowed from the intercourse of foreigners with the Polynesians, including the attempts to civilize and christianize them by the missionaries, Tahiti, on many accounts, is obviously the fairest practical example. Indeed, it may now be asserted, that the experiment of christianizing the Tahitians, and improving their social condition by the introduction of foreign customs, has been fully tried. The present generation have grown up under the auspices of their religious instructors. And although it may be urged, that the labours of the latter have at times been more or less obstructed by unprincipled foreigners, still, this in no wise renders Tahiti any the less a fair illustration; for, with obstacles like these, the missionaries in Polynesia must always, and everywhere struggle.

Nearly sixty years have elapsed since the Tahitian mission was started; and during this period, it has received the unceasing prayers and contributions of its friends abroad. Nor has any enterprise of the kind called forth more devotion on the part of those directly employed in it.

It matters not, that the earlier labourers in the work, although strictly conscientious, were, as a class, ignorant, and, in many cases, deplorably bigoted: such traits have, in some degree, characterized the pioneers of all faiths. And although in zeal and disinterestedness, the missionaries now on the island are, perhaps, inferior to their predecessors, they have, nevertheless, in their own way at least, laboured hard to make a Christian people of their charge.

Let us now glance at the most obvious changes wrought in their condition.

The entire system of idolatry has been done away; together with several barbarous practices engrafted thereon. But this result is not so much to be ascribed to the missionaries, as to the civilizing effects of a long and constant intercourse with whites of all nations; to whom, for many years, Tahiti has been one of the principal places of resort in the South Seas. At the Sandwich Islands, the potent institution of the Taboo, together with the entire paganism of the land, was utterly abolished by a voluntary act of the natives, some time previous to the arrival of the first missionaries among them.

The next most striking change in the Tahitians is this. From the permanent residence among them of influential and respectable foreigners, as well as from the frequent visits of ships-of-war, recognizing the nationality of the island, its inhabitants are no longer deemed fit subjects for the atrocities practised upon mere savages; and hence, secure from retaliation, vessels of all kinds now enter their harbours with perfect safety.

But let us consider what results are directly ascribable to the missionaries alone.

In all cases, they have striven hard to mitigate the evils resulting from the commerce with the whites in general. Such attempts, however, have been rather injudicious, and often ineffectual: in truth, a barrier almost insurmountable is presented in the dispositions of the people themselves. Still, in this respect, the morality of the islanders is, upon the whole, improved by the presence of the missionaries.

But the greatest achievement of the latter, and one which in itself is most hopeful and gratifying is, that they have translated the entire Bible into the language of the island; and I have myself known several who were able to read it with facility. They have also established churches, and schools for both children and adults; the latter, I regret to say, are now much neglected; which must be ascribed, in a great measure, to the disorders growing out of the proceedings of the French.

It were unnecessary here, to enter diffusely into matters connected with the internal government of the Tahitian churches and schools. Nor, upon this head, is my information copious enough to warrant me in presenting details. But we do not need them. We are merely considering general *results*, as made apparent in the moral and religious condition of the island at large.

Upon a subject like this, however, it would be altogether too assuming for a single individual to decide; and, so, in place of my own random observations, which may be found elsewhere, I will here present those of several known authors, made under various circumstances, at different periods, and down to a comparative late date. A few very brief extracts will enable the reader to mark for himself what progressive improvement, if any, has taken place.

Nor must it be overlooked, that of these authorities, the two first in order are largely quoted by the Right Reverend M. Russell, in a work composed for the express purpose of imparting information on the subject of Christian missions in Polynesia. And he frankly acknowledges, moreover, that they are such as "cannot fail to have great weight with the public."

After alluding to the manifold evils entailed upon the natives by foreigners, and their singularly inert condition; and after somewhat too severely denouncing the undeniable errors of the mission, Kotzebue, the Russian navigator, says, "A religion like this, which forbids every innocent pleasure, and cramps or annihilates every mental power, is a libel on the divine founder of Christianity. It is true, that the religion of the missionaries has, with a great deal of evil, effected some good. It has restrained the vices of theft and incontinence; but it has given birth to ignorance, hypocrisy, and a hatred of all other modes of faith, which was once foreign to the open and benevolent character of the Tahitian."

Captain Beechy says, that while at Tahiti, he saw scenes "which must have convinced the greatest sceptic of the thoroughly immoral condition of the people, and which would force him to conclude, as Turnbull did, many years previous, that their intercourse with the Europeans had tended to debase, rather than exalt, their condition."

About the year 1834, Daniel Wheeler, an honest-hearted Quaker, prompted by motives of the purest philanthropy, visited, in a vessel of his own, most of the missionary settlements in the South Seas. He remained some time at Tahiti; receiving the hospitalities of the missionaries there, and, from time to time, exhorting the natives.

After bewailing their social condition, he frankly says of their religious state, "Certainly, appearances are unpromising; and however unwilling to adopt such a conclusion, there is reason to apprehend, that Christian principle is a great rarity."

Such, then, is the testimony of good and unbiased men, who have been upon the spot; but, how comes it to differ so widely from impressions of others at home? Simply thus: instead of estimating the result of missionary labours by the number of heathens who have actually been made to understand and practise (in some measure, at least) the precepts of Christianity, this result has been unwarrantably inferred from the number of those, who, without any understanding of these things, have in any way been induced to abandon idolatry and conform to certain outward observances.

By authority of some kind or other, exerted upon the natives through their chiefs, and prompted by the hope of some worldly benefit to the latter, and not.

by appeals to the reason, have conversions in Polynesia been in most cases brought about.

Even in one or two instances—so often held up as wonderful examples of divine power—where the natives have impulsively burned their idols, and rushed to the waters of baptism, the very suddenness of the change has but indicated its unsoundness. Williams, the martyr of Erromanga, relates an instance where the inhabitants of an island professing Christianity, voluntarily assembled, and solemnly revived all their heathen customs.

All the world over, facts are more eloquent than words; and the following will show in what estimation the missionaries themselves hold the present state of Christianity and morals among the converted Polynesians.

On the island of Imeeo (attached to the Tahitian mission), is a seminary under the charge of the Rev. Mr. Simpson and wife, for the education of the children of the missionaries, exclusively. Sent home—in many cases, at a very early age—to finish their education, the pupils here are taught nothing but the rudiments of knowledge; nothing more than may be learned in the native schools. Notwithstanding this, the two races are kept as far as possible from associating; the avowed reason being, to preserve the young whites from moral contamination. The better to insure this end, every effort is made to prevent them from acquiring the native language.

They went even further at the Sandwich Islands; where, a few years ago, a playground for the children of the missionaries was enclosed with a fence many feet high, the more effectually to exclude the wicked little Hawaiians.

And yet, strange as it may seem, the depravity among the Polynesians, which renders precautions like these necessary, was in a measure unknown before their intercourse with the whites. The excellent Captain Wilson, who took the first missionaries out to Tahiti, affirms, that the people of that island had, in many things, "more refined ideas of decency than ourselves." Vancouver, also, has some noteworthy ideas on this subject, respecting the Sandwich Islanders.

That the immorality alluded to is continually increasing, is plainly shown in the numerous, severe, and perpetually violated laws against licentiousness of all kinds, in both groups of islands.

It is hardly to be expected, that the missionaries would send home accounts of this state of things. Hence, Captain Beechey, in alluding to the *Polynesian Researches* of Ellis, says, that the author has impressed his readers with a far more elevated idea of the moral condition of the Tahitians, and the degree of civilization to which they have attained, than they deserve; or, at least, than the facts which came under his observation, authorized. He then goes on to say, that in his intercourse with the islanders, "they had no fear of him, and consequently acted from the impulse of their natural feelings; so that he was the better enabled to obtain a correct knowledge of their real disposition and habits."

From my own familiar intercourse with the natives, this last reflection still more forcibly applies to myself.

CHAPTER XLIX

SAME SUBJECT CONTINUED

WE have glanced at their moral and religious condition; let us see how it is with them socially, and in other respects.

It has been said, that the only way to civilize a people, is to form in them habits of industry. Judged by this principle, the Tahitians are less civilized now than formerly. True, their constitutional indolence is excessive; but surely, if the spirit of Christianity is among them, so unchristian a vice ought to be, at least, partially remedied. But the reverse is the fact. Instead of acquiring new occupations, old ones have been discontinued.

As previously remarked, the manufacture of tappa is nearly obsolete in many parts of the island. So, too, with that of the native tools and domestic utensils; very few of which are now fabricated, since the superiority of European wares has been made so evident.

This, however, would be all very well, were the natives to apply themselves to such occupations as would enable them to supply the few articles they need. But they are far from doing so; and the majority being unable to obtain European substitutes for many things before made by themselves, the inevitable consequence is seen in the present wretched and destitute mode of life among the common people. To me, so recently from a primitive valley of the Marquesas, the aspect of most of the dwellings of the poorer Tahitians, and their general habits, seemed anything but tidy; nor could I avoid a comparison, immeasurably to the disadvantage of these partially civilized islanders.

In Tahiti, the people have nothing to do; and idleness, everywhere, is the parent of vice. "There is scarcely anything," says the good old Quaker Wheeler, "so striking, or pitiable, as their aimless, nerveless mode of spending life."

Attempts have repeatedly been made to rouse them from their sluggishness; but in vain. Several years ago, the cultivation of cotton was introduced; and, with their usual love of novelty, they went to work with great alacrity; but the interest excited quickly subsided, and now, not a pound of the article is raised.

About the same time, machinery for weaving was sent out from London; and a factory was started at Afrehitoo, in Imeeo. The whiz of the wheels and spindles brought in volunteers from all quarters, who deemed it a privilege to be admitted to work: yet, in six months, not a boy could be hired; and the machinery was knocked down, and packed off to Sydney.

It was the same way with the cultivation of the sugar-cane, a plant indigenous to the island; peculiarly fitted to the soil and climate, and of so excellent a quality that Bligh took slips of it to the West Indies. All the plantations went on famously, for a while; the natives swarming in the fields, like ants, and making a prodigious stir. What few plantations now remain, are owned and worked by whites; who would rather pay a drunken sailor eighteen or twenty Spanish dollars a month, than hire a sober native for his "fish and taro."

It is well worthy remark here, that every evidence of civilization among the South Sea Islands, directly pertains to foreigners; though the fact of such evidence existing at all, is usually urged as a proof of the elevated condition of the natives. Thus, at Honolulu, the capital of the Sandwich Islands, there are fine dwelling-houses, several hotels, and barber-shops, aye, even billiard-rooms;

but all these are owned and used, be it observed, by whites. There are tailors, and blacksmiths, and carpenters also; but not one of them is a native.

The fact is, that the mechanical and agricultural employments of civilized life, require a kind of exertion altogether too steady and sustained, to agree with an indolent people like the Polynesians. Calculated for a state of nature, in a climate providentially adapted to it, they are unfit for any other. Nay, as a race, they cannot otherwise long exist.

The following statement speaks for itself.

About the year 1777, Captain Cook estimated the population of Tahiti at about two hundred thousand. By a regular census, taken some four or five years ago, it was found to be only nine thousand. This amazing decrease, not only shows the malignancy of the evils necessary to produce it; but, from the fact, the inference unavoidably follows, that all the wars, child murders, and other depopulating causes, alleged to have existed in former times, were nothing in comparison to them.

These evils, of course, are solely of foreign origin. To say nothing of the effects of drunkenness, the occasional inroads of the small-pox, and other things, which might be mentioned, it is sufficient to allude to a virulent disease, which now taints the blood of at least two-thirds of the common people of the island; and, in some form or other, is transmitted from father to son.

Their first horror and consternation at the earlier ravages of this scourge, were pitiable in the extreme. The very name bestowed upon it, is a combination of all that is horrid and unmentionable to a civilized being.

Distracted with their sufferings, they brought forth their sick before the missionaries, when they were preaching, and cried out, "Lies, lies! you tell us of salvation; and, behold, we are dying. We want no other salvation, than to live in this world. Where are there any saved through your speech? Pomaree is dead; and we are all dying with your cursed diseases. When will you give over?"

At present, the virulence of the disorder, in individual cases, has somewhat abated; but the poison is only the more widely diffused.

"How dreadful and appalling," breaks forth old Wheeler, "the consideration, that the intercourse of distant nations should have entailed upon these poor, untutored islanders, a curse unprecedented, and unheard of, in the annals of history."

In view of these things, who can remain blind to the fact, that, so far as mere temporal felicity is concerned, the Tahitians are far worse off now, than formerly; and although their circumstances, upon the whole, are bettered by the presence of the missionaries, the benefits conferred by the latter become utterly insignificant, when confronted with the vast preponderance of evil brought about by other means.

Their prospects are hopeless. Nor can the most devoted efforts, now exempt them from furnishing a marked illustration of a principle, which history has always exemplified. Years ago brought to a stand, where all that is corrupt in barbarism and civilization unite, to the exclusion of the virtues of either state; like other uncivilized beings, brought into contact with Europeans, they must here remain stationary until utterly extinct.

The islanders themselves are mournfully watching their doom. Several years since, Pomaree II said to Tyreman and Bennet, the deputies of the London Missionary Society, "You have come to see me at a very bad time. Your ancestors came in the time of men, when Tahiti was inhabited: you are come to behold just the remnant of my people."

Of like import, was the prediction of Teearmoar, the high-priest of Paree; who lived over a hundred years ago. I have frequently heard it chanted, in a low, sad tone by aged Tahitians:—

> "A harree ta fow,
> A toro ta farraro,
> A now ta tararta."

> The palm-tree shall grow,
> The coral shall spread,
> But man shall cease.

CHAPTER L

SOMETHING HAPPENS TO LONG GHOST

WE will now return to the narrative.

·The day before the *Julia* sailed, Dr. Johnson paid his last call. He was not quite so bland as usual. All he wanted was the men's names to a paper, certifying to their having received from him sundry medicaments, therein mentioned. This voucher, endorsed by Captain Guy, secured his pay. But he would not have obtained for it the sailors' signs manual, had either the doctor or myself been present at the time.

Now, my long friend wasted no love upon Johnson; but, for reasons of his own, hated him heartily: all the same thing in one sense; for either passion argues an object deserving thereof. And so, to be hated cordially, is only a left-handed compliment; which shows how foolish it is to be bitter against any one.

For my own part, I merely felt a cool, purely incidental, and passive contempt for Johnson, as a selfish, mercenary apothecary; and hence, I often remonstrated with Long Ghost, when he flew out against him, and heaped upon him all manner of scurrilous epithets. In his professional brother's presence, however, he never acted thus; maintaining an amiable exterior, to help along the jokes which were played.

I am now going to tell another story, in which my long friend figures with the physician: I do not wish to bring one or the other of them too often upon the stage; but as the thing actually happened, I must relate it.

A few days after Johnson *presented his bill*, as above mentioned, the doctor expressed to me his regret, that although he (Johnson) had apparently been played off for our entertainment, yet, nevertheless, he had made money out of the transaction. And I wonder, added the doctor, if that, now he cannot expect to receive any further pay, he could be induced to call again.

By a curious coincidence, not five minutes after making this observation, Doctor Long Ghost himself fell down in an unaccountable fit; and without asking anybody's leave, Captain Bob, who was by, at once dispatched a boy, hot foot, for Johnson.

Meanwhile, we carried him into the Calabooza; and the natives, who assembled in numbers, suggested various modes of treatment. One rather energetic practitioner was for holding the patient by the shoulders, while somebody tugged at his feet. This resuscitatory operation was called the "Potata"; but thinking our long comrade sufficiently lengthy without additional stretching, we declined *potataing* him.

Presently the physician was spied coming along the Broom Road at a great rate, and so absorbed in the business of locomotion, that he heeded not the imprudence of being in a hurry in a tropical climate. He was in a profuse perspiration; which must have been owing to the warmth of his feelings, notwithstanding we had supposed him a man of no heart. But his benevolent haste upon this occasion was subsequently accounted for: it merely arose from professional curiosity, to behold a case most unusual in his Polynesian practice. Now, under certain circumstances, sailors, generally so frolicsome, are exceedingly particular in having everything conducted with the strictest propriety. Accordingly, they deputed me, as his intimate friend, to sit at Long Ghost's head, so as to be ready to officiate as "spokesman"; and answer all questions propounded, the rest to keep silent.

"What's the matter?" exclaimed Johnson, out of breath, and bursting into the Calabooza: "how did it happen?—speak quick!" and he looked at Long Ghost.

I told him how the fit came on.

"Singular"—he observed—"very: good enough pulse;" and he let go of it, and placed his hand upon the heart.

"But what's all that frothing at the, mouth?" he continued; "and bless me! look at the abdomen!"

The region thus denominated, exhibited the most unaccountable symptoms. A low, rumbling sound was heard; and a sort of undulation was discernible beneath the thin cotton frock.

"Colic, sir?" suggested a by-stander.

"Colic be hanged!" shouted the physician; "who ever heard of anybody in a trance of the colic?"

During this, the patient lay upon his back, stark and straight, giving no signs of life except those above mentioned.

"I'll bleed him!" cried Johnson at last—"run for a calabash, one of you!"

"Life ho!" here sung out Navy Bob, as if he had just spied a sail.

"What under the sun's the matter with him!" cried the physician, starting at the appearance of the mouth, which had jerked to one side, and there remained fixed.

"Pr'aps it's St. Witus's hornpipe," suggested Bob.

"Hold the calabash!" and the lancet was out in a moment.

But before the deed could be done, the face became natural;—a sigh was heaved;—the eyelids quivered, opened, closed; and Long Ghost, twitching all over, rolled on his side, and breathed audibly. By degrees, he became sufficiently recovered to speak.

After trying to get something coherent out of him, Johnson withdrew; evidently disappointed in the scientific interest of the case. Soon after his departure, the doctor sat up; and upon being asked what upon earth ailed him, shook his head mysteriously. He then deplored the hardship of being an invalid in such a place, where there was not the slightest provision for his comfort. This awakened the compassion of our good old keeper, who offered to send him to a place where he would be better cared for. Long Ghost acquiesced; and being at once mounted upon the shoulders of four of Captain Bob's men, was marched off in state, like the Grand Lama of Thibet.

Now, I do not pretend to account for his remarkable swoon; but his reason for suffering himself to be thus removed from the Calabooza, was strongly suspected to be nothing more than a desire to insure more regularity in his dinner-hour; hoping that the benevolent native to whom he was going, would set a good table.

The next morning, we were all envying his fortune; when of a sudden, he bolted in upon us, looking decidedly out of humour.

"Hang it!" he cried, "I'm worse off than ever; let me have some breakfast!" We lowered our slender bag of ship-stores from a rafter, and handed him a biscuit. While this was being munched, he went on and told us his story.

"After leaving here, they trotted me back into a valley, and left me in a hut, where an old woman lived by herself. This must be the nurse, thought I: and so I asked her to kill a pig, and bake it; for I felt my appetite returning. "*Ita! ita!—oee mattee—mattee nuee*"—(no, no; you too sick). "The devil *mattee* ye," said I—"give me something to eat!" But nothing could be had. Night coming on, I had to stay. Creeping into a corner, I tried to sleep; but it was to no purpose;—the old crone must have had the quinsy, or something else; and she kept up such a wheezing and choking, that at last I sprang up, and groped after her; but she hobbled away like a goblin; and that was the last of her. As soon as the sun rose, I made the best of my way back; and here I am."

He never left us more, nor ever had a second fit.

CHAPTER LI

WILSON GIVES US THE CUT—DEPARTURE FOR IMEEO

About three weeks after the *Julia's* sailing, our condition began to be a little precarious. We were without any regular supply of food; the arrival of ships was growing less frequent; and, what was worse yet, all the natives but good old Captain Bob, began to tire of us. Nor was this to be wondered at; we were obliged to live upon their benevolence, when they had little enough for themselves. Besides, we were sometimes driven to acts of marauding: such as kidnapping pigs, and cooking them in the groves; at which their proprietors were by no means pleased.

In this state of affairs, we determined to march off to the consul in a body; and, as he had brought us to these straits, demand an adequate maintenance.

On the point of starting, Captain Bob's men raised the most outrageous cries, and tried to prevent us. Though hitherto we had strolled about wherever we pleased, this grand conjunction of our whole force upon one particular expedition, seemed to alarm them. But we assured them, that we were not going to assault the village; and so, after a good deal of gibberish, they permitted us to leave.

We went straight to the Pritchard residence, where the consul dwelt. This house—to which I have before referred—is quite commodious. It has a wide veranda, glazed windows, and other appurtenances of a civilized mansion. Upon the lawn in front are palm-trees standing erect here and there, like sentinels. The Consular Office, a small building by itself, is enclosed by the same picket which fences in the lawn.

We found the office closed, but, in the veranda of the dwelling-house, was a lady performing a tonsorial operation on the head of a prim-looking, elderly

European, in a low, white cravat;—the most domestic little scene I had witnessed since leaving home. Bent upon an interview with Wilson, the sailors now deputed the doctor to step forward as a polite inquirer after his health.

The pair stared very hard as he advanced; but no ways disconcerted, he saluted them gravely, and inquired for the consul.

Upon being informed that he had gone down to the beach, we proceeded in that direction; and soon met a native, who told us, that apprised of our vicinity, Wilson was keeping out of the way. We resolved to meet him; and passing through the village, he suddenly came walking towards us; having apparently made up his mind that any attempt to elude us would be useless.

"What do you want of me, you rascals?" he cried—a greeting which provoked a retort in no measured terms. At this juncture, the natives began to crowd round, and several foreigners strolled along. Caught in the very act of speaking to such disreputable acquaintances, Wilson now fidgeted, and moved rapidly toward his office; the men following. Turning upon them incensed, he bade them be off—he would have nothing more to say to us; and then, hurriedly addressing Captain Bob in Tahitian, he hastened on, and never stopped till the postern of Pritchard's wicket was closed behind him.

Our good old keeper was now highly excited, bustling about in his huge petticoats, and conjuring us to return to the Calabooza. After a little debate, we acquiesced.

This interview was decisive. Sensible that none of the charges brought against us would stand, yet unwilling formally to withdraw them, the consul now wished to get rid of us altogether; but without being suspected of encouraging our escape. Thus only could we account for his conduct.

Some of the party, however, with a devotion to principle truly heroic, swore they would never leave him, happen what might. For my own part, I began to long for a change; and as there seemed to be no getting away in a ship, I resolved to hit upon some other expedient. But first, I cast about for a comrade; and of course the long doctor was chosen. We at once laid our heads together; and for the present, resolved to disclose nothing to the rest.

A few days previous, I had fallen in with a couple of Yankee lads, twins, who, originally deserting their ship at Fanning's Island (an uninhabited spot, but exceedingly prolific in fruit of all kinds), had, after a long residence there, roved about among the Society group. They were last from Imeeo—the island immediately adjoining—where they had been in the employ of two foreigners, who had recently started a plantation there. These persons, they said, had charged them to send over from Papeetee, if they could, two white men for field-labourers.

Now, all but the prospect of digging and delving, suited us exactly; but the opportunity for leaving the island was not to be slighted; and so we held ourselves in readiness to return with the planters; who, in a day or two, were expected to visit Papeetee in their boat.

At the interview which ensued, we were introduced to them as Peter and Paul; and they agreed to give Peter and Paul fifteen silver dollars a month, promising something more, should we remain with them permanently. What they wanted, was men who would stay. To elude the natives—many of whom not exactly understanding our relations with the consul, might arrest us, were they to see us departing—the coming midnight was appointed for that purpose.

When the hour drew nigh, we disclosed our intention to the rest. Some upbraided us for deserting them; others applauded, and said, that on the first opportunity they would follow our example. At last, we bade them farewell.

And there would now be a serene sadness in thinking over the scene—since we never saw them again—had not all been dashed by M'Gee's picking the doctor's pocket of a jack-knife, in the very act of embracing him.

We stole down to the beach, where, under the shadow of a grove, the boat was waiting. After some delay, we shipped the oars, and pulling outside of the reef, set the sail; and with a fair wind, glided away for Imeeo.

It was a pleasant trip. The moon was up—the air, warm—the waves, musical—and all above was the tropical night, one purple vault hung round with soft, trembling stars.

The channel is some five leagues wide. On one hand, you have the three great peaks of Tahiti lording it over ranges of mountains and valleys; and on the other, the equally romantic elevations of Imeeo, high above which a lone peak, called by our companions "the Marling-spike," shot up its verdant spire.

The planters were quite sociable. They had been sea-faring men, and this, of course, was a bond between us. To strengthen it, a flask of wine was produced, one of several which had been procured in person from the French admiral's steward; for whom the planters, when on a former visit to Papeetee, had done a good turn, by introducing the amorous Frenchman to the ladies ashore. Besides this, they had a calabash filled with wild boar's meat, baked yams, breadfruit, and Tombez potatoes. Pipes and tobacco also were produced; and while regaling ourselves, plenty of stories were told about the neighbouring islands.

At last we heard the roar of the Imeeo reef; and gliding through a break, floated over the expanse within, which was smooth as a young girl's brow and beached the boat.

CHAPTER LII

THE VALLEY OF MARTAIR

We went up through groves to an open space, where we heard voices, and a light was seen glimmering from out a bamboo dwelling. It was the planters' retreat; and in their absence, several girls were keeping house, assisted by an old native, who, wrapped up in tappa, lay in the corner, smoking.

A hasty meal was prepared, and after it we essayed a nap; but, alas! a plague, little anticipated, prevented. Unknown in Tahiti, the mosquitoes here fairly eddied round us. But more of them anon.

We were up betimes, and strolled out to view the country. We were in the valley of Martair; shut in, on both sides, by lofty hills. Here and there, were steep cliffs, gay with flowering shrubs, or hung with pendulous vines, swinging blossoms in the air. Of considerable width at the sea, the vale contracts as it runs inland; terminating, at the distance of several miles, in a range of the most grotesque elevations, which seem embattled with turrets and towers, grown. over with verdure, and waving with trees. The valley itself, is a wilderness of woodland; with links of streams flashing through, and narrow pathways, fairly tunnelled through masses of foliage.

All alone, in this wild place, was the abode of the planters; the only one back from the beach—their sole neighbours, the few fishermen and their families, dwelling in a small grove of coco-nut trees, whose roots were washed by the sea.

The cleared tract which they occupied, comprised some thirty acres, level as a prairie, part of which was under cultivation; the whole being fenced in by a stout palisade of trunks and boughs of trees, staked firmly in the ground. This was necessary, as a defence against the wild cattle and hogs overrunning the island.

Thus far, Tombez potatoes were the principal crop raised; a ready sale for them being obtained among the shipping touching at Papeetee. There was a small patch of the *taro,* or Indian turnip, also; another of yams; and, in one corner, a thrifty growth of the sugar-cane, just ripening.

On the side of the enclosure, next the sea, was the house; newly built of bamboos, in the native style. The furniture consisted of a couple of sea-chests, an old box, a few cooking utensils, and agricultural tools; together with three fowling-pieces, hanging from a rafter; and two enormous hammocks, swinging in opposite corners, and composed of dried bullocks' hides, stretched out with poles.

The whole plantation was shut in by a dense forest; and, close by the house, a dwarfed "Aoa," or species of banian-tree, had purposely been left twisting over the palisade, in the most grotesque manner, and thus made a pleasant shade. The branches of this curious tree afforded low perches, upon which the natives frequently squatted, after the fashion of their race, and smoked and gossiped by the hour.

We had a good breakfast of fish—speared by the natives, before sunrise, on the reef—pudding of Indian turnip, fried bananas, and roasted breadfruit.

During the repast, our new friends were quite sociable and communicative. It seems that, like nearly all uneducated foreigners, residing in Polynesia, they had, some time previous, deserted from a ship; and, having heard a good deal about the money to be made by raising supplies for whaling-vessels, they determined upon embarking in the business. Strolling about, with this intention, they, at last, came to Martair; and, thinking the soil would suit, set themselves to work. They began, by finding out the owner of the particular spot coveted, and then making a "tayo" of him.

He turned out to be Tonoi, the chief of the fishermen; who, one day, when exhilarated with brandy, tore his meagre tappa from his loins, and gave me to know, that he was allied by blood with Pomaree herself; and that his mother came from the illustrious race of pontiffs, who, in old times, swayed their bamboo crosier over all the pagans of Imeeo. A regal and right reverend lineage! But, at the time I speak of, the dusky noble was in decayed circumstances, and therefore, by no means unwilling to alienate a few useless acres. As an equivalent, he received from the strangers two or three rheumatic old muskets, several red woollen shirts, and a promise to be provided for in his old age: he was always to find a home with the planters.

Desirous of living on the cosy footing of a father-in-law, he frankly offered his two daughters for wives; but as such, they were politely declined; the adventurers, though not averse to courting, being unwilling to entangle themselves in a matrimonial alliance, however splendid in point of family.

Tonoi's men, the fishermen of the grove, were a sad set. Secluded, in a great measure, from the ministrations of the missionaries, they gave themselves up to all manner of lazy wickedness. Strolling among the trees of a morning, you came upon them napping on the shady side of a canoe hauled up among the bushes; lying under a tree smoking; or, more frequently still, gambling with pebbles; though, a little tobacco excepted, what they gambled for at their outlandish games, it would be hard to tell. Other idle diversions they had also, in which they seemed to take great delight. As for fishing, it employed but a small part of their time. Upon the whole, they were a merry, indigent, godless race.

Tonoi, the old sinner, leaning against the fallen trunk of a coco-nut tree, invariably squandered his mornings at pebbles; a grey-headed rook of a native regularly plucking him of every other stick of tobacco obtained from his friends, the planters. Toward afternoon, he strolled back to their abode; where he tarried till the next morning, smoking and snoozing, and, at times, prating about the hapless fortunes of the House of Tonoi. But like any other easy-going old dotard, he seemed for the most part perfectly content with cheerful board and lodging.

On the whole, the valley of Martair was the quietest place imaginable. Could the mosquitoes be induced to emigrate, one might spend the month of August there quite pleasantly. But this was not the case with the luckless Long Ghost and myself; as will presently be seen.

CHAPTER LIII

FARMING IN POLYNESIA

The planters were both whole-souled fellows; but in other respects, as unlike as possible.

One was a tall, robust Yankee, born in the backwoods of Maine, sallow, and with a long face;—the other was a short little Cockney, who had first clapped his eyes on the Monument.

The voice of Zeke, the Yankee, had a twang like a cracked viol; and Shorty (as his comrade called him), clipped the aspirate from every word beginning with one. The latter, though not the tallest man in the world, was a good-looking young fellow of twenty-five. His cheeks were dyed with the fine Saxon red, burned deeper from his roving life; his blue eye opened well, and a profusion of fair hair curled over a well shaped head.

But 'Zeke was no beauty. A strong, ugly man, he was well adapted for manual labour; and that was all. His eyes were made to see with, and not for ogling. Compared with the Cockney, he was grave, and rather taciturn; but there was a deal of good old humour bottled up in him, after all. For the rest, he was frank, good-hearted, shrewd, and resolute; and like Shorty, quite illiterate.

Though a curious conjunction, the pair got along together famously. But, as no two men were ever united in any enterprise, without one getting the upper hand of the other; so, in most matters, Zeke had his own way. Shorty, too, had imbibed from him a spirit of invincible industry; and Heaven only knows what ideas of making a fortune on their plantation.

We were much concerned at this; for the prospect of their setting us in their own persons an example of downright hard labour, was anything but agreeable. But it was now too late to repent what we had done.

The first day—thank fortune—we did nothing. Having treated us as guests thus far, they no doubt thought it would be wanting in delicacy, to set us to work before the compliments of the occasion were well over. The next morning, however, they both looked business-like, and we were put to.

"Wall, b'ys" (boys), said Zeke, knocking the ashes out of his pipe, after breakfast—"we must get at it. Shorty, give Peter there (the doctor), the big hoe, and Paul the other, and let's be off." Going to a corner, Shorty brought forth three of the implements; and distributing them impartially, trudged on after his partner, who took the lead with something in the shape of an axe.

For a moment left alone in the house, we looked at each other, quaking. We were each equipped with a great, clumsy piece of a tree, armed at one end with a heavy, flat mass of iron.

The cutlery part—especially adapted to a primitive soil—was an importation from Sydney; the handles must have been of domestic manufacture. "Hoes" —so called—we had heard of, and seen; but they were harmless, in comparison with the tools in our hands.

"What's to be done with them?" inquired I of Peter.

"Lift them up and down," he replied; "or put them in motion, some way or other. Paul, we are in a scrape—but hark; they are calling;" and shouldering the hoes, off we marched.

Our destination was the farther side of the plantation, where the ground, cleared in part, had not yet been broken up; but they were now setting about it. Upon halting, I asked why a plough was not used: some of the young wild steers might be caught, and trained for draught.

Zeke replied, that, for such a purpose, no cattle, to his knowledge, had ever been used in any part of Polynesia. As for the soil of Martair, so obstructed was it with roots, crossing and recrossing each other at all points, that no kind of a plough could be used to advantage. The heavy Sydney hoes were the only thing for such land.

Our work was now before us; but, previous to commencing operations, I endeavoured to engage the Yankee in a little further friendly chat, concerning the nature of virgin soils in general, and that of the valley of Martair in particular. So masterly a stratagem made Long Ghost brighten up; and he stood by ready to join in. But what our friend had to say about agriculture, all referred to the particular part of his plantation upon which we stood; and having communicated enough on this head to enable us to set to work to the best advantage, he fell to, himself; and Shorty, who had been looking on, followed suit.

The surface, here and there, presented closely amputated branches of what had once been a dense thicket. They seemed purposely left projecting, as if to furnish a handle whereby to drag out the roots beneath. After loosening the hard soil, by dint of much thumping and pounding, the Yankee jerked one of the roots this way and that, twisting it round and round, and then tugging at it horizontally.

"Come! lend us a hand!" he cried, at last; and, running, up we all four strained away in concert. The tough obstacle convulsed the surface with throes and spasms; but stuck fast, notwithstanding.

"Dumn it!" cried Zeke, "we'll have to get a rope; run to the house, Shorty, and fetch one."

The end of this being attached, we took plenty of room, and strained away once more.

"Give us a song, Shorty," said the doctor; who was rather sociable, on a short acquaintance. Where the work to be accomplished is any way difficult, this mode of enlivening toil is quite efficacious among sailors. So, willing to make everything as cheerful as possible, Shorty struck up, "Were you ever in Dumbarton?" a marvellously inspiring, but somewhat indecorous windlass chorus.

At last, the Yankee cast a damper on his enthusiasm, by exclaiming, in a pet, "Oh! dumn your singing! keep quiet, and pull away!" This we now did, in the most uninteresting silence; until, with a jerk, that made every elbow hum, the root dragged out; and, most inelegantly, we all landed upon the ground. The doctor, quite exhausted, stayed there; and, deluded into believing, that, after so doughty a performance, we would be allowed a cessation of toil, took off his hat, and fanned himself.

"Rayther a hard customer, that, Peter," observed the Yankee, going up to him: "but it's no use for any on 'em to hang back; for, I'm dumned if they hain't got to come out, whether or not. Hurrah! let's get at it agin!"

"Mercy!" ejaculated the doctor, rising slowly, and turning round. "He'll be the death of us!"

Falling to with our hoes again, we worked singly, or together, as occasion required, until "Nooning Time" came.

The period, so called by the planters, embraced about three hours in the middle of the day; during which it was so excessively hot, in this still, brooding valley, shut out from the Trades, and only open toward the leeward side of the island, that labour in the sun was out of the question. To use a hyperbolical phrase of Shorty's, "It was 'ot enough to melt the nose h'off a brass monkey."

Returning to the house, Shorty, assisted by old Tonoi, cooked the dinner; and, after we had all partaken thereof, both the Cockney and Zeke threw themselves into one of the hammocks, inviting us to occupy the other. Thinking it no bad idea, we did so; and, after skirmishing with the mosquitoes, managed to fall into a doze. As for the planters, more accustomed to "Nooning," they, at once, presented a nuptial back to each other; and were soon snoring away at a great rate. Tonoi snoozed on a mat, in one corner.

At last, we were roused by Zeke's crying out, "Up! b'ys; up! rise, and shine; time to get at it agin!"

Looking at the doctor, I perceived, very plainly, that he had decided upon something.

In a languid voice, he told Zeke, that he was not very well: indeed, that he had not been himself for some time past; though a little rest, no doubt, would recruit him. The Yankee, thinking, from this, that our valuable services might be lost to him altogether, were he too hard upon us at the outset, at once begged us both to consult our own feelings, and not exert ourselves for the present, unless we felt like it. Then—without recognizing the fact, that my comrade claimed to be actually unwell—he simply suggested, that, since he was so *tired*, he had better, perhaps, swing in his hammock for the rest of the day. If agreeable, however, I myself might accompany him upon a little bullock hunting excursion, in the neighbouring hills. In this proposition, I gladly acquiesced; though Peter, who was a great sportsman, put on a long face. The muskets and ammunition were forthwith got down from overhead; and, everything being then ready, Zeke cried out, "Tonoi! come; aramai! (get up) we want you for pilot. Shorty, my lad, look arter things, you know; and, if you likes, why, there's them roots in the field yonder."

Having thus arranged his domestic affairs to please himself, though little to Shorty's satisfaction, I thought; he slung his powder-horn over his shoulder, and we started.   Tonoi was, at once, sent on in advance; and, leaving the plantation, he struck into a path, which led towards the mountains.

After hurrying through the thickets for some time, we came out into the sunlight, in an open glade, just under the shadow of the hills.   Here, Zeke pointed aloft, to a beetling crag, far distant; where a bullock, with horns thrown back, stood like a statue.

CHAPTER LIV

SOME ACCOUNT OF THE WILD CATTLE IN POLYNESIA

BEFORE we proceed further, a word or two concerning these wild cattle, and the way they came on the island.

Some fifty years ago, Vancouver left several bullocks, sheep, and goats, at various places in the Society group.   He instructed the natives to look after the animals carefully; and by no means to slaughter any, until a considerable stock had accumulated.

The sheep must have died off; for I never saw a solitary fleece in any part of Polynesia.   The pair left were an ill assorted couple, perhaps; separated in disgust, and died without issue.

As for the goats, occasionally you come across a black, misanthropic ram, nibbling the scant herbage of some height inaccessible to man, in preference to the sweet grasses of the valley below.   The goats are not very numerous.

The bullocks, coming of a prolific ancestry, are a hearty set, racing over the island of Imeeo in considerable numbers; though in Tahiti but few of them are seen.   At the former place, the original pair must have scampered off to the interior, since it is now so thickly populated by their wild progeny.   The herds are the private property of Queen Pomaree; from whom the planters had obtained permission to shoot for their own use as many as they pleased.

The natives stand in great awe of these cattle; and for this reason, are excessively timid in crossing the island, preferring rather to sail round to an opposite village in their canoes.

Tonoi abounded in bullock stories; most of which, by the by, had a spice of the marvellous.   The following is one of these.

Once upon a time, he was going over the hills with a brother—now no more—when a great bull came bellowing out of a wood, and both took to their heels.   The old chief sprang into a tree; his companion, flying in an opposite direction, was pursued, and in the very act of reaching up to a bough, trampled underfoot.   The unhappy man was then gored—tossed in the air—and finally run away with on the bull's horns.   More dead than alive, Tonoi waited till all was over, and then made the best of his way home.   The neighbours, armed with two or three muskets, at once started to recover, if possible, his unfortunate brother's remains.   At nightfall, they returned without discovering any trace of him; but the next morning, Tonoi himself caught a glimpse of a bullock, marching across the mountain's brow, with a long dark object borne aloft on his horns.

Having referred to Vancouver's attempts to colonize the islands with useful quadrupeds, we may as well say something concerning his success upon Hawaii, one of the largest islands in the whole Polynesian Archipelago; and which gives the native name to the well known cluster named by Cook in honour of Lord Sandwich.

Hawaii is some one hundred leagues in circuit, and covers an area of over four thousand square miles. Until within a few years past, its interior was almost unknown, even to the inhabitants themselves, who, for ages, had been prevented from wandering thither, by certain strange superstitions. Pelée, the terrific goddess of the volcanoes Mount Roa and Mount Kea, was supposed to guard all the passes to the extensive valleys lying round their base. There are legends of her having chased with streams of fire several impious adventurers. Near Hilo, a jet-black cliff is shown, with the vitreous torrent apparently pouring over into the sea: just as it cooled after one of these supernatural eruptions.

To these inland valleys, and the adjoining hillsides, which are clothed in the most luxuriant vegetation, Vancouver's bullocks soon wandered; and unmolested for a long period, multiplied in vast herds.

Some twelve or fifteen years ago, the natives, losing sight of their superstitions, and learning the value of the hides in commerce, began hunting the creatures that wore them; but being very fearful and awkward in a business so novel, their success was small; and it was not until the arrival of a party of Spanish hunters, men regularly trained to their calling upon the plains of California, that the work of slaughter was fairly begun.

The Spaniards were showy fellows, tricked out in gay blankets, leggings worked with porcupine quills, and jingling spurs. Mounted upon trained Indian mares, these heroes pursued their prey up to the very base of the burning mountains; making the profoundest solitudes ring with their shouts, and flinging the lasso under the very nose of the vixen goddess Pelée. Hilo, a village upon the coast, was their place of resort; and thither flocked roving whites from all the islands of the group. As pupils of the dashing Spaniards, many of these dissipated fellows, quaffing too freely of the stirrup-cup, and riding headlong after the herds, when they reeled in the saddle, were unhorsed and killed.

This was about the year 1835, when the present king, Tammahammaha III, was a lad. With royal impudence, laying claim to the sole property of the cattle, he was delighted with the idea of receiving one of every two silver dollars paid down for their hides; so, with no thought for the future, the work of extermination went madly on. In three years' time, eighteen thousand bullocks were slain, almost entirely upon the single island of Hawaii.

The herds being thus nearly destroyed, the sagacious young prince imposed a rigorous "taboo" upon the few surviving cattle, which was to remain in force for ten years. During this period—not yet expired—all hunting is forbidden, unless directly authorized by the king.

The massacre of the cattle extended to the hapless goats. In one year, three thousand of their skins were sold to the merchants of Honolulu, fetching a *quartilia*, or a shilling sterling apiece.

After this digression, it is time to run on after Tonoi and the Yankee.

CHAPTER LV

A HUNTING RAMBLE WITH ZEKE

AT the foot of the mountain, a steep path went up among rocks and clefts, mantled with verdure. Here and there were green gulfs, down which it made one giddy to peep. At last we gained an overhanging, wooded shelf of land which crowned the heights; and along this, the path, well shaded, ran like a gallery.

In every direction, the scenery was enchanting. There was a low, rustling breeze; and below, in the vale, the leaves were quivering; the sea lay, blue and serene, in the distance; and inland the surface swelled up, ridge after ridge, and peak upon peak, all bathed in the Indian haze of the Tropics, and dreamy to look upon. Still valleys, leagues away, reposed in the deep shadows of the mountains; and here and there, waterfalls lifted up their voices in the solitude. High above all, and central, the "Marling-spike" lifted its finger. Upon the hillsides, small groups of bullocks were seen; some quietly browsing; others slowly winding into the valleys.

We went on, directing our course for a slope of the hills, a mile or two farther, where the nearest bullocks were seen.

We were cautious in keeping to windward of them; their sense of smell and hearing being, like those of all wild creatures, exceedingly acute.

As there was no knowing that we might not surprise some other kind of game in the coverts through which we were passing, we crept along warily.

The wild hogs of the island are uncommonly fierce; and as they often attack the natives, I could not help following Tonoi's example of once in a while peeping in under the foliage. Frequent retrospective glances also served to assure me that our retreat was not cut off.

As we rounded a clump of bushes, a noise behind them, like the crackling of dry branches, broke the stillness. In an instant, Tonoi's hand was on a bough, ready for a spring, and Zeke's finger touched the trigger of his piece. Again the stillness was broken; and thinking it high time to get ready, I brought my musket to my shoulder.

"Look sharp!" cried the Yankee; and dropping on one knee, he brushed the twigs aside. Presently, off went his piece; and with a wild snort, a black, bristly boar—his cherry red lip curled up by two glittering tusks—dashed, unharmed, across the path, and crashed through the opposite thicket. I saluted him with a charge as he disappeared; but not the slightest notice was taken of the civility.

By this time, Tonoi, the illustrious descendant of the Bishops of Imeeo, was twenty feet from the ground. "Aramai! come down, you old fool!" cried the Yankee; "the pesky critter's on t'other side of the island afore this."

"I rayther guess," he continued, as we began reloading, "that we've spoiled sport by firing at that 'ere 'tarnal hog. Them bullocks heard the racket, and is flinging their tails about now on the keen jump. Quick, Paul, and let's climb that rock yonder, and see if so be there's any in sight."

But none were to be seen, except at such a distance that they looked like ants.

As evening was now at hand, my companion proposed our returning home forthwith; and then, after a sound night's rest, starting in the morning upon a good day's hunt with the whole force of the plantation.

Following another path, in descending into the valley, we passed through some nobly wooded land on the face of the mountain.

One variety of tree particularly attracted my attention. The dark mossy stem, over seventy feet high, was perfectly branchless for many feet above the ground, when it shot out in broad boughs laden with lustrous leaves of the deepest green. And all round the lower part of the trunk, thin, slab-like buttresses of bark, perfectly smooth, and radiating from a common centre projected along the ground for at least two yards. From below, these natural props tapered upward until gradually blended with the trunk itself. There were signs of the wild cattle having sheltered themselves behind them. Zeke called this the canoe-tree; as in old times it supplied the navies of the Kings of Tahiti. For canoe-building, the wood is still used. Being extremely dense, and impervious to worms, it is very durable.

Emerging from the forest, when half-way down the hillside, we came upon an open space, covered with ferns and grass, over which a few lonely trees were casting long shadows in the setting sun. Here, a piece of ground some hundred feet square, covered with weeds and brambles, and sounding hollow to the tread, was enclosed by a ruinous wall of stones. Tonoi said it was an almost forgotten burial-place, of great antiquity, where no one had been interred since the islanders had been Christians. Sealed up in dry, deep vaults, many a dead heathen was lying here.

Curious to prove the old man's statement, I was anxious to get a peep at the catacombs; but hermetically overgrown with vegetation, as they were, no aperture was visible.

Before gaining the level of the valley, we passed by the site of a village, near a water-course, long since deserted. There was nothing but stone walls, and rude dismantled foundations of houses, constructed of the same material. Large trees and brush-wood were growing rankly among them.

I asked Tonoi how long it was since any one had lived here. "Me, *tammaree* (boy)—plenty *kannaker* (men) Martair," he replied. "Now, only poor *pehe kannaka* (fishermen) left—me born here."

Going down the valley, vegetation of every kind presented a different aspect from that of the high land.

Chief among the trees of the plain on this island, is the *"Ati,"* large and lofty, with a massive trunk, and broad, laurel-shaped leaves. The wood is splendid. In Tahiti, I was shown a narrow, polished plank, fit to make a cabinet for a king. Taken from the heart of the tree, it was of a deep, rich scarlet, traced with yellow veins, and in some places clouded with hazel.

In the same grove with the regal *"Ati,"* you may see the beautiful flowering *"Hotoo;"* its pyramid of shining leaves diversified with numberless small, white blossoms.

Planted with trees as the valley is, almost throughout its entire length, I was astonished to observe so very few which were useful to the natives: not one in a hundred was a coco-nut or breadfruit tree.

But here Tonoi again enlightened me. In the sanguinary religious hostilities which ensued upon the conversion to Christianity of the first Pomaree, a war party from Tahiti destroyed (by "girdling" the bark) entire groves of these invaluable trees. For some time afterward, they stood stark and leafless in the sun; sad monuments of the fate which befell the inhabitants of the valley.

CHAPTER LVI

MOSQUITOES

THE night following the hunting trip, Long Ghost and myself, after a valiant defence, had to fly the house on account of the mosquitoes.

And here I cannot avoid relating a story, rife among the natives, concerning the manner in which these insects were introduced upon the island.

Some years previous, a whaling captain, touching at an adjoining bay, got into difficulty with its inhabitants, and at last carried his complaint before one of the native tribunals; but receiving no satisfaction, and deeming himself aggrieved, he resolved upon taking signal revenge. One night, he towed a rotten old water-cask ashore, and left it in a neglected *Taro* patch, where the ground was warm and moist. Hence the mosquitoes.

I tried my best to learn the name of this man: and hereby do what I can to hand it down to posterity. It was Coleman—Nathan Coleman. The ship belonged to Nantucket.

When tormented by the mosquitoes, I found much relief in coupling the word "Coleman" with another of one syllable, and pronouncing them together energetically.

The doctor suggested a walk to the beach, where there was a long, low shed tumbling to pieces, but open lengthwise to a current of air which he thought might keep off the mosquitoes. So thither we went.

The ruin partially sheltered a relic of times gone by, which, a few days after, we examined with much curiosity. It was an old war-canoe, crumbling to dust. Being supported by the same rude blocks upon which, apparently, it had years before been hollowed out, in all probability it had never been afloat.

Outside, it seemed originally stained of a green colour, which, here and there, was now changed into a dingy purple. The prow terminated in a high, blunt beak; both sides were covered with carving; and upon the stern was something which Long Ghost maintained to be the arms of the royal House of Pomaree. The device had an heraldic look, certainly—being two sharks with the talons of hawks clawing a knot left projecting from the wood.

The canoe was at least forty feet long, about two wide, and four deep. The upper part—consisting of narrow planks laced together with cords of sinnate—had in many places fallen off, and lay decaying upon the ground. Still, there were ample accommodations left for sleeping; and in we sprang—the doctor into the bow, and I, into the stern. I soon fell asleep; but waking suddenly, cramped in every joint from my constrained posture, I thought, for an instant, that I must have been prematurely screwed down in my coffin.

Presenting my compliments to Long Ghost, I asked how it fared with *him*.

"Bad enough," he replied, as he tossed about in the outlandish rubbish lying in the bottom of our couch. "Pah! how these old mats smell!"

As he continued talking in this exciting strain for some time, I at last made no reply, having resumed certain mathematical reveries to induce repose. But finding the multiplication-table of no avail, I summoned up a greyish image of chaos in a sort of sliding fluidity, and was just falling into a nap on the strength of it, when I heard a solitary and distinct buzz. The hour of my calamity was at hand. One blended hum, the creature darted into the canoe like a small swordfish; and I out of it.

Upon getting into the open air, to my surprise, there was Long Ghost, fanning himself wildly with an old paddle. He had just made a noiseless escape from a swarm, which had attacked his own end of the canoe.

It was now proposed to try the water; so a small fishing canoe, hauled up near by, was quickly launched; and paddling a good distance off, we dropped overboard the native contrivance for an anchor—a heavy stone, attached to a cable of braided bark. At this part of the island, the encircling reef was close to the shore, leaving the water within smooth, and extremely shallow.

It was a blessed thought! We knew nothing till sunrise, when the motion of our aquatic cot awakened us. I looked up, and beheld Zeke wading toward the shore, and towing us after him by the bark cable. Pointing to the reef, he told us we had had a narrow escape.

It was true enough; the water-sprites had rolled our stone out of its noose, and we had floated away.

CHAPTER LVII

THE SECOND HUNT IN THE MOUNTAINS

Fair dawned, over the hills of Martair, the jocund morning of our hunt.

Everything had been prepared for it overnight; and, when we arrived at the house, a good breakfast was spread by Shorty: and old Tonoi was bustling about like an innkeeper. Several of his men, also, were in attendance, to accompany us with calabashes of food; and, in case we met with any success, to officiate as bearers of burdens, on our return.

Apprised, the evening previous, of the meditated sport, the doctor had announced his willingness to take part therein.

Now, subsequent events made us regard this expedition as a shrewd device of the Yankee's. Once get us off on a pleasure trip, and with what face could we afterward refuse to work? Besides, he enjoyed all the credit of giving us a holiday. Nor did he omit assuring us, that, work or play, our wages were all the while running on.

A dilapidated old musket of Tonoi's was borrowed for the doctor. It was exceedingly short and heavy, with a clumsy lock, which required a strong finger to pull the trigger. On trying the piece, by firing at a mark, Long Ghost was satisfied that it could not fail of doing execution: the charge went one way, and he the other.

Upon this, he endeavoured to negotiate an exchange of muskets with Shorty; but the Cockney was proof against his blandishments; at last he entrusted his weapon to one of the natives to carry for him.

Marshalling our forces, we started for the head of the valley; near which, a path ascended to a range of high land, said to be a favourite resort of the cattle.

Shortly after gaining the heights, a small herd, some way off, was perceived entering a wood. We hurried on; and, dividing our party, went in after them, at four different points; each white man followed by several natives.

I soon found myself in a dense covert; and, after looking round, was just emerging into a clear space, when I heard a report, and a bullet knocked the bark from a tree near by. The same instant, there was a trampling and crashing; and five bullocks, nearly abreast, .broke into view across the opening, and plunged right toward the spot where myself and three of the islanders were standing.

They were small, black, vicious-looking creatures; with short, sharp horns, red nostrils, and eyes like coals of fire. On they came—their dark woolly heads hanging down.

By this time, my island backers were roosting among the trees. Glancing round, for an instant, to discover a retreat in case of emergency, I raised my piece, when a voice cried out, from the wood, "Right between the 'orns, Paul! right between the 'orns!" Down went my barrel, in range with a small white tuft on the forehead of the headmost one; and, letting him have it, I darted to one side. As I turned again, the five bullocks shot by like a blast, making the air eddy in their wake.

The Yankee now burst into view, and saluted them in flank. Whereupon, the fierce little bull with the tufted forehead, flirted his long tail over his buttocks; kicked out with his hind feet, and shot forward a full length. It was nothing but a graze; and, in an instant, they were out of sight, the thicket into which they broke rocking overhead, and marking their progress.

The action over, the heavy artillery came up, in the person of the Long Doctor, with his blunderbuss.

"Where are they?" he cried, out of breath.

"A mile or two h'off, by this time," replied the Cockney. "Lord, Paul! you ought to've sent an 'ail stone into that little black 'un."

While excusing my want of skill, as well as I could, Zeke, rushing forward, suddenly exclaimed, "Creation! what are you 'bout there, Peter?"

Peter, incensed at our ill luck, and ignorantly imputing it to the cowardice of our native auxiliaries, was bringing his piece to bear upon his trembling squire—the musket carrier—now descending a tree.

Pulling trigger, the bullet went high over his head; and, hopping to the ground, bellowing like a calf, the fellow ran away as fast as his heels could carry him. The rest followed us, after this, with fear and trembling.

After forming our line of march anew, we went on for several hours, without catching a glimpse of the game; the reports of the muskets having been heard at a great distance. At last, we mounted a craggy height, to obtain a wide view of the country. From this place, we beheld three cattle; quietly browsing in a green opening of a wood below; the trees shutting them in all round.

A general re-examination of the muskets now took place, followed by a hasty lunch from the calabashes: we then started. As we descended the mountain-side, the cattle were in plain sight, until we entered the forest, when we lost sight of them for a moment; but only to see them again, as we crept close up to the spot where they grazed.

They were a bull, a cow, and a calf. The cow was lying down in the shade, by the edge of the wood; the calf, sprawling out before her in the grass, licking her lips; while old Taurus himself stood close by, casting a paternal glance at this domestic little scene, and conjugally elevating his nose in the air.

"Now then," said Zeke, in a whisper, "let's take the poor creeturs, while they are huddled together. Crawl along, b'ys; crawl along. Fire together, mind; and not 'till I say the word."

We crept up to the very edge of the open ground, and knelt behind a clump of bushes; resting our levelled barrels among the branches. The slight rustling was heard. Taurus turned round, dropped his head to the ground, and sent forth a low, sullen bellow; then snuffed the air. The cow rose on her fore knees, pitched forward alarmedly, and stood upon her legs; while the calf, with ears pricked, got right underneath her. All three were now grouped, and, in an instant would be off.

"I take the bull," cried our leader; "fire!"

The calf fell like a clod; its dam uttered a cry, and thrust her head into the thicket; but she turned, and came moaning up to the lifeless calf, going round and round it, snuffing fiercely with her bleeding nostrils. A crashing in the wood, and a loud roar, announced the flying bull.

Soon, another shot was fired, and the cow fell. Leaving some of the natives to look after the dead cattle, the rest of us hurried on after the bull; his dreadful bellowings guiding us to the spot where he lay. Wounded in the shoulder, in his fright and agony he had bounded into the wood; but when we came up to him, he had sunk to the earth in a green hollow, thrusting his black muzzle into a pool of his own blood, and tossing it over his hide in clots.

The Yankee brought his piece to a rest; and, the next instant, the wild brute sprang into the air, and with his fore legs crouching under him, fell dead.

Our island friends were now in high spirits; all courage and alacrity. Old Tonoi thought nothing of taking poor Taurus himself by the horns, and peering into his glazed eyes.

Our ship knives were at once in request; and, skinning the cattle, we hung them high up by cords of bark from the boughs of a tree. Withdrawing into a covert, we there waited for the wild hogs; which, according to Zeke, would soon make their appearance, lured by the smell of blood. Presently, we heard them coming, in two or three different directions; and, in a moment, they were tearing the offal to pieces.

As only one shot at these creatures could be relied on, we intended firing simultaneously; but, somehow or other, the doctor's piece went off by itself, and one of the hogs dropped. The others then breaking into the thicket, the rest of us sprang after them; resolved to have another shot at all hazards.

The Cockney darted among some bushes; and, a few moments after, we heard the report of his musket, followed by a quick cry. On running up, we saw our comrade doing battle with a young devil of a boar, as black as night, whose snout had been partly torn away. Firing when the game was in full career, and coming directly toward him, Shorty had been assailed by the enraged brute; it was now crunching the breech of the musket, with which he had tried to club it; Shorty holding fast to the barrel, and fingering his waist for a knife. Being in advance of the others, I clapped my gun to the boar's head, and so put an end to the contest.

Evening now coming on, we set to work loading our carriers. The cattle were so small, that a stout native could walk off with an entire quarter; brushing through thickets, and descending rocks without an apparent effort: though, to tell the truth, no white man present could have done the thing with any ease. As for the wild hogs, none of the islanders could be induced to carry Shorty's; some invincible superstition being connected with its black colour. We were, therefore, obliged to leave it. The other, a spotted one, being slung by green thongs to a pole, was marched off with by two young natives.

With our bearers of burdens ahead, we then commenced our return down the valley. Half-way home, darkness overtook us in the woods; and torches became necessary. We stopped, and made them of dry palm branches; and then, sending two lads on in advance, for the purpose of gathering fuel to feed the flambeaux, we continued our journey.

It was a wild sight. The torches, waved aloft, flashed through the forest;

and, where the ground admitted, the islanders went along on a brisk trot, notwithstanding they bent forward under their loads.

Their naked backs were stained with blood; and occasionally, running by each other, they raised wild cries, which startled the hillsides.

CHAPTER LVIII

THE HUNTING-FEAST; AND A VISIT TO AFREHITOO

Two bullocks and a boar! No bad trophies of our day's sport. So by torchlight we marched into the plantation, the wild hog rocking from its pole, and the doctor singing an old hunting-song—Tallyho! the chorus of which swelled high above the yells of the natives.

We resolved to make a night of it. Kindling a great fire just outside the dwelling, and hanging one of the heifer's quarters from a limb of the banian-tree, every one was at liberty to cut and broil for himself. Baskets of roasted breadfruit, and plenty of taro pudding; bunches of bananas, and young coconuts, had also been provided by the natives against our return.

The fire burned bravely, keeping off the mosquitoes, and making every man's face glow like a beaker of Port. The meat had the true wild-game flavour, not at all impaired by our famous appetites, and a couple of flasks of white brandy, which Zeke, producing from his secret store, circulated freely.

There was no end to my long comrade's spirits. After telling his stories, and singing his songs, he sprang to his feet, clasped a young damsel of the grove round the waist, and waltzed over the grass with her. But there's no telling all the pranks he played that night. The natives, who delight in a wag, emphatically pronounced him "maitai."

It was long after midnight ere we broke up; but when the rest had retired, Zeke, with the true thrift of a Yankee, salted down what was left of the meat.

The next day was Sunday; and at my request, Shorty accompanied me to Afrehitoo—a neighbouring bay, and the seat of a mission, almost directly opposite Papeetee. In Afrehitoo is a large church and schoolhouse, both quite dilapidated; and planted amid shrubbery on a fine knoll, stands a very tasteful cottage, commanding a view across the channel. In passing, I caught sight of a graceful calico skirt disappearing from the piazza through a doorway. The place was the residence of the missionary.

A trim little sail-boat was dancing out at her moorings, a few yards from the beach.

Straggling over the lowlands in the vicinity were several native huts—untidy enough—but much better every way, than most of those in Tahiti.

We attended service at the church, where we found but a small congregation; and after what I had seen in Papeetee, nothing very interesting took place. But the audience had a curious, fidgety look, which I knew not how to account for, until we ascertained that a sermon with the eighth commandment for a text was being preached.

It seemed that there lived an Englishman in the district, who, like our friends, the planters, was cultivating Tombez potatoes for the Papeetee market.

In spite of all his precautions, the natives were in the habit of making nocturnal forays into his enclosure, and carrying off the potatoes. One night he fired a fowling-piece, charged with pepper and salt, at several shadows which he discovered stealing across his premises. They fled. But it was like seasoning anything else: the knaves stole again with a greater relish than ever; and the very next night, he caught a party in the act of roasting a basket full of potatoes under his own cooking-shed. At last, he stated his grievances to the missionary; who, for the benefit of his congregation, preached the sermon we heard.

Now, there were no thieves in Martair; but then, the people of the valley were bribed to be honest. It was a regular business transaction between them and the planters. In consideration of so many potatoes "to them in hand, duly paid," they were to abstain from all depredations upon the plantation. Another security against roguery, was the permanent resident upon the premises, of their chief, Tonoi.

On our return to Martair, in the afternoon, we found the doctor and Zeke making themselves comfortable. The latter was reclining on the ground, pipe in mouth, watching the doctor, who, sitting like a Turk, before a large iron kettle, was slicing potatoes and Indian turnip, and now and then shattering splinters from a bone; all of which, by turns, were thrown into the pot. He was making what he called "Bullock broth."

In gastronomic affairs, my friend was something of an artist; and by way of improving his knowledge, did nothing the rest of the day but practise in what might called Experimental Cookery: broiling and grilling, and devilling slices of meat, and subjecting them to all sorts of igneous operations. It was the first fresh beef that either of us had tasted in more than a year.

"Oh, ye'll pick up arter a while, Peter," observed Zeke toward night, as Long Ghost was turning a great rib over the coals—"what d'ye think, Paul?"

"He'll get along, I dare say," replied I; "he only wants to get those cheeks of his tanned." To tell the truth, I was not a little pleased to see the doctor's reputation as an invalid fading away so fast; especially, as on the strength of his being one, he had promised to have such easy times of it, and very likely, too, at my expense.

CHAPTER LIX

THE MURPHIES

DOZING in our canoe the next morning about daybreak, we were wakened by Zeke's hailing us loudly from the beach.

Upon paddling up, he told us that a canoe had arrived overnight, from Papeetee, with an order from a ship lying there, for a supply of his potatoes; and as they must be on board the vessel by noon, he wanted us to assist in bringing them down to his sail-boat.

My long comrade was one of those, who, from always thrusting forth the wrong foot foremost when they rise, or committing some other indiscretion of the limbs, are more or less crabbed or sullen before breakfast. It was in vain, therefore, that the Yankee deplored the urgency of the case, which obliged him to call us up thus early:—the doctor only looked the more glum, and said nothing in reply.

At last, by way of getting up a little enthusiasm for the occasion, the

Yankee exclaimed quite spiritedly, "What d'ye say, then, b'ys, shall we git at it?"

"Yes, in the devil's name!" replied the doctor, like a snapping turtle; and we moved on to the house. Notwithstanding his ungracious answer, he probably thought that after the gastronomic performance of the day previous, it would hardly do to hang back. At the house, we found Shorty ready with the hoes; and we at once repaired to the farther side of the enclosure, where the potatoes had yet to be taken out of the ground.

The rich, tawny soil seemed specially adapted to the crop; the great yellow murphies rolling out of the hills like eggs from a nest.

My comrade really surprised me by the zeal with which he applied himself to his hoe. For my own part, exhilarated by the cool breath of the morning, I worked away like a good fellow. As for Zeke and the Cockney, they seemed mightily pleased at this evidence of our willingness to exert ourselves.

It was not long ere all the potatoes were turned out; and then came the worst of it: they were to be lugged down to the beach, a distance of at least a quarter of a mile. And there being no such thing as a barrow, or cart, on the island, there was nothing for it but spinal-marrows and broad shoulders. Well knowing that this part of the business would be anything but agreeable, Zeke did his best to put as encouraging a face upon it as possible; and giving us no time to indulge in desponding thoughts, gleefully directed our attention to a pile of rude baskets—made of stout stalks—which had been provided for the occasion. So, without more ado, we helped ourselves from the heap; and soon we were all four staggering along under our loads.

The first trip down, we arrived at the beach together: Zeke's enthusiastic cries proving irresistible. A trip or two more, however, and my shoulders began to grate in their sockets; while the doctor's tall figure acquired an obvious stoop. Presently, we both threw down our baskets, protesting we could stand it no longer. But our employers, bent, as it were, upon getting the work out of us by a silent appeal to our moral sense, toiled away without pretending to notice us. It was as much as to say, "There, men, we've been boarding and lodging ye for the last three days; and yesterday ye did nothing earthly but eat; so stand by now, and look at us working, if ye dare." Thus driven to it, then, we resumed our employment. Yet, in spite of all we could do, we lagged behind Zeke and Shorty, who, breathing hard, and perspiring at every pore, toiled away without pause or cessation. I almost wickedly wished, that they would load themselves down with one potato too many.

Gasping as I was with my own hamper, I could not, for the life of me, help laughing at Long Ghost. There he went:—his long neck thrust forward, his arms twisted behind him to form a shelf for his basket to rest on; and his stilts of legs every once in a while giving way under him, as if his knee-joints slipped either way.

"There! I carry no more!" he exclaimed all at once, flinging his potatoes into the boat, where the Yankee was just then stowing them away.

"Oh, then," said Zeke, quite briskly, "I guess you and Paul had better try the '*barrel-machine*'—come along, I'll fix ye out in no time;" and, so saying, he waded ashore, and hurried back to the house, bidding us follow.

Wondering what upon earth the "*barrel-machine*" could be, and rather suspicious of it, we limped after. On arriving at the house, we found him getting ready a sort of sedan-chair. It was nothing more than an old barrel, suspended by a rope from the middle of a stout oar. Quite an ingenious contrivance of the Yankee's; and his proposed arrangement with regard to mine and the doctor's shoulders, was equally so.

"There now!" said he, when everything was ready, "there's no back-breaking about this; you can stand right up under it, you see: jist try it once;" and he politely rested the blade of the oar on my comrade's right shoulder, and the other end on mine, leaving the barrel between us.

"Jist the thing!" he added, standing off admiringly, while we remained in this interesting attitude.

There was no help for us; with broken hearts and backs we trudged back to the field; the doctor all the while saying masses.

Upon starting with the loaded barrel, for a few paces we got along pretty well, and were constrained to think the idea not a bad one. But we did not long think so. In less than five minutes we came to a dead halt, the springing and buckling of the clumsy oar being almost unendurable.

"Let's shift ends," cried the doctor, who did not quite relish the blade of the stick, which was cutting into the blade of his shoulder.

At last, by stages short and frequent, we managed to shamble down to the beach, where we again dumped our cargo, in something of a pet.

"Why not make the natives help?", asked Long Ghost, rubbing his shoulder.

"Natives be dumned!" said the Yankee, "twenty on 'em ain't worth one white man. They never was meant to work any, them chaps; and they knows it, too, for dumned little work any on 'em ever does."

But notwithstanding this abuse, Zeké was at last obliged to press a few of the bipeds into service. "Aramai!" (come here) he shouted to several, who, reclining on a bank, had hitherto been critical observers of our proceedings; and, among other things, had been particularly amused by the performance with the sedan-chair.

After making these fellows load their baskets together, the Yankee filled his own, and then drove them before him, down to the beach. Probably he had seen the herds of panniered mules, driven in this way by mounted Indians, along the great road from Callao to Lima.

The boat at last loaded, the Yankee, taking with him a couple of natives, at once hoisted sail, and stood across the channel for Papeetee.

The next morning at breakfast, old Tonoi ran in, and told us that the voyagers were returning. We hurried down to the beach, and saw the boat gliding toward us, with a dozing islander at the helm, and Zeke standing up in the bows, jingling a small bag of silver, the proceeds of his cargo.

CHAPTER LX

WHAT THEY THOUGHT OF US IN MARTAIR

SEVERAL quiet days now passed away, during which, we just worked sufficiently to sharpen our appetites; the planters leniently exempting us from any severe toil.

Their desire to retain us became more and more evident; which was not to be wondered at; for, besides esteeming us from the beginning a couple of civil, good-natured fellows, who would soon become quite at home with them, they were not slow in perceiving that we were far different from the common run of rovers; and that our society was both entertaining and instructive to a couple of solitary, illiterate men, like themselves.

In a literary point of view, indeed, they soon regarded us with emotions of envy and wonder; and the doctor was considered nothing short of a prodigy. The Cockney found out, that he (the doctor) could read a book upside down, without even so much as spelling the big words beforehand; and the Yankee, in the twinkling of an eye, received from him the sum total of several arithmetical items, stated aloud, with the view of testing the extent of his mathematical lore.

Then, frequently, in discoursing upon men and things, my long comrade employed such imposing phrases, that, upon one occasion, they actually remained uncovered while he talked.

In short, their favourable opinion of Long Ghost in particular, rose higher and higher every day; and they began to indulge in all manner of dreams concerning the advantages to be derived from employing so learned a labourer. Among other projects revealed, was that of building a small craft of some forty tons, for the purpose of trading among the neighbouring islands. With a native crew, we would then take turns cruising over the tranquil Pacific; touching here and there, as caprice suggested, and collecting romantic articles of commerce;—bêche-de-mer, the pearl-oyster, arrow-root, ambergris, sandalwood, coco-nut oil, and edible birds'-nests.

This South Sea yachting was delightful to think of; and straightway, the doctor announced his willingness to navigate the future schooner clear of all shoals and reefs whatsoever. His impudence was audacious. He enlarged upon the science of navigation; treated us to a dissertation on Mercator's Sailing and the Azimuth compass; and went into an inexplicable explanation of the Lord only knows what plan of his, for infallibly settling the longitude.

Whenever my comrade thus gave the reins to his fine fancy, it was a treat to listen, and therefore I never interfered; but, with the planters, sat in mute admiration before him. This apparent self-abasement on my part, must have been considered as truly indicative of our respective merits; for, to my no small concern, I quickly perceived that, in the estimate formed of us, Long Ghost began to be rated far above myself. For aught I knew, indeed, he might have privately thrown out a hint concerning the difference in our respective stations aboard the *Julia;* or else, the planters must have considered him some illustrious individual, for certain inscrutable reasons, going incog. With this idea of him, his undisguised disinclination for work became venial; and, entertaining such views of extending their business, they counted more upon his ultimate value to them as a man of science, than as a mere ditcher.

Nor did the humorous doctor forbear to foster an opinion every way so advantageous to himself; at times, for the sake of the joke, assuming airs of superiority over myself, which, though laughable enough, were sometimes annoying.

To tell the plain truth, things at last came to such a pass, that I told him, up and down, that I had no notion to put up with his pretensions; if he were going to play the gentleman, I was going to follow suit; and then, there would quickly be an explosion.

At this he laughed heartily; and after some mirthful chat, we resolved upon leaving the valley, as soon as we could do so with a proper regard to politeness.

At supper, therefore, the same evening, the doctor hinted at our intention.

Though much surprised, and vexed, Zeke moved not a muscle. "Peter," said he at last—very gravely—and after mature deliberation, "would you like to do the *cooking?* It's easy work; and you needn't do anything else. Paul's heartier; he can work in the field when it suits him; and before long, we'll have ye at something more agreeable:—won't we, Shorty?"

Shorty assented.

Doubtless, the proposed arrangement was a snug one; especially the sinecure for the doctor; but I by no means relished the functions allotted to myself— they were too indefinite. Nothing final, however, was agreed upon;—our intention to leave was revealed, and that was enough for the present. But, as we said nothing further about going, the Yankee must have concluded that we might yet be induced to remain. He redoubled his endeavours to make us contented.

It was during this state of affairs, that one morning, before breakfast, we were set to weeding in a potato-patch; and the planters being engaged at the house, we were left to ourselves.

Now, though the pulling of weeds was considered by our employers an easy occupation (for which reason they had assigned it to us), and although as a garden recreation, it may be pleasant enough for those who like it—still, long persisted in, the business becomes excessively irksome.

Nevertheless, we toiled away for some time, until the doctor, who, from his height, was obliged to stoop at a very acute angle, suddenly sprang upright; and, with one hand propping his spinal column, exclaimed, "Oh, that one's joints were but provided with holes to drop a little oil through!"

Vain as the aspiration was for this proposed improvement upon our species, I cordially responded thereto; for every vertebra in my spine was articulating its sympathy.

Presently, the sun rose over the mountains, inducing that deadly morning languor, so fatal to early exertion in a warm climate. We could stand it no longer; but, shouldering our hoes, moved on to the house, resolved to impose no more upon the good nature of the planters, by continuing one moment longer in an occupation so extremely uncongenial.

We freely told them so. Zeke was exceedingly hurt, and said everything he could think of to alter our determination; but finding all unavailing, he very hospitably urged us not to be in any hurry about leaving; for we might stay with him as guests until we had time to decide upon our future movements.

We thanked him sincerely; but replied, that the following morning, we must turn our backs upon the hills of Martair.

CHAPTER LXI

PREPARING FOR THE JOURNEY

DURING the remainder of the day we loitered about, talking over our plans.

The doctor was all eagerness to visit Tamai, a solitary inland village, standing upon the banks of a considerable lake of the same name, and embosomed among groves. From Afrehitoo you went to this place by a lonely pathway, leading through the wildest scenery in the world. Much, too, we had heard concerning the lake itself, which abounded in such delicious fish, that, in former times, angling parties occasionally came over to it, from Papeetee.

Upon its banks, moreover, grew the finest fruit of the islands, and in their greatest perfection. The "Ve," or Brazilian plum, here attained the size of an orange; and the gorgeous "Arheea," or red apple of Tahiti, blushed with deeper dyes than in any of the seaward valleys.

Besides all this, in Tamai dwelt the most beautiful and unsophisticated women in the entire Society group. In short, the village was so remote from the coast, and had been so much less affected by recent changes than other places that, in most things, Tahitian life was here seen, as formerly existing in the days of young Otoo, the boy-king, in Cook's time.

After obtaining from the planters all the information which was needed, we decided upon penetrating to the village; and after a temporary sojourn there, to strike the beach again, and journey round to Taloo, a harbour on the opposite side of the island.

We at once put ourselves in travelling trim. Just previous to leaving Tahiti, having found my wardrobe reduced to two suits (frock and trousers, both much the worse for wear), I had quilted them together for mutual preservation (after a fashion peculiar to sailors); engrafting a red frock upon a blue one, and producing thereby a choice variety in the way of clothing. This was the extent of my wardrobe. Nor was the doctor by any means better off. His improvidence had at last driven him to don the nautical garb; but by this time, his frock— a light cotton one—had almost given out, and he had nothing to replace it. Shorty very generously offered him one which was a little less ragged; but the alms was proudly refused; Long Ghost preferring to assume the ancient costume of Tahiti—the "*Roora*."

This garment, once worn as a festival dress, is now seldom met with; but Captain Bob had often shown us one which he kept as an heirloom. It was a cloak, or mantle of yellow tappa, precisely similar to the "*poncho*," worn by the South-American Spaniards. The head being slipped through a slit in the middle, the robe hangs about the person in ample drapery. Tonoi obtained sufficient coarse brown tappa to make a short mantle of this description; and in five minutes the doctor was equipped. Zeke, eyeing his *toga* critically, reminded its proprietor that there were many streams to ford, and precipices to scale, between Martair and Tamai; and if he travelled in petticoats, he had better hold them up.

Besides other deficiencies, we were utterly shoeless. In the free and easy Pacific, sailors seldom wear shoes; mine had been tossed overboard the day we met the Trades; and except in one or two tramps ashore, I had never worn any since. In Martair, they would have been desirable; but none were to be had. For the expedition we meditated, however, they were indispensable. Zeke, being the owner of a pair of huge, dilapidated boots, hanging from a rafter like saddlebags, the doctor succeeded in exchanging for them a case-knife, the last valuable article in his possession. For myself, I made sandals from a bullock's hide, such as are worn by the Indians in California. They are made in a minute; the sole, rudely fashioned to the foot, being confined across the instep by three straps of leather.

Our headgear deserves a passing word. My comrade's was a brave old Panama hat, made of grass, almost as fine as threads of silk; and so elastic, that upon rolling it up, it sprang into perfect shape again. Set off by the jaunty slouch of this Spanish sombrero, Doctor Long Ghost, in this and his Roora, looked like a mendicant grandee.

Nor was my own appearance in an Eastern turban less distinguished. The way I came to wear it was this. My hat having been knocked overboard, a few days before reaching Papeetee, I was obliged to mount an abominable wad of parti-coloured worsted—what sailors call a Scotch cap. Every one knows the elasticity of knit wool; and this Caledonian headdress crowned my temples so effectually, that the confined atmosphere engendered was prejudicial to my curls. In vain I tried to ventilate the cap: every gash made, seemed to heal whole in no time. Then such a continual chafing as it kept up in a hot sun.

Seeing my dislike to the thing, Kooloo, my worthy friend, prevailed upon me to bestow it upon him. I did so; hinting that a good boiling might restore the original brilliancy of the colours.

It was then that I mounted the turban. Taking a new Regatta frock of the doctor's, which was of a gay calico, and winding it round my head in folds, I allowed the sleeves to droop behind—thus forming a good defence against the sun, though in a shower it was best off. The pendent sleeves adding much to the effect, the doctor always called me the Bashaw with Two Tails.

Thus arrayed, we were ready for Tamai; in whose green saloons we counted upon creating no small sensation.

CHAPTER LXII

TAMAI

LONG before sunrise the next morning, my sandals were laced on, and the doctor had vaulted into Zeke's boots.

Expecting to see us again before we went to Taloo, the planters wished us a pleasant journey; and, on parting, very generously presented us with a pound or two of what sailors call "plug" tobacco; telling us to cut it up into small change; the Virginian weed being the principal circulating medium on the island.

Tamai, we were told, was not more than three or four leagues distant; so making allowances for a wild road, a few hours to rest at noon, and our determination to take the journey leisurely, we counted upon reaching the shores of the lake some time in the flush of the evening.

For several hours we went on slowly through wood and ravine, and over hill and precipice, seeing nothing but occasional herds of wild cattle, and often resting; until we found ourselves, about noon, in the very heart of the island.

It was a green, cool hollow among the mountains, into which we at last descended with a bound. The place was gushing with a hundred springs, and shaded over with great solemn trees, on whose mossy boles the moisture stood in beads. Strange to say, no traces of the bullocks ever having been here were revealed. Nor was there a sound to be heard, nor a bird to be seen, nor any breath of wind stirring the leaves. The utter solitude and silence were oppressive; and after peering about under the shades, and seeing nothing but ranks of dark, motionless trunks, we hurried across the hollow, and ascended a steep mountain opposite.

Midway up, we rested where the earth had gathered about the roots of three palms, and thus formed a pleasant lounge, from which we looked down upon the hollow, now one dark-green tuft of woodland at our feet. Here we brought forth a small calabash of "*poee*," a parting present from Tonoi. After eating heartily, we obtained fire by two sticks, and throwing ourselves back, puffed forth our fatigue in wreaths of smoke. At last we fell asleep; nor did we waken till the sun had sunk so low that its rays darted in upon us under the foliage.

Starting up, we then continued our journey; and as we gained the mountain top—there, to our surprise, lay the lake and village of Tamai. We had thought it a good league off. Where we stood, the yellow sunset was still lingering; but over the valley below, long shadows were stealing—the rippling green lake reflecting the houses and trees, just as they stood along its banks. Several small canoes, moored here and there to posts in the water, were dancing upon the waves; and one solitary fisherman was paddling over to a grassy point. In front of the houses, groups of natives were seen; some thrown at full length upon the ground, and others indolently leaning against the bamboos.

With whoop and halloo, we ran down the hills, the villagers soon hurrying forth to see who were coming. As we drew near, they gathered round, all curiosity to know what brought the "karhowries" into their quiet country. The doctor contriving to make them understand the purely social object of our visit, they gave us a true Tahitian welcome; pointing into their dwellings, and saying they were ours as long as we chose to remain.

We were struck by the appearance of these people, both men and women; so much more healthful than the inhabitants of the bays. As for the young girls, they were more retiring and modest, more tidy in their dress, and far fresher and more beautiful than the damsels of the coast. A thousand pities, thought I, that they should bury their charms in this nook of a valley.

That night we abode in the house of Rartoo, a hospitable old chief. It was right on the shore of the lake; and at supper, we looked out through a rustling screen of foliage upon the surface of the starlit water.

The next day we rambled about, and found a happy little community, comparatively free from many deplorable evils to which the rest of their countrymen are subject. Their time, too, was more occupied. To my surprise, the manufacture of tappa was going on in several buildings. European calicoes were seldom seen, and not many articles of foreign origin of any description.

The people of Tamai were nominally Christians; but being so remote from ecclesiastical jurisdiction, their religion sat lightly upon them. We had been told, even, that many heathenish games and dances still secretly lingered in their valley.

Now the prospect of seeing an old-fashioned "hevar," or Tahitian reel, was one of the inducements which brought us here; and so, finding Rartoo rather liberal in his religious ideas, we disclosed our desire. At first, he demurred; and shrugging his shoulders like a Frenchman, declared it could not be brought about—was a dangerous matter to attempt, and might bring all concerned into trouble. But we overcame all this, convinced him that the thing could be done, and a "hevar," a genuine pagan fandango, was arranged for that very night.

CHAPTER LXIII

A DANCE IN THE VALLEY

THERE were some ill-natured people—tell-tales—it seemed, in Tamai; and hence there was a deal of mystery about getting up the dance.

An hour or two before midnight, Rartoo entered the house, and, throwing

robes of tappa over us, bade us follow at a distance behind him; and, until out
of the village, hood our faces. Keenly alive to the adventure, we obeyed. At
last,•after taking a wide circuit, we came out upon the farthest shore of the
lake. It was a wide, dewy space; lighted up by a full moon, and carpeted with
a minute species of fern, growing closely together. It swept right down to
the water, showing the village opposite, glistening among the groves.

Near the trees, on one side of the clear space, was a ruinous pile of stones,
many rods in extent; upon which had formerly stood a temple of Oro. At present, there was nothing but a rude hut, planted on the lowermost terrace. It
seemed to have been used as a *"tappa herree";* or house for making the native
cloth.

Here, we saw lights gleaming from between the bamboos, and casting long,
rod-like shadows upon the ground without. Voices also were heard. We went
up, and had a peep at the dancers; who were getting ready for the ballet. They
were some twenty in number; waited upon by hideous old crones, who might
have been duennas. Long Ghost proposed to send the latter packing; but
Rartoo said it would never do, and so they were permitted to remain.

We tried to effect an entrance at the door, which was fastened; but, after
a noisy discussion with one of the old witches within, our guide became fidgety,
and, at last, told us to desist, or we would spoil all. He then led us off to
a distance, to await the performance; as the girls, he said, did not wish to be
recognized. He, furthermore, made us promise to remain where we were, until
all was over, and the dancers had retired.

We waited impatiently; and, at last, they came forth. They were arrayed
in short tunics of white tappa; with garlands of flowers on their heads. Following them, were the duennas, who remained clustering about the house, while
the girls advanced a few paces; and, in an instant, two of them, taller than
their companions, were standing, side by side, in the middle of a ring, formed
by the clasped hands of the rest. This movement was made in perfect silence.

Presently, the two girls join hands overhead; and, crying out, "Ahloo!
ahloo!" wave them to and fro. Upon which, the ring begins to circle slowly;
the dancers moving sideways, with their arms a little drooping. Soon they
quicken their pace; and, at last, fly round and round: bosoms heaving, hair
streaming, flowers dropping, and every sparkling eye circling in what seemed
a line of light.

Meanwhile, the pair within are passing and repassing each other incessantly. Inclining sideways, so that their long hair falls far over, they glide
this way and that; one foot continually in the air, and their fingers thrown
forth, and twirling in the moonbeams.

"Ahloo! ahloo!" again cry the dance queens; and, coming together in the
middle of the ring, they once more lift up the arch, and stand motionless.

"Ahloo! ahloo!" Every link of the circle is broken; and the girls, deeply
breathing, stand perfectly still. They pant hard and fast, a moment or two;
and then, just as the deep flush is dying away from their faces, slowly recede, all
round; thus enlarging the ring.

Again the two leaders wave their hands, when the rest pause; and now, far
apart, stand in the still moonlight, like a circle of fairies. Presently, raising
a strange chant, they softly sway themselves, gradually quickening the movement, until, at length, for a few passionate moments, with throbbing bosoms
and glowing cheeks, they abandon themselves to all the spirit of the dance,
apparently lost to everything around. But soon subsiding again into the same
languid measure, as before, they become motionless; and then, reeling forward

on all sides, their eyes swimming in their heads, join in one wild chorus, and
sink into each other's arms.

Such is the Lory-Lory, I think they call it; the dance of the backsliding
girls of Tamai.

While it was going on, we had as much as we could do to keep the doctor
from rushing forward and seizing a partner.

They would give us no more "hevars" that night; and Rartoo fairly dragged
us away to a canoe, hauled up on the lake shore; when we reluctantly embarked, and, paddling over to the village, arrived there in time for a good
nap before sunrise.

The next day, the doctor went about, trying to hunt up the overnight
dancers. He thought to detect them by their late rising; but never was man
more mistaken; for, on first sallying out, the whole village was asleep, waking
up in concert about an hour after. But, in the course of the day, he came
across several, whom he at once charged with taking part in the "hevar." There
were some prim-looking fellows standing by (visiting elders from Afrehitoo,
perhaps), and the girls looked embarrassed; but parried the charge most skilfully.

Though soft as doves, in general, the ladies of Tamai are, nevertheless,
flavoured with a slight tincture of what we queerly enough call the *"devil"*; and
they showed it on the present occasion. For when the doctor pressed one
rather hard, she all at once turned round upon him, and, giving him a box on
the ear, told him to "hanree perrar!" (be off with himself).

CHAPTER LXIV

MYSTERIOUS

THERE was a little old man, of a most hideous aspect, living in Tamai, who,
in a coarse mantle of tappa, went about the village, dancing, and singing, and
making faces. He followed us about, wherever we went; and, when unobserved by others, plucked at our garments, making frightful signs for us to
go along with him somewhere, and see something.

It was in vain that we tried to get rid of him. Kicks and cuffs, even, were
at last resorted to; but, though he howled like one possessed, he would not
go away, but still haunted us. At last, we conjured the natives to rid us of
him; but they only laughed; so, we were forced to endure the dispensation
as well as we could.

On the fourth night of our visit, returning home late from paying a few
calls through the village, we turned a dark corner of trees, and came full upon
our goblin friend; as usual, chattering, and motioning with his hands. The
doctor, venting a curse, hurried forward; but, from some impulse or other, I
stood my ground, resolved to find out what this unaccountable object wanted
of us. Seeing me pause, he crept close up to me, peered into my face, and
then retreated, beckoning me to follow; which I did.

In a few moments the village was behind us; and with my guide in advance,
I found myself in the shadow of the heights overlooking the farther side of
the valley. Here my guide paused until I came up with him; when, side by
side, and without speaking, we ascended the hill.

Presently, we came to a wretched hut, barely distinguishable in the shade cast by the neighbouring trees. Pushing aside a rude, sliding door, held together with thongs, the goblin signed me to enter. Within, it looked dark as pitch; so, I gave him to understand that he must strike a light, and go in before me. Without replying, he disappeared in the darkness; and, after groping about, I heard two sticks rubbing together, and directly saw a spark. A native taper was then lighted, and I stooped, and entered.

It was a mere kennel. Foul old mats, and broken coco-nut shells, and calabashes were strewn about the floor of earth; and overhead, I caught glimpses of the stars through chinks in the roof. Here and there, the thatch had fallen through, and hung down in wisps.

I now told him to set about what he was going to do, or produce whatever he had to show without delay. Looking round fearfully, as if dreading a surprise, he commenced turning over and over the rubbish in one corner. At last, he clutched a calabash, stained black, and with the neck broken off; on one side of it was a large hole. Something seemed to be stuffed away in the vessel; and after a deal of poking at the aperture, a musty old pair of sailor trousers was drawn forth; and, holding them up eagerly, he inquired how many pieces of tobacco I would give for them.

Without replying, I hurried away; the old man chasing me, and shouting as I ran, until I gained the village. Here, I dodged him, and made my way home, resolved never to disclose so inglorious an adventure.

To no purpose, the next morning, my comrade besought me to enlighten him: I preserved a mysterious silence.

The occurrence served me a good turn, however, so long as we abode in Tamai; for the old clothesman never afterward troubled me; but for ever haunted the doctor, who, in vain, supplicated Heaven to be delivered from him.

CHAPTER LXV

THE HEGIRA, OR FLIGHT

"I say, doctor," cried I, a few days after my adventure with the goblin, as, in the absence of our host, we were one morning lounging upon the matting in his dwellnig, smoking our reed pipes, "Tamai's a thriving place; why not settle down?"

"Faith!" said he, "not a bad idea, Paul. But do you fancy they'll let us stay, though?"

"Why, certainly: they would be overjoyed to have a couple of karhowrees for townsmen."

"Gad! you're right, my pleasant fellow. Ha! ha! I'll put up a banana leaf as physician from London—deliver lectures on Polynesian antiquities—teach English in five lessons, of one hour each—establish power-looms for the manufacture of tappa—lay out a public park in the middle of the village, and found a festival in honour of Captain Cook!"

"But, surely, not without stopping to take breath," observed I.

The doctor's projects, to be sure, were of a rather visionary cast; but we seriously thought, nevertheless, of prolonging our stay in the valley for an indefinite period; and, with this understanding, we were turning over various plans for spending our time pleasantly, when several women came running into the house, and hurriedly besought us to *heree! heree!* (make our escape), crying out something about the *mickonarees*.

Thinking that we were about to be taken up under the act for the suppression of vagrancy, we flew out of the house, sprang into a canoe before the door, and paddled with might and main over to the opposite side of the lake.

Approaching Rartoo's dwelling, was a great crowd, among which we perceived several natives, who, from their partly European dress, we were certain did not reside in Tamai.

Plunging into the groves, we thanked our stars that we had thus narrowly escaped being apprehended as runaway seamen, and marched off to the beach. This, at least, was what we thought we had escaped.

Having fled the village, we could not think of prowling about its vicinity, and then returning; in doing so, we might be risking our liberty again. We therefore determined upon journeying back to Martair; and setting our faces thitherward, we reached the planters' house about nightfall. They gave us a cordial reception, and a hearty supper; and we sat up talking until a late hour.

We now prepared to go round to Taloo, a place from which we were not far off when at Tamai; but wishing to see as much of the island as we could, we preferred returning to Martair, and then going round by way of the beach.

Taloo, the only frequented harbour of Imeeo, lies on the western side of the island, almost directly over against Martair. Upon one shore of the bay stands the village of Partoowye, a missionary station. In its vicinity is an extensive sugar plantation—the best in the South Seas, perhaps—worked by a person from Sydney.

The patrimonial property of the husband of Pomaree, and every way a delightful retreat, Partoowye was one of the occasional residences of the court. But at the time I write of, it was permanently fixed there, the queen having fled thither from Tahiti.

Partoowye, they told us, was, by no means, the place Papeetee was. Ships seldom touched, and very few foreigners were living ashore. A solitary whaler, however, was reported to be lying in the harbour, wooding and watering, and said to be in want of men.

All things considered, I could not help looking upon Taloo as offering "a splendid opening" for us adventurers. To say nothing of the facilities presented for going to sea in the whaler, or hiring ourselves out as day labourers in the sugar plantation, there were hopes to be entertained of being promoted to some office of high trust and emolument, about the person of her majesty, the queen.

Nor was this expectation altogether Quixotic. In the train of many Polynesian princes, roving whites are frequently found: gentlemen pensioners of state, basking in the tropical sunshine of the court, and leading the pleasantest lives in the world. Upon islands little visited by foreigners, the first seaman that settles down is generally domesticated in the family of the head chief or king; where he frequently discharges the functions of various offices, elsewhere filled by as many different individuals. As historiographer, for instance, he gives the natives some account of distant countries; as commissioner of the arts and sciences, he instructs them in the use of the jack-knife, and the best way of shaping bits of iron hoop into spearheads; and as interpreter to his majesty, he facilitates intercourse with strangers; besides instructing the people generally in the uses of the most common English phrases, civil and profane; but oftener the latter.

These men generally marry well; often—like Hardy of Hannamanoo—into the blood royal.

Sometimes they officiate as personal attendant, or First Lord in Waiting, to the king. At Amboi, one of the Tonga Islands, a vagabond Welshman bends his knee as cupbearer to his cannibal majesty. He mixes his morning cup of "arva," and, with profound genuflections, presents it in a coco-nut bowl, richly carved. Upon another island of the same group, where it is customary to bestow no small pains in dressing the hair—frizzing it out by a curious process, into an enormous Pope's-head—an old man-of-war's-man fills the post of barber to the king. And as his majesty is not very neat, his mop is exceedingly populous; so that, when Jack is not engaged in dressing the head entrusted to his charge, he busies himself in gently titillating it—a sort of skewer being actually worn about in the patient's hair for that special purpose.

Even upon the Sandwich Islands, a low rabble of foreigners is kept about the person of Tammahammaha, for the purpose of ministering to his ease or enjoyment.

Billy Loon, a jolly little negro, tricked out in a soiled blue jacket, studded all over with rusty bell-buttons, and garnished with shabby gold lace, is the royal drummer and pounder of the tambourine. Joe, a wooden-legged Portuguese, who lost his leg by a whale, is violinist; and Mordecai, as he is called, a villainous-looking scamp, going about with his cups and balls in a side pocket, diverts the court with his jugglery. These idle rascals receive no fixed salary, being altogether dependent upon the casual bounty of their master. Now and then they run up a score at the Dance Houses in Honolulu, where the illustrious Tammahammaha III afterward calls and settles the bill.

A few years since, an auctioneer to his majesty came near being added to the retinue of state. It seems that he was the first man who had practised his vocation on the Sandwich Islands; and delighted with the sport of bidding upon his wares, the king was one of his best customers. At last he besought the man to leave all and follow him, and he should be handsomely provided for at court. But the auctioneer refused; and so the ivory hammer lost the chance of being borne before him on a velvet cushion, when the next king went to be crowned.

But it was not as strolling players, nor as footmen out of employ, that the doctor and myself looked forward to our approaching introduction to the court of the Queen of Tahiti. On the contrary, as before hinted, we expected to swell the appropriations of breadfruit and coco-nuts on the Civil List, by filling some honourable office in her gift.

We were told, that to resist the usurpation of the French, the queen was rallying about her person all the foreigners she could. Her partiality for the English and Americans was well known; and this was an additional ground for our anticipating a favourable reception. Zeke had informed us, moreover, that by the queen's counsellors at Partoowye, a war of aggression against the invaders at Papeetee had been seriously thought of. Should this prove true, a surgeon's commission for the doctor, and a lieutenancy for myself, were certainly counted upon in our sanguine expectations.

Such, then, were our views, and such our hopes in projecting a trip to Taloo. But in our most lofty aspirations, we by no means lost sight of any minor matters which might help us to promotion. The doctor had informed me that he excelled in playing the fiddle. I now suggested, that as soon as we arrived at Partoowye, we should endeavour to borrow a violin for him; or if this could not be done, that he should manufacture some kind of a substitute, and thus equipped, apply for an audience of the queen. Her well-known passion for music would at once secure his admittance; and so, under the most favourable auspices, bring about our introduction to her notice.

"And who knows," said my waggish comrade, throwing his head back, and performing an imaginary air by briskly drawing one arm across the other, "who knows, that I may not fiddle myself into her majesty's good graces, so as to become a sort of Rizzio to the Tahitian princess."

CHAPTER LXVI

HOW WE WERE TO GET TO TALOO

THE inglorious circumstances of our somewhat premature departure from Tamai, filled the sagacious doctor, and myself, with sundry misgivings for the future.

Under Zeke's protection, we were secure from all impertinent interference in our concerns, on the part of the natives. But as friendless wanderers over the island, we ran the risk of being apprehended as runaways, and as such, sent back to Tahiti. The truth is, that the rewards constantly offered for the apprehension of deserters from ships, induce some of the natives to eye all strangers suspiciously.

A passport was therefore desirable; but such a thing had never been heard of in Imeeo. At last, Long Ghost suggested, that as the Yankee was well known, and much respected all over the island, we should endeavour to obtain from him some sort of paper, not only certifying to our having been in his employ, but also to our not being highwaymen, kidnappers, nor yet runaway seamen. Even written in English, a paper like this would answer every purpose; for the unlettered natives, standing in great awe of the document, would not dare to molest us until acquainted with its purport. Then, if it came to the worst, we might repair to the nearest missionary, and have the passport explained.

Upon informing Zeke of these matters, he seemed highly flattered with the opinion we entertained of his reputation abroad; and he agreed to oblige us. The doctor at once offered to furnish him with a draft of the paper; but he refused, saying he would write it himself. With a rooster's quill, therefore, a bit of soiled paper, and a stout heart, he set to work. Evidently, he was not accustomed to composition; for his literary throes were so violent, that the doctor suggested that some sort of a Cæsarian operation might be necessary.

The precious paper was at last finished; and a great curiosity it was. We were much diverted with his reasons for not dating it.

"In this here dumned climate," he observed, "a feller can't keep the run of the months, nohow; cause there's no seasons; no summer and winter, to go by. One's etarnally thinkin' it's always July, it's so pesky hot."

A passport provided, we cast about for some means of getting to Taloo.

The island of Imeeo is very nearly surrounded by a regular breakwater of coral, extending within a mile or less of the shore. The smooth canal within, furnishes the best means of communication with the different settlements; all of which, with the exception of Tamai, are right upon the water. And so indolent are the Imeeose, that they think nothing of going twenty or thirty miles round the island in a canoe, in order to reach a place not a quarter of that distance by land. But as hinted before, the fear of the bullocks has something to do with this.

The idea of journeying in a canoe struck our fancy quite pleasantly; and we at once set about chartering one, if possible. But none could we obtain. For not only did we have nothing to pay for hiring one, but we could not expect to have it loaned; inasmuch as the good-natured owner would, in all probability, have to walk along the beach as we paddled, in order to bring back his property when we had no further use for it.

At last, it was decided to commence our journey on foot; trusting that we would soon fall in with a canoe going our way, in which we might take passage.

The planters said we would find no beaten path:—all we had to do was to follow the beach; and however inviting it might look inland, on no account must we stray from it. In short, the longest way round was the nearest way to Taloo. At intervals, there were little hamlets along the shore, besides lonely fishermen's huts here and there, where we could get plenty to eat without pay; so there was no necessity to lay in any store.

Intending to be off before sunrise the next morning, so as to have the benefit of the coolest part of the day, we bade our kind hosts farewell, overnight; and then, repairing to the beach, we launched our floating pallet, and slept away merrily till dawn.

CHAPTER LXVII

THE JOURNEY ROUND THE BEACH

It was on the fourth day of the first month of the Hegira, or Flight from Tamai (we now reckoned our time thus), that, rising bright and early, we were up and away out of the valley of Martair, before the fishermen even were stirring.

It was the earliest dawn. The morning only showed itself along the lower edge of a bank of purple clouds, pierced by the misty peaks of Tahiti. The tropical day seemed too languid to rise. Sometimes, starting fitfully, it decked the clouds with faint edgings of pink and grey, which, fading away, left all dim again. Anon, it threw out thin, pale rays, growing lighter and lighter, until at last, the golden morning sprang out of the East with a bound—darting its bright beams hither and thither, higher and higher, and sending them, broadcast, over the face of the heavens.

All balmy from the groves of Tahiti, came an indolent air, cooled by its transit over the waters; and grateful under foot was the damp and slightly yielding beach, from which the waves seemed just retired.

The doctor was in famous spirits; removing his Roora, he went splashing into the sea; and, after swimming a few yards, waded ashore, hopping, skipping, and jumping along the beach; but very careful to cut all his capers in the direction of our journey.

Say what they will of the glowing independence one feels in the saddle, give me the first morning flush of your cheery pedestrian!

Thus exhilarated, we went on, as light-hearted and care-free, as we could wish.

And here, I cannot refrain from lauding the very superior inducements which most intertropical countries afford, not only to mere rovers like ourselves, but to penniless people, generally. In these genial regions, one's wants are naturally diminished; and those which remain are easily gratified: fuel, house-shelter, and, if you please, clothing, may be entirely dispensed with.

How different, our hard northern latitudes! Alas! the lot of a "poor devil," twenty degrees north of the tropic of Cancer, is indeed pitiable.

At last, the beach contracted to hardly a yard's width, and the dense thicket almost dipped into the sea. In place of the smooth sand, too, we had sharp fragments of broken coral, which made travelling exceedingly unpleasant. "Lord! my foot!" roared the doctor, fetching it up for inspection, with a galvanic fling of the limb. A sharp splinter had thrust itself into the flesh, through a hole in his boot. My sandals were worse yet; their soles taking a sort of fossil impression of everything trod upon.

Turning round a bold sweep of the beach, we came upon a piece of fine, open ground, with a fisherman's dwelling in the distance, crowning a knoll which rolled off into the water.

The hut proved to be a low, rude erection, very recently thrown up; for the bamboos were still green as grass, and the thatching, fresh and fragrant as meadow hay. It was open upon three sides; so that, upon drawing near, the domestic arrangements within were in plain sight. No one was stirring; and nothing was to be seen but a clumsy old chest of native workmanship, a few calabashes, and bundles of tappa hanging against a post; and a heap of something, we knew not what, in a dark corner. Upon close inspection, the doctor discovered it to be a loving old couple, locked in each other's arms, and rolled together in a tappa mantle.

"Halloa! Darby!" he cried, shaking the one with a beard. But Darby heeded him not; though Joan, a wrinkled old body, started up in affright, and yelled aloud. Neither of us attempting to gag her, she presently became quiet; and after staring hard, and asking some unintelligible questions, she proceeded to rouse her still slumbering mate.

What ailed him, we could not tell; but there was no waking him. Equally in vain were all his dear spouse's cuffs, pinches, and other endearments; he lay like a log, face up, and snoring away like a cavalry trumpeter.

"Here, my good woman," said Long Ghost, "just let *me* try;" and, taking the patient right by his nose, he so lifted him bodily, into a sitting position, and held him there until his eyes opened. When this event came to pass, Darby looked round like one stupefied; and then, springing to his feet, backed away into a corner, from which place we became the objects of his earnest and respectful attention.

"Permit me, my dear Darby, to introduce to you my esteemed friend and comrade, Paul," said the doctor, gallanting me up with all the grimace and flourish imaginable. Upon this, Darby began to recover his faculties, and surprised us not a little, by talking a few words of English. So far as could be understood, they were expressive of his having been aware, that there were two "karhowrees" in the neighbourhood; that he was glad to see us, and would have something for us to eat in no time.

How he came by his English, was explained to us before we left. Some time previous, he had been a denizen of Papeetee, where the native language is broidered over with the most classic sailor phrases. He seemed to be quite proud of his residence there; and alluded to it in the same significant way in which a provincial informs you, that in his time he has resided in the capital. The old fellow was disposed to be garrulous; but being sharp-set, we told him to get breakfast; after which we would hear his anecdotes. While employed among the calabashes, the strange, antiquated fondness between these old semi-savages was really amusing. I made no doubt, that they were saying to each other, "yes, my love"—"no, my life," just in the same way that some young couples do, at home.

They gave us a hearty meal; and while we were discussing its merits, they assured us, over and over again, that they expected nothing in return for their attentions; more: we were at liberty to stay as long as we pleased; and as long as we *did* stay, their house and everything they had, was no longer theirs, but ours; still more: they themselves were our slaves—the old lady, to a degree that was altogether superfluous. This, now, is Tahitian hospitality! Self-immolation upon one's own hearthstone for the benefit of the guest.

The Polynesians carry their hospitality to an amazing extent. Let a native of Waiurar, the westernmost part of Tahiti, make his appearance as a traveller at Partoowye, the most easterly village of Imeeo; though a perfect stranger, the inhabitants on all sides accost him at their doorways, inviting him to enter, and make himself at home. But the traveller passes on, examining every house attentively; until at last, he pauses before one which suits him, and then exclaiming, "ah, ena maita" (this one will do, I think), he steps in, and makes himself perfectly at ease; flinging himself upon the mats, and very probably calling for a nice young coco-nut, and a piece of toasted breadfruit, sliced thin, and done brown.

Curious to relate, however, should a stranger carrying it thus bravely, be afterward discovered to be without a house of his own, why, he may thenceforth go a-begging for his lodgings. The "karhowrees," or white men, are exceptions to this rule. Thus is it precisely as in civilized countries; where those who have houses and lands are incessantly bored to death with invitations to come and live in other people's houses; while many a poor gentleman who inks the seams of his coat, and to whom the like invitation would be really acceptable, may go and sue for it. But to the credit of the ancient Tahitians, it should here be observed, that this blemish upon their hospitality is only of recent origin, and was wholly unknown in old times. So told me, Captain Bob.

In Polynesia, it is esteemed "a great hit," if a man succeed in marrying into a family to which the best part of the community is related (Heaven knows it is otherwise with us). The reason is, that when he goes a-travelling, the greater number of houses are the more completely at his service.

Receiving a paternal benediction from old Darby and Joan, we continued our journey; resolved to stop at the very next place of attraction which offered.

Nor did we long stroll for it. A fine walk along a beach of shells, and we came to a spot, where, with trees here and there, the land was all meadow, sloping away to the water, which stirred a sedgy growth of reeds bordering its margin. Close by, was a little cove, walled in with coral, where a fleet of canoes was dancing up and down. A few paces distant, on a natural terrace overlooking the sea, were several native dwellings, newly thatched, and peeping into view out of the foliage, like summer-houses.

As we drew near, forth came a burst of voices; and presently, three gay girls, overflowing with life, health, and youth; and full of spirits and mischief. One was arrayed in a flaunting robe of calico; and her long black hair was braided behind in two immense tresses, joined together at the ends, and wreathed with the green tendrils of a vine. From her self-possessed and forward air,

I fancied she might be some young lady from Papeetee, on a visit to her country relations. Her companions wore mere slips of cotton cloth; their hair was dishevelled; and though very pretty, they betrayed the reserve and embarrassment characteristic of the provinces.

The little gipsy first mentioned, ran up to me with great cordiality; and giving the Tahitian salutation, opened upon me such a fire of questions, that there was no understanding, much less answering them. But our hearty welcome to Loohooloo, as she called the hamlet, was made plain enough. Meanwhile, Doctor Long Ghost gallantly presented an arm to each of the other young ladies; which, at first, they knew not what to make of; but at last, taking it for some kind of joke, accepted the civility.

The names of these three damsels were at once made known by themselves; and being so exceedingly romantic, I cannot forbear particularizing them. Upon my comrade's arms, then, were hanging Night and Morning, in the persons of Farnowar, or the Day-Born, and Farnoopoo, or the Night-Born. She with the tresses, was very appropriately styled Marhar-Rarrar, the Wakeful, or Bright-Eyed.

By this time, the houses were emptied of the rest of their inmates—a few old men and women, and several strapping young fellows rubbing their eyes and yawning. All crowded round, putting questions as to whence we came. Upon being informed of our acquaintance with Zeke, they were delighted; and one of them recognized the boots worn by the doctor. "Keehee (Zeke) maitai," they cried, "nuee nuee hanna hanna portarto"—(makes plenty of potatoes).

There was now a little friendly altercation, as to who should have the honour of entertaining the strangers. At last, a tall old gentleman, by name Marharvai, with a bald head and white beard, took us each by the hand, and led us into his dwelling. Once inside, Marharvai, pointing about with his staff, was so obsequious in assuring us that his house was ours, that Long Ghost suggested he might as well hand over the deed.

It was drawing near noon; so after a light lunch of roasted breadfruit, a few whiffs of a pipe, and some lively chatting, our host admonished the company to lie down, and take the everlasting siesta. We complied; and had a social nap all round.

CHAPTER LXVIII

A DINNER-PARTY IN IMEEO

It was just in the middle of the merry, mellow afternoon, that they ushered us to dinner, underneath a green shelter of palm boughs; open all round, and so low at the eaves that we stooped to enter.

Within, the ground was strewn over with aromatic ferns—called "nahee"—freshly gathered; which, stirred under foot, diffused the sweetest odour. On one side was a row of yellow mats, inwrought with fibres of bark, stained a bright red. Here, seated after the fashion of the Turk, we looked out, over a verdant bank, upon the mild, blue, endless Pacific. So far round had we skirted the island, that the view of Tahiti was now intercepted.

Upon the ferns before us, were laid several layers of broad, thick "pooroo" leaves; lapping over, one upon the other. And upon these were placed, side by side, newly plucked banana leaves, at least two yards in length, and very wide; the stalks were withdrawn, so as to make them lie flat. This green cloth was set out and garnished, in the manner following:—

First, a number of "pooroo" leaves, by way of plates, were ranged along on one side; and by each was a rustic nut-bowl, half-filled with sea-water, and a Tahitian roll, or small breadfruit, roasted brown. An immense flat calabash, placed in the centre, was heaped up with numberless small packages of moist, steaming leaves: in each was a small fish, baked in the earth, and done to a turn. This pyramid of a dish was flanked on either side by an ornamental calabash. One was brimming with the golden-hued "poee," or pudding, made from the red plantain of the mountains: the other was stacked up with cakes of the Indian turnip, previously macerated in a mortar, kneaded with the milk of the coco-nut, and then baked. In the spaces between the three dishes, were piled young coco-nuts, stripped of their husks. Their eyes had been opened and enlarged; so that each was a ready-charged goblet.

There was a sort of side-cloth in one corner, upon which, in bright, buff jackets, lay the fattest of bananas; "avees," red-ripe; guavas, with the shadows of their crimson pulp flushing through a transparent skin, and almost coming and going there like blushes; oranges, tinged, here and there, berry-brown; and great, jolly melons, which rolled about in very portliness. Such a heap! All ruddy, ripe, and round—bursting with the good cheer of the tropical soil, from which they sprang!

"A land of orchards!" cried the doctor, in a rapture; and he snatched a morsel from a sort of fruit of which gentlemen of the sanguine temperament are remarkably fond; namely, the ripe cherry lips of Miss Day-Born, who stood looking on.

Marharvai allotted seats to his guests; and the meal began. Thinking that his hospitality needed some acknowledgment, I rose, and pledged him in the vegetable wine of the coco-nut; merely repeating the ordinary salutation, "Yar onor boyoee." Sensible that some compliment, after the fashion of white men, was paid him, with a smile, and a courteous flourish of the hand, he bade me be seated. No people, however refined, are more easy and graceful in their manners than the Imeeose.

The doctor, sitting next our host, now came under his special protection. Laying before his guest one of the packages of fish, Marharvai opened it; and commended its contents to his particular regards. But my comrade was one of those, who, on convivial occasions, can always take care of themselves. He ate an indefinite number of "Peehee Lee Lees" (small fish), his own and next neighbour's breadfruit; and helped himself, to right and left, with all the ease of an accomplished diner-out.

"Paul," said he, at last, "you don't seem to be getting along; why don't you try the pepper sauce?" and, by way of example, he steeped a morsel of food into his nutful of sea-water. On following suit, I found it quite piquant, though rather bitter; but, on the whole, a capital substitute for salt. The Imeeose invariably use sea-water in this way, deeming it quite a treat; and considering that their country is surrounded by an ocean of catsup, the luxury cannot be deemed an expensive one.

The fish were delicious; the manner of cooking them in the ground, preserving all the juices, and rendering them exceedingly sweet and tender. The plantain pudding was almost cloying; the cakes of Indian turnip, quite palatable; and the roasted breadfruit, crisp as toast.

During the meal, a native lad walked round and round the party; carrying a long staff of bamboo. This he occasionally tapped upon the cloth, before each guest; when a white clotted substance dropped forth, with a savour not unlike that of a curd. This proved to be "Lownee," an excellent relish, prepared from the grated meat of ripe coco-nuts, moistened with coco-nut milk and salt water, and kept perfectly tight, until a little past the saccharine stage of fermentation.

Throughout the repast there was much lively chatting among the islanders, in which their conversational powers quite exceeded ours. The young ladies, too, showed themselves very expert in the use of their tongues, and contributed much to the gaiety which prevailed.

Nor did these lively nymphs suffer the meal to languish; for upon the doctor's throwing himself back, with an air of much satisfaction, they sprang to their feet, and pelted him with oranges and guavas. This, at last, put an end to the entertainment.

By a hundred whimsical oddities, my long friend became a great favourite with these people; and they bestowed upon him a long, comical title, expressive of his lank figure and Roora combined. The latter, by the by, never failed to excite the remark of everybody we encountered.

The giving of nicknames is quite a passion with the people of Tahiti and Imeeo. No one, with any peculiarity, whether of person or temper, is exempt; not even strangers.

A pompous captain of a man-of-war, visiting Tahiti for the second time, discovered that, among the natives, he went by the dignified title of "Atee Poee"—literally, Poee Head, or Pudding Head. Nor is the highest rank among themselves any protection. The first husband of the present queen was commonly known in the court circles as "Pot Belly." He carried the greater part of his person before him, to be sure; and so did the gentlemanly George IV— but what a title for a king consort!

Even "Pomaree" itself, the royal patronymic, was, originally, a mere nickname; and literally signifies, one talking through his nose. The first monarch of that name, being on a war party, and sleeping overnight among the mountains, awoke one morning with a cold in his head; and some wag of a courtier, had no more manners than to vulgarize him thus.

How different from the volatile Polynesian in this, as in all other respects, is our grave and decorous North American Indian. While the former bestows a name in accordance with some humorous or ignoble trait, the latter seizes upon what is deemed the most exalted or warlike: and hence, among the red tribes, we have the truly patrician appellations of "White Eagles," "Young Oaks," "Fiery Eyes," and "Bended Bows."

CHAPTER LXIX

THE COCO-PALM

WHILE the doctor and the natives were taking a digestive nap after dinner, I strolled forth to have a peep at the country, which could produce so generous a meal.

To my surprise, a fine strip of land in the vicinity of the hamlet, and protected seaward by a grove of coco-nut and breadfruit trees, was under high cultivation. Sweet potatoes, Indian turnips, and yams were growing; also melons, a few pine-apples, and other fruits. Still more pleasing was the sight of young breadfruit and coco-nut trees set out with great care, as if, for once, the improvident Polynesian had thought of his posterity. But this was the only instance of native thrift which ever came under my observation. For, in all my rambles over Tahiti and Imeeo, nothing so much struck me as the comparative scarcity of these trees in many places where they ought to abound. Entire valleys, like Martair, of inexhaustible fertility, are abandoned to all the rankness of untamed vegetation. Alluvial flats bordering the sea, and watered by streams from the mountains, are overgrown with a wild, scrub guava-bush, introduced by foreigners, and which spreads with such fatal rapidity, that the natives, standing still while it grows, anticipate its covering the entire island. Even tracts of clear land, which, with so little pains, might be made to wave with orchards, lie wholly neglected.

When I considered their unequalled soil and climate, thus unaccountably slighted, I often turned in amazement upon the natives about Papeetee; some of whom all but starve in their gardens run to waste. Upon other islands which I have visited, of similar fertility, and wholly unreclaimed from their first discovered condition, no spectacle of this sort was presented.

The high estimation in which many of their fruit-trees are held by the Tahitians and Imeeose—their beauty in the landscape—their manifold uses, and the facility with which they are propagated, are considerations which render the remissness alluded to still more unaccountable. The coco-palm is an example; a tree by far the most important production of Nature in the Tropics. To the Polynesian, it is emphatically the Tree of Life; transcending even the breadfruit in the multifarious uses to which it is applied.

Its very aspect is imposing. Asserting its supremacy by an erect and lofty bearing, it may be said to compare with other trees as man with inferior creatures.

The blessings it confers are incalculable. Year after year, the islander reposes beneath its shade, both eating and drinking of its fruit; he thatches his hut with its boughs, and weaves them into baskets to carry his food; he cools himself with a fan plaited from the young leaflets, and shields his head from the sun by a bonnet of the leaves; sometimes he clothes himself with the cloth-like substance which wraps round the base of the stalks, whose elastic rods, strung with filberts, are used as a taper; the larger nuts, thinned and polished, furnish him with a beautiful goblet: the smaller ones, with bowls for his pipes; the dry husks kindle his fires; their fibres are twisted into fishing-lines and cords for his canoes; he heals his wounds with a balsam compounded from the juice of the nut; and with the oil extracted from its meat, embalms the bodies of the dead.

The noble trunk itself is far from being valueless. Sawn into posts, it upholds the islander's dwelling; converted into charcoal, it cooks his food; and supported on blocks of stone, rails in his lands. He impels his canoe through the water with a paddle of the wood, and goes to battle with clubs and spears of the same hard material.

In pagan Tahiti a coco-nut branch was the symbol of regal authority. Laid upon the sacrifice in the temple, it made the offering sacred; and with it, the priests chastised and put to flight the evil spirits which assailed them. The supreme majesty of Oro, the great god of their mythology, was declared in the coco-nut log from which his image was rudely carved. Upon one of the Tonga Islands, there stands a living tree, revered itself as a deity. Even upon the Sandwich Islands, the coco-palm retains all its ancient reputation; the people there having thought of adopting it as the national emblem.

The coco-nut is planted as follows: Selecting a suitable place, you drop into the ground a fully ripe nut, and leave it. In a few days, a thin, lance-like shoot forces itself through a minute hole in the shell, pierces the husk, and soon unfolds three pale-green leaves in the air; while, originating in the same soft white sponge which now completely fills the nut, a pair of fibrous roots, pushing away the stoppers which close two holes in an opposite direction, penetrate the shell, and strike vertically into the ground. A day or two more, and the shell and husk, which, in the last and germinating stage of the nut, are so hard that a knife will scarcely make any impression, spontaneously burst by some force within; and, henceforth, the hardy young plant thrives apace; and needing no culture, pruning, or attention of any sort, rapidly advances to maturity. In four or five years it bears; in twice as many more, it begins to lift its head among the groves, where, waxing strong, it flourishes for near a century.

Thus, as some voyager has said, the man who but drops one of these nuts into the ground, may be said to confer a greater and more certain benefit upon himself and posterity, than many a life's toil in less genial climes.

The fruitfulness of the tree is remarkable. As long as it lives, it bears; and without intermission. Two hundred nuts, besides innumerable white blossoms of others, may be seen upon it at one time; and though a whole year is required to bring any one of them to the germinating point, no two, perhaps, are at one time in precisely the same stage of growth.

The tree delights in a maritime situation. In its greatest perfection, it is perhaps found right on the sea-shore, where its roots are actually washed. But such instances are only met with upon islands where the swell of the sea is prevented from breaking on the beach by an encircling reef. No saline flavour is perceptible in the nut produced in such a place. Although it bears in any soil, whether upland or bottom, it does not flourish vigorously inland; and I have frequently observed, that when met with far up the valleys, its tall stem inclines seaward, as if pining after a more genial region.

It is a curious fact, that if you deprive the coco-nut tree of the verdant tuft at its head, it dies at once; and if allowed to stand thus, the trunk, which, when alive, is encased in so hard a bark, as to be almost impervious to a bullet, moulders away, and, in an incredibly short period, becomes dust. This is, perhaps, partly owing to the peculiar constitution of the trunk, a mere cylinder of minute hollow reeds, closely packed, and very hard; but when exposed at top, peculiarly fitted to convey moisture and decay through the entire stem.

The finest orchard of coco-palms I know, and the only plantation of them I ever saw at the islands, is one that stands right upon the southern shore of Papeetee Bay. They were set out by the first Pomaree, almost half-a-century ago; and the soil being especially adapted to their growth, the noble trees now form a magnificent grove, nearly a mile in extent. No other plant, scarcely a bush, is to be seen within its precincts. The Broom Road passes through its entire length.

At noonday, this grove is one of the most beautiful, serene, witching places that ever was seen. High overhead, are ranges of green rustling arches; through which the sun's rays come down to you in sparkles. You seem to be wandering through illimitable halls of pillars; everywhere you catch glimpses of stately aisles, intersecting each other at all points. A strange silence, too, reigns far and near; the air flushed with the mellow stillness of a sunset.

But after the long morning calms, the sea-breeze comes in; and creeping over the tops of these thousand trees, they nod their plumes. Soon the breeze freshens; and you hear the branches brushing against each other; and the flexible trunks begin to sway. Toward evening, the whole grove is rocking to and fro; and the traveller on the Broom Road is startled by the frequent falling of the nuts, snapped from their brittle stems. They come flying through the air, ringing like jugglers' balls; and often bound along the ground for many rods.

CHAPTER LXX

LIFE AT LOOHOOLOO

FINDING the society at Loohooloo very pleasant, the young ladies, in particular, being extremely sociable; and, moreover, in love with the famous good cheer of old Marharvai, we acquiesced in an invitation of his, to tarry a few days longer. We might then, he said, join a small canoe party, which was going to a place a league or two distant. So averse to all exertion are these people, that they really thought the prospect of thus getting rid of a few miles' walking, would prevail with us, even if there were no other inducement.

The people of the hamlet, as we soon discovered, formed a snug little community of cousins; of which our host seemed the head. Marharvai, in truth, was a petty chief, who owned the neighbouring lands. And as the wealthy, in most cases, rejoice in a numerous kindred, the family footing upon which everybody visited him, was, perhaps, ascribable to the fact of his being the lord of the manor. Like Captain Bob, he was, in some things, a gentleman of the old school—a stickler for the customs of a past and pagan age.

Nowhere else except in Tamai, did we find the manners of the natives less vitiated by recent changes. The old-fashioned Tahitian dinner they gave us on the day of our arrival was a fair sample of their general mode of living.

Our time passed delightfully. The doctor went his way, and I mine. With a pleasant companion, he was for ever strolling inland, ostensibly to collect botanical specimens; while I, for the most part, kept near the sea; sometimes taking the girls an aquatic excursion in a canoe.

Often we went fishing; not dozing over stupid hooks and lines, but leaping right into the water, and chasing our prey over the coral rocks, spear in hand.

Spearing fish is glorious sport. The Imeeose, all round the island, catch them in no other way. The smooth shallows between the reef and the shore, and, at low water, the reef itself, being admirably adapted to this mode of capturing them. At almost any time of the day—save ever the sacred hour of noon—you may see the fish-hunters pursuing their sport; with loud halloos, brandishing their spears, and splashing through the water in all directions. Sometimes a solitary native is seen, far out upon a lonely shallow, wading slowly along, with eye intent and poised spear.

But the best sport of all, is going out upon the great reef itself, by torch-light. The natives follow this recreation with as much spirit as a gentleman of England does the chase; and take full as much delight in it.

The torch is nothing more than a bunch of dry reeds, bound firmly together: the spear, a long, light pole, with an iron head, on one side barbed.

I shall never forget the night that old Marharvai and the rest of us, paddling off to the reef, leaped at midnight upon the coral ledges with waving torches and spears. We were more than a mile from the land; the sullen ocean, thundering upon the outside of the rocks, dashed the spray in our faces, almost extinguishing the flambeaux; and, far as the eye could reach, the darkness of sky and water was streaked with a long, misty line of foam, marking the course of the coral barrier. The wild fishermen, flourishing their weapons, and yelling like so many demons to scare their prey, sprang from ledge to ledge, and sometimes darted their spears in the very midst of the breakers.

But fish-spearing was not the only sport we had at Loohooloo. Right on the beach was a mighty old coco-nut tree, the roots of which had been underwashed by the waves, so that the trunk inclined far over its base. From the tuft of the tree, a stout cord of bark depended, the end of which swept the water several yards from the shore. This was a Tahitian swing. A native lad seizes hold of the cord, and, after swinging to and fro quite leisurely, all at once sends himself fifty or sixty feet from the water, rushing through the air like a rocket. I doubt whether any of our rope-dancers would attempt the feat. For my own part, I had neither head nor heart for it; so, after sending a lad aloft with an additional cord; by way of security, I constructed a large basket of green boughs, in which I and some particular friends of mine, used to swing over sea and land by the hour.

CHAPTER LXXI

WE START FOR TALOO

BRIGHT was the morning, and brighter still the smiles of the young ladies who accompanied us, when we sprang into a sort of family canoe—wide and roomy— and bade adieu to the hospitable Marharvai and his tenantry. As we paddled away, they stood upon the beach, waving their hands, and crying out, "Aroha! aroha!" (farewell! farewell!) as long as we were within hearing.

Very sad at parting with them, we endeavoured, nevertheless, to console ourselves in the society of our fellow-passengers. Among these were two old ladies; but as they said nothing to us, we will say nothing about them; nor anything about the old men who managed the canoe. But of the three mischievous, dark-eyed young witches, who lounged in the stern of that comfortable old island gondola, I have a great deal to say.

In the first place, one of them was Marhar-Rarrar, the Bright-Eyed; and, in the second place, neither she nor the romps, her companions, ever dreamed of taking the voyage, until the doctor and myself announced our intention; their going along was nothing more than a madcap frolic; in short, they were a parcel of wicked hoydens, bent on mischief, who laughed in your face when you looked sentimental, and only tolerated your company when making merry at your expense.

Something or other about us was perpetually awaking their mirth. Attributing this to his own remarkable figure, the doctor increased their enjoyment, by assuming the part of a Merry Andrew. Yet his cap and bells never jingled but to some tune; and while playing the Tom-fool, I more than suspected that he was trying to play the rake. At home, it is deemed auspicious to go a-wooing in epaulets; but among the Polynesians, your best dress in courting is motley.

A fresh breeze springing up, we set our sail of matting, and glided along as tranquilly as if floating upon an inland stream; the white reef on one hand, and the green shore on the other.

Soon, as we turned a headland, we encountered another canoe, paddling with might and main in an opposite direction; the strangers shouting to each other, and a tall fellow, in the bow, dancing up and down like a crazy man. They shot by us like an arrow, though our fellow-voyagers shouted again and again, for them to cease paddling.

According to the natives, this was a kind of royal mail-canoe, carrying a message from the queen to her friends in a distant part of the island.

Passing several shady bowers, which looked quite inviting, we proposed touching, and diversifying the monotony of a sea-voyage by a stroll ashore. So, forcing our canoe among the bushes, behind a decayed palm, lying partly in the water, we left the old folks to take a nap in the shade, and gallanted the others among the trees, which were here trellised with vines and creeping shrubs.

In the early part of the afternoon, we drew near the place to which the party were going. It was a solitary house, inhabited by four or five old women, who, when we entered, were gathered in a circle about the mats, eating *poee* from a cracked calabash. They seemed delighted at seeing our companions, but rather drew up when introduced to ourselves. Eyeing us distrustfully, they whispered to know who we were. The answers they received were not satisfactory; for they treated us with marked coolness and reserve, and seemed desirous of breaking off our acquaintance with the girls. Unwilling, therefore, to stay where our company was disagreeable, we resolved to depart, without even eating a meal.

Informed of this, Marhar-Rarrar and her companions evinced the most lively concern; and equally unmindful of their former spirits, and the remonstrances of the old ladies, broke forth into sobs and lamentations, which were not to be withstood. We agreed, therefore, to tarry until they left for home; which would be at the "Aheharar," or Falling of the Sun; in other words, at sunset.

When the hour arrived, after much leave-taking, we saw them safely embarked. As the canoe turned a bluff, they seized the paddles from the hands of the old men, and waved them silently in the air. This was meant for a touching farewell, as the paddle is only waved thus, when the parties separating never more expect to meet.

We now continued our journey; and following the beach, soon came to a level and lofty overhanging bank, which, planted here and there with trees, took a broad sweep round a considerable part of the island. A fine pathway skirted the edge of the bank; and often we paused to admire the scenery. The evening was still and fair, even for so heavenly a climate; and all round, far as the eye could reach, was the blending blue sky and ocean.

As we went on, the reef-belt still accompanied us; turning as we turned, and thundering its distant bass upon the ear, like the unbroken roar of a cataract. Dashing for ever against their coral rampart, the breakers looked, in the distance, like a line of rearing white chargers, reined in, tossing their white manes, and bridling with foam.

These great natural breakwaters are admirably designed for the protection of the land. Nearly all the Society Islands are defended by them. Were the vast swells of the Pacific to break against the soft alluvial bottoms which in many places border the sea, the soil would soon be washed away, and the natives be thus deprived of their most productive lands. As it is, the banks of no rivulet are firmer.

But the coral barriers answer another purpose. They form all the harbours of this group, including the twenty-four round about the shores of Tahiti. Curiously enough, the openings in the reefs, by which alone vessels enter to their anchorage, are invariably opposite the mouths of running streams: an advantage fully appreciated by the mariner who touches for the purpose of watering his ship.

It is said, that the fresh water of the land, mixing with the salts held in solution by the sea, so acts upon the latter, as to resist the formation of the coral; and hence the breaks. Here and there, these openings are sentinelled, as it were, by little fairy islets, green as emerald, and waving with palms. Strangely and beautifully diversifying the long line of breakers, no objects can strike the fancy more vividly. Pomaree II, with a taste in watering-place truly Tahitian, selected one of them as a royal retreat. We passed it on our journey.

Omitting several further adventures which befell us after leaving the party from Loohooloo, we must now hurry on, to relate what happened just before reaching the place of our destination.

CHAPTER LXXII

A DEALER IN THE CONTRABAND

It must have been at least the tenth day, reckoning from the Hegira, that we found ourselves the guests of Varvy, an old hermit of an islander, who kept house by himself, perhaps a couple of leagues from Taloo.

A stone's cast from the beach there was a fantastic rock, moss-grown, and deep in a dell. It was insulated by a shallow brook, which, dividing its waters, flowed on both sides, until united below. Twisting its roots round the rock, a gnarled "Aoa" spread itself overhead in a wilderness of foliage; the elastic branch-roots depending from the larger boughs, insinuating themselves into every cleft, thus forming supports to the parent stem. In some places, these pendulous branches, half-grown, had not yet reached the rock; swinging their loose fibrous ends in the air like whip-lashes.

Varvy's hut, a mere coop of bamboos, was perched upon a level part of the rock, the ridge-pole resting at one end in a crotch of the "Aoa," and the other, propped by a forked bough planted in a fissure.

Notwithstanding our cries as we drew near, the first hint the old hermit received of our approach was the doctor's stepping up and touching his shoulder, as he was kneeling over on a stone, cleaning fish in the brook. He leaped up, and stared at us. But with a variety of uncouth gestures, he soon made us welcome; informing us, by the same means, that he was both deaf and dumb; he then motioned us into his dwelling.

Going in, we threw ourselves upon an old mat, and peered round. The soiled bamboos and calabashes looked so uninviting, that the doctor was for pushing on to Taloo that night, notwithstanding it was near sunset. But at length we concluded to stay where we were.

After a good deal of bustling outside under a decrepit shed, the old man made his appearance with our supper. In one hand he held a flickering taper, and in the other, a huge, flat calabash, scantily filled with viands. His eyes were dancing in his head, and he looked from the calabash to us, and from us to the calabash, as much as to say, "Ah, my lads, what do ye think of this, eh? Pretty good cheer, eh?" But the fish and Indian turnip being none of the best, we made but a sorry meal. While discussing it, the old man tried hard to make himself understood by signs; most of which were so excessively ludicrous, that we made no doubt he was perpetrating a series of pantomimic jokes.

The remnants of the feast removed, our host left us for a moment, returning with a calabash of portly dimensions, and furnished with a long, hooked neck, the mouth of which was stopped with a wooden plug. It was covered with particles of earth, and looked as if just taken from some place under ground.

With sundry winks and horrible giggles peculiar to the dumb, the vegetable demijohn was now tapped; the old fellow looking round cautiously, and pointing at it; as much as to intimate, that it contained something which was "taboo," or forbidden.

Aware that intoxicating liquors were strictly prohibited to the natives, we now watched our entertainer with much interest. Charging a coco-nut shell, he tossed it off, and then filling up again, presented the goblet to me. Disliking the smell, I made faces at it; upon which he became highly excited; so much so, that a miracle was wrought upon the spot. Snatching the cup from my hands, he shouted out, "Ah, karhowree sabbee lee-lee, ena arva tee maitai" in other words, What a blockhead of a white man! this is the real stuff!

We could not have been more startled, had a frog leaped from his mouth. For an instant, he looked confused enough himself; and then placing a finger mysteriously upon his mouth, he contrived to make us understand, that at times he was subject to a suspension of the powers of speech.

Deeming the phenomenon a remarkable one, every way, the doctor desired him to open his mouth, so that he might have a look down. But he refused.

This occurrence made us rather suspicious of our host; nor could we afterward account for his conduct, except by supposing that his feigning dumbness might in some way or other assist him in the nefarious pursuits in which it afterward turned out that he was engaged. This conclusion, however, was not altogether satisfactory.

To oblige him, we at last took a sip of his "arva tee," and found it very crude, and strong as Lucifer. Curious to know whence it was obtained, we questioned him; when, lighting up with pleasure, he seized the taper, and led us outside the hut, bidding us follow.

After going some distance through the woods, we came to a dismantled old shed of boughs, apparently abandoned to decay. Underneath, nothing was to be seen but heaps of decaying leaves and an immense, clumsy jar, wide-mouthed, and, by some means, rudely hollowed out from a ponderous stone.

Here, for a while, we were left to ourselves; the old man placing the light in the jar, and then disappearing. He returned, carrying a long, large bamboo, and a crotched stick. Throwing these down, he poked under a pile of rubbish, and brought out a rough block of wood, pierced through and through with a hole, which was immediately clapped on top of the jar. Then planting the crotched stick upright about two yards distant, and making it sustain one end of the bamboo, he inserted the other end of the latter into the hole in the block; concluding these arrangements, by placing an old calabash under the farther end of the bamboo.

Coming up to us now with a sly, significant look, and pointing admiringly at his apparatus, he exclaimed, "Ah, karhowree, ena hannahanna arva tee!" as much as to say, "*This*, you see, is the way it's done."

His contrivance was nothing less than a native still, where he manufactured his island "poteen." The disarray in which we found it, was probably intentional, as a security against detection. Before we left the shed, the old fellow toppled the whole concern over, and dragged it away piecemeal.

His disclosing his secret to us thus, was characteristic of the "Tootai Owrees," or contemners of the missionaries among the natives; who, presuming that all foreigners are opposed to the ascendancy of the missionaries, take pleasure in making them confidants, whenever the enactments of their rulers are secretly set at naught.

The substance from which the liquor is produced is called "Tee," which is a large, fibrous root, something like a yam, but smaller. In its green state, it is exceedingly acrid; but boiled or baked, has the sweetness of the sugar-cane. After being subjected to the fire, macerated, and reduced to a certain stage of fermentation, the "Tee" is stirred up with water, and is then ready for distillation.

On returning to the hut, pipes were introduced; and, after a while, Long Ghost, who, at first, had relished the "Arva Tee" as little as myself, to my surprise, began to wax sociable over it, with Varvy; and, before long, absolutely got mellow, the old toper keeping him company.

It was a curious sight. Every one knows, that, so long as the occasion lasts, there is no stronger bond of sympathy and good-feeling among men, than getting tipsy together. And how earnestly, nay, movingly, a brace of worthies, thus employed, will endeavour to shed light upon, and elucidate their mystical ideas!

Fancy Varvy and the doctor, then, lovingly tippling, and brimming over with a desire to become better acquainted; the doctor politely bent upon carrying on the conversation in the language of his host, and the old hermit persisting in trying to talk English. The result was, that between the two, they made such a fricassee of vowels and consonants, that it was enough to turn one's brain.

The next morning, on waking, I heard a voice from the tombs. It was the doctor, solemnly pronouncing himself a dead man. He was sitting up, with both hands clasped over his forehead, and his pale face a thousand times paler than ever.

"That infernal stuff has murdered me!" he cried. "Heavens! my head's all wheels and springs, like the automaton chess-player! What's to be done, Paul? I'm poisoned."

But, after drinking an herbal draught, concocted by our host and eating a light meal, at noon, he felt much better; so much so, that he declared himself ready to continue our journey.

When we came to start, the Yankee's boots were missing; and, after a diligent search, were not to be found. Enraged beyond measure, their proprietor said that Varvy must have stolen them; but, considering his hospitality, I thought this extremely improbable; though, to whom else to impute the theft, I knew not. The doctor maintained, however, that one who was capable of drugging an innocent traveller with "Arva Tee," was capable of anything.

But it was in vain that he stormed, and Varvy and I searched; the boots were gone.

Were it not for this mysterious occurrence, and Varvy's detestable liquors, I would here recommend all travellers going round by the beach to Partoowye, to stop at the Rock, and patronize the old gentleman—the more especially as he entertains gratis.

CHAPTER LXXIII

OUR RECEPTION IN PARTOOWYE

Upon starting, at last, I flung away my sandals—by this time quite worn out—with the view of keeping company with the doctor, now forced to go barefooted. Recovering his spirits in good time, he protested that boots were a bore after all, and going without them decidedly manly.

This was said, be it observed, while strolling along over a soft carpet of grass; a little moist, even at midday, from the shade of the wood, through which we were passing.

Emerging from this, we entered upon a blank, sandy tract, upon which the sun's rays fairly flashed; making the loose gravel underfoot well-nigh as hot as the floor of an oven. Such yelling and leaping as there was in getting over this ground, would be hard to surpass. We could not have crossed at all,—until toward sunset,—had it not been for a few small, wiry bushes, growing here and there; into which we every now and then thrust our feet to cool. There was no little judgement necessary in selecting your bush; for if not chosen judiciously, the chances were that, on springing forward again, and finding the next bush so far off, that an intermediate cooling was indispensable, you would have to run back to your old place again.

Safely passing the Sahara, or Fiery Desert, we soothed our half-blistered feet by a pleasant walk through a meadow of long grass, which soon brought us in sight of a few straggling houses, sheltered by a grove on the outskirts of the village of Partoowye.

My comrade was for entering the first one we came to; but, on drawing near they had so much of an air of pretension, at least for native dwellings, that I hesitated; thinking they might be the residences of the higher chiefs, from whom no very extravagant welcome was to be anticipated.

While standing irresolute, a voice from the nearest house hailed us: "Aramai! aramai, karhowree!" ("come in! come in, strangers!")

We at once entered, and were warmly greeted. The master of the house was an aristocratic-looking islander; dressed in loose linen drawers, a fine white shirt, and a sash of red silk, tied about the waist, after the fashion of the Spaniards in Chili. He came up to us with a free, frank air, and, striking his chest with his hand, introduced himself as Eereemear Po-Po; or, to render the Christian name back again into English—Jeremiah Po-Po.

These curious combinations of names, among the people of the Society Islands, originate in the following way. When a native is baptized, his patronymic often gives offence to the missionaries, and they insist upon changing to something else whatever is objectionable therein. So, when Jeremiah came to the font, and gave his name as Narmo-Nana Po-Po (something equivalent to The-Darer-of-Devils-by-Night), the reverend gentleman officiating told him, that such a heathenish appellation would never do, and a substitute must be had; at least for the devil part of it. Some highly respectable Christian appellations were then submitted, from which the candidate for admission into the church was at liberty to choose. There was Adamo (Adam), Nooar (Noah),

Daveedar (David), Earcobar (James), Eorna (John), Patoora (Peter), Eree-mear (Jeremiah), &c. And thus did he come to be named Jeremiah Po-Po; or, Jeremiah-in-the-Dark—which he certainly was, I fancy, as to the ridiculous-ness of his new cognomen.

We gave our names in return; upon which he bade us be seated; and, sit-ting down himself, asked us a great many questions, in mixed English and Tahitian. After giving some directions to an old man, to prepare food, our host's wife, a large, benevolent-looking woman, upward of forty, also sat down by us. In our soiled and travel-stained appearance, the good lady seemed to find abundant matter for commiseration; and all the while kept looking at us piteously, and making mournful exclamations.

But Jeremiah and his spouse were not the only inmates of the mansion.

In one corner, upon a large native couch, elevated upon posts, reclined a nymph; who, half-veiled in her own long hair, had yet to make her toilet for the day. She was the only daughter of Po-Po; and a very beautiful little daughter she was; not more than fourteen; with the most delightful shape—like a bud just blown; and large hazel eyes. They called her Loo: a name rather pretty and genteel, and, therefore, quite appropriate; for a more genteel and lady-like little damsel there was not in all Imeeo.

She was a cold and haughty young beauty though, this same little Loo, and never deigned to notice us; further than now and then to let her eyes float over our persons, with an expression of indolent indifference. With the tears of the Loohooloo girls hardly dry from their sobbing upon our shoulders, this contemptuous treatment stung us not a little.

When we first entered, Po-Po was raking smooth the carpet of dried ferns which had that morning been newly laid; and now that our meal was ready, it was spread on a banana leaf, right upon this fragrant floor. Here, we lounged at our ease; eating baked pig and breadfruit off earthen plates, and using, for the first time in many a long month, real knives and forks.

These, as well as other symptoms of refinement, somewhat abated our sur-prise at the reserve of the little Loo; her parents, doubtless, were magnates in Partoowye, and she herself was an heiress.

After being informed of our stay in the vale of Martair, they were very curious to know on what errand we came to Taloo. We merely hinted, that the ship lying in the harbour was the reason of our coming.

Arfretee, Po-Po's wife, was a right motherly body. The meal over, she recommended a nap; and upon our waking much refreshed, she led us to the doorway, and pointed down among the trees; through which we saw the gleam of water. Taking the hint, we repaired thither; and finding a deep shaded pool, bathed, and returned to the house. Our hostess now sat down by us; and after looking with great interest at the doctor's cloak, felt of my own soiled and tat-tered garments for the hundredth time, and exclaimed plaintively—"Ah nuee nuee olee manee! olee manee!" (alas! they are very, very old! very old!)

When Arfretee, good soul, thus addressed us, she thought she was talking very respectable English. The word "nuee" is so familiar to foreigners, throughout Polynesia, and is so often used by them in their intercourse with the natives, that the latter suppose it to be common to all mankind. "Olee manee" is the native pronunciation of *"old man,"* which, by Society Islanders talking Saxon, is applied indiscriminately to all aged things and persons what-soever.

Going to a chest filled with various European articles, she took out two suits of new sailor frocks and trousers; and presenting them with a gracious smile, pushed us behind a calico screen, and left us. Without any fastidious scruples, we donned the garments; and what with the meal, the nap, and the bath, we now came forth like a couple of bridegrooms.

Evening drawing on, lamps were lighted. They were very simple: the half of a green melon, about one third full of coco-nut oil, and a wick of twisted tappa floating on the surface. As a night lamp, this contrivance cannot be excelled; a soft dreamy light being shed through the transparent rind.

As the evening advanced, other members of the household, whom as yet we had not seen, began to drop in. There was a slender young dandy in a gay striped shirt, and whole fathoms of bright figured calico tucked about his waist, and falling to the ground. He wore a new straw hat also, with three distinct ribbons tied about the crown; one black, one green, and one pink. Shoes or stockings, however, he had none.

There were a couple of delicate, olive-cheeked little girls—twins—with mild eyes and beautiful hair, who ran about the house, half-naked, like a couple of gazelles. They had a brother, somewhat younger—a fine dark boy, with an eye like a woman's. All these were the children of Po-Po, begotten in lawful wedlock.

Then, there were two or three queer-looking old ladies, who wore shabby mantles of soiled sheeting; which fitted so badly, and withal, had such a second-hand look, that I at once put their wearers down as domestic paupers —poor relations, supported by the bounty of My Lady Arfretee. They were sad, meek old bodies; said little and ate less; and either kept their eyes on the ground, or lifted them up deferentially. The semi-civilization of the island must have had something to do with making them what they were.

I had almost forgotten Monee, the grinning old man who prepared our meal. His head was a shining, bald globe. He had a round little paunch, and legs like a cat. He was Po-Po's factotum—cook, butler, and climber of the breadfruit and coco-nut trees; and, added to all else, a mighty favourite with his mistress; with whom he would sit smoking and gossiping by the hour.

Often you saw the indefatigable Monee working away at a great rate; then dropping his employment all at once—never mind what—run off to a little distance, and after rolling himself away in a corner, and taking a nap, jump up again, and fall to with fresh vigour.

From a certain something in the behaviour of Po-Po, and his household, I was led to believe, that he was a pillar of the church; though, from what I had seen in Tahiti, I could hardly reconcile such a supposition with his frank, cordial, unembarrassed air. But I was not wrong in my conjecture: Po-Po turned out to be a sort of elder, or deacon; he was also accounted a man of wealth, and was nearly related to a high chief.

Before retiring, the entire household gathered upon the floor; and in their midst, he read aloud a chapter from a Tahitian Bible. Then kneeling with the rest of us, he offered up a prayer. Upon its conclusion, all separated without speaking. These devotions took place regularly, every night and morning. Grace, too, was invariably said, by this family, both before and after eating.

After becoming familiarized with the almost utter destitution of anything like practical piety upon these islands, what I observed in our host's house astonished me much. But whatever others might have been, Po-Po was, in truth, a Christian: the only one, Arfretee excepted, whom I personally knew to be such, among all the natives of Polynesia.

CHAPTER LXXIV

RETIRING FOR THE NIGHT—THE DOCTOR GROWS DEVOUT

THEY put us to bed very pleasantly.

Lying across the foot of Po-Po's nuptial couch, was a smaller one, made of Koar-wood; a thin, strong cord, twisted from the fibres of the husk of the coco-nut, and woven into an exceedingly light sort of network, forming its elastic body. Spread upon this, was a single, fine mat, with a roll of dried ferns for a pillow, and a strip of white tappa for a sheet. This couch was mine. The doctor was provided for in another corner.

Loo reposed alone on a little settee, with a taper burning by her side; the dandy, her brother, swinging overhead in a sailor's hammock. The two gazelles frisked upon a mat near by; and the indigent relations borrowed a scant corner of the old butler's pallet, who snored away by the open door. After all had retired, Po-Po placed the illuminated melon in the middle of the apartment; and so, we all slumbered till morning.

Upon awaking, the sun was streaming brightly through the open bamboos, but no one was stirring. After surveying the fine attitudes, into which forgetfulness had thrown at least one of the sleepers, my attention was called off to the general aspect of the dwelling, which was quite significant of the superior circumstances of our host.

The house itself was built in the simple, but tasteful native style. It was a long, regular oval, some fifty feet in length, with low sides of cane-work, and a roof thatched with palmetto-leaves. The ridge-pole was, perhaps, twenty feet from the ground. There was no foundation whatever; the bare earth being merely covered with ferns: a kind of carpeting which serves very well, if frequently renewed; otherwise, it becomes dusty, and the haunt of vermin, as in the huts of the poorer natives.

Besides the couches, the furniture consisted of three or four sailor chests; in which were stored the fine wearing-apparel of the household—the ruffled linen shirts of Po-Po, the calico dresses of his wife and children, and divers odds and ends of European articles—strings of beads, ribbons, Dutch looking-glasses, knives, coarse prints, bunches of keys, bits of crockery, and metal buttons. One of these chests—used as a bandbox by Arfretee—contained several of the native hats (coal-scuttles), all of the same pattern, but trimmed with variously coloured ribbons. Of nothing was our good hostess more proud than of these hats, and her dresses. On Sundays, she went abroad a dozen times; and every time, like Queen Elizabeth, in a different robe.

Po-Po, for some reason or other, always gave us our meals before the rest of the family were served; and the doctor, who was very discerning in such matters, declared that we fared much better than they. Certain it was, that had Eeremear's guests travelled with purses, portmanteaux, and letters of introduction to the queen, they could not have been better cared for.

The day after our arrival, Monee, the old butler, brought us in for dinner a small pig, baked in the ground. All savoury, it lay in a wooden trencher, surrounded by roasted hemispheres of the breadfruit. A large calabash, filled with taro pudding, or poee, followed; and the young dandy, overcoming his customary languor, threw down our coco-nuts from an adjoining tree.

When all was ready, and the household looking on, Long Ghost, devoutly clasping his hands over the fated pig, implored a blessing. Hereupon, every-body present looked exceedingly pleased; Po-Po coming up, and addressing the doctor with much warmth; and Arfretee, regarding him with almost ma-ternal affection, exclaimed delightedly, "Ah mickonaree tata maitai!" in other words, "What a pious young man!"

It was just after this meal, that she brought me a roll of grass sinnate (of the kind which sailors sew into the frame of their tarpaulins), and then, hand-ing me needle and thread, bade me begin at once, and make myself the hat which I so much needed. An accomplished hand at the business, I finished it that day—merely stitching the braid together; and Arfretee, by way of re-warding my industry, with her own olive hands ornamented the crown with a band of flame-coloured ribbon; the two long ends of which streaming be-hind, sailor-fashion, still preserved for me the Eastern title bestowed by Long Ghost.

CHAPTER LXXV

A RAMBLE THROUGH THE SETTLEMENT

THE following morning, making our toilets carefully, we donned our sombreros, and sallied out on a tour. Without meaning to reveal our designs upon the court, our principal object was, to learn what chances there were for white men to obtain employment under the queen. On this head, it is true, we had questioned Po-Po; but his answers had been very discouraging; so we deter-mined to obtain further information elsewhere.

But first, to give some little description of the village.

The settlement of Partoowye is nothing more than some eighty houses, scattered here and there, in the midst of an immense grove, where the trees have been thinned out, and the underbrush cleared away. Through the grove flows a stream; and the principal avenue crosses it; over an elastic bridge of coco-nut trunks, laid together side by side. The avenue is broad and ser-pentine; well shaded, from one end to the other; and as pretty a place for a morning promenade, as any lounger could wish. The houses, constructed with-out the slightest regard to the road, peep into view from among the trees on either side; some looking you right in the face as you pass, and others, with-out any manners, turning their backs. Occasionally, you observe a rural retreat, enclosed by a picket of bamboos, or with a solitary pane of glass mas-sively framed in the broadside of the dwelling, or with a rude, strange-looking door, swinging upon dislocated wooden hinges. Otherwise, the dwellings are built in the original style of the natives; and never mind how mean and filthy some of them may appear within, they all look picturesque enough without.

As we sauntered along, the people we met saluted us pleasantly, and in-vited us into their houses; and in this way we made a good many brief morn-ing calls. But the hour could not have been the fashionable one in Partoowye; since the ladies were invariably in dishabille. But they always gave us a cordial reception, and were particularly polite to the doctor; caressing him, and amorously hanging about his neck; wonderfully taken up, in short, with a gay handkerchief he wore there. Arfretee had that morning bestowed it upon the pious youth.

With some exceptions the general appearance of the natives of Partoowye, was far better than that of the inhabitants of Papeetee: a circumstance only to be imputed to their restricted intercourse with foreigners.

Strolling on, we turned a sweep of the road, when the doctor gave a start; and no wonder. Right before us, in the grove, was a block of houses: regular square frames, boarded over, furnished with windows and doorways, and two stories high. We ran up, and found them fast going to decay; very dingy, and here and there covered with moss; no sashes nor doors; and on one side, the entire block had settled down nearly a foot. On going into the basement, we looked clean up through the unboarded timbers to the roof; where rays of light, glimmering through many a chink, illuminated the cobwebs which swung all round.

The whole interior was dark, and close. Burrowing among some old mats in one corner, like a parcel of Gipsies in a ruin, were a few vagabond natives. They had their dwelling here.

Curious to know, who on earth could have been thus trying to improve the value of real estate in Partoowye, we made inquiries; and learned that, some years previous, the block had been thrown up by a veritable Yankee (one might have known that), a house carpenter by trade, and a bold, enterprising fellow by nature.

Put ashore from his ship, sick, he first went to work and got well; then sallied out with chisel and plane, and made himself generally useful. A sober, steady man, it seems, he at last obtained the confidence of several chiefs, and soon filled them with all sorts of ideas concerning the alarming want of public spirit in the people of Imeeo. More especially did he dwell upon the humiliating fact of their living in paltry huts of bamboo, when magnificent palaces of boards might so easily be mortised together.

In the end, these representations so far prevailed with one old chief, that the carpenter was engaged to build a batch of these wonderful palaces. Provided with plenty of men, he at once set to work: built a saw-mill among the mountains, felled trees, and sent over to Papeetee for nails.

Presto! the castle rose; but alas, the roof was hardly on, when the Yankee's patron, having speculated beyond his means, broke all to pieces, and was absolutely unable to pay one "plug" of tobacco in the pound. His failure involved the carpenter, who sailed away from his creditors in the very next ship that touched at the harbour.

The natives despised the rickety palace of boards; and often lounged by, wagging their heads, and jeering.

We were told that the queen's residence was at the extreme end of the village; so, without waiting for the doctor to procure a fiddle, we suddenly resolved upon going thither at once, and learning whether any privy counsellorships were vacant.

Now, although there was a good deal of my waggish comrade's nonsense about what has been said concerning our expectations of court preferment, we nevertheless, really thought that something to our advantage might turn up in that quarter.

On approaching the palace grounds, we found them rather peculiar. A broad pier of hewn coral rocks was built right out into the water; and upon this, and extending into a grove adjoining, were some eight or ten very large native houses, constructed in the handsomest style, and enclosed together by a low picket of bamboos, which embraced a considerable area.

Throughout the Society Islands, the residences of the chiefs are mostly found in the immediate vicinity of the sea; a site which gives them the full benefit of a cooling breeze; nor are they so liable to the annoyance of insects; besides enjoying, when they please, the fine shade afforded by the neighbouring groves, always most luxuriant near the water.

Lounging about the grounds, were some sixty or eighty handsomely dressed natives, men and women; some reclining on the shady side of the houses, others under the trees, and a small group conversing close by the railing, facing us.

We went up to the latter; and giving the usual salutation, were on the point of vaulting over the bamboos, when they turned upon us angrily, and said we could not enter. We stated our earnest desire to see the queen; hinting that we were bearers of important dispatches. But it was to no purpose; and not a little vexed, we were obliged to return to Po-Po's without effecting anything.

CHAPTER LXXVI

AN ISLAND JILT—WE VISIT THE SHIP

Upon arriving home, we fully laid open to Po-Po our motives in visiting Taloo, and begged his friendly advice. In his broken English, he cheerfully gave us all the information we needed.

It was true, he said, that the queen entertained some idea of making a stand against the French; and it was currently reported, also, that several chiefs from Borabora, Huwyenee, Raiatair, and Tahar, the leeward islands of the group, were at that very time taking counsel with her, as to the expediency of organizing a general movement throughout the entire cluster, with a view of anticipating any further encroachments on the part of the invaders Should warlike measures be actually decided upon, it was quite certain that Pomaree would be glad to enlist all the foreigners she could; but as to her making officers of either the doctor or me, that was out of the question; because, already, a number of Europeans, well known to her, had volunteered as such. Concerning our getting immediate access to the queen, Po-po told us it was rather doubtful; she living at that time very retire ', in poor health and spirits, and averse to receiving calls. Previous to her misfortunes, however, no one, however humble, was denied admittance to her presence; sailors, even, attended her levees.

Not at all disheartened by these things, we concluded to kill time in Partoowye, until some event turned up more favourable to our projects. So that very day we sallied out on an excursion to the ship, which, lying land-locked, far up the bay, yet remained to be visited.

Passing, on our route, a long, low shed, a voice, hailed us—"White men ahoy!" Turning round, who should we see but a rosy-cheeked Englishman (you could tell his country at a glance), up to his knees in shavings, and planing away at a bench. He turned out to be a runaway ship's carpenter, recently from Tahiti, and now doing a profitable business in Imeeo, by fitting up the dwellings of opulent chiefs with cupboards and other conveniences, and once in a while trying his hand at a lady's work-box. He had been in the settlement but a few months, and already possessed houses and lands.

But though blessed with prosperity and high health, there was one thing wanting—a wife. And when he came to speak of the matter, his countenance fell, and he leaned dejectedly upon his plane.

"It's too bad!" he sighed, "to wait three long years; and all the while, dear little Lullee living in the same house with that infernal chief from Tahar!"

Our curiosity was piqued; the poor carpenter, then, had been falling in love with some island coquette, who was going to jilt him.

But such was not the case. There was a law prohibiting, under a heavy penalty, the marriage of a native with a foreigner, unless the latter, after being three years a resident on the island, was willing to affirm his settled intention of remaining for life.

William was therefore in a sad way. He told us that he might have married the girl half-a-dozen times, had it not been for this odious law; but, latterly, she had become less loving and more giddy, particularly with the strangers from Tahar. Desperately smitten, and desirous of securing her at all hazards, he had proposed to the damsel's friends a nice little arrangement, introductory to marriage; but they would not hear of it; besides, if the pair were discovered living together upon such a footing, they would be liable to a degrading punishment:—sent to work making stone walls and opening roads for the queen.

Doctor Long Ghost was all sympathy. "Bill, my good fellow," said he, tremulously, "let *me* go and talk to her." But Bill, declining the offer, would not even inform us where his charmer lived.

Leaving the disconsolate Willie planing a plank of New Zealand pine (an importation from the Bay of Islands), and thinking the while of Lullee, we went on our way. How his suit prospered in the end, we never learned.

Going from Po-Po's house toward the anchorage of the harbour of Taloo, you catch no glimpse of the water, until coming out from deep groves, you all at once find yourself upon the beach. A bay, considered by many voyagers the most beautiful in the South Seas, then lies before you. You stand upon one side of what seems a deep, green river, flowing through mountain passes to the sea. Right opposite, a majestic promontory divides the inlet from another, called after its discoverer, Captain Cook. The face of this promontory toward Taloo is one verdant wall; and at its base the waters lie still, and fathomless. On the left hand, you just catch a peep of the widening mouth of the bay, the break in the reef by which ships enter, and beyond, the sea. To the right, the inlet, sweeping boldly round the promontory, runs far away into the land; where, save in one direction, the hills close in on every side, knee-deep in verdure, and shooting aloft in grotesque peaks. The open space lies at the head of the bay; in the distance it extends into a broad, hazy plain lying at the foot of an amphitheatre of hills. Here is the large sugar plantation previously alluded to. Beyond the first range of hills, you descry the sharp pinnacles of the interior; and among these, the same silent Marling-spike, which we so often admired from the other side of the island.

All alone in the harbour lay the good ship *Leviathan*. We jumped into the canoe; and paddled off to her. Though early in the afternoon, everything was quiet; but upon mounting the side, we found four or five sailors lounging about the forecastle, under an awning. They gave us no very cordial reception; and though otherwise, quite hearty in appearance, seemed to assume a look of ill humour on purpose to honour our arrival. There was much eagerness to learn whether we wanted to "ship"; and by the unpleasant accounts they gave of the vessel, they seemed desirous to prevent such a thing, if possible.

We asked where the rest of the ship's company were; a gruff old fellow made answer, "One boat's crew of 'em is gone to Davy Jones's locker:—went off after a whale, last cruise, and never come back agin. All the starboard watch ran away last night, and the skipper's ashore kitching 'em."

"And it's *shipping* ye're after, my jewels, is it?" cried a curly-pated little Belfast sailor, coming up to us, "thin arrah! my livelies, jist be after sailing ashore in a jiffy:—the divil of a skipper will carry yees both to sea, whether or no. Be off wid ye, thin, darlints, and steer clear of the likes of this bally-hoo of blazes as long as ye live. They murther us here everyday, and starve us into the bargain. Here, Dick, lad, harl the poor divils' canow alongside; and paddle away wid yees for dear life."

But we loitered awhile, listening to more inducements to ship; and at last concluded to stay to supper. My sheath-knife never cut into better sea-beef than that which we found lying in the kid in the forecastle. The bread, too, was hard, dry, and brittle as glass; and there was plenty of both.

While we were below, the mate of the vessel called out for some one to come on deck. I liked his voice. Hearing it was as good as a look at his face. It betokened a true sailor, and no taskmaster.

The appearance of the *Leviathan* herself was quite pleasing. Like all large, comfortable old whalers, she had a sort of motherly look:—broad in the beam, flush decks, and four chubby boats hanging at the breast. Her sails were furled loosely upon the yards, as if they had been worn long, and fitted easy; her shrouds swung negligently slack; and as for the "running rigging," it never worked hard as it does in some of your "dandy ships," jamming in the sheaves of blocks, like Chinese slippers, too small to be useful; on the contrary, the ropes ran glibly through, as if they had many a time travelled the same road, and were used to it.

When evening came, we dropped into our canoe, and paddled ashore; fully convinced that the good ship never deserved the name which they gave her.

CHAPTER LXXVII

A PARTY OF ROVERS—LITTLE LOO AND THE DOCTOR

WHILE in Partoowye, we fell in with a band of six veteran rovers, prowling about the village and harbour, who had just come overland from another part of the island.

A few weeks previous, they had been paid off, at Papeetee, from a whaling vessel, on board of which they had, six months before, shipped for a single cruise; that is to say, to be discharged at the next port. Their cruise was a famous one; and each man stepped upon the beach at Tahiti, jingling his dollars in a sock.

Weary at last of the shore, and having some money left, they clubbed, and purchased a sail-boat; proposing a visit to a certain uninhabited island, concerning which they had heard strange and golden stories. Of course, they never could think of going to sea without a medicine-chest filled with flasks of spirits, and a small cask of the same in the hold, in case the chest should give out.

Away they sailed; hoisted a flag of their own, and gave three times three, as they staggered out of the bay of Papeetee with a strong breeze, and under all the "muslin" they could carry.

Evening coming on, and feeling in high spirits, and no ways disposed to

sleep, they concluded to make a night of it; which they did; all hands getting tipsy, and the two masts going over the side about midnight, to the tune of

"Sailing down, sailing down,
On the coast of *Barbaree.'*

Fortunately, one worthy could stand, by holding on to the tiller; and the
rest managed to crawl about, and hack away the lanyards of the rigging, so
as to break clear from the fallen spars.   While thus employed, two sailors got
tranquilly over the side, and went plumb to the bottom; under the erroneous
impression, that they were stepping upon an imaginary wharf, to get at their
work better.   .
After this, it blew quite a gale; and the commodore, at the helm, instinctively kept the boat before the wind; and by so doing, ran over for the opposite island of Imeeo.   Crossing the channel, by almost a miracle they went
straight through an opening in the reef, and shot upon a ledge of coral, where
the waters were tolerably smooth.   Here, they lay until morning, when the natives came off to them in their canoes.   By the help of the islanders, the schooner
was hove over on her beam-ends; when, finding the bottom knocked to pieces,
the adventurers sold the boat for a trifle to the chief of the district, and went
ashore, rolling before them their precious cask of spirits.   Its contents soon
evaporated, and they came to Partoowye.
The day after encountering these fellows, we were strolling among the
groves in the neighbourhood, when we came across several parties of natives,
armed with clumsy muskets, rusty cutlasses, and outlandish clubs.   They were
beating the bushes, shouting aloud, and apparently, trying to scare somebody.   They were in pursuit of the strangers, who, having in a single night
set at naught all the laws of the place, had thought best to decamp.
In the daytime, Po-Po's house was as pleasant a lounge as one could wish.
So, after strolling about, and seeing all there was to be seen, we spent the
greater part of our mornings there; breakfasting late, and dining about two
hours after noon.   Sometimes we lounged on the floor of ferns, smoking, and
telling stories; of which the doctor has as many as a half-pay captain in the
army.   Sometimes we chatted, as well as we could, with the natives; and,
one day—joy to us!—Po-Po brought in three volumes of Smollett's novels,
which had been found in the chest of a sailor, who sometime previous had
died on the island.
Amelia!—Peregrine!—you hero of rogues, Count Fathom!—what a debt
do we owe you!
I know not, whether it was the reading of these romances, or the want of
some sentimental pastime, which led the doctor, about this period, to lay siege
to the heart of the little Loo.
Now, as I have said before, the daughter of Po-Po was most cruelly reserved, and never deigned to notice us.   Frequently I addressed her with a
long face, and an air of the profoundest and most distant respect—but in vain;
she wouldn't even turn up her pretty olive nose.   Ah! it's quite plain, thought
I; she knows very well what graceless dogs sailors are, and won't have anything
to do with us.
But thus thought not my comrade.   Bent he was upon firing the cold
glitter of Loo's passionless eyes.
He opened the campaign with admirable tact: making cautious approaches,
and content, for three days, with ogling the nymph, for about five minutes after

every meal. On the fourth day, he asked her a question; on the fifth she dropped a nut of ointment, and he picked it up and gave it to her; on the sixth, he went over and sat down within three yards of the couch where she lay; and, on the memorable morn of the seventh, he proceeded to open his batteries in form.

The damsel was reclining on the ferns; one hand supporting her cheek, and the other listlessly turning over the leaves of a Tahitian Bible. The doctor approached.

Now the chief disadvantage under which he laboured, was his almost complete ignorance of the love vocabulary of the island. But French counts, they say, make love delightfully in broken English; and what hindered the doctor from doing the same in dulcet Tahitian? So at it he went.

"Ah!" said he, smiling bewitchingly, "oee mickonaree? oee ready Biblee?"

No answer; not even a look.

"Ah! maitai! very goody ready Biblee mickonaree."

Loo, without stirring, began reading, in a low tone, to herself.

"Mickonaree Biblee ready goody maitai," once more observed the doctor, ingeniously transposing his words for the third time.

But all to no purpose; Loo gave no sign.

He paused despairingly; but it would never do to give up; so he threw himself at full length beside her, and audaciously commenced turning over the leaves.

Loo gave a start, just one little start, barely perceptible, and then fumbling something in her hand, lay perfectly motionless; the doctor rather frightened at his own temerity, and knowing not what to do next. At last, he placed one arm cautiously about her waist; almost in the same instant he bounded to his feet, with a cry; the little witch had pierced him with a thorn. But there she lay, just as quietly as ever; turning over the leaves, and reading to herself.

My long friend raised the siege incontinently, and made a disorderly retreat to the place where I reclined, looking on.

I am pretty sure that Loo must have related this occurrence to her father, who came in shortly afterward; for he looked queerly at the doctor. But he said nothing; and, in ten minutes, was quite as affable as ever. As for Loo, there was not the slightest change in her; and the doctor, of course, for ever afterward held his peace.

CHAPTER LXXVIII

MRS. BELL

ONE day, taking a pensive afternoon stroll along one of the many bridle-paths which wind among the shady groves in the neighbourhood of Taloo, I was startled by a sunny apparition. It was that of a beautiful young Englishwoman, charmingly dressed, and mounted upon a spirited little white pony. Switching a green branch, she came cantering toward me.

I looked round to see whether I could possibly be in Polynesia. There were the palm-trees; but how to account for the lady?

Stepping to one side, as the apparition drew near, I made a polite obeisance.

It gave me a bold, rosy look; and then, with a gay air, patted its palfrey, crying out, "Fly away, Willie!" and galloped among the trees.

I would have followed; but Willie's heels were making such a pattering among the dry leaves, that pursuit would have been useless.

So I went straight home to Po-Po's, and related my adventure to the doctor.

The next day, our inquiries resulted in finding out, that the stranger had been on the island about two years; that she came from Sydney; and was the wife of Mr. Bell (happy dog!), the proprietor of the sugar plantation, to which I have previously referred.

To the sugar plantation we went, the same day.

The country round about was very beautiful: a level basin of verdure, surrounded by sloping hillsides. The sugar-cane—of which there were about one hundred acres, in various stages of cultivation—looked thrifty. A considerable tract of land, however, which seemed to have been formerly tilled, was now abandoned.

The place where they extracted the saccharine matter, was under an immense shed of bamboos. Here we saw several clumsy pieces of machinery for breaking the cane; also great kettles for boiling the sugar. But, at present, nothing was going on. Two or three natives were lounging in one of the kettles, smoking; the other was occupied by three sailors from the *Leviathan*, playing cards.

While we were conversing with these worthies, a stranger approached. He was a sun-burnt, romantic-looking European, dressed in a loose suit of nankeen; his fine throat and chest were exposed, and he sported a Guayaquil hat, with a brim like a Chinese umbrella. This was Mr. Bell. He was very civil; showed us the grounds, and, taking us into a sort of arbour, to our surprise, offered to treat us to some wine. People often do the like; but Mr. Bell did more: he produced the bottle. It was spicy sherry; and we drank out of the halves of fresh citron melons. Delectable goblets!

The wine was a purchase from the French in Tahiti.

Now all this was extremely polite in Mr. Bell; still, we came to see *Mrs.* Bell. But she proved to be a phantom, indeed; having left the same morning for Papeetee, on a visit to one of the missionaries' wives there.

I went home, much chagrined.

To be frank, my curiosity had been wonderfully piqued concerning the lady. In the first place, she was the most beautiful white woman I ever saw in Polynesia. But this is saying nothing. She had such eyes, such moss-roses in her cheeks, such a divine air in the saddle, that, to my dying day, I shall never forget Mrs. Bell.

The sugar-planter himself was young, robust, and handsome. So, merrily may the little Bells increase, and multiply, and make music in the Land of Imeeo.

CHAPTER LXXIX

TALOO CHAPEL—HOLDING COURT IN POLYNESIA

In Partoowye is to be seen one of the best constructed and handsomest chapels in the South Seas. Like the buildings of the palace, it stands upon an artificial pier, presenting a semi-circular sweep to the bay. The chapel is built of hewn blocks of coral; a substance which, although extremely friable, is said to harden by exposure to the atmosphere. To a stranger, these blocks look extremely curious. Their surface is covered with strange fossil-like impressions, the seal of which must have been set before the flood. Very nearly white when hewn from the reefs, the coral darkens with age; so that several churches in Polynesia now look almost as sooty and venerable as famed St. Paul's.

In shape, the chapel is an octagon, with galleries all round. It will seat, perhaps, four hundred people. Everything within is stained a tawny red; and there being but few windows, or rather embrasures, the dusky benches and galleries, and the tall spectre of a pulpit look anything but cheerful.

On Sundays, we always went to worship here. Going in the family suite of Po-Po, we, of course, maintained a most decorous exterior; and hence, by all the elderly people of the village, were doubtless regarded as pattern young men.

Po-Po's seat was in a snug corner; and it being particularly snug, in the immediate vicinity of one of the Palm pillars supporting the gallery, I invariably leaned against it: Po-po and his lady on one side, the doctor and the dandy on the other, and the children and poor relations seated behind.

As for Loo, instead of sitting (as she ought to have done) by her good father and mother, she must needs run up into the gallery, and sit with a parcel of giddy creatures of her own age; who, all through the sermon, did nothing but look down on the congregation; pointing out, and giggling at the queer-looking old ladies in dowdy bonnets and scant tunics. But Loo, herself, was never guilty of these improprieties.

Occasionally during the week, they have afternoon service in the chapel, when the natives themselves have something to say; although their auditors are but few. An introductory prayer being offered by the missionary, and a hymn sung, communicants rise in their places, and exhort in pure Tahitian, and with wonderful tone and gesture. And among them all, Deacon Po-Po, though he talked most, was the one whom you would have liked best to hear. Much would I have given to have understood some of his impassioned bursts; when he tossed his arms overhead, stamped, scowled, and glared, till he looked like the very Angel of Vengeance.

"Deluded man!" sighed the doctor, on one of these occasions, "I fear he takes the fanatical view of the subject." One thing was certain: when Po-Po spoke, all listened; a great deal more than could be said for the rest; for under the discipline of two or three I could mention, some of the audience napped; others fidgeted; a few yawned; and one irritable old gentleman, in a night-cap of coco-nut leaves, used to clutch his long staff in a state of excessive nervousness, and stride out of the church; making all the noise he could, to emphasize his disgust.

Right adjoining the chapel is an immense, rickety building, with windows and shutters, and a half-decayed board flooring laid upon trunks of palm-trees. They called it a school-house; but as such we never saw it occupied. It was often used as a court-room, however; and here we attended several trials; among others, that of a decayed naval officer, and a young girl of fourteen; the latter, charged with having been very naughty on a particular occasion, set forth in the pleadings; and the former, with having aided and abetted her in her naughtiness, and with other misdemeanours.

The foreigner was a tall, military-looking fellow, with a dark cheek and black whiskers. According to his own account, he had lost a colonial armed brig on the coast of New Zealand; and since then, had been leading the life of a man about town, among the islands of the Pacific.

The doctor wanted to know why he did not go home and report the loss of his brig; but Captain Crash, as they called him, had some incomprehensible reasons for not doing so, about which he could talk by the hour, and no one be any the wiser. Probably, he was a discreet man, and thought it best to waive an interview with the lords of the admiralty.

For some time past, this extremely suspicious character, had been carrying on the illicit trade in French wines and brandies, smuggled over from the men-of-war lately touching at Tahiti. In a grove near the anchorage, he had a rustic shanty and arbour; where, in quiet times, when no ships were in Taloo, a stray native once in a while got boozy, and staggered home, catching at the coco-nut trees as he went. The captain himself lounged under a tree during the warm afternoons, pipe in mouth; thinking, perhaps, over old times, and occasionally feeling his shoulders for his lost epaulets.

But, sail ho! a ship is descried coming into the bay. Soon, she drops her anchor in its waters; and the next day Captain Crash entertains the sailors in his grove. And rare times they have of it:—drinking and quarrelling together, as sociably as you please.

Upon one of these occasions, the crew of the *Leviathan* made so prodigious a tumult, that the natives, indignant at the insult offered their laws, plucked up a heart, and made a dash at the rioters, one hundred strong. The sailors fought like tigers; but were at last overcome, and carried before a native tribunal; which, after a mighty clamour, dismissed everybody but Captain Crash, who was asserted to be the author of the disorders.

Upon this charge, then, he had been placed in confinement against the coming on of the assizes; the judges being expected to lounge along in the course of the afternoon. While waiting his Honour's arrival, numerous additional offences were preferred against the culprit (mostly by the old women); among others was the bit of a slip in which he stood implicated along with the young lady. Thus, in Polynesia as elsewhere;—charge a man with one misdemeanour, and all his peccadilloes are raked up and assorted before him.

Going to the school-house for the purpose of witnessing the trial, the din of it assailed our ears a long way off; and upon entering the building, we were almost stunned. About five hundred natives were present; each, apparently, having something to say, and determined to say it. His Honour—a handsome, benevolent-looking old man—sat cross-legged on a little platform; seemingly resigned with all Christian submission to the uproar. He was an hereditary chief in this quarter of the island, and judge for life in the district of Partoowye.

There were several cases coming on; but the captain and girl were first tried together. They were mixing freely with the crowd; and as it afterward turned out that every one—no matter who—had a right to address the court, for aught we knew they might have been arguing their own case. At what precise moment the trial began, it would be hard to say. There was no swearing of witnesses, and no regular jury. Now and then somebody leaped up and shouted out something which might have been evidence; the rest, meanwhile, keeping up an incessant jabbering. Presently, the old judge himself began to get excited; and springing to his feet, ran in among the crowd, wagging his tongue as hard as anybody.

The tumult lasted about twenty minutes; and toward the end of it, Captain

Crash might have been seen, tranquilly regarding, from his Honour's platform, the judicial uproar, in which his fate was about being decided.

The result of all this was, that both he and the girl were found guilty. The latter was adjudged to make six mats for the queen; and the former, in consideration of his manifold offences, being deemed incorrigible, was sentenced to eternal banishment from the island. Both these decrees seemed to originate in the general hubbub. His Honour, however, appeared to have considerable authority, and it was quite plain that the decision received his approval.

The above penalties were by no means indiscriminately inflicted. The missionaries have prepared a sort of penal tariff to facilitate judicial proceedings. It costs so many days' labour on the Broom Road to indulge in the pleasures of the calabash; so many fathoms of stone wall to steal a musket; and so on to the end of the catalogue. The judge being provided with a book, in which all these matters are cunningly arranged, the thing is vastly convenient. For instance: a crime is proved,—say, bigamy; turn to letter B.—and there you have it. Bigamy:—forty days on the Broom Road, and twenty mats for the queen. Read the passage aloud, and sentence is pronounced.

After taking part in the first trial, the other delinquents present were put upon their own; in which, also, the convicted culprits seemed to have quite as much to say as the rest. A rather strange proceeding; but strictly in accordance with the glorious English principle, that every man should be tried by his peers.

They were all found guilty.

CHAPTER LXXX

QUEEN POMAREE

It is well to learn something about people before being introduced to them; and so, we will here give some account of Pomaree and her family.

Every reader of Cook's Voyages must remember "Otoo," who, in that navigator's time, was king of the larger peninsula of Tahiti. Subsequently, assisted by the muskets of the *Bounty's* men, he extended his rule over the entire island. This Otoo, before his death, had his name changed into Pomaree, which has ever since been the royal patronymic.

He was succeeded by his son, Pomaree II, the most famous prince in the annals of Tahiti. Though a sad debauchee and drunkard, and even charged with unnatural crimes, he was a great friend of the missionaries, and one of their very first proselytes. During the religious wars into which he was hurried, by his zeal for the new faith, he was defeated, and expelled from the island. After a short exile, he returned from Imeeo, with an army of eight hundred warriors; and, in the battle of Narii, routed the rebellious pagans with great slaughter, and re-established himself upon the throne. Thus, by force of arms, was Christianity finally triumphant in Tahiti.

Pomaree II dying, in 1821, was succeeded by his infant son, under the title of Pomaree III. This young prince survived his father but six years; and the government then descended to his elder sister, Aimata, the present queen, who is commonly called Pomaree Vahinee I, or the first female Pomaree. Her majesty must be now upward of thirty years of age. She has been twice married. Her first husband was a son of the old King of Tahar, an island about one hundred miles from Tahiti. This proving an unhappy alliance, the pair were soon after divorced. The present husband of the queen is a chief of Imeeo.

The reputation of Pomaree is not what it ought to be. She, and also her mother, were, for a long time, excommunicated members of the Church; and the former, I believe, still is. Among other things, her conjugal fidelity is far from being unquestioned. Indeed, it was upon this ground, chiefly, that she was excluded from the communion of the Church.

Previous to her misfortunes, she spent the greater portion of her time sailing about from one island to another, attended by a licentious court; and wherever she went, all manner of games and festivities celebrated her arrival.

She was always given to display. For several years, the maintenance of a regiment of household troops drew largely upon the royal exchequer. They were trouserless fellows, in a uniform of calico shirts and pasteboard hats; armed with muskets of all shapes and calibres, and commanded by a great noisy chief, strutting it in a coat of fiery red. These heroes escorted their mistress whenever she went abroad.

Some time ago, the queen received from her English sister, Victoria, a very showy, though uneasy, headdress—a crown; probably made to order, at some tinman's in London. Having no idea of reserving so pretty a bauble for coronation days, which come so seldom, her majesty sported it whenever she appeared in public; and, to show her familiarity with European customs, politely touched it to all foreigners of distinction—whaling captains, and the like—whom she happened to meet in her evening walk on the Broom Road.

The arrival and departure of royalty were always announced at the palace by the court artilleryman—a fat old gentleman, who, in a prodigious hurry and perspiration, discharged minute fowling-pieces, as fast as he could load and fire the same.

The Tahitian princess leads her husband a hard life. Poor fellow! he not only caught a queen, but a Tartar, when he married her. The style by which he is addressed is rather significant—"Pomaree-Tanee" (Pomaree's man). All things considered, as appropriate a title for a king-consort as could be hit upon.

If ever there were a henpecked husband, that man is the prince. One day, his cara-sposa, giving audience to a deputation from the captains of the vessels lying in Papeetee, he ventured to make a suggestion which was very displeasing to her. She turned round, and, boxing his ears, told him to go over to his beggarly island of Imeoo, if he wanted to give himself airs.

Cuffed and contemned, poor Tanee flies to the bottle, or rather, to the calabash, for solace. Like his wife and mistress, he drinks more than he ought.

Six or seven years ago, when an American man-of-war was lying at Papeetee, the town was thrown into the greatest commotion by a conjugal assault and battery, made upon the sacred person of Pomaree by her intoxicated Tanee.

Captain Bob once told me the story. And by way of throwing more spirit into the description, as well as to make up for his oral deficiencies, the old man went through the accompanying action: myself being proxy for the Queen of Tahiti.

It seems, that on a Sunday morning, being dismissed contemptuously from the royal presence, Tanee was accosted by certain good fellows, friends and boon companions, who condoled with him on his misfortunes—railed against the queen, and finally dragged him away to an illicit vender of spirits, in whose house the party got gloriously mellow. In this state, Pomaree Vahinee I was the topic upon which all dilated—"A vixen of a queen," probably suggested one. "It's infamous," said another; and "I'd have satisfaction," cried a third.

"And so I will!"—Tanee must have hiccoughed; for off he went; and ascertaining that his royal half was out riding, he mounted his horse, and galloped after her.

Near the outskirts of the town, a cavalcade of women came cantering toward him, in the centre of which was the object of his fury. Smiting his beast right and left, he dashed in among them; completely overturning one of the party, leaving her on the field, and dispersing everybody else except Pomaree. Backing her horse dexterously, the incensed queen heaped upon him every scandalous epithet she could think of; until at last, the enraged Tanee leaped out of his saddle, caught Pomaree by her dress, and dragging her to the earth, struck her repeatedly in the face, holding on meanwhile by the hair of her head. He was proceeding to strangle her on the spot, when the cries of the frightened attendants brought a crowd of natives to the rescue, who bore the nearly insensible queen away.

But his frantic rage was not yet sated. He ran to the palace; and before it could be prevented, demolished a valuable supply of crockery, a recent present from abroad. In the act of perpetrating some other atrocity, he was seized from behind, and carried off with rolling eyes and foaming at the mouth.

This is a fair example of a Tahitian in a passion. Though the mildest of mortals in general, and hard to be roused, when once fairly up, he is possessed with a thousand devils.

The day following, Tanee was privately paddled over to Imeoo, in a canoe; where, after remaining in banishment for a couple of weeks, he was allowed to return, and once more give in his domestic adhesion.

Though Pomaree Vahinee I be something of a Jezebel in private life, in her public rule, she is said to have been quite lenient and forbearing. This was her true policy; for an hereditary hostility to her family had always lurked in the hearts of many powerful chiefs, the descendants of the old Kings of Taiarboo, dethroned by her grandfather Otoo. Chief among these, and in fact the leader of his party, was Poofai; a bold, able man, who made no secret of his enmity to the missionaries, and the government which they controlled. But while events were occurring calculated to favour the hopes of the disaffected and turbulent, the arrival of the French gave a most unexpected turn to affairs.

During my sojourn in Tahiti, a report was rife—which I knew to originate with what is generally called the "missionary party"—that Poofai and some other chiefs of note, had actually agreed, for a stipulated bribe, to acquiesce in the appropriation of their country. But subsequent events have rebutted the calumny. Several of these very men have recently died in battle against the French.

Under the sovereignty of the Pomarees, the great chiefs of Tahiti were something like the barons of King John. Holding feudal sway over their patrimonial valleys, and on account of their descent, warmly beloved by the people, they frequently cut off the royal revenues by refusing to pay the customary tribute due from them as vassals.

The truth is, that with the ascendancy of the missionaries, the regal office in Tahiti lost much of its dignity and influence. In the days of Paganism, it was supported by all the power of a numerous priesthood, and was solemnly connected with the entire superstitious idolatry of the land. The monarch claimed to be a sort of by-blow of Tararroa, the Saturn of the Polynesian mythology, and cousin-german to inferior deities. His person was thrice holy; if he entered an ordinary dwelling, never mind for how short a time, it was demolished when he left; no common mortal being thought worthy to inhabit it afterward.

"I'm a greater man than King George," said the incorrigible young Otoo, to the first missionaries; "he rides on a horse, and I on a man." Such was the case. He travelled post through his dominions on the shoulders of his subjects; and relays of immortal beings were provided in all the valleys.

But alas! how times have changed; how transient human greatness. Some years since, Pomaree Vahinee I, the grand-daughter of the proud Otoo, went into the laundry business; publicly soliciting, by her agents, the washing of the linen belonging to the officers of ships touching in her harbours.

It is a significant fact, and one worthy of record, that while the influence of the English missionaries at Tahiti has tended to so great a diminution of the regal dignity there, that of the American missionaries at the Sandwich Islands, has been purposely exerted to bring about a contrary result.

CHAPTER LXXXI

WE VISIT THE COURT

IT was about the middle of the second month of the Hegira, and therefore some five weeks after our arrival in Partoowye, that we at last obtained admittance to the residence of the queen.

It happened thus. There was a Marquesan in the train of Pomaree, who officiated as nurse to her children. According to the Tahitian custom, the royal youngsters are carried about until it requires no small degree of strength to stand up under them. But Marbonna was just the man for this—large and muscular, well made as a statue, and with an arm like a degenerate Tahitian's thigh.

Embarking at his native island, as a sailor, on board of a French whaler, he afterward ran away from the ship at Tahiti; where, being seen and admired by Pomaree, he had been prevailed upon to enlist in her service.

Often, when visiting the grounds, we saw him walking about in the shade, carrying two handsome boys, who encircled his neck with their arms. Marbonna's face, tattooed as it was in the ornate style of his tribe, was as good as a picture-book to these young Pomarees. They delighted to trace with their fingers the outlines of the strange shapes there delineated.

The first time my eyes lighted upon the Marquesan, I knew his country in a moment; and hailing him in his own language, he turned round, surprised that a person so speaking should be a stranger. He proved to be a native of Tior, a glen of Nukuheva. I had visited the place more than once; and so, on the island of Imeeo, we met like old friends.

In my frequent conversations with him over the bamboo picket, I found this islander a philosopher of nature—a wild heathen, moralizing upon the vices and follies of the Christian court of Tahiti—a savage, scorning the degeneracy of the people among whom fortune had thrown him.

I was amazed at the national feelings of the man. No European, when abroad, could speak of his country with more pride than Marbonna. He assured me, again and again, that so soon as he had obtained sufficient money

to purchase twenty muskets, and as many bags of powder, he was going to
return to a place, with which Imeeo was not worthy to be compared.

It was Marbonna, who, after one or two unsuccessful attempts, at last
brought about our admission into the queen's grounds. Through a considerable
crowd, he conducted us along the pier to where an old man was sitting; to whom
he introduced us as a couple of "karhowrees" of his acquaintance, anxious to
see the sights of the palace. The venerable chamberlain stared at us, and
shook his head: the doctor, thinking he wanted a fee, placed a plug of tobacco
in his hand. This was ingratiating, and we were permitted to pass on. Upon
the point of entering one of the houses, Marbonna's name was shouted in half-
a-dozen different directions, and he was obliged to withdraw.

Thus left at the very threshold to shift for ourselves, my companion's assurance stood us in good stead. He stalked right in, and I followed. The
place was full of women, who, instead of exhibiting the surprise we expected,
accosted us as cordially as if we had called to take our Souchong with them,
by express invitation. In the first place, nothing would do but we must each
devour a calabash of "poee," and several roasted bananas. Pipes were then
lighted, and a brisk conversation ensued.

These ladies of the court, if not very polished, were surprisingly free and
easy in their manners; quite as much so as King Charles's Beauties. There was
one of them—an arch little miss, who could converse with us pretty fluently
—to whom we strove to make ourselves particularly agreeable, with the view
of engaging her services as cicerone.

As such, she turned out to be everything we could desire. No one disputing her will, every place was entered without ceremony, curtains brushed aside,
mats lifted, and each nook and corner explored. Whether the little damsel
carried her mistress' signet, that everything opened to her thus, I know not;
but Marbonna himself, the bearer of infants, could not have been half so
serviceable.

Among other houses which we visited, was one of large size and fine exterior;
the special residence of a European—formerly the mate of a merchant vessel,
—who had done himself the honour of marrying into the Pomaree family. The
lady he wedded being a near kinswoman of the queen, he became a permanent
member of her majesty's household. This adventurer rose late, dressed the-
atrically in calico and trinkets, assumed a dictatorial tone in conversation, and
was evidently upon excellent terms with himself.

We found him reclining on a mat, smoking a reedpipe of tobacco, in the midst
of an admiring circle of chiefs and ladies. He must have noticed our approach; but instead of rising and offering civilities, he went on talking and
smoking, without even condescending to look at us.

"His Highness feels his 'poee,' " carelessly observed the doctor. The rest
of the company gave us the ordinary salutation, our guide announcing us beforehand.

In answer to our earnest requests to see the queen, we were now conducted
to an edifice, by far the most spacious, in the enclosure. It was at least one
hundred and fifty feet in length, very wide, with low eaves, and an exceedingly
steep roof of pandannas leaves. There were neither doors nor windows—nothing along the sides but the slight posts supporting the rafters. Between these
posts, curtains of fine matting and tappa were rustling, all round; some of
them were festooned, or partly withdrawn, so as to admit light and air, and
afford a glimpse now and then of what was going on within.

Pushing aside one of the screens, we entered. The apartment was one immense hall; the long and lofty ridge-pole fluttering with fringed matting and tassels, full forty feet from the ground. Lounges of mats, piled one upon another, extended on either side; while here and there were slight screens, forming as many recesses, where groups of natives—all females—were reclining at their evening meal.

As we advanced, these various parties ceased their buzzing, and in explanation of our appearance among them, listened to a few cabalistic words from our guide.

The whole scene was a strange one; but what most excited our surprise, was the incongruous assemblage of the most costly objects from all quarters of the globe. Cheek by jowl, they lay beside the rudest native articles, without the slightest attempt at order. Superb writing-desks of rose-wood, inlaid with silver and mother-of-pearl; decanters and goblets of cut glass; embossed volumes of plates; gilded candelabras; sets of globes and mathematical instruments; the finest porcelain; richly mounted sabres and fowling-pieces; laced hats and sumptuous garments of all sorts, with numerous other matters of European manufacture, were strewn about among greasy calabashes half-filled with *"poee,"* rolls of old tappa and matting, paddles and fish-spears, and the ordinary furniture of a Tahitian dwelling.

All the articles first mentioned, were, doubtless, presents from foreign powers. They were more or less injured: the fowling-pieces and swords were rusted; the finest woods were scratched; and a folio volume of Hogarth lay open, with a coco-nut shell of some musty preparation capsized among the miscellaneous furniture of the Rake's apartment, where that inconsiderate young gentleman is being measured for a coat.

While we were amusing ourselves in this museum of curiosities, our conductor plucked us by the sleeve, and whispered, "Pomaree! Pomaree! aramai kow kow."

"She is coming to sup then," said the doctor, staring in the direction indicated. "What say you, Paul, suppose we step up?" Just then a curtain near by, lifted; and from a private building a few yards distant, the queen entered, unattended.

She wore a loose gown of blue silk, with two rich shawls, one red and the other yellow, tied about her neck. Her royal majesty was barefooted.

She was about the ordinary size, rather matronly; her features not very handsome; her mouth, voluptuous; but there was a care-worn expression in her face, probably attributable to her late misfortunes. From her appearance, one would judge her about forty; but she is not so old.

As the queen approached one of the recesses, her attendants hurried up, escorted her in, and smoothed the mats on which she at last reclined. Two girls soon appeared, carrying their mistress's repast; and then, surrounded by cut-glass and porcelain, and jars of sweetmeats and confections, Pomaree Vahinee I, the titular Queen of Tahiti, ate fish and poee out of her native calabashes, disdaining either knife or spoon.

"Come on," whispered Long Ghost, "let's have an audience at once;" and he was on the point of introducing himself, when our guide, quite alarmed, held him back, and implored silence. The other natives also interfered; and as he was pressing forward, raised such an outcry, that Pomaree lifted her eyes, and saw us for the first time.

She seemed surprised, and offended; and issuing an order in a commanding tone to several of her women waved us out of the house. Summary as the dismissal was, court etiquette, no doubt, required our compliance. We with-

drew; making a profound inclination as we disappeared behind the tappa
arras.

We departed the grounds without seeing Marbonna; and previous to
vaulting over the picket, fee'd our pretty guide, after a fashion of our own.
Looking round a few moments after, we saw the damsel escorted back by two
men, who seemed to have been sent after her. I trust she received nothing
more than a reprimand.

The next day Po-Po informed us that strict orders had been issued, to admit
no strangers within the palace precincts.

CHAPTER LXXXII

WHICH ENDS THE BOOK

DISAPPOINTED in going to court, we determined upon going to sea. It would
never do, longer to trespass on Po-Po's hospitality; and then, weary somewhat
of life in Imeeo, like all sailors ashore, I at last pined for the billows.

Now, if her crew were to be credited, the *Leviathan* was not the craft to our
mind. But I had seen the captain, and liked him. He was an uncommonly
tall, robust, fine-looking man, in the prime of life. There was a deep crimson
spot in the middle of each sunburnt cheek, doubtless the effect of his sea-pota-
tions. He was a Vineyarder, or native of the island of Martha's Vineyard (adjoining Nantucket), and—I would have sworn it—a sailor, and no tyrant.

Previous to this, we had rather avoided the *Leviathan's* men, when they came
ashore; but now, we purposely threw ourselves in their way, in order to learn
more of the vessel.

We became acquainted with the third mate, a Prussian, and an old merchant seaman—a right jolly fellow, with a face like a ruby. We took him to
Po-Po's, and gave him a dinner of baked pig and breadfruit; with pipes and
tobacco for dessert. The account he gave us of the ship, agreed with my own
surmises. A cosier old craft never floated; and the captain was the finest man
in the world. There was plenty to eat, too; and, at sea, nothing to do but sit
on the windlass and sail. The only bad trait about the vessel was this: she
had been launched under some baleful star; and so, was a luckless ship in the
fishery. She dropped her boats into the brine often enough, and they frequently got fast to the whales; but lance and harpoon almost invariably "drew"
when darted by the men of the *Leviathan*. But what of that? We would have
all the sport of chasing the monsters, with none of the detestable work which
follows their capture. So, hurrah for the coast of Japan! Thither the ship
was bound.

A word now, about the hard stories we heard, the first time we visited the
ship. They were nothing but idle fictions, got up by the sailors for the purpose of frightening us away, so as to oblige the captain, who was in want of
more hands, to lie the longer in a pleasant harbour.

The next time the Vineyarder came ashore, we flung ourselves in his path.
When informed of our desire to sail with him, he wanted to know our history;
and, above all, what countrymen we were. We said, that we had left a whaler
in Tahiti, some time previous; and, since then, had been—in the most praise-

worthy manner—employed upon a plantation. As for our country, sailors belong to no nation in particular; we were, on this occasion, both Yankees. Upon this he looked decidedly incredulous; and freely told us, that he verily believed we were both from Sydney.

Be it known here, that American sea captains, in the Pacific, are mortally afraid of these Sydney gentry; who, to tell the truth, wherever known, are in excessively bad odour. Is there a mutiny on board a ship in the South Seas, ten to one a Sydney man is the ringleader. Ashore, these fellows are equally riotous.

It was on this account, that we were anxious to conceal the fact of our having belonged to the *Julia;* though it annoyed me much, thus to deny the dashing little craft. For the same reason, also, the doctor fibbed about his birth-place.

Unfortunately, one part of our raiment—Arfretee's blue frocks—was deemed a sort of collateral evidence against us. For, curiously enough, an American sailor is generally distinguished by his red frock; and an English tar, by his blue one: thus reversing the national colours. The circumstance was pointed out by the captain; and we quickly explained the anomaly. But, in vain: he seemed inveterately prejudiced against us; and, in particular, eyed the doctor most distrustfully.

By way of propping the latter's pretensions, I was throwing out a hint concerning Kentucky, as a land of tall men, when our Vineyarder turned away abruptly, and desired to hear nothing more. It was evident that he took Long Ghost for an exceedingly problematical character.

Perceiving this, I resolved to see what a private interview would do. So, one afternoon, I found the captain smoking a pipe in the dwelling of a portly old native—one Mai-Mai—who, for a reasonable compensation, did the honours of Partoowye, to illustrious strangers.

His guest had just risen from a sumptuous meal of baked pig and taro pudding; and the remnants of the repast were still visible. Two reeking bottles, also, with their necks wrenched off, lay upon the mat. All this was encouraging; for, after a good dinner, one feels affluent and amiable, and peculiarly open to conviction. So, at all events, I found the noble Vineyarder.

I began by saying, that I called for the purpose of setting him right, touching certain opinions of his concerning the place of my nativity:—I was an American—thank Heaven!—and wanted to convince him of the fact.

After looking me in the eye for some time, and, by so doing, revealing an obvious unsteadiness in his own visual organs, he begged me to reach forth my arm. I did so; wondering what upon earth that useful member had to do with the matter in hand.

He placed his fingers upon my wrist; and holding them there for a moment, sprang to his feet; and, with much enthusiasm, pronounced me a Yankee, every beat of my pulse.

"Here, Mai-Mai!" he cried, "another bottle!" And when it came, with one stroke of a knife, he summarily beheaded it, and commanded me to drain it to the bottom. He then told me, that if I would come on board his vessel the following morning, I would find the ship's articles on the cabin transom.

This was getting along famously. But what was to become of the doctor?

I forthwith made an adroit allusion to my long friend. But it was worse than useless. The Vineyarder swore he would have nothing to do with him —he (my long friend) was a "bird" from Sydney, and nothing would make him (the man of little faith) believe otherwise.

I could not help loving the free-hearted captain; but indignant of this most unaccountable prejudice against my comrade, I abruptly took leave.

Upon informing the doctor of the result of the interview, he was greatly amused; and laughingly declared, that the Vineyarder must be a penetrating fellow. He then insisted upon my going to sea in the ship, since he well knew how anxious I was to leave. As for himself, on second thoughts, he was no sailor; and although "landsmen" very often compose part of a whaler's crew, he did not quite relish the idea of occupying a position so humble. In short, he had made up his mind to tarry awhile in Imeeo.

I turned the matter over; and at last decided upon quitting the island. The impulse urging me to sea once more, and the prospect of eventually reaching home, were too much to be resisted; especially, as the *Leviathan* was so comfortable a craft, was now bound on her last whaling cruise, and, in little more than a year's time, would be going round Cape Horn.

I did not, however, covenant to remain in the vessel for the residue of the voyage; which would have been needlessly binding myself. I merely stipulated for the coming cruise, leaving any subsequent movements unrestrained; for, there was no knowing that I might not change my mind, and prefer journeying home by short and easy stages.

The next day I paddled off to the ship, signed and sealed, and stepped ashore with my "advance"—fifteen Spanish dollars, tasselling the ends of my neck-handkerchief.

I forced half of the silver on Long Ghost; and having little use for the remainder, would have given it to Po-Po as some small return for his kindness; but, although he well knew the value of the coin, not a dollar would he accept.

In three days' time, the Prussian came to Po-Po's, and told us that the captain, having made good the number of his crew by shipping several islanders, had determined upon sailing with the land breeze, at dawn the following morning. These tidings were received in the afternoon. The doctor immediately disappeared, returning soon after with a couple of flasks of wine concealed in the folds of his frock. Through the agency of the Marquesan, he had purchased them from an understrapper of the court.

I prevailed upon Po-Po to drink a parting shell; and even little Loo, actually looking conscious that one of her hopeless admirers was about leaving Partoowye for ever, sipped a few drops from a folded leaf. As for the warm-hearted Arfretee, her grief was unbounded. She even besought me to spend my last night under her own palm-thatch; and then, in the morning, she would herself paddle me off to the ship.

But this I would not consent to; and so, as something to remember her by, she presented me with a roll of fine matting, and another of tappa. These gifts placed in my hammock, I afterward found very agreeable in the warm latitudes to which we were bound; nor did they fail to awaken most grateful remembrances.

About nightfall, we broke away from this generous-hearted household, and hurried down to the water.

It was a mad, merry night among the sailors: they had on tap a small cask of wine, procured in the same way as the doctor's flasks.

An hour or two after midnight, everything was noiseless; but when the first streak of the dawn showed itself over the mountains, a sharp voice hailed the forecastle, and ordered the ship unmoored. The anchors came up cheerily; the sails were soon set; and with the early breath of the tropical morning, fresh and fragrant from the hillsides, we slowly glided down the bay, and were swept through the opening in the reef. Presently, we "hove to," and the canoes came alongside to take off the islanders who had accompanied us thus far. As he stepped over the side, I shook the doctor long and heartily by the hand. I have never seen or heard of him since.

Crowding all sail, we braced the yards square; and, the breeze freshening, bowled straight away from the land. Once more the sailor's cradle rocked under me, and I found myself rolling in my gait.

By noon, the island had gone down in the horizon; and all before us was the wide Pacific.

BOOK THREE

TYPEE: *A Peep at Polynesian Life*

AUTHOR'S PREFACE

More than three years have elapsed since the occurrence of the events recorded in this volume. The interval, with the exception of the last few months, has been chiefly spent by the author tossing about on the wide ocean. Sailors are the only class of men who nowadays see anything like stirring adventure; and many things which to fireside people appear strange and romantic, to them seem as common-place as a jacket out at elbows. Yet, notwithstanding the familiarity of sailors with all sorts of curious adventure, the incidents recorded in the following pages have often served, when "spun as a yarn," not only to relieve the weariness of many a night-watch at sea, but to excite the warmest sympathies of the author's shipmates. He has been therefore led to think that his story could scarcely fail to interest those who are less familiar than the sailor with a life of adventure.

In his account of the singular and interesting people among whom he was thrown, it will be observed that he chiefly treats of their more obvious peculiarities; and, in describing their customs, refrains in most cases from entering into explanations concerning their origin and purposes. As writers of travels among barbarous communities are generally very diffuse on these subjects, he deems it right to advert to what may be considered a culpable omission. No one can be more sensible than the author of his deficiencies in this and many other respects; but when the very peculiar circumstances in which he was placed are understood, he feels assured that all these omissions will be excused.

In very many published narratives no little degree of attention is bestowed upon dates; but, as the author lost all knowledge of the days of the week, during the occurrence of the scenes herein related, he hopes that the reader will charitably pass over his shortcomings in this particular.

In the Polynesian words used in this volume—except in those cases where the spelling has been previously determined by others—that form of orthography has been employed, which might be supposed most easily to convey their sound to a stranger. In several works descriptive of the islands in the Pacific, many of the most beautiful combinations of vocal sounds have been altogether lost to the ear of the reader by an over-attention to the ordinary rules of spelling.

There are a few passages in the ensuing chapters which may be thought to bear rather hard upon a reverend order of men, the account of whose proceedings in different quarters of the globe—transmitted to us through their own hands—very generally, and often very deservedly, receives high commendation. Such passages will be found, however, to be based upon facts admitting of no contradiction, and which have come immediately under the writer's cognizance. The conclusions deduced from these facts are unavoidable, and in stating them the author has been influenced by no feeling of animosity, either to the individuals themselves or to that glorious cause which has not always been served by the proceedings of some of its advocates.

The great interest with which the important events lately occurring at the Sandwich, Marquesas, and Society Islands, have been regarded in America and England, and indeed throughout the world, will, he trusts, justify a few otherwise unwarrantable digressions.

545

There are some things related in the narrative which will be sure to appear strange, or perhaps entirely incomprehensible, to the reader; but they cannot appear more so to him than they did to the author at the time. He has stated such matters just as they occurred, and leaves every one to form his own opinion concerning them; trusting that his anxious desire to speak the unvarnished truth will gain for him the confidence of his readers.

CONTENTS

CHAPTER I

CHAPTER XXIX

CHAPTER XXX

CHAPTER XXXI

CHAPTER XXXII

CHAPTER XXXIII

CHAPTER XXXIV

APPENDIX

TYPEE

CHAPTER I

THE SEA—LONGINGS FOR SHORE—A LAND-SICK SHIP—DESTINATION OF THE
VOYAGERS—THE MARQUESAS—ADVENTURE OF A MISSIONARY'S WIFE AMONG
THE SAVAGES—CHARACTERISTIC ANECDOTE OF THE QUEEN OF NUKUHEVA.

SIX months at sea! Yes, reader, as I live, six months out of sight of land;
cruising after the sperm-whale beneath the scorching sun of the Line, and
tossed on the billows of the wide-rolling Pacific—the sky above, the sea around,
and nothing else! Weeks and weeks ago our fresh provisions were all exhausted.
There is not a sweet potato left; not a single yam. Those glorious bunches of
bananas which once decorated our stern and quarter-deck have, alas, disappeared! and the delicious oranges which hung suspended from our tops and
stays—they, too, are gone! Yes, they are all departed, and there is nothing
left us but salt-horse and sea-biscuit. Oh! ye state-room sailors, who make
so much ado about a fourteen-days' passage across the Atlantic; who so pa-
thetically relate the privations and hardships of the sea, where, after a day of
breakfasting, lunching, dining off five courses, chatting, playing whist, and
drinking champagne-punch, it was your hard lot to be shut up in little cabinets
of mahogany and maple, and sleep for ten hours, with nothing to disturb you
but "those good-for-nothing tars, shouting and tramping overhead,"—what
would ye say to our six months out of sight of land?

Oh! for a refreshing glimpse of one blade of grass—for a snuff at the fragrance of a handful of the loamy earth! Is there nothing fresh around us?
Is there no green thing to be seen? Yes, the inside of our bulwarks is painted
green; but what a vile and sickly hue it is, as if nothing bearing even the
semblance of verdure could flourish this weary way from land. Even the bark
that once clung to the wood we use for fuel has been gnawed off and devoured
by the captain's pig; and so long ago, too, that the pig himself has in turn
been devoured.

There is but one solitary tenant in the chicken-coop, once a gay and dapper
young cock, bearing him so bravely among the coy hens. But look at him
now; there he stands, moping all the day long on that everlasting one leg of
his. He turns with disgust from the mouldy corn before him and the brackish
water in his little trough. He mourns no doubt his lost companions, literally
snatched from him one by one, and never seen again. But his days of mourning will be few; for Mungo, our black cook, told me yesterday that the word
had at last gone forth, and poor Pedro's fate was sealed. His attenuated body
will be laid out upon the captain's table next Sunday, and long before night
will be buried with all the usual ceremonies beneath that worthy individual's
vest. Who would believe that there could be any one so cruel as to long for
the decapitation of the luckless Pedro; yet the sailors pray every minute,

selfish fellows, that the miserable fowl may be brought to his end. They say the captain will never point the ship for the land so long as he has in antici-pation a mess of fresh meat. This unhappy bird can alone furnish it; and when he is once devoured, the captain will come to his senses. I wish thee no harm, Peter; but as thou art doomed, sooner or later, to meet the fate of all thy race; and if putting a period to thy existence is to be the signal for our deliverance, why—truth to speak—I wish thy throat cut this very moment; for, oh! how I wish to see the living earth again! The old ship herself longs to look out upon the land from her hawse-holes once more, and Jack Lewis said right the other day when the captain found fault with his steering.

"Why, d'ye see, Captain Vangs," says bold Jack, "I'm as good a helmsman as ever put hand to spoke; but none of us can steer the old lady now. We can't keep her full and bye, sir: watch her ever so close, she will fall off; and then, sir, when I put the helm down so gently, and try like to coax her to the work, she won't take it kindly, but will fall round off again; and it's all because she knows the land is under the lee, sir, and she won't go any more to wind-ward." Aye, and why should she, Jack? Didn't every one of her stout timbers grow on shore, and hasn't she sensibilities as well as we?

Poor old ship! Her very looks denote her desires: how deplorably she appears! The paint on her sides, burnt up by the scorching sun, is puffed out and cracked. See the weeds she trails along with her, and what an un-sightly bunch of those horrid barnacles has formed about her stern-piece; and every time she rises on a sea, she shows her copper torn away, or hanging in jagged strips.

Poor old ship! I say again: for six months she has been rolling and pitching about, never for one moment at rest. But courage, old lass, I hope to see thee soon within a biscuit's toss of the merry land, riding snugly at anchor in some green cove, and sheltered from the boisterous winds.

.   .   .   .

"Hurra, my lads! It's a settled thing; next week we shape our course to the Marquesas!" The Marquesas! What strange visions of outlandish things does the very name spirit up! Naked houris—cannibal banquets—groves of coco-nut—coral-reefs—tatooed chiefs—and bamboo temples; sunny valleys planted with breadfruit-trees—carved canoes dancing on the flashing blue waters —savage woodlands guarded by horrible idols—*heathenish rites and human sacrifices*.

Such were the strangely jumbled anticipations that haunted me during our passage from the cruising ground. I felt an irresistible curiosity to see those islands which the olden voyagers had so glowingly described.

The group for which we were now steering (although among the earliest of European discoveries in the South Seas, having been first visited in the year 1595) still continues to be tenanted by beings as strange and barbarous as ever. The missionaries, sent on a heavenly errand, had sailed by their lovely shores, and had abandoned them to their idols of wood and stone. How inter-esting the circumstances under which they were discovered! In the watery path of Mendanna, cruising in quest of some region of gold, these isles had sprung up like a scene of enchantment, and for a moment the Spaniard be-lieved his bright dream was realized. In honour of the Marquess de Mendoza, then viceroy of Peru—under whose auspices the navigator sailed—he bestowed upon them the name which denoted the rank of his patron, and gave to the world on his return a vague and magnificent account of their beauty. But these islands, undisturbed for years, relapsed into their previous obscurity; and it is only recently that anything has been known concerning them. Once in the course of a half century, to be sure, some adventurous rover would break in upon their peaceful repose, and, astonished at the unusual scene, would be almost tempted to claim the merit of a new discovery.

Of this interesting group, but little account has ever been given, if we except the slight mention made of them in the sketches of South-Sea voyages. Cook, in his repeated circumnavigations of the globe, barely touched at their shores; and all that we know about them is from a few general narratives. Among these, there are two that claim particular notice. Porter's *Journal of the Cruise of the U. S. frigate "Essex," in the Pacific, during the late War,* is said to contain some interesting particulars concerning the islanders. This is a work, however, which I have never happened to meet with; and Stewart, the chaplain of the American sloop-of-war *Vincennes,* has likewise devoted a portion of his book, entitled *A Visit to the South Seas,* to the same subject.

Within the last few years American and English vessels engaged in the extensive whale fisheries of the Pacific have occasionally, when short of provisions, put into the commodious harbor which there is in one of the islands; but a fear of the natives, founded on a recollection of the dreadful fate which many white men have received at their hands, has deterred their crews from intermixing with the population sufficiently to gain any insight into their peculiar customs and manners.

The Protestant Missions appear to have despaired of reclaiming these islands from heathenism. The usage they in every case received from the natives has been such as to intimidate the boldest of their number. Ellis, in his *Polynesian Researches,* gives some interesting accounts of the abortive attempts made by the Tahiti Mission to establish a branch Mission upon certain islands of the group. A short time before my visit to the Marquesas, a somewhat amusing incident took place in connexion with these efforts, which I cannot avoid relating.

An intrepid missionary, undaunted by the ill-success that had attended all previous endeavours to conciliate the savages, and believing much in the efficacy of female influence, introduced among them his young and beautiful wife, the first white woman who had ever visited their shores. The islanders at first gazed in mute admiration at so unusual a prodigy, and seemed inclined to regard it as some new divinity. But after a short time, becoming familiar with its charming aspect, and jealous of the folds which encircled its form, they sought to pierce the sacred veil of calico in which it was enshrined, and in the gratification of their curiosity so far overstepped the limits of good breeding as deeply to offend the lady's sense of decorum. Her sex once ascertained, their idolatry was changed into contempt; and there was no end to the contumely showered upon her by the savages, who were exasperated at the deception which they conceived had been practised upon them. To the horror of her affectionate spouse, she was stripped of her garments, and given to understand that she could no longer carry on her deceits with impunity. The gentle dame was not sufficiently evangelized to endure this, and, fearful of further improprieties, she forced her husband to relinquish his undertaking, and together they returned to Tahiti.

Not thus shy of exhibiting her charms was the Island Queen, herself, the beauteous wife of Mowanna, the king of Nukuheva. Between two and three years after the adventures recorded in this volume, I chanced, while aboard of a man-of-war, to touch at these islands. The French had then held possession of the Marquesas some time, and already prided themselves upon the beneficial effects of their jurisdiction, as discernible in the deportment of the natives. To be sure, in one of their efforts at reform they had slaughtered about a hundred and fifty of them at Whitihoo—but let that pass. At the time I mention, the French squadron was rendezvousing in the bay of Nukuheva, and, during an interview between one of their captains and our worthy Commodore, it was suggested by the former that we, as the flag ship of the American squadron, should receive, in state, a visit from the royal pair. The French officer likewise represented, with evident satisfaction, that under their tuition the king and queen had imbibed proper notions of their elevated station, and on all ceremonious occasions conducted themselves with suitable dignity. Accordingly, preparations were made to give their majesties a reception on board in a style corresponding with their rank.

One bright afternoon, a gig, gaily bedizened with streamers, was observed to shove off from the side of one of the French frigates, and pull directly for our gangway. In the stern sheets reclined Mowanna and his consort. As they approached, we paid them all the honours due to royalty—manning our yards, firing a salute, and making a prodigious hubbub.

They ascended the accommodation ladder, were greeted by the Commodore, hat in hand, and passing along the quarter-deck, the marine guard presented arms, while the band struck up "The king of the Cannibal Islands." So far all went well. The French officers grimaced and smiled in exceedingly high spirits, wonderfully pleased with the discreet manner in which these distinguished personages behaved themselves.

Their appearance was certainly calculated to produce an effect. His majesty was arrayed in a magnificent military uniform, stiff with gold lace and embroidery, while his shaven crown was concealed by a huge *chapeau bras,* waving with ostrich plumes. There was one slight blemish, however, in his appearance. A broad patch of tattooing stretched completely across his face, in a line with his eyes, making him look as if he wore a huge pair of goggles, and royalty in goggles suggested some ludicrous ideas. But it was in the adornment of the fair person of his dark-complexioned spouse that the tailors of the fleet had evinced the gaiety of their national taste. She was hal ted in a gaudy tissue of scarlet cloth, trimmed with yellow silk, which, descending a little below the knees, exposed to view her bare legs, embellished with spiral tattooing, and somewhat resembling two miniature Trajan's columns. Upon her head was a fanciful turban of purple velvet, figured with silver sprigs, and surmounted by a tuft of variegated feathers.

The ship's company, crowding into the gangway to view the sight, soon arrested her majesty's attention. She singled out from their number an old salt, whose bare arms and feet and exposed breast were covered with as many inscriptions in India ink as the lid of an Egyptian sarcophagus. Notwithstanding all the sly hints and remonstrances of the French officers, she immediately approached the man, and pulling further open the bosom of his duck frock, and rolling up the leg of his wide trousers, she gazed with admiration at the bright blue and vermilion pricking, thus disclosed to view. She hung over the fellow, caressing him, and expressing her delight in a variety of wild exclamations and gestures. The embarrassment of the polite Gauls at such an unlooked-for occurrence may be easily imagined; but picture their consternation, when all at once the royal lady, eager to display the hieroglyphics on her own sweet form, bent forward for a moment, and turning sharply round, threw up the skirts of her mantle, and revealed a sight from which the aghast Frenchmen retreated precipitately, and, tumbling into their boat, fled the scene of so shocking a catastrophe.

CHAPTER II

PASSAGE FROM THE CRUISING GROUND TO THE MARQUESAS—SLEEPY TIMES ABOARD SHIP—SOUTH SEA SCENERY—LAND HO!—THE FRENCH SQUADRON DISCOVERED AT ANCHOR IN THE BAY OF NUKUHEVA—STRANGE PILOT—ESCORT OF CANOES—A FLOTILLA OF COCO-NUTS—SWIMMING VISITORS—THE "DOLLY" BOARDED BY THEM—STATE OF AFFAIRS THAT ENSUE.

I CAN never forget the eighteen or twenty days during which the light trade-winds were silently sweeping us toward the islands. In pursuit of the sperm-whale, we had been cruising on the Line some twenty degrees to the westward of the Gallipagos; and all that we had to do, when our course was determined on, was to square in the yards and keep the vessel before the breeze, and then the good ship and the steady gale did the rest between them. The man at the wheel never vexed the old lady with any superfluous steering, but, comfortably adjusting his limbs at the tiller, would doze away by the hour. True to her work, the *Dolly* headed to her course, and, like one of those characters who always do best when let alone, she jogged on her way like a veteran old sea-pacer—as she was.

What a delightful, lazy, languid time we had whilst we were thus gliding along! There was nothing to be done; a circumstance that happily suited our disinclination to do anything. We abandoned the forepeak altogether, and spreading an awning over the forecastle, slept, ate, and lounged under it the livelong day. Every one seemed to be under the influence of some narcotic. Even the officers aft, whose duty required them never to be seated whilst keeping a deck watch, vainly endeavoured to keep on their pins; and were obliged invariably to compromise the matter by leaning up against the bulwarks and gazing abstractedly over the side. Reading was out of the question; take a book in your hand, and you were asleep in an instant.

Although I could not avoid yielding in a great measure to the general languor, still at times I contrived to shake off the spell, and to appreciate the beauty of the scene around me. The sky presented a clear expanse of the most delicate blue, except along the skirts of the horizon, where you might see a thin drapery of pale clouds which never varied their form or colour. The long, measured, dirge-like swell of the Pacific came rolling along, with its surface broken by little tiny waves, sparkling in the sunshine. Every now and then a shoal of flying-fish, scared from the water under the bows, would leap into the air, and fall the next moment like a shower of silver into the sea. Then you would see the superb albicore, with his glittering sides, sailing aloft, and, often describing an arc in his descent, disappear on the surface of the water. Far off, the lofty jet of the whale might be seen, and nearer at hand the prowling shark, that villainous footpad of the seas, would come skulking along, and, at a wary distance, regard us with his evil eye. At times some shapeless monster of the deep, floating on the surface, would, as we approached, sink slowly into the blue waters, and fade away from the sight.

But the most impressive feature of the scene was the almost unbroken silence that reigned over sky and water. Scarcely a sound could be heard but the occasional breathing of the grampus and the rippling at the cutwater.

As we drew nearer the land, I hailed with delight the appearance of innumerable sea-fowl. Screaming and whirling in spiral tracks, they would accompany the vessel, and at times alight on our yards and stays. That piratical-looking fellow, appropriately named the man-of-war's hawk, with his blood-red bill and raven plumage, would come sweeping round us in gradually diminishing circles, till you could distinctly mark the strange flashings of his eye; and then, as if satisfied with his observation, would sail up into the air and disappear from the view. Soon, other evidences of our vicinity to the land were apparent, and it was not long before the glad announcement of its being in sight was heard from aloft—given with that peculiar prolongation of sound that a sailor loves—"Land ho!"

The captain, darting on deck from the cabin, bawled lustily for his spyglass; the mate in still louder accents hailed the masthead with a tremendous "where-away?" The black cook thrust his woolly head from the gallery, and Boats-wain, the dog, leaped up between the knight-heads, and barked most furiously. Land ho! Aye, there it was. A hardly perceptible blue irregular outline, indicating the bold contour of the lofty heights of Nukuheva.

This island, although generally called one of the Marquesas, is by some navigators considered as forming one of a distinct cluster, comprising the islands of Ruhooka, Ropo, and Nukuheva; upon which three the appellation of the Washington Group has been bestowed. They form a triangle, and lie within the parallels of 8° 38″ and 9° 32″ South latitude, and 139° 20′ and 140° 10′ West longitude from Greenwich. With how little propriety they are to be regarded as forming a separate group will be at once apparent, when it is considered that they lie in the immediate vicinity of the other islands, that is to say, less than a degree to the north-west of them, that their inhabitants speak the Marquesan dialect, and that their laws, religion, and general customs are identical. The only reason why they were ever thus arbitrarily distinguished may be attributed to the singular fact that their existence was altogether unknown to the world until the year 1791, when they were discovered by Captain Ingraham, of Boston, Massachusetts, nearly two centuries after the discovery of the adjacent islands by the agent of the Spanish Viceroy. Notwithstanding this, I shall follow the example of most voyagers, and treat of them as forming part and parcel of the Marquesas.

Nukuheva is the most important of these islands, being the only one at which ships are much in the habit of touching, and is celebrated as being the place where the adventurous Captain Porter refitted his ships during the late war between England and the United States, and whence he sallied out upon the large whaling fleet then sailing under the enemy's flag in the surrounding seas. This island is about twenty miles in length and nearly as many in breadth. It has three good harbours on its coast; the largest and best of which is called by the people living in its vicinity "Tyohee," and by Captain Porter was denominated Massachusetts Bay. Among the adverse tribes dwelling about the shores of the other bays, and by all voyagers, it is generally known by the name bestowed upon the island itself—Nukuheva. Its inhabitants have become somewhat corrupted owing to their recent commerce with Europeans; but so far as regards their peculiar customs and general mode of life, they retain their original primitive character, remaining very nearly in the same state of nature in which they were first beheld by white men. The hostile clans, residing in the more remote sections of the island, and very seldom holding any communication with foreigners, are in every respect unchanged from their earliest known condition.

In the bay of Nukuheva was the anchorage we desired to reach. We had perceived the loom of the mountains about sunset; so that after running all night with a very light breeze, we found ourselves close in with the island the next morning, but as the bay we sought lay on its farther side, we were obliged to sail some distance along the shore, catching, as we proceeded, short glimpses of blooming valleys, deep glens, waterfalls, and waving groves, hidden here and there by projecting and rocky headlands, every moment opening to the view some new and startling scene of beauty.

Those who for the first time visit the South Seas, generally are surprised at the appearance of the islands when beheld from the sea. From the vague accounts we sometimes have of their beauty, many people are apt to picture to themselves enamelled and softly swelling plains, shaded over with delicious groves, and watered by purling brooks, and the entire country but little elevated above the surrounding ocean. The reality is very different; bold rock-bound coasts, with the surf beating high against the lofty cliffs, and broken here and there into deep inlets, which open to the view thickly-wooded valleys, separated by the spurs of mountains clothed with tufted grass, and sweeping down towards the sea from an elevated and furrowed interior, form the principal features of these islands.

Towards noon we drew abreast the entrance to the harbour, and at last we slowly swept by the intervening promontory, and entered the bay of Nukuheva. No description can do justice to its beauty; but that beauty was lost to me then, and I saw nothing but the tri-coloured flag of France trailing over the stern of six vessels, whose black hulls and bristling broadsides proclaimed their warlike character. There they were, floating in that lovely bay, the green eminences of the shore looking down so tranquilly upon them, as if rebuking the sternness of their aspect. To my eye nothing could be more out of keeping than the presence of these vessels; but we soon learnt what brought them there. The whole group of islands had just been taken possession of by Rear-Admiral Du Petit Thouars, in the name of the invincible French nation.

This item of information was imparted to us by a most extraordinary individual, a genuine South-Sea vagabond, who came alongside of us in a whale-boat as soon as we entered the bay, and, by the aid of some benevolent persons at the gangway, was assisted on board, for our visitor was in that interesting stage of intoxication when a man is amiable and helpless. Although he was utterly unable to stand erect or to navigate his body across the deck, he still magnanimously proffered his services to pilot the ship to a good and secure anchorage. Our captain, however, rather distrusted his ability in this respect, and refused to recognize his claim to the character he assumed; but our gentleman was determined to play his part, for by dint of much scrambling he succeeded in getting into the weather-quarter boat, where he steadied himself by holding on to a shroud, and then commenced issuing his commands with amazing volubility and very peculiar gestures. Of course no one obeyed his orders; but as it was impossible to quiet him, we swept by the ships of the squadron with this strange fellow performing his antics in full view of all the French officers.

We afterwards learned that our eccentric friend had been a lieutenant in the English navy; but, having disgraced his flag by some criminal conduct in one of the principal ports on the main, he had deserted his ship, and spent many years wandering among the islands of the Pacific, until accidentally being at Nukuheva when the French took possession of the place, he had been appointed pilot of the harbour by the newly constituted authorities.

As we slowly advanced up the bay, numerous canoes pushed off from the surrounding shores, and we were soon in the midst of quite a flotilla of them, their savage occupants struggling to get aboard of us, and jostling one another in their ineffectual attempts. Occasionally the projecting outriggers of their slight shallops, running foul of one another, would become entangled beneath the water, threatening to capsize the canoes, when a scene of confusion would ensue that baffles description. Such strange outcries and passionate gesticulations I never certainly heard or saw before. You would have thought the islanders were on the point of flying at one another's throats, whereas they were only amicably engaged in disentangling their boats.

Scattered here and there among the canoes might be seen numbers of coco-nuts floating closely together in circular groups, and bobbing up and down with every wave. By some inexplicable means these coco-nuts were all steadily approaching towards the ship. As I leaned curiously over the side endeavouring to solve their mysterious movements, one mass far in advance of the rest attracted my attention. In its centre was something I could take for nothing else than a coco-nut, but which I certainly considered one of the most extraordinary specimens of the fruit I had ever seen. It kept twirling and dancing about among the rest in the most singular manner, and as it drew nearer I thought it bore a remarkable resemblance to the brown shaven skull of one of the savages. Presently it betrayed a pair of eyes, and soon I became aware that what I had supposed to have been one of the fruit was nothing else than the head of an islander, who had adopted this singular method of bringing his produce to market. The coco-nuts were all attached to one another by strips of the husk, partly torn from the shell and rudely fastened together. Their proprietor, inserting his head into the midst of them, impelled his necklace of coco-nuts through the water by striking out beneath the surface with his feet.

I was somewhat astonished to perceive that among the number of natives that surrounded us not a single female was to be seen. At that time I was ignorant of the fact that by the operation of the "taboo" the use of canoes in all parts of the island is rigorously prohibited to the entire sex, for whom it is death even to be seen entering one when hauled on shore; consequently, whenever a Marquesan lady voyages by water, she puts in requisition the paddles of her own fair body.

We had approached within a mile and a half perhaps of the foot of the bay, when some of the islanders, who by this time had managed to scramble aboard of us at the risk of swamping their canoes, directed our attention to a singular commotion in the water ahead of the vessel. At first I imagined it to be produced by a shoal of fish sporting on the surface, but our savage friends assured us that it was caused by a shoal of "whinhenies" (young girls), who in this manner were coming off from the shore to welcome us. As they drew nearer, and I watched the rising and sinking of their forms, and beheld the uplifted right arm bearing above the water the girdle of tappa, and their long dark hair trailing beside them as they swam, I almost fancied they could be nothing else than so many mermaids—and very like mermaids they behaved too.

We were still some distance from the beach, and under slow headway, when we sailed right into the midst of these swimming nymphs, and they boarded us at every quarter; many seizing hold of the chainplates and springing into the chains; others, at the peril of being run over by the vessel in her course, catching at the bob-stays, and wreathing their slender forms about the ropes, hung suspended in the air. All of them at length succeeded in getting up the the ship's side, where they clung dripping with the brine and glowing from the bath, their jet-black tresses streaming over their shoulders, and half enveloping their otherwise naked forms. There they hung, sparkling with savage vivacity, laughing gaily at one another, and chattering away with infinite glee. Nor were they idle the while, for each one performed the simple offices of the toilet for the other. Their luxuriant locks, wound up and twisted into the smallest possible compass, were freed from the briny element; the whole person carefully dried and, from a little round shell that passed from hand to hand, anointed with a fragrant oil: their adornments were completed by passing a few loose folds of white tappa, in a modest cincture, around the waist. Thus arrayed they no longer hesitated, but flung themselves lightly over the bulwarks, and were quickly frolicking about the decks. Many of them went forward, perching upon the head-rails or running out upon the bowsprit, while others seated themselves upon the taffrail, or reclined at full length upon the boats. What a sight for us bachelor sailors! how avoid so dire a temptation? For who could think of tumbling these artless creatures overboard, when they had swam miles to welcome us?

Their appearance perfectly amazed me; their extreme youth, the light clear brown of their complexions, their delicate features, and inexpressibly graceful figures, their softly moulded limbs, and free unstudied action, seemed as strange as beautiful.

The *Dolly* was fairly captured; and never I will say was vessel carried before by such a dashing and irresistible party of boarders! The ship taken, we could not do otherwise than yield ourselves prisoners, and, for the whole period that she remained in the bay, the *Dolly,* as well as her crew, were completely in the hands of the mermaids.

In the evening after we had come to an anchor the deck was illuminated with lanterns, and this picturesque band of sylphs, tricked out with flowers, and dressed in robes of variegated tappa, got up a ball in great style. These females are passionately fond of dancing, and in the wild grace and spirit of their style excel everything that I have ever seen. The varied dances of the Marquesan girls are beautiful in the extreme, but there is an abandoned voluptuousness in their character which I dare not attempt to describe.

Our ship was now wholly given up to every species of riot and debauchery. Not the feeblest barrier was interposed between the unholy passions of the crew and their unlimited gratification. The grossest licentiousness and the most shameful inebriety prevailed, with occasional and but short-lived interruptions, through the whole period of her stay. Alas for the poor savages when exposed to the influence of these polluting examples! Unsophisticated and confiding, they are easily led into every vice, and humanity weeps over the ruin thus remorselessly inflicted upon them by their European civilizers. Thrice happy are they who, inhabiting some yet undiscovered island in the midst of the ocean, have never been brought into contaminating contact with the white man.

CHAPTER III

SOME ACCOUNT OF THE LATE OPERATIONS OF THE FRENCH AT THE MARQUESAS
—PRUDENT CONDUCT OF THE ADMIRAL—SENSATION PRODUCED BY THE AR-
RIVAL OF THE STRANGERS—THE FIRST HORSE SEEN BY THE ISLANDERS—
REFLECTIONS—MISERABLE SUBTERFUGE OF THE FRENCH—DIGRESSION CON-
CERNING TAHITI—SEIZURE OF THE ISLAND BY THE ADMIRAL—SPIRITED
CONDUCT OF AN ENGLISH LADY.

IT was in the summer of 1842 that we arrived at the islands: the French
had then held possession of them for several weeks. During this time they
had visited some of the principal places in the group, and had disembarked
at various points about five hundred troops. These were employed in constructing works of defence, and otherwise providing against the attacks of
the natives, who at any moment might be expected to break out in open hostility. The islanders looked upon the people who made this cavalier appropriation of their shores with mingled feelings of fear and detestation. They
cordially hated them; but the impulses of their resentment were neutralized
by their dread of the floating batteries, which lay with their fatal tubes ostentatiously pointed, not at fortifications and redoubts, but at a handful of bamboo sheds, sheltered in a grove of coco-nuts! A valiant warrior doubtless,
but a prudent one too, was this same Rear-Admiral Du Petit Thouars. Four
heavy, double-banked frigates and three corvettes to frighten a parcel of naked
heathen into subjection! Sixty eight-pounders to demolish huts of coco-nut
boughs, and Congreve rockets to set on fire a few canoe sheds!

At Nukuheva, there were about one hundred soldiers ashore. They were
encamped in tents, constructed of the old sails and spare spars of the squadron,
within the limits of a redoubt mounted with a few nine-pounders, and surrounded with a fosse. Every other day, these troops were marched out in
martial array, to a level piece of ground in the vicinity, and there for hours
went through all sorts of military evolutions, surrounded by flocks of the natives,
who looked on with savage admiration at the show, and as savage a hatred of
the actors. A regiment of the Old Guard, reviewed on a summer's day in
the Champs Elysées, could not have made a more critically correct appearance. The officers' regimentals, resplendent with gold lace and embroidery, as
if purposely calculated to dazzle the islanders, looked as if just unpacked from
their Parisian cases.

The sensation produced by the presence of the strangers had not in the
least subsided at the period of our arrival at the islands. The natives still
flocked in numbers about the encampment, and watched with the liveliest
curiosity everything that was going forward. A blacksmith's forge, which had
been set up in the shelter of a grove near the beach, attracted so great a
crowd that it required the utmost efforts of the sentries posted around to keep
the inquisitive multitude at a sufficient distance to allow the workmen to ply
their vocation. But nothing gained so large a share of admiration as a horse,
which had been brought from Valparaiso by the *Achille*, one of the vessels of
the squadron. The animal, a remarkably fine one, had been taken ashore and
stabled in a hut of coco-nut boughs within the fortified enclosure. Occasionally
it was brought out, and, being gaily caparisoned, was ridden by one of the
officers at full speed over the hard sand beach. This performance was sure to

be hailed with loud plaudits, and the "puarkee nuee" (big hog) was unanimously pronounced by the islanders to be the most extraordinary specimen of zoology that had ever come under their observation.

The expedition for the occupation of the Marquesas had sailed from Brest in the spring of 1842, and the secret of its destination was solely in the possession of its commander. No wonder that those who contemplated such a signal infraction of the rights of humanity should have sought to veil the enormity from the eyes of the world. And yet, notwithstanding their iniquitous conduct in this and in other matters, the French have ever plumed themselves upon being the most humane and polished of nations. A high degree of refinement, however, does not seem to subdue our wicked propensities so much after all; and were civilization itself to be estimated by some of its results, it would seem perhaps better for what we call the barbarous part of the world to remain unchanged.

One example of the shameless subterfuges under which the French stand prepared to defend whatever cruelties they may hereafter think fit to commit in bringing the Marquesan natives into subjection is well worthy of being recorded. On some flimsy pretext or other Mowanna, the king of Nukuheva, whom the invaders by extravagant presents have cajoled over to their interests, and move about like a mere puppet, has been set up as the rightful sovereign of the entire island—the alleged ruler by prescription of various clans who for ages perhaps have treated with each other as separate nations. To reinstate this much-injured prince in the assumed dignities of his ancestors, the disinterested strangers have come all the way from France: they are determined that his title shall be acknowledged. If any tribe shall refuse to recognize the authority of the French, by bowing down to the laced chapeau of Mowanna, let them abide the consequences of their obstinacy. Under cover of a similar pretence, have the outrages and massacres at Tahiti the beautiful, the queen of the South Seas, been perpetrated.

On this buccaneering expedition, Rear-Admiral Du Petit Thouars, leaving the rest of his squadron at the Marquesas—which had then been occupied by his forces about five months—set sail for the doomed island in the *Reine Blanche* frigate. On his arrival, as an indemnity for alleged insults offered to the flag of his country, he demanded some twenty or thirty thousand dollars to be placed in his hands forthwith, and, in default of payment, threatened to land and take possession of the place.

The frigate, immediately upon coming to an anchor, got springs on her cables, and with her guns cast loose and her men at their quarters, lay in the circular basin of Papeete, with her broadside bearing upon the devoted town; while her numerous cutters, hauled in order alongside, were ready to effect a landing, under cover of her batteries. She maintained this belligerent attitude for several days, during which time a series of informal negotiations were pending, and wide alarm spread over the island. Many of the Tahitians were at first disposed to resort to arms, and drive the invaders from their shores; but more pacific and feebler councils ultimately prevailed. The unfortunate queen, Pomare, incapable of averting the impending calamity, terrified at the arrogance of the insolent Frenchman, and driven at last to despair, fled by night in a canoe to Emio.

During the continuance of the panic there occurred an instance of feminine heroism that I cannot omit to record.

In the grounds of the famous missionary consul, Pritchard, then absent in London, the consular flag of Britain waved as usual during the day, from a lofty staff planted within a few yards of the beach, and in full view of the frigate. One morning an officer, at the head of a party of men, presented himself at the verandah of Mr. Pritchard's house, and inquired in broken English for the lady his wife. The matron soon made her appearance; and the polite Frenchman making one of his best bows, and playing gracefully with the aiguillettes that danced upon his breast, proceeded in courteous accents to deliver his mission. "The admiral desired the flag to be hauled down—hoped it would be perfectly agreeable—and his men stood ready to perform the duty." "Tell the pirate your master," replied the spirited Englishwoman, pointing to the staff, "that if he wished to strike those colours, he must come and perform the act himself; I will suffer no one else to do it." The lady then bowed haughtily and withdrew into the house. As the discomfited officer slowly walked away, he looked up to the flag, and perceived that the cord by which it was elevated to its place, led from the top of the staff, across the lawn, to an open upper window of the mansion, where sat the lady, from whom he had just parted, tranquilly engaged in knitting. Was that flag hauled down? Mrs. Pritchard thinks not; and Rear-Admiral Du Petit Thouars is believed to be of the same opinion.

CHAPTER IV

STATE OF AFFAIRS ABOARD THE SHIP—CONTENTS OF HER LARDER—LENGTH OF SOUTH SEAMEN'S VOYAGES—ACCOUNT OF A FLYING WHALEMAN—DETERMINATION TO LEAVE THE VESSEL—THE BAY OF NUKUHEVA—THE TYPEES—INVASION OF THEIR VALLEY BY PORTER—REFLECTIONS—GLEN OF TIOR—INTERVIEW BETWEEN THE OLD KING AND THE FRENCH ADMIRAL.

OUR ship had not been many days in the harbour of Nukuheva before I came to the determination of leaving her. That my reasons for resolving to take this step were numerous and weighty, may be inferred from the fact that I chose rather to risk my fortunes among the savages of the island than to endure another voyage on board the *Dolly*. To use the concise, point-blank phrase of the sailors, I had made up my mind to "run away." Now as a meaning is generally attached to these two words no way flattering to the individual to whom they are applied, it behooves me, for the sake of my own character, to offer some explanation of my conduct.

When I entered on board the *Dolly*, I signed as a matter of course the ship's articles, thereby voluntarily engaging and legally binding myself to serve in a certain capacity for the period of the voyage; and, special considerations apart, I was of course bound to fulfil the agreement. But in all contracts, if one party fail to perform his share of the compact, is not the other virtually absolved from his liability? Who is there who will not answer in the affirmative?

Having settled the principle, then, let me apply it to the particular case in question. In numberless instances had not only the implied but the specified conditions of the articles been violated on the part of the ship in which I served. The usage on board of her was tyrannical; the sick had been inhumanly neglected; the provisions had been doled out in scanty allowance; and her cruises were unreasonably protracted. The captain was the author of these abuses; it was in vain to think that he would either remedy them, or alter his conduct, which was arbitrary and violent in the extreme. His prompt reply to all complaints and remonstrances was—the butt end of a hand-spike, so convincingly administered as effectually to silence the aggrieved party.

To whom could we apply for redress? We had left both law and equity on the other side of the Cape; and unfortunately, with a very few exceptions, our crew was composed of a parcel of dastardly and mean-spirited wretches, divided among themselves, and only united in enduring without resistance the unmitigated tyranny of the captain. It would have been mere madness for any two or three of the number, unassisted by the rest, to attempt making a stand against his ill-usage. They would only have called down upon themselves the particular vengeance of this "Lord of the Plank," and subjected their shipmates to additional hardships.

But, after all, these things could have been endured awhile, had we entertained the hope of being speedily delivered from them by the due completion of the term of our servitude. But what a dismal prospect awaited us in this quarter! The longevity of Cape Horn whaling voyages is proverbial, frequently extending over a period of four or five years.

Some long-haired bare-necked youths who, forced by the united influences of Captain Marryat and hard times, embark at Nantucket for a pleasure excursion to the Pacific, and whose anxious mothers provide them with bottled milk for the occasion, oftentimes return very respectable middle-aged gentlemen.

The very preparations made for one of these expeditions are enough to frighten one. As the vessel carries out no cargo, her hold is filled with provisions for her own consumption. The owners, who officiate as caterers for the voyage, supply the larder with an abundance of dainties. Delicate morsels of beef and pork, cut on scientific principles from every part of the animal, and of all conceivable shapes and sizes, are carefully packed in salt, and stored away in barrels; affording a never-ending variety in their different degrees of toughness, and in the peculiarities of their saline properties. Choice old water, too, decanted into stout six-barrel-casks, and two pints of which are allowed every day to each soul on board; together with ample store of sea-bread, previously reduced to a state of petrifaction with a view to preserve it either from decay or consumption in the ordinary mode, are likewise provided for the nourishment and gastronomic enjoyment of the crew.

But not to speak of the quality of these articles of sailors' fare, the abundance in which they are put on board a whaling vessel is almost incredible. Oftentimes when we had occasion to break out in the hold, and I beheld the successive tiers of casks and barrels, whose contents were all destined to be consumed in due course by the ship's company, my heart has sunk within me.

Although, as a general case, a ship unlucky in falling in with whales continues to cruise after them until she has barely sufficient provisions remaining to take her home, turning round then quietly and making the best of her way to her friends; yet there are instances when even this natural obstacle to the further prosecution of the voyage is overcome by headstrong captains, who, bartering the fruits of their hard-earned toils for a new supply of provisions in some of the ports of Chile or Peru, begin the voyage afresh with unabated zeal and perseverance. It is in vain that the owners write urgent letters to him to sail for home, and for their sake to bring back the ship, since it appears he can put nothing in her. Not he. He has registered a vow: he will fill his vessel with good sperm oil, or, failing to do so, never again strike Yankee soundings.

I heard of one whaler, which after many years' absence was given up for lost.

The last that had been heard of her was a shadowy report of her having touched at some of those unstable islands in the far Pacific, whose eccentric wanderings are carefully noted in each new edition of the South-Sea charts. After a long interval, however, *The Perseverance*—for that was her name—was spoken somewhere in the vicinity of the ends of the earth, cruising along as leisurely as ever, her sails all bepatched and bequilted with rope-yarns, her spars fished with old pipe staves, and her rigging knotted and spliced in every possible direction. Her crew was composed of some twenty venerable Greenwich-pensioner-looking old salts, who just managed to hobble about deck. The ends of all the running ropes, with the exception of the signal halyards and poop-down-haul, were rove through snatch-blocks, and led to the capstan or windlass, so that not a yard was braced or a sail set without the assistance of machinery.

Her hull was incrusted with barnacles, which completely encased her. Three pet sharks followed in her wake and every day came alongside to regale themselves from the contents of the cook's bucket, which were pitched over to them. A vast shoal of bonetas and albicores always kept her company.

Such was the account I heard of this vessel, and the remembrance of it always haunted me; what eventually became of her I never learned; at any rate she never reached home, and I suppose she is still regularly tacking twice in the twenty-four hours somewhere off Buggerry Island, or the Devil's-Tail Peak.

Having said thus much touching the usual length of these voyages, when I inform the reader that ours had as it were just commenced, we being only fifteen months out, and even at that time hailed as a late arrival, and boarded for news, he will readily perceive that there was little to encourage one in looking forward to the future, especially as I had always had a presentiment that we should make an unfortunate voyage, and our experience so far had justified the expectation.

I may here state, and on my faith as an honest man, that though more than three years have elapsed since I left this same identical vessel, she still continues in the Pacific, and but a few days since I saw her reported in the papers as having touched at the Sandwich Islands previous to going on the coast of Japan.

But to return to my narrative. Placed in these circumstances then, with no prospect of matters mending if I remained aboard the *Dolly*, I at once made up my mind to leave her: to be sure it was rather an inglorious thing to steal away privily from those at whose hands I had received wrongs and outrages that I could not resent; but how was such a course to be avoided when it was the only alternative left me? Having made up my mind, I proceeded to acquire all the information I could obtain relating to the island and its inhabitants, with a view of shaping my plans of escape accordingly. The result of these inquiries I will now state, in order that the ensuing narrative may be the better understood.

The bay of Nukuheva in which we were then lying is an expanse of water not unlike in figure the space included within the limits of a horse-shoe. It is, perhaps, nine miles in circumference. You approach it from the sea by a narrow entrance, flanked on either side by two small twin islets which soar conically to the height of some five hundred feet. From these the shore recedes on both hands, and describes a deep semicircle.

From the verge of the water the land rises uniformly on all sides, with green and sloping acclivities, until from gently rolling hill-sides and moderate elevations it insensibly swells into lofty and majestic heights, whose blue outlines, ranged all around, close in the view. The beautiful aspect of the shore is heightened by deep and romantic glens, which come down to it at almost equal distances, all apparently radiating from a common centre, and the upper extremities of which are lost to the eye beneath the shadow of the mountains. Down each of these little valleys flows a clear stream, here and there assuming the form of a slender cascade, then stealing invisibly along until it burst upon the sight again in larger and more noisy waterfalls, and at last demurely wanders along to the sea.

The houses of the natives, constructed of the yellow bamboo, tastefully twisted together in a kind of wickerwork, and thatched with the long tapering leaves of the palmetto, are scattered irregularly along these valleys beneath the shady branches of the coco-nut trees.

Nothing can exceed the imposing scenery of this bay. Viewed from our ship as she lay at anchor in the middle of the harbour, it presented the appearance of a vast natural amphitheatre in decay, and overgrown with vines, the deep glens that furrowed its sides appearing like enormous fissures caused by the ravages of time. Very often when lost in admiration at its beauty, I have experienced a pang of regret that a scene so enchanting should be hidden from the world in these remote seas, and seldom meet the eyes of devoted lovers of nature.

Besides this bay the shores of the island are indented by several other extensive inlets, into which descend broad and verdant valleys. These are inhabited by as many distinct tribes of savages, who, although speaking kindred dialects of a common language, and having the same religion and laws, have from time immemorial waged hereditary warfare against each other. The intervening mountains, generally two or three thousand feet above the level of the sea, geographically define the territories of each of these hostile tribes, who never cross them, save on some expedition of war or plunder. Immediately adjacent to Nukuheva, and only separated from it by the mountains seen from the harbour, lies the lovely valley of Happar, whose inmates cherish the most friendly relations with the inhabitants of Nukuheva. On the other side of Happar, and closely adjoining it, is the magnificent valley of the dreaded Typees, the unappeasable enemies of both these tribes.

These celebrated warriors appear to inspire the other islanders with unspeakable terrors. Their very name is a frightful one; for the word "Typee" in the Marquesan dialect signifies a lover of human flesh. It is rather singular that the title should have been bestowed upon them exclusively, inasmuch as the natives of all this group are irreclaimable cannibals. The name may, perhaps, have been given to denote the peculiar ferocity of this clan, and to convey a special stigma along with it.

These same Typees enjoy a prodigious notoriety all over the islands. The natives of Nukuheva would frequently recount in pantomime to our ship's company their terrible feats, and would show the marks of wounds they had received in desperate encounters with them. When ashore they would try to frighten us by pointing to one of their own number, and calling him a Typee, manifesting no little surprise that we did not take to our heels at so terrible an announcement. It was quite amusing, too, to see with what earnestness they disclaimed all cannibal propensities on their own part while they denounced their enemies—the Typees—as inveterate gormandizers of human flesh; but this is a peculiarity to which I shall hereafter have occasion to allude.

Although I was convinced that the inhabitants of our bay were as arrant cannibals as any of the other tribes on the island, still I could not but feel a particular and most unqualified repugnance to the aforesaid Typees. Even before visiting the Marquesas, I had heard from men who had touched at the group on former voyages some revolting stories in connection with these savages; and fresh in my remembrance was the adventure of the master of the *Katherine*, who, only a few months previous, imprudently venturing into this bay in an armed boat for the purpose of barter, was seized by the natives, carried back a little distance into their valley, and was only saved from a cruel death by the intervention of a young girl, who facilitated his escape by night along the beach to Nukuheva.

I had heard too of an English vessel that many years ago, after a weary cruise, sought to enter the bay of Nukuheva, and, arriving within two or three miles of the land, was met by a large canoe filled with natives, who offered to lead the way to the place of their destination. The captain, unacquainted with the localities of the island, joyfully acceded to the proposition—the canoe paddled on and the ship followed. She was soon conducted to a beautiful inlet, and dropped her anchor in its waters beneath the shadows of the lofty shore. That same night the perfidious Typees, who had thus inveigled her into their fatal bay, flocked aboard the doomed vessel by hundreds, and at a given signal murdered every soul on board.

I shall never forget the observation of one of our crew as we were passing slowly by the entrance of this bay in our way to Nukuheva. As we stood gazing over the side at the verdant headlands, Ned, pointing with his hand in the direction of the treacherous valley exclaimed, "There—there's Typee. Oh, the bloody cannibals, what a meal they'd make of us if we were to take it into our heads to land! but they say they don't like sailor's flesh, it's too salt. I say, matey, how should you like to be shoved ashore there, eh?" I little thought, as I shuddered at the question, that in the space of a few weeks I should actually be a captive in that self-same valley.

The French, although they had gone through the ceremony of hoisting their colours for a few hours at all the principal places of the group, had not as yet visited the bay of Typee, anticipating a fierce resistance on the part of the savages there, which for the present at least they wished to avoid. Perhaps they were not a little influenced in the adoption of this unusual policy from a recollection of the warlike reception given by the Typees to the forces of Captain Porter, about the year 1814, when that brave and accomplished officer endeavoured to subjugate the clan merely to gratify the mortal hatred of his allies the Nukuhevas and Happars.

On that occasion I have been told that a considerable detachment of sailors and marines from the frigate *Essex*, accompanied by at least two thousand warriors of Happar and Nukuheva, landed in boats and canoes at the head of the bay, and, after penetrating a little distance into the valley, met with the stoutest resistance from its inmates. Valiantly, although with much loss, the Typees disputed every inch of ground, and after some hard fighting obliged their assailants to retreat and abandon their design of conquest.

The invaders, on their march back to the sea, consoled themselves for their repulse by setting fire to every house and temple in their route; and a long line of smoking ruins defaced the once-smiling bosom of the valley, and proclaimed to its pagan inhabitants the spirit that reigned in the breasts of Christian soldiers. Who can wonder at the deadly hatred of the Typees to all foreigners after such unprovoked atrocities?

Thus it is that they whom we denominate "savages" are made to deserve the title. When the inhabitants of some sequestered island first descry the "big canoe" of the European rolling through the blue waters towards their shores, they rush down to the beach in crowds, and with open arms stand ready to embrace the strangers. Fatal embrace! They fold to their bosoms the vipers whose sting is destined to poison all their joys; and the instinctive feeling of love within their breasts is soon converted into the bitterest hate.

The enormities perpetrated in the South Seas upon some of the inoffensive islanders well nigh pass belief. These things are seldom proclaimed at home; they happen at the very ends of the earth; they are done in a corner, and there are none to reveal them. But there is, nevertheless, many a petty trader that has navigated the Pacific whose course from island to island might be traced by a series of cold-blooded robberies, kidnappings, and murders, the iniquity of which might be considered almost sufficient to sink her guilty timbers to the bottom of the sea.

Sometimes vague accounts of such things reach our firesides, and we coolly censure them as wrong, impolitic, needlessly severe, and dangerous to the crews of other vessels. How different is our tone when we read the highly wrought description of the massacre of the crew of the *Hobomak* by the Feejees; how we sympathise for the unhappy victims, and with what horror do we regard the diabolical heathens, who, after all, have but avenged the unprovoked injuries which they have received. We breathe nothing but vengeance, and equip armed vessels to traverse thousands of miles of ocean in order to execute summary punishment upon the offenders. On arriving at their destination, they burn, slaughter, and destroy, according to the tenor of written instructions, and sailing away from the scene of devastation call upon all Christendom to applaud their courage and their justice.

How often is the term "savages" incorrectly applied! None really deserving of it were ever yet discovered by voyagers or by travellers. They have discovered heathens and barbarians, whom by horrible cruelties they have exasperated into savages. It may be asserted without fear of contradiction, that in all the cases of outrages committed by Polynesians, Europeans have at some time or other been the aggressors, and that the cruel and bloodthirsty disposition of some of the islanders is mainly to be ascribed to the influence of such examples.

But to return. Owing to the mutual hostilities of the different tribes I have mentioned, the mountainous tracts which separate their respective territories remain altogether uninhabited; the natives invariably dwelling in the depths of the valleys, with a view of securing themselves from the predatory incursions of their enemies, who often lurk along their borders, ready to cut off any imprudent straggler, or make a descent upon the inmates of some sequestered habitation. I several times met with very aged men, who from this cause had never passed the confines of their native vale, some of them having never even ascended midway up the mountains in the whole course of their lives, and who, accordingly, had little idea of the appearance of any other part of the island, the whole of which is not perhaps more than sixty miles in circuit. The little space in which some of these clans pass away their days would seem almost incredible.

The glen of Tior will furnish a curious illustration of this. The inhabited part is not more than four miles in length, and varies in breadth from half a mile to less than a quarter. The rocky vine-clad cliffs on one side tower almost perpendicularly from their base to the height of at least fifteen hundred feet; while across the vale—in‐striking contrast to the scenery opposite— grass-grown elevations rise one above another in blooming terraces. Hemmed in by these stupendous barriers, the valley would be altogether shut out from the rest of the world, were it not that it is accessible from the sea at one end, and by a narrow defile at the other.

The impression produced upon my mind, when I first visited this beautiful glen, will never be obliterated.

I had come from Nukuheva by water in the ship's boat, and when we entered the bay of Tior it was high noon. The heat had been intense, as we had been floating upon the long smooth swell of the ocean, for there was but little wind. The sun's rays had expended all their fury upon us; and to add to our discomfort, we had omitted to supply ourselves with water previous to starting. What with heat and thirst together, I became so impatient to get ashore that, when at last we glided towards it, I stood up in the bow of the boat ready for a spring. As she shot two-thirds of her length high upon the beach, propelled by three or four strong strokes of the oars, I leaped among a parcel of juvenile savages, who stood prepared to give us a kind reception, and with them at my heels, yelling like so many imps, I rushed forward across the open ground in the vicinity of the sea, and plunged, diver fashion, into the recesses of the first grove that offered.

What a delightful sensation did I experience! I felt as if floating in some new element, while all sorts of gurgling, trickling, liquid sounds fell upon my ear. People may say what they will about the refreshing influences of a cold-water bath, but commend me when in a perspiration to the shade baths of Tior, beneath the coco-nut trees, and amidst the cool delightful atmosphere which surrounds them.

How shall I describe the scenery that met my eye, as I looked out from this verdant recess! The narrow valley, with its steep and close-adjoining sides draperied with vines, and arched overhead with a fretwork of interlacing boughs, nearly hidden from view by masses of leafy verdure, seemed from where I stood like an immense arbour disclosing its vista to the eye, whilst as I advanced it insensibly widened into the loveliest vale eye ever beheld.

It so happened that the very day I was in Tior the French admiral, attended by all the boats of his squadron, came down in state from Nukuheva to take formal possession of the place. He remained in the valley about two hours, during which time he had a ceremonious interview with the king.

The patriarch-sovereign of Tior was a man very far advanced in years; but though age had bowed his form and rendered him almost decrepit, his gigantic frame retained all its original magnitude and grandeur of appearance. He advanced, slowly and with evident pain, assisting his tottering steps with the heavy war-spear he held in his hand, and attended by a group of grey-bearded chiefs, on one of whom he occasionally leaned for support. The admiral came forward with head uncovered and extended hand, while the old king saluted him by a stately flourish of his weapon. The next moment they stood side by side, these two extremes of the social scale—the polished, splendid Frenchman, and the poor tatooed savage. They were both tall and noble-looking men; but in other respects how strikingly contrasted! Du Petit Thouars exhibited upon his person all the paraphernalia of his naval rank. He wore a richly decorated admiral's frock-coat, a laced *chapeau bras,* and upon his breast were a variety of ribbons and orders; while the simple islander, with the exception of a slight cincture about his loins, appeared in all the nakedness of nature.

At what an immeasurable distance, thought I, are these two beings removed from each other. In the one is shown the result of long centuries of progressive civilization and refinement, which have gradually converted the mere creature into the semblance of all that is elevated and grand; while the other, after the lapse of the same period, has not advanced one step in the career of improvement. "Yet, after all," quoth I to myself, "insensible as he is to a thousand wants, and removed from harassing cares, may not the savage be the happier man of the two?" Such were the thoughts that arose in my mind as I gazed upon the novel spectacle before me. In truth it was an impressive one, and little likely to be effaced. I can recall even now with vivid distinctiveness every feature of the scene. The umbrageous shades where the interview took place—the glorious tropical vegetation around—the picturesque grouping of the mingled throng of soldiery and natives—and even the golden-hued bunch of bananas that I held in my hand at the time, and of which I occasionally partook while making the aforesaid philosophical reflections.

CHAPTER V

THOUGHTS PREVIOUS TO ATTEMPTING AN ESCAPE—TOBY, A FELLOW SAILOR, AGREES TO SHARE THE ADVENTURE—LAST NIGHT ABOARD THE SHIP.

HAVING fully resolved to leave the vessel clandestinely, and having acquired all the knowledge concerning the bay that I could obtain under the circumstances in which I was placed, I now deliberately turned over in my mind every plan of escape that suggested itself, being determined to act with all possible prudence in an attempt where failure would be attended with so many disagreeable consequences. The idea of being taken and brought back ignominiously to the ship was so inexpressibly repulsive to me that I was determined by no hasty and imprudent measures to render such an event probable.

I knew that our worthy captain, who felt such a paternal solicitude for the welfare of his crew, would not willingly consent that one of his best hands should encounter the perils of a sojourn among the natives of a barbarous island; and I was certain that in the event of my disappearance, his fatherly anxiety would prompt him to offer, by way of a reward, yard upon yard of gaily printed calico for my apprehension. He might even have appreciated my services at the value of a musket, in which case I felt perfectly certain that the whole population of the bay would be immediately upon my track, incited by the prospect of so magnificent a bounty.

Having ascertained the fact before alluded to, that the islanders, from motives of precaution, dwelt altogether in the depths of the valleys, and avoided wandering about the more elevated portions of the shore, unless bound on some expedition of war or plunder, I concluded that if I could effect unperceived a passage to the mountains, I might easily remain among them, supporting myself by such fruits as came in my way until the sailing of the ship, an event of which I could not fail to be immediately apprised, as from my lofty position I should command a view of the entire harbour.

The idea pleased me greatly. It seemed to combine a great deal of practicability with no inconsiderable enjoyment in a quiet way; for how delightful it would be to look down upon the detested old vessel from the height of some thousand feet, and contrast the verdant scenery about me with the recollection of her narrow decks and gloomy forecastle! Why, it was really refreshing even to think of it; and so I straightway fell to picturing myself seated beneath a coco-nut tree on the brow of the mountain, with a cluster of plantains within easy reach, criticizing her nautical evolutions as she was working her way out of the harbour.

To be sure there was one rather unpleasant drawback to these agreeable anticipations—the possibility of falling in with a foraging party of these same bloody-minded Typees, whose appetites, edged perhaps by the air of so elevated a region, might prompt them to devour one. This, I must confess, was a most disagreeable view of the matter.

Just to think of a party of these unnatural gormands taking it into their heads to make a convivial meal of a poor devil, who would have no means of escape or defence; however, there was no help for it. I was willing to encounter some risks in order to accomplish my object, and counted much upon my ability to elude these prowling cannibals amongst the many coverts which the mountains afforded. Besides, the chances were ten to one in my favour that they would none of them quit their own fastnesses.

I had determined not to communicate my design of withdrawing from the vessel to any of my shipmates, and least of all to solicit any one to accompany me in my flight. But it so happened one night that being upon deck, revolving over in my mind various plans of escape, I perceived one of the ship's company leaning over the bulwarks, apparently plunged in a profound reverie. He was a young fellow about my own age, for whom I had all along entertained a great regard, and Toby, such was the name by which he went among us, for his real name he would never tell us, was every way worthy of it. He was active, ready, and obliging, of dauntless courage, and singularly open and fearless in the expression of his feelings. I had on more than one occasion got him out of scrapes into which this had led him; and I know not whether it was from this cause, or a certain congeniality of sentiment between us, that he had always shown a partiality for my society. We had battled out many a long watch together, beguiling the weary hours with chat, song, and story, mingled with a good many imprecations upon the hard destiny it seemed our common fortune to encounter.

Toby, like myself, had evidently moved in a different sphere of life, and his conversation at times betrayed this, although he was anxious to conceal it. He was one of that class of rovers you sometimes meet at sea, who never reveal their origin, never allude to home, and go rambling over the world as if pursued by some mysterious fate they cannot possibly elude.

There was much even in the appearance of Toby calculated to draw me towards him, for while the greater part of the crew were as coarse in person as in mind, Toby was endowed with a remarkably prepossessing exterior. Arrayed in his blue frock and duck trousers, he was as smart a looking sailor as ever stepped upon a deck; he was singularly small and slightly made, with great flexibility of limb. His naturally dark complexion had been deepened by exposure to the tropical sun, and a mass of jetty locks clustered about his temples and threw a darker shade into his large black eyes. He was a strange, wayward being, moody, fitful, and melancholy—at times almost morose. He had a quick and fiery temper too, which, when thoroughly roused, transported him into a state bordering on delirium.

It is strange the power that a mind of deep passion has over feebler natures. I have seen a brawny fellow, with no lack of ordinary courage, fairly quail before this slender stripling, when in one of his furious fits. But these paroxysms seldom occurred, and in them my big-hearted shipmate vented the bile which more calm-tempered individuals get rid of by a continual pettishness at trivial annoyances.

No one ever saw Toby laugh; I mean in the hearty abandonment of broad-mouthed mirth. He did smile sometimes, it is true; and there was a good deal of dry sarcastic humour about him, which told the more from the imperturbable gravity of his tone and manner.

Latterly I had observed that Toby's melancholy had greatly increased, and I had frequently seen him since our arrival at the island gazing wistfully upon the shore, when the remainder of the crew would be rioting below. I was aware that he entertained a cordial detestation of the ship, and believed that, should a fair chance of escape present itself, he would embrace it willingly. But the attempt was so perilous in the place where we then lay, that I supposed myself the only individual on board the ship who was sufficiently reckless to think of it. In this, however, I was mistaken.

When I perceived Toby leaning, as I have mentioned, against the bulwarks and buried in thought, it struck me at once that the subject of his meditations might be the same as my own. And if it be so, thought I, is he not the very one of all my shipmates whom I would choose for the partner of my adventure? and why should I not have some comrade with me to divide its dangers and alleviate its hardships? Perhaps I might be obliged to lie concealed among the mountains for weeks. In such an event what a solace would a companion be?

These thoughts passed rapidly through my mind, and I wondered why I had not before considered the matter in this light. But it was not too late. A tap upon the shoulder served to rouse Toby from his reverie; I found him ripe for the enterprise, and a very few words sufficed for a mutual understanding between us. In an hour's time we had arranged all the preliminaries, and decided upon our plan of action. We then ratified our engagement with an affectionate wedding of palms, and to elude suspicion repaired each to his hammock, to spend the last night on board the *Dolly*.

The next day the starboard watch, to which we both belonged, was to be sent ashore on liberty; and, availing ourselves of this opportunity, we determined, as soon after landing as possible, to separate ourselves from the rest of the men without exciting their suspicions, and strike back at once for the mountains. Seen from the ship, their summits appeared inaccessible, but here and there sloping spurs extended from them almost into the sea, buttressing the lofty elevations with which they were connected, and forming those radiating valleys I have before described. One of these ridges, which appeared more practicable than the rest, we determined to climb, convinced that it would conduct us to the heights beyond. Accordingly, we carefully observed its bearings and locality from the ship, so that when ashore we should run no chance of missing it.

In all this the leading object we had in view was to seclude ourselves from sight until the departure of the vessel; then to take our chance as to the reception the Nukuheva natives might give us; and, after remaining upon the island as long as we found our stay agreeable, to leave it the first favourable opportunity that offered.

CHAPTER VI

A SPECIMEN OF NAUTICAL ORATORY—CRITICISMS OF THE SAILORS—THE STAR-
BOARD WATCH ARE GIVEN A HOLIDAY—THE ESCAPE TO THE MOUNTAINS.

EARLY the next morning the starboard watch were mustered upon the quarter-
deck, and our worthy captain, standing in the cabin gangway, harangued us as
follows:—

"Now, men, as we are just off a six months' cruise, and have got through
most all our work in port here, I suppose you want to go ashore. Well, I mean
to give your watch liberty to-day, so you may get ready as soon as you please,
and go; but understand this, I am going to give you liberty because I suppose
you would growl like so many old quarter gunners if I didn't; at the same
time, if you'll take my advice, every mother's son of you will stay aboard, and
keep out of the way of the bloody cannibals altogether. Ten to one, men, if
you go ashore, you will get into some infernal row, and that will be the end of
you; for if those tattooed scoundrels get you a little ways back into their
valleys, they'll nab you—that you may be certain of. Plenty of white men
have gone ashore here and never been seen any more. There was the old *Dido*,
she put in here about two years ago, and sent one watch off on liberty; they
never were heard of again for a week—the natives swore they didn't know
where they were—and only three of them ever got back to the ship again,
and one with his face damaged for life, for the cursed heathens tattooed a broad
patch clean across his figurehead. But it will be no use talking to you, for go
you will, that I see plainly; so all I have to say is, that you need not blame
me if the islanders make a meal of you. You may stand some chance of
escaping them though, if you keep close about the French encampment, and
are back to the ship again before sunset. Keep that much in your mind, if
you forget all the rest I've been saying to you. There, go forward; bear a
hand and rig yourselves, and stand by for a call. At two bells the boat will
be manned to take you off, and the Lord have mercy on you!"

Various were the emotions depicted upon the countenances of the starboard
watch whilst listening to this address; but on its conclusion there was a general
move towards the forecastle, and we soon were all busily engaged in getting
ready for the holiday so auspiciously announced by the skipper. During these
preparations his harangue was commented upon in no very measured terms;
and one of the party, after denouncing him as a lying old son of a sea-cook
who begrudged a fellow a few hours' liberty, exclaimed with an oath, "But
you don't bounce me out of my liberty, old chap, for all your yarns; for I
would go ashore if every pebble on the beach was a live coal, and every stick
a gridiron, and the cannibals stood ready to broil me on landing."

The spirit of this sentiment was responded to by all hands, and we resolved that in spite of the captain's croakings we would make a glorious day
of it.

But Toby and I had our own game to play, and we availed ourselves of
the confusion which always reigns among a ship's company preparatory to going
ashore, to confer together and complete our arrangements. As our object was to
effect as rapid a flight as possible to the mountains, we determined not to
encumber ourselves with any superfluous apparel; and, accordingly, while the
rest were rigging themselves out with some idea of making a display, we were

content to put on new stout duck trousers, serviceable pumps, and heavy Havre-frocks which, with a Payta hat, completed our equipment.

When our shipmates wondered at this, Toby exclaimed in his odd grave way that the rest might do as they liked, but that he for one preserved his go-ashore traps for the Spanish main, where the tie of a sailor's neckerchief might make some difference; but as for a parcel of unbreeched heathen, he wouldn't go to the bottom of his chest for any of them, and was half disposed to appear among them in buff himself. The men laughed at what they thought was one of his strange conceits, and so we escaped suspicion.

It may appear singular that we should have been thus on our guard with our own shipmates; but there were some among us who, had they possessed the least inkling of our project, would, for a paltry hope of reward, have immediately communicated it to the captain.

As soon as two bells were struck, the word was passed for the liberty men to get into the boat. I lingered behind in the forecastle a moment to take a parting glance at its familiar features, and just as I was about to ascend to the deck my eye happened to light on the bread-barge and beef-kid, which contained the remnants of our hasty meal. Although I had never before thought of providing anything in the way of food for our expedition, as I fully relied upon the fruits of the island to sustain us wherever we might wander, yet I could not resist the inclination I felt to provide luncheon from the relics before me. Accordingly I took a double handful of these small, broken, flinty bits of biscuit which generally go by the name of "midshipmen's nuts," and thrust them into the bosom of my frock; in which same ample receptacle I had previously stowed away several pounds of tobacco and a few yards of cotton cloth—articles with which I intended to purchase the good-will of the natives as soon as we should appear among them after the departure of our vessel.

This last addition to my stock caused a considerable protuberance in front, which I abated in a measure by shaking the bits of bread around my waist, and distributing the plugs of tobacco among the folds of the garment.

Hardly had I completed these arrangements when my name was sung out by a dozen voices, and I sprang upon the deck, where I found all the party in the boat, and impatient to shove off. I dropped over the side and seated myself with the rest of the watch in the stern sheets, while the poor larborders shipped their oars, and commenced pulling us ashore.

This happened to be the rainy season at the islands, and the heavens had nearly the whole morning betokened one of those heavy showers which during this period so frequently occur. The large drops fell bubbling into the water shortly after our leaving the ship, and by the time we had effected a landing it poured down in torrents. We fled for shelter under cover of an immense canoe-house which stood hard by the beach, and waited for the first fury of the storm to pass.

It continued, however, without cessation; and the monotonous beating of the rain overhead began to exert a drowsy influence upon the men, who, throwing themselves here and there upon the large war-canoes, after chatting awhile, all fell asleep.

This was the opportunity we desired, and Toby and I availed ourselves of it at once by stealing out of the canoe-house and plunging into the depths of an extensive grove that was in its rear. After ten minutes' rapid progress we gained an open space from which we could just descry the ridge we intended to mount looming dimly through the mists of the tropical shower, and distant from us, as we estimated, something more than a mile. Our direct course towards it lay through a rather populous part of the bay; but desirous as we were of evading the natives, and securing an unmolested retreat to the mountains, we determined, by taking a circuit through some extensive thickets, to avoid their vicinity altogether.

The heavy rain that still continued to fall without intermission favoured our enterprise, as it drove the islanders into their houses, and prevented any casual meeting with them. Our heavy frocks soon became completely saturated with water, and by their weight, and that of the articles we had concealed beneath them, not a little impeded our progress. But it was no time to pause when at any moment we might be surprised by a body of the savages, and forced at the very outset to relinquish our undertaking.

Since leaving the canoe-house we had scarcely exchanged a single syllable with one another; but when we entered a second narrow opening in the wood, and again caught sight of the ridge before us, I took Toby by the arm and, pointing along its sloping outline to the lofty heights at its extremity, said in a low tone, "Now, Toby, not a word, nor a glance backward, till we stand on the summit of yonder mountain—so no more lingering, but let us shove ahead while we can, and in a few hours' time we may laugh aloud. You are the lightest and the nimblest, so lead on, and I will follow."

"All right, brother," said Toby, "quick's our play; only let's keep close together, that's all;" and so saying, with a bound like a young roe, he cleared a brook which ran across our path, and rushed forward with a quick step.

When we arrived within a short distance of the ridge, we were stopped by a mass of tall yellow reeds, growing together as thickly as they could stand, and as tough and stubborn as so many rods of steel; and we perceived, to our chagrin, that they extended midway up the elevation we purposed to ascend.

For a moment we gazed about us in quest of a more practicable route; it was, however, at once apparent that there was no resource but to pierce this thicket of canes at all hazards. We now reversed our order of march, I, being the heaviest, taking the lead, with a view of breaking a path through the obstruction, while Toby fell into the rear.

Two or three times I endeavoured to insinuate myself between the canes and by dint of coaxing and bending them to make some progress; but a bull-frog might as well have tried to work a passage through the teeth of a comb, and I gave up the attempt in despair.

Half wild with meeting an obstacle we had so little anticipated, I threw myself desperately against it, crushing to the ground the canes with which I came in contact; and, rising to my feet again, repeated the action with like effect. Twenty minutes of this violent exercise almost exhausted me, but it carried us some way into the thicket; when Toby, who had been reaping the benefit of my labours by following close at my heels, proposed to become pioneer in turn, and accordingly passed ahead with a view of affording me a respite from my exertions. As however with his slight frame he made but bad work of it, I was soon obliged to resume my old place again.

On we toiled, the perspiration starting from our bodies in floods, our limbs torn and lacerated with the splintered fragments of the broken canes, until we had proceeded perhaps as far as the middle of the brake, when suddenly it ceased raining, and the atmosphere around us became close and sultry beyond expression. The elasticity of the reeds, quickly recovering from the temporary pressure of our bodies, caused them to spring back to their original position; so that they closed in upon us as we advanced, and prevented the circulation of the little air which might otherwise have reached us. Besides this, their great height completely shut us out from the view of surrounding objects, and we were not certain but that we might have been going all the time in a wrong direction.

Fatigued with my long-continued efforts, and panting for breath, I felt myself completely incapacitated for any further exertion. I rolled up the sleeve of my frock, and squeezed the moisture it contained into my parched mouth. But the few drops I managed to obtain gave me little relief, and I sank down for a moment with a sort of dogged apathy, from which I was aroused by Toby, who had devised a plan to free us from the net in which we had become entangled.

He was laying about him lustily with his sheath-knife, lopping the canes right and left, like a reaper, and soon made quite a clearing around us. This sight reanimated me, and seizing my own knife, I hacked and hewed away without mercy. But alas! the farther we advanced, the thicker and taller, and apparently the more interminable, the reeds became.

I began to think we were fairly snared, and had almost made up my mind that without a pair of wings we should never be able to escape from the toils, when all at once I discerned a peep of daylight through the canes on my right, and, communicating the joyful tidings to Toby, we both fell to with fresh spirit, and speedily opening a passage towards it we found ourselves clear of perplexities, and in the near vicinity of the ridge.

After resting for a few moments we began the ascent, and after a little vigorous climbing found ourselves close to its summit. Instead however of walking along its ridge, where we should have been in full view of the natives in the vales beneath, and at a point where they could easily intercept us were they so inclined, we cautiously advanced on one side, crawling on our hands and knees, and screened from observation by the grass through which we glided, much in the fashion of a couple of serpents. After an hour employed in this unpleasant kind of locomotion, we started to our feet again and pursued our way boldly along the crest of the ridge.

This salient spur of the lofty elevations that encompassed the bay rose with a sharp angle from the valleys at its base, and presented, with the exception of a few steep acclivities, the appearance of a vast inclined plane, sweeping down towards the sea from the heights in the distance. We had ascended it near the place of its termination and at its lowest point, and now saw our route to the mountains distinctly defined along its narrow crest, which was covered with a soft carpet of verdure, and was in many parts only a few feet wide.

Elated with the success which had so far attended our enterprise, and invigorated by the refreshing atmosphere we now inhaled, Toby and I in high spirits were making our way rapidly along the ridge when suddenly from the valleys below which lay on either side of us we heard the distant shouts of the natives, who had just descried us, and to whom our figures, brought in bold relief against the sky, were plainly revealed.

Glancing our eyes into these valleys, we perceived their savage inhabitants hurrying to and fro, seemingly under the influence of some sudden alarm, and appearing to the eye scarcely bigger than so many pigmies; while their white-thatched dwellings dwarfed by the distance, looked like baby-houses. As we looked down upon the islanders from our lofty elevation, we experienced a sense of security; feeling confident that, should they undertake a pursuit, it would, from the start we had, prove entirely fruitless, unless they followed us into the mountains, where we knew they cared not to venture.

However, we thought it as well to make the most of our time; and accordingly, where the ground would admit of it, we ran swiftly along the summit of the ridge, until we were brought to a stand by a steep cliff, which at first seemed to interpose an effectual barrier to our further advance. By dint of much hard scrambling, however, and at some risk to our necks, we at last surmounted it, and continued our flight with unabated celerity.

We had left the beach early in the morning, and after an uninterrupted, though at times difficult and dangerous ascent, during which we had never once turned our faces to the sea, we found ourselves, about three hours before sunset, standing on the top of what seemed to be the highest land on the island, an immense overhanging cliff composed of basaltic rocks, hung round with parasitical plants. We must have been more than three thousand feet above the level of the sea, and the scenery viewed from this height was magnificent.

The lonely bay of Nukuheva, dotted here and there with the black hulls of the vessels composing the French squadron, lay reposing at the base of a circular range of elevations, whose verdant sides, perforated with deep glens or diversified with smiling valleys, formed altogether the loveliest view I ever beheld, and were I to live a hundred years, I should never forget the feeling of admiration which I then experienced.

CHAPTER VII

THE OTHER SIDE OF THE MOUNTAIN—DISAPPOINTMENT—INVENTORY OF ARTICLES BROUGHT FROM THE SHIP—DIVISION OF THE STOCK OF BREAD—APPEARANCE OF THE INTERIOR OF THE ISLAND—A DISCOVERY—A RAVINE AND WATERFALL —A SLEEPLESS NIGHT—FURTHER DISCOVERIES—MY ILLNESS—A MARQUESAN LANDSCAPE.

My curiosity had been not a little raised with regard to the description of country we should meet on the other side of the mountains; and I had supposed, with Toby, that immediately on gaining the heights we should be enabled to view the large bays of Happar and Typee reposing at our feet on one side, in the same way that Nukuheva lay spread out below on the other. But here we were disappointed. Instead of finding the mountain we had ascended sweeping down in the opposite direction into broad and capacious valleys, the land appeared to retain its general elevation, only broken into a series of ridges and inter-vales, which as far as the eye could reach stretched away from us, with their precipitous sides covered with the brightest verdure, and waving here and there with the foliage of clumps of woodland; among which, however, we perceived none of those trees upon whose fruit we had relied with such certainty.

This was a most unlooked-for discovery, and one that promised to defeat our plans altogether, for we could not think of descending the mountain on the Nukuheva side in quest of food. Should we for this purpose be induced to retrace our steps, we should run no small chance of encountering the natives, who in that case, if they did nothing worse to us, would be certain to convey us back to the ship for the sake of the reward in calico and trinkets, which we had no doubt our skipper would hold out to them as an inducement to our capture.

What was to be done? The *Dolly* would not sail perhaps for ten days and how were we to sustain life during this period? I bitterly repented our improvidence in not providing ourselves, as we easily might have done, with a supply of biscuit. With a rueful visage I now bethought me of the scanty handful of bread I had stuffed into the bosom of my frock, and felt somewhat desirous to ascertain what part of it had weathered the rather rough usage it had experienced in ascending the mountain. I accordingly proposed to Toby that we should enter into a joint examination of the various articles we had brought from the ship. With this intent we seated ourselves upon the grass; and a little curious to see with what kind of judgment my companion had filled his frock—which I remarked seemed about as well lined as my own—I requested him to commence operations by spreading out its contents.

Thrusting his hand, then, into the bosom of this capacious receptacle, he first brought to light about a pound of tobacco, whose component parts still adhered together, the whole outside being covered with soft particles of sea-bread. Wet and dripping, it had the appearance of having just been recovered from the bottom of the sea. But I paid slight attention to a substance of so little value to us in our present situation, as soon I perceived the indications it gave of Toby's foresight in laying in a supply of food for the expedition.

I eagerly inquired what quantity he had brought with him, when, rummaging once more beneath his garment, he produced a small handful of something so soft, pulpy, and discoloured, that for a few moments he was as much puzzled as myself to tell by what possible instrumentality such a villainous compound had become engendered in his bosom. I can only describe it as a hash of soaked bread and bits of tobacco, brought to a doughy consistency by the united agency of perspiration and rain. But repulsive as it might otherwise have been, I now regarded it as an invaluable treasure, and proceeded with great care to transfer this paste-like mass to a large leaf which I had plucked from a bush beside me. Toby informed me that in the morning he had placed two whole biscuits in his bosom, with a view of munching them, should he feel so inclined, during our flight. These were now reduced to the equivocal substance which I had just placed on the leaf.

Another dive into the frock brought to view some four or five yards of calico print, whose tasteful pattern was rather disfigured by the yellow stains of the tobacco with which it had been brought in contact. In drawing this calico slowly from his bosom inch by inch, Toby reminded me of a juggler performing the feat of the endless ribbon. The next cast was a small one, being a sailor's little "ditty-bag," containing needles, thread, and other sewing utensils; then came a razor-case, followed by two or three separate plugs of negro-head, which were fished up from the bottom of the now empty receptacle. These various matters being inspected, I produced the few things that I had myself brought.

As might have been anticipated from the state of my companion's edible supplies, I found my own in a deplorable condition, and diminished to a quantity that would have formed half a dozen mouthfuls for a hungry man who was partial enough to tobacco not to mind swallowing it. A few morsels of bread, with a fathom or two of white cotton cloth, and several pounds of choice pigtail, composed the extent of my possessions.

Our joint stock of miscellaneous articles was now made up into a compact bundle, which it was agreed we should carry alternately. But the sorry remains of the biscuit were not to be disposed of so summarily: the precarious circumstances in which we were placed made us regard them as something on which very probably depended the fate of our adventure.   After a brief discussion in which we both of us expressed our resolution of not descending into the bay until the ship's departure, I suggested to my companion that little of it as there was, we should divide the bread into six equal portions, each of which should be a day's allowance for both of us. This proposition he assented to; so I took the silk kerchief from my neck, and, cutting it with my knife into half a dozen equal pieces, proceeded to make an exact division.

At first, Toby, with a degree of fastidiousness that seemed to me ill-timed, was for picking out the minute particles of tobacco with which the spongy mass was mixed; but against this proceeding I protested, as by such an operation we must have greatly diminished its quantity.

When the division was accomplished, we found that a day's allowance for the two was not a great deal more than what a table-spoon might hold. Each separate portion we immediately rolled up in the bit of silk prepared for it, and joining them altogether into a small package, I committed them, with solemn injunctions of fidelity, to the custody of Toby.   For the remainder of that day we resolved to fast, as we had been fortified by a breakfast in the morning; and now starting again to our feet, we looked about us for a shelter during the night, which, from the appearance of the heavens, promised to be a dark and tempestuous one.

There was no place near us which would in any way answer our purpose; so turning our backs upon Nukuheva, we commenced exploring the unknown regions which lay upon the other side of the mountain.

In this direction, as far as our vision extended, not a sign of life, nor anything that denoted even the transient residence of man, could be seen. The whole landscape seemed one unbroken solitude, the interior of the island having apparently been untenanted since the morning of the creation; and as we advanced through this wilderness, our voices sounded strangely in our ears, as though human accents had never before disturbed the fearful silence of the place, interrupted only by the low murmurings of distant water-falls.

Our disappointment, however, in not finding the various fruits with which we had intended to regale ourselves during our stay in these wilds, was a good deal lessened by the consideration that from this very circumstance we should be much less exposed to a casual meeting with the savage tribes about us, who we knew always dwelt beneath the shadows of those trees which supplied them with food.

We wandered along, casting eager glances into every bush we passed, until just as we had succeeded in mounting one of the many ridges that inter-sected the ground, I saw in the grass before me something like an indistinctly traced footpath, which appeared to lead along the top of the ridge, and to descend with it into a deep ravine about half a mile in advance of us.

Robinson Crusoe could not have been more startled at the footprint in the sand than we were at this unwelcome discovery.   My first impulse was to make as rapid a retreat as possible, and bend our steps in some other direction; but our curiosity to see whither this path might lead, prompted us to pursue it.   So on we went, the track becoming more and more visible the farther we proceeded, until it conducted us to the verge of the ravine, where it abruptly terminated.

"And so," said Toby, peering down into the chasm, "every one that travels this path takes a jump here, eh?"

"Not so," said I, "for I think they might manage to descend without it; what say you—shall we attempt the feat?"

"And what, in the name of caves and coal-holes, do you expect to find at the bottom of that gulf but a broken neck—why it looks blacker than our ship's hold, and the roar of those waterfalls down there would batter one's brains to pieces."

"Oh, no, Toby," I exclaimed, laughing; "but there's something to be seen here, that's plain, or there would have been no path, and I am resolved to find out what it is."

"*I* will tell you what, my pleasant fellow," rejoined Toby quickly, "if you are going to pry into everything you meet with here that excites your curiosity, you will marvellously soon get knocked on the head; to a dead certainty you will come bang upon a party of those savages in the midst of your discovery-makings, and I doubt whether such an event would particularly delight you. Just take my advice for once, and let us 'bout ship and steer in some other direction; besides, it's getting late, and we ought to be mooring ourselves for the night."

"That is just the thing I have been driving at," replied I; "and I am thinking that this ravine will exactly answer our purpose, for it is roomy, secluded, well watered, and may shelter us from the weather."

"Aye, and from sleep too, and by the same token will give us sore throats and rheumatisms into the bargain," cried Toby with evident dislike at the idea.

"Oh, very well then, my lad," said I, "since you will not accompany me, here I go alone. You will see me in the morning"; and advancing to the edge of the cliff upon which we had been standing, I proceeded to lower myself down by the tangled roots which clustered about all the crevices of the rock. As I had anticipated, Toby, in spite of his previous remonstrances, followed my example, and dropping himself with the activity of a squirrel from point to point, he quickly outstripped me, and effected a landing at the bottom before I had accomplished two-thirds of the descent.

The sight that now greeted us was one that will ever be vividly impressed upon my mind. Five foaming streams, rushing through as many gorges, and swelled and turbid by the recent rains, united together in one mad plunge of nearly eighty feet, and fell with wild uproar into a deep black pool scooped out of the gloomy-looking rocks that lay piled around, and thence in one collected body dashed down a narrow sloping channel which seemed to penetrate into the very bowels of the earth. Overhead, vast roots of trees hung down from the sides of the ravine, dripping with moisture, and trembling with the concussions produced by the fall. It was now sunset, and the feeble uncertain light that found its way into these caverns and woody depths heightened their strange appearance, and reminded us that in a short time we should find ourselves in utter darkness.

As soon as I had satisfied my curiosity by gazing at this scene, I fell to wondering how it was that what we had taken for a path should have conducted us to so singular a place, and began to suspect that after all I might have been deceived in supposing it to have been a track formed by the islanders. This was rather an agreeable reflection than otherwise, for it diminished our dread of accidentally meeting with any of them, and I came to the conclusion that perhaps we could not have selected a more secure hiding-place than this very spot we had so accidentally hit upon. Toby agreed with me in this view of the matter, and we immediately began gathering together the limbs of trees which lay scattered about, with the view of constructing a temporary hut for the night. This we were obliged to build close to the foot of the cataract, for the current of water extended very nearly to the sides of the gorge. The few moments of light that remained we employed in covering our hut with a species of broad-bladed grass that grew in every fissure of the ravine. Our hut, if it deserved to be called one, consisted of six or eight of the straightest branches we could find laid obliquely against the steep wall of rock, with their lower ends within a foot of the stream. Into this space thus covered over we managed to crawl, and dispose our wearied bodies as best we could.

Shall I ever forget that horrid night? As for poor Toby, I could scarcely get a word out of him. It would have been some consolation to have heard his voice, but he lay shivering the livelong night like a man with the palsy, with his knees drawn up to his head, while his back was supported against the dripping side of the rock. During this wretched night there seemed nothing wanting to complete the perfect misery of our condition. The rain descended in such torrents that our poor shelter proved a mere mockery. In vain did I try to elude the incessant streams that poured upon me; by protecting one part I only exposed another, and the water was continually finding some new opening through which to drench us.

I have had many a ducking in the course of my life, and in general cared little about it; but the accumulated horrors of that night, the death-like coldness of the place, the appalling darkness and the dismal sense of our forlorn condition, almost unmanned me.

It will not be doubted that the next morning we were early risers, and as soon as I could reach the faintest glimpse of anything like daylight I shook my companion by the arm, and told him it was sunrise. Poor Toby lifted up his head, and after a moment's pause said in a husky voice, "Then, shipmate, my toplights have gone out, for it appears darker now with my eyes open than it did when they were shut."

"Nonsense!" exclaimed I, "you are not awake yet."

"Awake!" roared Toby in a rage, "awake! You mean to insinuate I've been asleep, do you? It is an insult to a man to suppose he could sleep in such an infernal place as this."

By the time I had apologized to my friend for having misconstrued his silence, it had become somewhat more light, and we crawled out of our lair. The rain had ceased, but everything around us was dripping with moisture. We stripped off our saturated garments, and wrung them as dry as we could. We contrived to make the blood circulate in our benumbed limbs by rubbing them vigorously with our hands; and after performing our ablutions in the stream, and putting on our still wet clothes, we began to think it advisable to break our long fast, it being now twenty-four hours since we had tasted food.

Accordingly our day's ration was brought out, and seating ourselves on a detached fragment of rock, we proceeded to discuss it. First we divided it into two equal portions, and, carefully rolling one of them up for our evening's repast, divided the remainder again as equally as possible, and then drew lots for the first choice. I could have placed the morsel that fell to my share upon the tip of my finger; but notwithstanding this I took care that it should be full ten minutes before I had swallowed the last crumb. What a true saying it is that "appetite furnishes the best sauce." There was a flavour and a relish to this small particle of food that under other circumstances it would have been impossible for the most delicate viands to have imparted. A copious draught of the pure water which flowed at our feet served to complete the meal, and after it we rose sensibly refreshed, and prepared for whatever might befall us.

We now carefully examined the chasm in which we had passed the night. We crossed the stream, and gaining the farther side of the pool I have mentioned, discovered proofs that the spot must have been visited by some one but a short time previous to our arrival. Further observation convinced us that it had been regularly frequented, and, as we afterwards conjectured from particular indications, for the purpose of obtaining a certain root, from which the natives obtain a kind of ointment.

These discoveries immediately determined us to abandon a place which had presented no inducement for us to remain, except the promise of security; and as we looked about us for the means of ascending again into the upper regions, we at last found a practicable part of the rock, and half an hour's toil carried us to the summit of the same cliff from which the preceding evening we had descended.

I now proposed to Toby that instead of rambling about the island, exposing ourselves to discovery at every turn, we should select some place as our fixed abode for as long a period as our food should hold out, build ourselves a comfortable hut, and be as prudent and circumspect as possible. To all this my companion assented, and we at once set about carrying the plan into execution.

With this view, after exploring without success a little glen near us, we crossed several of the ridges of which I have before spoken; and about noon found ourselves ascending a long and gradually rising slope, but still without having discovered any place adapted to our purpose. Low and heavy clouds betokened an approaching storm, and we hurried on to gain a covert in a clump of thick bushes which appeared to terminate the long ascent. We threw ourselves under the lee of these bushes, and pulling up the long grass that grew around, covered ourselves completely with it, and awaited the shower.

But it did not come as soon as we had expected, and before many minutes my companion was fast asleep, and I was rapidly falling into the same state of happy forgetfulness. Just at this juncture, however, down came the rain with a violence that put all thoughts of slumber to flight. Although in some measure sheltered, our clothes soon became as wet as ever: this, after all the trouble we had taken to dry them, was provoking enough: but there was no help for it; and I recommend all adventurous youths who abandon vessels in romantic islands during the rainy seasons to provide themselves with umbrellas.

After an hour or so the shower passed away. My companion slept through it all, or at least appeared so to do; and now that it was over I had not the heart to awaken him. As I lay on my back completely shrouded with verdure, the leafy branches drooping over me, and my limbs buried in grass, I could not avoid comparing our situation with that of the interesting babes in the wood. Poor little sufferers!—no wonder their constitutions broke down under the hardships to which they were exposed.

During the hour or two spent under the shelter of these bushes, I began to feel symptoms which I at once attributed to the exposure of the preceding night. Cold shiverings and a burning fever succeeded one another at intervals, while one of my legs was swelled to such a degree, and pained me so acutely, that I half suspected I had been bitten by some venomous reptile, the congenial inhabitant of the chasm from which we had lately emerged. I may here remark by the way—what I subsequently learned—that all the islands of Polynesia enjoy the reputation, in common with the Hibernian isle, of being free from the presence of any vipers; though whether Saint Patrick ever visited them, is a question I shall not attempt to decide.

As the feverish sensation increased upon me, I tossed about, still unwilling to disturb my slumbering companion, from whose side I removed two or three yards. I chanced to push aside a branch, and by so doing suddenly disclosed to my view a scene which even now I can recall with all the vividness of the first impression. Had a glimpse of the gardens of Paradise been revealed to me I could scarcely have been more ravished with the sight.

From the spot where I lay transfixed with surprise and delight, I looked straight down into the bosom of a valley, which swept away in long wavy undulations to the blue waters in the distance. Midway towards the sea, and peering here and there amidst the foliage, might be seen the palmetto-thatched houses of its inhabitants glistening in the sun that had bleached them to a dazzling whiteness. The vale was more than three leagues in length, and about a mile across at its greatest width.

On either side it appeared hemmed in by steep and green acclivities, which, uniting near the spot where I lay, formed an abrupt and semicircular termination of grassy cliffs and precipices hundreds of feet in height, over which flowed numberless small cascades. But the crowning beauty of the prospect was its universal verdure; and in this indeed consists, I believe, the peculiar charm of every Polynesian landscape. Everywhere below me, from the base of the precipice upon whose very verge I had been unconsciously reposing, the surface of the vale presented a mass of foliage, spread with such rich profusion that it was impossible to determine of what description of trees it consisted.

But perhaps there was nothing about the scenery I beheld more impressive than those silent cascades, whose slender threads of water, after leaping down the steep cliffs, were lost amidst the rich herbage of the valley.

Over all the landscape there reigned the most hushed repose, which I almost feared to break, lest, like the enchanted gardens in the fairy tale, a single syllable might dissolve the spell. For a long time, forgetful alike of my own situation and the vicinity of my still slumbering companion, I remained gazing around me, hardly able to comprehend by what means I had thus suddenly been made a spectator of such a scene.

CHAPTER VIII

THE IMPORTANT QUESTION, TYPEE OR HAPPAR?—A WILD-GOOSE CHASE—MY SUFFERINGS—DISHEARTENING SITUATION—A NIGHT IN A RAVINE—MORNING MEAL—HAPPY IDEA OF TOBY—JOURNEY TOWARDS THE VALLEY.

RECOVERING from my astonishment at the beautiful scene before me, I quickly awakened Toby, and informed him of the discovery I had made. Together we now repaired to the border of the precipice, and my companion's admiration was equal to my own. A little reflection, however, abated our surprise at coming so unexpectedly upon this valley, since the large vales of Happar and Typee, lying upon this side of Nukuheva, and extending a considerable distance from the sea towards the interior, must necessarily terminate somewhere about this point.

The question now was as to which of those two places we were looking down upon. Toby insisted that it was the abode of the Happars, and I that it was tenanted by their enemies the ferocious Typees. To be sure I was not entirely convinced by my own arguments, but Toby's proposition to descend at once into the valley, and partake of the hospitality of its inmates, seemed to me to be risking so much upon the strength of a mere supposition, that I resolved to oppose it until we had more evidence to proceed upon.

The point was one of vital importance, as the natives of Happar were not only at peace with Nukuheva, but cultivated with its inhabitants the most friendly relations, and enjoyed beside a reputation for gentleness and humanity which led us to expect from them, if not a cordial reception, at least a shelter during the short period we should remain in their territory.

On the other hand, the very name of Typee struck a panic into my heart which I did not attempt to disguise. The thought of voluntarily throwing ourselves into the hands of these cruel savages, seemed to me an act of mere madness; and almost equally so the idea of venturing into the valley, uncertain by which of these two tribes it was inhabited. That the vale at our feet was tenanted by one of them, was a point that appeared to us past all doubt, since we knew that they resided in this quarter, although our information did not enlighten us further.

My companion, however, incapable of resisting the tempting prospect which the place held out of an abundant supply of food and other means of enjoyment, still clung to his own inconsiderate view of the subject, nor could all my reasoning shake it. When I reminded him that it was impossible for either of us to know anything with certainty, and when I dwelt upon the horrible fate we should encounter were we rashly to descend into the valley, and discover too late the error we had committed, he replied by detailing all the evils of our present condition, and the sufferings we must undergo should we continue to remain where we then were.

Anxious to draw him away from the subject, if possible—for I saw that it would be in vain to attempt changing his mind—I directed his attention to a long bright unwooded tract of land which, sweeping down from the elevations in the interior, descended into the valley before us. I then suggested to him that beyond this ridge might lie a capacious and untenanted valley, abounding with all manner of delicious fruits; for I had heard that there were several such upon the island, and proposed that we should endeavor to reach it, and if we found our expectations realized we should at once take refuge in it and remain there as long as we pleased.

He acquiesced in the suggestion; and we immediately, therefore, began surveying the country lying before us, with a view of determining upon the best route for us to pursue; but it presented little choice, the whole interval being broken into steep ridges, divided by dark ravines, extending in parallel lines at right angles to our direct course. All these we would be obliged to cross before we could hope to arrive at our destination.

A weary journey! But we decided to undertake it, though, for my own part, I felt little prepared to encounter its fatigues, shivering and burning by turns with the ague and fever; for I know not how else to describe the alternate sensations I experienced, and suffering not a little from the lameness which afflicted me. Added to this was the faintness consequent on our meagre diet— a calamity in which Toby participated to the same extent as myself.

These circumstances, however, only augmented my anxiety to reach a place which promised us plenty and repose, before I should be reduced to a state which would render me altogether unable to perform the journey. Accordingly we now commenced it by descending the almost perpendicular side of a steep and narrow gorge, bristling with a thick growth of reeds. Here there was but one mode for us to adopt. We seated ourselves upon the ground, and guided our descent by catching at the canes in our path. The velocity with which we thus slid down the side of the ravine soon brought us to a point where we could use our feet, and in a short time we arrived at the edge of the torrent, which rolled impetuously along the bed of the chasm.

After taking a refreshing draught from the water of the stream, we addressed ourselves to a much more difficult undertaking than the last. Every foot of our late descent had to be regained in ascending the opposite side of the gorge—an operation rendered the less agreeable from the consideration that in these perpendicular episodes we did not progress a hundred yards on our journey. But, ungrateful as the task was, we set about it with exemplary patience, and, after a snail-like progress of an hour or more, had scaled perhaps one half of the distance, when the fever which had left me for awhile returned with such violence, and accompanied by so raging a thirst, that it required all the entreaties of Toby to prevent me from losing all the fruits of my late exertion, by precipitating myself madly down the cliffs we had just climbed in quest of the water which flowed so temptingly at their base. At the moment all my hopes and fears appeared to be merged in this one desire, careless of the consequences that might result from its gratification. I am aware of no feeling, either of pleasure or of pain, that so completely deprives one of all power to resist its impulses as this same raging thirst.

Toby earnestly conjured me to continue the ascent, assuring me that a little more exertion would bring us to the summit, and that then in less than five minutes we should find ourselves at the brink of the stream, which must necessarily flow on the other side of the ridge.

"Do not," he exclaimed, "turn back now, now that we have proceeded thus far; for I tell you that neither of us will have the courage to repeat the attempt, if once more we find ourselves looking up to where we now are from the bottom of these rocks!"

I was not yet so perfectly beside myself as to be heedless of these representations, and therefore toiled on, ineffectually endeavouring to appease the thirst which consumed me, by thinking that in a short time I should be able to gratify it to my heart's content.

At last we gained the top of the second elevation, the loftiest of those I have described as extending in parallel lines between us and the valley we desired to reach. It commanded a view of the whole intervening distance; and, discouraged as I was by other circumstances, this prospect plunged me into the very depths of despair. Nothing but dark and fearful chasms, separated by sharp-crested and perpendicular ridges as far as the eye could reach. Could we have stepped from summit to summit of these steep but narrow elevations we could easily have accomplished the distance; but we must penetrate to the bottom of every yawning gulf, and scale in succession every one of the eminences before us. Even Toby, although not suffering as I did, was not proof against the disheartening influences of the sight.

But we did not long stand to contemplate it, impatient as I was to reach the waters of the torrent which flowed beneath us. With an insensibility to danger which I cannot call to mind without shuddering, we threw ourselves down the depths of the ravine, startling its savage solitudes with the echoes produced by the falling fragments of rock we every moment dislodged from their places, careless of the insecurity of our footing, and reckless whether the slight roots and twigs we clutched at sustained us for the while, or treacherously yielded to our grasp. For my own part I scarcely knew whether I was helplessly falling from the heights above, or whether the fearful rapidity with which I descended was an act of my own volition.

In a few minutes we reached the foot of the gorge, and, kneeling upon a small ledge of dripping rocks, I bent over to the stream. What a delicious sensation was I now to experience! I paused for a second to concentrate all my capabilities of enjoyment, and then immerged my lips in the clear element before me. Had the apples of Sodom turned to ashes in my mouth, I could not have felt a more startling revulsion. A single drop of the cold fluid seemed to freeze every drop of blood in my body; the fever that had been burning in my veins gave place on the instant to death-like chills, which shook me one after another like so many shocks of electricity, while the perspiration produced by my late violent exertions congealed in icy beads upon my forehead. My thirst was gone, and I fairly loathed the water. Starting to my feet, the sight of those dank rocks, oozing forth moisture at every crevice, and the dark stream shooting along its dismal channel, sent fresh chills through my shivering frame, and I felt as uncontrollable a desire to climb up towards the genial sunlight as I before had to descend the ravine.

After two hours' perilous exertions we stood upon the summit of another ridge, and it was with difficulty I could bring myself to believe that we had ever penetrated the black and yawning chasm which then gaped at our feet. Again we gazed upon the prospect which the height commanded, but it was just as depressing as the one which had before met our eyes. I now felt that in our present situation it was in vain for us to think of ever overcoming the obstacles in our way, and I gave up all thoughts of reaching the vale which lay beyond this series of impediments; while at the same time I could not devise any scheme to extricate ourselves from the difficulties in which we were involved.

The remotest idea of returning to Nukuheva, unless assured of our vessel's departure, never once entered my mind, and indeed it was questionable whether we could have succeeded in reaching it, divided as we were from the bay by a distance we could not compute, and perplexed too in our remembrance of localities by our recent wanderings. Besides, it was unendurable the thought of retracing our steps and rendering all our painful exertions of no avail.

There is scarcely anything when a man is in difficulties that he is more disposed to look upon with abhorrence than a right-about retrograde movement—a systematic going over of the already trodden ground; and, especially if he has a love of adventure, such a course appears indescribably repulsive, so long as there remains the least hope to be derived from braving untried difficulties.

It was this feeling that prompted us to descend the opposite side of the elevation we had just scaled, although with what definite object in view it would have been impossible for either of us to tell.

Without exchanging a syllable upon the subject, Toby and myself simultaneously renounced the design which had lured us thus far—perceiving in each other's countenances that desponding expression which speaks more eloquently than words.

Together we stood towards the close of this weary day in the cavity of the third gorge we had entered, wholly incapacitated for any further exertion, until restored to some degree of strength by food and repose.

We seated ourselves upon the least uncomfortable spot we could select, and Toby produced from the bosom of his frock the sacred package. In silence we partook of the small morsel of refreshment that had been left from the morning's repast, and, without once proposing to violate the sanctity of our engagement with respect to the remainder, we rose to our feet and proceeded to construct some sort of shelter under which we might obtain the sleep we so greatly needed.

Fortunately the spot was better adapted to our purpose than the one in which we had passed the last wretched night. We cleared away the tall reeds from a small but almost level bit of ground, and twisted them into a low basket-like hut, which we covered with a profusion of long thick leaves, gathered from a tree near at hand. We disposed them thickly all around, reserving only a slight opening that barely permitted us to crawl under the shelter we had thus obtained.

These deep recesses, though protected from the winds that assail the summits of their lofty sides, are damp and chill to a degree that one would hardly anticipate in such a climate; and being unprovided with anything but our woollen frocks and thin duck trousers to resist the cold of the place, we were the more solicitous to render our habitation for the night as comfortable as we could. Accordingly, in addition to what we had already done, we plucked down all the leaves within our reach and threw them in a heap over our little hut, into which we now crept, raking after us a reserved supply to form our couch.

That night nothing but the pain I suffered prevented me from sleeping most refreshingly. As it was, I caught two or three naps, while Toby slept away at my side as soundly as though he had been sandwiched between two Holland sheets. Luckily it did not rain, and we were preserved from the misery which a heavy shower would have occasioned us.

In the morning I was awakened by the sonorous voice of my companion ringing in my ears and bidding me rise. I crawled out from our heap of leaves and was astonished at the change which a good night's rest had wrought in his appearance. He was as blithe and joyous as a young bird, and was staying the keenness of his morning's appetite by chewing the soft bark of a delicate branch he held in his hand, and he recommended the like to me as an admirable antidote against the gnawings of hunger.

For my own part, though feeling materially better than I had done the preceding evening, I could not look at the limb that had pained me so violently at intervals during the last twenty-four hours without experiencing a sense of alarm that I strove in vain to shake off. Unwilling to disturb the flow of my comrade's spirits, I managed to stifle the complaints to which I might otherwise have given vent, and calling upon him good-humouredly to speed our banquet, I prepared myself for it by washing in the stream. This operation concluded, we swallowed, or rather absorbed, by a peculiar kind of slow sucking process, our respective morsels of nourishment, and then entered into a discussion as to the steps it was necessary for us to pursue.

"What's to be done now?" inquired I, rather dolefully.

"Descend into that same valley we descried yesterday," rejoined Toby, with a rapidity and loudness of utterance that almost led me to suspect he had been slyly devouring the broadside of an ox in some of the adjoining thickets. "What else," he continued, "remains for us to do but that, to be sure? Why, we shall both starve to a certainty if we remain here; and as to your fears of those Typees—depend upon it, it is all nonsense.

"It is impossible that the inhabitants of such a lovely place as we saw can be anything else but good fellows; and if you choose rather to perish with hunger in one of these soppy caverns, I for one prefer to chance a bold descent into the valley, and risk the consequences."

"And who is to pilot us thither," I asked, "even if we should decide upon the measure you propose? Are we to go again up and down those precipices that we crossed yesterday, until we reach the place we started from, and then take a flying leap from the cliffs to the valley?'

" 'Faith, I didn't think of that," said Toby; "sure enough both sides of the valley appeared to be hemmed in by precipices, didn't they?"

"Yes," answered I, "as steep as the sides of a line-of-battle ship, and about a hundred times as high." My companion sank his head upon his breast and remained for a while in deep thought. Suddenly he sprang to his feet, while his eyes lighted up with that gleam of intelligence that marks the presence of some bright idea.

"Yes, yes," he exclaimed; "the streams all run in the same direction, and must necessarily flow into the valley before they reach the sea; all we have to do is just to follow this stream, and sooner or later it will lead us into the vale."

"You are right, Toby," I exclaimed, "you are right; it must conduct us thither, and quickly too; for see with what a steep inclination the water descends."

"It does, indeed," burst forth my companion, overjoyed at my verification of his theory, "it does indeed; why, it is as plain as a pikestaff. Let us proceed at once; come, throw away all those stupid ideas about the Typees, and hurrah for the lovely valley of the Happars!"

"You will have it to be Happar, I see, my dear fellow; pray Heaven you may not find yourself deceived," observed I, with a shake of my head.

"Amen to all that, and much more," shouted Toby, rushing forward; "but Happar it is, for nothing else than Happar can it be. So glorious a valley—such forests of breadfruit-trees—such groves of coco-nut—such wildernesses of guava-bushes! Ah, shipmate! don't linger behind: in the name of all delightful fruits, I am dying to be at them. Come on, come on; shove ahead, there's a lively lad; never mind the rocks; kick them out of the way, as I do; and to-morrow, old fellow, take my word for it, we shall be in clover. Come on;" and so saying, he dashed along the ravine like a madman, forgetting my inability to keep up with him. In a few minutes, however, the exuberance of his spirits abated, and, pausing for a while, he permitted me to overtake him.

CHAPTER IX

PERILOUS PASSAGE OF THE RAVINE—DESCENT INTO THE VALLEY.

THE fearless confidence of Toby was contagious, and I began to adopt the Happar side of the question. I could not, however, overcome a certain feeling of trepidation as we made our way along these gloomy solitudes. Our progress, at first comparatively easy, became more and more difficult. The bed of the watercourse was covered with fragments of broken rocks, which had fallen from above, offering so many obstructions to the course of the rapid stream, which vexed and fretted about them—forming at intervals small waterfalls, pouring over into deep basins, or splashing wildly upon heaps of stones.

From the narrowness of the gorge, and the steepness of its sides, there was no mode of advancing but by wading through the water; stumbling every moment over the impediments which lay hidden under its surface, or tripping against the huge roots of trees. But the most annoying hindrance we encountered was from a multitude of crooked boughs, which, shooting out almost horizontally from the sides of the chasm, twisted themselves together in fantastic masses almost to the surface of the stream, affording us no passage except under the low arches which they formed. Under these we were obliged to crawl on our hands and feet, sliding along the oozy surface of the rocks, or slipping into the deep pools, and with scarce light enough to guide us. Occasionally we would strike our heads against some projecting limb of a tree; and while imprudently engaged in rubbing the injured part, would fall sprawling amongst flinty fragments, cutting and bruising ourselves, whilst the unpitying waters flowed over our prostrate bodies. Belzoni, worming himself through the subterranean passages of the Egyptian catacombs, could not have met with greater impediments than those we here encountered. But we struggled against them manfully, well knowing our only hope lay in advancing.

Towards sunset we halted at a spot where we made preparations for passing the night. Here we constructed a hut, in much the same way as before, and crawling into it, endeavoured to forget our sufferings. My companion, I believe, slept pretty soundly; but at daybreak, when we rolled out of our dwelling, I felt nearly disqualified for any further efforts. Toby prescribed as a remedy for my illness the contents of one of our little silk packages, to be taken at once in a single dose. To this species of medical treatment, however, I would by no means accede, much as he insisted upon it; and so we partook of our usual morsel, and silently resumed our journey. It was now the fourth day since we left Nukuheva, and the gnawings of hunger became painfully acute. We were fain to pacify them by chewing the tender bark of roots and twigs, which, if they did not afford us nourishment, were at least sweet and pleasant to the taste.

Our progress along the steep watercourse was necessarily slow, and by noon we had not advanced more than a mile. It was somewhere near this part of the day that the noise of falling waters, which we had faintly caught in the early morning, became more distinct; and it was not long before we were arrested by a rocky precipice of nearly a hundred feet in depth, that extended all across the channel, and over which the wild stream poured in an unbroken leap. On either hand the walls of the ravine presented their overhanging sides both above and below the fall, affording no means whatever of avoiding the cataract by taking a circuit round it.

"What's to be done now, Toby?" said I.

"Why," rejoined he, "as we cannot retreat, I suppose we must keep shoving along."

"Very true, my dear Toby; but how do you purpose accomplishing that desirable object?"

"By jumping from the top of the fall, if there be no other way," unhesitatingly replied my companion: "it will be much the quickest way of descent; but as you are not quite as active as I am, we will try some other way."

And, so saying, he crept cautiously along and peered over into the abyss, while I remained wondering by what possible means we could overcome this apparently insuperable obstruction. As soon as my companion had completed his survey, I eagerly inquired the result.

"The result of my observations you wish to know, do you?" began Toby, deliberately, with one of his odd looks: "well, my lad, the result of my observations is very quickly imparted. It is at present uncertain which of our two necks will have the honour to be broken first; but about a hundred to one would be a fair bet in favour of the man who takes the first jump."

"Then it is an impossible thing, isn't it?" inquired I, gloomily.

"No, shipmate; on the contrary, it is the easiest thing in life: the only awkward point is the sort of usage which our unhappy limbs may receive when we arrive at the bottom and what sort of travelling trim we shall be in afterwards. But follow me now, and I will show you the only chance we have."

With this he conducted me to the verge of the cataract, and pointed along the side of the ravine to a number of curious-looking roots, some three or four inches in thickness, and several feet long, which after twisting among the fissures of the rock, shot perpendicularly from it and ran tapering to a point in the air, hanging over the gulf like so many dark icicles. They covered nearly the entire surface of one side of the gorge, the lowest of them reaching even to the water. Many were moss-grown and decayed, with their extremities snapped short off, and those in the immediate vicinity of the fall were slippery with moisture.

Toby's scheme, and it was a desperate one, was to entrust ourselves to these treacherous-looking roots, and by slipping down from one to another to gain the bottom.

"Are you ready to venture it?" asked Toby, looking at me earnestly, but without saying a word as to the practicability of the plan.

"I am," was my reply; for I saw it was our only resource if we wished to advance, and as for retreating, all thoughts of that sort had been long abandoned.

After I had signified my assent, Toby, without uttering a single word, crawled along the dripping ledge until he gained a point from when he could just reach one of the largest of the pendant roots; he shook it—it quivered in his grasp, and when he let it go it twanged in the air like a strong wire sharply struck. Satisfied by his scrutiny, my light-limbed companion swung himself nimbly upon it, and twisting his legs round it in sailor fashion, slipped down eight or ten feet, where his weight gave it a motion not unlike that of a pendulum. He could not venture to descend any further; so holding on with one hand, he with the other shook one by one all the slender roots around him, and at last, finding one which he thought trustworthy, shifted himself to it and continued his downward progress.

So far so well; but I could not avoid comparing my heavier frame and disabled condition with his light figure and remarkable activity; but there was no help for it, and in less than a minute's time I was swinging directly over his head. As soon as his upturned eyes caught a glimpse of me, he exclaimed in his usual dry tone, for the danger did not seem to daunt him in the least, "Mate, do me the kindness not to fall until I get out of your way;" and then swinging himself more on one side, he continued his descent. In the meantime I cautiously transferred myself from the limb down which I had been slipping to a couple of others that were near it, deeming two strings to my bow better than one, and taking care to test their strength before I trusted my weight to them.

On arriving towards the end of the second stage in this vertical journey, and shaking the long roots which were round me, to my consternation they snapped off one after another like so many pipe stems, and fell in fragments against the side of the gulf, splashing at last into the waters beneath.

As one after another the treacherous roots yielded to my grasp, and fell into the torrent, my heart sank within me. The branches on which I was suspended over the yawning chasm swung to and fro in the air, and I expected them every moment to snap in twain. Appalled at the dreadful fate that menaced me, I clutched at the only large root which remained near me, but in vain; I could not reach it, though my fingers were within a few inches of it. Again and again I tried to reach it, until at length, maddened with the thought of my situation, I swayed myself violently by striking my foot against the side of the rock, and at the instant that I approached the large root caught desperately at it, and transferred myself to it. It vibrated violently under the sudden weight, but fortunately did not give way.

My brain grew dizzy with the idea of the frightful risk I had just run, and I involuntarily closed my eyes to shut out the view of the depth beneath me. For the instant I was safe, and I uttered a devout ejaculation of thanksgiving for my escape.

"Pretty well done," shouted Toby underneath me; "you are nimbler than I thought you to be—hopping about up there from root to root like any young squirrel. As soon as you have diverted yourself sufficiently, I would advise you to proceed."

"Aye, aye, Toby, all in good time: two or three more such famous roots as this, and I shall be with you."

The residue of my downward progress was comparatively easy; the roots were in greater abundance, and in one or two places jutting out points of rock assisted me greatly. In a few moments I was standing by the side of my companion.

Substituting a stout stick for the one I had thrown aside at the top of the precipice, we now continued our course along the bed of the ravine. Soon we were saluted by a sound in advance, that grew by degrees louder and louder, as the noise of the cataract we were leaving behind gradually died on our ears.

"Another precipice for us, Toby."

"Very good; we can descend them, you know—come on."

Nothing indeed appeared to depress or intimidate this intrepid fellow. Typees or Niagaras, he was as ready to engage one as the other, and I could not avoid a thousand times congratulating myself upon having such a companion in an enterprise like the present.

After an hour's painful progress, we reached the verge of another fall, still loftier than the preceding, and flanked both above and below with the same steep masses of rock, presenting, however, here and there narrow irregular ledges, supporting a shallow soil, on which grew a variety of bushes and trees, whose bright verdure contrasted beautifully with the foamy waters that flowed between them.

Toby, who invariably acted as pioneer, now proceeded to reconnoitre. On his return, he reported that the shelves of rock on our right would enable us to gain with little risk the bottom of the cataract. Accordingly, leaving the bed of the stream at the very point where it thundered down, we began crawling along one of these sloping ledges until it carried us to within a few feet of another that inclined downward at a still sharper angle, and upon which, by assisting each other, we managed to alight in safety. We warily crept along this, steadying ourselves by the naked roots of the shrubs that clung to every fissure. As we proceeded, the narrow path became still more contracted, rendering it difficult for us to maintain our footing, until suddenly, as we reached an angle of the wall of rock where we had expected it to widen, we perceived to our consternation that a yard or two farther on it abruptly terminated at a place we could not possibly hope to pass.

Toby as usual led the van, and in silence I waited to learn from him how he proposed to extricate us from this new difficulty.

"Well, my boy," I exclaimed, after the expiration of several minutes, during which time my companion had not uttered a word; "what's to be done now?"

He replied in a tranquil tone, that probably the best thing we could do in our present strait was to get out of it as soon as possible.

"Yes, my dear Toby, but tell me *how* we are to get out of it."

"Something in this sort of style," he replied; and at the same moment to my horror he slipped sideways off the rock, and, as I then thought, by good fortune merely, alighted among the spreading branches of a species of palm tree, that, shooting its hardy roots along a ledge below, curved its trunk upwards into the air, and presented a thick mass of foliage about twenty feet below the spot where we had thus suddenly been brought to a standstill. I involuntarily held my breath, expecting to see the form of my companion, after being sustained for a moment by the branches of the tree, sink through their frail support, and fall headlong to the bottom. To my surprise and joy, however, he recovered himself, and disentangling his limbs from the fractured branches, he peered out from his leafy bed, and shouted lustily, "Come on, my hearty, there is no other alternative!" and with this he ducked beneath the foliage, and slipping down the trunk, stood in a moment at least fifty feet beneath me, upon the broad shelf of rock from which sprang the tree he had descended.

What would I not have given at that moment to have been by his side! The feat he had just accomplished seemed little less than miraculous, and I could hardly credit the evidence of my senses when I saw the wide distance that a single daring act had so suddenly placed between us.

Toby's animating "come on!" again sounded in my ears, and dreading to lose all confidence in myself if I remained meditating upon the step, I once more gazed down to assure myself of the relative bearing of the tree and my own position, and then, closing my eyes and uttering one comprehensive ejaculation of prayer, I inclined myself over towards the abyss, and after one breathless instant fell with a crash into the tree, the branches snapping and crackling with my weight, as I sank lower and lower among them, until I was stopped by coming in contact with a sturdy limb.

In a few moments I was standing at the foot of the tree, manipulating myself all over with a view of ascertaining the extent of the injuries I had received. To my surprise the only effects of my feat were a few slight contusions too trifling to care about. The rest of our descent was easily accomplished, and in half an hour after regaining the ravine we had partaken of our evening morsel, built our hut as usual, and crawled under its shelter.

The next morning, in spite of our debility and the agony of hunger under which we were now suffering, though neither of us confessed to the fact, we struggled along our dismal and still difficult and dangerous path, cheered by the hope of soon catching a glimpse of the valley before us, and towards evening the voice of a cataract which had for some time sounded like a low deep bass to the music of the smaller waterfalls, broke upon our ears in still louder tones, and assured us that we were approaching its vicinity.

That evening we stood on the brink of a precipice, over which the dark stream bounded in one final leap of full 300 feet. The sheer descent terminated in the region we so long had sought. On either side of the fall, two lofty and perpendicular bluffs buttressed the sides of the enormous cliff, and projected into the sea of verdure with which the valley waved, and a range of similar projecting eminences stood disposed in a half circle about the head of the vale. A thick canopy of trees hung over the very verge of the fall, leaving an arched aperture for the passage of the waters, which imparted a strange picturesqueness to the scene.

The valley was now before us; but instead of being conducted into its smiling bosom by the gradual descent of the deep watercourse we had thus far pursued, all our labours now appeared to have been rendered futile by its abrupt termination. But, bitterly disappointed, we did not entirely despair.

As it was now near sunset we determined to pass the night where we were, and on the morrow, refreshed by sleep and by eating at one meal all our stock of food, to accomplish a descent into the valley, or perish in the attempt.

We laid ourselves down that night on a spot, the recollection of which still makes me shudder. A small table of rock which projected over the precipice on one side of the stream, and was drenched by the spray of the fall, sustained a huge trunk of a tree which must have been deposited there by some heavy freshet. It lay obliquely, with one end resting on the rock and the other supported by the side of the ravine. Against it we placed in a sloping direction a number of the half-decayed boughs that were strewn about, and covering the whole with twigs and leaves, awaited the morning's light beneath such shelter as it afforded.

During the whole of this night the continual roaring of the cataract—the dismal moaning of the gale through the trees—the pattering of the rain—and the profound darkness, affected my spirits to a degree which nothing had ever before produced. Wet, half famished, and chilled to the heart with the dampness of the place, and nearly wild with the pain I endured, I fairly cowered down to the earth under this multiplication of hardships, and abandoned myself to frightful anticipations of evil; and my companion, whose spirit at last was a good deal broken, scarcely uttered a word during the whole night.

At length the day dawned upon us, and, rising from our miserable pallet, we stretched our stiffened joints, and after eating all that remained of our bread, prepared for the last stage of our journey.

I will not recount every hairbreadth escape, and every fearful difficulty that occurred before we succeeded in reaching the bosom of the valley. As I have already described similar scenes, it will be sufficient to say that at length, after great toil and great dangers, we both stood with no limbs broken at the head of that magnificent vale which five days before had so suddenly burst upon my sight, and almost beneath the shadows of those very cliffs from whose summits we had gazed upon the prospect.

CHAPTER X

THE HEAD OF THE VALLEY—CAUTIOUS ADVANCE—A PATH—FRUIT—DISCOVERY OF TWO OF THE NATIVES—THEIR SINGULAR CONDUCT—APPROACH TOWARDS THE INHABITED PARTS OF THE VALE—SENSATION PRODUCED BY OUR APPEARANCE—RECEPTION AT THE HOUSE OF ONE OF THE NATIVES.

How to obtain the fruit which we felt convinced must grow near at hand was our first thought.

Typee or Happar? A frightful death at the hands of the fiercest of cannibals, or a kindly reception from a gentler race of savages? Which? But it was too late now to discuss a question which would so soon be answered.

The part of the valley in which we found ourselves appeared to be altogether uninhabited. An almost impenetrable thicket extended from side to side, without presenting a single plant affording the nourishment we had confidently calculated upon; and with this object, we followed the course of the stream, casting quick glances as we proceeded into the thick jungles on either hand.

My companion—to whose solicitations I had yielded in descending into the valley—now that the step was taken, began to manifest a degree of caution I had little expected from him. He proposed that, in the event of our finding an adequate supply of fruit, we should remain in this unfrequented portion of the country—where we should run little chance of being surprised by its occupants, whoever they might be—until sufficiently recruited to resume our journey; when laying in a store of food equal to our wants, we might easily regain the bay of Nukuheva, after the lapse of a sufficient interval to ensure the departure of our vessel.

I objected strongly to this proposition, plausible as it was, as the difficulties of the route would be almost insurmountable, unacquainted as we were with the general bearings of the country, and I reminded my companion of the hardships which we had already encountered in our uncertain wanderings; in a word, I said that since we had deemed it advisable to enter the valley, we ought manfully to face the consequences, whatever they might be; the more especially as I was convinced there was no alternative left us but to fall in with the natives at once, and boldly risk the reception they might give us; and that, as to myself, I felt the necessity of rest and shelter, and that until I had obtained them I should be wholly unable to encounter such sufferings as we had lately passed through. To the justice of these observations Toby somewhat reluctantly assented.

We were surprised that, after moving as far as we had along the valley, we should still meet with the same impervious thickets; and thinking that although the borders of the stream might be lined for some distance with them, yet beyond there might be more open ground, I requested Toby to keep a bright look-out upon one side, while I did the same on the other, in order to discover some opening in the bushes, and especially to watch for the slightest appearance of a path or anything else that might indicate the vicinity of the islanders.

What furtive and anxious glances we cast into those dim-looking shades! With what apprehensions we proceeded, ignorant at what moment we might be greeted by the javelin of some ambushed savage! At last my companion paused, and directed my attention to a narrow opening in the foliage. We struck into it and it soon brought us by an indistinctly traced path to a comparatively clear space, at the farther end of which we descried a number of the trees, the native name of which is "annuee," and which bear a most delicious fruit.

What a race! I hobbling over the ground like some decrepit wretch, and Toby leaping forward like a greyhound. He quickly cleared one of the trees on which there were two or three of the fruit, but to our chagrin they proved to be much decayed; the rinds partly opened by the birds, and their hearts half devoured. However, we quickly dispatched them, and no ambrosia could have been more delicious.

We looked about us uncertain whither to direct our steps, since the path we had so far followed appeared to be lost in the open space around us. At last we resolved to enter a grove near at hand, and had advanced a few rods when, just upon its skirts, I picked up a slender breadfruit shoot perfectly green, and with the tender bark freshly stripped from it. It was still slippery with moisture, and appeared as if it had been but that moment thrown aside. I said nothing, but merely held it up to Toby, who started at this undeniable evidence of the vicinity of the savages.

The plot was now thickening. A short distance farther lay a little faggot of the same shoots bound together with a strip of bark. Could it have been thrown down by some solitary native who, alarmed at seeing us, had hurried forward to carry the tidings of our approach to his countrymen?—Typee or Happar?—But it was too late to recede, so we moved on slowly, my companion in advance casting eager glances under the trees on either side, until all at once I saw him recoil as if stung by an adder. Sinking on his knee, he waved me off with one hand, while with the other he held aside some intervening leaves and gazed intently at some object.

Disregarding his injunction, I quickly approached him and caught a glimpse of two figures partly hidden by the dense foliage; they were standing close together, and were perfectly motionless. They must have previously perceived us, and withdrawn into the depths of the wood to elude our observation.

My mind was at once made up. Dropping my staff, and tearing open the package of things we had brought from the ship, I unrolled the cotton cloth, and holding it in one hand plucked with the other a twig from the bushes beside me, and, telling Toby to follow my example, I broke through the covert and advanced, waving the branch in token of peace towards the shrinking forms before me.

They were a boy and girl, slender and graceful, and completely naked, with the exception of a slight girdle of bark, from which depended at opposite points two of the russet leaves of the breadfruit-tree. An arm of the boy, half screened from sight by her wild tresses, was thrown about the neck of the girl, while with the other he held one of her hands in his; and thus they stood together, their heads inclined forward, catching the faint noise we made in our progress, and with one foot in advance, as if half inclined to fly from our presence.

As we drew near, their alarm evidently increased. Apprehensive that they might fly from us altogether, I stopped short and motioned them to advance and receive the gift I extended towards them, but they would not; I then uttered a few words of their language with which I was acquainted, scarcely expecting that they would understand me, but to show that we had not dropped from the clouds upon them. This appeared to give them a little confidence, so I approached nearer, presenting the cloth with one hand and holding the bough with the other, while they slowly retreated. At last they suffered us to approach so near to them that we were enabled to throw the cotton cloth across their shoulders, giving them to understand that it was theirs, and by a variety of gestures endeavouring to make them understand that we entertained the highest possible regard for them.

The frightened pair now stood still, whilst we endeavoured to make them comprehend the nature of our wants. In doing this Toby went through with a complete series of pantomimic illustrations—opening his mouth from ear to ear, and thrusting his fingers down his throat, gnashing his teeth and rolling his eyes about, till I verily believe the poor creatures took us for a couple of white cannibals who were about to make a meal of them. When, however, they understood us, they showed no inclination to relieve our wants. At this juncture it began to rain violently, and we motioned them to lead us to some place of shelter. With this request they appeared willing to comply, but nothing could evince more strongly the apprehension with which they regarded us, than the way in which, whilst walking before us, they kept their eyes constantly turned back to watch every movement we made, and even our very looks.

"Typee or Happar, Toby?" asked I as we walked after them.

"Of course Happar," he replied with a show of confidence which was intended to disguise his doubts.

"We shall soon know," I exclaimed; and at the same moment I stepped forward towards our guides, and pronouncing the two names interrogatively and pointing to the lowest part of the valley, endeavoured to come to the point at once. They repeated the words after me again and again, but without giving any peculiar emphasis to either, so that I was completely at a loss to understand them; for a couple of wilier young things than we afterwards found them to have been on this particular occasion never probably fell in any traveller's way.

More and more curious to ascertain our fate, I now threw together in the form of a question the words "Happar" and "Mortarkee," the latter being equivalent to the word "good.' The two natives interchanged glances of peculiar meaning with one another at this, and manifested no little surprise; but on the repetition of the question, after some consultation together, to the great joy of Toby, they answered in the affirmative. Toby was now in ecstasies, especially as the young savages continued to reiterate their answer with great energy, as though desirous of impressing us with the idea that being among the Happars, we ought to consider ourselves perfectly secure.

Although I had some lingering doubts, I feigned great delight with Toby at this announcement, while my companion broke out into a pantomimic abhorrence of Typee, and immeasurable love for the particular valley in which we were; our guides all the while gazing uneasily at one another as if at a loss to account for our conduct.

They hurried on, and we followed them; until suddenly they set up a strange halloo, which was answered from beyond the grove through which we were passing, and the next moment we entered upon some open ground, at the extremity of which we descried a long, low hut and in front of it were several young girls. As soon as they perceived us they fled with wild screams into the adjoining thickets, like so many startled fawns. A few moments after the whole valley resounded with savage outcries, and the natives came running towards us from every direction.

Had an army of invaders made an irruption into their territory they could not have evinced greater excitement. We were soon completely encircled by a dense throng, and in their eager desire to behold us they almost arrested our progress; an equal number surrounding our youthful guides, who with amazing volubility appeared to be detailing the circumstances which had attended their meeting with us. Every item of intelligence appeared to redouble the astonishment of the islanders, and they gazed at us with inquiring looks.

At last we reached a large and handsome building of bamboos, and were by signs told to enter it, the natives opening a lane for us through which to pass; on entering without ceremony, we threw our exhausted frames upon the mats that covered the floor. In a moment the slight tenement was completely full of people, whilst those who were unable to obtain admittance gazed at us through its open cane-work.

It was now evening, and by the dim light we could just discern the savage countenances around us, gleaming with wild curiosity and wonder; the naked forms and tattooed limbs of brawny warriors, with here and there the slighter figures of young girls, all engaged in a perfect storm of conversation, of which we were of course the one only theme; whilst our recent guides were fully occupied in answering the innumerable questions which every one put to them. Nothing can exceed the fierce gesticulation of these people when animated in conversation, and on this occasion they gave loose to all their natural vivacity, shouting and dancing about in a manner that well-nigh intimidated us.

Close to where we lay, squatting upon their haunches, were some eight or ten noble-looking chiefs—for such they subsequently proved to be—who, more reserved than the rest, regarded us with a fixed and stern attention, which not a little discomposed our equanimity. One of them in particular, who appeared to be the highest in rank, placed himself directly facing me; looking at me with a rigidity of aspect under which I absolutely quailed. He never once opened his lips, but maintained his severe expression of countenance, without turning his face aside for a single moment. Never before had I been subjected to so strange and steady a glance; it revealed nothing of the mind of the savage, but it appeared to be reading my own.

After undergoing this scrutiny till I grew absolutely nervous, with a view of diverting it if possible, and conciliating the good opinion of the warrior, I took some tobacco from the bosom of my frock and offered it to him. He quietly rejected the proffered gift, and, without speaking, motioned me to return it to its place.

In my previous intercourse with the natives of Nukuheva and Tior, I had found that the present of a small piece of tobacco would have rendered any of them devoted to my service. Was this act of the chief a token of his enmity? Typee or Happar? I asked within myself. I started, for at the same moment this identical question was asked by the strange being before me. I turned to Toby; the flickering light of a native taper showed me his countenance pale with trepidation at this fatal question. I paused for a second, and I know not by what impulse it was that I answered "Typee." The piece of dusky statuary nodded in approval, and then murmured "Mortarkee!" "Mortarkee," said I, without further hesitation—"Typee mortarkee."

What a transition! The dark figures around us leaped to their feet, clapped their hands in transport, and shouted again and again the talismanic syllables, the utterance of which appeared to have settled everything.

When this commotion had a little subsided, the principal chief squatted once more before me, and throwing himself into a sudden rage, poured forth a string of philippics, which I was at no loss to understand, from the frequent recurrence of the word Happar, as being directed against the natives of the adjoining valley. In all these denunciations my companion and I acquiesced while we extolled the character of the warlike Typees. To be sure our panegyrics were somewhat laconic, consisting in the repetition of that name, united with the potent adjective "mortarkee." But this was sufficient, and served to conciliate the good will of the natives, with whom our congeniality of sentiment on this point did more towards inspiring a friendly feeling than anything else that could have happened.

At last the wrath of the chief evaporated, and in a few moments he was as placid as ever. Laying his hand upon his breast, he now gave me to understand that his name was Mehevi, and that, in return, he wished me to communicate my appellation. I hesitated for an instant, thinking that it might be difficult for him to pronounce my real name, and then with the most praiseworthy intentions intimated that I was known as Tom. But I could not have made a worse selection; the chief could not master it: "Tommo," "Tomma," "Tommee," everything but plain "Tom." As he persisted in garnishing the word with an additional syllable, I compromised the matter with him at the word "Tommo;" and by that name I went during the entire period of my stay in the valley. The same proceeding was gone through with Toby whose mellifluous appellation was more easily caught.

An exchange of names is equivalent to a ratification of good-will and amity among these simple people; and as we were aware of this fact, we were delighted that it had taken place on the present occasion.

Reclining upon our mats, we now held a kind of levee, giving audience to successive troops of the natives, who introduced themselves to us by pronouncing their respective names, and retired in high good humour on receiving ours in return. During this ceremony the greatest merriment prevailed, nearly every announcement on the part of the islanders being followed by a fresh sally of gaiety which induced me to believe that some of them at least were innocently diverting the company at our expense, by bestowing upon themselves a string of absurd titles, of the humour of which we were of course entirely ignorant.

All this occupied about an hour, when the throng having a little diminished, I turned to Mehevi and gave him to understand that we were in need of food and sleep. Immediately the attentive chief addressed a few words to one of the crowd who disappeared and returned in a few moments with a calabash of "poee-poee," and two or three young coco-nuts stripped of their husks, and with their shells partly broken. We both of us forthwith placed one of these natural goblets to our lips, and drained it in a moment of the refreshing draught it contained. The poee-poee was then placed before us, and even famished as I was, I paused to consider in what manner to convey it to my mouth.

This staple article of food among the Marquese islanders is manufactured from the produce of the breadfruit-tree. It somewhat resembles in its plastic nature our bookbinder's paste, is of a yellow colour, and somewhat tart to the taste.

Such was the dish, the merits of which I was now eager to discuss. I eyed it wistfully for a moment, and then unable any longer to stand on ceremony, plunged my hand into the yielding mass, and to the boisterous mirth of the natives drew it forth laden with the poee-poee, which adhered in lengthy strings to every finger. So stubborn was its consistency, that in conveying my heavily freighten hand to my mouth, the connecting links almost raised the calabash from the mats on which it had been placed. This display of awkwardness—in which, by the by, Toby kept me company—convulsed the bystanders with uncontrollable laughter.

As soon as their merriment had somewhat subsided, Mehevi, motioning us to be attentive, dipped the forefinger of his right hand in the dish, and giving it a rapid and scientific twirl, drew it out coated smoothly with the preparation. With a second peculiar flourish he prevented the poee-poee from dropping to the ground as he raised it to his mouth, into which the finger was inserted and drawn forth perfectly free from any adhesive matter. This performance was evidently intended for our instruction; so I again essayed the feat on the principles inculcated, but with very ill success.

A starving man, however, little heeds conventional proprieties, especially on a South Sea island, and accordingly Toby and I partook of the dish after our own clumsy fashion, beplastering our faces all over with the glutinous compound, and daubing our hands nearly to the wrist. This kind of food is by no means disagreeable to the palate of a European, though at first the mode of eating it may be. For my own part, after the lapse of a few days I became accustomed to its singular flavour, and grew remarkably fond of it.

So much for the first course; several other dishes followed it, some of which were positively delicious. We concluded our banquet by tossing off the contents of two more young coco-nuts, after which we regaled ourselves with the soothing fumes of tobacco, inhaled from a quaintly carved pipe which passed round the circle.

During the repast, the natives eyed us with intense curiosity, observing our minutest motions, and appearing to discover abundant matter for comment in the most trifling occurrences. Their surprise mounted the highest, when we began to remove our uncomfortable garments, which were saturated with rain. They scanned the whiteness of our limbs, and seemed utterly unable to account for the contrast they presented to the swarthy hue of our faces, embrowned from a six months' exposure to the scorching sun of the Line. They felt our skin, much in the same way that a silk mercer would handle a remarkably fine piece of satin; and some of them went so far in their investigation as to apply the olfactory organ.

Their singular behaviour almost led me to imagine that they never before had beheld a white man; but a few moments' reflection convinced me that this could not have been the case; and a more satisfactory reason for their conduct has since suggested itself to my mind.

Deterred by the frightful stories related of its inhabitants, ships never enter this bay, while their hostile relations with the tribes in the adjoining valleys prevent the Typees from visiting that section of the island where vessels occasionally lie. At long intervals, however, some intrepid captain will touch on the skirts of the bay, with two or three armed boats' crews, and accompanied by an interpreter. The natives who live near the sea descry the strangers long before they reach their waters, and aware of the purpose for which they come, proclaim loudly the news of their approach. By a species of vocal telegraph the intelligence reaches the inmost recesses of the vale in an inconceivably short space of time, drawing nearly its whole population down to the beach laden with every variety of fruit. The interpreter, who is invariably a ":tabooed Kannaka," leaps ashore with the goods intended for barter, while the boats, with their oars shipped, and every man on his thwart, lie just outside the surf, heading off from the shore, in readiness at the first untoward event to escape to the open sea. As soon as the traffic is concluded, one of the boats pulls in under cover of the muskets of the others, the fruit is quickly thrown into her, and the transient visitors precipitately retire from what they justly consider so dangerous a vicinity.

The intercourse occurring with Europeans being so restricted, no wonder that the inhabitants of the valley manifested so much curiosity with regard to us, appearing as we did among them under such singular circumstances. I have no doubt that we were the first white men who ever penetrated thus far back into their territories, or at least the first who had ever descended from the head of the vale. What had brought us thither must have appeared a complete mystery to them, and from our ignorance of the language it was impossible for us to enlighten them. In answer to inquiries which the eloquence of their gestures enabled us to comprehend, all that we could reply was, that we had come from Nukuheva, a place, be it remembered, with which they were at open war. This intelligence appeared to affect them with the most lively emotions. "Nukuheva mortarkee?" they asked. Of course we replied most energetically in the negative.

They then plied us with a thousand questions, of which we could understand nothing more than that they had reference to the recent movements of the French, against whom they seemed to cherish the most fierce hatred. So eager were they to obtain information on this point, that they still continued to propound their queries long after we had shown that we were utterly unable to answer them. Occasionally we caught some indistinct idea of their meaning, when we would endeavour by every method in our power to communicate the desired intelligence. At such times their gratification was boundless, and they would redouble their efforts to make us comprehend them more perfectly. But all in vain; and in the end they looked at us despairing, as if we were the receptacles of invaluable information, but how to come at it they knew not.

After a while the group around us gradually dispersed, and we were left about midnight (as we conjectured) with those who appeared to be permanent residents of the house. These individuals now provided us with fresh mats to lie upon, covered us with several folds of tappa, and then, extinguishing the tapers that had been burning, threw themselves down beside us, and after a little desultory conversation were soon sound asleep.

CHAPTER XI

MIDNIGHT REFLECTIONS—MORNING VISITORS—A WARRIOR IN COSTUME—A SAVAGE ÆSCULAPIUS—PRACTICE OF THE HEALING ART—BODY SERVANT— A DWELLING-HOUSE OF THE VALLEY DESCRIBED—PORTRAITS OF ITS INMATES.

VARIOUS and conflicting were the thoughts which oppressed me during the silent hours that followed the events related in the preceding chapter. Toby, wearied with the fatigues of the day, slumbered heavily by my side; but the pain under which I was suffering effectually prevented my sleeping, and I remained distressingly alive to all the fearful circumstances of our present situation. Was it possible that, after all our vicissitudes, we were really in the terrible valley of Typee, and at the mercy of its inmates, a fierce and unrelenting tribe of savages?

Typee or Happar? I shuddered when I reflected that there was no longer any room for doubt; and that beyond all hope of escape, we were now placed in those very circumstances from the bare thought of which I had recoiled with such abhorrence but a few days before. What might not be our fearful destiny? To be sure, as yet we had been treated with no violence; nay, had been even kindly and hospitably entertained. But what dependence could be placed upon the fickle passions which sway the bosom of a savage? His inconstancy and treachery are proverbial. Might it not be that beneath these fair appearances the islanders covered some perfidious design, and that their friendly reception of us might only precede some horrible catastrophe? How strongly did these forebodings spring up in my mind as I lay restlessly upon a couch of mats, surrounded by the dimly revealed forms of those whom I so greatly dreaded.

From the excitement of these fearful thoughts I sank towards morning into an uneasy slumber; and on awaking, with a start, in the midst of an appalling dream, looked up into the eager countenances of a number of the natives, who were bending over me.

It was broad day; and the house was nearly filled with young females, fancifully decorated with flowers, who gazed upon me as I rose with faces in which childish delight and curiosity were vividly portrayed. After waking Toby, they seated themselves .round us on the mats, and gave full play to that prying inquisitiveness which time out of mind has been attributed to the adorable sex.

As these unsophisticated young creatures were attended by no jealous duennas, their proceedings were altogether informal, and void of artificial restraint. Long and minute was the investigation with which they honoured us, and so uproarious their mirth, that I felt infinitely sheepish; and Toby was immeasurably outraged at their familiarity.

These lively young ladies were at the same time wonderfully polite and humane; fanning aside the insects that occasionally lighted on our brows; presenting us with food; and compassionately regarding me in the midst of my afflictions. But in spite of all their blandishments, my feelings of propriety were exceedingly shocked, for I could not but consider them as having over-stepped the due limits of female decorum.

Having diverted themselves to their heart's content, our young visitants now withdrew, and gave place to successive troops of the other sex, who continued flocking towards the house until near noon; by which time I have no doubt that the greater part of the inhabitants of the valley had bathed themselves in the light of our benignant countenances.

At last, when their numbers began to diminish, a superb-looking warrior stooped the towering plumes of his head-dress beneath the low portal, and entered the house. I saw at once that he was some distinguished personage, the natives regarding him with the utmost deference, and making room for him as he approached. His aspect was imposing. The splendid long drooping tail-feathers of the tropical bird, thickly interspersed with the gaudy plumage of the cock, were disposed in an immense upright semicircle upon his head, their lower extremities being fixed in a crescent of guinea-beads which spanned the forehead. Around his neck were several enormous necklaces of boars' tusks, polished like ivory, and disposed in such a manner as that the longest and largest were upon his capacious chest. Thrust forward through the large apertures in his ears were two small and finely shaped sperm-whale teeth, presenting their cavities in front, stuffed with freshly plucked leaves, and curiously wrought at the other end into strange little images and devices. These barbaric trinkets, garnished in this manner at their open extremities, and tapering and curving round to a point behind the ear, resembled not a little a pair of cornucopias.

The loins of the warrior were girt about with heavy folds of a dark-coloured tappa, hanging before and behind in clusters of braided tassels, while anklets and bracelets of curling human hair completed his unique costume. In his right hand he grasped a beautifully carved paddle-spear, nearly fifteen feet in length, made of the bright koar-wood, one end sharply pointed, and the other flattened like an oar-blade. Hanging obliquely from his girdle by a loop of sinnate, was a richly decorated pipe; the slender reed forming its stem was coloured with a red pigment, and round it, as well as the idol-bowl, fluttered little streamers of the thinnest tappa.

But that which was most remarkable in the appearance of the splendid islander was the elaborated tattooing displayed on every noble limb. All imaginable lines and curves and figures were delineated over his whole body, and in their grotesque variety and infinite profusion I could only compare them to the crowded groupings of quaint patterns we sometimes see in costly pieces of lacework. The most simple and remarkable of all these ornaments was that which decorated the countenance of the chief. Two broad stripes of tattooing, diverging from the centre of his shaven crown, obliquely crossed both eyes— staining the lids—to a little below either ear, where they united with another stripe which swept in a straight line along the lips and formed the base of the triangle. The warrior, from the excellence of his physical proportions, might certainly have been regarded as one of Nature's noblemen, and the lines drawn upon his face may possibly have denoted his exalted rank.

This warlike personage upon entering the house seated himself at some distance from the spot where Toby and myself reposed, while the rest of the savages looked alternately from us to him, as if in expectation of something they were disappointed in not perceiving. Regarding the chief attentively, I thought his lineaments appeared familiar to me. As soon as his full face was turned upon me and I again beheld its extraordinary embellishment, and met the strange gaze to which I had been subjected the preceding night, I immediately, in spite of the alteration in his appearance, recognized the noble Mehevi. On addressing him, he advanced at once in the most cordial manner, and, greeting me warmly, seemed to enjoy not a little the effect his barbaric costume had produced upon me.

I forthwith determined to secure, if possible, the good will of this individual, as I easily perceived he was a man of great authority in his tribe, and one who might exert a powerful influence upon our subsequent fate. In the endeavour I was not repulsed; for nothing could surpass the friendliness he manifested towards both my companion and myself. He extended his sturdy limbs by our side, and endeavoured to make us comprehend the full extent of the kindly feelings by which he was actuated. The almost insuperable difficulty in communicating to one another our ideas affected the chief with no little mortification. He evinced a great desire to be enlightened with regard to the customs and peculiarities of the far-off country we had left behind us, and to which under the name of Maneeka he frequently alluded.

But that which more than any other subject engaged his attention was the late proceedings of the "Franee," as he called the French, in the neighbouring bay of Nukuheva. This seemed a never-ending theme with him, and one concerning which he was never weary of interrogating us. All the information we succeeded in imparting to him on this subject was little more than that we had seen six men-of-war lying in the hostile bay at the time we had left it. When he received this intelligence, Mehevi, by the aid of his fingers, went through a long numerical calculation, as if estimating the number of Frenchmen the squadron might contain.

It was just after employing his faculties in this way that he happened to notice the swelling in my limb. He immediately examined it with the utmost attention, and after doing so despatched a boy who happened to be standing by with some message.

After the lapse of a few moments the stripling re-entered the house with an aged islander who might have been taken for old Hippocrates himself. His head was as bald as the polished surface of a coco-nut shell, which article it precisely resembled in smoothness and colour, while a long silvery beard swept almost to his girdle of bark. Encircling his temples was a bandeau of the twisted leaves of the Omoo tree, pressed closely over the brows to shield his feeble vision from the glare of the sun. His tottering steps were supported by a long slim staff, resembling the wand with which a theatrical magician appears on the stage, and in one hand he carried a freshly plaited fan of the green leaflets of the coco-nut tree. A flowing robe of tappa, knotted over the shoulder, hung loosely round his stooping form, and heightened the venerableness of his aspect.

Mehevi, saluting this old gentleman, motioned him to a seat between us, and then uncovering my limb, desired him to examine it. The leech gazed intently from me to Toby, and then proceeded to business. After diligently observing the ailing member, he commenced manipulating it; and on the supposition probably that the complaint had deprived the leg of all sensation, began to pinch and hammer it in such a manner that I absolutely roared with the pain. Thinking that I was as capable of making an application of thumps and pinches to the part as any one else, I endeavoured to resist this species of medical treatment. But it was not so easy a matter to get out of the clutches of the old wizard; he fastened on the unfortunate limb as if it were something for which he had been long seeking, and muttering some kind of incantation continued his discipline, pounding it after a fashion that set me wellnigh crazy; while Mehevi, upon the same principle which prompts an affectionate mother to hold a struggling child in a dentist's chair, restrained me in his powerful grasp, and actually encouraged the wretch in his infliction of torture.

Almost frantic with rage and pain, I yelled like a Bedlamite; while Toby, throwing himself into all the attitudes of a posture-master, vainly endeavoured to expostulate with the natives by signs and gestures. To have looked at my companion, as, sympathizing with my sufferings, he strove to put an end to them, one would have thought that he was the deaf and dumb alphabet incarnated. Whether my tormentor yielded to Toby's entreaties, or paused from sheer exhaustion, I do not know; but all at once he ceased his operations, and at the same time the chief relinquishing his hold upon me, I fell back, faint and breathless with the agony I had endured.

My unfortunate limb was now left much in the same condition as a rumpsteak after undergoing the castigating process which precedes cooking. My physician, having recovered from the fatigues of his exertions, as if anxious to make amends for the pain to which he had subjected me, now took some herbs out of a little wallet that was suspended from his waist, and moistening them in water, applied them to the inflamed part, stooping over it at the same time, and either whispering a spell, or having a little confidential chat with some imaginary demon located in the calf of my leg. My limb was now swathed in leafy bandages, and, grateful to Providence for the cessation of hostilities, I was suffered to rest.

Mehevi shortly after rose to depart; but before he went he spoke authoritatively to one of the natives whom he addressed as Kory-Kory; and from the little I could understand of what took place, pointed him out to me as a man whose peculiar business thenceforth would be to attend upon my person. I am not certain that I comprehended as much as this at the time, but the subsequent conduct of my trusty body-servant fully assured me that such must have been the case.

I could not but be amused at the manner in which the chief addressed me upon this occasion, talking to me for at least fifteen or twenty minutes as calmly as if I could understand every word that he said. I remarked this peculiarity very often afterwards in many other of the islanders.

Mehevi having now departed, and the family physician having likewise made his exit, we were left about sunset with the ten or twelve natives, who by this time I had ascertained composed the household of which Toby and I were members. As the dwelling to which we had been first introduced was the place of my permanent abode while I remained in the valley, and as I was necessarily placed upon the most intimate footing with its occupants, I may as well here enter into a little description of it and its inhabitants. This description will apply also to nearly all the other dwelling-places in the vale, and will furnish some idea of the generality of the natives.

Near one side of the valley, and about midway up the ascent of a rather abrupt rise of ground waving with the richest verdure, a number of large stones were laid in successive courses, to the height of nearly eight feet, and disposed in such a manner that their level surface corresponded in shape with the habitation which was perched upon it. A narrow space, however, was reserved in front of the dwelling, upon the summit of this pile of stones (called by the natives a "pi-pi"), which being enclosed by a little picket of canes, gave it somewhat the appearance of a verandah. The frame of the house was constructed of large bamboos planted uprightly, and secured together at intervals by transverse stalks of the light wood of the habiscus, lashed with thongs of bark. The rear of the tenement—built up with successive ranges of coco-nut boughs bound one upon another, with their leaflets cunningly woven together—inclined a little from the vertical, and extended from the extreme edge of the "pi-pi" to about twenty feet from its surface; whence the shelving roof—thatched with the long tapering leaves of the palmetto—sloped steeply off to within about five feet of the floor; leaving the eaves drooping with tassel-like appendages over the front of the habitation. This was constructed of light and elegant canes, in a kind of open screen work, tastefully adorned with bindings of variegated sinnate, which served to hold together its various parts. The sides of the house were similarly built; thus presenting three quarters for the circulation of the air, while the whole was impervious to the rain.

In length this picturesque building was perhaps twelve yards, while in breadth it could not have exceeded as many feet. So much for the exterior; which, with its wire-like reed-twisted sides, not a little reminded me of an immense aviary.

Stooping a little, you passed through a narrow aperture in its front; and facing you, on entering, lay two long, perfectly straight, and well-polished trunks of the coco-nut tree, extending the full length of the dwelling; one of them placed closely against the rear, and the other lying parallel with it some two yards distant, the interval between them being spread with a multitude of gaily worked mats, nearly all of a different pattern. This space formed the common couch and lounging place of the natives, answering the purpose of a divan in Oriental countries. Here would they slumber through the hours of the night, and recline luxuriously during the greater part of the day. The remainder of the floor presented only the cool shining surfaces of the large stones of which the "pi-pi" was composed.

From the ridge-pole of the house hung suspended a number of large packages enveloped in coarse tappa; some of which contained festival dresses, and various other matters of the wardrobe, held in high estimation. These were easily accessible by means of a line, which, passing over the ridge-pole, had one end attached to a bundle, while with the other, which led to the side of the dwelling and was there secured, the package could be lowered or elevated at pleasure.

Against the farther wall of the house were arranged in tasteful figures a variety of spears and javelins, and other implements of savage warfare. Outside of the habitation, and built upon the piazza-like area in its front, was a little shed used as a sort of larder or pantry, and in which were stored various articles of domestic use and convenience. A few yards from the "pi-pi" was a large shed built of coco-nut boughs, where the process of preparing the "poee-poee" was carried on, and all culinary operations attended to.

Thus much for the house, and its appurtenances; and it will be readily acknowledged that a more commodious and appropriate dwelling for the climate and the people could not possibly be devised. It was cool, free to admit the air, scrupulously clean, and elevated above the dampness and impurities of the ground.

But now to sketch the inmates; and here I claim for my tried servitor and faithful valet Kory-Kory the precedence of a first description. As his character will be gradually unfolded in the course of my narrative, I shall for the present content myself with delineating his personal appearance. Kory-Kory, though the most devoted and best-natured serving-man in the world, was, alas! a hideous object to look upon. He was some twenty-five years of age, and about six feet in height, robust and well made, and of the most extraordinary aspect. His head was carefully shaven, with the exception of two circular spots, about the size of a dollar, near the top of the cranium, where the hair, permitted to grow of an amazing length, was twisted up in two prominent knots, that gave him the appearance of being decorated with a pair of horns. His beard, plucked out by the roots from every other part of his face, was suffered to droop in hairy pendants, two of which garnished his upper lip, and an equal number hung from the extremity of his chin.

Kory-Kory, with a view of improving the handiwork of nature, and perhaps prompted by a desire to add to the engaging expression of his countenance, had seen fit to embellish his face with three broad longitudinal stripes of tattoo-ing, which, like those country roads that go straight forward in defiance of all obstacles, crossed his nasal organ, descended into the hollow of his eyes, and even skirted the borders of his mouth. Each completely spanned his physiog-nomy; one extending in a line with his eyes, another crossing the face in the vicinity of the nose, and the third sweeping along his lips from ear to ear. His countenance thus triply hooped, as it were, with tattooing, always reminded me of those unhappy wretches whom I have sometimes observed gazing out senti-mentally from behind the grated bars of a prison window; whilst the entire body of my savage valet, covered all over with representations of birds and fishes, and a variety of most unaccountable-looking creatures, suggested to me the idea of a pictorial museum of natural history, or an illustrated copy of Goldsmith's *Animated Nature*.

But it seems really heartless in me to write thus of the poor islander, when I owe perhaps to his unremitting attentions the very existence I now enjoy. Kory-Kory, I mean thee no harm in what I say in regard to thy outward adorn-ings; but they were a little curious to my unaccustomed sight, and therefore I dilate upon them. But to underrate or forget thy faithful services is something I could never be guilty of, even in the giddiest moment of my life.

The father of my attached follower was a native of gigantic frame, and had once possessed prodigious physical powers; but the lofty form was now yielding to the inroads of time, though the hand of disease seemed never to have been laid upon the aged warrior. Marheyo—for such was his name—appeared to have retired from all active participation in the affairs of the valley, seldom or never accompanying the natives in their various expeditions; and employing the greater part of his time in throwing up a little shed just outside the house, upon which he was engaged to my certain knowledge for four months, without appearing to make any sensible advance. I suppose the old gentleman was in his dotage, for he manifested in various ways the characteristics which mark this particular stage of life.

I remember in particular his having a choice pair of ear-ornaments, fabricated from the teeth of some sea-monster: These he would alternately wear and take off at least fifty times in the course of the day, going and coming from his little hut on each occasion with all the tranquillity imaginable. Sometimes slipping them through the slits in his ears, he would seize his spear—which in length and slightness resembled a fishing-pole—and go stalking beneath the shadows of the neighbouring groves, as if about to give a hostile meeting to some cannibal knight. But he would soon return again, and hiding his weapon under the projecting eaves of the house, and rolling his clumsy trinkets carefully in a piece of tappa, would resume his more pacific operations as quietly as if he had never interrupted them.

But despite his eccentricities, Marheyo was a most paternal and warm-hearted old fellow, and in this particular not a little resembled his son Kory-Kory. The mother of the latter was the mistress of the family, and a notable housewife, and a most industrious old lady she was. If she did not understand the art of making jellies, jams, custards, tea-cakes, and such-like trashy affairs, she was profoundly skilled in the mysteries of preparing "amar," "poee-poee," and "kokoo," with other substantial matters. She was a genuine busybody; bustling about the house like a country landlady at an unexpected arrival; forever giving the young girls tasks to perform, which the little hussies as often neglected; poking into every corner, and rummaging over bundles of old tappa, or making a prodigious clatter among the calabashes. Sometimes she might have been seen squatting upon her haunches in front of a huge wooden basin, and kneading "poee-poee" with terrific vehemence, dashing the stone pestle about as if she would shiver the vessel into fragments; on other occasions, galloping about the valley in search of a particular kind of leaf used in some of her recondite operations, and returning home, toiling and sweating, with a bundle of it, under which most women would have sunk.

To tell the truth, Kory-Kory's mother was the only industrious person in all the valley of Typee; and she could not have employed herself more actively had she been left an exceedingly muscular and destitute widow, with an inordinate supply of young children in the bleakest part of the civilized world. There was not the slightest necessity for the greater portion of the labour performed by the old lady: but she seemed to work from some irresistible impulse; her limbs continually swaying to and fro, as if there were some indefatigable engine concealed within her body which kept her in perpetual motion.

Never suppose that she was a termagant or a shrew for all this; she had the kindliest heart in the world, and acted towards me in particular in a truly maternal manner, occasionally putting some little morsel of choice food into my hand, some outlandish kind of savage sweetmeat or pastry, like a doting mother petting a sickly urchin with tarts and sugar-plums. Warm indeed are my remembrances of the dear, good, affectionate old Tinor!

Besides the individuals I have mentioned, there belonged to the household three young men, dissipated, good-for-nothing, roystering blades of savages, who were either employed in prosecuting love-affairs with the maidens of the tribe, or grew boozy on "arva" and tobacco in the company of congenial spirits, the scapegraces of the valley.

Among the permanent inmates of the house were likewise several lovely damsels, who instead of thrumming pianos and reading novels, like more enlightened young ladies, substituted for these employments the manufacture of a fine species of tappa; but for the greater portion of the time were skipping from house to house, gadding and gossiping with their acquaintances.

From the rest of these, however, I must except the beauteous nymph Fayaway, who was my peculiar favourite. Her free, pliant figure was the very perfection of female grace and beauty. Her complexion was a rich and mantling olive, and when watching the glow upon her cheeks I could almost swear that beneath the transparent medium there lurked the blushes of a faint vermilion. The face of this girl was a rounded oval, and each feature as perfectly formed as the heart or imagination of man could desire. Her full lips, when parted with a smile, disclosed teeth of a dazzling whiteness; and when her rosy mouth opened with a burst of merriment, they looked like the milk-white seeds of the "arta," a fruit of the valley, which, when cleft in twain, shows them reposing in rows on either side, imbedded in the rich and juicy pulp. Her hair of the deepest brown, parted irregularly in the middle, flowed in natural ringlets over her shoulders, and whenever she chanced to stoop, fell over and hid from view her lovely bosom. Gazing into the depths of her strange blue eyes, when she was in a contemplative mood, they seemed most placid yet unfathomable; but when illuminated by some lively emotion, they beamed upon the beholder like stars. The hands of Fayaway were as soft and delicate as those of any countess; for an entire exemption from rude labour marks the girlhood and even prime of a Typee woman's life. Her feet, though wholly exposed, were as diminutive and fairly shaped as those which peep from beneath the skirts of a Lima lady's dress. The skin of this young creature, from continual ablutions and the use of mollifying ointments, was inconceivably smooth and soft.

I may succeed, perhaps, in particularizing some of the individual features of Fayaway's beauty, but that general loveliness of appearance which they all contributed to produce I will not attempt to describe. The easy unstudied graces of a child of nature like this, breathing from infancy an atmosphere of perpetual summer, and nurtured by the simple fruits of the earth; enjoying a perfect freedom from care and anxiety, and removed effectually from all injurious tendencies, strike the eye in a manner which cannot be portrayed. This picture is no fancy sketch; it is drawn from the most vivid recollections of the person delineated.

Were I asked if the beauteous form of Fayaway was altogether free from the hideous blemish of tattooing, I should be constrained to answer that it was not. But the practitioners of the barbarous art, so remorseless in their inflictions upon the brawny limbs of the warriors of the tribe, seem to be conscious that it needs not the resources of their profession to augment the charms of the maidens of the vale.

The females are very little embellished in this way, and Fayaway, with all the other young girls of her age, were even less so than those of their sex more advanced in years. The reason of this peculiarity will be alluded to hereafter. All the tattooing that the nymph in question exhibited upon her person may be easily described. Three minute dots, no bigger than pin-heads, decorated either lip, and at a little distance were not at all discernible. Just upon the fall of the shoulder were drawn two parallel lines half an inch apart, and perhaps three inches in length, the interval being filled with delicately executed figures. These narrow bands of tattooing, thus placed, always reminded me of those stripes of gold lace worn by officers in undress, and which are in lieu of epaulets to denote their rank.

Thus much was Fayaway tattooed—the audacious hand which had gone so far in its desecrating work stopping short, apparently wanting the heart to proceed.

But I have omitted to describe the dress worn by this nymph of the valley.

Fayaway—I must avow the fact—for the most part clung to the primitive and summer garb of Eden. But how becoming the costume! It showed her fine figure to the best possible advantage; and nothing could have been better adapted to her peculiar style of beauty. On ordinary occasions she was habited precisely as I have described the two youthful savages whom we had met on first entering the valley. !At other times, when rambling among the groves, or visiting at the houses of her acquaintances, she wore a tunic of white tappa, reaching from her waist to a little below the knees; and when exposed for any length of time to the sun, she invariably protected herself from its rays by a floating mantle of the same material, loosely gathered about the person. Her gala dress will be described hereafter.

As the beauties of our own land delight in bedecking themselves with fanciful articles of jewellery, suspending them from their ears, hanging them about their necks, and clasping them around their wrists, so Fayaway and her companions were in the habit of ornamenting themselves with similar appendages.

Flora was their jeweller. Sometimes they wore necklaces of small carnation flowers, strung like rubies upon a fibre of tappa, or displayed in their ears a single white bud, the stem thrust backward through the aperture, and showing in front the delicate petals folded together in a beautiful sphere, and looking like a drop of the purest pearl. Chaplets too, resembling in their arrangement the strawberry coronal worn by an English peeress, and composed of intertwined leaves and blossoms, often crowned their temples; and bracelets and anklets of the same tasteful pattern were frequently to be seen. Indeed, the maidens of the island were passionately fond of flowers, and never wearied of decorating their persons with them; a lovely trait in their character, and one that ere long will be more fully alluded to.

Though, in my eyes at least, Fayaway was indisputably the loveliest female I saw in Typee, yet the description I have given of her will in some measure apply to nearly all the youthful portion of her sex in the valley. Judge ye then, reader, what beautiful creatures they must have been.

CHAPTER XII

OFFICIOUSNESS OF KORY-KORY—HIS DEVOTION—A BATH IN THE STREAM—WANT OF REFINEMENT OF THE TYPEE DAMSELS—STROLL WITH MEHEVI—A TYPEE HIGHWAY—THE TABOO GROVES—THE HOOLAH-HOOLAH GROUND—THE TI— TIME-WORN SAVAGES—HOSPITALITY OF MEHEVI—MIDNIGHT MISGIVINGS— ADVENTURE IN THE DARK—DISTINGUISHED HONOURS PAID TO THE VISITORS —STRANGE PROCESSION AND RETURN TO THE HOUSE OF MARHEYO.

WHEN Mehevi had departed from the house, as related in the preceding chapter, Kory-Kory commenced the functions of the post assigned him. He brought us various kinds of food; and, as if I were an infant, insisted upon feeding me with his own hands. To this procedure I, of course, most earnestly objected, but in vain; and having laid a calabash of kokoo before me, he washed his fingers in a vessel of water, and then putting his hand into the dish and rolling the food into little balls, put them one after another into my mouth. All my remonstrances against this measure only provoked so great a clamour on his part, that I was obliged to acquiesce; and the operation of feeding being thus facilitated, the meal was quickly dispatched. As for Toby, he was allowed to help himself after his own fashion.

The repast over, my attendant arranged the mats for repose, and, bidding me lie down, covered me with a large robe of tappa, at the same time looking approvingly upon me, and exclaiming, "Ki-Ki, muee muee, ah! moee moee mortarkee" (eat plenty, ah! sleep very good). The philosophy of this sentiment I did not pretend to question; for deprived of sleep for several preceding nights, and the pain in my limb having much abated, I now felt inclined to avail myself of the opportunity afforded me.

The next morning, on waking, I found Kory-Kory stretched out on one side of me, while my companion lay upon the other. I felt sensibly refreshed after a night of sound repose, and immediately agreed to the proposition of my valet that I should repair to the water and wash, although dreading the suffering that the exertion might produce. From this apprehension, however, I was quickly relieved; for Kory-Kory, leaping from the pi-pi, and then backing himself up against it, like a porter in readiness to shoulder a trunk, with loud vociferations and a superabundance of gestures, gave me to understand that I was to mount upon his back and be thus transported to the stream, which flowed perhaps two hundred yards from the house.

Our appearance upon the verandah in front of the habitation drew together quite a crowd, who stood looking on and conversing with one another in the most animated manner. They reminded one of a group of idlers gathered about the door of a village tavern when the equipage of some distinguished traveller is brought round previous to his departure. As soon as I clasped my arms about the neck of the devoted fellow, and he jogged off with me, the crowd—composed chiefly of young girls and boys—followed after, shouting and capering with infinite glee, and accompanied us to the banks of the stream.

On gaining it, Kory-Kory, wading up to his hips in the water, carried me half-way across, and deposited me on a smooth black stone which rose a few inches above the surface. The amphibious rabble at our heels plunged in after us, and, climbing to the summit of the grass-grown rocks with which the bed of the brook was here and there broken, waited curiously to witness our morning ablutions.

Somewhat embarrassed by the presence of the female portion of the company, and feeling my cheeks burning with bashful timidity, I formed a primitive basin by joining my hands together, and cooled my blushes in the water it contained; then removing my frock bent over and washed myself down to my waist in the stream. As soon as Kory-Kory comprehended from my motions that this was to be the extent of my performance, he appeared perfectly aghast with astonishment, and rushing towards me, poured out a torrent of words in eager deprecation of so limited an operation, enjoining me by unmistakable signs to immerse my whole body. To this I was forced to consent; and the honest fellow, regarding me as a froward, inexperienced child, whom it was his duty to serve at the risk of offending, lifted me from the rock, and tenderly bathed my limbs. This over, and resuming my seat, I could not avoid bursting into admiration of the scene around me.

From the verdant surfaces of the large stones that lay scattered about, the natives were now sliding off into the water, diving and ducking beneath the surface in all directions—the young girls springing buoyantly into the air, and revealing their naked forms to the waist, with their long tresses dancing about their shoulders, their eyes sparkling like drops of dew in the sun, and their gay laughter pealing forth at every frolicsome incident.

On the afternoon of the day that I took my first bath in the valley, we received another visit from Mehevi. The noble savage seemed to be in the same pleasant mood, and was quite as cordial in his manner as before. After remaining about an hour, he rose from the mats, and motioning to leave the house, invited Toby and myself to accompany him. I pointed to my leg; but Mehevi in his turn pointed to Kory-Kory, and removed that objection; so, mounting upon the faithful fellow's shoulders again—like the old man of the sea astride of Sindbad—I followed after the chief.

The nature of the route we now pursued struck me more forcibly than any, thing I had yet seen, as illustrating the indolent disposition of the islanders. The path was obviously the most beaten one in the valley, several others leading from either side into it, and perhaps for successive generations it had formed the principal avenue of the place. And yet, until I grew more familiar with its impediments, it seemed as difficult to travel as the recesses of a wilderness. Part of it swept round an abrupt rise of ground, the surface of which was broken by frequent inequalities, and thickly strewn with projecting masses of rocks, whose summits were often hidden from view by the drooping foliage of the luxuriant vegetation. Sometimes directly over, sometimes evading these obstacles with a wide circuit, the path wound along;—one moment climbing over a sudden eminence smooth with continued wear, then descending on the other side into a steep glen, and crossing the flinty channel of a brook. Here it pursued the depths of a glade, occasionally obliging you to stoop beneath vast horizontal branches; and now you stepped over huge trunks and boughs that lay rotting across the track.

Such was the grand thoroughfare of Typee. After proceeding a little distance along it—Kory-Kory panting and blowing with the weight of his burden—I dismounted from his back, and grasping the long spear of Mehevi in my hand, assisted my steps over the numerous obstacles of the road; preferring this mode of advance to one which, from the difficulties of the way, was equally painful to myself and my wearied servitor.

Our journey was soon at an end; for, scaling a sudden height, we came abruptly upon the place of our destination. I wish that it were possible to sketch in words this spot as vividly as I recollect it.

Here were situated the Taboo groves of the valley—the scene of many a prolonged feast, of many a horrid rite. Beneath the dark shadows of the consecrated breadfruit-trees there reigned a solemn twilight—a cathedral-like gloom. The frightful genius of pagan worship seemed to brood in silence over the place, breathing its spell upon every object around. Here and there, in the depths of these awful shades, half screened from sight by masses of overhanging foliage, rose the idolatrous altars of the savages, built of enormous blocks of black and polished stone, placed one upon another, without cement, to the height of twelve or fifteen feet, and surmounted by a rustic open temple, enclosed with a low picket of canes, within which might be seen, in various stages of decay, offerings of breadfruit and coco-nuts, and the putrefying relics of some recent sacrifice.

In the midst of the wood was the hallowed "hoolah-hoolah" ground—set apart for the celebration of the fantastic religious ritual of these people—comprising an extensive oblong "pi-pi," terminating at either end in a lofty terraced altar, guarded by ranks of hideous wooden idols, and with the two remaining sides flanked by ranges of bamboo sheds, opening towards the interior of the quadrangle thus formed. Vast trees, standing in the middle of this space, and throwing over it an umbrageous shade, had their massive trunks built round with slight stages, elevated a few feet above the ground, and railed in with canes, forming so many rustic pulpits, from which the priests harangued their devotees.

This holiest of spots was defended from profanation by the strictest edicts of the all-pervading "taboo," which condemned to instant death the sacrilegious female who should enter or touch its sacred precincts, or even so much as press with her feet the ground made holy by the shadows that it cast.

Access was had to the enclosure through an embowered entrance on one side, facing a number of towering coco-nut trees, planted at intervals along a level area of a hundred yards. At the farther extremity of this space was to be seen a building of considerable size, reserved for the habitation of the priests and religious attendants of the groves.

In its vicinity was another remarkable edifice, built as usual upon the summit of a pi-pi, and at least two hundred feet in length, though not more than twenty in breadth. The whole front of this latter structure was completely open, and from one end to the other ran a narrow verandah, fenced in on the edge of the pi-pi with a picket of canes. Its interior presented the appearance of an immense lounging-place, the entire floor being strewn with successive layers of mats, lying between parallel trunks of coco-nut trees, selected for the purpose from the straightest and most symmetrical the vale afforded.

To this building, denominated in the language of the natives the "Ti," Mehevi now conducted us. Thus far we had been accompanied by a troop of the natives of both sexes; but as soon as we approached its vicinity, the females gradually separated themselves from the crowd, and standing aloof, permitted us to pass on. The merciless prohibitions of the taboo extended likewise to this edifice, and were enforced by the same dreadful penalty that secured the hoolah-hoolah ground from the imaginary pollution of a woman's presence.

On entering the house, I was surprised to see six muskets ranged against the bamboo on one side, from the barrels of which depended as many small canvas pouches, partly filled with powder. Disposed about these muskets, like the cutlasses that decorate the bulkhead of a man-of-war's cabin, were a great variety of rude spears and paddles, javelins, and war-clubs. This then, said I to Toby, must be the armoury of the tribe.

As we advanced farther along the building, we were struck with the aspect of four or five hideous old wretches, on whose decrepit forms time and tattooing seemed to have obliterated every trace of humanity. Owing to the continued operation of this latter process, which only terminates among the warriors of the island after all the figures stretched upon their limbs in youth have been blended together—an effect, however, produced only in cases of extreme longevity—the bodies of these men were of a uniform dull green colour—the hue which the tattooing gradually assumes as the individual advances in age. Their skin had a frightful scaly appearance, which, united with its singular colour, made their limbs not a little resemble dusty specimens of verde-antique. Their flesh, in parts, hung upon them in huge folds, like the overlapping plaits on the flank of a rhinoceros. Their heads were completely bald, whilst their faces were puckered into a thousand wrinkles, and they presented no vestige of a beard. But the most remarkable peculiarity about them was the appearance of their feet; the toes, like the radiating lines of the mariner's compass, pointed to every quarter of the horizon. This was doubtless attributable to the fact, that during nearly a hundred years of existence the said toes never had been subjected to any artificial confinement, and in their old age, being averse to close neighborhood, bid one another keep open order.

These repulsive-looking creatures appeared to have lost the use of their lower limbs altogether; sitting upon the floor cross-legged in a state of torpor. They never heeded us in the least, scarcely looking conscious of our presence, while Mehevi seated us upon the mats, and Kory-Kory gave utterance to some unintelligible gibberish.

In a few moments a boy entered with a wooden trencher of poee-poee; and in regaling myself with its contents I was obliged again to submit to the officious intervention of my indefatigable servitor. Various other dishes followed, the chief manifesting the most hospitable importunity in pressing us to partake, and to remove all bashfulness on our part, set us no despicable example in his own person.

The repast concluded, a pipe was lighted, which passed from mouth to mouth, and yielding to its soporific influence, the quiet of the place, and the deepening shadows of approaching night, my companion and I sank into a kind of drowsy repose, while the chief and Kory-Kory seemed to be slumbering beside us.

I awoke from an uneasy nap, about midnight, as I supposed; and, raising myself partly from the mat, became sensible that we were enveloped in utter darkness. Toby lay still asleep, but our late companion had disappeared. The only sound that interrupted the silence of the place was the asthmatic breathing of the old men I have mentioned, who reposed at a little distance from us. Beside them, as well as I could judge, there was no one else in the house.

Apprehensive of some evil, I roused my comrade, and we were engaged in a whispered conference concerning the unexpected withdrawal of the natives when all at once, from the depths of the grove, in full view of us where we lay, shoots of flame were seen to rise, and in a few moments illuminated the surrounding trees, casting, by contrast, into still deeper gloom the darkness around us.

While we continued gazing at this sight, dark figures appeared moving to and fro before the flames; while others, dancing and capering about, looked like so many demons.

Regarding this new phenomenon with no small degree of trepidation, I said to my companion, "What can all this mean, Toby?"

"Oh, nothing," replied he; "getting the fire ready, I suppose."

"Fire!" exclaimed I, while my heart took to beating like a trip-hammer, "what fire?"

"Why, the fire to cook us, to be sure; what else would the cannibals be kicking up such a row about if it were not for that?"

"Oh, Toby! have done with your jokes; this is no time for them; something is about to happen, I feel confident."

"Jokes, indeed!" exclaimed Toby, indignantly. "Did you ever hear me joke? Why, for what do you suppose the devils have been feeding us up in this kind of style during the last three days, unless it were for something that you are too much frightened at to talk about? Look at that Kory-Kory there! —has he not been stuffing you with his confounded mushes, just in the way they treat swine before they kill them? Depend upon it, we will be eaten this blessed night, and there is the fire we shall be roasted by."

This view of the matter was not at all calculated to allay my apprehensions, and I shuddered when I reflected that we were indeed at the mercy of a tribe of cannibals, and that the dreadful contingency to which Toby had alluded was by no means removed beyond the bounds of possibility.

"There! I told you so! they are coming for us!" exclaimed my companion the next moment, as the forms of four of the islanders were seen in bold relief against the illuminated background, mounting the pi-pi and approaching towards us.

They came on noiselessly, nay stealthily, and glided along through the gloom that surrounded us as if about to spring upon some object they were fearful of disturbing before they should make sure of it.—Gracious heaven! the horrible reflections which crowded upon me that moment.—A cold sweat stood upon my brow, and spell-bound with terror I awaited my fate!

Suddenly the silence was broken by the well-remembered tones of Mehevi, and at the kindly accents of his voice my fears were immediately dissipated.

"Tommo, Toby, ki ki?" (eat).—He had waited to address us until he had assured himself that we were both awake, at which he seemed somewhat surprised.

"Ki ki! is it?" said Toby in his gruff tones; "well, cook us first, will you?— but what's this?" he added, as another savage appeared, bearing before him a large trencher of wood, containing some kind of steaming meat, as appeared from the odours it diffused, and which he deposited at the feet of Mehevi. "A baked baby, I dare say! but I will have none of it, never mind what it is.— A pretty fool I should make of myself, indeed, waked up here in the middle of the night, stuffing and guzzling, and all to make a fat meal for a parcel of bloody-minded cannibals one of these mornings!—No, I see what they are at very plainly, so I am resolved to starve myself into a bunch of bones and gristle, and then, if they serve me up, they are welcome! But I say, Tommo, you are not going to eat any of that mess there, in the dark, are you? Why, how can you tell what it is?"

"By tasting it, to be sure," said I, masticating a morsel that Kory-Kory had just put in my mouth; "and excellently good it is too, very much like veal."

"A baked baby, by the soul of Captain Cook!" burst forth Toby, with amazing vehemence; "Veal! why there never was a calf on the island till you landed. I tell you you are bolting down mouthfuls from a dead Happar's carcass, as sure as you live, and no mistake!"

Emetics and lukewarm water! What a sensation in the abdominal regions! Sure enough, where could the fiends incarnate have obtained meat? But I resolved to satisfy myself at all hazards; and, turning to Mehevi, I soon made the ready chief understand that I wished a light to be brought. When the taper came, I gazed eagerly into the vessel, and recognized the mutilated remains of a juvenile porker! "Puarkee!" exclaimed Kory-Kory, looking complacently at the dish; and from that day to this I have never forgotten that such is the designation of a pig in the Typee lingo.

The next morning, after being again abundantly feasted by the hospitable Mehevi, Toby and myself arose to depart. But the chief requested us to postpone our intention. "Abo, abo" (Wait, wait), he said, and accordingly we resumed our seats, while, assisted by the zealous Kory-Kory, he appeared to be engaged in giving directions to a number of the natives outside, who were busily employed in making arrangements, the nature of which we could not comprehend. But we were not left long in our ignorance, for a few moments only had elapsed when the chief beckoned us to approach, and we perceived that he had been marshalling a kind of guard of honour to escort us on our return to the house of Marheyo.

The procession was led off by two venerable-looking savages, each provided with a spear, from the end of which streamed a pennon of milk-white tappa. After them went several youths, bearing aloft calabashes of poee-poee; and followed in their turn by four stalwart fellows, sustaining long bamboos, from the tops of which hung suspended, at least twenty feet from the ground, large baskets of green breadfruit. Then came a troop of boys, carrying bunches of ripe bananas, and baskets made of the woven leaflets of coco-nut boughs, filled with the young fruit of the tree, the naked shells stripped of their husks peeping forth from the verdant wicker-work that surrounded them. Last of all came a burly islander, holding over his head a wooden trencher, in which lay disposed the remnants of our midnight feast, hidden from view, however, by a covering of breadfruit leaves.

Astonished as I was at this exhibition, I could not avoid smiling at its grotesque appearance, and the associations it naturally called up. Mehevi, it seemed, was bent on replenishing old Marheyo's larder, fearful perhaps that without this precaution his guests might not fare as well as they could desire.

As soon as I descended from the pi-pi, the procession formed anew, enclosing us in its centre; where I remained part of the time, carried by Kory-Kory, and occasionally relieving him from his burden by limping along with a spear. When we moved off in this order, the natives struck up a musical recitative, which, with various alternations, they continued until we arrived at the place of our destination.

As we proceeded on our way, bands of young girls, darting from the surrounding groves, hung upon our skirts, and accompanied us with shouts of merriment and delight, which almost drowned the deep notes of the recitative. On approaching old Marheyo's domicile, its inmates rushed out to receive us; and while the gifts of Mehevi were being disposed of, the superannuated warrior did the honours of his mansion with all the warmth of hospitality evinced by an English squire when he regales his friends at some fine old patrimonial mansion.

CHAPTER XIII

ATTEMPT TO PROCURE RELIEF FROM NUKUHEVA—PERILOUS ADVENTURE OF TOBY IN THE HAPPAR MOUNTAIN—ELOQUENCE OF KORY-KORY.

AMIDST these novel scenes a week passed away almost imperceptibly. The natives, actuated by some mysterious impulse, day after day redoubled their attentions to us. Their manner towards us was unaccountable. Surely, thought I, they would not act thus if they meant us any harm. But why this excess of deferential kindness, or what equivalent can they imagine us capable of rendering them for it?

We were fairly puzzled. But despite the apprehensions I could not dispel, the horrible character imputed to these Typees appeared to me wholly undeserved.

"Why, they are cannibals!" said Toby on one occasion when I eulogized the tribe. "Granted," I replied, "but a more humane, gentlemanly, and amiable set of epicures do not probably exist in the Pacific."

But, notwithstanding the kind treatment we received, I was too familiar with the fickle disposition of savages not to feel anxious to withdraw from the valley, and put myself beyond the reach of that fearful death which, under all these smiling appearances, might yet menace us. But here there was an obstacle in the way of doing so. It was idle for me to think of moving from the place until I should have recovered from the severe lameness that afflicted me; indeed my malady began seriously to alarm me; for, despite the herbal remedies of the natives, it continued to grow worse and worse. Their mild applications, though they soothed the pain, did not remove the disorder, and I felt convinced that without better aid I might anticipate long and acute suffering.

But how was this aid to be procured? From the surgeons of the French fleet, which probably still lay in the bay of Nukuheva, it might easily have been obtained, could I have made my case known to them. But how could that be effected?

At last, in the exigency to which I was reduced, I proposed to Toby that he should endeavour to go round to Nukuheva, and if he could not succeed in returning to the valley by water, in one of the boats of the squadron, and taking me off, he might at least procure me some proper medicines, and effect his return overland.

My companion listened to me in silence, and at first did not appear to relish the idea. The truth was he felt impatient to escape from the place, and wished to avail himself of our present high favour with the natives to make good our retreat, before we should experience some sudden alteration in their behaviour. As he could not think of leaving me in my helpless condition, he implored me to be of good cheer, assured me that I should soon be better and enabled in a few days to return with him to Nukuheva.

Added to this, he could not bear the idea of again returning to this danger-ous place; and as for the expectation of persuading the Frenchmen to detach a boat's crew for the purpose of rescuing me from the Typees, he looked upon it as idle; and, with arguments that I could not answer, urged the improbability of their provoking the hostilities of the clan by any such measure; especially as, for the purpose of quieting its apprehensions, they had as yet refrained from making any visit to the bay. "And even should they consent," said Toby, "they would only produce a commotion in the valley, in which we might both be sacrificed by these ferocious islanders." This was unanswerable; but still I clung to the belief that he might succeed in accomplishing the other part of my plan; and at last I overcame his scruples, and he agreed to make the attempt.

As soon as we succeeded in making the natives understand our intention, they broke out into the most vehement opposition to the measure, and for a while I almost despaired of obtaining their consent. At the bare thought of one of us leaving them, they manifested the most lively concern. The grief and consternation of Kory-Kory, in particular, was unbounded; he threw him-self into a perfect paroxysm of gestures, which were intended to convey to us not only his abhorrence of Nukuheva and its uncivilized inhabitants, but also his astonishment that after becoming acquainted with the enlightened Typees, we should evince the least desire to withdraw, even for a time, from their agreeable society.

However, I overbore his objections by appealing to my lameness; from which I assured the natives I should speedily recover, if Toby were permitted to obtain the supplies I needed.

It was agreed that on the following morning my companion should depart, accompanied by some one or two of the household, who should point out to him an easy route, by which the bay might be reached before sunset.

At early dawn of the next day, our habitation was astir. One of the young men mounted into an adjoining coco-nut tree, and threw down a number of the young fruit, which old Marheyo quickly stripped of the green husks, and strung together upon a short pole. These were intended to refresh Toby on his route.

The preparations being completed, with no little emotion I bade my companion adieu. He promised to return in three days at farthest; and, bidding me keep up my spirits in the interval, turned round the corner of the pi-pi, and, under the guidance of the venerable Marheyo, was soon out of sight. His departure oppressed me with melancholy, and, re-entering the dwelling, I threw myself almost in despair upon the matting of the floor.

In two hours' time the old warrior returned, and gave me to understand that, after accompanying my companion a little distance, and showing him the route, he had left him journeying on his way.

It was about noon of this same day, a season which these people are wont to pass in sleep, that I lay in the house, surrounded by its slumbering inmates, and painfully affected by the strange silence which prevailed. All at once I thought I heard a faint shout, as if proceeding from some persons in the depth of the grove which extended in front of our habitation.

The sounds grew louder and nearer, and gradually the whole valley rang with wild outcries. The sleepers around me started to their feet in alarm, and hurried outside to discover the cause of the commotion. Kory-Kory, who had been the first to spring up, soon returned almost breathless and nearly frantic with the excitement under which he seemed to be labouring. All that I could understand from him was that some accident had happened to Toby. Apprehensive of some dreadful calamity, I rushed out of the house, and caught sight of a tumultuous crowd, who, with shrieks and lamentations, were just emerging from the grove bearing in their arms some object, the sight of which produced all this transport of sorrow. As they drew near, the men redoubled their cries, while the girls, tossing their bare arms in the air, exclaimed plaintively, "Awha! awha! Toby muckee mooee!"—Alas! alas! Toby is killed!

In a moment the crowd opened, and disclosed the apparently lifeless body of my companion borne between two men, the head hanging heavily against the breast of the foremost. The whole face, neck, and bosom were covered with blood, which still trickled slowly from a wound behind the temple. In the midst of the greatest uproar and confusion the body was carried into the house and laid on a mat. Waving the natives off to give room and air, I bent eagerly over Toby, and, laying my hand upon the breast, ascertained that the heart still beat. Overjoyed at this, I seized a calabash of water, and dashed its contents upon his face, then wiping away the blood, anxiously examined the wound. It was about three inches long, and on removing the clotted hair from about it, showed the skull laid completely bare. Immediately with my knife I cut away the heavy locks, and bathed the part repeatedly in water.

In a few moments Toby revived, and, opening his eyes for a second, closed them again without speaking. Kory-Kory, who had been kneeling beside me, now chafed his limbs gently with the palms of his hands, while a young girl at his head kept fanning him, and still continued to moisten his lips and brow. Soon my poor comrade showed signs of animation, and I succeeded in making him swallow from a coco-nut shell a few mouthfuls of water.

Old Tinor now appeared, holding in her hand some simples she had gathered, the juice of which she by signs besought me to squeeze into the wound. Having done so, I thought it best to leave Toby undisturbed until he should have had time to rally his faculties. Several times he opened his lips, but fearful for his safety I enjoined silence. In the course of two or three hours, however, he sat up, and was sufficiently recovered to tell me what had occurred.

"After leaving the house with Marheyo," said Toby, "we struck across the valley, and ascended the opposite heights. Just beyond them, my guide informed me, lay the valley of Happar, while along their summits, and skirting the head of the vale, was my route to Nukuheva. After mounting a little way up the elevation my guide paused, and gave me to understand that he could not accompany me any farther, and by various signs intimated that he was afraid to approach any nearer the territories of the enemies of his tribe. He, however, pointed out my path, which now lay clearly before me, and bidding me farewell hastily descended the mountain.

"Quite elated at being so near the Happars, I pushed up the acclivity, and soon gained its summit. It tapered up to a sharp ridge, from whence I beheld both the hostile valleys. Here I sat down and rested for a moment, refreshing myself with my coco-nuts. I was soon again pursuing my way along the height, when suddenly I saw three of the islanders, who must have just come out of Happar valley, standing in the path ahead of me. They were each armed with a heavy spear, and one from his appearance I took to be a chief. They sung out something, I could not understand what, and beckoned me to come on.

"Without the least hesitation I advanced towards them, and had approached within about a yard of the foremost, when, pointing angrily into the Typee valley, and uttering some savage exclamation, he wheeled round his weapon like lightning, and struck me in a moment to the ground. The blow inflicted this wound, and took away my senses. As soon as I came to myself, I perceived the three islanders standing a little distance off, and apparently engaged in some violent altercation respecting me.

"My first impulse was to run for it; but, in endeavouring to rise, I fell back, and rolled down a little grassy precipice. The shock seemed to rally my faculties; so, starting to my feet, I fled down the path I had just ascended. I had no need to look behind me, for, from the yells I heard, I knew that my enemies were in full pursuit. Urged on by their fearful outcries, and heedless of the injury I had received—though the blood flowing from the wound trickled over into my eyes and almost blinded me—I rushed down the mountain-side with the speed of the wind. In a short time I had descended nearly a third of the distance, and the savages had ceased their cries, when suddenly a terrific howl burst upon my ear, and at the same moment a heavy javelin darted past me as I fled, and stuck quivering in a tree close to me. Another yell followed, and a second spear and a third shot through the air within a few feet of my body, both of them piercing the ground obliquely in advance of me. The fellows gave a roar of rage and disappointment; but they were afraid, I suppose, of coming down farther into the Typee valley, and so abandoned the chase. I saw them recover their weapons and turn back; and I continued my descent as fast as I could.

"What could have caused this ferocious attack on the part of these Happars I could not imagine, unless it were that they had seen me ascending the mountain with Marheyo, and that the mere fact of coming from the Typee valley was sufficient to provoke them.

"As long as I was in danger I scarcely felt the wound I had received; but when the chase was over I began to suffer from it. I had lost my hat in my flight, and the sun scorched my bare head. I felt faint and giddy; but, fearful of falling to the ground beyond the reach of assistance, I staggered on as well as I could, and at last gained the level of the valley and then down I sank; and I knew nothing more until I found myself lying upon these mats, and you stooping over me with the calabash of water."

Such was Toby's account of this sad affair. I afterwards learned that fortunately he had fallen close to a spot where the natives go for fuel. A party of them caught sight of him as he fell, and sounding the alarm, had lifted him up; and, after ineffectually endeavouring to restore him at the brook, had hurried forward with him to the house.

This incident threw a dark cloud over our prospects. It reminded us that we were hemmed in by hostile tribes, whose territories we could not hope to pass, on our route to Nukuheva, without encountering the effects of their savage resentment. There appeared to be no avenue opened to our escape but the sea, which washed the lower extremity of the vale.

Our Typee friends availed themselves of the recent disaster of Toby to exhort us to a due appreciation of the blessings we enjoyed among them; contrasting their own generous reception of us with the animosity of their neighbours. They likewise dwelt upon the cannibal propensities of the Happars, a subject which they were perfectly aware could not fail to alarm us; while at the same time they earnestly disclaimed all participation in so horrid a custom. Nor did they omit to call upon us to admire the natural loveliness of their own abode, and the lavish abundance with which it produced all manner of luxuriant fruits; exalting it in this particular above any of the surrounding valleys.

Kory-Kory seemed to experience so heartfelt a desire to infuse into our minds proper views on these subjects, that, assisted in his endeavours by the little knowledge of the language we had acquired, he actually succeeded in making us comprehend a considerable part of what he said. To facilitate our correct apprehension of his meaning, he at first condensed his ideas into the smallest possible compass.

"Happar keekeeno nuee," he exclaimed; "nuee, nuee, ki ki kannaka!—ah! owle mortarkee!" which signifies, "Terrible fellows those Happars!—devour an amazing quantity of men!—ah, shocking bad!" Thus far he explained himself by a variety of gestures, during the performance of which he would dart out of the house, and point abhorrently towards the Happar valley; running in to us again with a rapidity that showed he was fearful we would lose one part of his meaning before he could complete the other; and continuing his illustrations by seizing the fleshy part of my arm in his teeth, intimating by the operation that the people who lived over in that direction would like nothing better than to treat me in that manner.

Having assured himself that we were fully enlightened on this point, he proceeded to another branch of his subject. "Ah! Typee mortarkee!—nuee, nuee mioree—nuee, nuee wai—nuee, nuee poee-poee—nuee, nuee kokoo—ah! nuee, nuee kiki—ah! nuee, nuee, nuee!" Which, literally interpreted as before, would imply, "Ah, Typee! isn't it a fine place though!—no danger of starving here, I tell you!—plenty of breadfruit—plenty of water—plenty of pudding—ah! plenty of everything!—ah! heaps, heaps, heaps!" All this was accompanied by a running commentary of signs and gestures which it was impossible not to comprehend.

As he continued his harangue, however, Kory-Kory, in emulation of our more polished orators, began to launch out rather diffusely into other branches of his subject, enlarging, probably, upon the moral reflections it suggested; and proceeded in such a strain of unintelligible and stunning gibberish, that he actually gave me the headache for the rest of the day.

CHAPTER XIV

A GREAT EVENT HAPPENS IN THE VALLEY—THE ISLAND TELEGRAPH—SOMETHING BEFALLS TOBY—FAYAWAY DISPLAYS A TENDER HEART—MELANCHOLY RE-FLECTIONS—MYSTERIOUS CONDUCT OF THE ISLANDERS—DEVOTION OF KORY-KORY—A RURAL COUCH—A LUXURY—KORY-KORY STRIKES A LIGHT A LA TYPEE.

In the course of a few days Toby had recovered from the effects of his adventure with the Happar warriors; the wound on his head rapidly healing under the vegetable treatment of the good Tinor. Less fortunate than my companion, however, I still continued to languish under a complaint the origin and nature of which were still a mystery. Cut off as I was from all intercourse with the civilized world, and feeling the inefficiency of anything the natives could do to relieve me; knowing too, that so long as I remained in my present condition, it would be impossible for me to leave the valley, whatever opportunity might present itself; and apprehensive that ere long we might be exposed to some caprice on the part of the islanders, I now gave up all hopes of recovery, and became a prey to the most gloomy thoughts. A deep dejection fell upon me, which neither the friendly remonstrances of my companion, the devoted attentions of Kory-Kory, nor all the soothing influences of Fayaway could remove.

One morning as I lay on the mats in the house, plunged in melancholy reverie, and regardless of everything around me, Toby, who had left me about an hour, returned in haste, and with great glee told me to cheer up and be of good heart; for he believed from what was going on among the natives, that there were boats approaching the bay.

These tidings operated upon me like magic. The hour of our deliverance was at hand, and starting up, I was soon convinced that something unusual was about to occur. The word "botee! botee!" was vociferated in all directions; and shouts were heard in the distance, at first feebly and faintly: but growing louder and nearer at each successive repetition, until they were caught up by a fellow in a coco-nut tree a few yards off, who sounding them in turn, they were reiterated from a neighbouring grove, and so died away gradually from point to point, as the intelligence penetrated into the farthest recesses of the valley. This was the vocal telegraph of the islanders; by means of which condensed items of information could be carried in a very few minutes from the sea to their remotest habitation, a distance of at least eight or nine miles. On the present occasion it was in active operation; one piece of information following another with inconceivable rapidity.

The greatest commotion now appeared to prevail. At every fresh item of intelligence the natives betrayed the liveliest interest, and redoubled the energy with which they employed themselves in collecting fruit to sell to the expected visitors. Some were tearing off the husks from coco-nuts; some perched in the trees were throwing down breadfruit to their companions, who gathered them into heaps as they fell; while others were plying their fingers rapidly in weaving leafen baskets in which to carry the fruit.

There were other matters too going on at the same time. Here you would see a stout warrior polishing his spear with a bit of old tappa, or adjusting the folds of the girdle about his waist; and there you might descry a young damsel decorating herself with flowers, as if having in her eye some maidenly conquest; while, as in all cases of hurry and confusion in every part of the world, a number of individuals kept hurrying to and fro, with amazing vigour and perseverance, doing nothing themselves, and hindering others.

Never before had we seen the islanders in such a state of bustle and excitement; and the scene furnished abundant evidence of the fact—that it was only at long intervals any such events occurred.

When I thought of the length of time that might intervene before a similar chance of escape would be presented, I bitterly lamented that I had not the power of availing myself effectually of the present opportunity.

From all that we could gather, it appeared that the natives were fearful of arriving too late upon the beach, unless they made extraordinary exertions. Sick and lame as I was, I would have started with Toby at once, had not Kory-Kory not only refused to carry me, but manifested the most invincible repugnance to our leaving the neighbourhood of the house. The rest of the savages were equally opposed to our wishes, and seemed grieved and astonished at the earnestness of my solicitations. I clearly perceived that while my attendant avoided all appearance of constraining my movements, he was nevertheless determined to thwart my wish. He seemed to me on this particular occasion, as well as often afterwards, to be executing the orders of some other person with regard to me, though at the same time feeling towards me the most lively affection.

Toby, who had made up his mind to accompany the islanders if possible, as soon as they were in readiness to depart, and who for that reason had refrained from showing the same anxiety that I had done, now represented to me that it was idle for me to entertain the hope of reaching the beach in time to profit by any opportunity that might then be presented.

"Do you not see," said he, "the savages themselves are fearful of being too late, and I should hurry forward myself at once did I not think that if I showed too much eagerness I should destroy all our hopes of reaping any benefit from this fortunate event. If you will only endeavour to appear tranquil or unconcerned, you will quiet their suspicions, and I have no doubt they will then let me go with them to the beach, supposing that I merely go out of curiosity. Should I succeed in getting down to the boats, I will make known the condition in which I have left you, and measures may then be taken to secure our escape."

In the expediency of this I could not but acquiesce; and as the natives had now completed their preparations, I watched with the liveliest interest the reception that Toby's application might meet with. As soon as they understood from my companion that I intended to remain, they appeared to make no objection to his proposition, and even hailed it with pleasure. Their singular conduct on this occasion not a little puzzled me at the time, and imparted to subsequent events an additional mystery.

The islanders were now to be seen hurrying along the path which led to the sea. I shook Toby warmly by the hand, and gave him my Payta hat to shield his wounded head from the sun, as he had lost his own. He cordially returned the pressure of my hand, and solemnly promising to return as soon as the boats should leave the shore, sprang from my side, and the next minute disappeared in a turn of the grove.

In spite of the unpleasant reflections that crowded upon my mind, I could not but be entertained by the novel and animated sight which now met my view. One after another the natives crowded along the narrow path, laden with every variety of fruit. Here, you might have seen one, who, after ineffectually endeavouring to persuade a surly porker to be conducted in leading strings, was obliged at last to seize the perverse animal in his arms, and carry him struggling against his naked breast, and squealing without intermission. There went two, who at a little distance might have been taken for the Hebrew spies, on their return to Moses with the goodly bunch of grapes. One trotted before the other at a distance of a couple of yards, while between them, from a pole resting on their shoulders, was suspended a huge cluster of bananas, which swayed to and fro with the rocking gait at which they proceeded. Here ran another, perspiring with his exertions, and bearing before him a quantity of coco-nuts, who, fearful of being too late, heeded not the fruit that dropped from his basket, and appeared solely intent upon reaching his destination, careless how many of his coco-nuts kept company with him.

In a short time the last straggler was seen hurrying on his way, and the faint shouts of those in advance died insensibly upon the ear. Our part of the valley now appeared nearly deserted by its inhabitants, Kory-Kory, his aged father, and a few decrepit old people being all that were left.

Towards sunset the islanders in small parties began to return from the beach, and among them, as they drew near to the house, I sought to descry the form of my companion. But one after another they passed the dwelling, and I caught no glimpse of him. Supposing, however, that he would soon appear with some of the members of the household, I quieted my apprehensions, and waited patiently to see him advancing in company with the beautiful Fayaway. At last, I perceived Tinor coming forward, followed by the girls and young men who usually resided in the house of Marheyo; but with them came not my comrade, and, filled with a thousand alarms, I eagerly sought to discover the cause of his delay.

My earnest questions appeared to embarrass the natives greatly. All their accounts were contradictory: one giving me to understand that Toby would be with me in a very short time; another that he did not know where he was; while a third, violently inveighing against him, assured me that he had stolen away, and would never come back. It appeared to me, at the time, that in making these various statements they endeavoured to conceal from me some terrible disaster, lest the knowledge of it should overpower me.

Fearful lest some fatal calamity had overtaken him, I sought out young Fayaway, and endeavoured to learn from her, if possible, the truth.

This gentle being had early attracted my regard, not only from her extraordinary beauty, but from the attractive cast of her countenance, singularly expressive of intelligence and humanity. Of all the natives she alone seemed to appreciate the effect which the peculiarity of the circumstances in which we were placed had produced upon the minds of my companion and myself. In addressing me—especially when I lay reclining upon the mats suffering from pain—there was a tenderness in her manner which it was impossible to misunderstand or resist. Whenever she entered the house, the expression of her face indicated the liveliest sympathy for me; and moving towards the place where I lay, with one arm slightly elevated in a gesture of pity, and her large glistening eyes gazing intently into mine, she would murmur plaintively, "Awha! awha! Tommo," and seat herself mournfully beside me.

Her manner convinced me that she deeply compassionated my situation, as being removed from my country and friends, and placed beyond the reach of all relief. Indeed, at times I was almost led to believe that her mind was swayed by gentle impulses hardly to be anticipated from one in her condition; that she appeared to be conscious there were ties rudely severed, which had once bound us to our homes; that there were sisters and brothers anxiously looking forward to our return, who were, perhaps, never more to behold us.

In this amiable light did Fayaway appear in my eyes; and reposing full confidence in her candour and intelligence, I now had recourse to her, in the midst of my alarm, with regard to my companion.

My questions evidently distressed her. She looked round from one to another of the bystanders, as if hardly knowing what answer to give me. At last, yielding to my importunities, she overcame her scruples, and gave me to understand that Toby had gone away with the boats which had visited the bay, but had promised to return at the expiration of three days. At first I accused him of perfidiously deserting me; but as I grew more composed, I upbraided myself for imputing so cowardly an action to him, and tranquillized myself with the belief that he had availed himself of the opportunity to go round to Nukuheva, in order to make some arrangement by which I could be removed from the valley. At any rate, thought I, he will return with the medicines I require, and then, as soon as I recover, there will be no difficulty in the way of our departure.

Consoling myself with these reflections, I lay down that night in a happier frame of mind than I had done for some time. The next day passed without any allusion to Toby on the part of the natives, who seemed desirous of avoiding all reference to the subject. This raised some apprehensions in my breast; but when night came, I congratulated myself that the second day had now gone by and that on the morrow Toby would again be with me. But the morrow came and went, and my companion did not appear. Ah! thought I, he reckons three days from the morning of his departure—to-morrow he will arrive. But that weary day also closed upon me, without his return. Even yet I would not despair; I thought that something detained him—that he was waiting for the sailing of a boat, at Nukuheva, and that in a day or two at farthest I should see him again. But day after day of renewed disappointment passed by; at last hope deserted me, and I fell a victim to despair.

Yes, thought I, gloomily, he has secured his own escape, and cares not what calamity may befall his unfortunate comrade. Fool that I was to suppose any one would willingly encounter the perils of this valley, after having once got beyond its limits! He has gone, and has left me to combat alone all the dangers by which I am surrounded. Thus would I sometimes seek to derive a desperate consolation from dwelling upon the perfidy of Toby: whilst at other times I sunk under the bitter remorse which I felt as having by my own imprudence brought upon myself the fate which I was sure awaited me.

At other times I thought that perhaps after all these treacherous savages had made away with him, and thence the confusion into which they were thrown by my questions, and their contradictory answers, or he might be a captive in some other part of the valley; or, more dreadful still, might have met with that fate at which my very soul shuddered. But all these speculations were vain; no tidings of Toby ever reached me; he had gone never to return.

The conduct of the islanders appeared inexplicable. All reference to my lost comrade was carefully evaded, and if at any time they were forced to make some reply to my frequent inquiries on the subject, they would uniformly denounce him as an ungrateful runaway, who had deserted his friend, and taken himself off to that vile and detestable place Nukuheva.

But whatever might have been his fate, now that he was gone, the natives multiplied their acts of kindness and attention towards myself, treating me with a degree of deference which could hardly have been surpassed had I been some celestial visitant. Kory-Kory never for one moment left my side, unless it were to execute my wishes. The faithful fellow, twice every day, in the cool of the morning and in the evening, insisted upon carrying me to the stream, and bathing me in its refreshing water.

Frequently in the afternoon he would carry me to a particular part of the stream, where the beauty of the scene produced a soothing influence upon my mind. At this place the waters flowed between grassy banks, planted with enormous breadfruit-trees, whose vast branches, interlacing overhead, formed a leafy canopy; near the stream were several smooth black rocks. One of these, projecting several feet above the surface of the water, had upon its summit a shallow cavity, which, filled with freshly gathered leaves, formed a delightful couch.

Here I often lay for hours, covered with a gauze-like veil of tappa, while Fayaway, seated beside me, and holding in her hand a fan woven from the leaflets of a young coco-nut bough, brushed aside the insects that occasionally lighted on my face, and Kory-Kory, with a view of chasing away my melancholy, performed a thousand antics in the water before us.

As my eye wandered along this romantic stream, it would fall upon the half-immersed figure of a beautiful girl, standing in the transparent water, and catching in a little net a species of diminutive shell-fish, of which these people are extravagantly fond. Sometimes a chattering group would be seated upon the edge of a low rock in the midst of the brook, busily engaged in thinning and polishing the shells of coco-nuts, by rubbing them briskly with a small stone in the water, an operation which soon converts them into a light and elegant drinking-vessel, somewhat resembling goblets made of tortoiseshell.

But the tranquillizing influences of beautiful scenery, and the exhibition of human life under so novel and charming an aspect, were not my only sources of consolation.

Every evening the girls of the house gathered about me on the mats, and after chasing away Kory-Kory from my side—who, nevertheless, retired only to a little distance and watched their proceedings with the most jealous attention—would anoint my whole body with a fragrant oil, squeezed from a yellow root, previously pounded between a couple of stones, and which in their language is denominated "aka." And most refreshing and agreeable are the juices of the "aka," when applied to one's limbs by the soft palms of sweet nymphs, whose bright eyes are beaming upon you with kindness; and I used to hail with delight the daily recurrence of this luxurious operation, in which I forgot all my troubles, and buried for the time every feeling of sorrow.

Sometimes in the cool of the evening my devoted servitor would lead me out upon the pi-pi in front of the house, and seating me near its edge, protect my body from the annoyances of the insects which occasionally hovered in the air, by wrapping me round with a large roll of tappa. He then bustled about, and employed himself at least twenty minutes in adjusting everything to secure my personal comfort.

Having perfected his arrangements, he would get my pipe, and, lighting it, would hand it to me. Often he was obliged to strike a light for the occasion, and as the mode he adopted was entirely different from what I had ever seen or heard of before, I will describe it.

A straight, dry, and partly decayed stick of the Habiscus, about six feet in length, and half as many inches in diameter, with a smaller bit of wood not more than a foot long, and scarcely an inch wide, is as invariably to be met with in every house in Typee as a box of lucifer matches in the corner of a kitchen cupboard at home.

The islander, placing the larger stick obliquely against some object, with one end elevated at an angle of forty-five degrees, mounts astride of it like an urchin about to gallop off upon a cane, and then, grasping the smaller one firmly in both hands, he rubs its pointed end slowly up and down the extent of a few inches on the principal stick, until at last he makes a narrow groove in the wood, with an abrupt termination at the point furthest from him, where all the dusty articles which the friction creates are accumulated in a little heap.

At first Kory-Kory goes to work quite leisurely, but gradually quickens his pace, and waxing warm in the employment, drives the stick furiously along the smoking channel, plying his hands to and fro with amazing rapidity, the perspiration starting from every pore. As he approaches the climax of his effort, he pants and gasps for breath, and his eyes almost start from their sockets with the violence of his exertions. This is the critical stage of the operation; all his previous labours are vain if he cannot sustain the rapidity of the movement until the reluctant spark is produced. Suddenly he stops, becomes perfectly motionless. His hands still retain their hold of the smaller stick, which is pressed convulsively against the farther end of the channel among the fine powder there accumulated, as if he had just pierced through and through some little viper that was wriggling and struggling to escape from his clutches. The next moment a delicate wreath of smoke curls spirally into the air, the heap of dusty particles glows with fire, and Kory-Kory almost breathless, dismounts from his steed.

This operation appeared to me to be the most laborious species of work performed in Typee; and had I possessed a sufficient intimacy with the language to have conveyed my ideas upon the subject, I should certainly have suggested to the most influential of the natives the expediency of establishing a college of vestals to be centrally located in the valley, for the purpose of keeping alive the indispensable article of fire; so as to supersede the necessity of such a vast outlay of strength and good temper, as were usually squandered on these occasions. There might, however, be special difficulties in carrying this plan into execution.

What a striking evidence does this operation furnish of the wide difference between the extreme of savage and civilized life. A gentleman of Typee can bring up a numerous family of children and give them all a highly respectable cannibal education, with infinitely less toil and anxiety than he expends in the simple process of striking a light; whilst a poor European artisan, who through the instrumentality of a lucifer performs the same operation in one second, is put to his wits' end to provide for his starving offspring that food which the children of a Polynesian father, without troubling their parent, pluck from the branches of every tree around them.

CHAPTER XV

KINDNESS OF MARHEYO AND THE REST OF THE ISLANDERS—A FULL DESCRIPTION
OF THE BREADFRUIT-TREE—DIFFERENT MODES OF PREPARING THE FRUIT.

ALL the inhabitants of the valley treated me with great kindness; but as to
the household of Marheyo, with whom I was now permanently domiciled,
nothing could surpass their efforts to minister to my comfort. To the gratification of my palate they paid the most unwearied attention. They continually
invited me to partake of food, and when after eating heartily I declined the
viands they continued to offer me, they seemed to think that my appetite stood
in need of some piquant stimulant to excite its activity.

In pursuance of this idea, old Marheyo himself would hie him away to
the sea-shore by the break of day, for the purpose of collecting various species
of rare sea-weed; some of which among these people are considered a great
luxury. After a whole day spent in this employment, he would return about
nightfall with several coco-nut shells filled with different descriptions of kemp.
In preparing these for use he manifested all the ostentation of a professed cook,
although the chief mystery of the affair appeared to consist in pouring water
in judicious quantities upon the slimy contents of his coco-nut shells.

The first time he submitted one of these saline salads to my critical attention
I naturally thought that anything collected at such pains must possess peculiar
merits; but one mouthful was a complete dose; and great was the consternation of the old warrior at the rapidity with which I ejected his epicurean treat.

How true it is, that the rarity of any particular article enhances its value
amazingly. In some part of the valley—I know not where, but probably in the
neighbourhood of the sea—the girls were sometimes in the habit of procuring
small quantities of salt, a thimble-full or so being the result of the united labours
of a party of five or six employed for the greater part of the day. This precious
commodity they brought to the house, enveloped in multitudinous folds of
leaves; and as a special mark of the esteem in which they held me, would spread
an immense leaf on the ground, and dropping one by one a few minute particles
of the salt upon it, invite me to taste them.

From the extravagant value placed upon the article I verily believe, that
with a bushel of common Liverpool salt all the real estate in Typee might
have been purchased. With a small pinch of it in one hand, and a quarter
section of a breadfruit in the other, the greatest chief in the valley would have
laughed at all the luxuries of a Parisian table.

The celebrity of the breadfruit-tree, and the conspicuous place it occupies
in a Typee bill of fare, induce me to give at some length a general description
of the tree, and the various modes in which the fruit is prepared.

The breadfruit-tree, in its glorious prime, is a grand and towering object,
forming the same feature in a Marquesan landscape that the patriarchal elm
does in New England scenery. The latter tree it not a little resembles in
height, in the wide spread of its stalwart branches, and in its venerable and
imposing aspect.

The leaves of the breadfruit are of great size, and their edges are cut and
scalloped as fantastically as those of a lady's lace collar. As they annually
tend towards decay, they almost rival in the brilliant variety of their gradually
changing hues the fleeting shades of the expiring dolphin. The autumnal tints

of our American forests, glorious as they are, sink into nothing in comparison with this tree.

The leaf, in one particular stage, when nearly all the prismatic colours are blended on its surface, is often converted by the natives into a superb and striking head-dress. The principal fibre traversing its length being split open a convenient distance, and the elastic sides of the aperture pressed apart, the head is inserted between them, the leaf drooping on one side, with its forward half turned jauntily up on the brows, and the remaining part spreading laterally behind the ears.

The fruit somewhat resembles in magnitude and general appearance one of our citron melons of ordinary size; but, unlike the citron it has no sectional lines drawn along the outside. Its surface is dotted all over with little conical prominences, looking not unlike the knobs on an antiquated church door. The rind is perhaps an eighth of an inch in thickness; and denuded of this, at the time when it is in the greatest perfection, the fruit presents a beautiful globe of white pulp, the whole of which may be eaten, with the exception of a slender core, which is easily removed.

The breadfruit, however, is never used, and is indeed altogether unfit to be eaten, until submitted in one form or other to the action of fire.

The most simple manner in which this operation is performed, and, I think, the best, consists in placing any number of the freshly plucked fruit, when in a particular stage of greenness, among the embers of a fire, in the same way that you would roast a potato. After the lapse of ten or fifteen minutes, the green rind embrowns and cracks, showing through the fissures in its sides the milk-white interior. As soon as it cools, the rind drops off, and you then have the soft round pulp in its purest and most delicious state. Thus eaten, it has a mild and pleasing flavour.

Sometimes, after having been roasted in the fire, the natives snatch it briskly from the embers, and permitting it to slip out of the yielding rind into a vessel of cold water, stir up the mixture, which they call "bo-a-sho." I never could endure this compound, and indeed the preparation is not greatly in vogue among the more polite Typees.

There is one form, however, in which the fruit is occasionally served, that renders it a dish fit for a king. As soon as it is taken from the fire the exterior is removed, and the core extracted, and the remaining part is placed in a sort of shallow stone mortar, and briskly worked with a pestle of the same substance. While one person is performing this operation, another takes a ripe coco-nut, and breaking it in half, which they also do very cleverly, proceeds to grate the juicy meat into fine particles. This is done by means of a piece of mother-of-pearl shell, lashed firmly to the extreme end of a heavy stick, with its straight side accurately notched like a saw. The stick is sometimes a grotesquely-formed limb of a tree, with three or four branches twisting from its body like so many shapeless legs, and sustaining it two or three feet from the ground.

The native, first placing a calabash beneath the nose, as it were, of his curious-looking log-steed, for the purpose of receiving the grated fragments as they fall, mounts astride of it as if it were a hobby-horse, and twirling the inside of one of his hemispheres of coco-nut around the sharp teeth of the mother-of-pearl shell, the pure white meat falls in snowy showers into the receptacle provided. Having obtained a quantity sufficient for his purpose, he places it in a bag made of the net-like fibrous substance attached to all coco-nut trees, and compressing it over the breadfruit, which, being now sufficiently pounded, is put into a wooden bowl—extracts a thick creamy milk. The delicious liquid soon bubbles round the fruit, and leaves it at last just peeping above its surface.

This preparation is called "kokoo," and a most luscious preparation it is. The hobby-horse and the pestle and mortar were in great requisition during the time I remained in the house of Marheyo, and Kory-Kory had frequent occasion to show his skill in their use.

But the great staple articles of food into which the breadfruit is converted by these natives are known respectively by the names of amar and poee-poee.

At a certain season of the year, when the fruit of the hundred groves of the valley has reached its maturity, and hangs in golden spheres from every branch, the islanders assemble in harvest groups, and garner in the abundance which surrounds them. The trees are stripped of their nodding burdens, which, easily freed from the rind and core, are gathered together in capacious wooden vessels, where the pulpy fruit is soon worked by a stone pestle, vigorously applied, into a blended mass of a doughy consistency, called by the natives "tutao." This is then divided into separate parcels, which, after being made up into stout packages, enveloped in successive folds of leaves, and bound round with thongs of bark, are stored away in large receptacles hollowed in the earth, from whence they are drawn as occasion may require.

In this condition the tutao sometimes remains for years, and even is thought to improve by age. Before it is fit to be eaten, however, it has to undergo an additional process. A primitive oven is scooped in the ground, and its bottom being loosely covered with stones, a large fire is kindled within it. As soon as the requisite degree of heat is attained, the embers are removed, and the surface of the stones being covered with thick layers of leaves, one of the larger packages of tutao is deposited upon them, and overspread with another layer of leaves. The whole is then quickly heaped up with earth, and forms a sloping mound.

The tutao thus baked is called "amar;" the action of the oven having converted it into an amber-coloured caky substance, a little tart, but not at all disagreeable to the taste.

By another and final process the "amar" is changed into "poee-poee." This transition is rapidly effected. The amar is placed in a vessel, and mixed with water until it gains a proper pudding-like consistency, when, without further preparation, it is in readiness for use. This is the form in which the "tutao" is generally consumed. The singular mode of eating it I have already described.

Were it not that the breadfruit is thus capable of being preserved for a length of time, the natives might be reduced to a state of starvation; for owing to some unknown cause the trees sometimes fail to bear fruit; and on such occasions the islanders chiefly depend upon the supplies they have been enabled to store away.

This stately tree, which is rarely met with upon the Sandwich Islands, and then only of a very inferior quality, and at Tahiti, does not abound to a degree that renders its fruit the principal article of food, attains its greatest excellence in the genial climate of the Marquesan group, where it grows to an enormous magnitude, and flourishes in the utmost abundance.

CHAPTER XVI

MELANCHOLY CONDITION—OCCURRENCE AT THE TI—ANECDOTE OF MARHEYO—
SHAVING THE HEAD OF A WARRIOR.

In looking back to this period, and calling to remembrance the numberless proofs of kindness and respect which I received from the natives of the valley, I can scarcely understand how it was that, in the midst of so many consolatory circumstances, my mind should still have been consumed by the most dismal forebodings, and have remained a prey to the profoundest melancholy. It is true that the suspicious circumstances which had attended the disappearance of Toby were enough of themselves to excite distrust with regard to the savages, in whose power I felt myself to be entirely placed, especially when it was combined with the knowledge that these very men, kind and respectful as they were to me, were, after all, nothing better than a set of cannibals.

But my chief source of anxiety, and that which poisoned every temporary enjoyment, was the mysterious disease in my leg, which still remained unabated. All the herbal applications of Tinor, united with the severer discipline of the old leech, and the affectionate nursing of Kory-Kory, had failed to relieve me. I was almost a cripple, and the pain I endured at intervals was agonizing. The unaccountable malady showed no signs of amendment; on the contrary, its violence increased day by day, and threatened the most fatal results, unless some powerful means were employed to counteract it. It seemed as if I were destined to sink under this grievous affliction, or at least that it would hinder me from availing myself of any opportunity of escaping from the valley.

An incident which occurred as nearly as I can estimate about three weeks after the disappearance of Toby, convinced me that the natives, from some reason or other, would interpose every possible obstacle to my leaving them.

One morning there was no little excitement evinced by the people near my abode, and which I soon discovered proceeded from a vague report that boats had been seen at a great distance approaching the bay. Immediately all was bustle and animation. It so happened that day that the pain I suffered having somewhat abated, and feeling in much better spirits than usual, I had complied with Kory-Kory's invitation to visit the chief Mehevi at the place called the "Ti," which I have before described as being situated within the precincts of the Taboo Groves. These sacred recesses were at no great distance from Marheyo's habitation, and lay between it and the sea; the path that conducted to the beach passing directly in front of the Ti, and thence skirting along the border of the groves.

I was reposing upon the mats, within the sacred building, in company with Mehevi and several other chiefs, when the announcement was first made. It sent a thrill of joy through my whole frame;—perhaps Toby was about to return. I rose at once to my feet, and my instinctive impulse was to hurry down to the beach, equally regardless of the distance that separated me from it and of my disabled condition. As soon as Mehevi noticed the effect the intelligence had produced upon me, and the impatience I betrayed to reach the sea, his countenance assumed that inflexible rigidity of expression which had so awed me on the afternoon of our arrival at the house of Marheyo. As I was proceeding to leave the Ti, he laid his hand upon my shoulder, and said gravely, "abo, abo" (wait, wait). Solely intent upon the one thought that occupied my mind, and heedless of his request, I was brushing past him, when suddenly he assumed a tone of authority, and told me to "moee" (sit down). Though struck by the alteration in his demeanour, the excitement under which I laboured was too strong to permit me to obey the unexpected command, and I was still limping towards the edge of the pi-pi with Kory-Kory clinging to one arm in his efforts to restrain me, when the natives around starting to their feet, ranged themselves along the open front of the building, while Mehevi looked at me scowlingly, and reiterated his commands still more sternly.

It was at this moment, when fifty savage countenances were glaring upon me, that I first truly experienced I was indeed a captive in the valley. The conviction rushed upon me with staggering force, and I was overwhelmed by this confirmation of my worst fears. I saw at once that it was useless for me to resist, and sick at heart, I reseated my self upon the mats, and for the moment abandoned myself to despair.

I now perceived the natives one after the other hurrying past the Ti and pursuing the route that conducted to the sea. These savages, thought I, will soon be holding communication with some of my own countrymen perhaps, who with ease could restore me to liberty did they know of the situation I was in. No language can describe the wretchedness which I felt; and in the bitterness of my soul I imprecated a thousand curses on the perfidious Toby, who had thus abandoned me to destruction. It was in vain that Kory-Kory tempted me with food, or lighted my pipe, or sought to attract my attention by performing the uncouth antics that had sometimes diverted me. I was fairly knocked down by this last misfortune, which, much as I had feared it, I had never before had the courage calmly to contemplate.

Regardless of everything but my own sorrow, I remained in the Ti for several hours, until shouts proceeding at intervals from the groves beyond the house proclaimed the return of the natives from the beach.

Whether any boats visited the bay that morning or not, I never could ascertain. The savages assured me that there had not—but I was inclined to believe that by deceiving me in this particular they sought to allay the violence of my grief. However that might be, this incident showed plainly that the Typees intended to hold me a prisoner. As they still treated me with the same sedulous attention as before, I was utterly at a loss how to account for their singular conduct. Had I been in a situation to instruct them in any of the rudiments of the mechanic arts, or had I manifested a disposition to render myself in any way useful among them, their conduct might have been attributed to some adequate motive, but as it was, the matter seemed to me inexplicable.

During my whole stay on the island there occurred but two or three instances where the natives applied to me with the view of availing themselves of my superior information. And these now appear so ludicrous that I cannot forbear relating them.

The few things we had brought from Nukuheva had been done up into a small bundle which we had carried with us in our descent to the valley. This bundle, the first night of our arrival, I had used as a pillow, but on the succeeding morning, opening it for the inspection of the natives, they gazed upon the miscellaneous contents as though I had just revealed to them a casket of diamonds, and they insisted that so precious a treasure should be properly secured. A line was accordingly attached to it, and the other end being passed over the ridge-pole of the house, it was hoisted up to the apex of the roof, where it nung suspended directly over the mats where I usually reclined. When I desired anything from it I merely raised my finger to a bamboo beside me, and taking hold of the string which was there fastened, lowered the package. This was exceedingly handy, and I took care to let the natives understand how much I applauded the invention. Of this package the chief contents were a razor with its case, a supply of needles and thread, a pound or two of tobacco, and a few yards of a bright-coloured calico.

I should have mentioned that shortly after Toby's disappearance, perceiving the uncertainty of the time I might be obliged to remain in the valley—if, indeed, I ever should escape from it—and considering that my whole wardrobe consisted of a shirt and a pair of trousers, I resolved to doff these garments at once, in order to preserve them in a suitable condition for wear should I again appear among civilized beings. I was consequently obliged to assume the Typee costume, a little altered, however, to suit my own views of propriety, and in which I have no doubt I appeared to as much advantage as a senator of Rome enveloped in the folds of his toga. A few folds of yellow tappa tucked about my waist, descended to my feet in the style of a lady's petticoat, only I did not have recourse to those voluminous paddings in the rear with which our gentle dames are in the habit of augmenting the sublime rotundity of their figures. This usually comprised my indoor dress: whenever I walked out, I superadded to it an ample robe of the same material, which completely enveloped my person, and screened it from the rays of the sun.

One morning I made a rent in this mantle; and to show the islanders with what facility it could be repaired, I lowered my bundle, and taking from it a needle and thread, proceeded to stitch up the opening. They regarded this wonderful application of science with intense admiration; and whilst I was stitching away, old Marheyo, who was one of the lookers-on, suddenly clapped his hand to his forehead, and rushing to a corner of the house, drew forth a soiled and tattered strip of faded calico—which he must have procured some time or other in traffic on the beach—and besought me eagerly to exercise a little of my art upon it. I willingly complied, though certainly so stumpy a needle as mine never took such gigantic strides over calico before. The repairs completed, old Marheyo gave me a paternal hug; and divesting himself of his "maro" (girdle), swathed the calico about his loins, and slipping the beloved ornaments into his ears, grasped his spear and sallied out of the house, like a valiant Templar arrayed in a new and costly suit of armour.

I never used my razor during my stay in the island, but, although a very subordinate affair, it had been vastly admired by the Typees; and Narmonee, a great hero among them, who was exceedingly precise in the arrangements of his toilet and the general adjustment of his person, being the most accurately tattooed and laboriously horrified individual in all the valley, thought it would be a great advantage to have it applied to the already shaven crown of his head.

The implement they usually employ is a shark's tooth, which is about as well adapted to the purpose as a one-pronged fork for pitching hay. No wonder, then, that the acute Narmonee perceived the advantage my razor possessed over the usual implement. Accordingly, one day he requested as a personal favour that I would just run over his head with the razor. In reply, I gave him to understand that it was too dull, and could not be used to any purpose without being previously sharpened. To assist my meaning, I went through an imaginary honing process on the palm of my hand. Narmonee took my meaning in an instant, and running out of the house, returned the next moment with a huge rough mass of rock as big as a milestone, and indicated to me that that was exactly the thing I wanted. Of course there was nothing left for me but to proceed to business, and I began scraping away at a great rate. He writhed and wriggled under the infliction, but, fully convinced of my skill, endured the pain like a martyr.

Though I never saw Narmonee in battle, I will, from what I then observed, stake my life upon his courage and fortitude. Before commencing operations, his head had presented a surface of short bristling hairs, and by the time I had concluded my unskilful operation it resembled not a little a stubble field after being gone over with a harrow. However, as the chief expressed the liveliest satisfaction at the result, I was too wise to dissent from his opinion.

CHAPTER XVII

IMPROVEMENT IN HEALTH AND SPIRITS—FELICITY OF THE TYPEES—THEIR EN-
JOYMENTS COMPARED WITH THOSE OF MORE ENLIGHTENED COMMUNITIES—
COMPARATIVE WICKEDNESS OF CIVILIZED AND UNENLIGHTENED PEOPLE—A
SKIRMISH IN THE MOUNTAIN WITH THE WARRIORS OF HAPPAR.

DAY after day wore on, and still there was no perceptible change in the conduct of the islanders towards me. Gradually I lost all knowledge of the regular occurrence of the days of the week, and sank insensibly into that kind of apathy which ensues after some violent outbreak of despair. My limb suddenly healed, the swelling went down, the pain subsided, and I had every reason to suppose I should soon completely recover from the affliction that had so long tormented me.

As soon as I was enabled to ramble about the valley in company with the natives, troops of whom followed me whenever I sallied out of the house, I began to experience an elasticity of mind which placed me beyond the reach of those dismal forebodings to which I had so lately been a prey. Received wherever I went with the most deferential kindness; regaled perpetually with the most delightful fruits; ministered to by dark-eyed nymphs; and enjoying besides all the services of the devoted Kory-Kory, I thought that for a sojourn among cannibals, no man could have well made a more agreeable one.

To be sure there were limits set to my wanderings. Toward the sea my progress was barred by an express prohibition of the savages; and after having made two or three ineffectual attempts to reach it, as much to gratify my curiosity as anything else, I gave up the idea. It was in vain to think of reaching it by stealth, since the natives escorted me in numbers wherever I went, and not for one single moment that I can recall to mind was I ever permitted to be alone.

The green and precipitous elevations that stood ranged around the head of the vale where Marheyo's habitation was situated effectually precluded all hope of escape in that quarter, even if I could have stolen away from the thousand eyes of the savages.

But these reflections now seldom obtruded upon me; I gave myself up to the passing hour, and if ever disagreeable thoughts arose in my mind, I drove them away. When I looked around the verdant recess in which I was buried, and gazed up to the summits of the lofty eminence that hemmed me in, I was well disposed to think that I was in the "Happy Valley," and that beyond those heights there was naught but a world of care and anxiety.

As I extended my wanderings in the valley and grew more familiar with the habits of its inmates, I was fain to confess that, despite the disadvantages of his condition, the Polynesian savage, surrounded by all the luxurious provisions of nature, enjoyed an infinitely happier, though certainly a less intellectual existence, than the self-complacent European.

The naked wretch who shivers beneath the bleak skies, and starves among the inhospitable wilds of Tierra del Fuego, might indeed be made happier by civilization, for it would alleviate his physical wants. But the voluptuous Indian, with every desire supplied, whom Providence has bountifully provided with all the sources of pure and natural enjoyment, and from whom are removed so many of the ills and pains of life—what has he to desire at the hands of Civilization? She may "cultivate his mind," may "elevate his thoughts"—these I believe are the established phrases—but will he be the happier? Let the once smiling and populous Hawaiian islands, with their now diseased, starving, and dying natives, answer the question. The missionaries may seek to disguise the matter as they will, but the facts are incontrovertible; and the devoutest Christian who visits that group with an unbiased mind, must go away mournfully asking—"Are these, alas! the fruits of twenty-five years of enlightening?"

In a primitive state of society, the enjoyments of life, though few and simple, are spread over a great extent, and are unalloyed; but Civilization, for every advantage she imparts, holds a hundred evils in reserve—the heart burnings, the jealousies, the social rivalries, the family dissensions, and the thousand self-inflicted discomforts of refined life, which make up in units the swelling aggregate of human misery, are unknown among these unsophisticated people.

But it will be urged that these shocking unprincipled wretches are cannibals. Very true; and a rather bad trait in their character it must be allowed. But they are such only when they seek to gratify the passion of revenge upon their enemies; and I ask whether the mere eating of human flesh so very far exceeds in barbarity that custom which only a few years since was practised in enlightened England—a convicted traitor, perhaps a man found guilty of honesty, patriotism, and such-like heinous crimes, had his head lopped off with a huge axe, his bowels dragged out and thrown into a fire; while his body, carved into four quarters, was with his head exposed upon pikes, and permitted to rot and fester among the public haunts of men!

The fiend-like skill we display in the invention of all manner of death-dealing engines, the vindictiveness with which we carry on our wars, and the misery and desolation that follow in their train, are enough of themselves to distinguish the white civilized man as the most ferocious animal on the face of the earth.

His remorseless cruelty is seen in many of the institutions of our own favoured land. There is one in particular lately adopted in one of the States of the Union, which purports to have been dictated by the most merciful considerations. To destroy our malefactors piecemeal, drying up in their veins, drop by drop, the blood we are too chicken-hearted to shed by a single blow which would at once put a period to their sufferings, is deemed to be infinitely preferable to the old-fashioned punishment of gibbeting—much less annoying to the victim, and more in accordance with the refined spirit of the age; and yet how feeble is all language to describe the horrors we inflict upon these wretches, whom we mason up in the cells of our prisons, and condemn to perpetual solitude in the very heart of our population!

But it is needless to multiply the examples of civilized barbarity; they far exceed in the amount of misery they cause the crimes which we regard with such abhorrence in our less enlightened fellow-creatures.

The term "Savage" is, I conceive, often misapplied, and indeed when I consider the vices, cruelties, and enormities of every kind that spring up in the tainted atmosphere of a feverish civilization, I am inclined to think that so far as the relative wickedness of the parties is concerned, four or five Marquesan Islanders sent to the United States as Missionaries might be quite as useful as an equal number of Americans dispatched to the Islands in a similar capacity.

I once heard it given as an instance of the frightful depravity of a certain tribe in the Pacific, that they had no word in their language to express the idea of virtue. The assertion was unfounded; but were it otherwise, it might be met by stating that their language is almost entirely destitute of terms to express the delightful ideas conveyed by our endless catalogue of civilized crimes.

In the altered frame of mind to which I have referred, every object that presented itself to my notice in the valley struck me in a new light, and the opportunities I now enjoyed of observing the manners of its inmates, tended to strengthen my favourable impressions. One peculiarity that fixed my admiration was the perpetual hilarity reigning through the whole extent of the vale. There seemed to be no cares, griefs, troubles, or vexations in all Typee. The hours tripped along as gaily as the laughing couples down a country dance.

There were none of those thousand sources of irritation that the ingenuity of civilized man has created to mar his own felicity. There were no foreclosures of mortgages, no protested notes, no bills payable, no debts of honour in Typee; no unreasonable tailors and shoemakers, perversely bent on being paid; no duns of any description; no assault and battery attorneys, to foment discord, backing their clients up to a quarrel, and then knocking their heads together; no poor relations, everlastingly occupying the spare bed-chamber, and diminishing the elbow room at the family table; no destitute widows with their children starving on the cold charities of the world; no beggars; no debtors' prisons; no proud and hard-hearted nabobs in Typee; or to sum up all in one word— no Money! "That root of all evil" was not to be found in the valley.

In this secluded abode of happiness there were no cross old women, no cruel step-dames, no withered spinsters, no love-sick maidens, no sour old bachelors, no inattentive husbands, no melancholy young men, no blubbering youngsters, and no squalling brats. All was mirth, fun, and high good humour. Blue devils, hypochondria, and doleful dumps, went and hid themselves among the nooks and crannies of the rocks.

Here you would see a parcel of children frolicking together the livelong day, and no quarrelling, no contention, among them. The same number in our own land could not have played together for the space of an hour without biting or scratching one another. There you might have seen a throng of young females, not filled with envyings of each other's charms, nor displaying the ridiculous affectations of gentility, nor yet moving in whalebone corsets, like so many automatons, but free, inartificially happy, and unconstrained.

There were some spots in that sunny vale where they would frequently resort to decorate themselves with garlands of flowers. To have seen them reclining beneath the shadows of one of the beautiful groves; the ground about them strewn with freshly gathered buds and blossoms, employed in weaving chaplets and necklaces, one would have thought that all the train of Flora had gathered together to keep a festival in honour of their mistress.

With the young men there seemed almost always some matter of diversion or business on hand that afforded a constant variety of enjoyment. But whether fishing, or carving canoes, or polishing their ornaments, never was there exhibited the least sign of strife or contention among them.

As for the warriors, they maintained a tranquil dignity of demeanour, journeying occasionally from house to house, where they were always sure to be received with the attention bestowed upon distinguished guests. The old men, of whom there were many in the vale, seldom stirred from their mats, where they would recline for hours and hours, smoking and talking to one another with all the garrulity of age.

But the continual happiness, which so far as I was able to judge appeared to prevail in the valley, sprang principally from that all-pervading sensation which Rousseau has told us he at one time experienced, the mere buoyant sense of a healthful physical existence. And indeed in this particular the Typees had ample reason to felicitate themselves, for sickness was almost unknown. During the whole period of my stay I saw but one invalid among them; and on their smooth clear skins you observed no blemish or mark of disease.

The general repose, however, upon which I have just been descanting, was broken in upon about this time by an event which proved that the islanders were not entirely exempt from those occurrences which disturb the quiet of more civilized communities.

Having now been a considerable time in the valley I began to feel surprised that the violent hostility, subsisting between its inhabitants and those of the adjoining bay of Happar, should never have manifested itself in any warlike encounter. Although the valiant Typees would often by gesticulations declare their undying hatred against their enemies, and the disgust they felt at their cannibal propensities; although they dilated upon the manifold injuries they had received at their hands, yet with a forbearance truly commendable, they appeared patiently to sit down under their grievances, and to refrain from making any reprisals. The Happars, entrenched behind their mountains, and never even showing themselves on their summits, did not appear to me to furnish adequate cause for that excess of animosity evinced towards them by the heroic tenants of our vale, and I was inclined to believed that the deeds of blood attributed to them had been greatly exaggerated.

On the other hand, as the clamours of war had not up to this period disturbed the serenity of the tribe, I began to distrust the truth of those reports which ascribe so fierce and belligerent a character to the Typee nation. Surely, thought I, all these terrible stories I have heard about the inveteracy with which they carried on the feud, their deadly intensity of hatred, and the diabolical malice with which they glutted their revenge upon the inanimate forms of the slain, are nothing more than fables, and I must confess that I experienced something like a sense of regret at having my hideous anticipations thus disappointed. I felt in some sort like a 'prentice-boy who, going to the play in the expectation of being delighted with a cut-and-thrust tragedy, is almost moved to tears of disappointment at the exhibition of a genteel comedy.

I could not avoid thinking that I had fallen in with a greatly traduced people, and I moralized not a little upon the disadvantage of having a bad name, which in this instance had given a tribe of savages, who were as pacific as so many lambkins, the reputation of a confederacy of giant-killers.

But subsequent events proved that I had been a little too premature in coming to this conclusion. One day about noon, happening to be at the Ti, I had lain down on the mats with several of the chiefs, and had gradually sunk into a most luxurious siesta, when I was awakened by a tremendous outcry, and starting up beheld the natives seizing their spears and hurrying out, while the most puissant of the chiefs, grasping the six muskets which were ranged against the bamboos, followed after, and soon disappeared in the groves. These movements were accompanied by wild shouts, in which "Happar, Happar," greatly predominated. The islanders were now to be seen running past the Ti, and striking across the valley to the Happar side. Presently I heard the sharp report of a musket from the adjoining hills, and then a burst of voices in the same direction. At this the women, who had congregated in the groves, set up the most violent clamours, as they invariably do here as else-where on every occasion of excitement and alarm, with a view of tranquil-lizing their own minds and disturbing other people. On this particular occasion they made such an outrageous noise, and continued it with such perseverance, that for awhile, had entire volleys of musketry been fired off in the neighbouring mountains, I should not have been able to have heard them.

When this female commotion had a little subsided I listened eagerly for further information. At last bang went another shot, and then a second volley of yells from the hills. Again all was quiet, and continued so for such a length of time that I began to think the contending armies had agreed upon a sus-pension of hostilities; when pop went a third gun, followed as before with a yell. After this, for nearly two hours nothing occurred worthy of comment, save some straggling shouts from the hill-side, sounding like the halloos of a parcel of truant boys who had lost themselves in the woods.

During this interval I had remained standing on the piazza of the Ti, which directly fronted the Happar mountain, and with no one near me but Kory-Kory and the old superannuated savages I have before described. These latter never stirred from their mats, and seemed altogether unconscious that anything unusual was going on.

As for Kory-Kory, he appeared to think that we were in the midst of great events, and sought most zealously to impress me with a due sense of their importance. Every sound that reached us conveyed some momentous item of intelligence to him. At such times, as if he were gifted with second sight, he would go through a variety of pantomimic illustrations, showing me the pre-cise manner in which the redoubtable Typees were at that very moment chas-tising the insolence of the enemy. "Mehevi hanna pippee nuee Happar," he exclaimed every five minutes, giving me to understand that under that dis-tinguished captain the warriors of his nation were performing prodigies of valour.

Having heard only four reports from the muskets I was led to believe that they were worked by the islanders in the same manner as the Sultan Solyman's ponderous artillery at the siege of Byzantium, one of them taking an hour or two to load and train. At last, no sound whatever proceeding from the mountains, I concluded that the contest had been determined one way or the other. Such appeared, indeed, to be the case, for in a little while a courier arrived at the Ti, almost breathless with his exertions, and commu-nicated the news of a great victory having been achieved by his countrymen: "Happar poo arva!—Happar poo arva" (the cowards had fled). Kory-Kory was in ecstasies, and commenced a vehement harangue, which, so far as I understood it, implied that the result exactly agreed with his expectations, and which, moreover, was intended to convince me that it would be a perfectly useless undertaking, even for an army of fire-eaters, to offer battle to the irre-sistible heroes of our valley. In all this I of course acquiesced, and looked forward with no little interest to the return of the conquerors, whose victory I feared might not have been purchased without cost to themselves.

But here I was again mistaken; for Mehevi, in conducting his warlike operations, rather inclined to the Fabian than to the Bonapartean tactics, husbanding his resources and exposing his troops to no unnecessary hazards. The total loss of the victors in this obstinately contested affair was, in killed, wounded, and missing—one forefinger and part of a thumb-nail (which the late proprietor brought along with him in his hand), a severely contused arm, and a considerable effusion of blood flowing from the thigh of a chief, who had received an ugly thrust from a Happar spear. What the enemy had suffered I could not discover, but I presume they had succeeded in taking off with them the bodies of their slain.

Such was the issue of the battle, as far as its results came under my observation; and as it appeared to be considered an event of prodigious importance, I reasonably concluded that the wars of the natives were marked by no very sanguinary traits. I afterwards learned how the skirmish had originated. A number of the Happars had been discovered prowling for no good purpose on the Typee side of the mountain; the alarm was sounded, and the invaders, after a protracted resistance, had been chased over the frontier. But why had not the intrepid Mehevi carried the war into Happar? Why had he not made a descent into the hostile vale, and brought away some trophy of his victory—some materials for the cannibal entertainment which I had heard usually terminated every engagement? After all, I was much inclined to believe that such shocking festivals must occur very rarely among the islanders, if, indeed, they ever take place.

For two or three days the late event was the theme of general comment; after which the excitement gradually wore away, and the valley resumed its accustomed tranquillity.

CHAPTER XVIII

SWIMMING IN COMPANY WITH THE GIRLS OF THE VALLEY—A CANOE—EFFECTS OF THE TABOO—A PLEASURE EXCURSION ON THE POND—BEAUTIFUL FREAK OF FAYAWAY—MANTUA-MAKING—A STRANGER ARRIVES IN THE VALLEY— HIS MYSTERIOUS CONDUCT—NATIVE ORATORY—THE INTERVIEW—ITS RE- SULTS—DEPARTURE OF THE STRANGER.

RETURNING health and peace of mind gave a new interest to everything around me. I sought to diversify my time by as many enjoyments as lay within reach. Bathing in company with troops of girls formed one of my chief amusements. We sometimes enjoyed the recreation in the waters of a miniature lake, into which the central stream of the valley expanded. This lovely sheet of water was almost circular in figure, and about three hundred yards across. Its beauty was indescribable. All around its banks waved luxuriant masses of tropical foliage, soaring high above which were to be seen, here and there, the symmetrical shaft of the coco-nut tree, surmounted by its tuft of graceful branches, drooping in the air like so many waving ostrich plumes.

The ease and grace with which the maidens of the valley propelled themselves through the water, and their familiarity with the element, were truly

astonishing. Sometimes they might be seen gliding along just under the surface, without apparently moving hand or foot—then throwing themselves on
their sides, they darted through the water, revealing glimpses of their forms, as,
in the course of their rapid progress, they shot for an instant partly into the air
—at one moment they dived deep down into the water and the next they rose
bounding to the surface.

I remember upon one occasion plunging in among a parcel of these river-
nymphs, and counting vainly upon my superior strength, sought to drag some
of them under the water, but I quickly repented my temerity. The amphibious
young creatures swarmed about me like a shoal of dolphins, and seizing hold of
my devoted limbs, tumbled me about and ducked me under the surface, until
from the strange noises which rang in my ears, and the supernatural visions
dancing before my eyes, I thought I was in the land of spirits. I stood indeed
as littie chance among them as a cumbrous whale attacked on all sides by a
legion of sword-fish. When at length they relinquished their hold of me, they
swam away in every direction, laughing at my clumsy endeavours to reach
them.

There was no boat on the lake; but at my solicitation and for my special
use, some of the young men attached to Marheyo's household, under the direction of the indefatigable Kory-Kory, brought up a light and tastefully carved
canoe from the sea. It was launched upon the sheet of water, and floated there
as gracefully as a swan. But, melancholy to relate, it produced an effect I had
not anticipated. The sweet nymphs, who had sported with me before in the
lake, now all fled its vicinity. The prohibited craft, guarded by the edicts of
the "taboo," extended the prohibition to the waters in which it lay.

For a few days, Kory-Kory, with one or two other youths, accompanied ме
in my excursions to the lake, and while I paddled about in my light canoe,
would swim after me shouting and gamboling in pursuit. But I was ever
partial to what is termed in the *Young Men's Own Book*—"the society of virtuous and intelligent young ladies;" and in the absence of the mermaids, the
amusement became dull and insipid. One morning I expressed to my faithful
servitor my desire for the return of the nymphs. The honest fellow looked at
me bewildered for a moment, and then shook his head solemnly, and murmured
"taboo! taboo!" giving me to understand that unless the canoe was removed,
I could not expect to have the young ladies back again. But to this procedure
I was averse; I not only wanted the canoe to stay where it was, but I wanted
the beauteous Fayaway to get into it, and paddle with me about the lake.
This latter proposition completely horrified Kory-Kory's notions of propriety.
He inveighed against it, as something too monstrous to be thought of. It not
only shocked their established notions of propriety, but was at variance with
all their religious ordinances.

However, although the "taboo" was a ticklish thing to meddle with, I determined to test its capabilities of resisting an attack. I consulted the chiet
Mehevi, who endeavoured to dissuade me from my object: but I was not to be
repulsed; and accordingly increased the warmth of my solicitations. At last
he entered into a long, and I have no doubt a very learned and eloquent, expo-
sition of the history and nature of the "taboo" as affecting this particular case;
employing a variety of most extraordinary words, which, from their amazing
length and sonorousness, I have every reason to believe were of a theological
nature. But all that he said failed to convince me: partly, perhaps, because
I could not comprehend a word that he uttered; but chiefly, that for the life of
me I could not understand why a woman should not have as much right to

enter a canoe as a man. At last he became a little more rational, and intimated that, out of the abundant love he bore me, he would consult with the priests and see what could be done.

How it was that the priesthood of Typee satisfied the affair with their consciences, I know not; but so it was, and Fayaway's dispensation from this portion of the taboo was at length procured. Such an event I believe never before had occurred in the valley; but it was high time the islanders should be taught a little gallantry, and I trust that the example I set them may produce beneficial effects. Ridiculous, indeed, that the lovely creatures should be obliged to paddle about in the water, like so many ducks, while a parcel of great strapping fellows skimmed over its surface in their canoes.

The first day after Fayaway's emancipation I had a delightful little party on the lake—the damsel, Kory-Kory, and myself. My zealous body-servant brought from the house a calabash of poee-poee, half a dozen young coco-nuts —stripped of their husks—three pipes, as many yams, and me on his back a part of the way. Something of a load; but Kory-Kory was a very strong man for his size, and by no means brittle in the spine. We had a very pleasant day; my trusty valet plied the paddle and swept us gently along the margin of the water, beneath the shades of the overhanging thickets. Fayaway and I reclined in the stern of the canoe, on the very best terms possible with one another; the gentle nymph occasionally placing her pipe to her lip, and exhaling the mild fumes of the tobacco, to which her rosy breath added a fresh perfume. Strange as it may seem, there is nothing in which a young and beautiful female appears to more advantage than in the act of smoking. How captivating is a Peruvian lady, swinging in her gaily woven hammock of grass, extended between two orange trees, and inhaling the fragrance of a choice cigarro! But Fayaway, holding in her delicately formed olive hand the long yellow reed of her pipe, with its quaintly carved bowl, and every few moments languishingly giving forth light wreaths of vapour from her mouth and nostrils, looked still more engaging.

We floated about thus for several hours, when I looked up to the warm, glowing, tropical sky, and then down into the transparent depths below; and when my eye, wandering from the bewitching scenery around, fell upon the grotesquely-tattooed form of Kory-Kory, and finally encountered the pensive gaze of Fayaway, I thought I had been transported to some fairy region, so unreal did everything appear.

This lovely piece of water was the coolest spot in all the valley, and I now made it a place of continual resort during the hottest period of the day. One side of it lay near the termination of a long, gradually expanding gorge, which mounted to the heights that environed the vale. The strong trade wind, met in its course by these elevations, circled and eddied about their summits, and was sometimes driven down the steep ravine and swept across the valley, ruffling in its passage the otherwise tranquil surface of the lake.

One day, after we had been paddling about for some time, I disembarked Kory-Kory, and paddled the canoe to the windward side of the lake. As I turned the canoe, Fayaway, who was with me, seemed all at once to be struck with some happy idea. With a wild exclamation of delight, she disengaged from her person the ample robe of tappa which was knotted over her shoulder (for the purpose of shielding her from the sun), and spreading it out like a sail, stood erect with upraised arms in the head of the canoe. We American sailors pride ourselves upon our straight clean spars, but a prettier little mast than Fayaway made was never shipped a-board of any craft.

In a moment the tappa was distended by the breeze—the long brown tresses of Fayaway streamed in the air—and the canoe glided rapidly through the water, and shot towards the shore. Seated in the stern, I directed its course with my paddle until it dashed up the soft sloping bank, and Fayaway, with a light spring, alighted on the ground; whilst Kory-Kory, who had watched our manœuvres with admiration, now clapped his hands in transport, and shouted like a madman. Many a time afterwards was this feat repeated.

If the reader have not observed ere this that I was the declared admirer of Miss Fayaway, all I can say is that he is little conversant with affairs of the heart, and I certainly shall not trouble myself to enlightened him any farther. Out of the calico I had brought from the ship I made a dress for this lovely girl. In it she looked, I must confess, something like an opera dancer. The drapery of the latter damsel generally commences a little above the elbows, but my island beauty's began at the waist, and terminated sufficiently far above the ground to reveal the most bewitching ankle in the universe.

The day that Fayaway first wore this robe was rendered memorable by a new acquaintance being introduced to me. In the afternoon I was lying in the house, when I heard a great uproar outside; but being by this time pretty well accustomed to the wild halloos which were almost continually ringing through the valley, I paid little attention to it, until old Marheyo, under the influence of some strange excitement, rushed into my presence and communicated the astounding tidings, "Marnoo pemi!" which being interpreted, implied that an individual by the name of Marnoo was approaching. My worthy old friend evidently expected that this intelligence would produce a great effect upon me, and for a time he stood earnestly regarding me, as if curious to see how I should conduct myself, but as I remained perfectly unmoved, the old gentleman darted out of the house again, in as great a hurry as he had entered it.

"Marnoo, Marnoo," cogitated I, "I have never heard that name before. Some distinguished character, I presume, from the prodigious riot the natives are making;" the tumultuous noise drawing nearer and nearer every moment, while "Marnoo!—Marnoo!" was shouted by every tongue.

I made up my mind that some savage warrior of consequence, who had not yet enjoyed the honour of an audience, was desirous of paying his respects on the present occasion. So vain had I become by the lavish attention to which I had been accustomed that I felt half inclined, as a punishment for such neglect, to give this Marnoo a cold reception, when the excited throng came within view, convoying one of the most striking specimens of humanity that I ever beheld.

The stranger could not have been more than twenty-five years of age, and was a little above the ordinary height; had he been a single hair's breadth taller, the matchless symmetry of his form would have been destroyed. His unclad limbs were beautifully formed; whilst the elegant outline of his figure, together with his beardless cheeks, might have entitled him to the distinction of standing for the statue of the Polynesian Apollo; and indeed the oval of his countenance and the regularity of every feature reminded me of an antique bust. But the marble repose of art was supplied by a warmth and liveliness of expression only to be seen in the South Sea Islander under the most favourable developments of nature. The hair of Marnoo was a rich curling brown, and twined about his temples and neck in little close curling ringlets, which danced up and down continually when he was animated in conversation. His cheek was of a feminine softness, and his face was free from the least blemish of tattooing, although the rest of his body was drawn all over with fanciful figures, which—unlike the unconnected sketching usual among these natives—appeared to have been executed in conformity with some general design.

The tattooing on his back in particular attracted my attention. The artist employed must indeed have excelled in his profession. Traced along the course of the spine was accurately delineated the slender, tapering, and diamond-checkered shaft of the beautiful "artu" tree. Branching from the stem on either side, and disposed alternately, were the graceful branches drooping with leaves all correctly drawn. and elaborately finished. Indeed, this piece of tattooing was the best specimen of the Fine Arts I had yet seen in Typee. A rear view of the stranger might have suggested the idea of a spreading vine tacked against a garden wall. Upon his breast, arms, and legs, were exhibited an infinite variety of figures; every one of which, however, appeared to have reference to the general effect sought to be produced. The tattooing I have described was of the brightest blue, and when contrasted with the light olive colour of the skin, produced an unique and even elegant effect. A slight girdle of white tappa, scarcely two inches in width, but hanging before and behind in spreading tassels, composed the entire costume of the stranger.

He advanced surrounded by the islanders, carrying under one arm a small roll of the native cloth, and grasping in his other hand a long and richly decorated spear. His manner was that of a traveller conscious that he is approaching a comfortable stage in his journey. Every moment he turned good-humoredly to the throng around him, and gave some dashing sort of reply to their incessant queries, which appeared to convulse them with uncontrollable mirth.

Struck by his demeanour, and the peculiarity of his appearance, so unlike that of the shaven-crowned and face-tattooed natives in general, I involuntarily rose as he entered the house, and proffered him a seat on the mats beside me. But without deigning to notice the civility, or even the more incontrovertible fact of my existence, the stranger passed on, utterly regardless of me, and flung himself upon the farther end of the long couch that traversed the sole apartment of Marheyo's habitation.

Had the belle of the season, in the pride of her beauty and power, been cut in a place of public resort by some supercilious exquisite, she could not have felt greater indignation than I did at this unexpected slight.

I was thrown into utter astonishment. The conduct of the savages had prepared me to anticipate from every new-comer the same extravagant expressions of curiosity and regard. The singularity of his conduct, however, only roused my desire to discover who this remarkable personage might be, who now engrossed the attention of every one.

Tinor placed before him a calabash of poee-poee, from which the stranger regaled himself, alternating every mouthful with some rapid exclamation which was eagerly caught up and echoed by the crowd that completely filled the house. When I observed the striking devotion of the natives to him, and their temporary withdrawal of all attention from myself I felt not a little piqued. The glory of Tommo is departed, thought I, and the sooner he removes from the valley the better. These were my feelings at the moment, and they were prompted by that glorious principle inherent in all heroic natures—the strong-rooted determination to have the biggest share of the pudding or go without any of it.

Marnoo, this all-attractive personage, having satisfied his hunger, and inhaled a few whiffs from a pipe which was handed to him, launched out into an harangue which completely enchained the attention of his auditors.

Little as I understood of the language, yet from his animated gestures and the varying expression of his features—reflected as from so many mirrors in the countenances around him—I could easily discover the nature of those passions which he sought to arouse. From the frequent recurrence of the words "Nukuheva" and "Franee" (French), and some others with the meaning of which I was acquainted, he appeared to be rehearsing to his auditors events which had recently occurred in the neighbouring bays. But how he had gained the knowledge of these matters I could not understand, unless it were that he had just come from Nukuheva—a supposition which his travel-stained appearance not a little supported. But, if a native of that region, I could not account for his friendly reception at the hands of the Typees.

Never, certainly, had I beheld so powerful an exhibition of natural eloquence as Marnoo displayed during the course of his oration. The grace of the attitudes into which he threw his flexible figure, the striking gestures of his naked arms, and above all, the fire which shot from his brilliant eyes, imparted an effect to the continually changing accents of his voice, of which the most accomplished orator might have been proud. At one moment reclining sideways upon the mat, and leaning calmly upon his bended arm, he related circumstantially the aggressions of the French—their hostile visits to the surrounding bays, enumerating each one in succession—Happar, Puerka, Nukuheva, Tior—and then, starting to his feet and precipitating himself forward with clenched hands and a countenance distorted with passion, he poured out a tide of invectives. Falling back into an attitude of lofty command, he exhorted the Typees to resist these encroachments; reminding them, with a fierce glance of exultation, that as yet the terror of their name had preserved them from attack, and with a scornful sneer he sketched in ironical terms the wondrous intrepidity of the French, who, with five war-canoes and hundreds of men, had not dared to assail the naked warriors of their valley.

The effect he produced upon his audience was electric; one and all they stood regarding him with sparkling eyes and trembling limbs, as though they were listening to the inspired voice of a prophet.

But it soon appeared that Marnoo's powers were as versatile as they were extraordinary. As soon as he had finished this vehement harangue, he threw himself again upon the mats, and, singling out individuals in the crowd, addressed them by name, in a sort of bantering style, the humour of which, though nearly hidden from me, filled the whole assembly with uproarious delight.

He had a word for everybody; and, turning rapidly from one to another, gave utterance to some hasty witticism, which was sure to be followed by peals of laughter. To the females, as well as to the men, he addressed his discourse. Heaven only knows what he said to them, but he caused smiles and blushes to mantle their ingenuous faces. I am, indeed, very much inclined to believe that Marnoo, with his handsome person and captivating manners, was a sad deceiver among the simple maidens of the island.

During all this time he had never, for one moment, deigned to regard me. He appeared, indeed, to be altogether unconscious of my presence. I was utterly at a loss how to account for this extraordinary conduct. I easily perceived that he was a man of no little consequence among the islanders; that he possessed uncommon talents; and was gifted with a higher degree of knowledge than the inmates of the valley. For these reasons, I therefore greatly feared lest having, from some cause or other, unfriendly feelings toward me, he might exert his powerful influence to do me mischief.

It seemed evident that he was not a permanent resident of the vale, and yet, whence could he have come? On all sides the Typees were girt in by hostile tribes, and how could he possibly, if belonging to any of these, be received with so much cordiality?

The personal appearance of the enigmatical stranger suggested additional perplexities. The face, free from tattooing, and the unshaven crown, were peculiarities I have never before remarked in any part of the island, and I had always heard that the contrary were considered the indispensable distinctions of a Marquesan warrior. Altogether the matter was perfectly incomprehensible to me, and I awaited its solution with no small degree of anxiety.

At length, from certain indications, I suspected that he was making me the subject of his remarks, although he appeared cautiously to avoid either pronouncing my name, or looking in the direction where I lay. All at once he rose from the mats where he had been reclining, and, still conversing, moved towards me, his eye purposely evading mine, and seated himself within less than a yard of me. I had hardly recovered from my surprise, when he suddenly turned round, and, with a most benignant countenance, extended his right hand gracefully towards me. Of course I accepted the courteous challenge, and as soon as our palms met, he bent towards me, and murmured in musical accents,—"How you do?" "How long you been in this bay?" "You like this bay?"

Had I been pierced simultaneously by three Happar spears, I could not have started more than I did at hearing these simple questions! For a moment I was overwhelmed with astonishment, and then answered something I know not what; but as soon as I regained my self-possession, the thought darted through my mind that from this individual I might obtain that information regarding Toby which I suspected the natives had purposely withheld from me. Accordingly I questioned him concerning the disappearance of my companion, but he denied all knowledge of the matter. I then inquired from whence he had come? He replied, from Nukuheva. When I expressed my surprise, he looked at me for a moment, as if enjoying my perplexity, and then, with his strange vivacity, exclaimed—"Ah! me taboo—me go Nukuheva—me go Tior—me go Typee— me go everywhere—nobody harm me—me taboo."

This explanation would have been altogether unintelligible to me, had it not recalled to my mind something I had previously heard concerning a singular custom among these islanders. Though the country is possessed by various tribes, whose mutual hostilities almost wholly preclude any intercourse between them; yet there are instances where a person having ratified friendly relations with some individual belonging to the valley, whose inmates are at war with his own, may, under particular restrictions, venture with impunity into the country of his friend, where, under other circumstances, he would have been treated as an enemy. In this light are personal friendships regarded among them, and the individual so protected is said to be "taboo," and his person, to a certain extent, is held as sacred. Thus the stranger informed me he had access to all the valleys in the island.

Curious to know how he had acquired his knowledge of English, I questioned him on the subject. At first, for some reason or other, he evaded the inquiry, but afterwards told me that, when a boy, he had been carried to sea by the captain of a trading vessel, with whom he had stayed three years, living part of the time with him at Sydney, in Australia, and that, at a subsequent visit to the island, the captain had, at his own request, permitted him to remain among his countrymen. The natural quickness of the savage had been wonderfully improved by his intercourse with the white men, and his partial knowledge of a foreign language gave him a great ascendency over his less accomplished countrymen.

When I asked the now affable Marnoo why it was that he had not previously spoken to me, he eagerly inquired what I had been led to think of him from his conduct in that respect. I replied, that I had supposed him to be some great chief or warrior, who had seen plenty of white men before, and did not think it worth while to notice a poor sailor. At this declaration of the exalted opinion I had formed of him, he appeared vastly gratified, and gave me to understand that he had purposely behaved in that manner, in order to increase my astonishment, as soon as he should see proper to address me.

Marnoo now sought to learn my version of the story as to how I came to be an inmate of the Typee valley. When I related to him the circumstances under which Toby and I had entered it, he listened with evident interest; but as soon as I alluded to the absence, yet unaccounted for, of my comrade, he endeavoured to change the subject, as if it were something he desired not to agitate. It seemed, indeed, as if everything connected with Toby was destined to beget distrust and anxiety in my bosom. Notwithstanding Marnoo's denial of any knowledge of his fate, I could not avoid suspecting that he was deceiving me; and this suspicion revived those frightful apprehensions with regard to my own fate, which, for a short time past, had subsided in my breast.

Influenced by these feelings, I now felt a strong desire to avail myself of the stranger's protection, and under his safeguard to return to Nukuheva. But as soon as I hinted at this, he unhesitatingly pronounced it to be entirely impracticable; assuring me that the Typees would never consent to my leaving the valley. Although what he said merely confirmed the impression which I had before entertained, still it increased my anxiety to escape from a captivity which, however endurable, nay, delightful it might be in some respects, involved in its issues a fate marked by the most frightful contingencies.

I could not conceal from my mind that Toby had been treated in the same friendly manner as I had been, and yet all their kindness had terminated in his mysterious disappearance. Might not the same fate await me?—a fate too dreadful to think of. Stimulated by these considerations, I urged anew my request to Marnoo; but he only set forth in stronger colours the impossibility of my escape and repeated his previous declaration that the Typees would never be brought to consent to my departure.

When I endeavoured to learn from him the motives which prompted them to hold me a prisoner, Marnoo again assumed that mysterious tone which had tormented me with apprehensions when I had questioned him with regard to the fate of my companion.

Thus repulsed, in a manner which only served, by arousing the most dreadful forebodings, to excite me to renewed attempts, I conjured him to intercede for me with the natives, and endeavour to procure their consent to my leaving them. To this he appeared strongly averse; but, yielding at last to my importunities, he addressed several of the chiefs, who with the rest had been eyeing us intently during the whole of our conversation. His petition, however, was at once met with the most violent disapprobation, manifesting itself in angry glances and gestures, and a perfect torrent of passionate words, directed to both him and myself. Marnoo, evidently repenting the step he had taken, earnestly deprecated the resentment of the crowd, and in a few moments succeeded in pacifying to some extent the clamours which had broken out as soon as his proposition had been understood.

With the most intense interest had I watched the reception his intercession might receive; and a bitter pang shot through my heart at the additional evidence, now furnished, of the unchangeable determination of the islanders. Marnoo told me, with evident alarm in his countenance, that although admitted into the bay on a friendly footing with its inhabitants, he could not presume to meddle with their concerns, as such a procedure, if persisted in, would at once absolve the Typees from the restraints of the "Taboo," although so long as he refrained from any such conduct, it screened him effectually from the consequences of the enmity they bore his tribe.

At this moment, Mehevi, who was present, angrily interrupted him; and the words which he uttered, in a commanding tone, evidently meant that he must at once cease talking to me, and withdraw to the other part of the house. Marnoo immediately started up, hurriedly enjoining me not to address him again, and, as I valued my safety, to refrain from all further allusion to the subject of my departure; and then, in compliance with the order of the determined chief, but not before it had again been angrily repeated, he withdrew to a distance.

I now perceived, with no small degree of apprehension, the same savage expression in the countenance of the natives which had startled me during the scene at the Ti. They glanced their eyes suspiciously from Marnoo to me, as if distrusting the nature of an intercourse carried on, as it was, in a language they could not understand, and they seemed to harbour the belief that already we had concerted measures calculated to elude their vigilance.

The lively countenances of these people are wonderfully indicative of the emotions of the soul, and the imperfections of their oral language are more than compensated for by the nervous eloquence of their looks and gestures. I could plainly trace, in every varying expression of their faces, all those passions which had been thus unexpectedly aroused in their bosoms.

It required no reflection to convince me, from what was going on, that the injunction of Marnoo was not to be rashly slighted; and accordingly, great as was the effort to suppress my feelings, I accosted Mehevi in a good-humoured tone, with a view of dissipating any ill impression he might have received. But the ireful, angry chief was not so easily mollified. He rejected my advances with that peculiarly stern expression I have before described, and took care by the whole of his behaviour towards me to show the displeasure and resentment which he felt.

Marnoo, at the other extremity of the house, apparently desirous of making a diversion in my favour, exerted himself to amuse with his pleasantries the crowd about him; but his lively attempts were not so successful as they had previously been, and, foiled in his efforts, he rose gravely to depart. No one expressed any regret at this movement, so seizing his roll of tappa, and grasping his spear, he advanced to the front of the pi-pi, and waving his hand in adieu to the now silent throng, cast upon me a glance of mingled pity and reproach, and flung himself into the path which led from the house. I watched his receding figure until it was lost in the obscurity of the grove and then gave myself up to the most desponding reflections.

CHAPTER XIX

REFLECTIONS AFTER MARNOO'S DEPARTURE—BATTLE OF THE POP-GUNS—STRANGE
CONCEIT OF MARHEYO—PROCESS OF MAKING TAPPA.

THE knowledge I had now obtained as to the intention of the savages deeply
affected me.

Marnoo, I perceived, was a man who, by reason of his superior acquirements,
and the knowledge he possessed of the events which were taking place in the
different bays of the island, was held in no little estimation by the inhabitants
of the valley. He had been received with the most cordial welcome and respect.
The natives had hung upon the accents of his voice, and had manifested the
highest gratification at being individually noticed by him. And yet, despite
all this, a few words urged in my behalf, with the intent of obtaining my release
from captivity, had sufficed not only to banish all harmony and good-will; but,
if I could believe what he told me, had gone nigh to endanger his own personal
safety.

How strongly rooted, then, must be the determination of the Typees with
regard to me, and how suddenly could they display the strangest passions!
The mere suggestion of my departure had estranged from me, for the time at
least, Mehevi, who was the most influential of all the chiefs, and who had
previously exhibited so many instances of his friendly sentiments. The rest of
the natives had likewise evinced their strong repugnance to my wishes, and even
Kory-Kory himself seemed to share in the general disapprobation bestowed
upon me.

In vain I racked my invention to find out some motive for the strange
desire these people manifested to retain me among them; but I could discover
none.

But however this might be, the scene which had just occurred admonished
me of the danger of trifling with the wayward and passionate spirits against
whom it was vain to struggle, and might even be fatal to do so. My only hope
was to induce the natives to believe that I was reconciled to my detention in the
valley, and, by assuming a tranquil and cheerful demeanour, to allay the suspicions which I had so unfortunately aroused. Their confidence revived, they
might in a short time remit in some degree their watchfulness over my movements, and I should then be the better enabled to avail myself of any opportunity which presented itself for escape. I determined, therefore, to make the
best of a bad bargain, and to bear up manfully against whatever might betide.
In this endeavour I succeeded beyond my own expectations. At the period
of Marnoo's visit, I had been in the valley, as nearly as I could conjecture, some
two months. Although not completely recovered from my strange illness which
still lingered about me, I was free from pain and able to take exercise. In
short, I had every reason to anticipate a perfect recovery. Freed from apprehensions on this point, and resolved to regard the future without flinching,
I flung myself anew into all the social pleasures of the valley, and sought to
bury all regrets, and all remembrances of my previous existence, in the wild
enjoyments it afforded. In my various wanderings through the vale, and as
I became better acquainted with the character of its inhabitants, I was more
struck with the light-hearted joyousness that everywhere prevailed. The minds
of these simple savages, unoccupied by matters of graver moment, were capable

of deriving the utmost delight from circumstances which would have passed unnoticed in more intelligent communities. All their enjoyment, indeed, seemed to be made up of the little trifling incidents of the passing hour; but these diminutive items swelled altogether to an amount of happiness seldom experienced by more enlightened individuals, whose pleasures are drawn from more elevated but rarer sources.

What community, for instance, of refined and intellectual mortals would derive the least satisfaction from shooting pop-guns? The mere supposition of such a thing being possible would excite their indignation, and yet the whole population of Typee did little else for ten days but occupy themselves with that childish amusement, fairly screaming, too, with the delight it afforded them.

One day I was frolicking with a little spirited urchin, some six years old, who chased me with a piece of bamboo about three feet long, with which he occasionally belaboured me. Seizing the stick from him, the idea happened to suggest itself, that I might make for the youngster, out of the slender tube, one of those nursery muskets with which I had sometimes seen children playing. Accordingly, with my knife I made two parallel slits in the cane several inches in length, and cutting loose at one end the elastic strip between them, bent it back and slipped the point into a little notch made for the purpose. Any small substance placed against this would be projected with considerable force through the tube, by merely springing the bent strip out of the notch.

Had I possessed the remotest idea of the sensation this piece of ordnance was destined to produce, I should certainly have taken out a patent for the invention. The boy scampered away with it, half delirious with ecstasy, and in twenty minutes afterwards I might have been seen surrounded by a noisy crowd—venerable old greybeards—responsible fathers of families—valiant warriors—matrons—young men—girls and children, all holding in their hand bits of bamboo, and each clamouring to be served first.

For three or four hours I was engaged in manufacturing pop-guns, but at last made over my goodwill and interest in the concern to a lad of remarkable quick parts, whom I soon initiated into the art and mystery.

Pop, Pop, Pop, Pop, now resounded all over the valley. Duels, skirmishes, pitched battles, and general engagements were to be seen on every side. Here, as you walked along a path which led through a thicket, you fell into a cunningly laid ambush, and became a target for a body of musketeers whose tattooed limbs you could just see peeping into view through the foliage. There, you were assailed by the intrepid garrison of a house, who levelled their bamboo rifles at you from between the upright canes which composed its sides. Farther on you were fired upon by a detachment of sharpshooters, mounted upon the top of a pi-pi.

Pop, Pop, Pop, Pop! green guavas, seeds, and berries were flying about in every direction, and during this dangerous state of affairs I was half afraid that, like the man and his brazen bull, I should fall a victim to my own ingenuity. Like everything else, however, the excitement gradually wore away, though ever after occasional pop-guns might be heard at all hours of the day.

It was towards the close of the pop-gun war, that I was infinitely diverted with a strange freak of Marheyo's.

I had worn, when I quitted the ship, a pair of thick pumps, which, from the rough usage they had received in scaling precipices and sliding down gorges, were so dilapidated as to be altogether unfit for use—so, at least, would have thought the generality of people, and so they most certainly were, when considered in the light of shoes. But things unserviceable in one way, may with advantage be applied in another, that is, if one have genius enough for the purpose. This genius Marheyo possessed in· a superlative degree, as he abundantly evinced by the use to which he put these sorely bruised and battered old shoes.

Every article, however trivial, which belonged to me, the natives appeared to regard as sacred; and I observed that for several days after becoming an inmate of the house, my pumps were suffered to remain, untouched, where I had first happened to throw them. I remembered, however, that after awhile I had missed them from their accustomed place; but the matter gave me no concern, supposing that Tinor—like any other tidy housewife, having come across them in some of her domestic occupations—had pitched the useless things out of the house. But I was soon undeceived.

One day I observed old Marheyo bustling about me with unusual activity, and to such a degree as almost to supersede Kory-Kory in the functions of his office. One moment he volunteered to trot off with me on his back to the stream; and when I refused, noways daunted by the repulse, he continued to frisk about me like a superannuated house-dog. I could not for the life of me conjecture what possessed the old gentleman, until all at once, availing himself of the temporary absence of the household, he went through a variety of uncouth gestures, pointing eagerly down to my feet, and then up to a little bundle which swung from the ridge-pole overhead. At last I caught a faint idea of his meaning, and motioned him to lower the package. He executed the order in the twinkling of an eye, and unrolling a piece of tappa displayed to my astonished gaze the identical pumps which I thought had been destroyed long before.

I immediately comprehended his desires, and very generously gave him the shoes, which had become quite mouldy, wondering for what earthly purpose he could want them.

The same afternoon I descried the venerable warrior approaching the house, with a slow, stately gait, ear-rings in ears, and spear in hand, with this highly ornamental pair of shoes suspended from his neck by a strip of bark, and swinging backwards and forwards on his capacious chest. In the gala costume of the tasteful Marheyo, these calf-skin pendants ever after formed the most striking feature.

But to turn to something a little more important. Although the whole existence of the inhabitants of the valley seemed to pass away exempt from toil, yet there were some light employments which, although amusing rather than laborious as occupations, contributed to their comfort and luxury. Among these, the most important was the manufacture of the native cloth —"tappa"—so well known, under various modifications, throughout the whole Polynesian Archipelago. As is generally understood, this useful and sometimes elegant article is fabricated from the bark of different trees. But, as I believe that no description of its manufacture has ever been given, I shall state what I know regarding it.

In the manufacture of the beautiful white tappa generally worn on the Marquesan Islands, the preliminary operation consists in gathering a certain quantity of the young branches of the cloth-tree. The exterior green bark being pulled off as worthless, there remains a slender fibrous substance, which is carefully stripped from the stick, to which it closely adheres. When a sufficient quantity of it has been collected, the various strips are enveloped in a covering of large leaves, which the natives use precisely as we do wrapping-paper, and which are secured by a few turns of a line passed round them. The package is then laid in the bed of some running stream, with a heavy stone placed over it, to prevent its being swept away. After it has remained for two or three days in this state, it is drawn out, and exposed, for a short time, to the action of the air, every distinct piece being attentively inspected, with a view of ascertaining whether it has yet been sufficiently affected by the operation. This is repeated again and again, until the desired result is obtained.

When the substance is in a proper state for the next process, it betrays evidences of incipient decomposition; the fibres are relaxed and softened, and rendered perfectly malleable. The different strips are now extended, one by one, in successive layers, upon some smooth surface—generally the prostrate trunk of a coco-nut tree—and the heap thus formed is subjected, at every new increase, to a moderate beating, with a sort of wooden mallet, leisurely applied. The mallet is made of a hard heavy wood resembling ebony, is about twelve inches in length, and perhaps two in breadth, with a rounded handle at one end, and in shape is the exact counterpart of one of our four-sided razor-strops. The flat surfaces of the implement are marked with shallow parallel indentations, varying in depth on the different sides, so as to be adapted to the several stages of the operation. These marks produce the corduroy sort of stripes discernible in the tappa in its finished state. After being beaten in the manner I have described, the material soon becomes blended in one mass, which, moistened occasionally with water, is at intervals hammered out, by a kind of gold-beating process, to any degree of thinness required. In this way the cloth is easily made to vary in strength and thickness, so as to suit the numerous purposes to which it is applied.

When the operation last described has been concluded the new-made tappa is spread out on the grass to bleach and dry, and soon becomes of a dazzling whiteness. Sometimes, in the first stages of the manufacture, the substance is impregnated with a vegetable juice, which gives it a permanent colour. A rich brown and a bright yellow are occasionally seen, but the simple taste of the Typee people inclines them to prefer the natural tint.

The notable wife of Kammahammaha, the renowned conqueror and king of the Sandwich Islands, used to pride herself in the skill she displayed in dyeing her tappa with contrasting colours disposed in regular figures; and, in the midst of the innovations of the times, was regarded, towards the decline of her life, as a lady of the old school, clinging as she did to the national cloth, in preference to the frippery of the European calicoes. But the art of printing the tappa is unknown upon the Marquesan Islands.

In passing along the valley, I was often attracted by the noise of the mallet, which, when employed in the manufacture of the cloth, produces at every stroke of its hard, heavy wood, a clear, ringing, and musical sound, capable of being heard at a great distance. When several of these implements happen to be in operation at the same time, and near one another, the effect upon the ear of a person, at a little distance, is really charming.

CHAPTER XX

HISTORY OF A DAY AS USUALLY SPENT IN THE TYPEE VALLEY—DANCES OF THE
MARQUESAN GIRLS.

NOTHING can be more uniform and undiversified than the life of the Typees;
one tranquil day of ease and happiness follows another in quiet succession;
and with these unsophisticated savages the history of a day is the history of
a life. I will, therefore, as briefly as I can, describe one of our days in the
valley.

To begin with the morning. We were not very early risers—the sun would
be shooting his golden spikes above the Happar mountains, ere I threw aside
my tappa robe, and girding my long tunic about my waist, sallied out with
Fayaway and Kory-Kory and the rest of the household, and bent my steps
towards the stream. Here we found congregated all those who dwelt in our
section of the valley; and here we bathed with them. The fresh morning
air and the cool flowing waters put both soul and body in a glow, and after
a half-hour employed in this recreation, we sauntered back to the house—
Tinor and Marheyo gathering dry sticks by the way for firewood; some of
the young men laying the coco-nut trees under contribution as they passed
beneath them; while Kory-Kory played his outlandish pranks for my particular diversion, and Fayaway and I, not arm in arm to be sure, but sometimes hand in hand, strolled along, with feelings of perfect charity for all
the world, and especial good-will towards each other.

Our morning meal was soon prepared. The islanders are somewhat abstemious at this repast; reserving the more powerful efforts of their appetite to a later period of the day. For my own part, with the assistance of
my valet, who, as I have before stated, always officiated as spoon on these
occasions, I ate sparingly from one of Tinor's trenchers of poee-poee; which
was devoted exclusively for my own use, being mixed with the milky meat
of ripe coco-nut. A section of a roasted breadfruit, a small cake of "Amar,"
or a mess of "Cokoo," two or three bananas, or a Mawmee apple; an annuee,
or some other agreeable and nutritious fruit served from day to day to diversify the meal, which was finished by tossing off the liquid contents of a
young coco-nut or two.

While partaking of this simple repast, the inmates of Marheyo's house,
after the style of the indolent Romans, reclined in sociable groups upon the
divan of mats, and digestion was promoted by cheerful conversation.

After the morning meal was concluded, pipes were lighted; and among
them my own especial pipe, a present from the noble Mehevi. The islanders,
who only smoke a whiff or two at a time, and at long intervals, and who
keep their pipes going from hand to hand continually, regarded my systematic
smoking of four or five pipefuls of tobacco in succession, as something quite
wonderful. When two or three pipes had circulated freely, the company
gradually broke up. Marheyo went to the little hut he was for ever building. Tinor began to inspect her rolls of tappa, or employed her busy fingers
in plaiting grass-mats. The girls anointed themselves with their fragrant oils,
dressed their hair, or looked over their curious finery, and compared together
their ivory trinkets, fashioned out of boars' tusks or whales' teeth. The young
men and warriors produced their spears, paddles, canoe-gear, battle-clubs,

and war-conchs, and occupied themselves in carving all sorts of figures upon them with pointed bits of shell or flint, and adorning them, especially the war-conchs, with tassels of braided bark and tufts of human hair. Some, immediately after eating, threw themselves once more upon the inviting mats, and resumed the employment of the previous night, sleeping as soundly as if they had not closed their eyes for a week. Others sallied out into the groves, for the purpose of gathering fruit or fibres of bark and leaves; the last two being in constant requisition, and applied to a hundred uses. A few, perhaps, among the girls, would slip into the woods after flowers, or repair to the stream with small calabashes and coco-nut shells, in order to polish them by friction with a smooth stone in the water. In truth these innocent people seemed to be at no loss for something to occupy their time; and it would be no light task to enumerate all their employments, or rather pleasures.

My own mornings I spent in a variety of ways. Sometimes I rambled about from house to house, sure of receiving a cordial welcome wherever I went; or from grove to grove, and from one shady place to another, in company with Kory-Kory and Fayaway, and a rabble rout of merry young idlers. Sometimes I was too indolent for exercise, and accepting one of the many invitations I was continually receiving, stretched myself out on the mats of some hospitable dwelling, and occupied myself pleasantly either in watching the proceedings of those around me or taking part in them myself. Whenever I chose to do the latter, the delight of the islanders was boundless; and there was always a throng of competitors for the honour of instructing me in any particular craft. I soon became quite an accomplished hand at making tappa—could braid a grass sling as well as the best of them—and once, with my knife, carved the handle of a javelin so exquisitely, that I have no doubt, to this day, Karnoonoo, its owner, preserves it as a surprising specimen of my skill. As noon approached, all those who had wandered forth from our habitation, began to return; and when mid-day was fairly come scarcely a sound was to be heard in the valley: a deep sleep fell upon all. The luxurious siesta was hardly ever omitted, except by old Marheyo, who was so eccentric a character, that he seemed to be governed by no fixed principles whatever; but, acting just according to the humour of the moment, slept, ate, or tinkered away at his little hut, without regard to the proprieties of time or place. Frequently he might have been seen taking a nap in the sun at noonday, or a bath in the stream at midnight. Once I beheld him perched eighty feet from the ground, in the tuft of a coco-nut tree, smoking; and often I saw him standing up to the waist in water, engaged in plucking out the stray hairs of his beard, using a piece of mussel-shell for tweezers.

The noontide slumber lasted generally an hour and a half; very often longer; and after the sleepers had arisen from their mats they again had recourse to their pipes, and then made preparations for the most important meal of the day.

I, however, like those gentlemen of leisure who breakfast at home and dine at their club, almost invariably, during my intervals of health, enjoyed the afternoon repast with the bachelor chiefs of the Ti, who were always rejoiced to see me, and lavishly spread before me all the good things which their larder afforded. Mehevi generally produced among other dainties a baked pig, an article which I have every reason to suppose was provided for my sole gratification.

The Ti was a right jovial place. It did my heart, as well as my body, good to visit it. Secure from female intrusion, there was no restraint upon the hilarity of the warriors, who, like the gentlemen of Europe after the cloth is drawn and the ladies retire, freely indulged their mirth.

After spending a considerable portion of the afternoon at the Ti, I usually found myself, as the cool of the evening came on, either sailing on the little lake with Fayaway, or bathing in the waters of the stream with a number of the savages, who, at this hour, always repaired thither. As the shadows of night approached, Marheyo's household were once more assembled under his roof: tapers were lit, long and curious chants were raised, interminable stories were told (for which one present was little the wiser), and all sorts of social festivities served to while away the time.

The young girls very often danced by moonlight in front of their dwellings. There are a great variety of these dances, in which, however, I never saw the men take part. They all consist of active, romping, mischievous evolutions, in which every limb is brought into requisition. Indeed, the Marquesan girls dance all over, as it were; not only do their feet dance, but their arms, hands, fingers, ay, their very eyes, seem to dance in their heads. In good sooth, they so sway their floating forms, arch their necks, toss aloft their naked arms, and glide, and swim, and whirl, that it was almost too much for a quiet, sober-minded, modest young man like myself.

The damsels wear nothing but flowers and their compendious gala tunics; and when they plume themselves for the dance, they look like a band of olive-coloured Sylphides on the point of taking wing.

Unless some particular festivity was going forward, the inmates of Marheyo's house retired to their mats rather early in the evening; but not for the night, since, after slumbering lightly for a while, they rose again, relit their tapers, partook of the third and last meal of the day, at which poee-poee alone was eaten, and then, after inhaling a narcotic whiff from a pipe of tobacco, disposed themselves for the great business of night, sleep. With the Marquesans it might almost be styled the great business of life, for they pass a large portion of their time in the arms of Somnus. The native strength of their constitutions is no way shown more emphatically than in the quantity of sleep they can endure. To many of them, indeed, life is little else than an often interrupted and luxurious nap.

CHAPTER XXI

THE SPRING OF ARVA WAI—REMARKABLE MONUMENTAL REMAINS—SOME IDEAS WITH REGARD TO THE HISTORY OF THE PI-PIS FOUND IN THE VALLEY.

ALMOST every country has its medicinal springs famed for their healing virtues. The Cheltenham of Typee is embosomed in the deepest solitude, and but seldom receives a visitor. It is situated remote from any dwelling, a little way up the mountain, near the head of the valley; and you approach it by a pathway shaded by the most beautiful foliage and adorned with a thousand fragrant plants.

The mineral waters of Arva Wai ooze forth from the crevices of a rock, and gliding down its mossy side, fall at last, in many clustering drops into a natural basin of stone fringed round with grass and dewy-looking little violet-coloured flowers, as fresh and beautiful as the perpetual moisture they enjoy can make them.

The water is held in high estimation by the islanders, some of whom consider it an agreeable as well as a medicinal beverage; they bring it from the mountain in their calabashes, and store it away beneath heaps of leaves in some shady nook near the house. Old Marheyo had a great love for the waters of the spring. Every now and then he lugged off to the mountain a great round demijohn of a calabash, and, panting with his exertions, brought it back filled with his darling fluid.

The water tasted like a solution of a dozen disagreeable things, and was sufficiently nauseous to have made the fortune of the proprietor, had the spa been situated in the midst of any civilized community.

As I am no chemist, I cannot give a scientific analysis of the water. All I know about the matter is, that one day Marheyo in my presence poured out the last drop from his huge calabash, and I observed at the bottom of the vessel a small quantity of gravelly sediment very much resembling our common sand. Whether this is always found in the water, and gives it its peculiar flavour and virtues, or whether its presence was merely incidental, I was not able to ascertain.

One day in returning from this spring by a circuitous path, I came upon a scene which reminded me of Stonehenge and the architectural labours of the Druids.

At the base of one of the mountains, and surrounded on all sides by dense groves, a series of vast terraces of stone rises, step by step, for a considerable distance up the hill-side. These terraces cannot be less than one hundred yards in length and twenty in width. Their magnitude, however, is less striking than the immense size of the blocks composing them. Some of the stones, of an oblong shape, are from ten to fifteen feet in length, and five or six feet thick. Their sides are quite smooth, but though square, and of pretty regular formation, they bear no mark of the chisel. They are laid together without cement, and here and there show gaps between. The topmost terrace and the lower ones are somewhat peculiar in their construction. They have both a quadrangular depression in the center, leaving the rest of the terrace elevated several feet above it. In the intervals of the stones immense trees have taken root, and their broad boughs stretching far over, and interlacing together, support a canopy almost impenetrable to the sun. Overgrowing the greater part of them, and climbing from one to another, is a wilderness of vines, in whose sinewy embrace many of the stones lie half hidden, while in some places a thick growth of bushes entirely covers them. There is a wild pathway which obliquely crosses two of these terraces; and so profound is the shade, so dense the vegetation, that a stranger to the place might pass along it without being aware of their existence.

These structures bear every indication of a very high antiquity. and Kory-Kory, who was my authority in all matters of scientific research, gave me to understand that they were coeval with the creation of the world; that the great gods themselves were the builders; and that they would endure until time shall be no more. Kory-Kory's prompt explanation, and his attributing the work to a divine origin, at once convinced me that neither he nor the rest of his countrymen knew anything about them.

As I gazed upon this monument, doubtless the work of an extinct and forgotten race, thus buried in the great nook of an island at the ends of the earth, the existence of which was yesterday unknown, a stronger feeling of awe came over me than if I had stood musing at the mighty base of the Pyramid of Cheops. There are no inscriptions, no sculpture, no clue, by which to conjecture its history: nothing but the dumb stones. How many generations of those majestic trees which overshadow them have grown and flourished and decayed since first they were erected!

These remains naturally suggest many interesting reflections. They establish the great age of the island, an opinion which the builders of theories concerning the creation of the various groups in the South Seas are not always inclined to admit. For my own part, I think it just as probable that human beings were living in the valleys of the Marquesas three thousand years ago as that they were inhabiting the land of Egypt. The origin of the island of Nukuheva cannot be imputed to the coral insect; for indefatigable as that wonderful creature is, it would be hardly muscular enough to pile rocks one upon the other more than three thousand feet above the level of the sea. That the land may have been thrown up by a submarine volcano is as possible as anything else. No one can make an affidavit to the contrary, and therefore I will say nothing against the supposition: indeed, were geologists to assert that the whole continent of America had in like manner been formed by the simultaneous explosion of a train of Etnas laid under the water all the way from the North Pole to the parallel of Cape Horn, I am the last man in the world to contradict them.

I have already mentioned that the dwellings of the islanders were almost invariably built upon massive stone foundations, which they call pi-pis. The dimensions of these, however, as well as of the stones composing them, are comparatively small: but there are other and larger erections of a similar description comprising the "morais," or burying-grounds, and festival-places, in nearly all the valleys of the island. Some of these piles are so extensive, and so great a degree of labour and skill must have been requisite in constructing them, that I can scarcely believe they were built by the ancestors of the present inhabitants. If indeed they were, the race has sadly deteriorated in their knowledge of the mechanic arts. To say nothing of their habitual indolence, by what contrivance within the reach of so simple a people could such enormous masses have been moved or fixed in their places? and how could they with their rude implements have chiselled and hammered them into shape?

All of these larger pi-pis—like that of the Hoolah Hoolah ground in the Typee valley—bore incontestable marks of great age; and I am disposed to believe that their erection may be ascribed to the same race of men who were the builders of the still more ancient remains I have just described.

According to Kory-Kory's account, the pi-pi upon which stands the Hoolah-Hoolah ground was built a great many moons ago, under the direction of Monoo, a great chief and warrior, and, as it would appear, master-mason among the Typees. It was erected for the express purpose to which it is at present devoted in the incredibly short period of one sun; and was dedicated to the immortal wooden idols by a grand festival, which lasted ten days and nights.

Among the smaller pi-pis, upon which stand the dwelling-houses of the natives, I never observed any which intimated a recent erection. There are in every part of the valley a great many of these massive stone foundations which have no houses upon them. This is vastly convenient, for whenever an enterprising islander chooses to emigrate a few hundred yards from the place where he was born, all he has to do in order to establish himself in some new locality, is to select one of the many unappropriated pi-pis, and without further ceremony pitch his bamboo tent upon it.

CHAPTER XXII

PREPARATIONS FOR A GRAND FESTIVAL IN THE VALLEY—STRANGE DOINGS IN THE TABOO GROVES—MONUMENT OF CALABASHES—GALA COSTUME OF THE TYPEE DAMSELS—DEPARTURE FOR THE FESTIVAL.

FROM the time that my lameness had decreased, I had made a daily practice of visiting Mehevi at the Ti, who invariably gave me a most cordial reception. I was always accompanied in these excursions by Fayaway and the ever-present Kory-Kory. The former, as soon as we reached the vicinity of the Ti—which was rigourously tabooed to the whole female sex—withdrew to a neighbouring hut, as if her feminine delicacy restrained her from approaching a habitation which might be regarded as a sort of Bachelors' Hall.

And in good truth it might well have been so considered. Although it was the permanent residence of several distinguished chiefs, and of the noble Mehevi in particular, it was still at certain seasons the favourite haunt of all the jolly, talkative, and elderly savages of the vale, who resorted thither in the same way that similar characters frequent a tavern in civilized countries. There they would remain hour after hour, chatting, smoking, eating poee-poee, or busily engaged in sleeping for the good of their constitutions.

This building appeared to be the headquarters of the valley, where all flying rumours concentrated; and to have seen it filled with a crowd of the natives, all males, conversing in animated clusters, while multitudes were continually coming and going, one would have thought it a kind of savage Exchange, where the rise and fall of Polynesian Stock was discussed.

Mehevi acted as supreme lord over the place, spending the greater portion of his time there: and often when, at particular hours of the day, it was deserted by nearly every one else except the verd-antique looking centenarians, who were fixtures in the building, the chief himself was sure to be found enjoying his "otium cum dignitate," upon the luxurious mats which covered the floor. Whenever I made my appearance he invariably rose, and, like a gentleman doing the honours of his mansion, invited me to repose myself wherever I pleased, and calling out "tammaree!" (boy), a little fellow would appear, and then retiring for an instant, return with some savoury mess, from which the chief would press me to regale myself. To tell the truth, Mehevi was indebted to the excellence of his viands for the honour of my repeated visits —a matter which cannot appear singular when it is borne in mind that bachelors, all the world over, are famous for serving up unexceptionable repasts.

One day, on drawing near to the Ti, I observed that extensive preparations were going forward, plainly betokening some approaching festival. Some of the symptoms reminded me of the stir produced among the scullions of a large hotel where a grand jubilee dinner is about to be given. The natives were hurrying about hither and thither, engaged in various duties; some lugging off to the stream enormous hollow bamboos, for the purpose of filling them with water; others chasing furious-looking hogs through the bushes, in their endeavours to capture them; and numbers employed in kneading great mountains of poee-poee heaped up in huge wooden vessels.

After observing these lively indications for a while, I was attracted to a neighbouring grove by a prodigious squeaking which I heard there. On reaching the spot I found it proceeded from a large hog which a number of natives were forcibly holding to the earth, while a muscular fellow, armed with a bludgeon, was ineffectually aiming murderous blows at the skull of the unfortunate porker. Again and again he missed his writhing and struggling victim, but though puffing and panting with his exertions, he still continued them; and after striking a sufficient number of blows to have demolished an entire drove of oxen, with one crashing stroke he laid him dead at his feet.

Without letting any blood from the body, it was immediately carried to a fire which had been kindled near at hand, and four savages taking hold of the carcass by its legs, passed it rapidly to and fro in the flames. In a moment the smell of burning bristles betrayed the object of this procedure. Having got thus far in the matter, the body was removed to a little distance; and, being disembowelled, the entrails were laid aside as choice parts, and the whole carcass thoroughly washed with water. An ample thick green cloth, composed of the long thick leaves of a species of palm-tree, ingeniously tacked together with little pins of bamboo, was now spread upon the ground, in which the body being carefully rolled, it was borne to an oven previously prepared to receive it. Here it was at once laid upon the heated stones at the bottom, and covered with thick layers of leaves, the whole being quickly hidden from sight by a mound of earth raised over it.

Such is the summary style in which the Typees convert perverse-minded and rebellious hogs into the most docile and amiable pork; a morsel of which placed on the tongue melts like a soft smile from the lips of Beauty.

I commend their peculiar mode of proceeding to the consideration of all butchers, cooks, and housewives. The hapless porker whose fate I have just rehearsed, was not the only one who suffered on that memorable day. Many a dismal grunt, many an imploring squeak, proclaimed what was going on throughout the whole extent of the valley; and I verily believe the first-born of every litter perished before the setting of that fatal sun.

The scene around the Ti was now most animated. Hogs and poee-poee were baking in numerous ovens, which, heaped up with fresh earth into slight elevations, looked like so many ant-hills. Scores of the savages were vigorously plying their stone pestles in preparing masses of poee-poee, and numbers were gathering green breadfruit and young coco-nuts in the surrounding groves; while an exceeding great multitude, with a view of encouraging the rest in their labours, stood still, and kept shouting most lustily without intermission.

It is a peculiarity among these people, that when engaged in any employment they always make a prodigious fuss about it. So seldom do they ever exert themselves, that when they do work they seem determined that so meritorious an action shall not escape the observation of those around. If, for example, they have occasion to remove a stone to a little distance, which perhaps might be carried by two able-bodied men, a whole swarm gather about it, and, after a vast deal of palavering, lift it up among them, every one struggling to get hold of it, and bear it off yelling and panting as if accomplishing some mighty achievement. Seeing them on these occasions, one is reminded of an infinity of black ants clustering about and dragging away to some hole the leg of a deceased fly.

Having for some time attentively observed these demonstrations of good cheer, I entered the Ti, where Mehevi sat complacently looking out upon the busy scene, and occasionally issuing his orders. The chief appeared to be in an extraordinary flow of spirits, and gave me to understand that on the morrow there would be grand doings in the Groves generally, and at the Ti in particular; and urged me by no means to absent myself. In commemoration of what event, however, or in honour of what distinguished personage, the feast was to be given, altogether passed my comprehension. Mehevi sought to enlighten my ignorance, but he failed as signally as when he had endeavoured to initiate me into the perplexing arcana of the taboo.

On leaving the Ti, Kory-Kory, who had as a matter of course accompanied me, observing that my curiosity remained unabated, resolved to make everything plain and satisfactory. With this intent, he escorted me through the Taboo Groves, pointing out to my notice a variety of objects, and endeavoured to explain them in such an indescribable jargon of words, that it almost put me in bodily pain to listen to him. In particular, he led me to a remarkable pyramidical structure some three yards square at the base, and perhaps ten feet in height, which had lately been thrown up, and occupied a very conspicuous position. It was composed principally of large empty calabashes, with a few polished coco-nut shells, and looked not unlike a cenotaph of skulls. My cicerone perceived the astonishment with which I gazed at this monument of savage crockery, and immediately addressed himself to the task of enlightening me: but all in vain; and to this hour the nature of the monument remains a complete mystery to me. As, however, it formed so prominent a feature in the approaching revels, I bestowed upon the latter, in my own mind, the title of the "Feast of Calabashes."

The following morning, awakening rather late, I perceived the whole of Marheyo's family busily engaged in preparing for the festival. The old warrior himself was arranging in round balls the two grey locks of hair that were suffered to grow from the crown of his head; his earrings and spear, both well polished, lay beside him, while the highly decorative pair of shoes hung suspended from a projecting cane against the side of the house. The young men were similarly employed; and the fair damsels, including Fayaway, were anointing themselves with "aka," arranging their long tresses, and performing other matters connected with the duties of the toilet.

Having completed their preparations, the girls now exhibited themselves in gala costume; the most conspicuous feature of which was a necklace of beautiful white flowers, with the stems removed, and strung closely together upon a single fibre of tappa. Corresponding ornaments were inserted in their ears, and woven garlands upon their heads. About their waists they wore a short tunic of spotless white tappa, and some of them superadded to this a mantle of the same material, tied in an elaborate bow upon the left shoulder, and falling about the figure in picturesque folds.

Thus arrayed, I would have matched the charming Fayaway against any beauty in the world.

People may say what they will about the taste evinced by our fashionable ladies in dress. Their jewels, their feathers, their silks, and their furbelows would have sunk into utter insignificance beside the exquisite simplicity of attire adopted by the nymphs of the vale on this festive occasion. I should like to have seen a gallery of coronation beauties, at Westminster Abbey, confronted for a moment by this band of Island girls; their stiffness, formality, and affectation contrasted with the artless vivacity and unconcealed natural graces of these savage maidens. It would be the Venus dei Medici placed beside a milliner's doll.

It was not long before Kory-Kory and myself were left alone in the house, the rest of its inmates having departed for the Taboo Groves. My valet was all impatience to follow them; and was as fidgety about my dilatory movements as a diner-out waiting hat in hand at the bottom of the stairs for some lagging companion. At last, yielding to his importunities, I set out for the Ti. As we passed the houses peeping out from the groves through which our route lay, I noticed that they were entirely deserted by their inhabitants.

When we reached the rock that abruptly terminated the path, and concealed from us the festive scene, wild shouts and a confused blending of voices assured me that the occasion, whatever it might be, had drawn together a great multitude. Kory-Kory, previous to mounting the elevation, paused for a moment, like a dandy at a ballroom door, to put a hasty finish to his toilet. During this short interval, the thought struck me that I ought myself perhaps to be taking some little pains with my appearance. But as I had no holiday raiment, I was not a little puzzled to devise some means of decorating myself. However, as I felt desirous to create a sensation, I determined to do all that lay in my power; and knowing that I could not delight the savages more than by conforming to their style of dress, I removed from my person the large robe of tappa which I was accustomed to wear over my shoulders whenever I sallied into the open air, and remained merely girt about with a short tunic descending from my waist to my knees.

My quick-witted attendant fully appreciated the compliment I was paying to the costume of his race, and began more sedulously to arrange the folds of the one only garment which remained to me. Whilst he was doing this, I caught sight of a knot of young lasses, who were sitting near us on the grass surrounded by heaps of flowers which they were forming into garlands. I motioned to them to bring some of their handiwork to me; and in an instant a dozen wreaths were at my disposal. One of them I put round the apology of a hat which I had been forced to construct for myself out of palmetto-leaves, and some of the others I converted into a splendid girdle. These operations finished, with the slow and dignified step of a full-dressed beau I ascended the rock.

CHAPTER XXIII

THE FEAST OF CALABASHES.

THE whole population of the valley seemed to be gathered within the precincts of the grove. In the distance could be seen the long front of the Ti, its immense piazza swarming with men, arrayed in every variety of fantastic costume, and all vociferating with animated gestures; while the whole interval between it and the place where I stood was enlivened by groups of females fancifully decorated, dancing, capering, and uttering wild exclamations. As soon as they descried me they set up a shout of welcome; and a band of

them came dancing towards me chanting as they approached some wild recitative. The change in my garb seemed to transport them with delight, and
clustering about me on all sides, they accompanied me towards the Ti. When,
however, we drew near it these joyous nymphs paused in their career, and
parting on either side, permitted me to pass on to the now densely thronged
building.

So soon as I mounted to the pi-pi I saw at a glance that the revels were
fairly under way.

What lavish plenty reigned around!—Warwick feasting his retainers with
beef and ale was a niggard to the noble Mehevi!—All along the piazza of the
Ti were arranged elaborately carved canoe-shaped vessels, some twenty feet
in length, filled with newly made poee-poee, and sheltered from the sun by
the broad leaves of the banana. At intervals were heaps of green breadfruit,
raised in pyramidical stacks, resembling the regular piles of heavy shot to be
seen in the yard of an arsenal. Inserted into the interstices of the huge stones
which formed the pi-pi were large boughs of trees; hanging from the branches
of which, and screened from the sun by their foliage, were innumerable little
packages with leafy coverings, containing the meat of the numerous hogs
which had been slain, done up in this manner to make it more accessible to
the crowd. Leaning against the railing of the piazza were an immense number of long, heavy bamboos, plugged at the lower end, and with their projecting muzzles stuffed with a wad of leaves. These were filled with water
from the stream, and each of them might hold from four to five gallons.

The banquet being thus spread, nought remained but for every one to
help himself at his pleasure. Accordingly not a moment passed but the
transplanted boughs I have mentioned were rifled by the throng of the fruit
they certainly had never borne before. Calabashes of poee-poee were continually being replenished from the extensive receptable in which that article
was stored, and multitudes of little fires were kindled about the Ti for the
purpose of roasting the breadfruit.

Within the building itself was presented a most extraordinary scene. The
immense lounge of mats lying between the parallel rows of the trunks of coco-
nut trees, and extending the entire length of the house, at least two hundred
feet, was covered by the reclining forms of a host of chiefs and warriors, who
were eating at a great rate, or soothing the cares of Polynesian life in the
sedative fumes of tobacco. The smoke was inhaled from large pipes, the
bowls of which, made out of small coco-nut shells, were curiously carved in
strange heathenish devices. These were passed from mouth to mouth by the
recumbent smokers, who, taking two or three prodigious whiffs, handed the
pipe to his neighbour; sometimes for that purpose stretching indolently across
the body of some dozing individual whose exertions at the dinner-table had
already induced sleep.

The tobacco used among the Typees was of a very mild and pleasing
flavour, and as I always saw it in leaves, and the natives appeared pretty well
supplied with it, I was led to believe that it must have been the growth of
the valley. Indeed Kory-Kory gave me to understand that this was the
case; but I never saw a single plant growing on the island. At Nukuheva,
and, I believe, in all the other valleys, the weed is very scarce, being only
obtained in small quantities from foreigners, and smoking is consequently
with the inhabitants of these places a very great luxury. How it was that
the Typees were so well furnished with it I cannot divine. I should think
them too indolent to devote any attention to its culture; and indeed, as far

as my observation extended, not a single atom of the soil was under any other cultivation than that of shower and sunshine. The tobacco-plant, however, like the sugar-cane, may grow wild in some remote part of the vale.

There were many in the Ti for whom the tobacco did not furnish a sufficient stimulus, and who accordingly had recourse to "arva," as a more powerful agent in producing the desired effect.

"Arva" is a root very generally dispersed over the South Seas and from it is extracted a juice, the effects of which upon the system are at first stimulating in a moderate degree; but it soon relaxes the muscles, and exerting a narcotic influence produces a luxurious sleep. In the valley this beverage was universally prepared in the following way:—Some half-dozen young boys seated themselves in a circle around an empty wooden vessel, each one of them being supplied with a certain quantity of the roots of the "arva," broken into small bits and laid by his side. A coco-nut goblet of water was passed around the juvenile company, who, rinsing their mouths with its contents, proceeded to the business before them. This merely consisted in thoroughly masticating the "arva," and throwing it mouthful after mouthful into the receptacle provided. When a sufficient quantity had thus been obtained water was poured upon the mass, and being stirred about with the forefinger of the right hand, the preparation was soon in readiness for use. The "arva" has medicinal qualities.

Upon the Sandwich Islands it has been employed with no small success in the treatment of scrofulous affections, and in combating the ravages of a disease for whose frightful inroads the ill-starred inhabitants of that group are indebted to their foreign benefactors. But the tenants of the Typee valley, as yet exempt from these inflictions, generally employ the "arva" as a minister to social enjoyment, and a calabash of the liquid circulates among them as the bottle with us. Mehevi, who was greatly delighted with the change in my costume, gave me a cordial welcome. He had reserved for me a most delectable mess of "cockoo," well knowing my partiality for that dish; and had likewise selected three or four young coco-nuts, several roasted breadfruit, and a magnificent bunch of bananas, for my special comfort and gratification. These various matters were at once placed before me; but Kory-Kory deemed the banquet entirely insufficient for my wants until he had supplied me with one of the leafy packages of pork, which, notwithstanding the somewhat hasty manner in which it had been prepared, possessed a most excellent flavour, and was surprisingly sweet and tender.

Pork is not a staple article of food among the people of the Marquesas, consequently they pay little attention to the *breeding* of the swine. The hogs are permitted to roam at large in the groves, where they obtain no small part of their nourishment from the coco-nuts which continually fall from the trees. But it is only after infinite labour and difficulty, that the hungry animal can pierce the husk and shell so as to get at the meat. I have frequently been amused at seeing one of them, after crunching the obstinate nut with his teeth for a long time unsuccessfully, get into a violent passion with it. He would then root furiously under the coco-nut, and, with a fling of his snout, toss it before him on the ground. Following it up he would crunch at it again savagely for a moment, and the next knock it on one side, pausing immediately after, as if wondering how it could so suddenly have disappeared. In this way the persecuted coco-nuts were often chased half across the valley.

The second day of the Feast of Calabashes was ushered in by still more uproarious noises than the first. The skins of innumerable sheep seemed to be resounding to the blows of an army of drummers. Startled from my slumbers by the din, I leaped up, and found the whole household engaged in making preparations for immediate departure. Curious to discover of what strange events these novel sounds might be the precursers, and not a little desirous to catch a sight of the instruments which produced the terrific noise, I accompanied the natives as soon as they were in readiness to depart for the Taboo Groves.

The comparatively open space that extended from the Ti toward the rock, to which I have before alluded as forming the ascent to the place, was, with the building itself, now altogether deserted by the men, the whole distance being filled by bands of females, shouting and dancing under the influence of some strange excitement.

I was amused at the appearance of four or five old women who, in a state of utter nudity, with their arms extended flatly down their sides, and holding themselves perfectly erect, were leaping stiffly into the air, like so many sticks bobbing to the surface after being pressed perpendicularly into the water. They preserved the utmost gravity of countenance, and continued their extraordinary movements without a single moment's cessation. They did not appear to attract the observation of the crowd around them, but I must candidly confess that, for my own part, I stared at them most pertinaciously.

Desirous of being enlightened with regard to the meaning of this peculiar diversion, I turned inquiringly to Kory-Kory; that learned Typee immediately proceeded to explain the whole matter thoroughly. But all that I could comprehend from what he said was, that the leaping figures before me were bereaved widows, whose partners had been slain in battle many moons previously; and who, at every festival, gave public evidence in this manner of their calamities. It was evident that Kory-Kory considered this an all-sufficient reason for so indecorous a custom; but I must say that it did not satisfy me as to its propriety.

Leaving these afflicted females, we passed on to the Hoolah-Hoolah ground. Within the spacious quadrangle, the whole population of the valley seemed to be assembled, and the sight presented was truly remarkable. Beneath the sheds of bamboo which opened towards the interior of the square, reclined the principal chiefs and warriors, while a miscellaneous throng lay at their ease under the enormous trees which spread a majestic canopy overhead. Upon the terraces of the gigantic altars, at either end, were deposited green breadfruit in baskets of coco-nut leaves, large rolls of tappa, bunches of ripe bananas, clusters of mammee-apples, the golden-hued fruit of the artu-tree, and baked hogs, laid out in large wooden trenches, fancifully decorated with freshly plucked leaves, whilst a variety of rude implements of war were piled in confused heaps before the ranks of hideous idols. Fruits of various kinds were likewise suspended in leafen baskets, from the tops of poles planted uprightly, and at regular intervals, along the lower terraces of both altars. At their base were arranged two parallel rows of cumbersome drums, standing at least fifteen feet in height, and formed from the hollow trunks of large trees. Their heads were covered with shark-skins, and their barrels were elaborately carved with various quaint figures and devices. At regular intervals they were bound round by a species of sinnate of various colours, and strips of native cloth flattened upon them here and there. Behind these instruments were built slight platforms, upon which stood a number of young men who, beating violently with the palms of their hands upon the drum-heads, produced those outrageous sounds which had awakened me in the morning.

Every few minutes these musical performers hopped down from their elevation into the crowd below, and their places were immediately supplied by fresh recruits. Thus an incessant din was kept up that might have startled Pandemonium.

Precisely in the middle of the quadrangle were placed perpendicularly in the ground, a hundred or more slender, fresh-cut poles, stripped of their bark, and decorated at the end with a floating pennon of white tappa; the whole being fenced about with a little picket of canes. For what purpose these singular ornaments were intended I in vain endeavoured to discover.

Another most striking feature of the performance was exhibited by a score of old men, who sat cross-legged in the little pulpits, which encircled the trunks of the immense trees growing in the middle of the enclosure. These venerable gentlemen, who I presume were the priests, kept up an uninterrupted monotonous chant, which was nearly drowned in the roar of the drums. In the right hand they held a finely woven grass fan, with a heavy black wooden handle curiously chased; these fans they kept in continual motion.

But no attention whatever seemed to be paid to the drummers or to the old priests; the individuals who composed the vast crowd present being entirely taken up in chatting and laughing with one another, smoking, drinking arva, and eating. For all the observation it attracted, or the good it achieved, the whole savage orchestra might, with great advantage to its own members and the company in general, have ceased the prodigious uproar they were making.

In vain I questioned Kory-Kory and others of the natives, as to the meaning of the strange things that were going on; all their explanations were conveyed in such a mass of outlandish gibberish and gesticulation that I gave up the attempt in despair. All that day the drums resounded, the priests chanted, and the multitude feasted and roared till sunset, when the throng dispersed, and the Taboo Groves were again abandoned to quiet and repose. The next day the same scene was repeated until night, when this singular festival terminated.

CHAPTER XXIV

IDEAS SUGGESTED BY THE FEAST OF THE CALABASHES—INACCURACY OF CERTAIN
PUBLISHED ACCOUNTS OF THE ISLANDS—A REASON—NEGLECTED STATE OF
HEATHENISM IN THE VALLEY—EFFIGY OF A DEAD WARRIOR—A SINGULAR
SUPERSTITION—THE PRIEST KOLORY AND THE GOD MOA ARTUA—AMAZING
RELIGIOUS OBSERVANCE—A DILAPIDATED SHRINE—KORY-KORY AND THE
IDOL—AN INFERENCE.

ALTHOUGH I had been baffled in my attempts to learn the origin of the Feast of Calabashes, yet it seemed very plain to me that it was principally, if not wholly, of a religious character. As a religious solemnity, however, it had not at all corresponded with the horrible descriptions of Polynesian worship which we have received in some published narratives, and especially in those accounts of the evangelized islands with which the missionaries have favoured us. Did not the sacred character of these persons render the purity of their intentions unquestionable, I should certainly be led to suppose that they had exaggerated the evils of Paganism, in order to enhance the spirit of their own disinterested labours.

In a certain work incidentally treating of the "Washington, or Northern Marquesas Islands," I have seen the frequent immolation of human victims upon the altars of their gods, positively and repeatedly charged upon the inhabitants. The same work gives also a rather minute account of their religion—enumerates a great many of their superstitions—and makes known the particular designations of numerous orders of the priesthood. One would almost imagine from the long list that is given of cannibal primates, bishops, archdeacons, prebendaries, and other inferior ecclesiastics, that the sacerdotal order far outnumbered the rest of the population, and that the poor natives were more severely priest-ridden than even the inhabitants of the papal states. These accounts are likewise calculated to leave upon the reader's mind an impression that human victims are daily cooked and served up upon the altars; that heathenish cruelties of every description are continually practised; and that these ignorant Pagans are in a state of the extremest wretchedness in consequence of the grossness of their superstitions. Be it observed, however, that all this information is given by a man who, according to his own statement, was only at one of the islands, and remained there but two weeks, sleeping every night on board his ship, and taking little kid-glove excursions ashore in the daytime, attended by an armed party.

Now, all I can say is, that in all my excursions through the valley of Typee, I never saw any of these alleged enormities. If any of them are practiced upon the Marquesas Islands they must certainly have come to my knowledge while living for months with a tribe of savages, wholly unchanged from their original primitive condition, and reputed the most ferocious in the South Seas.

The fact is, that there is a vast deal of unintentional humbuggery in some of the accounts we have from scientific men concerning the religious institutions of Polynesia. These learned tourists generally obtain the greater part of their information from the retired old South Sea rovers, who have domesticated themselves among the barbarous tribes of the Pacific. Jack, who has long been accustomed to the long-bow, and to spin tough yarns on a ship's forecastle, invariably officiates as showman of the island on which he has settled, and having mastered a few dozen words of the language, is supposed to know all about the people who speak it. A natural desire to make himself of consequence in the eyes of the strangers, prompts him to lay claim to a much greater knowledge of such matters than he actually possesses. In reply to incessant queries, he communicates not only all he knows but a good deal more, and if there be any information deficient still he is at no loss to supply it. The avidity with which his anecdotes are noted down tickles his vanity, and his powers of invention increase with the credulity of his auditors. He knows just the sort of information wanted, and furnishes it to any extent.

This is not a supposed case; I have met with several individuals like the one described, and I have been present at two or three of their interviews with strangers.

Now when the scientific voyager arrives at home with his collection of wonders, he attempts, perhaps, to give a description of some of the strange people he has been visiting. Instead of representing them as a community of lusty savages, who are leading a merry, idle, innocent life, he enters into a very circumstantial and learned narrative of certain unaccountable superstitions and practices, about which he knows as little as the islanders do themselves. Having had little time, and scarcely any opportunity, to become acquainted with the customs he pretends to describe, he writes them down one after another in an off-hand, haphazard style; and were the book thus produced to be translated into the tongue of the people of whom it purports to give the history, it would appear quite as wonderful to them as it does to the American public, and much more improbable.

For my own part, I am free to confess my almost entire inability to gratify any curiosity that may be felt with regard to the theology of the valley. I doubt whether the inhabitants themselves could do so. They are either too lazy or too sensible to worry themselves about abstract points of religious belief. While I was among them they never held any synods or councils to settle the principles of their faith by agitating them. An unbounded liberty of conscience seemed to prevail. Those who pleased to do so were allowed to repose implicit faith in an ill-favoured god with a large bottle-nose and fat shapeless arms crossed upon his breast; whilst others worshipped an image which, having no likeness either in heaven or on earth, could hardly be called an idol. As the islanders always maintained a discreet reserve with regard to my own peculiar views on religion, I thought it would be excessively ill-bred in me to pry into theirs.

But, although my knowledge of the religious faith of the Typees was unavoidably limited, one of their superstitious observances with which I became acquainted interested me greatly.

In one of the most secluded portions of the valley, within a stone's cast of Fayaway's Lake—for so I christened the scene of our island yachting—and hard by a growth of palms, which stood ranged in order along both banks of the stream, waving their green arms as if to do honour to its passage, was the mausoleum of a deceased warrior-chief. Like all the other edifices of any note, it was raised upon a small pi-pi of stones, which, being of unusual height, was a conspicuous object from a distance. A light thatching of bleached palmetto-leaves hung over it like a self-supported canopy; for it was not until you came very near that you saw it was supported by four slender columns of bamboo rising at each corner to a little more than the height of a man. A clear area of a few yards surrounded the pi-pi, and was enclosed by four trunks of coco-nut trees resting at the angles on massive blocks of stone. The place was sacred. The sign of the inscrutable taboo was seen in the shape of a mystic roll of white tappa, suspended by a twisted cord of the same material from the top of a slight pole planted within the enclosure. The sanctity of the spot appeared never to have been violated. The stillness of the grave was there, and the calm solitude around was beautiful and touching. The soft shadows of those lofty palm-trees!—I can see them now—hanging over the little temple, as if to keep out the intrusive sun.

On all sides as you approached this silent spot you caught sight of the dead chief's effigy, seated in the stern of a canoe, which was raised on a light frame a few inches above the level of the pi-pi. The canoe was about seven feet in length; of a rich, dark-coloured wood, handsomely carved and adorned in many places with variegated bindings of stained sinnate, into which were ingeniously wrought a number of sparkling seashells, and a belt of the same shells ran all round it. The body of the figure—of whatever material it might have been made—was effectually concealed in a heavy robe of brown tappa, revealing only the hands and head; the latter skilfully carved in wood, and surmounted by a superb arch of plumes. These plumes, in the subdued and gentle gales which found access to this sequestered spot, were never for one moment at rest, but kept nodding and waving over the chief's brow. The long leaves of the palmetto dropped over the eaves, and through them you saw the warrior holding his paddle with both hands in the act of rowing, leaning forward and inclining his head, as if eager to hurry on his voyage. Glaring at him forever, and face to face, was a polished human skull, which crowned the prow of the canoe. The spectral figurehead, reversed in its position, glancing backwards, seemed to mock the impatient attitude of the warrior.

When I first visited this singular place with Kory-Kory, he told me—or at least I so understood him—that the chief was paddling his way to the realms of bliss, and breadfruit—the Polynesian heaven—where every moment the breadfruit trees dropped their ripened spheres to the ground, and where there was no end to the coco-nuts and bananas; there they reposed through the livelong eternity upon mats much finer than those of Typee; and every day bathed their glowing limbs in rivers of coco-nut oil. In that happy land there were plenty of plumes and feathers, and boars' tusks and sperm-whale teeth, far preferable to all the shining trinkets and gay tappa of the white men; and, best of all, women far lovelier than the daughters of earth were there in abundance. "A very pleasant place," Kory-Kory said it was; "but after all, not much pleasanter, he thought, than Typee." "Did he not then," I asked him, "wish to accompany the warrior?" "Oh, no: he was very happy where he was; but supposed that some time or other he would go in his own canoe."

Thus far, I think, I clearly comprehended Kory-Kory. But there was a singular expression he made use of at the time, enforced by as singular a gesture, the meaning of which I would have given much to penetrate. I am inclined to believe it must have been a proverb he uttered; for I afterwards heard him repeat the same words several times and in what appeared to me to be a somewhat similar sense. Indeed, Kory-Kory had a great variety of short, smart-sounding sentences, with which he frequently enlivened his discourse; and he introduced them with an air which plainly intimated, that in his opinion, they settled the matter in question, whatever it might be.

Could it have been then, that when I asked him whether he desired to go to this heaven of breadfruit, coco-nuts, and young ladies, which he had been describing, he answered by saying something equivalent to our old adage— "A bird in the hand is worth two in the bush?"—if he did, Kory-Kory was a discreet and sensible fellow, and I cannot sufficiently admire his shrewdness.

Whenever in the course of my rambles through the valley I happened to be near the chief's mausoleum, I always turned aside to visit it. The place had a peculiar charm for me; I hardly know why; but so it was. As I leaned over the railing and gazed upon the strange effigy and watched the play of the feathery head-dress, stirred by the same breeze which in low tones breathed amidst the lofty palm-trees, I loved to yield myself up to the fanciful superstition of the islanders, and could almost believe that the grim warrior was bound heavenward. In this mood when I turned to depart, I bade him "God speed, and a pleasant voyage." Aye, paddle away, brave chieftain, to the land of spirits! To the material eye thou makest but little progress; but with the eye of faith, I see thy canoe cleaving the bright waves, which die away on those dimly looming shores of Paradise.

The strange superstition affords another evidence of the fact, that however ignorant man may be, he still feels within him his immortal spirit yearning after the unknown future.   Although the religious theories of the islands were a complete mystery to me, their practical every-day operation could not be concealed.   I frequently passed the little temples reposing in the shadows of the Taboo Groves and beheld the offerings—mouldy fruit spread out upon a rude altar, or hanging in half-decayed baskets around some uncouth jolly-looking image; I was present during the continuance of the festival; I daily beheld the grinning idols marshalled rank and file in the Hoolah-Hoolah ground, and was often in the habit of meeting those whom I supposed to be the priests.   But the temples seemed abandoned to solitude; the festival had been nothing more than a jovial mingling of the tribe; the idols were quite as harmless as any other logs of wood; and the priests were the merriest dogs in the valley.

In fact religious affairs in Typee were at a very low ebb; all such matters sat very lightly upon the thoughtless inhabitants; and, in the celebration of many of their strange rites, they appeared merely to seek a sort of childish amusement.

A curious evidence of this was given in a remarkable ceremony in which I frequently saw Mehevi and several other chiefs and warriors of note take part; but never a single female.

Among those whom I looked upon as forming the priesthood of the valley, there was one in particular who often attracted my notice, and whom I could not help regarding as the head of the order.   He was a noble-looking man, in the prime of his life, and of a most benignant aspect.   The authority this man, whose name was Kolory, seemed to exercise over the rest, the episcopal part he took in the Feast of Calabashes, his sleek and complacent appearance, the mystic characters which were tatooed upon his chest, and above all the mitre he frequently wore, in the shape of a towering head-dress, consisting of part of a coco-nut branch, the stalk planted uprightly on his brow, and the leaflets gathered together and passed round the temples and behind the ears, all these pointed him out as Lord Primate of Typee.   Kolory was a sort of Knight Templar—a soldier-priest; for he often worse the dress of a Marquesan warrior, and always carried a long spear, which, instead of terminating in a paddle at the lower end, after the general fashion of these weapons, was curved into a heathenish-looking little image.   This instrument, however, might perhaps have been emblematic of his double functions.   With one end in carnal combat he transfixed the enemies of his tribe; and with the other as a pastoral crook he kept in order his spiritual flock.   But this is not all I have to say about Kolory.   His martial grace very often carried about with him what seemed to me the half of a broken war-club.   It was swathed round with ragged bits of white tappa, and the upper part, which was intended to represent a human head, was embellished with a strip of scarlet cloth of European manufacture.   It required little observation to discover that this strange object was revered as a god.   By the side of the big and lusty images standing sentinel over the altars of the Hoolah-Hoolah ground, it seemed a mere pigmy in tatters.   But appearances all the world over are deceptive.   Little men are sometimes very potent, and rags sometimes cover very extensive pretensions.   In fact, this funny little image was the "crack" god of the island; lording it over all the wooden lubbers who looked so grim and dreadful; its name was Moa Artua.   And it was in honour of Moa Artua, and for the entertainment of those who believe in him, that the curious ceremony I am about to describe was observed.

Mehevi and the chieftains of the Ti have just risen from their noontide slumbers. There are no affairs of state to dispose of; and having eaten two or three breakfasts in the course of the morning, the magnates of the valley feel no appetite as yet for dinner. How are their leisure moments to be occupied? They smoke, they chat, and at last one of their number makes a proposition to the rest, who joyfully acquiescing, he darts out of the house, leaps from the pi-pi, and disappears in the grove. Soon you see him returning with Kolory, who bears the god Moa Artua in his arms, and carries in one hand a small trough, hollowed out in the likeness of a canoe. The priest comes along dandling his charge as if it were a lachrymose infant he was endeavouring to put into a good humour. Presently, entering the Ti, he seats himself on the mats as composedly as a juggler about to perform his sleight-of-hand tricks; and with the chiefs disposed in a circle around him, commences his ceremony.

In the first place he gives Moa Artua an affectionate hug, then caressingly lays him to his breast, and, finally, whispers something in his ear; the rest of the company listening eagerly for a reply. But the baby-god is deaf or dumb—perhaps both, for never a word does he utter. At last Kolory speaks a little louder, and soon growing angry, comes boldly out with what he has to say and bawls to him. He put me in mind of a choleric fellow, who, after trying in vain to communicate a secret to a deaf man, all at once flies into a passion and screams it out so that every one may hear. Still Moa Artua remains as quiet as ever; and Kolory, seemingly losing his temper, fetches him a box over the head, strips him of his tappa and red cloth, and laying him in a state of nudity in the little trough, covers him from sight. At this proceeding all present loudly applaud and signify their approval by uttering the adjective "mortarkee" with violent emphasis. Kolory, however, is so desirous his conduct should meet with unqualified approbation, that he inquires of each individual separately whether, under existing circumstances, he has not done perfectly right in shutting up Moa Artua. The invariable response is "Aa, Aa" (yes, yes), repeated over again and again in a manner which ought to quiet the scruples of the most conscientious. After a few moments Kolory brings forth his doll again, and while arraying it very carefully in the tappa and red cloth, alternately fondles and chides it. The toilet being completed, he once more speaks to it aloud. The whole company hereupon show the greatest interest; while the priest holding Moa Artua to his ear interprets to them what he pretends the god is confidentially communicating to him. Some items of intelligence appear to tickle all present amazingly; for one claps his hands in a rapture; another shouts with merriment; and a third leaps to his feet and capers about like a madman.

What under the sun Moa Artua on these occasions had to say to Kolory I never could find out; but I could not help thinking that the former showed a sad want of spirit in being disciplined into making those disclosures, which at first he seemed bent on withholding. Whether the priest honestly interpreted what he believed the divinity said to him or whether he was not all the while guilty of a vile humbug, I shall not presume to decide. At any rate whatever as coming from the god was imparted to those present seemed to be generally of a complimentary nature: a fact which illustrates the sagacity of Kolory, or else the time-serving disposition of this hardly used deity.

Moa Artua having nothing more to say, his bearer goes to nursing him again, in which occupation, however, he is soon interrupted by a question put by one of the warriors to the god. Kolory hereupon snatches it up to his

ear again, and after listening attentively, once more officiates as the organ
of communication. A multitude of questions and answers having passed between the parties, much to the satisfaction of those who propose them, the
god is put tenderly to bed in the trough, and the whole company unite in a
long chant, led off by Kolory. This ended, the ceremony is over; the chiefs
rise to their feet in high good humour, and my Lord Archbishop, after chatting awhile, and regaling himself with a whiff or two from a pipe of tobacco,
tucks the canoe under his arm and marches off with it.

The whole of these proceedings were like those of a parcel of children
playing with dolls and baby houses.

For a youngster scarcely ten inches high, and with so few early advantages
as he doubtless had had, Moa Artua was certainly a precocious little fellow
if he really said all that was imputed to him; but for what reason this poor
devil of a deity, thus cuffed about, cajoled and shut up in a box, was held in
greater estimation than the full-grown and dignified personages of the Taboo
Groves, I cannot divine. And yet Mehevi, and other chiefs of unquestionable
veracity—to say nothing of the Primate himself—assured me over and over
again that Moa Artua was the tutelary deity of Typee, and was more to be
held in honour than a whole battalion of the clumsy idols in the Hoolah-
Hoolah grounds. Kory-Kory—who seemed to have devoted considerable attention to the study of theology, as he knew the names of all the graven images
in the valley, and often repeated them over to me—likewise entertained some
rather enlarged ideas with regard to the character and pretensions of Moa
Artua. He once gave me to understand, with a gesture there was no miscon-
ceiving, that if he (Moa Artua) were so minded, he could cause a coco-nut
tree to sprout out of his (Kory-Kory's) head; and that it would be the easiest
thing in life for him (Moa Artua) to take the whole island of Nukuheva in
his mouth and dive down to the bottom of the sea with it.

But in sober seriousness, I hardly knew what to make of the religion of
the valley. There was nothing that so much perplexed the illustrious Cook, in
his intercourse with the South Sea islanders, as their sacred rites. Although
this prince of navigators was in many instances assisted by interpreters in the
prosecution of his researches, he still frankly acknowledges that he was at
a loss to obtain anything like a clear insight into the puzzling arcana of their
faith. A similar admission has been made by other eminent voyagers: by
Carteret, Byron, Kotzebue, and Vancouver.

For my own part, although hardly a day passed while I remained upon
the island that I did not witness some religious ceremony or other, it was very
much like seeing a parcel of "Freemasons" making secret signs to each other;
I saw everything, but could comprehend nothing.

On the whole, I am inclined to believe that the islanders in the Pacific have
no fixed and definite ideas whatever on the subject of religion. I am persuaded that Kolory himself would be effectually posed were he called upon
to draw up the articles of his faith and pronounce the creed by which he hoped
to be saved. In truth, the Typees, so far as their actions evince, submitted
to no laws, human or divine—always excepting the thrice mysterious Taboo.
The "independent electors" of the valley were not to be brow-beaten by chiefs,
priests, idols, or devils. As for the luckless idols, they received more hard knocks
than supplications. I do not wonder that some of them looked so grim, and
stood so bolt upright, as if fearful of looking to the right or the left lest they
should give any one offence. The fact is, they had to carry themselves *"pretty
straight,"* or suffer the consequences. Their worshippers were such a precious

set of fickle-minded and irreverent heathens, that there was no telling when they might topple one of them over, break it to pieces, and making a fire with it on the very altar itself, fall to roasting the offerings of breadfruit, and eat them in spite of its teeth.

In how little reverence these unfortunate deities were held by the natives was on one occasion most convincingly proved to me. Walking with Kory-Kory through the deepest recesses of the groves, I perceived a curious-looking image, about six feet in height, which originally had been placed upright against a low pi-pi, surmounted by a ruinous bamboo temple, but having become fatigued and weak in the knees, was now carelessly leaning against it. The idol was partly concealed by the foliage of a tree which stood near, and whose leafy boughs drooped over the pile of stones, as if to protect the rude fane from the decay to which it was rapidly hastening. The image itself was nothing more than a grotesquely shaped log, carved in the likeness of a portly, naked man with the arms clasped over the head, the jaws thrown wide apart, and its thick, shapeless legs bowed into an arch. It was much decayed. The lower part was overgrown with a bright silky moss. Thin spears of grass sprouted from the distended mouth and fringed the outline of the head and arms. His god-ship had literally attained a green old age. All its prominent points were bruised and battered, or entirely rotted away. The nose had taken its departure, and from the general appearance of the head it might have been supposed that the wooden divinity, in despair at the neglect of its worshippers, had been trying to beat its own brains out against the surrounding trees.

I drew near to inspect more closely this strange object of idolatry; but halted reverently at the distance of two or three paces, out of regard to the religious prejudices of my valet. As soon, however, as Kory-Kory perceived that I was in one of my inquiring, scientific moods, to my astonishment, he sprang to the side of the idol, and pushing it away from the stones against which it rested, endeavoured to make it stand upon its legs. But the divinity had lost the use of them altogether; and while Kory-Kory was trying to prop it up, by placing a stick between it and the pi-pi, the monster fell clumsily to the ground, and would infallibly have broken its neck had not Kory-Kory providentially broken its fall by receiving its whole weight on his own half-crushed back. I never saw the honest fellow in such a rage before. He leaped furiously to his feet, and seizing the stick, began beating the poor image: every moment or two pausing and talking to it in the most violent manner, as if upbraiding it for the accident. When his indignation had subsided a little he whirled the idol about most profanely, so as to give me an opportunity of examining it on all sides. I am quite sure I never should have presumed to have taken such liberties with the god myself, and I was not a little shocked at Kory-Kory's impiety.

This anecdote speaks for itself. When one of the inferior order of natives could show such contempt for a venerable and decrepit God of the Groves, what the state of religion must be among the people in general is easily to be imagined. In truth, I regard the Typees as a back-slidden generation. They are sunk in religious sloth, and require a spiritual revival. A long prosperity of breadfruit and coco-nuts has rendered them remiss in the performance of their higher obligations. The wood-rot malady is spreading among the idols—the fruit upon their altars is becoming offensive—the temples themselves need re-thatching—the tattooed clergy are altogether too light-hearted and lazy—and their flocks are going astray.

CHAPTER XXV

GENERAL INFORMATION GATHERED AT THE FESTIVAL—PERSONAL BEAUTY OF THE
TYPEES—THEIR SUPERIORITY OVER THE INHABITANTS OF THE OTHER
ISLANDS—DIVERSITY OF COMPLEXION—A VEGETABLE COSMETIC AND OINT-
MENT—TESTIMONY OF VOYAGERS TO THE UNCOMMON BEAUTY OF THE
MARQUESANS—FEW EVIDENCES OF INTERCOURSE WITH CIVILIZED BEINGS
—DILAPIDATED MUSKET—PRIMITIVE SIMPLICITY OF GOVERNMENT—REGAL
DIGNITY OF MEHEVI.

ALTHOUGH I had been unable during the late festival to obtain information on
many interesting subjects which had much excited my curiosity, still that important event had not passed by without adding materially to my general
knowledge of the islanders.

I was especially struck by the physical strength and beauty which they
displayed, by their great superiority in these respects over the inhabitants of
the neighbouring bay of Nukuheva, and by the singular contrasts they presented
among themselves in their various shades of complexion.

In beauty of form they surpassed anything I had ever seen. Not a single
instance of natural deformity was observable in all the throng attending the
revels. Occasionally I noticed among the men the scars of wounds they had
received in battle; and sometimes, though very seldom, the loss of a finger,
an eye, or an arm, attributable to the same cause. With these exceptions, every
individual appeared free from those blemishes which sometimes mar the effect
of an otherwise perfect form. But their physical excellence did not merely consist in an exemption from these evils; nearly every individual of their number
might have been taken for a sculptor's model.

When I remembered that these islanders derived no advantage from dress,
but appeared in all the naked simplicity of nature, I could not avoid comparing
them with the fine gentlemen and dandies who promenade such unexceptionable
figures in our frequented thoroughfares. Stripped of the cunning artifices of
the tailor, and standing forth in the garb of Eden—what a sorry set of round-
shouldered, spindle-shanked, crane-necked varlets would civilized men appear!
Stuffed calves, padded breasts, and scientifically cut pantaloons would then
avail them nothing, and the effect would be truly deplorable.

Nothing in the appearance of the islanders struck me more forcibly than the
whiteness of their teeth. The novelist always compares the masticators of his
heroine to ivory; but I boldly pronounce the teeth of the Typees to be far more
beautiful than ivory itself. The jaws of the oldest greybeards among them
were much better garnished than those of most of the youths of civilized countries; while the teeth of the young and middle-aged, in their purity and whiteness, were actually dazzling to the eye. This marvellous whiteness of the teeth
is to be ascribed to the pure vegetable diet of these people, and the uninterrupted healthfulness of their natural mode of life.

The men, in almost every instance, are of lofty stature, scarcely ever less
than six feet in height, while the other sex are uncommonly diminutive. The
early period of life at which the human form arrives at maturity in this generous
tropical climate, likewise deserves to be mentioned. A little creature, not more
than thirteen years of age, and who in other particulars might be regarded as
a mere child, is often seen nursing her own baby; whilst lads who, under less

ripening skies, would be still at school, are here responsible fathers of families.

On first entering the Typee Valley, I had been struck with the marked contrast presented by its inhabitants with those of the bay I had previously left. In the latter place, I had not been favourably impressed with the personal appearance of the male portion of the population; although with the females, excepting in some truly melancholy instances, I had been wonderfully pleased. I had observed that even the little intercourse Europeans had carried on with the Nukuheva natives had not failed to leave its traces amongst them. One of the most dreadful curses under which humanity labours had commenced its havocs, and betrayed, as it ever does among the South Sea islanders, the most aggravated symptoms. From this, as from all other foreign inflictions, the yet uncontaminated tenants of the Typee Valley were wholly exempt; and long may they continue so. Better will it be for them for ever to remain the happy and innocent heathens and barbarians that they now are, than, like the wretched inhabitants of the Sandwich Islands, to enjoy the mere name of Christians without experiencing any of the vital operations of true religion, whilst, at the same time, they are made the victims of the worst vices and evils of civilized life.

Apart, however, from these considerations, I am inclined to believe that there exists a radical difference between the two tribes, if indeed they are not distinct races of men. To those who have merely touched at Nukuheva Bay, without visiting other portions of the island, it would hardly appear credible the diversities presented between the various small clans inhabiting so diminutive a spot. But the hereditary hostility which has existed between them for ages fully accounts for this.

Not so easy, however, is it to assign an adequate cause for the endless variety of complexions to be seen in the Typee Valley. During the festival, I had noticed several young females whose skins were almost as white as any Saxon damsels; a slight dash of the mantling brown being all that marked the difference. This comparative fairness of complexion, though in a great degree perfectly natural, is partly the result of an artificial process, and of an entire exclusion from the sun. The juice of the "papa" root, found in great abundance at the head of the valley, is held in great esteem as a cosmetic, with which many of the females daily anoint their whole person. The habitual use of it whitens and beautifies the skin. Those of the young girls who resort to this method of heightening their charms, never expose themselves to the rays of the sun; an observance, however, that produces little or no inconvenience, since there are but few of the inhabited portions of the vale which are not shaded over with a spreading canopy of boughs, so that one may journey from house to house, scarcely deviating from the direct course, and yet never once see his shadow cast upon the ground.

The "papa," when used, is suffered to remain upon the skin for several hours; being of a light green colour, it consequently imparts for the time a similar hue to the complexion. Nothing, therefore, can be imagined more singular than the appearance of these nearly naked damsels immediately after the application of the cosmetic. To look at one of them you would almost suppose she was some vegetable in an unripe state; and that, instead of living in the shade for ever, she ought to be placed out in the sun to ripen.

All the islanders are more or less in the habit of anointing themselves; the women preferring the "aker" or "papa," and the men using the oil of the coconut. Mehevi was remarkably fond of mollifying his entire cuticle with this ointment. Sometimes he might be seen, with his whole body fairly reeking with the perfumed oil of the nut, looking as if he had just emerged from a soap-boiler's vat, or had undergone the process of dipping in a tallow-chandlery. To this cause perhaps, united to their frequent bathing and extreme cleanliness, is ascribable, in a great measure, the marvellous purity and smoothness of skin exhibited by the natives in general.

The prevailing tint among the women of the valley was a light olive, and of this style of complexion Fayaway afforded the most beautiful example. Others were still darker, while not a few were of a genuine golden colour, and some of a swarthy hue.

As agreeing with much previously mentioned in this narrative, I may here observe, that Mendanna, their discoverer, in his account of the Marquesas, described the natives as wondrously beautiful to behold, and as nearly resembling the people of southern Europe. The first of these islands seen by Mendanna was La Madelena, which is not far distant from Nukuheva; and its inhabitants in every respect resemble those dwelling on that and the other islands of the group. Figueroa, the chronicler of Mendanna's voyage, says, that on the morning the land was descried, when the Spaniards drew near the shore, there sallied forth, in rude procession, about seventy canoes, and at the same time many of the inhabitants (females, I presume) made towards the ship by swimming. He adds, that "in complexion they were nearly white; of good stature, and finely formed; and on their faces and bodies were delineated representations of fishes and other devices." The old Don then goes on to say, "There came, among others, two lads paddling their canoe, whose eyes were fixed on the ship; they had beautiful faces and the most promising animation of countenance; and were in all things so becoming, that the pilot-mayor Quiros affirmed, nothing in his life ever caused him so much regret as the leaving such fine creatures to be lost in that country." More than two hundred years have gone by since the passage of which the above is a translation was written; and it appears to me now, as I read it, as fresh and true as if written but yesterday. The islanders are still the same; and I have seen boys in the Typee Valley of whose "beautiful faces" and "promising animation of countenance" no one who has not beheld them can form any adequate idea. Cook, in the account of his voyages, pronounces the Marquesans as by far the most splendid islanders in the South Seas. Stewart, the chaplain of the U.S. ship *Vincennes*, in his *Scenes in the South Seas*, expresses, in more than one place, his amazement at the surpassing loveliness of the women; and says that many of the Nukuheva damsels reminded him forcibly of the most celebrated beauties in his own land. Fanning, a Yankee mariner of some reputation, likewise records his lively impressions of the physical appearance of these people; and Commodore David Porter of the U.S. frigate *Essex*, is said to have been vastly smitten by the beauty of the ladies. Their great superiority over all other Polynesians cannot fail to attract the notice of those who visit the principal groups in the Pacific. The voluptuous Tahitians are the only people who at all deserve to be compared with them; while the dark-hued Hawaiians and the woolly-headed Feegees are immeasurably inferior to them. The distinguishing characteristic of the Marquesan islanders, and that which at once strikes you, is the European cast of their features—a peculiarity seldom observable among other uncivilized people. Many of their faces present a profile classically beautiful, and in the valley of Typee, I saw several who, like the stranger Marnoo, were in every respect models of beauty.

Some of the natives present at the Feast of Calabashes had displayed a few articles of European dress; disposed, however, about their persons after their own peculiar fashion. Among these I perceived the two pieces of cotton-cloth which poor Toby and myself had bestowed upon our youthful guides the afternoon we entered the valley. They were evidently reserved for gala days; and during those of the festival they rendered the young islanders who wore them very distinguished characters. The small number who were similarly adorned, and the great value they appeared to place upon the most common and most trivial articles, furnished ample evidence of the very restricted intercourse they held with vessels touching at the island. A few cotton handkerchiefs, of a gay pattern, tied about the neck, and suffered to fall over the shoulders; strips of fanciful calico, swathed about the loins, were nearly all I saw.

Indeed, throughout the valley, there were few things of any kind to be seen of European origin. All I ever saw beside the articles just alluded to, were the six muskets preserved in the Ti, and three or four similar implements of warfare hung up in other houses; some small canvas bags, partly filled with bullets and powder, and half a dozen old hatchet-heads, with the edges blunted and battered to such a degree as to render them utterly useless. These last seemed to be regarded as nearly worthless by the natives; and several times they held up one of them before me, and throwing it aside with a gesture of disgust, manifested their contempt for anything that could so soon become unserviceable.

But the muskets, the powder, and the bullets were held in most extravagant esteem. The former, from their great age and the peculiarities they exhibited, were well worthy a place in any antiquarian's armory. I remember in particular one that hung in the Ti, and which Mehevi—supposing as a matter of course that I was able to repair it—had put into my hands for that purpose. It was one of those clumsy, old-fashioned, English pieces known generally as Tower Hill muskets, and, for aught I know, might have been left on the island by Wallace, Carteret, Cook, or Vancouver. The stock was half-rotten and worm-eaten; the lock was as rusty and about as well adapted to its ostensible purpose as an old door-hinge; the threading of the screws about the trigger was completely worn away; while the barrel shook in the wood. Such was the weapon the chief desired me to restore to its original condition. As I did not possess the accomplishments of a gunsmith, and was likewise destitute of the necessary tools, I was reluctantly obliged to signify my inability to perform the task. At this unexpected communication Mehevi regarded me, for a moment, as if he half suspected I was some inferior sort of white man, who after all did not know much more than a Typee. However, after a most laboured explanation of the matter, I succeeded in making him understand the extreme difficulty of the task. Scarcely satisfied with my apologies, however, he marched off with the superannuated musket in something of a huff as if he would no longer expose it to the indignity of being manipulated by such unskilful fingers.

During the festival I had not failed to remark the simplicity of manner, the freedom from all restraint, and, to a certain degree, the quality of condition manifested by the natives in general. No one appeared to assume any arrogant pretensions. There was little more than a slight difference in costume to distinguish the chiefs from the other natives. All appeared to mix together freely, and without any reserve; although I noticed that the wishes of a chief, even when delivered in the mildest tone, received the same immediate obedience which elsewhere would have been only accorded to a peremptory command. What may be the extent of the authority of the chiefs over the rest of the tribe, I will not venture to assert; but from all I saw during my stay in the valley, I was induced to believe that in matters concerning the general welfare it was very limited. The required degree of deference towards them, however, was willingly and cheerfully yielded; and as all authority is transmitted from father to son, I have no doubt that one of the effects here, as elsewhere, of high birth, is to induce respect and obedience.

The civil institutions of the Marquesas Islands appear to be in this, as in other respects, directly the reverse of those of the Tahitian and Hawaiian groups, where the original power of the king and chiefs was far more despotic than that of any tyrant in civilized countries. At Tahiti it used to be death for one of the inferior orders to approach, without permission, under the shadow of the king's house; or to fail in paying the customary reverence when food destined for the king was borne past them by his messengers. At the Sandwich Islands, Kaahumanu, the gigantic old dowager queen—a woman of nearly four hundred pounds weight, and who is said to be still living at Mowee—was accustomed, in some of her terrific gusts of temper, to snatch up an ordinary-sized man who had offended her, and snap his spine across her knee. Incredible as this may seem, it is a fact. While at Lahainaluna—the residence of this monstrous Jezebel—a humpbacked wretch was pointed out to me, who, some twenty-five years previously, had had the vertebræ of his backbone very seriously discomposed by his gentle mistress.

The particular grades of rank existing among the chiefs of Typee, I could not in all cases determine. Previous to the Feast of Calabashes I had been puzzled what particular station to assign to Mehevi. But the important part he took upon that occasion convinced me that he had no superior among the inhabitants of the valley. I had invariably noticed a certain degree of deference paid to him by all with whom I had ever seen him brought in contact; but when I remembered that my wanderings had been confined to a limited portion of the valley, and that towards the sea a number of distinguished chiefs resided, some of whom had separately visited me at Marheyo's house, and whom, until the festival, I had never seen in the company of Mehevi, I felt disposed to believe that his rank after all might not be particularly elevated.

The revels, however, had brought together all the warriors whom I had seen individually and in groups at different times and places. Among them Mehevi moved with an easy air of superiority which was not to be mistaken; and he whom I had only looked at as the hospitable host of the Ti, and one of the military leaders of the tribe, now assumed in my eyes the dignity of royal station. His striking costume, no less than his naturally commanding figure, seemed indeed to give him pre-eminence over the rest. The towering helmet of feathers that he wore raised him in height above all who surrounded him; and though some others were similarly adorned, the length and luxuriance of their plumes were far inferior to his.

Mehevi was in fact the greatest of the chiefs—the head of his clan—the sovereign of the valley; and the simplicity of the social institutions of the people could not have been more completely proved than by the fact, that after having been several weeks in the valley, and almost in daily intercourse with Mehevi, I should have remained until the time of the festival ignorant of his regal character. But a new light had now broken in upon me. The Ti was the palace—and Mehevi the king. Both the one and the other of a most simple and patriarchal nature it must be allowed, and wholly unattended by the ceremonious pomp which usually surrounds the purple.

After having made this discovery I could not avoid congratulating myself that Mehevi had from the first taken me as it were under his royal protection, and that he still continued to entertain for me the warmest regard, as far at least as I was enabled to judge from appearances. For the future I determined to pay most assiduous court to him, hoping that eventually through his kindness I might obtain my liberty.

CHAPTER XXVI

KING MEHEVI—ALLUSION TO HIS HAWAIIAN MAJESTY—CONDUCT OF MARHEYO AND MEHEVI IN CERTAIN DELICATE MATTERS—PECULIAR SYSTEM OF MAR-RIAGE—NUMBER OF POPULATION—UNIFORMITY—EMBALMING—PLACES OF SEPULTURE—FUNERAL OBSEQUIES AT NUKUHEVA—NUMBER OF INHABITANTS IN TYPEE—LOCATION OF THE DWELLINGS—HAPPINESS ENJOYED IN THE VALLEY—A WARNING—SOME IDEAS WITH REGARD TO THE CIVILIZATION OF THE ISLANDS—REFERENCE TO THE PRESENT STATE OF THE HAWAIIANS—STORY OF A MISSIONARY'S WIFE—FASHIONABLE EQUIPAGES AT OAHU—REFLECTIONS.

KING MEHEVI!—A goodly sounding title!—and why should I not bestow it upon the foremost man in the valley of Typee? The republican missionaries of Oahu cause to be gazetted in the Court Journal, published at Honolulu, the most trivial movements of "his gracious majesty" King Kammehammaha III, and "their highnesses the princes of the blood royal."—And who is his "gracious majesty," and what the quality of this "blood-royal?"—His "gracious majesty" is a fat, lazy, negro-looking blockhead, with as little character as power. He has lost the noble traits of the barbarian, without acquiring the redeeming graces of a civilized being; and, although a member of the Hawaiian Temperance Society, is a most inveterate dram-drinker.

The "blood royal" is an extremely thick, depraved fluid; formed princi-pally of raw fish, bad brandy, and European sweetmeats, and is charged with a variety of eruptive humours, which are developed in sundry blotches and pimples upon the august face of "majesty itself," and the angelic countenances of the "princes and princesses of the blood-royal"!

Now, if the farcical puppet of a chief magistrate in the Sandwich Islands be allowed the title of King, why should it be withheld from the noble savage Mehevi, who is a thousand times more worthy of the appellation? All hail, therefore, Mehevi, King of the Cannibal Valley, and long life and prosperity to his Typeean majesty! May Heaven for many a year preserve him, the un-compromising foe of Nukuheva and the French, if a hostile attitude will secure his lovely domain from the remorseless inflictions of South Sea civilization.

Previously to seeing the Dancing Widows I had little idea that there were any matrimonial relations subsisting in Typee, and I should as soon have thought of a Platonic affection being cultivated between the sexes, as of the solemn connexion of man and wife. To be sure, there were old Marheyo and Tinor, who seemed to have a sort of nuptial understanding with one another; but for all that, I had sometimes observed a comical-looking old gentleman dressed in a suit of shabby tattooing, who had the audacity to take various liberties with the lady, and that too in the very presence of the old warrior her husband, who looked on, as good-naturedly as if nothing was happening. This behaviour, until subsequent discoveries enlightened me, puzzled me more than anything else I witnessed in Typee.

As for Mehevi, I had supposed him a confirmed bachelor, as well as most of the principal chiefs. At any rate, if they had wives and families, they ought

to have been ashamed of themselves; for sure I am, they never troubled themselves about any domestic affairs. In truth, Mehevi seemed to be the president
of a club of hearty fellows, who kept "Bachelors' Hall" in fine style at the Ti.
I had no doubt but that they regarded children as odious encumbrances; and
their ideas of domestic felicity were sufficiently shown in the fact, that they
allowed no meddlesome housekeepers to turn topsy-turvy those snug little arrangements they had made in their comfortable dwelling. I strongly suspected,
however, that some of these jolly bachelors were carrying on love intrigues
with the maidens of the tribe; although they did not appear publicly to acknowledge them. I happened to pop upon Mehevi three or four times when
he was romping—in a most undignified manner for a warrior king—with one of
the prettiest little witches in the valley. She lived with an old woman and a
young man in a house near Marheyo's; and although in appearance a mere
child herself, had a noble boy about a year old, who bore a marvellous resemblance to Mehevi, whom I should certainly have believed to have been
the father, were it not that the little fellow had no triangle on his face—but
on second thoughts, tattooing is not hereditary. Mehevi, however, was not
the only person upon whom the damsel Moonoony smiled—the young fellow
of fifteen, who permanently resided in the house with her, was decidedly in
her good graces. I sometimes beheld both him and the chief making love at
the same time. Is it possible, thought I, that the valiant warrior can consent
to give up a corner in the thing he loves? This too was a mystery which, with
others of the same kind, was afterwards satisfactorily explained.

During the second day of the Feast of Calabashes, Kory-Kory—being determined that I should have some understanding on these matters—had, in the
course of his explanations, directed my attention to a peculiarity I had frequently remarked among many of the females;—principally those of a mature
age and rather matronly appearance. This consisted in having the right hand
and the left foot most elaborately tattooed; while the rest of the body was
wholly free from the operation of the art, with the exception of the minutely
dotted lips and slight marks on the shoulders, to which I have previously referred as comprising the sole tattooing exhibited by Fayaway, in common
with other young girls of her age. The hand and foot thus embellished were, according to Kory-Kory, the distinguishing badge of wedlock, so far as
that social and highly commendable institution is known among these people.
It answers, indeed, the same purpose as the plain gold ring worn by our fairer
spouses.

After Kory-Kory's explanation of the subject, I was for some time studiously
respectful in the presence of all females thus distinguished, and never ventured
to indulge in the slightest approach to flirtation with any of their number.
Married women, to be sure!—I knew better than to offend them.

A further insight however into the peculiar domestic customs of the inmates
of the valley did away in a measure with the severity of my scruples, and
convinced me that I was deceived in some at least of my conclusions. A regular
system of polygamy exists among the islanders; but of a most extraordinary
nature—a plurality of husbands, instead of wives; and this solitary fact speaks
volumes for the gentle disposition of the male population. Where else, indeed,
could such a practice exist, even for a single day?—Imagine a revolution
brought about in a Turkish seraglio, and the harem rendered the abode of
bearded men; or conceive some beautiful woman in our own country running
distracted at the sight of her numerous lovers murdering one another before
her eyes, out of jealousy for the unequal distribution of her favours!—Heaven

defend us from such a state of things!—We are scarcely amiable and forbearing enough to submit to it.

I was not able to learn what particular ceremony was observed in forming the marriage contract, but am inclined to think that it must have been of a very simple nature. Perhaps the mere "popping the question," as it is termed with us, might have been followed by an immediate nuptial alliance. At any rate, I have more than one reason to believe that tedious courtships are unknown in the valley of Typee.

The males considerably outnumber the females. This holds true of many of the islands of Polynesia, although the reverse of what is the case in most civilized countries. The girls are first wooed and won, at a very tender age, by some stripling in the household in which they reside. This, however, is a mere frolic of the affections, and no formal engagement is contracted. By the time this first love has a little subsided a second suitor presents himself, of graver years, and carries both boy and girl away to his own habitation. This disinterested and generous-hearted fellow now weds the young couple—marrying damsel and lover at the same time—and all three thenceforth live together as harmoniously as so many turtles. I have heard of some men who in civilized countries rashly marry large families with their wives, but had no idea that there was any place where people married supplementary husbands with them. Infidelity on either side is very rare. No man has more than one wife, and no wife of mature years has less than two husbands—sometimes she has three, but such instances are not frequent. The marriage tie, whatever it may be, does not appear to be indissoluble; for separations occasionally happen. These, however, when they do take place, produce no unhappiness, and are preceded by no bickerings; for the simple reason, that an ill-used wife or a henpecked husband is not obliged to file a bill in Chancery to obtain a divorce. As nothing stands in the way of a separation, the matrimonial yoke sits easily and lightly, and a Typee wife lives on very pleasant and sociable terms with her husbands. On the whole, wedlock, as known among these Typees, seems to be of a more distinct and enduring nature than is usually the case with barbarous people. A baneful promiscuous intercourse of the sexes is hereby avoided, and virtue, without being clamorously invoked, is, as it were, unconsciously practised.

The contrast exhibited between the Marquesas and other islanders of the Pacific in this respect, is worthy of being noticed. At Tahiti the marriage tie was altogether unknown; and the relation of husband and wife, father and son, could hardly be said to exist. The Arreory Society—one of the most singular institutions that ever existed in any part of the world—spread universal licentiousness over the island. It was the voluptuous character of these people which rendered the disease introduced among them by De Bougainville's ships, in 1768, doubly destructive. It visited them like a plague, sweeping them off by hundreds.

Notwithstanding the existence of wedlock among the Typees, the Scriptural injunction to increase and multiply seems to be but indifferently attended to. I never saw any of those large families in arithmetical or step-ladder progression which one often meets with at home. I never knew of more than two youngsters living together in the same home, and but seldom even that number. As for the women it was very plain that the anxieties of the nursery but seldom disturbed the serenity of their souls; and they were never to be seen going about the valley with half a score of little ones tagging at their apron-strings, or rather at the breadfruit-leaf they usually wore in the rear.

The ratio of increase among all the Polynesian nations is very small; and in some places as yet uncorrupted by intercourse with Europeans, the births would appear but very little to outnumber the deaths; the population in such instances remaining nearly the same for several successive generations, even upon those islands seldom or never desolated by wars, and among people with whom the crime of infanticide is altogether unknown. This would seem expressly ordained by Providence to prevent the overstocking of the islands with a race too indolent to cultivate the ground, and who, for that reason alone, would, by any considerable increase in their numbers, be exposed to the most deplorable misery. During the entire period of my stay in the valley of Typee, I never saw more than ten or twelve children under the age of six months, and only became aware of two births.

It is to the absence of the marriage tie that the late rapid decrease of the population of the Sandwich Islands and of Tahiti is in part to be ascribed. The vices and diseases introduced among these unhappy people annually swell the ordinary mortality of the islands, while, from the same cause, the originally small number of births is proportionally decreased. Thus the progress of the Hawaiians and Tahitians to utter extinction is accelerated in a sort of compound ratio.

I have before had occasion to remark that I never saw any of the ordinary signs of a place of sepulture in the village, a circumstance which I attributed, at the time, to my living in a particular part of it, and being forbidden to extend my rambles to any considerable distance towards the sea. I have since thought it probable, however, that the Typees, either desirous of removing from their sight the evidences of mortality, or prompted by a taste for rural beauty, may have some charming cemetery situated in the shadowy recesses along the base of the mountains. At Nukuheva, two or three large quadrangular "pi-pis," heavily flagged, enclosed with regular stone walls and shaded over and almost hidden from view by the interlacing branches of enormous trees, were pointed out to me as burial-places. The bodies, I understood, were deposited in rude vaults beneath the flagging, and were suffered to remain there without being disinterred. Although nothing could be more strange and gloomy than the aspect of these places where the lofty trees threw their dark shadows over rude blocks of stone, a stranger in looking at them would have discerned none of the ordinary evidences of a place of sepulture.

During my stay in the valley, as none of its inmates were so accommodating as to die and be buried in order to gratify my curiosity with regard to their funeral rites, I was reluctantly obliged to remain in ignorance of them. As I have reason to believe, however, that the observances of the Typees in these matters are the same with those of all the other tribes on the island, I will here relate a scene I chanced to witness at Nukuheva.

A young man had died, about daybreak, in a house near the beach. I had been sent ashore that morning, and saw a good deal of the preparations they were making for his obsequies. The body, neatly wrapped in new white tappa, was laid out in an open shed of coco-nut boughs, upon a bier constructed of elastic bamboos ingeniously twisted together. This was supported, about two feet from the ground, by large canes planted upright in the earth. Two females, of a dejected appearance, watched by its side, plaintively chanting and beating the air with large grass fans whitened with pipeclay. In the dwelling-house adjoining a numerous company were assembled, and various articles of food were being prepared for consumption. Two or three individuals, distinguished by head-dresses of beautiful tappa, and wearing a great number of ornaments, appeared to officiate as masters of the ceremonies. By noon the entertainment had fairly begun, and we were told that it would last during the whole of the two following days. With the exception of those who mourned by the corpse, every one seemed disposed to drown the sense of the late bereavement in convivial indulgence. The girls, decked out in their savage finery, danced; the old men chanted; the warriors smoked and chatted; and the young and lusty, of both sexes, feasted plentifully, and seemed to enjoy themselves as pleasantly as they could have done had it been a wedding.

The islanders understand the art of embalming, and practise it with such success, that the bodies of their great chiefs are frequently preserved for many years in the very houses where they died. I saw three of these in my visit to the Bay of Tior. One was enveloped in immense folds of tappa, with only the face exposed, and hung erect against the side of the dwelling. The others were stretched out upon biers of bamboo, in open, elevated temples, which seemed consecrated to their memory. The heads of enemies killed in battle are invariably preserved and hung up as trophies in the house of the conqueror. I am not acquainted with the process which is in use, but believe that fumigation is the principal agency employed. All the remains which I saw presented the appearance of a ham after being suspended for some time in a smoky chimney.

But to return from the dead to the living. The late festival had drawn together, as I had every reason to believe, the whole population of the vale, and consequently I was enabled to make some estimate with regard to its numbers. I should imagine that there were about two thousand inhabitants in Typee; and no number could have been better adapted to the extent of the valley. The valley is some nine miles in length, and may average one in breadth; the houses being distributed at wide intervals throughout its whole extent, principally, however, towards the head of the vale. There are no villages: the houses stand here and there in the shadow of the groves, or are scattered along the banks of the winding stream; their golden-hued bamboo sides and gleaming white thatch forming a beautiful contrast to the perpetual verdure in which they are embowered. There are no roads of any kind in the valley—nothing but a labyrinth of footpaths twisting and turning among the thickets without end.

The penalty of the Fall presses very lightly upon the valley of Typee; for, with the one solitary exception of striking a light, I scarcely saw any piece of work performed there which caused the sweat to stand upon a single brow. As for digging and delving for a livelihood, the thing is altogether unknown. Nature had planted the breadfruit and the banana, and in her own good time she brings them to maturity, when the idle savage stretches forth his hand, and satisfies his appetite.

Ill-fated people! I shudder when I think of the change a few years will produce in their paradisaical abode; and probably when the most destructive vices, and the worst attendances on civilization, shall have driven all peace and happiness from the valley, the magnanimous French will proclaim to the world that the Marquesas Islands have been converted to Christianity! and this the Catholic world will doubtless consider as a glorious event. Heaven help the "Isles of the Sea"!—The sympathy which Christendom feels for them has, alas! in too many instances proved their bane.

How little do some of these poor islanders comprehend when they look around them, that no inconsiderable part of their disasters originate in certain tea-party excitements, under the influence of which benevolent-looking gentlemen in white cravats solicit alms, and old ladies in spectacles, and young ladies in sober russet low gowns, contribute sixpences towards the creation of a fund, the object of which is to ameliorate the spiritual condition of the Polynesians, but whose end has almost invariably been to accomplish their temporal destruction!

Let the savages be civilized, but civilize them with benefits, and not with evils; and let heathenism be destroyed, but not by destroying the heathen. The Anglo-Saxon hive have extirpated Paganism from the greater part of the North American continent; but with it they have likewise extirpated the greater portion of the Red race. Civilization is gradually sweeping from the earth the lingering vestiges of Paganism, and at the same time the shrinking forms of its unhappy worshippers.

Among the islands of Polynesia, no sooner are the images overturned, the temples demolished, and the idolaters converted into *nominal* Christians, than disease, vice, and premature death make their appearance. The depopulated land is then recruited from the rapacious hordes of enlightened individuals who settle themselves within its borders, and clamorously announce the progress of the Truth. Neat villas, trim gardens, shaven lawns, spires, and cupolas arise, while the poor savage soon finds himself an interloper in the country of his fathers, and that too on the very site of the hut where he was born. The spontaneous fruits of the earth, which God in his wisdom had ordained for the support of the indolent natives, remorselessly seized upon and appropriated by the stranger, are devoured before the eyes of the starving inhabitants, or sent on board the numerous vessels which now touch at their shores.

When the famished wretches are cut off in this manner from their natural supplies, they are told by their benefactors to work and earn their support by the sweat of their brows! But to no fine gentleman born to hereditary opulence does manual labour come more unkindly than to the luxurious Indian when thus robbed of the bounty of Heaven. Habituated to a life of indolence, he cannot and will not exert himself; and want, disease, and vice, all evils of foreign growth, soon terminate his miserable existence.

But what matters all this? Behold the glorious result!—The abominations of Paganism have given way to the pure rites of the Christian worship, the ignorant savage has been supplanted by the refined European! Look at Honolulu, the metropolis of the Sandwich Islands!—A community of disinterested merchants, and devoted self-exiled heralds of the Cross, located on the very spot that twenty years ago was defiled by the presence of idolatry. What a subject for an eloquent Bible-meeting orator! Nor has such an opportunity for a display of missionary rhetoric been allowed to pass by unimproved!—But when these philanthropists send us such glowing accounts of one half of their labours, why does their modesty restrain them from publishing the other half of the good they have wrought?—Not until I visited Honolulu was I aware of the fact that the small remnant of the natives had been civilized into draught horses, and evangelized into beasts of burden. But so it is. They have been literally broken into the traces, and are harnessed to the vehicles of their spiritual instructors like so many dumb brutes!

Among a multitude of similar exhibitions that I saw, I shall never forget a robust, red-faced, and very lady-like personage, a missionary's spouse, who day after day for months together took her regular airings in a little go-cart drawn by two of the islanders, one an old grey-headed man, and the other a roguish stripling, both being, with the exception of the fig-leaf, as naked as when they were born. Over a level piece of ground this pair of *draught* bipeds would go with a shambling, unsightly trot, the youngster hanging back all the time like a knowing horse, while the old hack plodded on and did all the work.

Rattling along through the streets of the town in this stylish equipage, the lady looks about her as magnificently as any queen driven in state to her coronation. A sudden elevation, and a sandy road however, soon disturb her serenity. The small wheels become imbedded in the loose soil,— the old stager stands tugging and sweating, while the young one frisks about and does nothing; not an inch does the chariot budge. Will the tender-hearted lady, who has left friends and home for the good of the souls of the poor heathen, will she think a little about their bodies and get out, and ease the wretched old man until the ascent is mounted? Not she; she could not dream of it. To be sure, she used to think nothing of driving the cows to pasture on the old farm in New England; but times have changed since then. So she retains her seat and bawls out, "Hookee! hookee!" (Pull, pull.) The old gentleman, frightened at the sound, labours away harder than ever; and the younger one makes a great show of straining himself, but takes care to keep one eye on his mistress, in order to know when to dodge out of harm's way. At last the good lady loses all patience; "Hookee! hookee!" and rap goes the heavy handle of her huge fan over the naked skull of the old savage; while the young one shies to one side and keeps beyond its range. "Hookee! hookee!" again she cries—"Hookee tata kannaka!" (Pull strong, men,)—but all in vain, and she is obliged in the end to dismount and, sad necessity! actually to walk to the top of the hill.

At the town where this paragon of humility resides, is a spacious and elegant American chapel, where divine service is regularly performed. Twice every Sabbath towards the close of the exercises may be seen a score or two of little wagons ranged along the railing in front of the edifice, with two squalid native footmen in the livery of nakedness standing by each, and waiting for the dismission of the congregation to draw their superiors home.

Lest the slightest misconception should arise from anything thrown out in this chapter, or indeed in any other part of the volume, let me here observe, that against the cause of missions in the abstract no Christian can possibly be opposed: it is in truth a just and holy cause. But if the great end proposed by it be spiritual, the agency employed to accomplish that end is purely earthly; and, although the object in view be the achievement of much good, that agency may nevertheless be productive of evil. In short, missionary undertaking, however it may be blessed of Heaven, is in itself but human; and subject, like everything else, to errors and abuses. And have not errors and abuses crept into the most sacred places, and may there not be unworthy or incapable missionaries abroad, as well as ecclesiastics of a similar character at home? May not the unworthiness or incapacity of those who assume apostolic functions upon the remote islands of the sea more easily escape detection by the world at large than if it were displayed in the heart of a city? An unwarranted confidence in the sanctity of its apostles—a proneness to regard them as incapable of guile—and an impatience of the least suspicion as to their rectitude as men or Christians, have ever been prevailing faults in the Church. Nor is this to be wondered at: for subject as Christianity is to the assaults of unprincipled foes, we are naturally disposed to regard everything like an exposure of ecclesiastical misconduct as the offspring of malevolence or irreligious feeling. Not even this last consideration, however, shall deter me from the honest expression of my sentiments.

There is something decidedly wrong in the practical operations of the Sandwich Island Missions. Those who from pure religious motives contribute to the support of this enterprise, should take care to ascertain that their donations, flowing through many devious channels, at last effect their legitimate object, the conversion of the Hawaiians. I urge this not because I doubt the moral probity of those who disburse these funds, but because I know that they are not rightly applied. To read pathetic accounts of missionary hardships, and glowing descriptions of conversions, and baptisms taking place beneath palm-trees, is one thing; and to go to the Sandwich Islands and see the missionaries dwelling in picturesque and prettily furnished coral-rock villas, whilst the miserable natives are committing all sorts of immoralities around them, is quite another.

In justice to the missionaries, however, I will willingly admit, that whatever evils may have resulted from their collective mismanagement of the business of the mission, and from the want of vital piety evinced by some of their number, still the present deplorable condition of the Sandwich Islands is by no means wholly chargeable against them. The demoralizing influence of a dissolute foreign population, and the frequent visits of all descriptions of vessels, have tended not a little to increase the evils alluded to. In a word, here, as in every case where Civilization has in any way been introduced among those whom we call savages, she has scattered her vices, and withheld her blessings.

As wise a man as Shakespeare has said, that the bearer of evil tidings hath but a losing office; and so I suppose will it prove with me, in communicating to the trusting friends of the Hawaiian Mission what has been disclosed in various portions of this narrative. I am persuaded, however, that as these disclosures will by their very nature attract attention, so they will lead to something which will not be without ultimate benefit to the cause of Christianity in the Sandwich Islands.

I have but one thing more to add in connexion with this subject—those things which I have stated as facts will remain facts, in spite of whatever the bigoted or incredulous may say or write against them. My reflections, however, on those facts may not be free from error. If such be the case, I claim no further indulgence than should be conceded to every man whose object is to do good.

CHAPTER XXVII

THE SOCIAL CONDITION AND GENERAL CHARACTER OF THE TYPEES.

I HAVE already mentioned that the influence exerted over the people of the valley by their chiefs was mild in the extreme: and as to any general rule or standard of conduct by which the commonalty were governed in their intercourse with each other, so far as my observation extended, I should be almost tempted to say that none existed on the island, except, indeed, the mysterious "Taboo" be considered as such. During the time I lived among the Typees, no one was ever put upon his trial for any offence against the public. To all appearances there were no courts of law or equity. There was no municipal police for the purpose of apprehending vagrants and disorderly characters. In short, there were no legal provisions whatever for the well-being and conservation of society, the enlightened end of civilized legislation. And yet everything went on in the valley with a harmony and smoothness unparalleled, I will venture to assert, in the most select, refined, and pious associations of mortals in Christendom. How are we to ·explain this enigma? These islanders were heathens! savages! ay, cannibals! and how came they, without the aid of established law, to exhibit, in so eminent a degree, that social order which is the greatest blessing and highest pride of the social state?

It may reasonably be inquired, how were these people governed? How were their passions controlled in their everyday transactions? It must have been by an inherent principle of honesty and charity towards each other. They seemed to be governed by that sort of tacit common-sense law which, say what they will of the inborn lawlessness of the human race, has its precepts graven on every breast. The grand principles of virtue and honour, however they may be distorted by arbitrary codes, are the same all the world over: and where these principles are concerned, the right or wrong of any action appears the same to the uncultivated as to the enlightened mind. It is to this indwelling, this universally diffused perception of what is *just* and *noble,* that the integrity of the Marquesans in their intercourse with each other is to be attributed. In the darkest nights they slept securely, with all their worldly wealth around them, in houses the doors of which were never fastened. The disquieting ideas of theft or assassination never disturbed them. Each islander reposed beneath his own palmetto thatching, or sat under his own breadfruit-tree, with none to molest or alarm him. There was not a padlock in the valley, nor anything that answered the purpose of one: still there was no community of goods. This long spear, so elegantly carved and highly polished, belongs to Wormoonoo: it is far handsomer than the one which old Marheyo so greatly prizes; it is the most valuable article belonging to its owner. And yet I have seen it leaning against a coco-nut tree in the grove, and there it was found when sought for. Here is a sperm-whale tooth, graven all over with cunning devices: it is the property of Karluna: it is the most precious of the damsel's ornaments. In her estimation its price is far above rubies—and yet there hangs the dental jewel by its cord of braided bark, in the girl's house, which is far back in the valley; the door is left open, and all the inmates have gone off to bathe in the stream.

So much for the respect in which "personal property" is held in Typee; how secure an investment of "real property" may be, I cannot take upon me to say. Whether the land of the valley was the joint property of its inhabitants, or whether it was parcelled out among a certain number of landed proprietors who allowed everybody to "squat" and "poach" as much as he or she pleased, I never could ascertain. At any rate, musty parchments and title-deeds there were none on the island; and I am half inclined to believe that its inhabitants hold their broad valleys in fee simple from Nature herself; to have and to hold, so long as grass grows and water runs; or until their French visitors, by a summary mode of conveyancing, shall appropriate them to their own benefit and behoof.

Yesterday I saw Kory-Kory hie him away, armed with a long pole, with which, standing on the ground, he knocked down the fruit from the topmost boughs of the trees, and brought them home in his basket of coco-nut leaves. To-day I see an islander, whom I know to reside in a distant part of the valley, doing the self-same thing. On the sloping bank of the stream are a number of banana-trees. I have often seen a score or two of young people making a merry foray on the great golden clusters, and bearing them off, one after another, to different parts of the vale, shouting and tramping as they went. No churlish old curmudgeon could have been the owner of that grove of breadfruit trees, or of these gloriously yellow bunches of bananas.

From what I have said it will be perceived that there is a vast difference between "personal property" and "real estate" in the valley of Typee. Some individuals, of course, are more wealthy than others. For example: the ridge-pole of Marheyo's house bends under the weight of many a huge package of tappa; his long couch is laid with mats placed one upon the other seven deep. Outside, Tinor has ranged along in her bamboo cupboard—or whatever the place may be called—a goodly array of calabashes and wooden trenchers. Now, the house just beyond the grove, and next to Marheyo's, occupied by Ruaruga, is not quite so well furnished. There are only three moderate-sized packages swinging overhead: there are only two layers of mats beneath, and the calabashes and trenchers are not so numerous, nor so tastefully stained and carved. But then, Ruaruga has a house—not so pretty a one, to be sure—but just as com-modious as Marheyo's; and, I suppose, if he wished to vie with his neighbour's establishment, he could do so with very little trouble. These, in short, con-stituted the chief differences perceivable in the relative wealth of the people in Typee.

Civilization does not engross all the virtues of humanity: she has not even her full share of them. They flourish in greater abundance and attain greater strength among many barbarous people. The hospitality of the wild Arab, the courage of the North American Indian and the faithful friendships of some of the Polynesian nations, far surpass any thing of a similar kind among the polished communities of Europe. If truth and justice, and the better principles of our nature, cannot exist unless enforced by the statute-book, how are we to account for the social condition of the Typees? So pure and upright were they in all the relations of life, that entering their valley, as I did, under the most erroneous impressions of their character, I was soon led to exclaim in amazement: "Are these the ferocious savages, the bloodthirsty cannibals of whom I have heard such frightful tales! They deal more kindly with each other, and are more humane, than many who study essays on virtue and benev-olence, and who repeat every night that beautiful prayer breathed first by the lips of the divine and gentle Jesus." I will frankly declare, that after passing a few weeks in this valley of the Marquesas, I formed a higher estimate of human nature than I had ever before entertained. But alas! since then I have been one of the crew of a man-of-war, and the pent-up wickedness of five hun-dred men has nearly overturned all my previous theories.

There was one admirable trait in the general character of the Typees which, more than any thing else secured my admiration: it was the unanimity of feeling they displayed on every occasion. With them there hardly appeared to be any difference of opinion upon any subject whatever. They all thought and acted alike. I do not conceive that they could support a debating society for a single night: there would be nothing to dispute about; and were they to call a convention to take into consideration the state of the tribe, its session would be a remarkably short one. They showed this spirit of unanimity in every action of life: everything was done in concert and good fellowship. I will give an instance of this fraternal feeling.

One day, in returning with Kory-Kory from my accustomed visit to the Ti, we passed by a little opening in the grove; on one side of which, my at-tendant informed me, was that afternoon to be built a dwelling of bamboo. At least a hundred of the natives were bringing materials to the ground, some carrying in their hands one or two of the canes which were to form the sides, others slender rods of the habiscus, strung with palmetto leaves, for the roof. Every one contributed something to the work; and by the united, but easy, and even indolent, labours of all, the entire work was completed before sunset. The islanders, while employed in erecting this tenement, reminded me of a colony of beavers at work. To be sure, they were hardly as silent and demure as those wonderful creatures, nor were they by any means as diligent. To tell the truth, they were somewhat inclined to be lazy, but a perfect tumult of hilarity prevailed; and they worked together so unitedly, and seemed actuated by such an instinct of friendliness that it was truly beautiful to behold.

Not a single female took part in this employment: and if the degree of consideration in which the ever-adorable sex is held by the men be—as the philosophers affirm—a just criterion of the degree of refinement among a people, then I may truly pronounce the Typees to be as polished a community as ever the sun shone upon. The religious restrictions of the taboo alone excepted, the women of the valley were allowed every possible indulgence. Nowhere are the ladies more assiduously courted; nowhere are they better appreciated as the contributors to our highest enjoyments; and nowhere are they more sensible of their power. Far different from their condition among many rude nations, where the women are made to perform all the work while their ungallant lords and masters lie buried in sloth, the gentle sex in the valley of Typee were exempt from toil, if toil it might be called that, even in that tropical climate, never distilled one drop of perspiration. Their light household occupations, together with the manufacture of tappa, the platting of mats, and the polishing of drinking-vessels, were the only employments pertaining to the women. And even these resembled those pleasant avocations which fill up the elegant morning leisure of our fashionable ladies at home. But in these occupations, slight and agreeable though they were, the giddy young girls very seldom engaged. Indeed these wilful, care-killing damsels were averse to all useful employment. Like so many spoiled beauties, they ranged through the groves—bathed in the stream—danced—flirted—played all manner of mischievous pranks, and passed their days in one merry round of thoughtless happiness.

During my whole stay on the island I never witnessed a single quarrel, nor anything that in the slightest degree approached even to a dispute. The natives appeared to form one household, whose members were bound together by the ties of strong affection. The love of kindred I did not so much perceive, for it seemed blended in the general love; and where all were treated as brothers and sisters, it was hard to tell who were actually related to each other by blood.

Let it not be supposed that I have overdrawn this picture. I have not done so. Nor let it be urged, that the hostility of this tribe to foreigners, and the hereditary feuds they carry on against their fellow-islanders beyond the mountains, are facts which contradict me. Not so: these apparent discrepancies are easily reconciled. By many a legendary tale of violence and wrong, as well as by events which have passed before their eyes, these people have been taught to look upon white men with abhorrence. The cruel invasion of their country by Porter has alone furnished them with ample provocation; and I can sympathize in the spirit which prompts the Typee warrior to guard all the passes to his valley with the point of his levelled spear, and, standing upon the beach, with his back turned upon his green home, to hold at bay the intruding European.

As to the origin of the enmity of this particular clan towards the neighbouring tribes, I cannot so confidently speak. I will not say that their foes are the aggressors, nor will I endeavour to palliate their conduct. But surely, if our evil passions must find vent, it is far better to expend them on strangers and aliens, than in the bosom of the community in which we dwell. In many polished countries civil contentions, as well as domestic enmities, are prevalent at the same time that the most atrocious foreign wars are waged. How much less guilty, then, are our islanders, who of these three sins are only chargeable with one, and that the least criminal!

The reader will ere long have reason to suspect that the Typees are not free from the guilt of cannibalism; and he will then, perhaps, charge me with admiring a people against whóm so odious a crime is chargeable. But this only enormity in their character is not half so horrible as it is usually described. According to the popular fictions, the crews of vessels, shipwrecked on some barbarous coast, are eaten alive like so many dainty joints by the uncivil inhabitants; and unfortunate voyagers are lured into smiling and treacherous bays; knocked in the head with outlandish war-clubs; and served up without any preliminary dressing. In truth, so horrific and improbable are these accounts, that many sensible and well-informed people will not believe that any cannibals exist; and place every book of voyages which purports to give any account of them, on the same shelf with Blue Beard and Jack the Giant-Killer; while others, implicitly crediting the most extravagant fictions, firmly believe that there are people in the world with tastes so depraved that they would infinitely prefer a single mouthful of material humanity to a good dinner of roast beef and plum pudding. But here Truth, who loves to be centrally located, is again found between the two extremes; for cannibalism to a certain moderate extent is practised among several of the primitive tribes in the Pacific, but it is upon the bodies of slain enemies alone; and horrible and fearful as the custom is, immeasurably as it is to be abhorred and condemned, still I assert that those who indulge in it are in other respects humane and virtuous.

CHAPTER XXVIII

FISHING PARTIES—MODE OF DISTRIBUTING THE FISH—MIDNIGHT BANQUET—
TIMEKEEPING TAPERS—UNCEREMONIOUS STYLE OF EATING THE FISH.

THERE was no instance in which the social and kindly dispositions of the Typees were more forcibly evinced than in the manner they conducted their great fishing parties. Four times during my stay in the valley the young men assembled near the full of the moon, and went together on these excursions. As they were generally absent about forty-eight hours, I was led to believe that they went out towards the open sea, some distance from the bay. The Polynesians seldom use a hook and line, almost always employing large well-made nets, most ingeniously fabricated from the twisted fibres of a certain bark. I examined several of them which had been spread to dry upon the beach at Nukuheva. They resemble very much our own seines, and I should think were very nearly as durable.

All the South Sea Islanders are passionately fond of fish; but none of them can be more so than the inhabitants of Typee. I could not comprehend, therefore, why they so seldom sought it in their waters, for it was only at stated times that the fishing parties were formed, and these occasions were always looked forward to with no small degree of interest.

During their absence the whole population of the place were in a ferment, and nothing was talked of but "pehee, pehee" (fish, fish).   Towards the time when they were expected to return the vocal telegraph was put into operation— the inhabitants, who were scattered throughout the length of the valley, leaped upon rocks and into trees, shouting with delight at the thoughts of the antici- pated treat.   As soon as the approach of the party was announced, there was a general rush of the men towards the beach; some of them remaining, however, about the Ti, in order to get matters in readiness for the reception of the fish, which were brought to the Taboo groves in immense packages of leaves, each one of them being suspended from a pole carried on the shoulders of two men.

I was present at the Ti on one of these occasions, and the sight was most interesting.   After all the packages had arrived, they were laid in a row under the verandah of the building and opened.   The fish were all quite small, gener- ally about the size of a herring, and of every variety of colour.   About one- eighth of the whole being reserved for the use of the Ti itself, the remainder was divided into numerous smaller packages, which were immediately dispatched in every direction to the remotest parts of the valley.   Arrived at their desti- nation, these were in turn portioned out, and equally distributed among the various houses of each particular district.   The fish were under a strict Taboo, until the distribution was completed, which seemed to be effected in the most impartial manner.   By the operation of this system every man, woman, and child in the vale were at one and the same time partaking of this favourite article of food.

Once I remember the party arrived at midnight; but the unseasonableness of the hour did not repress the impatience of the islanders.   The carriers dis- patched from the Ti were to be seen hurrying in all directions through the deep groves; each individual preceded by a boy bearing a flaming torch of dried coco- nut boughs, which from time to time was replenished from the materials scat- tered along the path.   The wild glare of these enormous flambeaux, lighting up with a startling brilliancy the innermost recesses of the vale, and seen moving rapidly along beneath the canopy of leaves, the savage shout of the excited messengers sounding the news of their approach, which was answered on all sides, and the strange appearance of their naked bodies, seen against the gloomy background, produced altogether an effect upon my mind that I shall long remember.

It was on this same occasion that Kory-Kory awakened me at the dead hour of night, and in a sort of transport communicated the intelligence contained in the words "pehee perni" (fish come).   As I happened to have been in a re- markably sound and refreshing slumber, I could not imagine why the informa- tion had not been deferred until morning; indeed, I felt very much inclined to fly into a passion and box my valet's ears; but on second thoughts I got quietly up, and on going outside the house was not a little interested by the moving illumination which I beheld.

When old Marheyo received his share of the spoils, immediate preparations were made for a midnight banquet; calabashes of poee-poee were filled to the brim; green breadfruit were roasted; and a huge cake of "amar" was cut up with a sliver of bamboo and laid out on an immense banana-leaf.

At this supper we were lighted by several of the native tapers, held in the hands of young girls.   These tapers are most ingeniously made.   There is a nut abounding in the valley, called by the Typees "armor," closely resembling our common horse-chestnut.   The shell is broken, and the contents extracted whole. Any number of these are strung at pleasure upon the long elastic fibre that traverses the branches of the coco-nut tree.   Some of these tapers are eight and ten feet in length; but being perfectly flexible, one end is held in a coil, while the other is lighted. The nut burns with a fitful bluish flame, and the oil that it contains is exhausted in about ten minutes. As one burns down, the next becomes ignited, and the ashes of the former are knocked into a coco-nut shell kept for the purpose. This primitive candle requires continual attention, and must be constantly held in the hand. The person so employed marks the lapse of time by the number of nuts consumed, which is easily learned by counting the bits of tappa distributed at regular intervals along the string.

I grieve to state so distressing a fact, but the inhabitants of Typee were in the habit of devouring fish much in the same way that a civilized being would eat a radish, and without any more previous preparation. They eat it raw; scales, bones, gills, and all the inside. The fish is held by the tail, and the head being introduced into the mouth, the animal disappears with a rapidity that would at first nearly lead one to imagine it had been launched bodily down the throat.

Raw fish! Shall I ever forget my sensations when I first saw my island beauty devour one? Oh, heavens! Fayaway, how could you ever have contracted so vile a habit? However, after the first shock had subsided, the custom grew less odious in my eyes, and I soon accustomed myself to the sight. Let no one imagine, however, that the lovely Fayaway was in the habit of swallowing great vulgar-looking fishes: oh, no; with her beautiful small hand she would clasp a delicate, little, golden-hued love of a fish, and eat it as elegantly and as innocently as though it were a Naples biscuit. But, alas! it was after all a raw fish; and all I can say is, that Fayaway ate it in a more lady-like manner than any other girl of the valley.

When at Rome do as the Romans do, I held to be so good a proverb, that being in Typee I made a point of doing as the Typees did. Thus I ate poee-poee as they did; I walked about in a garb striking for its simplicity; and I reposed on a community of couches; besides doing many other things in conformity with their peculiar habits; but the farthest I ever went in the way of conformity, was on several occasions to regale myself with raw fish. These being remarkably tender, and quite small, the undertaking was not so disagreeable in the main, and after a few trials I positively began to relish them: however, I subjected them to a slight operation with my knife previously to making my repast.

CHAPTER XXIX

NATURAL HISTORY OF THE VALLEY—GOLDEN LIZARDS—TAMENESS OF THE BIRDS —MOSQUITOES—FLIES—DOGS—A SOLITARY CAT—THE CLIMATE—THE COCO-NUT TREE—SINGULAR MODES OF CLIMBING IT—AN AGILE YOUNG CHIEF— FEARLESSNESS OF THE CHILDREN—TOO-TOO AND THE COCO-NUT TREE—THE BIRDS OF THE VALLEY.

I THINK I must enlighten the reader a little about the natural history of the valley.

Whence, in the name of Count Buffon and Baron Cuvier, came those dogs that I saw in Typee? Dogs!—Big hairless rats rather; all with smooth, shining, speckled hides—fat sides, and very disagreeable faces. Whence could they have come? That they were not the indigenous production of the region, I am firmly convinced. Indeed they seemed aware of their being interlopers, looking fairly ashamed, and always trying to hide themselves in some dark corner. It was plain enough they did not feel at home in the vale—that they wished themselves well out of it, and back to the ugly country from which they must have come.

Scurvy curs! they were my abhorrence; I should have liked nothing better than to have been the death of every one of them. In fact, on one occasion, I intimated the propriety of a canine crusade to Mehevi; but the benevolent king would not consent to it. He heard me very patiently; but when I had finished, shook his head, and told me, in confidence, that they were "taboo."

As for the animal that made the fortune of the ex-lord-mayor Whittington: I shall never forget the day that I was lying in the house about noon; everybody else being fast asleep; and happening to raise my eyes, met those of a big black spectral cat, which sat erect in the doorway, looking at me with its frightful goggling green orbs, like one of those monstrous imps that torment some of Teniers' saints! I am one of those unfortunate persons to whom the sight of these animals is at any time an insufferable annoyance.

Thus constitutionally averse to cats in general, the unexpected apparition of this one in particular utterly confounded me. When I had a little recovered from the fascination of its glance, I started up; the cat fled, and emboldened by this, I rushed out of the house in pursuit; but it had disappeared. It was the only time I ever saw one in the valley, and how it got there I cannot imagine. It is just possible that it might have escaped from one of the ships at Nukuheva. It was in vain to seek information on the subject from the natives; since none of them had seen the animal, the appearance of which remains a mystery to me to this day.

Among the few animals which are to be met with in Typee, there were none which I looked upon with more interest than a beautiful golden-hued species of lizard. It measured perhaps five inches from head to tail, and was most gracefully proportioned. Numbers of these creatures were to be· seen basking in the sunshine upon the thatching of the houses, and multitudes at all hours of the day showed their glittering sides as they ran frolicking between the spears of grass or raced in troops up and down the tall shafts of the coco-nut trees. But the remarkable beauty of these little animals and their lively ways were not their only claims upon my admiration. They were perfectly tame and insensible to fear. Frequently after seating myself upon the ground in some shady place during the heat of the day, I would be completely overrun with them. If I brushed one off my arm, it would leap perhaps into my hair: when I tried to frighten it away by gently pinching its leg, it would turn for protection to the very hand that attacked it.

The birds are also remarkably tame. If you happened to see one perched upon a branch within reach of your arm, and advanced towards it, it did not fly away immediately, but waited quietly looking at you, until you could almost touch it, and then took wing slowly, less alarmed at your presence, it would seem, than desirous of removing itself from your path. Had salt been less scarce in the valley than it was, this was the very place to have gone birding with it.

I remember that once, on an uninhabited island of the Gallipagos, a bird alighted on my outstretched arm, while its mate chirped from an adjoining tree. Its tameness, far from shocking me, as a similar occurrence did Selkirk, imparted to me the most exquisite thrill of delight I ever experienced; and with somewhat of the same pleasure did I afterwards behold the birds and lizards of the valley show their confidence in the kindliness of man.

Among the numerous afflictions which the Europeans have entailed upon some of the natives of the South Seas, is the accidental introduction among them of that enemy of all repose and ruffler of even tempers—the Mosquito. At the Sandwich Islands and at two or three of the Society group there are now thriving colonies of these insects, who promise ere long to supplant altogether the aboriginal sand-flies. They sting, buzz, and torment, from one end of the year to the other, and by incessantly exasperating the natives materially obstruct the benevolent labours of the missionaries.

From this grievous visitation, however, the Typees are as yet wholly exempt; but its place is unfortunately in some degree supplied by the occasional presence of a minute species of fly, which, without stinging, is nevertheless productive of no little annoyance. The tameness of the birds and lizards is as nothing when compared to the fearless confidence of this insect. He will perch upon one of your eyelashes, and go to roost there, if you do not disturb him, or force his way through your hair, or along the cavity of the nostril, till you almost fancy he is resolved to explore the very brain itself. On one occasion I was so inconsiderate as to yawn while a number of them were hovering around me. I never repeated the act. Some half-dozen darted into the open apartment, and began walking about its ceiling; the sensation was dreadful. I involuntarily closed my mouth, and the poor creatures being enveloped in inner darkness, must in their consternation have stumbled over my palate, and been precipitated into the gulf beneath. At any rate, though I afterwards charitably held my mouth open for at least five minutes, with a view of affording egress to the stragglers, none of them ever availed themselves of the opportunity.

There are no wild animals of any kind on the island, unless it be decided that the natives themselves are such. The mountains and the interior present to the eye nothing but silent solitudes, unbroken by the roar of beasts of prey, and enlivened by few tokens even of minute animated existence. There are no venomous reptiles, and no snakes of any description to be found in any of the valleys.

In a company of Marquesan natives the weather affords no topic of conversation. It can hardly be said to have any vicissitudes. The rainy season, it is true, brings frequent showers, but they are intermitting and refreshing. When an islander bound on some expedition rises from his couch in the morning, he is never solicitous to peep out and see how the sky looks, or ascertain from what quarter the wind blows. He is always sure of a "fine day," and the promise of a few genial showers he hails with pleasure. There is never any of that "remarkable weather" on the island which from time immemorial has been experienced in America, and still continues to call forth the wondering conversational exclamations of its elderly citizens. Nor do there even occur any of those eccentric meteorological changes which elsewhere surprise us. In the valley of Typee ice-creams would never be rendered less acceptable by sudden frosts, nor would picnic parties be deferred on account of inauspicious snow-storms: for there day follows day in one unvarying round of summer and sunshine, and the whole year is one long tropical month of June just melting into July.

It is this genial climate which causes the coco-nuts to flourish as they do. This invaluable fruit, brought to perfection by the rich soil of the Marquesas, and borne aloft on a stately column more than a hundred feet from the ground, would seem at first almost inaccessible to the simple natives. Indeed the slender, smooth, and soaring shaft, without a single limb or protuberance of any kind to assist one in mounting it, presents an obstacle only to be overcome by the surprising agility and ingenuity of the islanders. It might be supposed that their indolence would lead them patiently to await the period when the ripened nuts, slowly parting from their stems, fall one by one to the ground. This certainly would be the case, were it not that the young fruit, encased in a soft green husk, with the incipient meat adhering in a jelly-like pellicle to its sides, and containing a bumper of the most delicious nectar, is what they chiefly prize. They have at least twenty different terms to express as many progressive stages in the growth of the nut. Many of them reject the fruit altogether except at a particular period of its growth, which, incredible as it may appear, they seemed to me to be able to ascertain within an hour or two. Others are still more capricious in their tastes; and after gathering together a heap of the nuts of all ages, and ingeniously tapping them, will sip first from one and then from another, as fastidiously as some delicate wine-bibber experimenting glass in hand among his dusty demijohns of different vintages.

Some of the young men, with more flexible frames than their comrades, and perhaps with more courageous souls, had a way of walking up the trunk of the coco-nut trees which to me seemed little less than miraculous; and when looking at them in the act, I experienced that curious perplexity a child feels when he beholds a fly moving feet uppermost along a ceiling.

I will endeavour to describe the way in which Narnee, a noble young chief, sometimes performed this feat for my peculiar gratification; but his preliminary performances must also be recorded. Upon my signifying my desire that he should pluck me the young fruit of some particular tree, the handsome savage, throwing himself into a sudden attitude of surprise, feigns astonishment at the apparent absurdity of the request. Maintaining this position for a moment, the strange emotions depicted on his countenance soften down into one of humorous resignation to my will, and then looking wistfully up to the tufted top of the tree, he stands on tip-toe, straining his neck and elevating his arm, as though endeavouring to reach the fruit from the ground where he stands. As if defeated in this childish attempt, he now sinks to the earth despondingly, beating his breast in well-acted despair; and then, starting to his feet all at once, and throwing back his head, raises both hands, like a schoolboy about to catch a falling ball. After continuing this for a moment or two, as if in expectation that the fruit was going to be tossed down to him by some good spirit in the tree-top, he turns wildly round in another fit of despair, and scampers off to the distance of thirty or forty yards. Here he remains awhile, eyeing the tree, the very picture of misery; but the next moment, receiving, as it were, a flash of inspiration, he rushes again towards it, and clasping both arms about the trunk, with one elevated a little above the other, he presses the soles of his feet close together against the tree, extending his legs from it until they are nearly horizontal, and his body becomes doubled into an arch; then, hand over hand and foot after foot, he rises from the earth with steady rapidity, and almost before you are aware of it, has gained the cradled and embowered nest of nuts, and with boisterous glee flings the fruit to the ground.

This mode of walking the tree is only practicable where the trunk declines considerably from the perpendicular. This, however, is almost always the case; some of the perfectly straight shafts of the trees leaning at an angle of thirty degrees.

The less active among the men, and many of the children of the valley, have another method of climbing. They take a broad and stout piece of bark, and secure either end of it to their ankles; so that when the feet thus confined are extended apart, a space of little more than twelve inches is left between them.   This contrivance greatly facilitates the act of climbing.   The band pressed against the tree, and closely embracing it, yields a pretty firm support; while with the arms clasped about the trunk, and at regular intervals sustaining the body, the feet are drawn up nearly a yard at a time, and a corresponding elevation of the hands immediately succeeds.   In this way I have seen little children, scarcely five years of age, fearlessly climbing the slender pole of a young coco-nut tree, and while hanging perhaps fifty feet from the ground, receive the plaudits of their parents beneath, who clapped their hands, and encouraged them to mount still higher.

What, thought I, on first witnessing one of these exhibitions, would the nervous mothers of America and England say to a similar display of hardihood in any of their children?   The Lacedemonian nations might have approved it, but most modern dames would have gone into hysterics at the sight.

At the top of the coco-nut tree the numerous branches, radiating on all sides from a common centre, form a sort of green and waving basket, between the leaflets of which you just discern the nuts thickly clustering together, and on the loftier trees looking no bigger from the ground than bunches of grapes. I remember one adventurous little fellow—Too-Too was the rascal's name— who had built himself a sort of aerial baby-house in the picturesque tuft of a tree adjoining Marheyo's habitation.   He used to spend hours there,—rustling among the branches, and shouting with delight every time the strong gusts of wind rushing down from the mountain's side swayed to and fro the tall and flexible column on which he was perched.   Whenever I heard Too-Too's musical voice, sounding strangely to the ear from so great a height, and beheld him peeping down upon me from out his leafy covert, he always recalled to my mind Dibdin's lines—

> "There's a sweet little cherub that sits up aloft,
> To look out for the life of poor Jack."

Birds—bright and beautiful birds—fly over the valley of Typee.   You see them perched aloft among the immovable boughs of the majestic breadfruit trees, or gently swaying on the elastic branches of the Omoo; skimming over the palmetto thatching of the bamboo huts; passing like spirits on the wing through the shadows of the grove, and sometimes descending into the bosom of the valley in gleaming flights from the mountains.   Their plumage is purple and azure, crimson and white, black and gold; with bills of every tint:—bright bloody-red, jet black, and ivory white; and their eyes are bright and sparkling; they go sailing through the air in starry throngs; but alas! the spell of dumb- ness is upon them all—there is not a single warbler in the valley!

I know not why it was, but the sight of these birds, generally the ministers of gladness, always oppressed me with melancholy.   As in their dumb beauty they hovered by me whilst I was walking, or looked down upon me with steady curious eyes from out the foliage, I was almost inclined to fancy that they knew they were gazing upon a stranger, and that they commiserated his fate.

CHAPTER XXX

A PROFESSOR OF THE FINE ARTS—HIS PERSECUTIONS—SOMETHING ABOUT TAT-
TOOING AND TABOOING—TWO ANECDOTES IN ILLUSTRATION OF THE LATTER
—A FEW THOUGHTS ON THE TYPEE DIALECT.

IN one of my strolls with Kory-Kory, in passing along the border of a thick growth of bushes, my attention was arrested by a singular noise. On entering the thicket I witnessed for the first time the operation of tattooing as performed by these islanders.

I beheld a man extended flat upon his back on the ground, and, despite the forced composure of his countenance, it was evident that he was suffering agony. His tormentor bent over him, working away for all the world like a stone-cutter with mallet and chisel. In one hand he held a short slender stick, pointed with a shark's tooth, on the upright end of which he tapped with a small hammer-like piece of wood, thus puncturing the skin, and charging it with the colouring matter in which the instrument was dipped. A coco-nut shell containing this fluid was placed upon the ground. It is prepared by mixing with a vegetable juice the ashes of the "armor," or candle-nut, always preserved for the purpose. Beside the savage, and spread out upon a piece of soiled tappa, were a great number of curious black-looking little implements of bone and wood, used in the various divisions of his art. A few terminated in a single fine point, and, like very delicate pencils, were employed in giving the finishing touches, or in operating upon the more sensitive portions of the body, as was the case in the present instance. Others presented several points distributed in a line, somewhat resembling the teeth of a saw. These were employed in the coarser parts of the work, and particularly in pricking in straight marks. Some presented their points disposed in small figures, and being placed upon the body, were, by a single blow of the hammer, made to leave their indelible impression. I observed a few the handles of which were mysteriously curved, as if intended to be introduced into the orifice of the ear, with a view perhaps of beating the tattoo upon the tympanum. Altogether, the sight of these strange instruments recalled to mind that display of cruel-looking mother-of-pearl-handled things which one sees in their velvet-lined cases at the elbow of a dentist.

The artist was not at this time engaged on an original sketch, his subject being a venerable savage, whose tattooing had become somewhat faded with age and needed a few repairs, and accordingly he was merely employed in touching up the works of some of the old masters of the Typee school, as delineated upon the human canvas before him. The parts operated upon were the eyelids, where a longitudinal streak, like the one which adorned Kory-Kory, crossed the countenance of the victim.

In spite of all the efforts of the poor old man, sundry twitchings and screwings of the muscles of the face denoted the exquisite sensibility of these shutters to the windows of his soul, which he was now having repainted. But the artist, with a heart as callous as that of an army surgeon, continued his performance, enlivening his labours with a wild chant, tapping away the while as merrily as a woodpecker.

So deeply engaged was he in his work, that he had not observed our approach, until, after having enjoyed an unmolested view of the operation, I chose to attract his attention. As soon as he perceived me, supposing that

I sought him in his professional capacity, he seized hold of me in a paroxysm of delight, and was all eagerness to begin the work. When, however, I gave him to understand that he had altogether mistaken my views, nothing could exceed his grief and disappointment. But recovering from this, he seemed determined not to credit my assertion and grasping his implements, he flourished them about in fearful vicinity to my face, going through an imaginary performance of his art, and every moment bursting into some admiring exclamation at the beauty of his designs.

Horrified at the bare thought of being rendered hideous for life if the wretch were to execute his purpose upon me, I struggled to get away from him, while Kory-Kory, turning traitor, stood by, and besought me to comply with the outrageous request.

On my reiterated refusals, the excited artist got half beside himself, and was overwhelmed with sorrow at losing so noble an opportunity of distinguishing himself in his profession.

The idea of engrafting his tattooing upon my white skin filled him with all a painter's enthusiasm: again and again he gazed into my countenance, and every fresh glimpse seemed to add to the vehemence of his ambition. Not knowing to what extremities he might proceed, and shuddering at the ruin he might inflict upon my figure-head, I now endeavoured to draw off his attention from it, and holding out my arm in a fit of desperation, signed to him to commence operations. But he rejected the compromise indignantly, and still continued his attack on my face, as though nothing short of that would satisfy him. When his fore-finger swept across my features, in laying out the borders of those parallel bands which were to encircle my countenance, the flesh fairly crawled upon my bones. At last, half wild with terror and indignation, I succeeded in breaking away from the three savages, and fled towards old Marheyo's house, pursued by the indomitable artist, who ran after me, implements in hand. Kory-Kory, however, at last interfered, and drew him off from the chase.

This incident opened my eyes to a new danger; and I now felt convinced that in some luckless hour I should be disfigured in such a manner as never more to have the *face* to return to my countrymen, even should an opportunity offer.

These apprehensions were greatly increased by the desire which King Mehevi and several of the inferior chiefs now manifested that I should be tattooed. The pleasure of the king was first signified to me some three days after my casual encounter with Karky the artist. Heavens! what imprecations I showered upon that Karky! Doubtless he had plotted a conspiracy against me and my countenance, and would never rest until his diabolical purpose was accomplished. Several times I met him in various parts of the valley, and, invariably, whenever he descried me, he came running after me with his mallet and chisel, flourishing them about my face as if he longed to begin. What an object he would have made of me!

When the king first expressed his wish to me, I made known to him my utter abhorrence of the measure, and worked myself into such a state of excitement, that he absolutely stared at me in amazement. It evidently surpassed his majesty's comprehension how any sober-minded and sensible individual could entertain the least possible objection to so beautifying an operation.

Soon afterwards he repeated his suggestion, and meeting with a like repulse, showed some symptoms of displeasure at my obduracy. On his a third time renewing his request, I plainly perceived that something must be done, or my visage was ruined for ever; I therefore screwed up my courage to the sticking point, and declared my willingness to have both arms tattooed from just above the wrist to the shoulder. His majesty was greatly pleased at the proposition, and I was congratulating myself with having thus compromised the matter, when he intimated that as a thing of course my face was first to undergo the operation. I was fairly driven to despair; nothing but the utter ruin of my "face divine," as the poets call it, would, I perceived, satisfy the inexorable Mehevi and his chiefs, or rather, that infernal Karky, for he was at the bottom of it all.

The only consolation afforded me was a choice of patterns: I was at perfect liberty to have my face spanned by three horizontal bars, after the fashion of my serving-man's; or to have as many oblique stripes slanting across it; or if, like a true courtier, I chose to model my style on that of royalty, I might wear a sort of freemason badge upon my countenance in the shape of a mystic triangle. However, I would have none of these, though the king most earnestly impressed upon my mind that my choice was wholly unrestricted. At last, seeing my unconquerable repugnance, he ceased to importune me.

But not so some other of the savages. Hardly a day passed but I was subjected to their annoying requests, until at last my existence became a burden to me; the pleasures I had previously enjoyed no longer afforded me delight, and all my former desire to escape from the valley now revived with additional force.

A fact which I soon afterwards learned augmented my apprehension. The whole system of tattooing was, I found, connected with their religion; and it was evident, therefore, that they were resolved to make a convert of me.

In the decoration of the chiefs it seems to be necessary to exercise the most elaborate pencilling; while some of the inferior natives looked as if they had been daubed over indiscriminately with a house-painter's brush. I remember one fellow who prided himself hugely upon a great oblong patch, placed high upon his back, and who always reminded me of a man with a blister of Spanish flies stuck between his shoulders. Another whom I frequently met had the hollow of his eyes tattooed in two regular squares, and his visual organs being remarkably brilliant, they gleamed forth from out this setting like a couple of diamonds inserted in ebony.

Although convinced that tattooing was a religious observance, still the nature of the connexion between it and the superstitious idolatry of the people was a point upon which I could never obtain any information. Like the still more important system of the "Taboo," it always appeared inexplicable to me.

There is a marked similarity, almost an identity, between the religious institutions of most of the Polynesian islands, and in all exists the mysterious "Taboo," restricted in its uses to a greater or less extent. So strange and complex in its arrangements is this remarkable system, that I have in several cases met with individuals who, after residing for years among the islands in the Pacific, and acquiring a considerable knowledge of the language, have nevertheless been altogether unable to give any satisfactory account of its operations. Situated as I was in the Typee valley, I perceived every hour the effects of this all-controlling power, without in the least comprehending it. Those effects were, indeed, widespread and universal, pervading the most important as well as the minutest transactions of life. The savage, in short, lives in the continual observance of its dictates, which guide and control every action of his being.

For several days after entering the valley I had been saluted at least fifty times in the twenty-four hours with the talismanic word "Taboo" shrieked in my ears, at some gross violation of its provisions, of which I had unconsciously been guilty. The day after our arrival I happened to hand some tobacco to Toby over the head of a native who sat between us. He started up, as if stung by an adder; while the whole company, manifesting an equal degree of horror, simultaneously screamed out "taboo!" I never again perpetrated a similar piece of ill-manners, which, indeed, was forbidden by the canons of good breeding, as well as by the mandates of the taboo. But it was not always so easy to perceive wherein you had contravened the spirit of this institution. I was many times called to order, if I may use the phrase, when I could not for the life of me conjecture what particular offence I had committed.

One day I was strolling through a secluded portion of the valley, and hearing the musical sound of the cloth-mallet at a little distance, I turned down a path that conducted me in a few moments to a house where there were some half-dozen girls employed in making tappa. This was an operation I had frequently witnessed, and had handled the bark in all the various stages of its preparation. On the present occasion the females were intent upon their occupation, and after looking up and talking gaily to me for a few moments, they resumed their employment. I regarded them for awhile in silence, and then carelessly picking up a handful of the material that lay around, proceeded unconsciously to pick it apart. While thus engaged, I was suddenly startled by a scream, like that of a whole boarding-school of young ladies just on the point of going into hysterics. Leaping up with the idea of seeing a score of Happar warriors about to perform anew the Sabine atrocity, I found myself confronted by the company of girls, who, having dropped their work, stood before me with starting eyes, swelling bosoms, and fingers pointed in horror towards me.

Thinking that some venomous reptile must be concealed in the bark which I held in my hand, I began cautiously to separate and examine it. Whilst I did so the horrified girls redoubled their shrieks. Their wild cries and frightened motions actually alarmed me, and throwing down the tappa, I was about to rush from the house, when in the same instant their clamours ceased, and one of them seizing me by the arm, pointed to the broken fibres that had just fallen from my grasp, and screamed in my ears the fatal word Taboo!

I subsequently found out that the fabric they were engaged in making was a peculiar kind, destined to be worn on the heads of the females, and through every stage of its manufacture was guarded by a vigorous taboo, which interdicted the whole masculine gender from even so much as touching it.

Frequently in walking through the groves I observed breadfruit and coconut trees, with a wreath of leaves twined in a peculiar fashion about their trunks. This was the mark of the taboo. The trees themselves, their fruit, and even the shadows they cast upon the ground, were consecrated by its presence. In the same way a pipe, which the king had bestowed upon me, was rendered sacred in the eyes of the natives, none of whom could I ever prevail upon to smoke from it. The bowl was encircled by a woven band of grass, somewhat resembling those Turks' heads occasionally worked in the handles of our whip-stalks.

A similar badge was once braided about my wrist by the royal hand of Mehevi himself, who, as soon as he had concluded the operation, pronounced me "Taboo." This occurred shortly after Toby's disappearance; and were it not that from the first moment I had entered the valley the natives had treated me with uniform kindness, I should have supposed that their conduct afterwards was to be ascribed to the fact that I had received this sacred investiture.

The capricious operations of the taboo is not its least remarkable feature:

to enumerate them all would be impossible. Black hogs—infants to a certain age—women in an interesting situation—young men while the operation of tattooing their faces is going on—and certain parts of the valley during the continuance of a shower—are alike fenced about by the operation of the taboo.

I witnessed a striking instance of its effects in the bay of Tior, my visit to which place has been alluded to in a former part of this narrative. On that occasion our worthy captain formed one of the party. He was a most insatiable sportsman. Outward bound, and off the pitch of Cape Horn, he used to sit on the taffrail, and keep the steward loading three or four old fowling-pieces, with which he would bring down albatrosses, Cape pigeons, jays, petrels, and divers other marine fowl, who followed chattering in our wake. The sailors were struck aghast at his impiety, and one and all attributed our forty days' beating about that horrid headland to his sacrilegious slaughter of these inoffensive birds.

At Tior he evinced the same disregard for the religious prejudices of the islanders, as he had previously shown for the superstitions of the sailors. Having heard that there were a considerable number of fowls in the valley—the progeny of some cocks and hens accidentally left there by an English vessel, and which being strictly tabooed, flew about almost in a wild state—he determined to break through all restraints, and be the death of them. Accordingly, he provided himself with a most formidable-looking gun, and announced his landing on the beach by shooting down a noble cock that was crowing what proved to be his own funeral dirge, on the limb of an adjoining tree. "Taboo," shrieked the affrighted savages. "Oh, hang your taboo," says the nautical sportsman; "talk taboo to the marines;" and bang went the piece again, and down came another victim. At this the natives ran scampering through the groves, horror-struck at the enormity of the act.

All that afternoon the rocky sides of the valley rang with successive reports, and the superb plumage of many a beautiful fowl was ruffled by the fatal bullet. Had it not been that the French admiral, with a large party, were then in the glen, I have no doubt that the natives, although their tribe was small and dispirited, would have inflicted summary vengeance upon the man who thus outraged their most sacred institutions; as it was, they contrived to annoy him not a little.

Thirsting with his exertions, the skipper directed his steps to a stream; but the savages, who had followed at a little distance, perceiving his object, rushed towards him and forced him away from its bank—his lips would have polluted it. Wearied at last, he sought to enter a house, that he might rest for a while on the mats; its inmates gathered tumultuously about the door and denied him admittance. He coaxed and blustered by turns, but in vain; the natives were neither to be intimidated nor appeased, and as a final resort he was obliged to call together his boat's crew, and pull away from what he termed the most infernal place he ever stepped upon.

Lucky was it for him and for us that we were not honoured on our departure by a salute of stones from the hands of the exasperated Tiors. In this way, on the neighbouring island of Ropo, were killed, but a few weeks previously, and for a nearly similar offence, the master and three of the crew of the K——.

I cannot determine with anything approaching to certainty, what power it is that imposes the taboo. When I consider the slight disparity of condition among the islanders—the very limited and inconsiderable prerogatives of the king and chiefs—and the loose and indefinite functions of the priesthood, most of whom were hardly to be distinguished from the rest of their countrymen, I am wholly at a loss where to look for the authority which regulates this potent institution. It is imposed upon something to-day, and withdrawn to-morrow; while its operations in other cases are perpetual. Sometimes its restrictions only affect a single individual—sometimes a particular family—sometimes a whole tribe; and in a few instances they extend not merely over the various clans on a single island, but over all the inhabitants of an entire group. In illustration of this latter peculiarity I may cite the law which forbids a female to enter a canoe—a prohibition which prevails upon all the northern Marquesas Islands.

The word itself (taboo) is used in more than one signification. It is sometimes used by a parent to his child, when in the exercise of parental authority he forbids it to perform a particular action. Anything opposed to the ordinary customs of the islanders, although not expressly prohibited, is said to be "taboo."

The Typee language is one very difficult to be acquired; it bears a close resemblance to the other Polynesian dialects, all of which show a common origin. The duplication of words, as "lumee lumee," "poee poee," "muee muee," is one of their peculiar features. But another, and a more annoying one, is the different senses in which one and the same word is employed; its various meanings all have a certain connexion, which only makes the matter more puzzling. So one brisk, lively little word is obliged, like a servant in a poor family, to perform all sorts of duties; for instance, one particular combination of syllables expresses the ideas of sleep, rest, reclining, sitting, leaning, and all other things anywise analogous thereto, the particular meaning being shown chiefly by a variety of gestures and the eloquent expression of the countenance.

The intricacy of these dialects is another peculiarity. In the Missionary College at Lahainaluna, or Mawee, one of the Sandwich Islands, I saw a tabular exhibition of a Hawaiian verb, conjugated through all its moods and tenses. It covered the side of a considerable apartment, and I doubt whether Sir William Jones himself would have not despaired of mastering it.

CHAPTER XXXI

STRANGE CUSTOM OF THE ISLANDERS—THEIR CHANTING AND THE PECULIARITY
    OF THEIR VOICE—RAPTURE OF THE KING AT FIRST HEARING A SONG—A NEW
    DIGNITY CONFERRED ON THE AUTHOR—MUSICAL INSTRUMENTS IN THE
    VALLEY—ADMIRATION OF THE SAVAGES AT BEHOLDING A PUGILISTIC PER-
    FORMANCE—SWIMMING INFANT—BEAUTIFUL TRESSES OF THE GIRLS—
    OINTMENT FOR THE HAIR.

SADLY discursive as I have already been, I must still further entreat the reader's patience, as I am about to string together, without any attempt at order, a few odds and ends of things not hitherto mentioned, but which are either curious in themselves or peculiar to the Typees.

There was one singular custom, observed in old Marheyo's domestic establishment, which often excited my surprise. Every night, before retiring, the inmates of the house gathered together on the mats, and squatting upon their haunches, after the universal practice of these islanders, would commence a low, dismal, and monotonous chant, accompanying the voice with the instrumental melody produced by two small half-rotten sticks tapped slowly together, a pair of which were held in the hands of each person present. Thus would they employ themselves for an hour or two, sometimes longer. Lying in the gloom which wrapped the further end of the house, I could not avoid looking at them, although the spectacle suggested nothing but unpleasant reflections. The flickering rays of the "armor" nut just served to reveal their savage lineaments, without dispelling the darkness that hovered about them.

Sometimes when, after falling into a kind of doze, and awaking suddenly in the midst of these doleful chantings, my eye would fall upon the wild-looking group engaged in their strange occupation, with their naked tattooed limbs, and shaven heads disposed in a circle, I was almost tempted to believe that I gazed upon a set of evil beings in the act of working a frightful incantation.

What was the meaning or purpose of this custom, whether it was practised merely as a diversion, or whether it was a religious exercise, a sort of family prayers, I never could discover.

The sounds produced by the natives on these occasions were of a most singular description; and had I not actually been present, I never would have believed that such curious noises could have been produced by human beings.

To savages generally is imputed a guttural articulation. This, however, is not always the case, especially among the inhabitants of the Polynesian Archipelago. The labial melody with which the Typee girls carry on an ordinary conversation, giving a musical prolongation to the final syllable of every sentence, and chirping out some of the words with a liquid, bird-like accent, was singularly pleasing.

The men, however, are not quite so harmonious in their utterance, and when excited upon any subject, would work themselves up into a sort of wordy paroxysm, during which all descriptions of rough-sided sounds were projected from their mouths, with a force and rapidity which was absolutely astonishing.

.   .   .   .

Although these savages are remarkably fond of chanting, still they appear to have no idea whatever of singing, at least as that art is practised among other nations.

I never shall forget the first time I happened to roar out a stave in the presence of the noble Mehevi. It was a stanza from the "Bavarian broomseller." His Typean majesty, with all his court, gazed upon me in amazement, as if I had displayed some preternatural faculty which Heaven had denied to them. The king was delighted with the verse; but the chorus fairly transported him. At his solicitation I sang it again and again, and nothing could be more ludicrous than his vain attempts to catch the air and the words. The royal savage seemed to think that by screwing all the features of his face into the end of his nose, he might possibly succeed in the undertaking, but it failed to answer the purpose, and in the end he gave it up, and consoled himself by listening to my repetition of the sounds fifty times over.

Previous to Mehevi's making the discovery, I had never been aware that there was anything of the nightingale about me; but I was now promoted to the place of court-minstrel, in which capacity I was afterwards perpetually called upon to officiate.

.   .   .   .

Besides the sticks and the drums, there are no other musical instruments among the Typees, except one which might appropriately be denominated a

nasal flute. It is somewhat longer than an ordinary fife; is made of a beautiful
scarlet-coloured reed; and has four or five stops, with a large hole near one
end, which latter is held just beneath the left nostril. The other nostril being
closed by a peculiar movement of the muscles about the nose, the breath is
forced into the tube, and produces a soft dulcet sound, which is varied by the
fingers running at random over the stops. This is a favourite recreation with
the females, and one in which Fayaway greatly excelled. Awkward as such an
instrument may appear, it was, in Fayaway's delicate little hands, one of the
most graceful I have ever seen. A young lady, in the act of tormenting a
guitar strung about her neck by a couple of yards of blue ribbon, is not half
so engaging.

Singing was not the only means I possessed of diverting the royal Mehevi
and his easy-going subjects. Nothing afforded them more pleasure than to see
me go through the attitude of pugilistic encounter. As not one of the natives
had soul enough in him to stand up like a man, and allow me to hammer away
at him, for my own personal gratification and that of the king, I was necessitated to fight with an imaginary enemy, whom I invariably made to knock
under to my superior prowess. Sometimes when this sorely battered shadow
retreated precipitately towards a group of the savages, and, following him up,
I rushed among them, dealing my blows right and left, they would disperse
in all directions, much to the enjoyment of Mehevi, the chiefs, and themselves.

The noble art of self-defence appeared to be regarded by them as the peculiar
gift of the white man; and I make little doubt but that they supposed armies
of Europeans were drawn up provided with nothing else but bony fists and
stout hearts, with which they set to in column, and pummelled one another at
the word of command.

One day, in company with Kory-Kory, I had repaired to the stream for the
purpose of bathing, when I observed a woman sitting upon a rock in the midst
of the current, and watching with the liveliest interest the gambols of something,
which at first I took to be an uncommonly large species of frog that was sporting in the water near her. Attracted by the novelty of the sight, I waded
towards the spot where she sat, and could hardly credit the evidence of my
senses when I beheld a little infant, the period of whose birth could not have
extended back many days, paddling about as if it had just risen to the surface,
after being hatched into existence at the bottom. Occasionally the delighted
parent reached out her hands towards it, when the little thing, uttering a faint
cry, and striking out its tiny limbs, would sidle for the rock, and the next
moment be clasped to its mother's bosom. This was repeated again and again,
the baby remaining in the stream about a minute at a time. Once or twice it
made wry faces at swallowing a mouthful of water, and choked and spluttered
as if on the point of strangling. At such times, however, the mother snatched
it up, and by a process scarcely to be mentioned obliged it to eject the fluid.
For several weeks afterwards I observed this woman bringing her child down to
the stream regularly every day, in the cool of the morning and evening, and
treating it to a bath. No wonder that the South Sea Islanders are so amphibious a race, when they are thus launched into the water as soon as they see the
light. I am convinced that it is as natural for a human being to swim as it is
for a duck. And yet in civilized communities how many able-bodied individuals

die, like so many drowning kittens, from the occurrence of the most trivial accidents!

.   .   .   .   .   .

The long, luxuriant, and glossy tresses of the Typee damsels often attracted my admiration. A fine head of hair is the pride and joy of every woman's heart. Whether, against the express will of Providence, it is twisted up on the crown of the head and there coiled away like a rope on a ship's deck; whether it be stuck behind the ears and hangs down like the swag of a small window-curtain; or whether it be permitted to flow over the shoulders in natural ringlets, it is always the pride of the owner, and the glory of the toilette.

The Typee girls devote much of their time to the dressing of their fair and redundant locks. After bathing, as they sometimes do five or six times every day, the hair is carefully dried, and if they have been in the sea, invariably washed in fresh water, and anointed with a highly scented oil extracted from the meat of the coco-nut. This oil is obtained in great abundance by the following very simple process:

A large vessel of wood, with holes perforated in the bottom, is filled with the pounded meat, and exposed to the rays of the sun. As the oleaginous matter exudes, it falls in drops through the apertures into a wide-mouthed calabash placed underneath. After a sufficient quantity has been thus collected, the oil undergoes a purifying process, and is then poured into the small spherical shells of the nuts of the moo-tree, which are hollowed out to receive it. These nuts are then hermetically sealed with a resinous gum, and the vegetable fragrance of their green rind soon imparts to the oil a delightful odour. After the lapse of a few weeks the exterior shell of the nuts becomes quite dry and hard, and assumes a beautiful carnation tint; and when opened they are found to be about two-thirds full of an ointment of a light yellow colour, and diffusing the sweetest perfume. This elegant little odourous globe would not be out of place even upon the toilette of a queen. Its merits as a preparation for the hair are undeniable—it imparts to it a superb gloss and a silky fineness.

CHAPTER XXXII

APPREHENSIONS OF EVIL—FRIGHTFUL DISCOVERY—SOME REMARKS ON CANNI-
BALISM—SECOND BATTLE WITH THE HAPPARS—SAVAGE SPECTACLE—MYS-
TERIOUS FEAST—SUBSEQUENT DISCLOSURES.

FROM the time of my casual encounter with Karky the artist, my life was one of absolute wretchedness. Not a day passed but I was persecuted by the solicitations of some of the natives to subject myself to the odious operation of tattooing. Their importunities drove me half wild, for I felt how easily they might work their will upon me regarding this or anything else which they took into their heads. Still, however, the behaviour of the islanders towards me was as kind as ever. Fayaway was quite as engaging; Kory-Kory was devoted; and Mehevi the king just as gracious and condescending as before. But I had now been three months in their valley, as nearly as I could estimate; I had grown familiar with the narrow limits to which my wanderings had been confined; and I began bitterly to feel the state of captivity in which I was held. There was no one with whom I could freely converse; no one to whom

I could communicate my thoughts; no one who could sympathize with my sufferings. A thousand times I thought how much more endurable would have been my lot had Toby still been with me. But I was left alone, and the thought was terrible to me. Still, despite my griefs, I did all in my power to appear composed and cheerful, well knowing that by manifesting any uneasiness, or any desire to escape, I should only frustrate my object.

It was during the period I was in this unhappy frame of mind that the painful malady under which I had been labouring—after having almost completely subsided—began again to show itself, and with symptoms as violent as ever. This added calamity nearly unmanned me; the recurrence of the complaint proved that without powerful remedial applications all hope of cure was futile; and when I reflected that just beyond the elevations which bound me in, was the medical relief I needed, and that, although so near, it was impossible for me to avail myself of it, the thought was misery.

In this wretched situation, every circumstance which evinced the savage nature of the beings at whose mercy I was, augmented the fearful apprehensions that consumed me. An occurrence which happened about this time affected me most powerfully.

I have already mentioned that from the ridge-pole of Marheyo's house were suspended a number of packages enveloped in tappa. Many of these I had often seen in the hands of the natives, and their contents had been examined in my presence. But there were three packages hanging very nearly over the place where I lay, which from their remarkable appearance had often excited my curiosity. Several times I had asked Kory-Kory to show me their contents; but my servitor, who in almost every other particular had acceded to my wishes, always refused to gratify me in this.

One day, returning unexpectedly from the "Ti," my arrival seemed to throw the inmates of the house into the greatest confusion. They were seated together on the mats, and by the lines which extended from the roof to the floor I immediately perceived that the mysterious packages were for some purpose or other under inspection. The evident alarm the savages betrayed filled me with forebodings of evil, and with an uncontrollable desire to penetrate the secret so jealously guarded. Despite the efforts of Marheyo and Kory-Kory to restrain me, I forced my way into the midst of the circle, and just caught a glimpse of three human heads, which others of the party were hurriedly enveloping in the coverings from which they had been taken.

One of the three I distinctly saw. It was in a state of perfect preservation, and, from the slight glimpse I had of it, seemed to have been subjected to some smoking operation which had reduced it to the dry, hard, and mummy-like appearance it presented. The two long scalp-locks were twisted up into balls upon the crown of the head in the same way that the individual had worn them during life. The sunken cheeks were rendered yet more ghastly by the rows of glistening teeth which protruded from between the lips, while the sockets of the eyes—filled with oval bits of mother-of-pearl shell, with a black spot in the centre—heightened the hideousness of its aspect.

Two of the three were heads of the islanders; but the third, to my horror, was that of a white man. Although it had been quickly removed from my sight, still the glimpse I had of it was enough to convince me that I could not be mistaken.

Gracious God! what dreadful thoughts entered my mind! In solving this mystery perhaps I had solved another, and the fate of my lost companion might be revealed in the shocking spectacle I had just witnessed. I longed to have torn off the folds of cloth, and satisfied the awful doubts under which I laboured. But before I had recovered from the consternation into which I had been thrown, the fatal packages were hoisted aloft and once more swung over my head. The natives now gathered round me tumultuously, and laboured to convince me that what I had just seen were the heads of three Happar warriors, who had been slain in battle. This glaring falsehood added to my alarm, and it was not until I reflected that I had observed the packages swinging from their elevation before Toby's disappearance, that I could at all recover my composure.

But although this horrible apprehension had been dispelled, I had discovered enough to fill me, in my present state of mind, with the most bitter reflections. It was plain that I had seen the last relic of some unfortunate wretch, who must have been massacred on the beach by the savages, in one of those perilous trading adventures which I have before described.

It was not, however, alone the murder of the stranger that overcame me with gloom. I shuddered at the idea of the subsequent fate his inanimate body might have met with. Was the same doom reserved for me? Was I destined to perish like him—like him, perhaps, to be devoured, and my head to be preserved as a fearful memento of the event? My imagination ran riot in these horrid speculations, and I felt certain that the worst possible evils would befall me. But whatever were my misgivings, I studiously concealed them from the islanders, as well as the full extent of the discovery I had made.

Although the assurances which the Typees had often given me, that they never eat human flesh, had not convinced me that such was the case, yet, having been so long a time in the valley without witnessing anything which indicated the existence of the practice, I began to hope that it was an event of very rare occurrence, and that I should be spared the horror of witnessing it during my stay among them; but, alas! these hopes were soon destroyed.

It is a singular fact, that in all our accounts of cannibal tribes we have seldom received the testimony of an eye-witness to the revolting practice. The horrible conclusion has almost always been derived either from the second-hand evidence of Europeans, or else from the admissions of the savages themselves, after they have in some degree become civilized. The Polynesians are aware of the detestation in which Europeans hold this custom, and therefore invariably deny its existence, and, with the craft peculiar to savages, endeavour to conceal every trace of it.

The excessive unwillingness betrayed by the Sandwich Islanders, even at the present day, to allude to the unhappy fate of Cook, has been often remarked. And so well have they succeeded in covering that event with mystery, that to this very hour, despite all that has been said and written on the subject, it still remains doubtful whether they wreaked upon his murdered body the vengeance they sometimes inflicted upon their enemies.

At Karakikova, the scene of that tragedy, a strip of ship's copper nailed against an upright post in the ground used to inform the traveller that beneath reposed the "remains" of the great circumnavigator. But I am strongly inclined to believe not only that the corpse was refused Christian burial, but that the heart which was brought to Vancouver some time after the event, and which the Hawaiians stoutly maintained was that of Captain Cook, was no such thing; and that the whole affair was a piece of imposture which was sought to be palmed off upon the credulous Englishman.

A few years since there was living on the island of Mowee (one of the Sandwich group) an old chief, who, actuated by a morbid desire for notoriety, gave himself out among the foreign residents of the place as the living tomb of Captain Cook's big toe!—affirming, that at the cannibal entertainment which ensued after the lamented Briton's death, that particular portion of his body had fallen to his share. His indignant countrymen actually caused him to be prosecuted in the native courts, on a charge nearly equivalent to what we term defamation of character; but the old fellow persisting in his assertion, and no invalidating proof being adduced, the plaintiffs were cast in the suit, and the cannibal reputation of the defendant fully established. This result was the making of his fortune; ever afterwards he was in the habit of giving very profitable audiences to all curious travellers who were desirous of beholding the man who had eaten the great navigator's great toe.

About a week after my discovery of the contents of the mysterious packages, I happened to be at the Ti, when another war-alarm was sounded, and the natives rushing to their arms, sallied out to resist a second incursion of the Happar invaders. The same scene was again repeated, only that on this occasion I heard at least fifteen reports of muskets from the mountains during the time that the skirmish lasted. An hour or two after its termination, loud pæans chanted through the valley announcing the approach of the victors. I stood with Kory-Kory leaning against the railing of the pi-pi awaiting their advance, when a tumultuous crowd of islanders emerged with wild clamours from the neighbouring groves. In the midst of them marched four men, one preceding the other at regular intervals of eight or ten feet, with poles of corresponding length, extended from shoulder to shoulder, to which were lashed with thongs of bark three long narrow bundles, carefully wrapped in ample coverings of freshly plucked palm-leaves, tacked together with slivers of bamboo. Here and there upon these green winding-sheets might be seen stains of blood, while the warriors who carried the frightful burdens displayed upon their naked limbs similar sanguinary marks. The shaven head of the foremost had a deep gash upon it, and the clotted gore which had flowed from the wound remained in dry patches around it. This savage seemed to be sinking under the weight he bore. The bright tattooing upon his body was covered with blood and dust; his inflamed eyes rolled in their sockets, and his whole appearance denoted extraordinary suffering and exertion; yet, sustained by some powerful impulse, he continued to advance, while the throng around him with wild cheers sought to encourage him. The other three men were marked about the arms and breasts with several slight wounds, which they somewhat ostentatiously displayed.

These four individuals, having been the most active in the late encounter, claimed the honour of bearing the bodies of their slain enemies to the Ti. Such was the conclusion I drew from my own observations, and, as far as I could understand, from the explanation which Kory-Kory gave me.

The royal Mehevi walked by the side of these heroes. He carried in one hand a musket, from the barrel of which was suspended a small canvas pouch of powder, and in the other he grasped a short javelin, which he held before him and regarded with fierce exultation. This javelin he had wrested from a celebrated champion of the Happars, who had ignominiously fled, and was pursued by his foe beyond the summit of the mountain.

When within a short distance of the Ti, the warrior with the wounded head, who proved to be Narmonee, tottered forward two or three steps, and fell helplessly to the ground; but not before another had caught the end of the pole from his shoulder, and placed it upon his own.

The excited throng of islanders, who surrounded the person of the king and the dead bodies of the enemy, approached the spot where I stood, brandishing their rude implements of warfare, many of which were bruised and broken, and uttering continual shouts of triumph. When the crowd drew up opposite the Ti, I set myself to watch their proceedings most attentively; but scarcely had they halted when my servitor, who had left my side for an instant, touched my arm, and proposed our returning to Marheyo's house. To this I objected; but, to my surprise, Kory-Kory reiterated his request, and with an unusual vehemence of manner. Still, however, I refused to comply, and was retreating before him, as in his importunity he pressed upon me, when I felt a heavy hand laid upon my shoulder, and turning round, encountered the bulky form of Mow-Mow, a one-eyed chief, who had just detached himself from the crowd below, and had mounted the rear of the pi-pi upon which we stood. His cheek had been pierced by the point of a spear, and the wound imparted a still more frightful expression to his hideously tattooed face, already deformed by the loss of an eye. The warrior, without uttering a syllable, pointed fiercely in the direction of Marheyo's house, while Kory-Kory, at the same time presenting his back, desired me to mount.

I declined this offer, but intimated my willingness to withdraw, and moved slowly along the piazza, wondering what could be the cause of this unusual treatment. A few minutes' consideration convinced me that the savages were about to celebrate some hideous rite in connection with their peculiar customs, and at which they were determined I should not be present. I descended from the pi-pi, and attended by Kory-Kory, who on this occasion did not show his usual commiseration for my lameness, but seemed only anxious to hurry me on, walked away from the place. As I passed through the noisy throng, which by this time completely environed the Ti, I looked with fearful curiosity at the three packages, which now were deposited upon the ground; but although I had no doubt as to their contents, still their thick coverings prevented my actually detecting the form of a human body.

The next morning, shortly after sunrise, the same thundering sounds which had awakened me from sleep on the second day of the Feast of Calabashes, assured me that the savages were on the eve of celebrating another, and, as I fully believed, a horrible solemnity.

All the inmates of the house, with the exception of Marheyo, his son, and Tinor, after assuming their gala dresses, departed in the direction of the Taboo Groves.

Although I did not anticipate a compliance with my request, still, with a view of testing the truth of my suspicions, I proposed to Kory-Kory that, according to our usual custom in the morning, we should take a stroll to the Ti: he positively refused; and when I renewed the request, he evinced his determination to prevent my going there; and, to divert my mind from the subject, he offered to accompany me to the stream. We accordingly went, and bathed. On our coming back to the house, I was surprised to find that all its inmates had returned, and were lounging upon the mats as usual, although the drums still sounded from the groves.

The rest of the day I spent with Kory-Kory and Fayaway, wandering about a part of the valley situated in an opposite direction from the Ti; and whenever I so much as looked towards that building, although it was hidden from view by intervening trees, and at the distance of more than a mile, my attendant would exclaim, "Taboo, taboo!"

At the various houses where we stopped, I found many of the inhabitants reclining at their ease, or pursuing some light occupation, as if nothing unusual were going forward; but amongst them all I did not perceive a single chief or warrior. When I asked several of the people why they were not at the "Hoolah Hoolah" (the feast), they uniformly answered the question in a manner which implied that it was not intended for them, but for Mehevi, Narmonee, Mow-Mow, Kolor, Womonoo, Kalow—running over, in their desire to make me comprehend their meaning, the names of all the principal chiefs.

Everything, in short, strengthened my suspicions with regard to the nature of the festival they were now celebrating; and which amounted almost to a certainty. While in Nukuheva I had frequently been informed that the whole tribe were never present at these cannibal banquets; but the chiefs and priests only, and everything I now observed agreed with the account.

The sound of the drums continued, without intermission, the whole day, and falling continually upon my ear, caused me a sensation of horror which I am unable to describe. On the following day, hearing none of those noisy indications of revelry, I concluded that the inhuman feast was terminated; and feeling a kind of morbid curiosity to discover whether the Ti might furnish any evidence of what had taken place there, I proposed to Kory-Kory to walk there. To this proposition he replied by pointing with his finger to the newly risen sun, and then up to the zenith, intimating that our visit must be deferred until noon. Shortly after that hour we accordingly proceeded to the Taboo Groves, and as soon as we entered their precincts, I looked fearfully round in quest of some memorial of the scenes which had so lately been acted there; but everything appeared as usual. On reaching the Ti, we found Mehevi and a few chiefs reclining on the mats, who gave me as friendly a reception as ever. No allusions of any kind were made by them to the recent events; and I refrained, for obvious reasons, from referring to them myself.

After staying a short time I took my leave. In passing along the piazza, previously to descending from the pi-pi, I observed a curiously carved vessel of wood, of considerable size, with a cover placed over it, of the same material, and which resembled in shape a small canoe. It was surrounded by a low railing of bamboos the top of which was scarcely a foot from the ground. As the vessel had been placed in its present position since my last visit, I at once concluded that it must have some connexion with the recent festival; and, prompted by a curiosity I could not repress, in passing it I raised one end of the cover; at the same moment the chiefs, perceiving my design, loudly ejaculated, "Taboo! taboo!" But the slight glimpse sufficed; my eyes fell upon the disordered members of a human skeleton, the bones still fresh with moisture, and with particles of flesh clinging to them here and there!

Kory-Kory, who had been a little in advance of me, attracted by the exclamations of the chiefs, turned round in time to witness the expression of horror on my countenance. He now hurried towards me, pointing at the same time to the canoe, and exclaiming rapidly, "Puarkee! puarkee!" (Pig, pig). I pretended to yield to the deception, and repeated the words after him several times, as though acquiescing in what he said. The other savages, either deceived by my conduct or unwilling to manifest their displeasure at what could not now be remedied, took no further notice of the occurrence, and I immediately left the Ti.

All that night I lay awake, revolving in my mind the fearful situation in which I was placed. The last horrid revelation had now been made, and the full sense of my condition rushed upon my mind with a force I had never before experienced.

Where, thought I, desponding, is there the slightest prospect of escape? The only person who seemed to possess the ability to assist me was the stranger Marnoo; but would he ever return to the valley? And if he did, should I be permitted to hold any communication with him? It seemed as if I were cut off from every source of hope, and that nothing remained but passively to await whatever fate was in store for me. A thousand times I endeavoured to account for the mysterious conduct of the natives. For what conceivable purpose did they thus retain me a captive? What could be their object in treating me with such apparent kindness, and did it not cover some treacherous scheme? Or, if they had no other design than to hold me a prisoner, how should I be able to pass away my days in this narrow valley, deprived of all intercourse with civilized beings, and for ever separated from friends and home?

One only hope remained to me. The French could not long defer a visit to the bay, and if they should permanently locate any of their troops in the valley, the savages could not for any length of time conceal my existence from them. But what reason had I to suppose that I should be spared until such an event occurred—an event which might be postponed by a hundred different contingencies?

CHAPTER XXXIII

THE STRANGER AGAIN ARRIVES IN THE VALLEY—SINGULAR INTERVIEW WITH HIM—ATTEMPT TO ESCAPE—FAILURE—MELANCHOLY SITUATION—SYMPATHY OF MARHEYO.

"MARNOO, Marnoo pemi!" Such were the welcome sounds which fell upon my ear some ten days after the events related in the preceding chapter. Once more the approach of the stranger was heralded, and the intelligence operated upon me like magic. Again I should be able to converse with him in my own language; and I resolved at all hazards to concert with him some scheme, however desperate, to rescue me from a condition that had now become insupportable.

As he drew near, I remembered with many misgivings, the inauspicious termination of our former interview; and when he entered the house, I watched with intense anxiety the reception he met with from its inmates. To my joy, his appearance was hailed with the liveliest pleasure; and accosting me kindly, he seated himself by my side, and entered into conversation with the natives around him. It soon appeared, however, that on this occasion he had not any intelligence of importance to communicate. I inquired of him from whence he had last come? He replied from Pueearka, his native valley, and that he intended to return to it the same day.

At once it struck me that, could I but reach the valley under his protection, I might easily from thence reach Nukuheva by water; and animated by the prospect which this plan held out, I disclosed it in a few brief words to the stranger, and asked him how it could be best accomplished. My heart sank within me when in his broken English he answered me that it could never be effected. "Kannaka no let you go no where," he said; "you taboo. Why you no like to stay? Plenty moee-moee (sleep)—plenty kiki (eat)—plenty whihe-nee (young girls)—Oh, very good place Typee! Suppose you no like this bay, why you come? You no hear about Typee. All white men afraid Typee, so no white men come."

These words distressed me beyond belief; and when I again related to
him the circumstances under which I had descended into the valley, and sought
to enlist his sympathies in my behalf by appealing to the bodily misery I endured, he listened to me with impatience and cut me short by exclaiming passionately, "Me no hear you talk any more; by by Kannaka get mad, kill you
and me too. No you see he no want you to speak to me at all?—you see—ah!
by by you no mind—you get well, he kill you, eat you, hang you head up there,
like Happar Kannaka.—Now you listen—but no talk any more. By by I
go;—you see why I go.—Ah! then some night Kannaka all moee-moee (sleep)
—you run away, you come Pueearka. I speak Pueearka Kannaka—he no harm
you—ah! then I take you my canoe Nukuheva—and you no run away ship
no more." With these words, enforced by a vehemence of gesture I cannot
describe, Marnoo started from my side, and immediately engaged in conversation with some of the chiefs who had entered the house.

It would have been idle for me to have attempted resuming the interview
so peremptorily terminated by Marnoo, who was evidently little disposed to
compromise his own safety by any rash endeavours to ensure mine. But the
plan he had suggested struck me as one which might possibly be accomplished,
and I resolved to act upon it as speedily as possible.

Accordingly, when he rose to depart, I accompanied him with the natives
outside of the house, with a view of carefully noting the path he would take
in leaving the valley. Just before leaping from the pi-pi he clasped my hand,
and looking significantly at me, exclaimed, "Now you see—you do what I tell
you—ah! then you do good;—you no do so—ah! then you die." The next
moment he waved his spear in adieu to the islanders, and following the route
that conducted to a defile in the mountains lying opposite the Happar side,
was soon out of sight.

A mode of escape was now presented to me, but how was I to avail myself
of it? I was continually surrounded by the savages; I could not stir from
one house to another without being attended by some of them; and even during
the hours devoted to slumber the slightest movement which I made seemed
to attract the notice of those who shared the mats with me. In spite of these
obstacles, however, I determined forthwith to make the attempt. To do so
with any prospect of success, it was necessary that I should have at least two
hours' start before the islanders should discover my absence; for with such
facility was any alarm spread through the valley, and so familiar, of course,
were the inhabitants with the intricacies of the groves, that I could not hope,
lame and feeble as I was, and ignorant of the route, to secure my escape unless
I had this advantage. It was also by night alone that I could hope to accomplish my object, and then only by adopting the utmost precaution.

The entrance to Marheyo's habitation was through a low narrow opening
in its wicker-work front. This passage, for no conceivable reason that I could
devise, was always closed after the household had retired to rest, by drawing
a heavy slide across it, composed of a dozen or more bits of wood, ingeniously
fastened together by seizings of sinnate. When any of the inmates chose to
go outside, the noise occasioned by the removing of this rude door awakened
everybody else; and on more than one occasion I had remarked that the
islanders were nearly as irritable as more civilized beings under similar circumstances.

The difficulty thus placed in my way I determined to obviate in the following
manner. I would get up boldly in the course of the night, and drawing the
slide, issue from the house, and pretend that my object was merely to procure

a drink from the calabash, which always stood without the dwelling on the corner of the pi-pi. On re-entering I would purposely omit closing the passage after me, and trusting that the indolence of the savages would prevent them from repairing my neglect, would return to my mat, and waiting patiently until all were again asleep, I would then steal forth, and at once take the route to Pueearka.

The very night which followed Marnoo's departure, I proceeded to put this project into execution. About midnight, as I imagined, I rose and drew the slide. The natives, just as I had expected, started up, while some of them asked, "Arware poo awa, Tommo?" (Where are you going, Tommo?) "Wai" (water), I laconically answered, grasping the calabash. On hearing my reply they sank back again, and in a minute or two I returned to my mat, anxiously awaiting the result of the experiment.

One after another the savages, turning restlessly, appeared to resume their slumbers, and rejoicing at the stillness which prevailed, I was about to rise again from my couch, when I heard a slight rustling—a dark form was intercepted between me and the doorway—the slide was drawn across it, and the individual, whoever he was, returned to his mat. This was a sad blow to me; but as it might have roused the suspicions of the islanders to have made another attempt that night, I was reluctantly obliged to defer it until the next. Several times after I repeated the same manœuvre but with as little success as before. As my pretence for withdrawing from the house was to allay my thirst, Kory-Kory, either suspecting some design on my part, or else prompted by a desire to please me, regularly every evening placed a calabash of water by my side.

Even under these inauspicious circumstances I again and again renewed the attempt; but when I did so my valet always rose with me, as if determined I should not remove myself from his observation. For the present, therefore, I was obliged to abandon the attempt; but I endeavoured to console myself with the idea that by this mode I might yet effect my escape.

Shortly after Marnoo's visit I was reduced to such a state, that it was with extreme difficulty I could walk, even with the assistance of a spear, and Kory-Kory, as formerly, was obliged to carry me daily to the stream.

For hours and hours during the warmest part of the day I lay upon my mat, and while those around me were nearly all dozing away in careless ease, I remained awake gloomily pondering over the fate which it appeared now idle for me to resist, when I thought of the loved friends who were thousands and thousands of miles from the savage island in which I was held a captive, when I reflected that my dreadful fate would for ever be concealed from them, and that with hope deferred they might continue to await my return long after my inanimate form had blended with the dust of the valley—I could not repress a shudder of anguish.

How vividly is impressed upon my mind every minute feature of the scene which met my view during those long days of suffering and sorrow! At my request my mats were always spread directly facing the door, opposite which, and at a little distance, was the hut of boughs that Marheyo was building.

Whenever my gentle Fayaway and Kory-Kory, laying themselves down beside me, would leave me awhile to uninterrupted repose, I took a strange interest in the slightest movements of the eccentric old warrior. All alone during the stillness of the tropical mid-day, he would pursue his quiet work, sitting in the shade and weaving together the leaflets of his coco-nut branches, or rolling upon his knee the twisted fibres of bark to form the cords with which he tied together the thatching of his tiny house. Frequently suspending his employment, and noticing my melancholy eye fixed upon him, he would raise his hand with a gesture expressive of deep commiseration, and then moving towards me slowly would enter on tip-toes, fearful of disturbing the slumbering natives, and, taking the fan from my hand, would sit before me, swaying it gently to and fro, and gazing earnestly into my face.

Just beyond the pi-pi, and disposed in a triangle before the entrance of the house, were three magnificent breadfruit-trees. At this moment I can recall to my mind their slender shafts, and the graceful inequalities of their bark, on which my eye was accustomed to dwell day after day in the midst of my solitary musings. It is strange how inanimate objects will twine themselves into our affections, especially in the hour of affliction. Even now, amidst all the bustle and stir of the proud and busy city in which I am dwelling, the image of those three trees seems to come as vividly before my eyes as if they were actually present, and I still feel the soothing quiet pleasure which I then had in watching hour after hour their topmost boughs waving gracefully in the breeze.

CHAPTER XXXIV

THE ESCAPE.

NEARLY three weeks had elapsed since the second visit of Marnoo, and it must have been more than four months since I entered the valley, when one day about noon, and whilst everything was in profound silence, Mow-Mow, the one-eyed chief, suddenly appeared at the door, and leaning forward towards me as I lay directly facing him, said in a low tone, "Toby pemi ena" (Toby has arrived here). Gracious heaven! What a tumult of emotions rushed upon me at this startling intelligence! Insensible to the pain that had before distracted me, I leaped to my feet, and called wildly to Kory-Kory, who was reposing by my side. The startled islanders sprang from their mats; the news was quickly communicated to them; and the next moment I was making my way to the Ti on the back of Kory-Kory, and surrounded by the excited savages.

All that I could comprehend of the particulars which Mow-Mow rehearsed to his auditors as we proceeded, was that my long-lost companion had arrived in a boat which had just entered the bay. These tidings made me most anxious to be carried at once to the sea, lest some untoward circumstance should prevent our meeting; but to this they would not consent, and continued their course towards the royal abode. As we approached it, Mehevi and several chiefs showed themselves from the piazza, and called upon us loudly to come to them.

As soon as we had approached, I endeavoured to make them understand that I was going down to the sea to meet Toby. To this the king objected and motioned Kory-Kory to bring me into the house. It was in vain to resist; and in a few moments I found myself within the Ti, surrounded by a noisy group engaged in discussing the recent intelligence. Toby's name was frequently repeated, coupled with violent exclamations of astonishment. It seemed as if they yet remained in doubt with regard to the fact of his arrival, and at every fresh report that was brought from the shore they betrayed the liveliest emotions.

Almost frenzied at being held in this state of suspense, I passionately besought Mehevi to permit me to proceed. Whether my companion had arrived or not, I felt a presentiment that my own fate was about to be decided. Again and again I renewed my petition to Mehevi. He regarded me with a fixed and serious eye, but at length yielding to my importunity, reluctantly granted my request.

Accompanied by some fifty of the natives, I now rapidly continued my journey; every few moments being transferred from the back of one to another, and urging my bearer forward all the while with earnest entreaties. As I thus hurried forward no doubt as to the truth of the information I had received ever crossed my mind. I was alive only to the one overwhelming idea, that a chance of deliverance was now afforded me, if the jealous opposition of the savages could be overcome.

Having been prohibited from approaching the sea during the whole of my stay in the valley, I had always associated with it the idea of escape. Toby too—if indeed he had ever voluntarily deserted me—must have effected his flight by the sea; and now that I was drawing near to it myself, I indulged in hopes which I had never felt before. It was evident that a boat had entered the bay, and I saw little reason to doubt the truth of the report that it had brought my companion. Every time therefore that we gained an elevation, I looked eagerly around, hoping to behold him.

In the midst of an excited throng, who by their violent gestures and wild cries appeared to be under the influence of some excitement as strong as my own, I was now borne along at a rapid trot, frequently stooping my head to avoid the branches which crossed the path, and never ceasing to implore those who carried me to accelerate their already swift pace.

In this manner we had proceeded about four or five miles, when we were met by a party of some twenty islanders, between whom and those who accompanied me ensured an animated conference. Impatient of the delay occasioned by this interruption, I was beseeching the man who carried me to proceed without his loitering companions, when Kory-Kory, running to my side, informed me, in three fatal words, that the news had all proved false—that Toby had not arrived—"Toby owlee permi." Heaven only knows how, in the state of mind and body I then was, I ever sustained the agony which this intelligence caused me: not that the news was altogether unexpected; but I had trusted that the fact might not have been made known until we should have arrived upon the beach. As it was, I at once foresaw the course the savages would pursue. They had only yielded thus far to my entreaties, that I might give a joyful welcome to my long-absent comrade; but now that it was known he had not arrived, they would at once oblige me to turn back.

My anticipations were but too correct. In spite of the resistance I made, they carried me into a house which was near the spot, and left me upon the mats. Shortly afterwards several of those who had accompanied me from the Ti, detaching themselves from the others, proceeded in the direction of the sea. Those who remained—among whom were Marheyo, Mow-Mow, Kory-Kory, and Tinor—gathered about the dwelling and appeared to be awaiting their return.

This convinced me that strangers—perhaps some of my own countrymen—had for some cause or other entered the bay. Distracted at the idea of their vicinity, and reckless of the pain which I suffered, I heeded not the assurances of the islanders, that there were no boats at the beach, but starting to my feet endeavoured to gain the door. Instantly the passage was blocked up by several men, who commanded me to resume my seat. The fierce looks of the irritated savages admonished me that I could gain nothing by force, and that it was by entreaty alone that I could hope to compass my object.

Guided by this consideration, I turned to Mow-Mow, the only chief present whom I had been much in the habit of seeing, and carefully concealing my real design, tried to make him comprehend that I still believed Toby to have arrived on the shore, and besought him to allow me to go forward to welcome him. To all his repeated assertions, that my companion had not been seen, I pretended to turn a deaf ear: while I urged my solicitations with an eloquence of gesture which the one-eyed chief appeared unable to resist. He seemed indeed to regard me as a froward child, to whose wishes he had not the heart to oppose force, and whom he must consequently humour. He spoke a few words to the natives, who at once retreated from the door, and I immediately passed out of the house.

Here I looked earnestly round for Kory-Kory; but that hitherto faithful servitor was nowhere to be seen. Unwilling to linger even for a single instant when every moment might be so important, I motioned to a muscular fellow near me to take me upon his back: to my surprise he angrily refused. I turned to another, but with a like result. A third attempt was as unsuccessful and I immediately perceived what had induced Mow-Mow to grant my request and why the other natives conducted themselves in so strange a manner. It was evident that the chief had only given me liberty to continue my progress towards the sea because he supposed that I was deprived of the means of reaching it.

Convinced by this of their determination to retain me a captive, I became desperate; and almost insensible to the pain which I suffered I seized a spear which was leaning against the projecting eaves of the house, and supporting myself with it, resumed the path that swept by the dwelling. To my surprise I was suffered to proceed alone, all the natives remaining in front of the house, and engaging in earnest conversation which every moment became more loud and vehement; and to my unspeakable delight I perceived that some difference of opinion had arisen between them; that two parties, in short, were formed, and consequently that in their divided counsels there was some chance of my deliverance.

Before I had proceeded a hundred yards I was again surrounded by the savages, who were still in all the heat of argument, and appeared every moment as if they would come to blows. In the midst of this tumult old Marheyo came to my side, and I shall never forget the benevolent expression of his countenance. He placed his arm upon my shoulder, and emphatically pronounced the only two English words I had taught him—"Home" and "Mother." I at once understood what he meant, and eagerly expressed my thanks to him. Fayaway and Kory-Kory were by his side, both weeping violently; and it was not until the old man had twice repeated the command that his son could bring himself to obey him, and take me again upon his back. The one-eyed chief opposed his doing so, but he was overruled, and, as it seemed to me, by some of his own party.

We proceeded onwards, and never shall I forget the ecstasy I felt when I first heard the roar of the surf breaking upon the beach. Before long I saw the flashing billows themselves through the opening between the trees. Oh, glorious sight and sound of ocean! with what rapture did I hail you as familiar friends! By this time the shouts of the crowd upon the beach were distinctly audible.

and in the blended confusion of sounds I almost fancied I could distinguish the voices of my own countrymen.

When we reached the open space which lay between the groves and the sea, the first object that met my view was an English whale-boat, lying with her bow pointed from the shore, and only a few fathoms distant from it. It was manned by five islanders, dressed in short tunics of calico. My first impression was that they were in the very act of pulling out from the bay; and that, after all my exertions, I had come too late. My soul sank within me: but a second glance convinced me that the boat was only hanging off to keep out of the surf; and the next moment I heard my own name shouted out by a voice from the midst of the crowd.

Looking in the direction of the sound, I perceived, to my indescribable joy, the tall figure of Karakoee, an Oahu Kannaka, who had often been aboard the *Dolly*, while she lay in Nukuheva. He wore the green shooting-jacket with gilt buttons, which had been given to him by an officer of the *Reine Blanche*—the French flag-ship—and in which I had always seen him dressed. I now remembered the Kannaka had frequently told me that his person was tabooed in all the valleys of the island, and the sight of him at such a moment as this filled my heart with a tumult of delight.

Karakoee stood near the edge of the water with a large roll of cotton-cloth thrown over one arm, and holding two or three canvas bags of powder; while with the other hand he grasped a musket, which he appeared to be proffering to several of the chiefs around him. But they turned with· disgust from his offers, and seemed to be impatient at his presence, with vehement gestures waving him off to his boat, and commanding him to depart.

The Kannaka, however, still maintained his ground, and I at once perceived that he was seeking to purchase my freedom. Animated by the idea, I called upon him loudly to come to me; but he replied, in broken English, that the islanders had threatened to pierce him with their spears, if he stirred a foot towards me. At this time I was still advancing, surrounded by a dense throng of the natives, several of whom had their hands upon me, and more than one javelin was threateningly pointed at me. Still I perceived clearly that many of those least friendly towards me looked irresolute and anxious.

I was still some thirty yards from Karakoee when my further progress was prevented by the natives, who compelled me to sit down upon the ground, while they still retained their hold upon my arms. The din' and tumult now became tenfold, and I perceived that several of the priests were on the spot, all of whom were evidently urging Mow-Mow and the other chiefs to prevent my departure; and the detestable word "Roo-ne! Roo-ne!" which I had heard repeated a thousand times during the day, was now shouted out on every side of me. Still I saw that the Kannaka continued his exertions in my favour—that he was boldly debating the matter with the savages, and was striving to entice them by displaying his cloth and powder, and snapping the lock of his musket. But all he said or did appeared only to augment the clamours of those around him, who seemed bent upon driving him into the sea.

When I remembered the extravagant value placed by these people upon the articles which were offered to them in exchange for me, and which were so indignantly rejected, I saw a new proof of the same fixed determination of purpose they had all along manifested with regard to me, and in despair, and reckless of consequences, I exerted all my strength, and shaking myself free from the grasp of those who held me, I sprang upon my feet and rushed towards Karakoee.

The rash attempt nearly decided my fate; for, fearful that I might slip from them, several of the islanders now raised a simultaneous shout, and pressing upon Karakoee, they menaced him with furious gestures, and actually forced him into the sea. Appalled at their violence, the poor fellow, standing nearly to the waist in the surf, endeavoured to pacify them; but at length, fearful that they would do him some fatal violence, he beckoned to his comrades to pull in at once, and take him into the boat.

It was at this agonizing moment, when I thought all hope was ended, that a new contest arose between the two parties who had accompanied me to the shore; blows were struck, wounds were given, and blood flowed. In the interest excited by the fray, every one had left me except Marheyo, Kory-Kory, and poor dear Fayaway, who clung to me, sobbing indignantly. I saw that now or never was the moment. Clasping my hands together, I looked imploringly at Marheyo, and moved towards the now almost deserted beach. The tears were in the old man's eyes, but neither he nor Kory-Kory attempted to hold me, and I soon reached the Kannaka who had been anxiously watching my movements; the rowers pulled in as near as they dared to the edge of the surf; I gave one parting embrace to Fayaway, who seemed speechless with sorrow, and the next instant I found myself safe in the boat, and Karakoee by my side, who told the rowers at once to give way. Marheyo and Kory-Kory, and a great many of the women, followed me into the water, and I was determined, as the only mark of gratitude I could show, to give them the articles which had been brought as my ransom. I handed the musket to Kory-Kory, with a rapid gesture which was equivalent to a "Deed of Gift"; threw the roll of cotton to old Marheyo, pointing as I did so to poor Fayaway, who had retired from the edge of the water and was sitting down disconsolate on the shingles; and tumbled the powder-bags out to the nearest young ladies, all of whom were vastly willing to take them. This distribution did not occupy ten seconds, and before it was over the boat was under full way; the Kannaka all the while exclaiming loudly against what he considered a useless throwing away of valuable property.

Although it was clear that my movements had been noticed by several of the natives, still they had not suspended the conflict in which they were engaged, and it was not until the boat was above fifty yards from the shore that Mow-Mow and some six or seven other warriors rushed into the sea and hurled their javelins at us. Some of the weapons passed quite as close to us as was desirable, but no one was wounded, and the men pulled away gallantly. But although soon out of the reach of the spears, our progress was extremely slow; it blew strong upon the shore, and the tide was against us; and I saw Karakoee, who was steering the boat, give many a look towards a jutting point of the bay round which we had to pass.

For a minute or two after our departure, the savages, who had formed into different groups, remained perfectly motionless and silent. All at once the enraged chief showed by his gestures that he had resolved what course he would take. Shouting loudly to his companions, and pointing with his tomahawk towards the headland, he set off at full speed in that direction, and was followed by about thirty of the natives, among whom were several of the priests, all yelling out "Roo-ne! Roo-ne!" at the very top of their voices. Their intention was evidently to swim off from the headland and intercept us in our course. The wind was freshening every minute, and was right in our teeth, and it was one of those chopping angry seas in which it is so difficult to row. Still the chances seemed in our favour, but when we came within a hundred yards of the point, the active savages were already dashing into the water, and we all feared that within five minutes' time we should have a score of the infuriated wretches around us. If so, our doom was sealed, for these savages, unlike the feeble swimmers of civilized countries, are, if anything, more formidable antagonists in the water than when on the land. It was all a trial of strength; our natives pulled till their oars bent again, and the crowd of swimmers shot through the water despite its roughness, with fearful rapidity.

By the time we had reached the headland, the savages were spread right across our course. Our rowers got out their knives and held them ready between their teeth, and I seized the boat-hook. We were well aware that if they succeeded in intercepting us they would practise upon us the manœuvre which has proved so fatal to many a boat's crew in these seas. They would grapple the oars, and seizing hold of the gunwale, capsize the boat, and then we should be entirely at their mercy.

After a few breathless moments I discerned Mow-Mow. The athletic islander, with his tomahawk between his teeth, was dashing the water before him till it foamed again. He was the nearest to us, and in another instant he would have seized one of the oars. Even at the moment I felt horror at the act I was about to commit; but it was no time for pity or compunction, and with a true aim, and exerting all my strength, I dashed the boat-hook at him. It struck him just below the throat, and forced him downwards. I had no time to repeat my blow, but I saw him rise to the surface in the wake of the boat, and never shall I forget the ferocious expression of his countenance.

Only one other of the savages reached the boat. He seized the gunwale, but the knives of our rowers so mauled his wrists, that he was forced to quit his hold, and the next minute we were past them all, and in safety. The strong excitement which had thus far kept me up, now left me, and I fell back fainting into the arms of Karakoee.

.　　　.　　　.　　　.　　　.　　　.　　　.

The circumstances connected with my most unexpected escape may be very briefly stated. The captain of an Australian vessel, being in distress for men in these remote seas, had put into Nukuheva in order to recruit his ship's company; but not a single man was to be obtained; and the barque was about to get under weigh, when she was boarded by Karakoee, who informed the disappointed Englishman that an American sailor was detained by the savages in the neighbouring bay of Typee; and he offered, if supplied with suitable articles of traffic, to undertake his release. The Kannaka had gained his intelligence from Marnoo, to whom, after all, I was indebted for my escape. The proposition was acceded to; and Karakoee, taking with him five tabooed natives of Nukuheva, again repaired aboard the barque, which in a few hours sailed to that part of the island, and threw her main-topsail aback right off the entrance to the Typee bay. The whale-boat, manned by the tabooed crew, pulled towards the head of the inlet, while the ship lay "off and on" awaiting its return.

The events which ensued have already been detailed, and little more remains to be related. On reaching the *Julia* I was lifted over the side, and my strange appearance and remarkable adventure occasioned the liveliest interest. Every attention was bestowed upon me that humanity could suggest. But to such a state was I reduced, that three months elapsed before I recovered my health.

The mystery which hung over the fate of my friend and companion Toby has never been cleared up. I still remain ignorant whether he succeeded in leaving the valley, or perished at the hands of the islanders.

APPENDIX

THE author of this volume arrived at Tahiti the very day that the iniquitous designs of the French were consummated by inducing the subordinate chiefs, during the absence of their queen, to ratify an artfully drawn treaty, by which she was virtually deposed. Both menaces and caresses were employed on this occasion, and the 32-pounders which peeped out of the portholes of the frigate were the principal arguments adduced to quiet the scruples of the more conscientious islanders.

And yet this piratical seizure of Tahiti, with all the woe and desolation which resulted from it, created not half so great a sensation, at least in America, as was caused by the proceedings of the English at the Sandwich Islands. No transaction has ever been more grossly misrepresented than the events which occurred upon the arrival of Lord George Paulet at Oahu. During a residence of four months at Honolulu, the metropolis of the group, the author was in the confidence of an Englishman who was much employed by his lordship; and great was the author's astonishment on his arrival at Boston, in the autumn of 1844, to read the distorted accounts and fabrications which had produced in the United States so violent an outbreak of indignation against the English. He deems it, therefore, a mere act of justice towards a gallant officer briefly to state the leading circumstances connected with the event in question.

It is needless to rehearse all the abuse that for some time previous to the spring of 1843 had been heaped upon the British residents, especially upon Captain Charlton, her Britannic Majesty's consul-general, by the native authorities of the Sandwich Islands. High in the favour of the imbecile king at this time was one Dr. Judd, a sanctimonious apothecary-adventurer, who, with other kindred and influential spirits, were animated by an inveterate dislike to England. The ascendancy of a junto of ignorant and designing Methodist elders in the councils of a half-civilized king, ruling with absolute sway over a nation just poised between barbarism and civilization, and exposed by the peculiarities of its relations with foreign States to unusual difficulties, was not precisely calculated to impart a healthy tone to the policy of the government.

At last matters were brought to such an extremity, through the iniquitous maladministration of affairs, that the endurance of further insults and injuries on the part of the British consul was no longer to be borne. Captain Charlton, insultingly forbidden to leave the islands, clandestinely withdrew, and arriving at Valparaiso, conferred with Rear-Admiral Thomas, the English commander-in-chief on the Pacific station. In consequence of this communication, Lord George Paulet was dispatched by the admiral in the *Carysfort* frigate, to inquire into and correct the alleged abuses. On arriving at his destination, he sent his first-lieutenant ashore with a letter to the king, couched in terms of the utmost courtesy, and soliciting the honour of an audience. The messenger was denied access to his Majesty, and Paulet was coolly referred to Doctor Judd, and informed that the apothecary was invested with plenary powers to treat with him. Rejecting this insolent proposition, his lordship again addressed the king by letter, and renewed his previous request; but he encountered another repulse. Justly indignant at this treatment, he penned a third epistle, enumerating the grievances to be redressed, and demanding a compliance with his requisitions, under penalty of immediate hostilities.

The government was now obliged to act, and an artful stroke of policy was decided upon by the despicable counsellors of the king to entrap the sympathies and rouse the indignation of Christendom. His Majesty was made to intimate to the British captain that he could not, as the conscientious ruler of his beloved people, comply with the arbitrary demands of his lordship, and in deprecation of the horrors of war, tendered to his acceptance the "provisional cession" of the islands, subject to the result of the negotiations then pending in London. Paulet, a bluff and straightforward sailor, took the king at his word, and after some preliminary arrangements, entered upon the administration of Hawaiian affairs, in the same firm and benignant spirit which marked the discipline of his frigate, and which had rendered him the idol of his ship's company. He soon endeared himself to nearly all orders of the islanders; but the king and the chiefs, whose feudal sway over the common people is laboriously sought to be perpetuated by their missionary advisers, regarded all his proceedings with the most vigilant animosity. Jealous of his growing popularity, and unable to counteract it, they endeavoured to assail his reputation abroad by ostentatiously protesting against his acts, and appealing in Oriental phrase to the *wide universe* to witness and compassionate their *unparalleled wrongs*.

Heedless of their idle clamours, Lord George Paulet addressed himself to the task of reconciling the differences among the foreign residents, remedying their grievances, promoting their mercantile interests, and ameliorating as far as lay in his power the condition of the degraded natives. The iniquities he brought to light and·instantly suppressed are too numerous to be here recorded; but one instance may be mentioned that will give some idea of the lamentable misrule to which these poor islanders are subjected.

It is well known that the laws at the Sandwich Islands are subject to the most capricious alterations, which, by confounding all ideas of right and wrong in the minds of the natives, produce the most pernicious effects. In no case is this mischief more plainly discernible than in the· continually shifting regulations concerning licentiousness. At one time the most innocent freedoms between the sexes are punished with fine and imprisonment; at another the revocation of the statute is followed by the most open and undisguised profligacy.

It so happened that at the period of Paulet's arrival the Connecticut blue laws had been for at least three weeks steadily enforced. In consequence of this, the fort at Honolulu was filled with a great number of young girls, who were confined there doing penance for their slips from virtue. Paulet, although at first unwilling to interfere with regulations having reference solely to the natives themselves, was eventually, by the prevalence of certain reports, induced to institute a strict inquiry into the internal administration of General Kekuanoa, governor of the island of Oahu, one of the pillars of the Hawaiian Church, and captain of the fort. He soon ascertained that numbers of the young females employed during the day at work intended for the benefit of the king, were at night smuggled over the ramparts of the fort—which on one side directly overhangs the sea—and were conveyed by stealth on board such vessels as had contracted with the General to be supplied with them. Before daybreak they returned to their quarters, and their own silence with regard to these secret excursions was purchased by a small portion of those wages of iniquity which were placed in the hands of Kekuanoa.

The vigour with which the laws concerning licentiousness were at that period enforced, enabled the General to monopolize in a great measure the detestable trade in which he was engaged, and there consequently flowed into his coffers—and some say into those of the government also—considerable sums of money. It is indeed a lamentable fact, that the principal revenue of the Hawaiian government is derived from the fines levied upon, or rather the licenses taken out by, Vice, the prosperity of which is linked with that of the government. Were the people to become virtuous the authorities would become poor; but from present indications there is little apprehension to be entertained on that score.

Some five months after the date of the cession, the *Dublin* frigate, carrying the flag of Rear-Admiral Thomas, entered the harbour of Honolulu. The excitement that her sudden appearance produced on shore was prodigious. Three days after her arrival an English sailor hauled down the red cross which had been flying from the heights of the fort, and the Hawaiian colours were again displayed upon the same staff. At the same moment the long 42-pounders upon Punchbowl Hill opened their iron throats in triumphant reply to the thunders of the five men-of-war in the harbour; and King Kammahamaha III, surrounded by a splendid group of British and American officers, unfurled the royal standard to assembled thousands of his subjects, who, attracted by the imposing military display of the foreigners, had flocked to witness the formal restoration of the islands to their ancient rulers.

The Admiral, after sanctioning the proceedings of his subaltern, had brought the authorities to terms; and so removed the necessity of acting any longer under the provisional cession.

The event was made an occasion of riotous rejoicing by the king and the principal chiefs, who easily secured a display of enthusiasm from the inferior orders, by remitting for a time the accustomed severity of the laws. Royal proclamations in English and Hawaiian were placarded in the streets of Honolulu, and posted up in the more populous villages of the group, in which his Majesty announced to his loving subjects the re-establishment of his throne, and called upon them to celebrate it by breaking through all moral, legal, and religious restraint for ten consecutive days, during which time all the laws of the land were solemnly declared to be suspended.

Who that happened to be at Honolulu during those ten memorable days will ever forget them! The spectacle of universal broad-day debauchery, which was then exhibited, beggars description. The natives of the surrounding islands flocked to Honolulu by hundreds, and the crews of two frigates, opportunely let loose like so many demons to swell the heathenish uproar, gave the crowning flourish to the scene. It was a sort of Polynesian saturnalia. Deeds too atrocious to be mentioned were done at noon-day in the open street, and some of the islanders caught in the very act of stealing from the foreigners, were, on being taken to the fort by the aggrieved party, suffered immediately to go at large and to retain the stolen property—Kekuanoa informing the white men, with a sardonic grin, that the laws were "hannapa" (tied up).

The history of these ten days reveals in their true colours the character of the Sandwich islanders, and furnishes an eloquent commentary on the results which have flowed from the labours of the missionaries. Freed from the restraints of severe penal laws, the natives almost to a man had plunged voluntarily into every species of wickedness and excess, and by their utter disregard of all decency plainly showed, that although they had been schooled into a seeming submission to the new order of things, they were in reality as depraved and vicious as ever.

Such were the events which produced in America so general an outbreak of indignation against the spirited and high-minded Paulet. He is not the first man who, in the fearless discharge of his duty, has awakened the senseless clamours of those whose narrow-minded suspicions blind them to a proper appreciation of measures which unusual exigencies may have rendered necessary.

It is almost needless to add that the British Cabinet never had any idea of appropriating the islands; and it furnishes a sufficient vindication of the acts of Lord George Paulet, that he not only received the unqualified approbation of his own government, but that to this hour the great body of the Hawaiian people invoke blessings on his head, and look back with gratitude to the time when his liberal and paternal sway diffused peace and happiness among them.

NOTE TO THE SEQUEL

THE author was more than two years in the South Seas, after escaping from the valley, as recounted in the last chapter. Some time after returning home the foregoing narrative was published, though it was little thought at the time that this would be the means of revealing the existence of Toby, who had long been given up for lost. But so it proved.

The story of his escape supplies a natural sequel to the adventure, and as such it is now added to the volume. It was related to the author by Toby himself not ten days since.

NEW YORK,
July 1846

SEQUEL

THE STORY OF TOBY

THE morning my comrade left me, as related in the narrative, he was accompanied by a large party of the natives, some of them carrying fruit and hogs for the purposes of traffic, as the report had spread that boats had touched at the bay.

As they proceeded through the settled parts of the valley, numbers joined them from every side, running with animated cries from every pathway. So excited were the whole party, that eager as Toby was to gain the beach, it was almost as much as he could do to keep up with them. Making the valley ring with their shouts, they hurried along on a swift trot, those in advance pausing now and then, and flourishing their weapons to urge the rest forward.

Presently they came to a place where the path crossed a band of the main stream of the valley. Here a strange sound came through the grove beyond, and the Islanders halted. It was Mow-Mow, the one-eyed chief, who had gone on before; he was striking his heavy lance against the hollow bough of a tree.

This was a signal of alarm;—for nothing was now heard but shouts of "Happar! Happar!"—the warriors tilting with their spears and brandishing them in the air, and the women and boys shouting to each other, and picking up the stones in the bed of the stream. In a moment or two Mow-Mow and two or three other chiefs ran out from the grove, and the din increased tenfold.

Now, thought Toby, for a fray; and being unarmed, he besought one of the young men domiciled with Marheyo for the loan of his spear. But he was refused; the youth roguishly telling him that the weapon was very good for him (the Typee), but that a white man could fight much better with his fists.

The merry humour of this young wag seemed to be shared by the rest, for in spite of their warlike cries and gestures, everybody was capering about and laughing, as if it was one of the funniest things in the world to be awaiting the flight of a score or two of Happar javelins from an ambush in the thickets.

While my comrade was in vain trying to make out the meaning of all this, a good number of the natives separated themselves from the rest and ran off into the grove on one side, the others now keeping perfectly still, as if awaiting the result. After a little while, however, Mow-Mow, who stood in advance, motioned them to come on stealthily, which they did, scarcely rustling a leaf. Thus they crept along for ten or fifteen minutes, every now and then pausing to listen.

Toby by no means relished this sort of skulking; if there was going to be a fight he wanted it to begin at once. But all in good time,—for just then, as they went prowling into the thickest of the wood, terrific howls burst upon them on all sides, and volleys of darts and stones flew across the path. Not an enemy was to be seen, and, what was still more surprising, not a single man dropped, though the pebbles fell among the leaves like hail.

There was a moment's pause, when the Typees, with wild shrieks, flung themselves into the covert, spear in hand; nor was Toby behindhand. Coming so near getting his skull broken by the stones, and animated by an old grudge he bore the Happars, he was among the first to dash at them. As he broke his way through the underbrush, trying, as he did so, to wrest a spear from a young chief, the shouts of battle all of a sudden ceased, and the wood was as still as death. The next moment, the party who had left them so mysteriously rushed out from behind every bush and tree, and united with the rest in long and merry peals of laughter.

It was all a sham, and Toby, who was quite out of breath with excitement, was much incensed at being made a fool of.

It afterwards turned out that the whole affair had been concerted for his particular benefit, though with what precise view it would be hard to tell. My comrade was the more enraged at this boys' play, since it had consumed so much time, every moment of which might be precious. Perhaps, however, it was partly intended for this very purpose; and he was led to think so, because, when the natives started again, he observed that they did not seem to be in so great a hurry as before. At last, after they had gone some distance, Toby, thinking all the while that they never would get to the sea, two men came running towards them, and a regular halt ensued, followed by a noisy discussion during which Toby's name was often repeated. All this made him more and more anxious to learn what was going on at the beach; but it was in vain that he now tried to push forward; the natives held him back.

In a few moments the conference ended, and many of them ran down the path in the direction of the water, the rest surrounding Toby, and entreating him to "Moce," or sit down and rest himself. As an additional inducement, several calabashes of food, which had been brought along, were now placed on the ground, and opened, and pipes also were lighted. Toby bridled his impatience a while, but at last sprang to his feet and dashed forward again. He was soon overtaken nevertheless, and again surrounded, but without further detention was then permitted to go down to the sea.

They came out upon a bright green space between the groves and the water, and close under the shadow of the Happar mountain, where a path was seen, winding out of sight through a gorge.

No sign of a boat, however, was beheld; nothing but a tumultuous crowd of men and women, and some one in their midst, earnestly talking to them. As my comrade advanced, this person came forward and proved to be no stranger. He was an old grizzled sailor, whom Toby and myself had frequently seen in Nukuheva, where he lived an easy devil-may-care life in the household of Mowanna the king, going by the name of "Jimmy." In fact, he was the royal favourite, and had a good deal to say in his master's councils. He wore a Manilla hat and a sort of tappa morning gown, sufficiently loose and negligent to show the verse of a song tatooed upon his chest, and a variety of spirited cuts by native artists in other parts of his body. He sported a fishing-rod in his hand, and carried a sooty old pipe slung about his neck.

This old rover having retired from active life, had resided in Nukuheva for some time, could speak the language, and for that reason was frequently employed by the French as an interpreter. He was an arrant old gossip too; for ever coming off in his canoe to the ships in the bay, and regaling their crews with choice little morsels of court scandal; such, for instance, as a shameful intrigue of his majesty with a Happar damsel, a public dancer at the feasts, and otherwise relating some incredible tales about the Marquesas generally. I remember in particular his telling the *Dolly's* crew what proved to be literally a cock and bull story, about two natural prodigies which he said were then on the island. One was an old monster of a hermit, having a marvellous reputation for sanctity, and reputed a famous sorcerer, who lived away off in a den among the mountains, where he hid from the world a great pair of horns that grew out of his temples. Notwithstanding his reputation for piety, this horrid old fellow was the terror of all the island round, being reported to come out from his retreat, and go a-man-hunting every dark night. Some anonymous Paul Pry, too, coming down the mountain, once got a peep at his den and found it full of bones. In short, he was a most unheard-of monster.

The other prodigy Jimmy told us about, was the younger son of a chief, who although but just turned of ten, had entered upon holy orders, because his superstitious countrymen thought him especially intended for the priesthood from the fact of his having a comb on his head like a rooster. But this was not all; for still more wonderful to relate, the boy prided himself upon this strange crest, being actually endowed with a cock's voice, and frequently crowing over his peculiarity.

But to return to Toby. The moment he saw the old rover on the beach, he ran up to him, the natives following after, and forming a circle round them.

After welcoming him to the shore, Jimmy went on to tell him how that he knew all about our having run away from the ship, and being among the Typees. Indeed, he had been urged by Mowanna to come over to the valley, and after visiting his friends there, to bring us back with him, his royal master being exceedingly anxious to share with him the reward which had been held out for our capture. He, however, assured Toby that he had indignantly spurned the offer.

All this astonished my comrade not a little, as neither of us had entertained the least idea that any white man ever visited the Typees sociably. But Jimmy told him that such was the case nevertheless, although he seldom came into the bay, and scarcely ever went back from the beach. One of the priests of the valley, in some way or other connected with an old tatooed divine in Nukuheva, was a friend of his, and through him he was "taboo."

He said, moreover, that he was sometimes employed to come round to the bay, and engage fruit for ships lying in Nukuheva. In fact, he was now on that very errand, according to his own account, having just come across the mountains by the way of Happar. By noon of the next day the fruit would be heaped up in stacks on the beach, in readiness for the boats which he then intended to bring into the bay.

Jimmy now asked Toby whether he wished to leave the island; if he did, there was a ship in want of men lying in the other harbour, and would be glad to take him over, and see him on board that very day.

"No," said Toby, "I cannot leave the island unless my comrade goes with me. I left him up the valley because they would not let him come down. Let us go now and fetch him."

"But how is he to cross the mountain with us," replied Jimmy, "even if we get him down to the beach? Better let him stay till to-morrow, and I will bring him round to Nukuheva in the boats."

"That will never do," said Toby; "but come along with me now, and let us get him down here at any rate;" and yielding to the impulse of the moment, he started to hurry back into the valley. But hardly was his back turned, when a dozen hands were laid on him, and he learned that he could not go a step farther.

It was in vain that he fought with them; they would not hear of his stirring from the beach. Cut to the heart at this unexpected repulse, Toby now conjured the sailor to go after me alone. But Jimmy replied, that in the mood the Typees then were they would not permit him so to do, though at the same time he was not afraid of their offering him any harm.

Little did Toby then think, as he afterwards had good reason to suspect, that this very Jimmy was a heartless villain, who, by his arts, had just incited the natives to restrain him as he was in the act of going after me. Well must the old sailor have known, too, that the natives would never consent to our leaving together, and he therefore wanted to get Toby off alone, for a purpose which he afterwards made plain. Of all this, however, my comrade now knew nothing.

He was still struggling with the islanders when Jimmy again came up to him, and warned him against irritating them, saying that he was only making matters worse for both of us, and if they became enraged, there was no telling what might happen. At last he made Toby sit down on a broken canoe by a pile of stones, upon which was a ruinous little shrine supported by four upright paddles, and in front partly screened by a net. The fishing parties met there when they came in from the sea, for their offerings were laid before an image, upon a smooth black stone within. This spot Jimmy said was strictly taboo, and no one would molest or come near him while he stayed by its shadow. The old sailor then went off, and began speaking very earnestly to Mow-Mow and some other chiefs, while all the rest formed a circle round the taboo place, looking intently at Toby, and talking to each other without ceasing.

Now, notwithstanding what Jimmy had just told him, there presently came up to my comrade an old woman, who seated herself beside him on the canoe.

"Typee Mortarkee?" said she. "Mortarkee nuee," said Toby.

She then asked him whether he was going to Nukuheva; he nodded yes; and with a plaintive wail and her eyes filling with tears she rose and left him.

This old woman, the sailor afterwards said, was the wife of an aged king of a small inland valley, communicating by a deep pass with the country of the Typees. The inmates of the two valleys were related to each other by blood, and were known by the same name. The old woman had gone down into the Typee valley the day before, and was now with three chiefs, her sons, on a visit to her kinsmen.

As the old king's wife left him, Jimmy again came up to Toby, and told him that he had just talked the whole matter over with the natives, and there was only one course for him to follow. They would not allow him to go back into the valley, and harm would certainly come to both him and me, if he remained much longer on the beach. "So," said he, "you and I had better go to Nukuheva now overland, and to-morrow I will bring Tommo, as they call him, by water; they have promised to carry him down to the sea for me early in the morning, so that there will be no delay."

"No, no," said Toby desperately, "I will not leave him that way; we must escape together."

"Then there is no hope for you," exclaimed the sailor; "for if I leave you here on the beach, as soon as I am gone you will be carried back into the valley, and then neither of you will ever look upon the sea again." And with many oaths he swore that if he would only go to Nukuheva with him that day, he would be sure to have me there the very next morning.

"But how do you know they will bring him down to the beach to-morrow, when they will not do so to-day?" asked Toby. But the sailor had many reasons, all of which were so mixed up with the mysterious customs of the islanders, that he was none the wiser. Indeed, their conduct, especially in preventing him from returning into the valley, was absolutely unaccountable to him; and added to everything else, was the bitter reflection, that the old sailor, after all, might possibly be deceiving him. And then again he had to think of me, left alone with the natives, and by no means well. If he went with Jimmy, he might at least hope to procure some relief for me. But might not the savages who had acted so strangely, hurry me off somewhere before his return? Then, even if he remained, perhaps they would not let him go back into the valley where I was.

Thus perplexed was my poor comrade; he knew not what to do, and his courageous spirit was of no use to him now. There he was, all by himself, seated upon the broken canoe—the natives grouped around him at a distance, and eyeing him more and more fixedly.

"It is getting late," said Jimmy, who was standing behind the rest. "Nukuheva is far off, and I cannot cross the Happar country by night. You see how it is: if you come along with me, all will be well; if you do not, depend upon it, neither of you will ever escape."

"There is no help for it," said Toby, at last, with a heavy heart, "I will have to trust you;" and he came out from the shadow of the little shrine, and cast a long look up the valley.

"Now keep close to my side," said the sailor, "and let us be moving quickly." Tinor and Fayaway here appeared; the kind-hearted old woman embracing Toby's knees, and giving way to a flood of tears; while Fayaway, hardly less moved, spoke some few words of English she had learned, and held up three fingers before him—in so many days he would return.

At last Jimmy pulled Toby out of the crowd, and after calling to a young Typee who was standing by with a young pig in his arms, all three started for the mountains.

"I have told them that you are coming back again," said the old fellow, laughing, as they began the ascent, "but they'll have to wait a long time." Toby turned, and saw the natives all in motion—the girls waving their tappas in adieu, and the men their spears. As the last figure entered the grove with one arm raised, and the three fingers spread, his heart smote him.

As the natives had at last consented to his going, it might have been that some of them, at least, really counted upon his speedy return, probably supposing, as indeed he had told them when they were coming down the valley, that his only object in leaving them was to procure the medicines I needed. This Jimmy also must have told them. And as they had done before, when my comrade, to oblige me, started on his perilous journey to Nukuheva, they looked upon me, in his absence, as one of two inseparable friends who was a sure guaranty for the other's return. This is only my own supposition, however, for as to all their strange conduct, it is still a mystery.

"You see what sort of a taboo man I am," said the sailor, after for some time silently following the path which led up the mountain. "Mow-Mow made me a present of this pig here, and the man who carries it will go right through Happar, and down into Nukuheva with us. So long as he stays by me he is safe, and just so it will be with you, and to-morrow with Tommo. Cheer up, then, and rely upon me, you will see him in the morning."

The ascent of the mountain was not very difficult owing to its being near to the sea, where the island ridges are comparatively low; the path, too, was a fine one, so that in a short time all three were standing on the summit with the two valleys at their feet. The white cascades marking the green head of the Typee valley first caught Toby's eye; Marheyo's house could easily be traced by them.

As Jimmy led the way along the ridge, Toby observed that the valley of the Happars did not extend near so far inland as that of the Typees. This accounted for our mistake in entering the latter valley as we had.

A path leading down from the mountain was soon seen, and, following it, the party were in a short time fairly in the Happar valley.

"Now," said Jimmy, as they hurried on, "we taboo men have wives in all the bays, and I am going to show you the two I have here."

So, when they came to the house where he said they lived,—which was close by the base of the mountain in a shady nook among the groves,—he went in, and was quite furious at finding it empty—the ladies had gone out. However, they soon made their appearance, and, to tell the truth, welcomed Jimmy quite cordially, as well as Toby, about whom they were very inquisitive. Nevertheless, as the report of their arrival spread, and the Happars began to assemble, it became evident that the appearance of a white stranger among them was not by any means deemed so wonderful an event as in the neighbouring valley.

The old sailor now bade his wives prepare something to eat, as he must be in Nukuheva before dark. A meal of fish, breadfruit, and bananas was accordingly served up, the party regaling themselves on the mats, in the midst of a numerous company.

The Happars put many questions to Jimmy about Toby; and Toby himself looked sharply at them, anxious to recognize the fellow who gave him the wound from which he was still suffering. But this fiery gentleman, so handy with his spear, had the delicacy, it seemed, to keep out of view. Certainly the sight of him would not have been any added inducement to making a stay in the valley,—some of the afternoon loungers in Happar having politely urged Toby to spend a few days with them,—there was a feast coming on. He, however, declined.

All this while the young Typee stuck to Jimmy like his shadow, and though as lively a dog as any of his tribe, he was now as meek as a lamb, never opening his mouth except to eat. Although some of the Happars looked queerly at him, others were more civil, and seemed desirous of taking him abroad and showing him the valley. But the Typee was not to be cajoled in that way. How many yards he would have to remove from Jimmy before the taboo would be powerless, it would be hard to tell, but probably he himself knew to a fraction.

On the promise of a red cotton handkerchief, and something else which he kept secret, this poor fellow had undertaken a rather ticklish journey, though, as far as Toby could ascertain, it was something that had never happened before.

The island-punch—arva—was brought in at the conclusion of the repast and passed round in a shallow calabash.

Now my comrade, while seated in the Happar house, began to feel more troubled than ever at leaving me: indeed, so sad did he feel that he talked about going back to the valley, and wanted Jimmy to escort him as far as the mountains. But the sailor would not listen to him, and, by way of diverting his thoughts, pressed him to drink of the arva. Knowing its narcotic nature, he refused; but Jimmy said he would have something mixed with it, which would convert it into an innocent beverage that would inspirit them for the rest of the journey. So at last he was induced to drink of it, and its effects were just as the sailor had predicted; his spirits rose at once, and all his gloomy thoughts left him.

The old rover now began to reveal his true character, though he was hardly suspected at the time. "If I get you off to a ship," said he, "you will surely give a poor fellow something for saving you." In short before they left the house, he made Toby promise that he would give him five Spanish dollars if he succeeded in getting any part of his wages advanced from the vessel, aboard of which they were going; Toby, moreover, engaging to reward him still further, as soon as my deliverance was accomplished.

A little while after this they started again, accompanied by many of the natives, and going up the valley, took a steep path near its head, which led to Nukuheva. Here the Happars paused, and watched them as they ascended the mountain, one group of bandit-looking fellows, shaking their spears and casting threatening glances at the poor Typee, whose heart as well as heels seemed much the lighter when he came to look down upon them.

On gaining the heights once more, their way led for a time along several ridges covered with enormous ferns. At last they entered upon a wooded tract, and here they overtook a party of Nukuheva natives, well armed, and carrying bundles of long poles. Jimmy seemed to know them all very well, and stopped for a while, and had a talk about the "Wee-Wees," as the people of Nukuheva call the Monsieurs.

The party with the poles were King Mowanna's men, and by his orders they had been gathering them in the ravines for his allies the French.

Leaving these fellows to trudge on with their loads, Toby and his companions now pushed forward again, as the sun was already low in the west. They came upon the valleys of Nukuheva on one side of the bay, where the highlands slope off into the sea. The men-of-war were still lying in the harbour, and as Toby looked down upon them, the strange events which had happened so recently seemed all a dream.

They soon descended towards the beach, and found themselves in Jimmy's house before it was well dark. Here he received another welcome from his Nukuheva wives, and after some refreshments in the shape of coco-nut milk and poee-poee, they entered a canoe (the Typee, of course, going along) and paddled off to a whale ship which was anchored near the shore. This was the vessel in want of men. Our own had sailed some time before. The captain professed great pleasure at seeing Toby, but thought, from his exhausted appearance, that he must be unfit for duty. However, he agreed to ship him, as well as his comrade, as soon as he should arrive.

Toby begged hard for an armed boat, in which to go round to Typee and rescue me, notwithstanding the promises of Jimmy. But this the captain would not hear of, and told him to have patience, for the sailor would be faithful to his word. When, too, he demanded the five silver dollars for Jimmy, the captain was unwilling to give them. But Toby insisted upon it, as he now began to think that Jimmy might be a mere mercenary, who would be ɛ ɪre to prove faithless if not well paid. Accordingly he not only gave him the money, but took care to assure him, over and over again, that as soon as he brought me aboard he would receive a still larger sum.

Before sunrise the next day, Jimmy and the Typee started in two of the ship's boats, which were manned by tabooed natives. Toby, of course, was all eagerness to go along, but the sailor told him that if he did, it would spoil all; so, hard as it was, he was obliged to remain.

Towards evening he was on the watch, and descried the boats turning the headland and entering the bay. He strained his eyes, and thought he saw me; but I was not there. Descending from the mast almost distracted, he grappled Jimmy as he struck the deck, shouting in a voice that startled him, "Where is Tommo?" The old fellow faltered, but soon recovering, did all he could to soothe him, assuring him that it had proved to be impossible to get me down to the shore that morning; assigning many plausible reasons, and adding that early on the morrow he was going to visit the bay again in a French boat, when, if he did not find me on the beach—as this time he certainly expected to—he would march right back into the valley, and carry me away at all hazards. He, however, again refused to allow Toby to accompany him.

Now, situated as Toby was, his sole dependence for the present was upon this Jimmy, and therefore he was fain to comfort himself as well as he could with what the old sailor had told him.

The next morning, however, he had the satisfaction of seeing the French boat start with Jimmy in it. To-night, then, I will see him, thought Toby; but many a long day passed before he ever saw Tommo again. Hardly was the boat out of sight, when the captain came forward and ordered the anchor to be weighed; he was going to sea.

Vain were all Toby's ravings,—they were disregarded; and when he came to himself the sails were set, and the ship fast leaving the land.

. . . Oh! said he to me at our meeting, what sleepless nights were mine. Often I started from my hammock, dreaming you were before me, and upbraiding me for leaving you on the island.

There is little more to be related. Toby left this vessel at New Zealand, and after some further adventures, arrived home in less than two years after leaving the Marquesas. He always thought of me as dead—and I had every reason to suppose that he too was no more; but a strange meeting was in store for us, one which made Toby's heart all the lighter.

BOOK
FOUR

ISRAEL POTTER: *His*
Fifty Years of Exile

TO

HIS HIGHNESS

THE

BUNKER-HILL MONUMENT

BIOGRAPHY, in its purer form, confined to the ended lives of the true and brave, may be held the fairest meed of human virtue—one given and received in entire disinterestedness—since neither can the biographer hope for acknowledgment from the subject, nor the subject at all avail himself of the biographical distinction conferred.

Israel Potter well merits the present tribute—a private of Bunker Hill, who for his faithful services was years ago promoted to a still deeper privacy under the ground, with a posthumous pension, in default of any during life, annually paid him by the spring in ever-new mosses and sward.

I am the more encouraged to lay this performance at the feet of your Highness, because, with a change in the grammatical person, it preserves, almost as in a reprint, Israel Potter's autobiographical story. Shortly after his return in infirm old age to his native land, a little narrative of his adventures, forlornly published on sleazy gray paper, appeared among the peddlers, written, probably, not by himself, but taken down from his lips by another. But like the crutch-marks of the cripple by the Beautiful Gate, this blurred record is now out of print. From a tattered copy, rescued by the merest chance from the rag-pickers, the present account has been drawn, which, with the exception of some expansions, and additions of historic and personal details, and one or two shiftings of scene, may, perhaps, be not unfitly regarded something in the light of a dilapidated old tombstone retouched.

Well aware that in your Highness' eyes the merit of the story must be in its general fidelity to the main drift of the original narrative, I forbore anywhere to mitigate the hard fortunes of my hero; and particularly towards the end, though sorely tempted, durst not substitute for the allotment of Providence any artistic recompense of poetical justice; so that no one can complain of the gloom of my closing chapters more profoundly than myself.

Such is the work, and such the man, that I have the honor to present to your Highness. That the name here noted should not have appeared in the volumes of Sparks, may or may not be a matter for astonishment; but Israel Potter seems purposely to have waited to make his popular advent under the present exalted patronage, seeing that your Highness, according to the definition above, may, in the loftiest sense, be deemed the Great Biographer: the national commemorator of such of the anonymous privates of June 17, 1775, who may never have received other requital than the solid reward of your granite.

Your Highness will pardon me, if, with the warmest ascriptions on this auspicious occasion, I take the liberty to mingle my hearty congratulations on the recurrence of the anniversary day we celebrate, wishing your Highness (though indeed your Highness be somewhat prematurely gray) many returns

731

of the same, and that each of its summer's suns may shine as brightly on your brow as each winter snow shall lightly rest on the grave of Israel Potter.

Your Highness'

Most devoted and obsequious,

THE EDITOR.

JUNE 17TH, 1854.

CONTENTS

CONTENTS

ISRAEL POTTER

CHAPTER I

THE BIRTHPLACE OF ISRAEL

THE traveller who at the present day is content to travel in the good old Asiatic style, neither rushed along by a locomotive, nor dragged by a stage-coach; who is willing to enjoy hospitalities at far-scattered farmhouses, instead of paying his bill at an inn; who is not to be frightened by any amount of loneliness, or to be deterred by the roughest roads or the highest hills; such a traveller in the eastern part of Berkshire, Massachusetts, will find ample food for poetic reflection in the singular scenery of a country, which, owing to the ruggedness of the soil and its lying out of the track of all public conveyances, remains almost as unknown to the general tourist as the interior of Bohemia.

Travelling northward from the township of Otis, the road leads for twenty or thirty miles towards Windsor, lengthwise upon that long broken spur of heights which the Green Mountains of Vermont send into Massachusetts. For nearly the whole of the distance, you have the continual sensation of being upon some terrace in the moon. The feeling of the plain or the valley is never yours; scarcely the feeling of the earth. Unless by a sudden precipitation of the road you find yourself plunging into some gorge, you pass on, and on, and on, upon the crests or slopes of pastoral mountains, while far below, mapped out in its beauty, the valley of the Housatonic lies endlessly along at your feet. Often, as your horse gaining some lofty level tract, flat as a table, trots gayly over the almost deserted and sodded road, and your admiring eye sweeps the broad landscape beneath, you seem to be Boötes driving in heaven. Save a potato field here and there, at long intervals, the whole country is either in wood or pasture. Horses, cattle, and sheep are the principal inhabitants of these mountains. But all through the year lazy columns of smoke, rising from the depths of the forest, proclaim the presence of that half-outlaw, the charcoal-burner; while in early spring added curls of vapor show that the maple sugar-boiler is also at work. But as for farming as a regular vocation, there is not much of it here. At any rate, no man by that means accumulates a fortune from this thin and rocky soil, all whose arable parts have long since been nearly exhausted.

Yet during the first settlement of the country, the region was not unproductive. Here it was that the original settlers came, acting upon the principle well known to have regulated their choice of site, namely, the high land in preference to the low, as less subject to the unwholesome miasmas generated by breaking into the rich valleys and alluvial bottoms of primeval regions. By degrees, however, they quitted the safety of this sterile elevation, to brave the dangers of richer though lower fields. So that, at the present day, some of those mountain townships present an aspect of singular abandonment. Though they have never known aught but peace and health, they, in one lesser aspect at least, look like countries depopulated by plague and war. Every mile or two a house is passed untenanted. The strength of the frame-work of these ancient buildings enables them long to resist the encroachments of decay. Spotted gray and green with the weather-stain, their timbers seem to have lapsed back into their woodland original, forming part now of the general picturesqueness of the natural scene. They are of extraordinary size, compared with modern farmhouses. One peculiar feature is the immense chimney, of light gray stone, perforating the middle of the roof like a tower.

On all sides are seen the tokens of ancient industry. As stone abounds throughout these mountains, that material was, for fences, as ready to the hand as wood, besides being much more durable. Consequently the landscape is inter-sected in all directions with walls of uncommon neatness and strength.

The number and length of these walls is not more surprising than the size of some of the blocks comprising them. The very Titans seemed to have been at work. That so small an army as the first settlers must needs have been, should have taken such wonderful pains to enclose so ungrateful a soil; that they should have accomplished such herculean undertakings with so slight pros-pect of reward; this is a consideration which gives us a significant hint of the temper of the men of the Revolutionary era.

Nor could a fitter country be found for the birthplace of the devoted patriot, Israel Potter.

To this day the best stone-wall builders, as the best woodchoppers, come from those solitary mountain towns; a tall, athletic, and hardy race, unerring with the axe as the Indian with the tomahawk; at stone-rolling, patient as Sisyphus, powerful as Samson.

In fine clear June days, the blooms of these mountains is beyond expression delightful. Last visiting these heights ere she vanishes, Spring, like the sunset, flings her sweetest charms upon them. Each tuft of upland grass is musked like a bouquet with perfume. The balmy breeze swings to and fro like a censer. On one side the eye follows for the space of an eagle's flight, the serpentine moun-tain chains, southwards from the great purple dome of Taconic—the St. Peter's of these hills—northwards to the twin summits of Saddleback, which is the two-steepled natural cathedral of Berkshire; while low down to the west the Housa-tonic winds on in her watery labyrinth, through charming meadows basking in the reflected rays from the hill-sides. At this season the beauty of every thing around you populates the loneliness of your way. You would not have the coun-try more settled if you could. Content to drink in such loveliness at all your senses, the heart desires no company but Nature.

With what rapture you behold, hovering over some vast hollow of the hills, or slowly drifting at an immense height over the far sunken Housatonic Valley, some lordly eagle, who in unshared exaltation looks down equally upon plain and mountain. Or you behold a hawk sallying from some crag, like a Rhenish baron of old from his pinnacled castle, and darting down towards the river for his prey. Or perhaps, lazily gliding about in the zenith, this ruffian fowl is suddenly beset by a crow, who with stubborn audacity pecks at him, and, spite of all his bravery, finally persecutes him back to his stronghold. The otherwise dauntless bandit, soaring at his topmost height, must needs succumb to this sable image of death. Nor are there wanting many smaller and less famous fowl, who without contributing to the grandeur, yet greatly add to the beauty of the scene. The yellow-bird flits like a winged jonquil here and there; like knots of violets the blue-birds sport in clusters upon the grass; while hurry-ing from the pasture to the grove, the red robin seems an incendiary putting torch to the trees. Meanwhile the air is vocal with their hymns, and your own soul joys in the general joy. Like a stranger in an orchestra, you cannot help singing yourself when all around you raise such hosannas.

But in autumn, those gay northerners, the birds, return to their southern plantations. The mountains are left bleak and sere. Solitude settles down upon them in drizzling mists. The traveller is beset, at perilous turns, by dense masses of fog. He emerges for a moment into more penetrable air; and passing some gray, abandoned house sees the lofty vapors plainly eddy by its desolate door; just as from the plain you may see it eddy by the pinnacles of distant and lonely heights. Or, dismounting from his frightened horse, he leads him down some scowling glen, where the road steeply dips among grim rocks, only to rise as abruptly again; and as he warily picks his way, uneasy at the menacing scene, he sees some ghost-like object looming through the mist at the roadside; and wending towards it, beholds a rude white stone, uncouthly inscribed, marking the spot where, some fifty or sixty years ago, some farmer was upset in his woodsled, and perished beneath the load.

In winter this region is blocked up with snow. Inaccessible and impassable, those wild, unfrequented roads, which in August are overgrown with high grass, in December are drifted to the arm-pit with the white fleece from the sky. As if an ocean rolled between man and man, intercommunication is often suspended for weeks and weeks.

Such, at this day, is the country which gave birth to our hero: prophetically styled Israel by the good Puritans, his parents: since, for more than forty years, poor Potter wandered in the wild wilderness of the world's extremest hardships and ills.

How little he thought, when, as a boy, hunting after his father's stray cattle among these New England hills, he himself like a beast should be hunted through half of Old England, as a runaway rebel. Or, how could he ever have dreamed, when involved in the autumnal vapors of these mountains, that worse bewilderments awaited him three thousand miles across the sea, wandering forlorn in the coal-fogs of London. But so it was destined to be. This little boy of the hills, born in sight of the sparkling Housatonic, was to linger out the best part of his life a prisoner or a pauper upon the grimy banks of the Thames.

CHAPTER II

THE YOUTHFUL ADVENTURES OF ISRAEL

IMAGINATION will easily picture the rural day of the youth of Israel. Let us pass on to a less immature period.

It appears that he began his wanderings very early; moreover, that ere, on just principles throwing off the yoke of his king, Israel, on equally excusable grounds, emancipated himself from his sire. He continued in the enjoyment of parental love till the age of eighteen when, having formed an attachment for a neighbor's daughter—for some reason, not deemed a suitable match by his father—he was severely reprimanded, warned to discontinue his visits, and threatened with some disgraceful punishment in case he persisted. As the girl was not only beautiful, but amiable—though, as will be seen, rather weak—and her family as respectable as any, though unfortunately but poor, Israel deemed his father's conduct unreasonable and oppressive; particularly as it turned out that he had taken secret means to thwart his son with the girl's connections, if not with the girl herself, so as to place almost insurmountable obstacles to an eventual marriage. For it had not been the purpose of Israel to marry at once, but at a future day, when prudence should approve the step. So, oppressed by his father, and bitterly disappointed in his love, the desperate boy formed the determination to quit them both, for another home and other friends.

It was on Sunday, while the family were gone to a farmhouse church near by, that he packed up as much of his clothing as might be contained in a handkerchief, which, with a small quantity of provision, he hid in a piece of woods in the rear of the house. He then returned, and continued in the house till about nine in the evening, when, pretending to go to bed, he passed out of a back door, and hastened to the woods for his bundle.

It was a sultry night in July; and that he might travel with the more ease on the succeeding day, he lay down at the foot of a pine tree, reposing himself till an hour before dawn, when, upon awaking, he heard the soft, prophetic sighing of the pine, stirred by the first breath of the morning. Like the leaflets of that evergreen, all the fibres of his heart trembled within him; tears fell from his eyes. But he thought of the tyranny of his father, and what seemed to him the faithlessness of his love; and shouldering his bundle, arose, and marched on.

His intention was to reach the new countries to the northward and westward, lying between the Dutch settlements on the Hudson, and the Yankee setlements on the Housatonic. This was mainly to elude all search. For the same reason, for the first ten or twelve miles, shunning the public roads, he travelled through the woods; for he knew that he would soon be missed and pursued.

He reached his destination in safety; hired out to a farmer for a month through the harvest; then crossed from the Hudson to the Connecticut. Meeting here with an adventurer to the unknown regions lying about the head waters of the latter river, he ascended with this man in a canoe, paddling and pulling for many miles. Here again he hired himself out for three months; at the end of that time, to receive for his wages two hundred acres of land lying in New Hampshire. The cheapness of the land was not alone owing to the newness of the country, but to the perils investing it. Not only was it a wilderness abounding with wild beasts, but the widely scattered inhabitants were in continual dread of being, at some unguarded moment, destroyed or made captive by the Canadian savages, who, ever since the French war, had improved every opportunity to make forays across the defenceless frontier.

His employer proving false to his contract in the matter of the land, and there being no law in the country to force him to fulfil it, Israel—who, however brave-hearted, and even much of a dare-devil upon a pinch, seems nevertheless to have evinced, throughout many parts of his career, a singular patience and mildness—was obliged to look round for other means of livelihood than clearing out a farm for himself in the wilderness. A party of royal surveyors were at this period surveying the unsettled regions bordering the Connecticut river to its source. At fifteen shillings per month, he engaged himself to this party as assistant chain-bearer, little thinking that the day was to come when he should clank the king's chains in a dungeon, even as now he trailed them a free ranger of the woods. It was midwinter; the land was surveyed upon snowshoes. At the close of the day, fires were kindled with dry hemlock, a hut thrown up, and the party ate and slept.

Paid off at last, Israel bought a gun and ammunition, and turned hunter.

Deer, beaver, &c., were plenty. In two or three months he had many skins to show. I suppose it never entered his mind that he was thus qualifying himself for a marksman of men. But thus were tutored those wonderful shots who did such execution at Bunker's Hill; these, the hunter-soldiers, whom Putnam bade wait till the white of the enemy's eye was seen.

With the result of his hunting he purchased a hundred acres of land, farther down the river, toward the more settled parts; built himself a log hut, and in two summers, with his own hands, cleared thirty acres for sowing. In the winter seasons he hunted and trapped. At the end of the two years, he sold back his land—now much improved—to the original owner, at an advance of fifty pounds. He conveyed his cash and furs to Charlestown, on the Connecticut (sometimes called No. 4), where he trafficked them away for Indian blankets, pigments, and other showy articles adapted to the business of a trader among savages. It was now winter again. Putting his goods on a hand-sled, he started towards Canada, a peddler in the wilderness, stopping at wigwams instead of cottages. One fancies that, had it been summer, Israel would have travelled with a wheel-barrow, and so trundled his wares through the primeval forests, with the same indifference as porters roll their barrows over the flagging of streets. In this way was bred that fearless self-reliance and independence which conducted our forefathers to national freedom.

This Canadian trip proved highly successful. Selling his glittering goods at a great advance, he received in exchange valuable peltries and furs at a corresponding reduction. Returning to Charlestown, he disposed of his return cargo again at a very fine profit. And now, with a light heart and a heavy purse, he resolved to visit his sweetheart and parents, of whom, for three years, he had had no tidings.

They were not less astonished than delighted at his reappearance; he had been numbered with the dead. But his love still seemed strangely coy; willing, but yet somehow mysteriously withheld. The old intrigues were still on foot. Israel soon discovered, that though rejoiced to welcome the return of the prodigal son—so some called him—his father still remained inflexibly determined against the match, and still inexplicably countermined his wooing. With a dolorous heart he mildly yielded to what seemed his fatality; and more intrepid in facing peril for himself, than in endangering others by maintaining his rights (for he was now one-and-twenty), resolved once more to retreat, and quit his blue hills for the bluer billows.

A hermitage in the forest is the refuge of the narrow-minded misanthrope; a hammock on the ocean is the asylum for the generous distressed. The ocean brims with natural griefs and tragedies; and into that watery immensity of terror, man's private grief is lost like a drop.

Travelling on foot to Providence, Rhode Island, Israel shipped on board a sloop, bound with lime to the West Indies. On the tenth day out, the vessel caught fire, from water communicating with the lime. It was impossible to extinguish the flames. The boat was hoisted out but, owing to long exposure to the sun, it needed continual bailing to keep it afloat. They had only time to put in a firkin of butter and a ten-gallon keg of water. Eight in number, the crew entrusted themselves to the waves; in a leaky tub, many leagues from land. As the boat swept under the burning bowsprit, Israel caught at a fragment of the flying-jib, which sail had fallen down the stay, owing to the charring, nigh the deck, of the rope which hoisted it. Tanned with the smoke, and its edge blackened with the fire, this bit of canvas helped them bravely on their way. Thanks to kind Providence, on the second day they were picked up by a Dutch ship, bound from Eustatia to Holland. The castaways were humanely received, and supplied with every necessary. At the end of a week, while unsophisticated Israel was sitting in the main-top, thinking what should befall him in Holland, and wondering what sort of unsettled, wild country it was, and whether there was any deer-shooting or beaver-trapping there, lo! an American brig, bound from Piscataqua to Antigua, comes in sight. The American took them aboard, and conveyed them safely to her port. There Israel shipped for Porto Rico; from thence, sailed to Eustatia.

Other rovings ensued; until at last, entering on board a Nantucket ship, he hunted the leviathan off the Western Islands and on the coast of Africa, for sixteen months; returning at length to Nantucket with a brimming hold. From that island he sailed again on another whaling voyage extending, this time, into the great South Sea. There, promoted to be harpooneer, Israel, whose eye and arm had been so improved by practice with his gun in the wilderness, now further intensified his aim, by darting the whale-lance; still, unwittingly, preparing himself for the Bunker Hill rifle.

In this last voyage, our adventurer experienced to the extreme all the hardships and privations of the whaleman's life on a long voyage to distant and barbarous waters—hardships and privations unknown at the present day, when science has so greatly contributed, in manifold ways, to lessen the sufferings, and add to the comforts of seafaring men. Heartily sick of the ocean, and longing once more for the bush, Israel, upon receiving his discharge at Nantucket at the end of the voyage, hied straight back for his mountain home.

But if hopes of his sweetheart winged his returning flight, such hopes were not destined to be crowned with fruition. The dear, false girl was another's.

CHAPTER III

ISRAEL GOES TO THE WARS; AND REACHING BUNKER HILL IN TIME TO BE OF SERVICE THERE, SOON IS FORCED TO EXTEND HIS TRAVELS ACROSS THE SEA INTO THE ENEMY'S LAND

LEFT to idle lamentations, Israel might now have planted deep furrows in his brow. But stifling his pain, he chose rather to plough, than be ploughed. Farming weans man from his sorrows. That tranquil pursuit tolerates nothing but tranquil meditations. There, too, in mother earth, you may plant and reap; not, as in other things, plant and see the planting torn up by the roots. But if wandering in the wilderness, and wandering upon the waters, if felling trees, and hunting, and shipwreck, and fighting with whales, and all his other strange adventures, had not as yet cured poor Israel of his now hopeless passion, events were at hand for ever to drown it.

It was the year 1774. The difficulties long pending between the colonies and England were arriving at their crisis. Hostilities were certain. The Americans were preparing themselves. Companies were formed in most of the New England towns, whose members, receiving the name of minute-men, stood ready to march anywhere at a minute's warning. Israel, for the last eight months, sojourning as a laborer on a farm in Windsor, enrolled himself in the regiment of Colonel John Patterson of Lenox, afterwards General Patterson.

The battle of Lexington was fought on the 18th of April, 1775; news of it arrived in the county of Berkshire on the 20th about noon. The next morning at sunrise, Israel swung his knapsack, shouldered his musket, and, with Patterson's regiment, was on the march, quick-step, towards Boston.

Like Putnam, Israel received the stirring tidings at the plough. But although not less willing than Putnam to fly to battle at an instant's notice, yet —only half an acre of the field remaining to be finished—he whipped up his team and finished it. Before hastening to one duty, he would not leave a prior one undone; and ere helping to whip the British, for a little practice' sake, he applied the gad to his oxen. From the field of the farmer, he rushed to that of the soldier, mingling his blood with his sweat. While we revel in broadcloth, let us not forget what we owe to linsey-woolsey.

With other detachments from various quarters, Israel's regiment remained encamped for several days in the vicinity of Charlestown. On the seventeenth of June, one thousand Americans, including the regiment of Patterson, were set about fortifying Bunker's Hill. Working all through the night, by dawn of the following day, the redoubt was thrown up. But every one knows all about the battle. Suffice it, that Israel was one of those marksmen whom Putnam harangued as touching the enemy's eyes. Forbearing as he was with his oppressive father and unfaithful love, and mild as he was on the farm, Israel was not the same at Bunker Hill. Putnam had enjoined the men to aim at the officers; so Israel aimed between the golden epaulettes, as, in the wilderness, he had aimed between the branching antlers. With dogged disdain of their foes, the English grenadiers marched up the hill with sullen slowness; thus furnishing still surer aims to the muskets which bristled on the redoubt. Modest Israel was used to aver, that considering his practice in the woods, he could hardly be regarded as an inexperienced marksman; hinting, that every shot which the epauletted grenadiers received from his rifle would, upon a different occasion, have procured him a deerskin. And like stricken deers the English, rashly brave as they were, fled from the opening fire. But the marksman's ammunition was expended; a hand-to-hand encounter ensued. Not one American musket in twenty had a bayonet to it. So, wielding the stock right and left, the terrible farmers, with hats and coats off, fought their way among the furred grenadiers, knocking them right and left, as seal-hunters on the beach, knock down with their clubs the Shetland seal. In the dense crowd and confusion, while Israel's musket got interlocked, he saw a blade horizontally menacing his feet from the ground. Thinking some fallen enemy sought to strike him at the last gasp, dropping his hold on his musket, he wrenched at the steel, but found that though a brave hand held it, that hand was powerless for ever. It was some British officer's laced sword-arm, cut from the trunk in the act of fighting, refusing to yield up its blade to the last. At that moment another sword was aimed at Israel's head by a living officer. In an instant the blow was parried by kindred steel, and the assailant fell by a brother's weapon, wielded by alien hands. But Israel did not come off unscathed. A cut on the right arm near the elbow; received in parrying the officer's blow, a long slit across the chest, a musket ball buried in his hip, and another mangling him near the ankle of the same leg, were the tokens of intrepidity which our Sicinius Dentatus carried from this memorable field. Nevertheless, with his comrades he succeeded in reaching Prospect Hill, and from thence was conveyed to the hospital at Cambridge. The bullet was extracted, his lesser wounds were dressed, and after much suffering from the fracture of the bone near the ankle, several pieces of which were extracted by the surgeon, ere long, thanks to the high health and pure blood of the farmer, Israel rejoined his regiment when they were throwing up intrenchments on Prospect Hill. Bunker Hill was now in possession of the foe, who in turn had fortified it.

On the third of July, Washington arrived from the South to take the command. Israel witnessed his joyful reception by the huzzahing companies.

The British now quartered in Boston suffered greatly from the scarcity of provisions. Washington took every precaution to prevent their receiving a supply. Inland, all aid could easily be cut off. To guard against their receiving any by water, from tories and other disaffected persons, the General equipped three armed vessels to intercept all traitorous cruisers. Among them was the brigantine *Washington*, of ten guns, commanded by Captain Martindale. Seamen were hard to be had. The soldiers were called upon to volunteer for these vessels. Israel was one who so did; thinking that as an experienced sailor he should not be backward in a juncture like this, little as he fancied the new service assigned.

Three days out of Boston harbor, the brigantine was captured by the enemy's ship *Foy*, of twenty guns. Taken prisoner with the rest of the crew, Israel was afterwards put on board the frigate *Tartar*, with immediate sailing orders for England. Seventy-two were captives in this vessel. Headed by Israel, these men—half way across the sea—formed a scheme to take the ship, but were betrayed by a renegade Englishman. As ringleader, Israel was put in irons, and so remained till the frigate anchored at Portsmouth. There he was brought on deck; and would have met perhaps some terrible fate, had it not come out, during the examination, that the Englishman had been a deserter from the army of his native country ere proving a traitor to his adopted one. Relieved of his irons, Israel was placed in the marine hospital on shore, where half of the prisoners took the small-pox, which swept off a third of their number. Why talk of Jaffa?

From the hospital the survivors were conveyed to Spithead, and thrust on board a hulk. And here in the black bowels of the ship, sunk low in the sunless sea, our poor Israel lay for a month, like Jonah in the belly of the whale.

But one bright morning, Israel is hailed from the deck. A bargeman of the commander's boat is sick. Known for a sailor, Israel for the nonce is appointed to pull the absent man's oar.

The officers being landed, some of the crew propose, like merry Englishman as they are, to hie to a neighboring ale-house, and have a cosy pot or two together. Agreed. They start, and Israel with them. As they enter the ale-house door, our prisoner is suddenly reminded of still more imperative calls. Unsuspected of any design, he is allowed to leave the party for a moment. No sooner does Israel see his companions housed, than putting speed into his feet, and letting grow all his wings, he starts like a deer. He runs four miles (so he afterwards affirmed) without halting. He sped towards London; wisely deeming that once in that crowd detection would be impossible.

Ten miles, as he computed, from where he had left the bargemen, leisurely passing a public house of a little village on the roadside, thinking himself now pretty safe—hark, what is this he hears?

"Ahoy!"

"No ship," says Israel, hurrying on.

"Stop."

"If you will attend to your business, I will endeavor to attend to mine," replies Israel coolly. And next minute he lets grow his wings again; flying, one dare say, at the rate of something less than thirty miles an hour.

"Stop thief!" is now the cry. Numbers rushed from the roadside houses. After a mile's chase, the poor panting deer is caught.

Finding it was no use now to prevaricate, Israel boldly confesses himself a prisoner-of-war. The officer, a good fellow as it turned out, had him escorted back to the inn; where, observing to the landlord that this must needs be a true-blooded Yankee, he calls for liquors to refresh Israel after his run. Two soldiers are then appointed to guard him for the present. This was towards evening; and up to a late hour at night, the inn was filled with strangers crowding to see the Yankee rebel, as they politely termed him. These honest rustics seemed to think that Yankees were a sort of wild creatures, a species of 'possum or kangaroo. But Israel is very affable with them. That liquor he drank from the hand of. his foe, has perhaps warmed his heart towards all the rest of his enemies. Yet this may not be wholly so. We shall see. At any rate, still he keeps his eye on the main chance—escape. Neither the jokes nor the insults of the mob does he suffer to molest him. He is cogitating a little plot to himself.

It seems that the good officer—not more true to the king his master than indulgent towards the prisoner which that same loyalty made—had left orders that Israel should be supplied with whatever liquor he wanted that night. So, calling for the can again and again, Israel invites the two soldiers to drink and be merry. At length, a wag of the company proposes that Israel should entertain the public with a jig, he (the wag) having heard that the Yankees were extraordinary dancers. A fiddle is brought in, and poor Israel takes the floor. Not a little cut to think that these people should so unfeelingly seek to be diverted at the expense of an unfortunate prisoner, Israel, while jigging it up and down, still conspires away at his private plot, resolving ere long to give the enemy a touch of certain Yankee steps, as yet undreamed of in their simple philosophy. They would not permit any cessation of his dancing till he had danced himself into a perfect sweat, so that the drops fell from his lank and flaxen hair. But Israel, with much of the gentleness of the dove, is not wholly without the wisdom of the serpent. Pleased to see the flowing bowl, he congratulates himself that his own state of perspiration prevents it from producing any intoxicating effect upon him.

Late at night the company break up. Furnished with a pair of handcuffs, the prisoner is laid on a blanket spread upon the floor at the side of the bed in which his two keepers are to repose. Expressing much gratitude for the blanket, with apparent unconcern, Israel stretches his legs. An hour or two passes. All is quiet without.

The important moment had now arrived. Certain it was, that if this chance were suffered to pass unimproved, a second would hardly present itself. For early, doubtless, on the following morning, if not some way prevented, the two soldiers would convey Israel back to his floating prison where he would thenceforth remain confined until the close of the war; years and years, perhaps. When he thought of that horrible old hulk, his nerves were restrung for flight. But intrepid as he must be to compass it, wariness too was needed. His keepers had gone to bed pretty well under the influence of the liquor. This was favorable. But still, they were full-grown, strong men; and Israel was handcuffed. So Israel resolved upon strategy first; and if that failed, force afterwards. He eagerly listened. One of the drunken soldiers muttered in his sleep, at first lowly, then louder and louder,—"Catch 'em! Grapple 'em! Have at 'em! Ha—long cutlasses! Take that, runaway!"

"What's the matter with ye, Phil?" hiccoughed the other, who was not yet asleep. "Keep quiet, will ye? Ye ain't at Fontenoy now."

"He's a runaway prisoner, I say. Catch him, catch him"

"Oh, stush with your drunken dreaming," again hiccoughed his comrade, violently nudging him. "This comes o' carousing."

Shortly after, the dreamer with loud snores fell back into dead sleep. But by something in the sound of the breathing of the other soldier, Israel knew that this man remained uneasily awake. He deliberated a moment what was best to do. At length he determined upon trying his old plea. Calling upon the two soldiers, he informed them that urgent necessity required his immediate presence somewhere in the rear of the house.

"Come, wake up here, Phil," roared the soldier who was awake; "the fellow here says he must step out; cuss these Yankees; no better edication than to be gettin' up on nateral necessities at this time o' night. It ain't nateral; its unnateral. D—n ye, Yankee, don't ye know no better?"

With many more denunciations, the two now staggered to their feet, and clutching hold of Israel, escorted him down stairs, and through a long, narrow, dark entry, rearward, till they came to a door. No sooner was this unbolted by the foremost guard, than, quick as a flash, manacled Israel, shaking off the grasp of the one behind him, butts him sprawling back into the entry; when, dashing in the opposite direction, he bounces the other head over heels into the garden, never using a hand; and then, leaping over the latter's head, darts blindly out into the midnight. Next moment he was at the garden wall. No outlet was discoverable in the gloom. But a fruit-tree grew close to the wall. Springing into it desperately, handcuffed as he was, Israel leaps atop of the barrier, and without pausing to see where he is, drops himself to the ground on the other side, and once more lets grow all his wings. Meantime, with loud outcries, the two baffled drunkards grope deliriously about in the garden.

After running two or three miles, and hearing no sound of pursuit, Israel reins up to rid himself of the handcuffs, which impede him. After much painful labor he succeeds in the attempt. Pressing on again with all speed, day broke, revealing a trim-looking, hedged, and beautiful country, soft, neat, and serene, all colored with the fresh early tints of the spring of 1776.

Bless me, thought Israel, all of a tremble, I shall certainly be caught now; I have broken into some nobleman's park.

But, hurrying forward again, he came to a turnpike road and then knew that, all comely and shaven as it was, this was simply the open country of England; one bright, broad park, paled in with white foam of the sea. A copse skirting the road was just bursting out into bud. Each unrolling leaf was in very act of escaping from its prison. Israel looked at the budding leaves, and round on the budding sod, and up at the budding dawn of the day. He was so sad, and these sights were so gay, that Israel sobbed like a child, while thoughts of his mountain home rushed like a wind on his heart. But conquering this fit, he marched on, and presently passed nigh a field, where two figures were working. They had rosy cheeks, short, sturdy legs, showing the blue stocking nearly to the knee, and were clad in long, coarse, white frocks, and had on coarse, broad-brimmed straw hats. Their faces were partly averted.

"Please, ladies," half roguishly says Israel, taking off his hat, "does this road go to London?"

At this salutation, the two figures turned in a sort of stupid amazement, causing an almost corresponding expression in Israel, who now perceived that they were men, and not women. He had mistaken them, owing to their frocks, and their wearing no pantaloons, only breeches hidden by their frocks.

"Beg pardon, ladies, but I thought ye were something else," said Israel again.

Once more the two figures stare at the stranger, and with added boorishness of surprise.

"Does this road go to London, gentlemen?"

"Gentlemen—egad!' cried one of the two.

"Egad!" echoed the second.

Putting their hoes before them, the two frocked boors now took a good long look at Israel, meantime scratching their heads under their plaited straw hats.

"Does it, gentlemen? Does it go to London? Be kind enough to tell a poor fellow, do."

"Yees goin' to Lunnun, are yees? Weel—all right—go along."

And without another word, having now satisfied their rustic curiosity, the two human steers, with wonderful phlegm, applied themselves to their hoes; supposing, no doubt, that they had given all requisite information.

Shortly after, Israel passed an old, dark, mossy-looking chapel, its roof all plastered with the damp yellow dead leaves of the previous autumn, showered there from a close cluster of venerable trees, with great trunks, and overstretching branches. Next moment he found himself entering a village. The silence of early morning rested upon it. But few figures were seen. Glancing through the window of a now noiseless public-house, Israel saw a table all in disorder, covered with empty flagons, and tobacco-ashes, and long pipes; some of the latter broken.

After pausing here a. moment, he moved on, and observed a man over the way standing still and watching him. Instantly Israel was reminded that he had on the dress of an English sailor, and that it was this probably which had arrested the stranger's attention. Well knowing that his peculiar dress exposed him to peril, he hurried on faster to escape the village; resolving at the first opportunity to change his garments. Ere long, in a secluded place about a mile from the village, he saw an old ditcher tottering beneath the weight of a pick-axe, hoe and shovel, going to his work; the very picture of poverty, toil and distress. His clothes were tatters.

Making up to this old man, Israel, after a word or two of salutation, offered to change clothes with him. As his own clothes were prince-like compared to the ditcher's, Israel thought that however much his proposition might excite the suspicion of the ditcher, yet self-interest would prevent his communicating the suspicions. To be brief, the two went behind a hedge, and presently Israel emerged, presenting the most forlorn appearance conceivable; while the old ditcher hobbled off in an opposite direction, correspondingly improved in his aspect; though it was rather ludicrous than otherwise, owing to the immense bagginess of the sailor-trowsers flapping about his lean shanks, to say nothing of the spare voluminousness of the pea-jacket. But Israel— how deplorable, how dismal his plight! Little did he ween that these wretched rags he now wore, were but suitable to that long career of destitution before him: one brief career of adventurous wanderings; and then, forty torpid years of pauperism. The coat was all patches. And no two patches were alike, and no one patch was the color of the original cloth. The stringless breeches gaped wide open at the knee; the long woollen stockings looked as if they had been set up at some time for a target. Israel looked suddenly metamorphosed from youth to old age; just like an old man of eighty he looked. But, indeed, dull, dreary adversity was now in store for him; and adversity, come it at eighteen or eighty, is the true old age of man. The dress befitted the fate.

From the friendly old ditcher, Israel learned the exact course he must steer for London; distant now between seventy and eighty miles. He was also apprised by his venerable friend, that the country was filled with soldiers on the constant look-out for deserters whether from the navy or army, for the capture of whom a stipulated reward was given, just as in Massachusetts at that time for prowling bears.

Having solemnly enjoined his old friend not to give any information, should any one he meet inquire for such a person as Israel, our adventurer walked briskly on, less heavy of heart, now that he felt comparatively safe in disguise.

Thirty miles he travelled that day. At night Israel stole into a barn, in hopes of finding straw or hay for a bed. But it was spring; all the hay and straw were gone. So after groping about in the dark, he was fain to content himself with an undressed sheep-skin. Cold, hungry, foot-sore, weary, and impatient for the morning dawn, Israel drearily dozed out the night.

By the first peep of day coming through the chinks of the barn, he was up and abroad. Ere long finding himself in the suburbs of a considerable village, the better to guard against detection he supplied himself with a rude crutch, and feigning himself a cripple, hobbled straight through the town; followed by a perverse-minded cur, which kept up a continual, spiteful, suspicious bark. Israel longed to have one good rap at him with his crutch, but thought it would hardly look in character for a poor old cripple to be vindictive.

A few miles farther, and he came to a second village. While hobbling through its main street, as through the former one, he was suddenly stopped by a genuine cripple, all in tatters, too, who, with a sympathetic air, inquired after the cause of his lameness.

"White swelling," says Israel.

"That's just my ailing," wheezed the other; "but you're lamer than me," he added with a forlorn sort of self-satisfaction, critically eyeing Israel's limp as once more he stumped on his way, not liking to tarry too long.

"But halloo, what's your hurry, friend?" seeing Israel fairly departing— "where're you going?"

"To London," answered Israel, turning round, heartily wishing the old fellow any where else than present.

"Going to limp to Lunnun, eh? Well, success to ye."

"As much to you, sir," answers Israel politely.

Nigh the opposite suburbs of this village, as good fortune would have it, an empty baggage-wagon bound for the metropolis turned into the main road from a side one. Immediately Israel limps most deplorably, and begs the driver to give a poor cripple a lift. So up he climbs; but after a time, finding the gait of the elephantine draught-horses intolerably slow, Israel craves permission to dismount, when, throwing away his crutch, he takes nimbly to his legs, much to the surprise of his honest friend the driver.

The only advantage, if any, derived from his trip in the wagon, was, when passing through a third village—but a little distant from the previous one— Israel, by lying down in the wagon, had wholly avoided being seen.

The villages surprised him by their number and proximity. Nothing like this was to be seen at home. Well knowing that in these villages he ran much more risk of detection than in the open country, he henceforth did his best to avoid them, by taking a roundabout course whenever they came in sight from a distance. This mode of travelling not only lengthened his journey, but put unlooked-for obstacles in his path—walls, ditches, and streams.

Not half an hour after throwing away his crutch, he leaped a great ditch ten feet wide, and of undiscoverable muddy depth. I wonder if the old cripple would think me the lamer one now, thought Israel to himself, arriving on the hither side.

CHAPTER IV

FURTHER WANDERINGS OF THE REFUGEE, WITH SOME ACCOUNT OF A GOOD KNIGHT OF BRENTFORD WHO BEFRIENDED HIM

At nightfall, on the third day, Israel had arrived within sixteen miles of the capital. Once more he sought refuge in a barn. This time he found some hay, and flinging himself down procured a tolerable night's rest.

Bright and early he arose refreshed, with the pleasing prospect of reaching his destination ere noon. Encouraged to find himself now so far from his original pursuers, Israel relaxed in his vigilance, and about ten o'clock, while passing through the town of Staines, suddenly encountered three soldiers. Unfortunately in exchanging clothes with the ditcher, he could not bring himself to include his shirt in the traffic, which shirt was a British navy shirt, a bargeman's shirt, and though hitherto he had crumpled the blue collar out of sight, yet, as it appeared in the present instance, it was not thoroughly concealed. At any rate, keenly on the lookout for deserters, and made acute by hopes of reward for their apprehension, the soldiers spied the fatal collar, and in an instant laid violent hands on the refugee.

"Hey, lad!" said the foremost soldier, a corporal, "you are one of his majesty's seamen! come along with ye."

So, unable to give any satisfactory account of himself, he was made prisoner on the spot, and soon after found himself handcuffed and locked up in the Round House of the place, a prison so called, appropriated to runaways, and those convicted of minor offences. Day passed dinnerless and supperless in this dismal durance, and night came on.

Israel had now been three days without food, except one twopenny loaf. The cravings of hunger now became sharper; his spirits, hitherto arming him with fortitude, began to forsake him. Taken captive once again upon the very brink of reaching his goal, poor Israel was on the eve of falling into helpless despair. But he rallied, and considering that grief would only add to his calamity, sought with stubborn patience to habituate himself to misery, but still hold aloof from despondency. He roused himself, and began to bethink him how to be extricated from this labyrinth.

Two hours sawing across the grating of the window, ridded him of his handcuffs. Next came the door, secured luckily with only a hasp and padlock. Thrusting the bolt of his handcuffs through a small window in the door, he succeeded in forcing the hasp and regaining his liberty about three o'clock in the morning.

Not long after sunrise, he passed nigh Brentford, some six or seven miles from the capital. So great was his hunger that downright starvation seemed before him. He chewed grass, and swallowed it. Upon first escaping from the hulk, six English pennies was all the money he had. With two of these he had bought a small loaf the day after fleeing the inn. The other four still remained in his pocket, not having met with a good opportunity to dispose of them for food.

Having torn off the collar of his shirt, and flung it into a hedge, he ventured to accost a respectable carpenter at a pale fence, about a mile this side of Brentford, to whom his deplorable situation now induced him to apply for work. The man did not wish himself to hire, but said that if he (Israel) understood farming or gardening, he might perhaps procure work from Sir John Millet, whose seat, he said, was not remote. He added that the knight was in the habit of employing many men at that season of the year, so he stood a fair chance.

Revived a little by this prospect of relief, Israel starts in quest of the gentleman's seat, agreeably to the direction received. But he mistook his way, and proceeding up a gravelled and beautifully decorated walk, was terrified at catching a glimpse of a number of soldiers thronging a garden. He made an instant retreat before being espied in turn. No wild creature of the American wilderness could have been more panic-struck by a firebrand, than at this period hunted Israel was by a red coat. It afterwards appeared that this garden was the Princess Amelia's.

Taking another path, ere long he came to some laborers shovelling gravel. These proved to be men employed by Sir John. By them he was directed towards the house, when the knight was pointed out to him, walking bareheaded in the inclosure with several guests. Having heard the rich men of England charged with all sorts of domineering qualities, Israel felt no little misgiving in approaching to an audience with so imposing a stranger. But, screwing up his courage, he advanced; while seeing him coming all rags and tatters, the group of gentlemen stood in some wonder awaiting what so singular a phantom might want.

"Mr. Millet," said Israel, bowing towards the bareheaded gentleman.

"Ha—who are you, pray?"

"A poor fellow, sir, in want of work."

"A wardrobe, too, I should say," smiled one of the guests, of a very youthful, prosperous, and dandified air.

"Where's your hoe?' said Sir John.

"I have none, sir."

"Any money to buy one?"

"Only four English pennies, sir."

"*English* pennies. What sort would you have?"

"Why, China pennies to be sure," laughed the youthful gentleman. "See his long, yellow hair behind; he looks like a Chinaman. Some broken-down Mandarin. Pity he's no crown to his old hat; if he had, he might pass it round, and make eight pennies of his four."

"Will you hire me, Mr. Millet," said Israel.

"Ha! that's queer again," cried the knight.

"Hark ye, fellow," said a brisk servant, approaching from the porch, "this is Sir John Millet."

Seeming to take pity on his seeming ignorance, as well as on his undisputable poverty, the good knight now told Israel that if he would come the next morning he would see him supplied with a hoe, and moreover would hire him.

It would be hard to express the satisfaction of the wanderer at receiving this encouraging reply. Emboldened by it, he now returns towards a baker's he had spied, and bravely marching in, flings down all four pennies, and demands bread. Thinking he would not have any more food till next morning, Israel resolved to eat only one of the pair of two-penny loaves. But having demolished one, it so sharpened his longing, that yielding to the irresistible temptation, he bolted down the second loaf to keep the other company.

After resting under a hedge, he saw the sun far descended, and so prepared himself for another hard night. Waiting till dark, he crawled into' an old carriage-house, finding nothing there but a dismantled old phaëton. Into this he climbed, and curling himself up like a carriage-dog, endeavored to sleep; but, unable to endure the constraint of such a bed, got out, and stretched himself on the bare boards of the floor.

No sooner was light in the east than he hastened to await the commands of one who, his instinct told him, was destined to prove his benefactor. On his father's farm accustomed to rise with the lark, Israel was surprised to discover, as he approached the house, that no soul was astir. It was four o'clock. For a considerable time he walked back and forth before the portal ere any one appeared. The first riser was a man servant of the household, who informed Israel that seven o'clock was the hour the people went to their work. Soon after he met an hostler of the place, who gave him permission to lie on some straw in an outhouse. There he enjoyed a sweet sleep till awakened at seven o'clock by the sounds of activity around him.

Supplied by the overseer of the men with a large iron fork and a hoe, he followed the hands into the field. He was so weak he could hardly support his tools. Unwilling to expose his debility, he yet could not succeed in concealing it. At last, to avoid worse imputations, he confessed the cause. His companions regarded him with compassion, and exempted him from the severer toil.

About noon the knight visited his workmen. Noticing that Israel made little progress, he said to him, that though he had long arms and broad shoulders, yet he was feigning himself to be a very weak man, or otherwise must in reality be so.

Hereupon one of the laborers standing by informed the gentleman how it was with Israel, when immediately the knight put a shilling into his hands and bade him go to a little roadside inn, which was nearer than the house, and buy him bread and a pot of beer. Thus refreshed he returned to the band, and toiled with them till four o'clock, when the day's work was over.

Arrived at the house he there again saw his employer, who, after attentively eyeing him without speaking, bade a meal be prepared for him; when the maid presenting a smaller supply than her kind master deemed necessary, she was ordered to return and bring out the entire dish. But aware of the danger of sudden repletion of heavy food to one in his condition, Israel, previously recruited by the frugal meat at the inn, partook but sparingly. The repast was spread on the grass, and being over, the good knight again looked inquisitively at Israel, ordered a comfortable bed to be laid in the barn, and here Israel spent a capital night.

After breakfast, next morning, he was proceeding to go with the laborers to their work, when his employer approaching him with a benevolent air, bade him return to his couch, and there remain till he had slept his fill, and was in a better state to resume his labors.

Upon coming forth again a little after noon, he found Sir John walking alone in the grounds. Upon discovering him, Israel would have retreated, fearing that he might intrude; but beckoning him to advance, the knight, as Israel drew nigh, fixed on him such a penetrating glance, that our poor hero quaked to the core. Neither was his dread of detection relieved by the knight's now calling in a loud voice for one from the house. Israel was just on the point of fleeing, when overhearing the words of the master to the servant who now appeared, all dread departed:

"Bring hither some wine!"

.It presently came; by order of the knight the salver was set down on a green bank near by, and the servant retired.

"My poor fellow," said Sir John, now pouring out a glass of wine, and handing it to Israel, "I perceive that you are an American; and, if I am not mistaken, you are an escaped prisoner of war. But no fear—drink the wine."

"Mr. Millet," exclaimed Israel aghast, the untasted wine trembling in his hand, "Mr. Millet, I——"

"*Mr.* Millet—there it is again. Why don't you say *Sir John* like the rest?"

"Why, sir—pardon me—but somehow, I can't. I've tried; but I can't. You won't betray me for that?"

"Betray—poor fellow! Hark ye, your history is doubtless a secret which you would not wish to divulge to a stranger; but whatever happens to you, I pledge you my honor I will never betray you."

"God bless you for that, Mr. Millet."

"Come, come; call me by my right name. I am not Mr. Millet. *You* have said *Sir* to me; and no doubt you have a thousand times said *John* to other people. Now can't you couple the two? Try once. Come. Only *Sir* and then *John—Sir John*—that's all."

"John—I can't—Sir, sir!—your pardon. I didn't mean that."

"My good fellow," said the knight looking sharply upon Israel, "tell me, are all your countrymen like you? If so, it's no use fighting them. To that effect, I must write to his Majesty myself. Well, I excuse you from Sir John-ning me. But tell me the truth, are you not a seafaring man, and lately a prisoner of war?"

Israel frankly confessed it, and told his whole story. The knight listened with much interest; and at its conclusion warned Israel to beware of the soldiers; for owing to the seats of some of the royal family being in the neighborhood, the red-coats abounded hereabout.

"I do not wish unnecessarily to speak against my own countrymen," he added; "I but plainly speak for your good. The soldiers you meet prowling on the roads, are not fair specimens of the army. They are a set of mean, dastardly banditti, who, to obtain their fee, would betray their best friends. Once more, I warn you against them. But enough; follow me now to the house, and as you tell me you have exchanged clothes before now, you can do it again. What say you? I will give you coat and breeches for your rags."

Thus generously supplied with clothes and other comforts by the good knight, and implicitly relying upon the honor of so kind-hearted a man, Israel cheered up, and in the course of two or three weeks had so fattened his flanks, that he was able completely to fill Sir John's old buckskin breeches, which at first had hung but loosely about him.

He was assigned to an occupation which removed him from the other workmen. The strawberry bed was put under his sole charge. And often, of mild, sunny afternoons, the knight, genial and gentle with dinner, would stroll bareheaded to the pleasant strawberry bed, and have nice little confidential chats with Israel; while Israel, charmed by the patriarchal demeanor of this true Abrahamic gentleman, with a smile on his lips, and tears of gratitude in his eyes, offered him, from time to time, the plumpest berries of the bed. When the strawberry season was over, other parts of the grounds were assigned him. And so six months elapsed, when, at the recommendation of Sir John, Israel procured a good berth in the garden of the Princess Amelia.

So completely now had recent events metamorphosed him in all outward things, that few suspected him of being any other than an Englishman. Not even the knight's domestics. But in the princess's garden, being obliged to work in company with many other laborers, the war was often a topic of discussion among them. And "the d—d Yankee rebels" were not seldom the object of scurrilous remark. Illy could the exile brook in silence such insults upon the country for which he had bled, and for whose honored sake he was that very instant a sufferer. More than once, his indignation came very nigh getting the better of his prudence. He longed for the war to end, that he might but speak a little bit of his mind.

Now, the superintendent of the garden was a harsh, overbearing man. The workmen with tame servility endured his worst affronts. But Israel, bred among mountains, found it impossible to restrain himself when made the undeserved object of pitiless epithets. Ere two months went by, he quitted the service of the princess, and engaged himself to a farmer in a small village not far from Brentford. But hardly had he been here three weeks, when a rumor again got afloat, that he was a Yankee prisoner of war. Whence this report arose he could never discover. No sooner did it reach the ears of the soldiers, than they were on the alert. Luckily, Israel was apprised of their intentions in time. But he was hard pushed. He was hunted after with a perseverance worthy a less ignoble cause. He had many hairbreadth escapes. Most assuredly he would have been captured, had it not been for the secret good offices of a few individuals, who, perhaps, were not unfriendly to the American side of the question, though they durst not avow it.

Tracked one night by the soldiers to the house of one of these friends, in whose garret he was concealed, he was obliged to force the skuttle, and running along the roof, passed to those of adjoining houses to the number of ten or twelve, finally succeeding in making his escape.

CHAPTER V

ISRAEL IN THE LION'S DEN

HARASSED day and night, hunted from food and sleep, driven from hole to hole like a fox in the woods, with no chance to earn an hour's wages, he was at last advised by one whose sincerity he could not doubt, to apply, on the good word of Sir John Millet, for a berth as laborer in the King's Gardens at Kew. There, it was said, he would be entirely safe, as no soldier durst approach those premises to molest any soul therein employed. It struck the poor exile as curious, that the very den of the British lion, the private grounds of the British King, should be commended to a refugee as his securest asylum.

His nativity carefully concealed and being personally introduced to the chief gardener by one who well knew him; armed, too, with a line from Sir John, and recommended by his introducer as uncommonly expert at horticulture; Israel was soon installed as keeper of certain less private plants and walks of the park.

It was here, to one of his near country retreats, that, coming from perplexities of state—leaving far behind him the dingy old bricks of St. James—George the Third was wont to walk up and down beneath the long arbors formed by the interlockings of lofty trees.

More than once, raking the gravel, Israel through intervening foliage would catch peeps in some private but parallel walk, of that lonely figure, not more shadowy with overhanging leaves than with the shade of royal meditations.

Unauthorized and abhorrent thoughts will sometimes invade the best human heart. Seeing the monarch unguarded before him; remembering that the war was imputed more to the self-will of the King than to the willingness of parliament or the nation; and calling to mind all his own sufferings growing out of that war, with all the calamities of his country; dim impulses, such as those to which the regicide Ravaillac yielded, would shoot balefully across the soul of the exile. But thrusting Satan behind him, Israel vanquished all such temptations. Nor did these ever more disturb him, after his only chance conversation with the monarch.

As he was one day gravelling a little by-walk, wrapped in thought, the King turning a clump of bushes, suddenly brushed Israel's person.

Immediately Israel touched his hat—but did not remove it—bowed, and was retiring; when something in his air arrested the King's attention.

"You ain't an Englishman—no Englishman—no, no."

Pale as death, Israel tried to answer something; but, knowing not what to say, stood frozen to the ground.

"You are a Yankee—a Yankee," said the King again in his rapid and half-stammering way.

Again Israel essayed to reply, but could not. What could he say? Cauld he lie to a King?

"Yes, yes—you are one of that stubborn race—that very stubborn race. What brought you here?"

"The fate of war, sir."

"May it please your Majesty," said a low cringing voice, approaching, "this man is in the walk against orders. There is some mistake, may it please your Majesty. Quit the walk, blockhead," he hissed at Israel.

It was one of the junior gardeners who thus spoke. It seems that Israel had mistaken his directions that morning.

"Slink, you dog," hissed the gardener again to Israel; then aloud to the King, "A mistake of the man, I assure your Majesty."

"Go you away—away with ye, and leave him with me," said the King.

Waiting a moment, till the man was out of hearing, the King again turned upon Israel.

"Were you at Bunker Hill?—that bloody Bunker Hill—eh, eh?"

"Yes, sir."

"Fought like a devil—like a very devil, I suppose?"

"Yes, sir."

"Helped flog—helped flog my soldiers?"

"Yes, sir; but very sorry to do it."

"Eh?—eh?—how's that?"

"I took it to be my sad duty, sir."

"Very much mistaken—very much mistaken, indeed. Why do ye sir me?— eh? I'm your king—your king."

"Sir," said Israel firmly, but with deep respect, "I have no king."

The King darted his eye incensedly for a moment; but without quailing, ·

Israel, now that all was out, still stood with mute respect before him. The King, turning suddenly, walked rapidly away from Israel a moment, but presently returning with a less hasty pace, said, "You are rumored to be a spy—a spy, or something of that sort—ain't you? But I know you are not— no, no. You are a runaway prisoner of war, eh? You have sought this place to be safe from pursuit, eh? eh? Is it not so?—eh? eh? eh?"

"Sir, it is."

"Well, ye're an honest rebel—rebel, yes, rebel. Hark ye, hark. Say nothing of this talk to any one. And hark again. So long as you remain here at Kew, I shall see that you are safe—safe."

"God bless your Majesty!"

"Eh?"

"God bless your noble Majesty?"

"Come—come—come," smiled the King in delight, "I thought I could conquer ye—conquer ye."

"Not the king, but the king's kindness, your Majesty."

"Join my army—army."

Sadly looking down, Israel silently shook his head.

"You won't? Well, gravel the walk then—gravel away. Very stubborn race—very stubborn race, indeed—very—very—very."

And still growling, the magnanimous lion departed.

How the monarch came by his knowledge of so humble an exile, whether through that swift insight into individual character said to form one of the miraculous qualities transmitted with a crown, or whether some of the rumors prevailing outside of the garden had come to his ear, Israel could never determine. Very probably, though, the latter was the case, inasmuch as some vague shadowy report of Israel not being an Englishman, had, a little previous to his interview with the King, been communicated to several of the inferior gardeners. Without any impeachment of Israel's fealty to his country, it must still be narrated, that from this his familiar audience with George the Third, he went away with very favorable views of that monarch. Israel now thought that it could not be the warm heart of the King, but the cold heads of his lords in council, that persuaded him so tyrannically to persecute America. Yet hitherto the precise contrary of this had been Israel's opinion, agreeably to the popular prejudice throughout New England.

Thus we see what strange and powerful magic resides in a crown, and how subtly that cheap and easy magnanimity, which in private belongs to most kings, may operate on good-natured and unfortunate souls. Indeed, had it not been for the peculiar disinterested fidelity of our adventurer's patriotism, he would have soon sported the red coat; and perhaps under the immediate patronage of his royal friend, been advanced in time to no mean rank in the army of Britain. Nor in that case would we have had to follow him, as at last we shall, through long, long years of obscure and penurious wandering.

Continuing in the service of the King's gardeners at Kew, until a season came when the work of the garden required a less number of laborers, Israel, with several others, was discharged; and the day after, engaged himself for a few months to a farmer in the neighborhood where he had been last employed. But hardly a week had gone by, when the old story of his being a rebel, or a runaway prisoner, or a Yankee! or a spy, began to be revived with added malignity. Like bloodhounds, the soldiers were once more on the track. The houses where he harbored were many times searched; but thanks to the fidelity of a few earnest well-wishers, and to his own unsleeping vigilance and activity, the hunted fox still continued to elude apprehension. To such extremities of harassment, however, did this incessant pursuit subject him, that in a fit of despair he was about to surrender himself, and submit to his fate, when Providence seasonably interposed in his favor.

CHAPTER VI

ISRAEL MAKES THE ACQUAINTANCE OF CERTAIN SECRET FRIENDS OF AMERICA, ONE OF THEM BEING THE FAMOUS AUTHOR OF THE "DIVERSIONS OF PURLEY." THESE DISPATCH HIM ON A SLY ERRAND ACROSS THE CHANNEL

AT this period, though made the victims indeed of British oppression, yet the colonies were not totally without friends in Britain. It was but natural that when Parliament itself held patriotic and gifted men, who not only recommended conciliatory measures, but likewise denounced the war as monstrous; it was but natural that throughout the nation at large there should be many private individuals cherishing similar sentiments, and some who made no scruple clandestinely to act upon them.

Late one night while hiding in a farmer's granary, Israel saw a man with a lantern approaching. He was about to flee, when the man hailed him in a well-known voice, bidding him have no fear. It was the farmer himself. He carried a message to Israel from a gentleman of Brentford, to the effect, that the refugee was earnestly requested to repair on the following evening to that gentleman's mansion.

At first, Israel was disposed to surmise that either the farmer was playing him false, or else his honest credulity had been imposed upon by evil-minded persons. At any rate, he regarded the message as a decoy, and for half an hour refused to credit its sincerity. But at length he was induced to think a little better of it. The gentleman giving the invitation was one Squire Woodcock, of Brentford, whose loyalty to the king had been under suspicion; so at least the farmer averred. This latter information was not without its effect.

At nightfall on the following day, being disguised in strange clothes by the farmer, Israel stole from his retreat, and after a few hours' walk, arrived before the ancient brick house of the Squire; who opening the door in person, and learning who it was that stood there, at once assured Israel in the most solemn manner, that no foul play was intended. So the wanderer suffered himself to enter, and be conducted to a private chamber in the rear of the mansion, where were seated two other gentlemen, attired, in the manner of that age, in long laced coats, with smallclothes, and shoes with silver buckles.

"I am John Woodcock," said the host, "and these gentlemen are Horne Tooke and James Bridges. All three of us are friends to America. We have heard of you for some weeks past, and inferring from your conduct, that you must be a Yankee of the true blue stamp, we have resolved to employ you in a way which you cannot but gladly approve; for surely, though an exile, you are still willing to serve your country; if not as a sailor or soldier, yet as a traveller?"

"Tell me how I may do it?" demanded Israel, not completely at ease.

"All that in good time," smiled the Squire. "The point is now—do you repose confidence in my statements?"

Israel glanced inquiringly upon the Squire; then upon his companions; and meeting the expressive, enthusiastic, candid countenance of Horne Tooke—then in the first honest ardor of his political career—turned to the Squire, and said, "Sir, I believe what you have said. Tell me now what I am to do."

"Oh, there is just nothing to be done to-night," said the Squire; "nor for some days to come perhaps, but we wanted to have you prepared."

And hereupon he hinted to his guest rather vaguely of his general intention; and that over, begged him to entertain them with some account of his adventures since he first took up arms for his country. To this Israel had no objections in the world, since all men love to tell the tale of hardships endured in a righteous cause. But ere beginning his story, the Squire refreshed him with some cold beef, laid in a snowy napkin, and a glass of Perry, and thrice during the narration of the adventures, pressed him with additional draughts.

But after his second glass, Israel declined to drink more, mild as the beverage was. For he noticed, that not only did the three gentlemen listen with the utmost interest to his story, but likewise interrupted him with questions and cross-questions in the most pertinacious manner. So this led him to be on his guard, not being absolutely certain yet, as to who they might really be, or what was their real design. But as it turned out, Squire Woodcock and his friends only sought to satisfy themselves thoroughly, before making their final disclosures, that the exile was one in whom implicit confidence might be placed.

And to this desirable conclusion they eventually came, for upon the ending of Israel's story, after expressing their sympathies for his hardships, and applauding his generous patriotism in so patiently enduring adversity, as well as singing the praises of his gallant fellow-soldiers of Bunker Hill, they openly revealed their scheme. They wished to know whether Israel would undertake a trip to Paris, to carry an important message—shortly to be received for transmission through them—to Doctor Franklin, then in that capital.

"All your expenses shall be paid, not to speak of a compensation besides," said the Squire; "will you go?"

"I must think of it," said Israel, not yet wholly confirmed in his mind. But once more he cast his glance on Horne Hooke, and his irresolution was gone.

The Squire now informed Israel that, to avoid suspicions, it would be necessary for him to remove to another place until the hour at which he should start for Paris. They enjoined upon him the profoundest secrecy, gave him a guinea, with a letter for a gentleman in White Waltham, a town some miles from Brentford, which point they begged him to reach as soon as possible, there to tarry for further instructions.

Having informed him of thus much, Squire Woodcock asked him to hold out his right foot.

"What for?" said Israel.

"Why, would you not like to have a pair of new boots against your return?" smiled Horne Tooke.

"Oh, yes; no objection at all," said Israel.

"Well, then, let the bootmaker measure you," smiled Horne Tooke.

"Do *you* do it, Mr. Tooke," said the Squire; "you measure men's parts better than I."

"Hold out your foot, my good friend," said Horne Tooke—"there—now let's measure your heart."

"For that, measure me round the chest," said Israel.

"Just the man we want," said Mr. Bridges, triumphantly.

"Give him another glass of wine, Squire," said Horne Tooke.

Exchanging the farmer's clothes for still another disguise, Israel now set out immediately, on foot, for his destination, having received minute directions as to his road; and arriving in White Waltham on the following morning was very cordially received by the gentleman to whom he carried the letter. This person, another of the active English friends of America, possessed a particular knowledge of late events in that land. To him Israel was indebted for much entertaining information. After remaining some ten days at this place, word came from Squire Woodcock, requiring Israel's immediate return, stating the hour at which he must arrive at the house, namely, two o'clock on the following morning. So, after another night's solitary trudge across the country, the wanderer was welcomed by the same three gentlemen as before, seated in the same room.

"The time has now come," said Squire Woodcock. "You must start this morning for Paris. Take off your shoes."

"Am I to steal from here to Paris on my stocking-feet?" said Israel, whose late easy good living at White Waltham had not failed to bring out the good-natured and mirthful part of him, even as his prior experiences had produced, for the most part, something like a contrary result.

"Oh, no," smiled Horne Tooke, who always lived well, "we have seven-league-boots for you. Don't you remember my measuring you?"

Hereupon going to the closet, the Squire brought out a pair of new boots. They were fitted with false heels. Unscrewing these, the Squire showed Israel the papers concealed beneath. They were of a fine tissuey fibre, and contained much writing in a very small compass. The boots, it need hardly be said, had been particularly made for the occasion.

"Walk across the room with them," said the Squire, when Israel had pulled them on.

"He'll surely be discovered," smiled Horne Tooke. "Hark, how he creaks."

"Come, come, it's too serious a matter for joking," said the Squire. "Now, my fine fellow, be cautious, be sober, be vigilant, and above all things be speedy."

Being furnished now with all requisite directions, and a supply of money, Israel, taking leave of Mr. Tooke and Mr. Bridges, was secretly conducted down stairs by the Squire, and in five minutes' time was on his way to Charing Cross in London, where taking the post-coach for Dover, he thence went in a packet to Calais, and in fifteen minutes after landing, was being wheeled over French soil towards Paris. He arrived there in safety, and freely declaring himself an American, the peculiarly friendly relations of the two nations at that period, procured him kindly attentions even from strangers.

CHAPTER VII

AFTER A CURIOUS ADVENTURE UPON THE PONT NEUF, ISRAEL ENTERS THE PRESENCE OF THE RENOWNED SAGE, DR. FRANKLIN, WHOM HE FINDS RIGHT LEARNEDLY AND MULTIFARIOUSLY EMPLOYED

FOLLOWING the directions given him at the place where the diligence stopped, Israel was crossing the Pont Neuf, to find Doctor Franklin, when he was suddenly called to by a man standing on one side of the bridge, just under the equestrian statue of Henry IV.

The man had a small, shabby-looking box before him on the ground, with a box of blacking on one side of it, and several shoe-brushes upon the other. Holding another brush in his hand, he politely seconded his verbal invitation by gracefully flourishing the brush in the air.

"What do you want of me, neighbor?" said Israel, pausing in somewhat uneasy astonishment.

"Ah, Monsieur," exclaimed the man, and with voluble politeness he ran on with a long string of French, which of course was all Greek to poor Israel. But what his language failed to convey, his gestures now made very plain. Pointing to the wet muddy state of the bridge, splashed by a recent rain, and then to the feet of the wayfarer, and lastly to the brush in his hand, he appeared to be deeply regretting that a gentleman of Israel's otherwise imposing appearance should be seen abroad with unpolished boots, offering at the same time to remove their blemishes.

"Ah, Monsieur, Monsieur," cried the man, at last running up to Israel. And with tender violence he forced him towards the box, and lifting this unwilling customer's right foot thereon, was proceeding vigorously to work, when suddenly illuminated by a dreadful suspicion, Israel, fetching the box a terrible kick, took to his false heels and ran like mad over the bridge.

Incensed that his politeness should receive such an ungracious return, the man pursued, which but confirming Israel in his suspicions he ran all the faster, and thanks to his fleetness, soon succeeded in escaping his pursuer.

Arrived at last at the street and the house to which he had been directed, in reply to his summons, the gate very strangely of itself swung open, and much astonished at this unlooked-for sort of enchantment, Israel entered a wide vaulted passage leading to an open court within. While he was wondering that no soul appeared, suddenly he was hailed from a dark little window, where sat an old man cobbling shoes, while an old woman standing by his side was thrusting her head into the passage, intently eyeing the stranger. They proved to be the porter and portress, the latter of whom, upon hearing his summons, had invisibly thrust open the gate to Israel, by means of a spring communicating with the little apartment.

Upon hearing the name of Doctor Franklin mentioned, the old woman, all alacrity, hurried out of her den, and with much courtesy showed Israel across the court, up three flights of stairs to a door in the rear of the spacious building. There she left him while Israel knocked.

"Come in," said a voice.

And immediately Israel stood in the presence of the venerable Doctor Franklin.

Wrapped in a rich dressing gown, a fanciful present from an admiring Marchesa, curiously embroidered with algebraic figures like a conjuror's robe, and with a skull-cap of black satin on his hive of a head, the man of gravity was seated at a huge claw-footed old table, round as the zodiac. It was covered with printed papers, files of documents, rolls of manuscripts, stray bits of strange models in wood and metal, odd-looking pamphlets in various languages, and all sorts of books, including many presentation-copies, embracing history, mechanics, diplomacy, agriculture, political economy, metaphysics, meteorology, and geometry. The walls had a necromantic look, hung round with barometers of different kinds, drawings of surprising inventions, wide maps of far countries in the New World, containing vast empty spaces in the middle, with the word DESERT diffusely printed there, so as to span five-and-twenty degrees of longitude with only two syllables—which printed word, however, bore a vigorous pen-mark, in the Doctor's hand, drawn straight through it, as if in summary repeal of it; crowded topographical and trigonometrical charts of various parts of Europe; with geometrical diagrams, and endless other surprising hangings and upholstery of science.

The chamber itself bore evident marks of antiquity. One part of the rough-finished wall was sadly cracked, and covered with dust, looked dim and dark. But the aged inmate, though wrinkled as well, looked neat and hale. Both wall and sage were compounded of like materials—lime and dust; both, too, were old; but while the rude earth of the wall had no painted lustre to shed off all fadings and tarnish, and still keep fresh without, though with long eld its core decayed: the living lime and dust of the sage was frescoed with defensive bloom of his soul.

The weather was warm; like some old West India hogshead on the wharf, the whole chamber buzzed with flies. But the sapient inmate sat still and cool in the midst. Absorbed in some other world of his occupations and thoughts, these insects, like daily cark and care, did not seem one whit to annoy him. It was a goodly sight to see this serene, cool and ripe old philosopher, who by sharp inquisition of man in the street, and then long meditating upon him, surrounded by all those queer old implements, charts and books, had grown at last so wondrous wise. There he sat, quite motionless among those restless flies; and, with a sound like the low noon murmur of foliage in the woods, turning over the leaves of some ancient and tattered folio, with a binding dark and shaggy as the bark of any old oak. It seemed as if supernatural lore must needs pertain to this gravely, ruddy personage; at least far foresight, pleasant wit, and working wisdom. Old age seemed in no wise to have dulled him, but to have sharpened; just as old dinner-knives—so they be of good steel—wax keen, spear-pointed, and elastic as whalebone with long usage. Yet though he was thus lively and vigorous to behold, spite of his seventy-two years (his exact date at that time) somehow, the incredible seniority of an antediluvian seemed his. Not the years of the calendar wholly, but also the years of sapience. His white hairs and mild brow, spoke of the future as well as the past. He seemed to be seven score years old; that is, three score and ten of prescience added to three score and ten of remembrance, makes just seven score years in all.

But when Israel stepped within the chamber, he lost the complete effect of all this; for the sage's back, not his face, was turned to him.

So, intent on his errand, hurried and heated with his recent run, our courier entered the room, inadequately impressed, for the time, by either it or its occupant.

"Bon jour, bon jour, monsieur," said the man of wisdom, in a cheerful voice, but too busy to turn round just then.

"How do you do, Doctor Franklin?" said Israel.

"Ah! I smell Indian corn," said the Doctor, turning round quickly on his chair. "A countryman; sit down, my good sir. Well, what news? Special?"

"Wait a minute, sir," said Israel, stepping across the room towards a chair.

Now there was no carpet on the floor, which was of dark-colored wood, set in lozenges, and slippery with wax, after the usual French style. As Israel walked this slippery floor, his unaccustomed feet slid about very strangely as if walking on ice, so that he came very near falling.

" 'Pears to me you have rather high heels to your boots,' said the grave man of utility, looking sharply down through his spectacles; "don't you know that it's both wasting leather and endangering your limbs to wear such high heels? I have thought, at my first leisure, to write a little pamphlet against that very abuse. But pray, what are you doing now? Do your boots pinch you, my friend, that you lift one foot from the floor that way?"

At this moment, Israel having seated himself, was just putting his right foot against his left knee.

"How foolish," continued the wise man, "for a rational creature to wear tight boots. Had nature intended rational creatures should do so, she would have made the foot of solid bone, or perhaps of solid iron, instead of bone, muscle, and flesh. But—I see. Hold!"

And springing to his own slippered feet, the venerable sage hurried to the door and shot-to the bolt. Then drawing the curtain carefully across the window looking out across the court to various windows on the opposite side, bade Israel proceed with his operations.

"I was mistaken this time," added the Doctor, smiling, as Israel produced his documents from their curious recesses—"your high heels, instead of being idle vanities, seem to be full of meaning."

"Pretty full, Doctor," said Israel, now handing over the papers. "I had a narrow escape with them just now."

"How? How's that?" said the sage, fumbling the papers eagerly.

"Why, crossing the stone bridge there over the *Seen*"—

"*Seine*"—interrupted the Doctor, giving the French pronunciation.—"Always get a new word right in the first place, my friend, and you will never get it wrong afterwards."

"Well, I was crossing the bridge there, and who should hail me, but a suspicious-looking man, who, under pretence of seeking to polish my boots, wanted slyly to unscrew their heels, and so steal all these precious papers I've brought you."

"My good friend," said the man of gravity, glancing scrutinizingly upon his guest, "have you not in your time undergone what they call hard times? Been set upon, and persecuted, and very illy entreated by some of your fellow-creatures?"

"That I have, Doctor; yes, indeed."

"I thought so. Sad usage has made you sadly suspicious, my honest friend. An indiscriminate distrust of human nature is the worst consequence of a miserable condition, whether brought about by innocence or guilt. And though want of suspicion more than want of sense sometimes leads a man into harm, yet too much suspicion is as bad as too little sense. The man you met, my friend, most probably had no artful intention; he knew just nothing about you or your heels; he simply wanted to earn two sous by brushing your boots. Those blackingmen regularly station themselves on the bridge."

"How sorry I am then that I knocked over his box, and then ran away. But he didn't catch me."

"How? surely, my honest friend, you—appointed to the conveyance of important secret dispatches—did not act so imprudently as to kick over an innocent man's box in the public streets of the capital, to which you had been especially sent?"

"Yes, I did, Doctor."

"Never act so unwisely again. If the police had got hold of you, think of what might have ensued."

"Well, it was not very wise of me, that's a fact, Doctor. But, you see, I thought he meant mischief."

"And because you only thought he *meant* mischief, *you* must straightway proceed to *do* mischief. That's poor logic. But think over what I have told you now, while I look over these papers."

In half an hour's time, the Doctor, laying down the documents, again turned towards Israel, and removing his spectacles very placidly, proceeded in the kindest and most familiar manner to read him a paternal detailed lesson upon the ill-advised act he had been guilty of, upon the Pont Neuf; concluding by taking out his purse, and putting three small silver coins into Israel's hands, charging him to seek out the man that very day, and make both apology and restitution for his unlucky mistake.

"All of us, my honest friend," continued the Doctor, "are subject to making mistakes; so that the chief art of life, is to learn how best to remedy mistakes. Now one remedy for mistakes is honesty. So pay the man for the damage done to his box. And now, who are you, my friend? My correspondents here mention your name—Israel Potter—and say you are an American, an escaped prisoner of war, but nothing further. I want to hear your story from your own lips."

Israel immediately began, and related to the Doctor all his adventures up to the present time.

"I suppose," said the Doctor, upon Israel's concluding, "that you desire to return to your friends across the sea?"

"That I do, Doctor," said Israel.

"Well, I think I shall be able to procure you a passage."

Israel's eyes sparkled with delight. The mild sage noticed it, and added:

"But events in these times are uncertain. At the prospect of pleasure never be elated; but, without depression, respect the omens of ill. So much my life has taught me, my honest friend."

Israel felt as though a plum-pudding had been thrust under his nostrils, and then as rapidly withdrawn.

"I think it is probable that in two or three days I shall want you to return with some papers to the persons who sent you to me. In that case you will have to come here once more, and then, my good friend, we will see what can be done towards getting you safely home again."

Israel was pouring out torrents of thanks when the Doctor interrupted him.

"Gratitude, my friend, cannot be too much towards God, but toward man, it should be limited. No man can possibly so serve his fellow, as to merit unbounded gratitude. Over-gratitude in the helped person, is apt to breed vanity or arrogance in the helping one. Now in assisting you to get home— if indeed I shall prove able to do so—I shall be simply doing part of my official duty as agent of our common country. So you owe me just nothing at all, but the sum of these coins I put in your hand just now. But that, instead of repaying to me hereafter, you can, when you get home, give to the first soldier's widow you meet. Don't forget it, for it is a debt, a pecuniary liability, owing to me. It will be about a quarter of a dollar, in the Yankee currency. A quarter of a dollar, mind. My honest friend, in pecuniary matters always be exact as a second-hand; never mind with whom it is, father or stranger, peasant or king, be exact to a tick of your honor."

"Well, Doctor," said Israel, "since exactness in these matters is so necessary, let me pay back my debt in the very coins in which it was loaned. There will be no chance of mistake then. Thanks to my Brentford friends, I have enough to spare of my own, to settle damages with the boot-black of the bridge. I only took the money from you, because I thought it would not look well to push it back after being so kindly offered."

"My honest friend," said the Doctor, "I like your straightforward dealing. I will receive back the money."

"No interest, Doctor, I hope," said Israel.

The sage looked mildly over his spectacles upon Israel and replied: "My good friend, never permit yourself to be jocose upon pecuniary matters. Never joke at funerals, or during business transactions. The affair between us two, you perhaps deem very trivial, but trifles may involve momentous principles. But no more at present. You had better go immediately and find the boot-black. Having settled with him, return hither, and you will find a room ready for you near this, where you will stay during your sojourn in Paris."

"But I thought I would like to have a little look round the town, before I go back to England," said Israel.

"Business before pleasure, my friend. You must absolutely remain in your room, just as if you were my prisoner, until you quit Paris for Calais. Not knowing now at what instant I shall want you to start, your keeping to your room is indispensable. But when you come back from Brentford again, then, if nothing happens, you will have a chance to survey this celebrated capital ere taking ship for America. Now go directly, and pay the boot-black. Stop, have you the exact change ready? Don't be taking out all your money in the open street."

"Doctor," said Israel, "I am not so simple."

"But you knocked over the box."

"That, Doctor, was bravery."

"Bravery in a poor cause, is the height of simplicity, my friend.—Count out your change. It must be French coin, not English, that you are to pay the man with.—Ah, that will do—those three coins will be enough. Put them in a pocket separate from your other cash. Now go, and hasten to the bridge."

"Shall I stop to take a meal anywhere, Doctor, as I return? I saw several cookshops as I came hither."

"Cafés and restaurants, they are called here, my honest friend. Tell me, are you the possessor of a liberal fortune?"

"Not very liberal," said Israel.

"I thought as much. Where little wine is drunk, it is good to dine out occasionally at a friend's; but where a poor man dines out at his own charge, it is bad policy. Never dine out that way, when you can dine in. Do not stop on the way at all, my honest friend, but come directly back hither, and you shall dine at home, free of cost, with me."

"Thank you very kindly, Doctor."

And Israel departed for the Pont Neuf. Succeeding in his errand thither, he returned to Doctor Franklin, and found that worthy envoy waiting his attendance at a meal, which, according to the Doctor's custom, had been sent from a neighboring restaurant. There were two covers; and without attendance the host and guest sat down. There was only one principal dish, lamb boiled with green peas. Bread and potatoes made up the rest. A decanter-like bottle of uncolored glass, filled with some uncolored beverage, stood at the venerable envoy's elbow.

"Let me fill your glass," said the sage.

"It's white wine, ain't it?" said Israel.

"White wine of the very oldest brand; I drink your health in it, my honest friend."

"Why, it's plain water," said Israel, now tasting it.

"Plain water is a very good drink for plain men," replied the wise man.

"Yes," said Israel, "but Squire Woodcock gave me perry, and the other gentleman at White Waltham gave me port, and some other friends have given me brandy."

"Very good, my honest friend; if you like perry and port and brandy, wait till you get back to Squire Woodcock, and the gentleman at White Waltham, and the other friends, and you shall drink perry and port and brandy. But while you are with me, you will drink plain water."

"So it seems, Doctor."

"What do you suppose a glass of port costs?"

"About three pence English, Doctor."

"That must be poor port. But how much good bread will three pence English purchase?"

"Three penny rolls, Doctor."

"How many glasses of port do you suppose a man may drink at a meal?"

"The gentleman at White Waltham drank a bottle at a dinner."

"A bottle contains just thirteen glasses—that's thirty-nine pence, supposing it poor wine. If something of the best, which is the only sort any sane man should drink, as being the least poisonous, it would be quadruple that sum, which is one hundred and fifty-six pence, which is seventy-eight two-penny loaves. Now, do you not think that for one man to swallow down seventy-two two-penny rolls at one meal is rather extravagant business?"

"But he drank a bottle of wine; he did not eat seventy-two two-penny rolls, Doctor."

"He drank the money worth of seventy-two loaves, which is drinking the loaves themselves; for money is bread."

"But he has plenty of money to spare, Doctor."

"To have to spare, is to have to give away. Does the gentleman give much away?"

"Not that I know of, Doctor."

"Then he thinks he has nothing to spare; and thinking he has nothing to spare, and yet prodigally drinking down his money as he does every day, it seems to me that that gentleman stands self-contradicted, and therefore is no good example for plain sensible folks like you and me to follow. My honest friend, if you are poor, avoid wine as a costly luxury; if you are rich, shun it as a fatal indulgence. Stick to plain water. And now, my good friend, if you are through with your meal, we will rise. There is no pastry coming. Pastry is poisoned bread. Never eat pastry. Be a plain man, and stick to plain things. Now, my friend, I shall have to be private until nine o'clock in the evening, when I shall be again at your service. Meantime you may go to your room. I have ordered the one next to this to be prepared for you. But you must not be idle. Here is Poor Richard's Almanac, which, in view of our late conversation, I commend to your earnest perusal. And here, too, is a Guide to Paris, an English one, which you can read. Study it well, so that when you come back from England, if you should then have an opportunity to travel about Paris, to see its wonders, you will have all the chief places made historically familiar to you. In this world, men must provide knowledge before it is wanted, just as our countrymen in New England get in their winter's fuel one season, to serve them the next."

So saying, this homely sage, and household Plato, showed his humble guest to the door, and standing in the hall, pointed out to him the one which opened into his allotted apartment.

CHAPTER VIII

WHICH HAS SOMETHING TO SAY ABOUT DR. FRANKLIN AND THE LATIN QUARTER

THE first, both in point of time and merit, of American envoys was famous not less for the pastoral simplicity of his manners than for the politic grace of his mind. Viewed from a certain point, there was a touch of primeval orientalness in Benjamin Franklin. Neither is there wanting something like his Scriptural parallel. The history of the patriarch Jacob is interesting not less from the unselfish devotion which we are bound to ascribe to him, than from the deep worldly wisdom and polished Italian tact, gleaming under an air of Arcadian unaffectedness. The diplomatist and the shepherd are blended; a union not without warrant; the apostolic serpent and dove. A tanned Machiavelli in tents.

Doubtless, too, notwithstanding his eminence as lord of the moving manor, Jacob's raiment was of homespun; the economic envoy's plain coat and hose, who has not heard of?

Franklin all over is of a piece. He dressed his person as his periods; neat, trim, nothing superfluous, nothing deficient. In some of his works his style is only surpassed by the unimprovable sentences of Hobbes of Malmsbury, the paragon of perspicuity. The mental habits of Hobbes and Franklin in several points, especially in one of some moment, assimilated. Indeed, making due allowance for soil and era, history presents few trios more akin, upon the whole, than Jacob, Hobbes, and Franklin; three labyrinth-minded, but plainspoken Broadbrims, at once politicians and philosophers; keen observers of the main chance; prudent courtiers; practical magians in linsey-woolsey.

In keeping with his general habitudes, Doctor Franklin while at the French Court did not reside in the aristocratical faubourgs. He deemed his worsted hose and scientific tastes more adapted in a domestic way to the other side of the Seine, where the Latin Quarter, at once the haunt of erudition and economy, seemed peculiarly to invite the philosophical Poor Richard to its venerable retreats. Here, of gray, chilly, drizzly November mornings, in the dark-stoned quadrangle of the time-honored Sorbonne, walked the lean and slippered metaphysician—oblivious for the moment that his sublime thoughts and tattered wardrobe were famous throughout Europe—meditating on the theme of his next lecture; at the same time, in the well-worn chambers overhead, some clayey-visaged chemist in ragged robe-de-chambre, and with a soiled green flap over his left eye, was hard at work stooping over retorts and crucibles, discovering new antipathies in acids, again risking strange explosions similar to that whereby he had already lost the use of one optic; while in the lofty lodging houses of the neighboring streets, indigent young students, from all parts of France, were ironing their shabby cocked hats, or inking the whity seams of their small-clothes, prior to a promenade with their pink-ribboned little grisettes in the Garden of the Luxembourg.

Long ago the haunt of rank, the Latin Quarter still retains many old buildings whose imposing architecture singularly contrasts with the unassuming habits of their present occupants. In some parts its general air is dreary and dim; monastic and theurgic. In those lonely narrow ways—long-drawn prospectives of desertion—lined with huge piles of silent, vaulted, old iron-grated buildings of dark gray stone, one almost expects to encounter Paracelsus or Friar Bacon turning the next corner, with some awful vial of Black-Art elixir in his hand.

But all the lodging-houses are not so grim. Not to speak of many of comparatively modern erection, the others of the better class, however stern. in exterior, evince a feminine gayety of taste, more or less, in their furnishings within. The embellishing, or softening, or screening hand of woman is to be seen all over the interiors of this metropolis. Like Augustus Cæsar with respect to Rome, the Frenchwoman leaves her obvious mark on Paris. Like the hand in nature, you know it can be none else but hers. Yet sometimes she overdoes it, as nature in the peony; or underdoes it, as nature in the bramble; or—what is still more frequent—is a little slatternly about it, as nature in the pig-weed.

In this congenial vicinity of the Latin Quarter, and in an ancient building something like those alluded to, at a point midway between the Palais des Beaux Arts and the College of the Sorbonne, the venerable American Envoy pitched his tent when not passing his time at his country retreat at Passy. The frugality of his manner of life did not lose him the good opinion even of the voluptuaries of the showiest of capitals, whose very iron railings are not free from gilt. Franklin was not less a lady's man, than a man's man, a wise man, and an old man. Not only did he enjoy the homage of the choicest Parisian literati, but at the age of seventy-two he was the caressed favorite of the highest born beauties of the Court; who through blind fashion having been originally attracted to him as a famous *savan*, were permanently retained as his admirers by his Plato-like graciousness of good humor. Having carefully weighed the world, Franklin could act in any part of it. By nature turned to knowledge, his mind was often grave, but never serious. At times he had seriousness—extreme seriousness—for others, but never for himself. Tranquillity was to him instead of it. This philosophical levity of tranquillity, so to speak, is shown in his easy variety of pursuits. Printer, postmaster, almanac maker, essayist, chemist, orator, tinker, statesman, humorist, philosopher, parlor man, political economist, professor of housewifery, ambassador, projector, maxim-monger, herb-doctor, wit:—Jack of all trades, master of each and mastered by none—the type and genius of his land. Franklin was everything but a poet. But since a soul with many qualities, forming of itself a sort of handy index and pocket congress of all humanity, needs the contact of just as many different men, or subjects, in order to the exhibition of its totality; hence very little indeed of the sage's multifariousness will be portrayed in a simple narrative like the present. This casual private intercourse with Israel, but served to manifest him in his far lesser lights; thrifty, domestic, dietarian, and, it may be, didactically waggish. There was much benevolent irony, innocent mischievousness, in the wise man. Seeking here to depict him in his less exalted habitudes, the narrator feels more as if he were playing with one of the sage's worsted hose, than reverentially handling the honored hat which once oracularly sat upon his brow.

So, then, in the Latin Quarter lived Doctor Franklin. And accordingly in the Latin Quarter tarried Israel for the time. And it was into a room of a house in this same Latin Quarter that Israel had been directed when the sage had requested privacy for a while.

CHAPTER IX

ISRAEL IS INITIATED INTO THE MYSTERIES OF LODGING-HOUSES IN THE LATIN QUARTER

CLOSING the door upon himself, Israel advanced to the middle of the chamber, and looked curiously round him.

A dark tessellated floor, but without a rug; two mahogany chairs, with embroidered seats, rather the worse for wear; one mahogany bed, with a gay but tarnished counterpane; a marble wash-stand, cracked, with a china vessel of water, minus the handle. The apartment was very large; this part of the house, which was a very extensive one, embracing the four sides of a quadrangle, having, in a former age, been the hotel of a nobleman. The magnitude of the chamber made its stinted furniture look meagre enough.

But in Israel's eyes, the marble mantel (a comparatively recent addition) and its appurtenances, not only redeemed the rest, but looked quite magnificent and hospitable in the extreme. Because, in the first place, the mantel was graced with an enormous old-fashioned square mirror, of heavy plate glass, set fast, like a tablet, into the wall. And in this mirror was genially reflected the following delicate articles:—first, two bouquets of flowers inserted in pretty vases of porcelain; second, one cake of white soap; third, one cake of rose-colored soap (both cakes very fragrant); fourth, one wax candle; fifth, one china tinder-box; sixth, one bottle of Eau de Cologne; seventh, one paper of loaf sugar, nicely broken into sugar-bowl size; eighth, one silver teaspoon; ninth, one glass tumbler; tenth, one glass decanter of cool pure water; eleventh, one sealed bottle containing a richly hued liquid, and marked "Otard."

"I wonder now what O-t-a-r-d is?" soliloquised Israel, slowly spelling the word. "I have a good mind to step in and ask Dr. Franklin. He knows everything. Let me smell it. No, it's sealed; smell is locked in. Those are pretty flowers. Let's smell them: no smell again. Ah, I see—sort of flowers in women's bonnets—sort of calico flowers. Beautiful soap. This smells anyhow —regular soap-roses—a white rose and a red one. That long-necked bottle there looks like a crane. I wonder what's in that? Hallo! E-a-u—d-e— C-o-l-o-g-n-e. I wonder if Dr. Franklin understands that? It looks like his white wine. This is nice sugar. Let's taste. Yes, this is very nice sugar, sweet as—yes, it's sweet as sugar; better than maple sugar, such as they make at home. But I'm crunching it too loud, the Doctor will hear me. But here's a teaspoon. What's this for? There's no tea, nor teacup; but here's a tumbler, and here's drinking water. Let me see. Seems to me, putting this and that and the other thing together, it's a sort of alphabet that spells something. Spoon, tumbler, water, sugar, —— brandy—that's it. O-t-a-r-d is brandy. Who put these things here? What does it all mean? Don't put sugar here for show, don't put a spoon here for ornament, nor a jug of water. There is only one meaning to it, and that is a very polite invitation from some invisible person to help myself, if I like, to a glass of brandy and sugar, and if I don't like, let it alone. That's my reading. I have a good mind to ask Doctor Franklin about it, though, for there's just a chance I may be mistaken, and these things here be some other person's private property, not at all meant for me to help myself from. Co-logne, what's that—never mind. Soap: soap's to wash with. I want to use soap, anyway. Let me see—no, there's no soap on the wash-stand. I see, soap is not given gratis here in Paris, to boarders. But if you want it, take it from the marble, and it will be charged in the bill. If you don't want it let it alone, and no charge. Well, that's fair, anyway. But then to a man who could not afford to use soap, such beautiful cakes as these lying before his eyes all the time, would be a strong temptation. And now that I think of it, the O-t-a-r-d looks rather tempting too. But if I don't like it now, I can let it alone. I've a good mind to try it. But it's sealed. I wonder now if I'm right in my understanding of this alphabet? Who knows? I'll venture one little sip, anyhow. Come, cork. Hark!"

There was a rapid knock at the door.

Clapping down the bottle, Israel said, "Come in."

It was the man of wisdom.

"My honest friend," said the Doctor, stepping with venerable briskness into the room, "I was so busy during your visit to the Pont Neuf, that I did not have time to see that your room was all right. I merely gave the order, and heard that it had been fulfilled. But it just occurred to me, that as the land-ladies of Paris have some curious customs which might puzzle an entire stranger, my presence here for a moment might explain any little obscurity. Yes, it is as I thought," glancing towards the mantel.

"Oh, Doctor, that reminds me; what is O-t-a-r-d, pray?"

"Otard is poison."

"Shocking."

"Yes, and I think I had best remove it from the room forthwith," replied the sage, in a business-like manner putting the bottle under his arm; "I hope you never use Cologne, do you?"

"What—what is that, Doctor?"

"I see. You never heard of the senseless luxury—a wise ignorance. You smelt flowers upon your mountains. You won't want this, either;" and the Cologne bottle was put under the other arm. "Candle—you'll want that. Soap —you want soap. Use the white cake."

"Is that cheaper, Doctor?"

"Yes, but just as good as the other. You don't ever munch sugar, do you? It's bad for the teeth. I'll take the sugar." So the paper of sugar was likewise dropped into one of the capacious coat pockets.

"Oh, you better take the whole furniture, Doctor Franklin. Here, I'll help you drag out the bedstead."

"My honest friend," said the wise man, pausing solemnly, with the two bottles, like swimmer's bladders, under his arm-pits; "my honest friend, the bedstead you will want; what I propose to remove you will not want."

"Oh, I was only joking, Doctor."

"I knew that. It's a bad habit, except at the proper time, and with the proper person. The things left on the mantel were there placed by the landlady to be used if wanted; if not, to be left untouched. To-morrow morning, upon the chambermaid's coming in to make your bed, all such articles as remained obviously untouched would have been removed, the rest would have been charged in the bill, whether you used them up completely or not."

"Just as I thought. Then why not let the bottles stay, Doctor, and save yourself all this trouble?"

"Ah! why indeed. My honest friend, are you not my guest? It were unhandsome in me to permit a third person superfluously to entertain you under what, for the time being, is my own roof."

These words came from the wise man in the most graciously bland and flowing tones. As he ended, he made a sort of conciliatory half bow towards Israel.

Charmed with his condescending affability, Israel, without another word, suffered him to march from the room, bottles and all. Not till the first impression of the venerable envoy's suavity had left him, did Israel begin to surmise the mild superiority of successful strategy which lurked beneath this highly ingratiating air.

"Ah," pondered Israel, sitting gloomily before the rifled mantel, with the empty tumbler and teaspoon in his hand, "it's sad business to have a Doctor Franklin lodging in the next room. I wonder if he sees to all the boarders this way. How the O-t-a-r-d merchants must hate him, and the pastry-cooks too. I wish I had a good pie to pass the time. I wonder if they ever make pumpkin pies in Paris? So I've got to stay in this room all the time. Somehow I'm bound to be a prisoner, one way or another. Never mind, I'm an ambassador; that's satisfaction. Hark! The Doctor again.—Come in."

No venerable doctor, but in tripped a young French lass, bloom on her cheek, pink ribbons in her cap, liveliness in all her air, grace in the very tips of her elbows. The most bewitching little chambermaid in Paris. All art, but the picture of artlessness.

"Monsieur! pardon!"

"Oh, I pardong ye freely," said Israel. "Come to call on the Ambassador?"

"Monsieur, is de—de—" but breaking down at the very threshold in her English, she poured out a long ribbon of sparkling French, the purpose of which was to convey a profusion of fine compliments to the stranger, with many tender inquiries as to whether he was comfortably roomed, and whether there might not be something, however trifling, wanting to his complete accommodation. But Israel understood nothing, at the time, but the exceeding grace, and trim, bewitching figure of the girl.

She stood eyeing him for a few moments more, with a look of pretty theatrical despair, and, after vaguely lingering a while, with another shower of incomprehensible compliments and apologies, tripped like a fairy from the chamber. Directly she was gone Israel pondered upon a singular glance of the girl. It seemed to him that he had, by his reception, in some way, unaccountably disappointed his beautiful visitor. It struck him very strangely that she had entered all sweetness and friendliness, but had retired as if slighted, with a sort of disdainful and sarcastic levity, all the more stinging from its apparent politeness.

Not long had she disappeared, when a noise in the passage apprised him that, in her hurried retreat, the girl must have stumbled against something.

The next moment he heard a chair scraping in the adjacent apartment, and there was another knock at the door.

It was the man of wisdom this time.

"My honest friend, did you not have a visitor, just now?"

"Yes, Doctor, a very pretty girl called upon me."

"Well, I just stopped in to tell you of another strange custom of Paris. That girl is the chambermaid, but she does not confine herself altogether to one vocation. You must beware of the chambermaids of Paris, my honest friend. Shall I tell the girl, from you, that, unwilling to give her the fatigue of going up and down so many flights of stairs, you will for the future waive her visits of ceremony?"

"Why, Doctor Franklin, she is a very sweet little girl."

"I know it, my honest friend; the sweeter the more dangerous. Arsenic is sweeter than sugar. I know you are a very sensible young man, not to be taken in by an artful Ammonite, and so I think I had better convey your message to the girl forthwith."

So saying, the sage withdrew, leaving Israel once more gloomily seated before the rifled mantel, whose mirror was not again to reflect the form of the charming chambermaid.

"Every time he comes in he robs me," soliloquised Israel, dolefully; "with an air all the time, too, as if he were making me presents. If he thinks me such a very sensible young man, why not let me take care of myself?"

It was growing dusk, and Israel, lighting the wax candle, proceeded to read in his Guide-book.

"This is poor sight-seeing," muttered he at last, "sitting here all by myself, with no company but an empty tumbler, reading about the fine things in Paris, and I myself a prisoner in Paris. I wish something extraordinary would turn up now; for instance, a man come in and give me ten thousand pounds. But here's 'Poor Richard;' I am a poor fellow myself; so let's see what comfort he has for a comrade."

Opening the little pamphlet, at random, Israel's eyes fell on the following passages: he read them aloud—

" 'So what signifies waiting and hoping for better times? We may make these times better, if we bestir ourselves. Industry need not wish, and he that lives upon hope will die fasting, as Poor Richard says. There are no gains, without pains. Then help hands, for I have no lands, as Poor Richard says.' Oh, confound all this wisdom! It's a sort of insulting to talk wisdom to a man like me. It's wisdom that's cheap, and it's fortune that's dear. That ain't in Poor Richard; but it ought to be," concluded Israel, suddenly slamming down the pamphlet.

He walked across the room, looked at the artificial flowers, and the rose-colored soap, and again went to the table and took up the two books.

"So here is the 'Way to Wealth,' and here is the 'Guide to Paris.' Wonder now whether Paris lies on the Way to Wealth? if so, I am on the road. More likely though, it's a parting-of-the-ways. I shouldn't be surprised if the Doctor meant something sly by putting these two books in my hand. Somehow, the old gentleman has an amazing sly look—a sort of wild slyness—about him, seems to me. His wisdom seems a sort of sly, too. But all in honor, though. I rather think he's one of these old gentlemen who say a vast deal of sense, but hint a world more. Depend upon it, he's sly, sly, sly. Ah, what's this Poor Richard says: 'God helps them that help themselves.' Let's consider that. Poor Richard ain't a Dunker, that's certain, though he has lived in Pennsylvania. 'God helps them that help themselves.' I'll just mark that saw, and leave the pamphlet open to refer to it again—Ah!"

At this point, the Doctor knocked, summoning Israel to his own apartment. Here, after a cup of weak tea, and a little toast, the two had a long, familiar talk together; during which, Israel was delighted with the unpretending talkativeness, serene insight, and benign amiability of the sage. But, for all this, he could hardly forgive him for the Cologne and Otard depredations.

Discovering that, in early life, Israel had been employed on a farm, the man of wisdom at length turned the conversation in that direction; among other things, mentioning to his guest a plan of his (the Doctor's) for yoking oxen, with a yoke to go by a spring instead of a bolt; thus greatly facilitating the operation of hitching on the team to the cart. Israel was very much struck with the improvement; and thought that, if he were home, upon his mountains, he would immediately introduce it among the farmers.

CHAPTER X

ANOTHER ADVENTURER APPEARS UPON THE SCENE

ABOUT half-past ten o'clock, as they were thus conversing, Israel's acquaintance, the pretty chambermaid, rapped at the door, saying, with a titter, that a very rude gentleman in the passage of the court, desired to see Doctor Franklin.

"A very rude gentleman?" repeated the wise man in French, narrowly looking at the girl; "that means, a very fine gentleman who has just paid you some energetic compliment. But let him come up, my girl," he added patriarchially.

In a few moments, a swift coquettish step was heard, followed, as if in chase, by a sharp and manly one. The door opened. Israel was sitting so that, accidentally, his eye pierced the crevice made by the opening of the door, which, like a theatrical screen, stood for a moment between Doctor Franklin and the just entering visitor. And behind that screen, through the crack, Israel caught one momentary glimpse of a little bit of by-play between the pretty chambermaid and the stranger. The vivacious nymph appeared to have affectedly run from him on the stairs—doubtless in freakish return for some liberal advances—but had suffered herself to be overtaken at last ere too late; and on the instant Israel caught sight of her, was with an insincere air of rosy resentment, receiving a roguish pinch on the arm, and a still more roguish salute on the cheek.

The next instant both disappeared from the range of the crevice; the girl departing whence she had come; the stranger—transiently invisible as he advanced behind the door—entering the room. When Israel now perceived him again, he seemed, while momentarily hidden, to have undergone a complete transformation.

He was a rather small, elastic, swarthy man, with an aspect as of a disinherited Indian Chief in European clothes. An unvanquishable enthusiasm, intensified to perfect sobriety, couched in his savage, self-possessed eye. He was elegantly and somewhat extravagantly dressed as a civilian; he carried himself with a rustic, barbaric jauntiness, strangly dashed with a superinduced touch of the Parisian *salon*. His tawny cheek, like a date, spoke of the tropic. A

wonderful atmosphere of proud friendliness and scornful isolation invested him.
Yet there was a bit of the poet as well as the outlaw in him, too. A cool
solemnity of intrepidity sat on his lip. He looked like one who of purpose
sought out harm's way. He looked like one who never had been, and never
would be, a subordinate.

Israel thought to himself that seldom before had he seen such a being.
Though dressed à-la-mode, he did not seem to be altogether civilized.

So absorbed was our adventurer by the person of the stranger, that a few
moments passed ere he began to be aware of the circumstance, that Dr. Franklin and this new visitor having saluted as old acquaintances, were now sitting
in earnest conversation together.

"Do as you please; but I will not bide a suitor much longer," said the
stranger in bitterness. "Congress gave me to understand that, upon my arrival
here, I should be given immediate command of the *Indien;* and now, for no
earthly reason that I can see, you Commissioners have presented her, fresh
from the stocks at Amsterdam, to the King of France, and not to me. What
does the King of France with such a frigate? And what can I *not* do with her?
Give me back the *Indien,* and in less than one month, you shall hear glorious
or fatal news of Paul Jones."

"Come, come, Captain," said Doctor Franklin, soothingly, "tell me now,
what would you do with her, if you had her?"

"I would teach the British that Paul Jones, though born in Britain, is no
subject to the British King, but an untrammelled citizen and sailor of the universe; and I would teach them, too, that if they ruthlessly ravage the American
coasts, their own coasts are vulnerable as New Holland's. Give me the *Indien,*
and I will rain down on wicked England like fire on Sodom."

These words of bravado were not spoken in the tone of a bravo, but a
prophet. Erect upon his chair, like an Iroquois, the speaker's look was like that
of an unflickering torch.

His air seemed slightly to disturb the old sage's philosophic repose, who,
while not seeking to disguise his admiration of the unmistakable spirit of the
man, seemed but illy to relish his apparent measureless boasting.

As if both to change the subject a little, as well as put his visitor in better
mood—though indeed it might have been but covertly to play with his enthusiasm—the man of wisdom now drew his chair confidentially nearer to the
stranger's and putting one hand in a very friendly, conciliatory way upon his
visitor's knee, and rubbing it gently to and fro there, much as a lion-tamer
might soothingly manipulate the aggravated king of beasts, said in a winning
manner:—"Never mind at present, Captain, about the *Indien* affair. Let that
sleep a moment. See now, the Jersey privateers do us a great deal of mischief
by intercepting our supplies. It has been mentioned to me, that if you had
a small vessel—say, even your present ship, the *Amphitrite,*—then, by your singular bravery, you might render great service, by following those privateers where
larger ships durst not venture their bottoms; or. if but supported by some
frigates from Brest at a proper distance, might draw them out, so that the larger
vessels could capture them."

"Decoy-duck to French frigates!—Very dignified office, truly!" hissed Paul
in a fiery rage. "Doctor Franklin, whatever Paul Jones does for the cause of
America, it must be done through unlimited orders: a separate, supreme command; no leader and no counsellor but himself. Have I not already by my
services on the American coast shown that I am well worthy all this? Why
then do you seek to degrade me below my previous level? I will mount, not

sink. I live but for honor and glory. Give me, then, something honorable and glorious to do, and something famous to do it with. Give me the *Indien*."

The man of wisdom slowly shook his head. "Everything is lost through this shillyshallying timidity, called prudence," cried Paul Jones, starting to his feet; "to be effectual, war should be carried on like a monsoon, one changeless determination of every particle towards the one unalterable aim. But in vacillating councils, statesmen idle about like the cats'-paws in calms. My God, why was I not born a Czar!"

"A Nor'wester, rather. Come, come, Captain," added the sage, "sit down, we have a third person present, you see," pointing towards Israel, who sat rapt at the volcanic spirit of the stranger.

Paul slightly started, and turned inquiringly upon Israel, who, equally owing to Paul's own earnestness of discourse and Israel's motionless bearing, had thus far remained undiscovered.

"Never fear, Captain," said the sage, "this man is true blue, a secret courier, and an American born. He is an escaped prisoner of war."

"Ah, captured in a ship?" asked Paul eagerly; "what ship? None of mine! Paul Jones never was captured."

"No, sir, in the brigantine *Washington*, out of Boston," replied Israel; "we were cruising to cut off supplies to the English."

"Did your shipmates talk much of me?" demanded Paul, with a look as of a parading Sioux demanding homage to his gewgaws; "what did they say of Paul Jones?"

"I never heard the name before this evening," said Israel.

"What? Ah—brigantine *Washington*—let me see; that was before I had outwitted the *Soleby* frigate, fought the *Milford*, and captured the *Mellish* and the rest off Louisbergh. You were long before the news, my lad," he added, with a sort of compassionate air.

"Our friend here gave you a rather blunt answer," said the wise man, sagely mischievous, and addressing Paul.

"Yes. And I like him for it. My man, will you go a cruise with Paul Jones? You fellows so blunt with the tongue, are apt to be sharp with the steel. Come, my lad, return with me to Brest. I go in a few days."

Fired by the contagious spirit of Paul, Israel, forgetting all about his previous desire to reach home, sparkled with response to the summons. But Doctor Franklin interrupted him.

"Our friend here," said he to the Captain, "is at present engaged for very different duty."

Much other conversation followed, during which Paul Jones again and again expressed his impatience at being unemployed, and his resolution to accept of no employ unless it gave him supreme authority; while in answer to all this Dr. Franklin, not uninfluenced by the uncompromising spirit of his guest, and well knowing that however unpleasant a trait in conversation, or in the transaction of civil affairs, yet in war this very quality was invaluable, as projectiles and combustibles, finally assured Paul, after many complimentary remarks, that he would immediately exert himself to the utmost to procure for him some enterprise which should come up to his merits.

"Thank you for your frankness," said Paul; "frank myself, I love to deal with a frank man. You, Doctor Franklin, are true and deep, and so you are frank."

The sage sedately smiled, a queer incredulity just lurking in the corner of his mouth.

"But how about our little scheme for new modelling ships-of-war?" said the Doctor, shifting the subject; "it will be a great thing for our infant navy, if we succeed. Since our last conversation on that subject, Captain, at odds and ends of time, I have thought over the matter, and have begun a little skeleton of the thing here, which I will show you. Whenever one has a new idea of anything mechanical, it is best to clothe it with a body as soon as possible. For you can't improve so well on ideas as you can on bodies."

With that, going to a little drawer, he produced a small basket, filled with a curious looking unfinished frame-work of wood, and several bits of wood unattached. It looked like a nursery basket containing broken odds and ends of playthings.

"Now look here, Captain, though the thing is but begun at present, yet there is enough to show that *one* idea at least of yours is not feasible."

Paul was all attention, as if having unbounded confidence in whatever the sage might suggest, while Israel looked on quite as interested as either, his heart swelling with the thought of being privy to the consultations of two such men; consultations, too, having ultimate reference to such momentous affairs as the freeing of nations.

"If," continued the Doctor, taking up some of the loose bits and piling them along on one side of the top of the frame, "if the better to shelter your crew in an engagement, you construct your rail in the manner proposed—as thus— then, by the excessive weight of the timber, you will too much interfere with the ship's centre of gravity. You will have that too high."

"Ballast in the hold in proportion," said Paul.

"Then you will sink the whole hull too low. But here, to have less smoke in time of battle, especially on the lower decks, you proposed a new sort of hatchway. But that won't do. See here now, I have invented certain ventilating pipes, they are to traverse the vessel thus"—laying some toilette pins along— "the current of air to enter here and be discharged there. What do you think of that? But now about the main things—fast sailing, driving little to leeward, and drawing little water. Look now at this keel. I whittled it only night before last, just before going to bed. Do you see now how"——

At this crisis, a knock was heard at the door, and the chambermaid reappeared, announcing that two gentlemen were that moment crossing the court below to see Doctor Franklin.

"The Duke de Chartres, and Count D'Estaing," said the Doctor; "they appointed for last night, but did not come. Captain, this has something indirectly to do with your affair. Through the Duke, Count D'Estaing has spoken to the King about the secret expedition, the design of which you first threw out. Call early to-morrow, and I will inform you of the result."

With his tawny hand Paul pulled out his watch, a small, richly-jewelled lady's watch.

"It is so late, I will stay here to-night," he said; "is there a convenient room?"

"Quick," said the Doctor, "it might be ill-advised of you to be seen with me just now. Our friend here will let you share his chamber. Quick, Israel, and show the Captain thither."

As the door closed upon them in Israel's apartment, Doctor Franklin's door closed upon the Duke and the Count. Leaving the latter to their discussion of profound plans for the timely befriending of the American cause, and the crippling of the power of England on the seas, let us pass the night with Paul Jones and Israel in the neighboring room.

CHAPTER XI

PAUL JONES IN A REVERIE

" 'God helps them that help themselves.' That's a clincher. That's been my experience. But I never saw it in words before. What pamphlet is this? 'Poor Richard,' hey!"

Upon entering Israel's room, Captain Paul, stepping towards the table and spying the open pamphlet there, had taken it up, his eye being immediately attracted to the passage previously marked by our adventurer.

"A rare old gentleman is 'Poor Richard,' " said Israel in response to Paul's observations.

"So he seems, so he seems," answered Paul, his eye still running over the pamphlet again; "why, 'Poor Richard' reads very much as Doctor Franklin speaks."

"He wrote it," said Israel.

"Aye? Good. So it is, so it is; it's the wise man all over. I must get me a copy of this and wear it around my neck for a charm. And now about our quarters for the night. I am not going to deprive you of your bed, my man. Do you go to bed and I will doze in the chair here. It's good dozing in the crosstrees."

"Why not sleep together?" said Israel; "see, it is a big bed. Or perhaps you don't fancy your bedfellow, Captain?"

"When, before the mast, I first sailed out of Whitehaven to Norway," said Paul, coolly, "I had for hammock-mate a full-blooded Congo. We had a white blanket spread in our hammock. Every time I turned in I found the Congo's black wool worked in with the white worsted. By the end of the voyage the blanket was of a pepper-and-salt look, like an old man's turning head. So it's not because I am notional at all, but because I don't care to, my lad. Turn in and go to sleep. Let the lamp burn. I'll see to it. There, go to sleep."

Complying with what seemed as much a command as a request, Israel, though in bed, could not fall into slumber for thinking of the little circumstance that this strange swarthy man, flaming with wild enterprises, sat in full suit in the chair. He felt an uneasy misgiving sensation, as if he had retired, not only without covering up the fire, but leaving it fiercely burning with spitting fagots of hemlock.

But his natural complaisance induced him at last to feign himself asleep; whereupon Paul, laying down "Poor Richard," rose from his chair, and, withdrawing his boots, began walking rapidly but noiselessly to and fro, in his stockings, in the spacious room, wrapped in Indian meditations. Israel furtively eyed him from beneath the coverlid, and was anew struck by his aspect, now that Paul thought himself unwatched. Stern relentless purposes, to be pursued to the points of adverse bayonets and the muzzles of hostile cannon, were expressed in the now rigid lines of his brow. His ruffled right hand was clutched by his side, as if grasping a cutlass. He paced the room as if advancing upon a fortification. Meantime a confused buzz of discussion came from the neighboring chamber. All else was profound midnight tranquillity. Presently, passing the large mirror over the mantel, Paul caught a glimpse of his person. He paused, grimly regarding it, while a dash of pleased coxcombry seemed to mingle with the otherwise savage satisfaction expressed in his face. But the latter predominated. Soon, rolling up his sleeve, with a queer wild smile, Paul lifted his right arm, and stood thus for an interval, eying its image in the glass. From where he lay, Israel could not see that side of the arm presented to the mirror, but he saw its reflection, and started at perceiving there, framed in the carved and gilded wood, certain large intertwisted ciphers covering the whole inside of the arm, so far as exposed, with mysterious tattooings. The design was wholly unlike the fanciful figures of anchors, hearts, and cables, sometimes decorating small portions of seamen's bodies. It was a sort of tattooing such as is seen only on thorough-bred savages—deep blue, elaborate, labyrinthine, cabalistic. Israel remembered having beheld, on one of his early voyages, something similar on the arm of a New Zealand warrior, once met, fresh from battle, in his native village. He concluded that on some similar early voyage Paul must have undergone the manipulations of some pagan artist.

Covering his arm again with his laced coat-sleeve, Paul glanced ironically at the hand of the same arm, now again half muffled in ruffles, and ornamented with several Parisian rings. He then resumed his walking with a prowling air, like one haunting an ambuscade; while a gleam of the consciousness of possessing a character as yet unfathomed, and hidden power to back unsuspected projects, irradiated his cold white brow, which, owing to the shade of his hat in equatorial climates, had been left surmounting his swarthy face, like the snow topping the Andes.

So at midnight, the heart of the metropolis of modern civilization was secretly trod by this jaunty barbarian in broadcloth; a sort of prophetical ghost, glimmering in anticipation upon the advent of those tragic scenes of the French Revolution which levelled the exquisite refinement of Paris with the bloodthirsty ferocity of Borneo; showing that broaches and finger-rings, not less than nose-rings and tattooing, are tokens of the primeval savageness which ever slumbers in human kind, civilized or uncivilized.

Israel slept not a wink that night. The troubled spirit of Paul paced the chamber till morning; when, copiously bathing himself at the wash-stand, Paul looked care-free and fresh as a day-break hawk. After a closeted consultation with Doctor Franklin, he left the place with a light and dandified air, switching his gold-headed cane, and throwing a passing arm round all the pretty chambermaids he encountered, kissing them resoundingly, as if saluting a frigate. All barbarians are rakes.

CHAPTER XII

RECROSSING THE CHANNEL, ISRAEL RETURNS TO THE SQUIRE'S ABODE—HIS ADVENTURES THERE

ON the third day, as Israel was walking to and fro in his room, having removed his courier's boots, for fear of disturbing the Doctor, a quick sharp rap at the door announced the American envoy. The man of wisdom entered, with two small wads of paper in one hand, and several crackers and a bit of cheese in the other. There was such an eloquent air of instantaneous dispatch about him, that Israel involuntarily sprang to his boots, and, with two vigorous jerks, hauled them on, and then seizing his hat, like any bird, stood poised for his flight across the channel.

"Well done, my honest friend," said the Doctor; "you have the papers in your heel, I suppose."

"Ah," exclaimed Israel, perceiving the mild irony; and in an instant his boots were off again; when, without another word, the Doctor took one boot, and Israel the other, and forthwith both parties proceeded to secrete the documents.

"I think I could improve the design," said the sage, as, notwithstanding his haste, he critically eyed the screwing apparatus of the boot. "The vacancy should have been in the standing part of the heel, not in the lid. It should go with a spring, too, for better dispatch. I'll draw up a paper on false heels one of these days, and send it to a private reading at the Institute. But no time for it now. My honest friend, it is now half-past ten o'clock. At half-past eleven the diligence starts from the Place-du-Carrousel for Calais. Make all haste till you arrive at Brentford. I have a little provender here for you to eat in the diligence, as you will not have time for a regular meal. A day-and-night courier should never be without a cracker in his pocket. You will probably leave Brentford in a day or two after your arrival there. Be wary, now, my good friend; heed well, that, if you are caught with these papers on British ground, you will involve both yourself and our Brentford friends in fatal calamities. Kick no man's box, never mind whose, in the way. Mind your own box. You can't be too cautious, but don't be too suspicious. God bless you, my honest friend. Go!"

And, flinging the door open for his exit, the Doctor saw Israel dart into the entry, vigorously spring down the stairs, and disappear with all celerity across the court into the vaulted way.

The man of wisdom stood mildly motionless a moment, with a look of sagacious, humane meditation on his face, as if pondering upon the chances of the important enterprise: one which, perhaps, might in the sequel affect the weal or woe of nations yet to come. Then suddenly clapping his hand to his capacious coat-pocket, dragged out a bit of cork with some hen's feathers, and hurrying to his room, took out his knife, and proceeded to whittle away at a shuttlecock of an original scientific construction, which at some prior time he had promised to send to the young Duchess D'Abrantes that very afternoon.

Safely reaching Calais, at night, Israel stepped almost from the diligence into the packet, and, in a few moments, was cutting the water. As on the diligence he took an outside and plebeian seat, so, with the same secret motive of preserving unsuspected the character assumed, he took a deck passage in the packet. It coming on to rain violently, he stole down into the forecastle, dimly lit by a solitary swinging lamp, where were two men industriously smoking, and filling the narrow hole with soporific vapors. These induced strange drowsiness in Israel, and he pondered how best he might indulge it, for a time, without imperilling the precious documents in his custody.

But this pondering in such soporific vapors had the effect of those mathematical devices whereby restless people cipher themselves to sleep. His languid head fell to his breast. In another moment, he drooped half-lengthwise upon a chest, his legs outstretched before him.

Presently he was awakened by some intermeddlement with his feet. Starting to his elbow, he saw one of the two men in the act of slyly slipping off his right boot, while the left one, already removed, lay on the floor, all ready against the rascal's retreat. Had it not been for the lesson learned on the Pont Neuf, Israel would instantly have inferred that his secret mission was known, and the operator some designed diplomatic knave or other, hired by the British Cabinet, thus to lie in wait for him, fume him into slumber with tobacco, and then rifle him of his momentous dispatches. But as it was, he recalled Doctor Franklin's prudent admonitions against the indulgence of premature suspicions.

"Sir," said Israel very civilly, "I will thank you for that boot which lies on the floor, and, if you please, you can let the other stay where it is."

"Excuse me," said the rascal, an accomplished, self-possessed practitioner in his thievish art; "I thought your boots might be pinching you, and only wished to ease you a little."

"Much obliged to ye for your kindness, sir," said Israel; "but they don't pinch me at all. I suppose, though, you think they wouldn't pinch *you* either; your foot looks rather small. Were you going to try 'em on, just to see how they fitted?"

"No," said the fellow, with sanctimonious seriousness; "but with your permission I should like to try them on, when we get to Dover. I couldn't try them well walking on this tipsy craft's deck, you know."

"No," answered Israel, "and the beach at Dover ain't very smooth either. I guess, upon second thought, you had better not try 'em on at all. Besides, I am a simple sort of a soul—eccentric they call me—and don't like my boots to go out of my sight. Ha! ha!"

"What are you laughing at?" said the fellow testily.

"Odd idea! I was just looking at those sad old patched boots there at your feet, and thinking to myself what leaky fire-buckets they would be to pass up a ladder on a burning building. It would hardly be fair now to swap my new boots for those old fire-buckets, would it?"

"By plunko!" cried the fellow, willing now by a bold stroke to change the subject, which was growing slightly annoying; "by plunko, I believe we are getting nigh Dover. Let's see."

And so saying, he sprang up the ladder to the deck. Upon Israel following, he found the little craft half becalmed, rolling on short swells almost in the exact middle of the channel. It was just before the break of the morning; the air clear and fine; the heavens spangled with moistly twinkling stars. The French and English coasts lay distinctly visible in the strange starlight, the white cliffs of Dover resembling a long gabled block of marble houses. Both shores showed a long straight row of lamps. Israel seemed standing in the middle of the crossing of some wide stately street in London. Presently a breeze sprang up, and ere long our adventurer disembarked at his destined port, and directly posted on for Brentford.

The following afternoon, having gained unobserved admittance into the house, according to preconcerted signals, he was sitting in Squire Woodcock's closet, pulling off his boots and delivering his dispatches.

Having looked over the compressed tissuey sheets, and read a line particularly addressed to himself, the Squire, turning round upon Israel, congratulated him upon his successful mission, placed some refreshment before him, and apprised him that, owing to certain suspicious symptoms in the neighborhood, he (Israel) must now remain concealed in the house for a day or two, till an answer should be ready for Paris.

It was a venerable mansion, as was somewhere previously stated, of a wide and rambling disorderly spaciousness, built, for the most part, of weather-stained old bricks, in the goodly style called Elizabethan. As without, it was all dark russet bricks, so within, it was nothing but tawny oak panels.

"Now, my good fellow," said the Squire, "my wife has a number of guests, who wander from room to room, having the freedom of the house. So I shall have to put you very snugly away, to guard against any chance of discovery."

So saying, first locking the door, he touched a spring nigh the open fireplace, whereupon one of the black sooty stone jambs of the chimney started ajar, just like the marble gate of a tomb. Inserting one leg of the heavy tongs in the crack, the Squire pried this cavernous gate wide open.

"Why, Squire Woodcock, what is the matter with your chimney?" said Israel.

"Quick, go in."

"Am I to sweep the chimney?" demanded Israel; "I didn't engage for that."

"Pooh, pooh, this is your hiding-place. Come, move in."

"But where does it go to, Squire Woodcock? I don't like the looks of it."

"Follow me. I'll show you."

Pushing his florid corpulence into the mysterious aperture, the elderly Squire led the way up steep stairs of stone, hardly two feet in width, till they reached a little closet, or rather cell, built into the massive main wall of the mansion, and ventilated and dimly lit by two little sloping slits, ingeniously concealed without, by their forming the sculptured mouths of two griffins cut in a great stone tablet decorating that external part of the dwelling. A mattress lay rolled up in one corner, with a jug of water, a flask of wine, and a wooden trencher containing cold roast beef and bread.

"And I am to be buried alive here?" said Israel, ruefully looking round.

"But your resurrection will soon be at hand," smiled the Squire; "two days at the furthest."

"Though to be sure I was a sort of prisoner in Paris, just as I seem about to be made here," said Israel, "yet Doctor Franklin put me in a better jug than this, Squire Woodcock. It was set out with bouquets and a mirror, and other fine things. Besides, I could step out into the entry whenever I wanted."

"Ah, but, my hero, that was in France, and this is in England. There you were in a friendly country: here you are in the enemy's. If you should be discovered in my house, and your connection with me became known, do you know that it would go very hard with me; very hard indeed?"

"Then, for your sake, I am willing to stay wherever you think best to put me," replied Israel.

"Well, then, you say you want bouquets and a mirror. If those articles will at all help you to solace your seclusion, I will bring them to you."

"They really would be company; the sight of my own face particularly."

"Stay here, then. I will be back in ten minutes."

In less than that time, the good old Squire returned, puffing and panting, with a great bunch of flowers, and a small shaving-glass.

"There," said he, putting them down; "now keep perfectly quiet; avoid making any undue noise, and on no account descend the stairs, till I come for you again."

"But when will that be?" asked Israel.

"I will try to come twice each day while you are here. But there is no knowing what may happen. If I should not visit you till I come to liberate you—on the evening of the second day, or the morning of the third—you must not be at all surprised, my good fellow. There is plenty of food and water to last you. But mind, on no account descend the stone-stairs till I come for you."

With that, bidding his guest adieu, he left him.

Israel stood glancing pensively around for a time. By and by, moving the rolled mattress under the two air-slits, he mounted, to try if aught were visible beyond. But nothing was to be seen but a very thin slice of blue sky peeping through the lofty foliage of a great tree planted near the side-portal of the mansion; an ancient tree, coeval with the ancient dwelling it guarded.

Sitting down on the mattress, Israel fell into a reverie.

"Poverty and liberty, or plenty and a prison, seem to be the two horns of the constant dilemma of my life," thought he. "Let's look at the prisoner."

And taking up the shaving-glass, he surveyed his lineaments.

"What a pity I didn't think to ask for razors and soap. I want shaving very badly. I shaved last in France. How it would pass the time here. Had I a comb now and a razor, I might shave and curl my hair, and keep making a continual toilet all through the two days, and look spruce as a robin when I get out. I'll ask the Squire for the things this very night when he drops in. Hark! ain't that a sort of rumbling in the wall? I hope there ain't any oven next door; if so, I shall be scorched out. Here I am, just like a rat in the wainscot. I wish there was a low window to look out of. I wonder what Doctor Franklin is doing now, and Paul Jones? Hark! there's a bird singing in the leaves. Bell for dinner, that."

And for pastime, he applied himself to the beef and bread, and took a draught of the wine and water.

At last night fell. He was left in utter darkness. No Squire.

After an anxious, sleepless night, he saw two long flecks of pale gray light slanting into the cell from the slits, like two long spears. He rose, rolled up his mattress, got upon the roll, and put his mouth to one of the griffins' mouths. He gave a low, just audible whistle, directing it towards the foliage of the tree. Presently there was a slight rustling among the leaves, then one solitary chirrup, and in three minutes a whole chorus of melody burst upon his ear.

"I've waked the first bird," said he to himself, with a smile, "and he's waked all the rest. Now then for breakfast. That over, I dare say the Squire will drop in."

But the breakfast was over, and the two flecks of pale light had changed to golden beams, and the golden beams grew less and less slanting, till they straightened themselves up out of sight altogether. It was noon, and no Squire.

"He's gone a-hunting before breakfast, and got belated," thought Israel.

The afternoon shadows lengthened. It was sunset; no Squire.

"He must be very busy trying some sheep-stealer in the hall," mused Israel. "I hope he won't forget all about me till to-morrow."

He waited and listened; and listened and waited.

Another restless night; no sleep; morning came. The second day passed like the first, and the night. On the third morning the flowers lay shrunken by his side. Drops of wet oozing through the air-slits, fell dully on the stone floor. He heard the dreary beatings of the tree's leaves against the mouths of the griffins, bedashing them with the spray of the rain-storm without. At intervals a burst of thunder rolled over his head, and lightning flashing down through the slits, lit up the cell with a greenish glare, followed by sharp splashings and rattlings of the redoubled rain-storm.

"This is the morning of the third day," murmured Israel to himself; "he said he would at the furthest come to me on the morning of the third day. This is it. Patience, he will be here yet. Morning lasts till noon."

But, owing to the murkiness of the day, it was very hard to tell when noon came. Israel refused to credit that noon had come and gone, till dusk set plainly in. Dreading he knew not what, he found himself buried in the darkness of still another night. However patient and hopeful hitherto, fortitude now presently left him. Suddenly, as if some contagious fever had seized him, he was afflicted with strange enchantments of misery, undreamed of till now.

He had eaten all the beef, but there were bread and water sufficient to last, by economy, for two or three days to come. It was not the pang of hunger then, but a nightmare originating in his mysterious incarceration, which appalled him. All through the long hours of this particular night, the sense of being masoned up in the wall, grew, and grew, and grew upon him, till again and again he lifted himself convulsively from the floor, as if vast blocks of stone had been laid on him; as if he had been digging a deep well, and the stonework with all the excavated earth had caved in upon him, where he burrowed ninety feet beneath the clover. In the blind tomb of the midnight he stretched his two arms sideways, and felt as if coffined at not being able to extend them straight out, on opposite sides, for the narrowness of the cell. He seated himself against one side of the wall, crosswise with the cell, and pushed with his feet at the opposite wall. But still mindful of his promise in this extremity, he uttered no cry. He mutely raved in the darkness. The delirious sense of the absence of light was soon added to his other delirium as to the contraction of space. The lids of his eyes burst with impotent distension. Then he thought the air itself was getting unbearable. He stood up at the griffin slits, pressing his lips far into them till he moulded his lips there, to suck the utmost of the open air possible.

And continually, to heighten his frenzy, there recurred to him again and again what the Squire had told him as to the origin of the cell. It seemed that this part of the old house, or rather this wall of it, was extremely ancient, dating far beyond the era of Elizabeth, having once formed portions of a religious retreat belonging to the Templars. The domestic discipline of this order was rigid and merciless in the extreme. In a sidewall of their second-story chapel, horizontal and on a level with the floor, they had an internal vacancy left, exactly of the shape and average size of a coffin. In this place, from time to time, inmates convicted of contumacy were confined; but, strange to say, not till they were penitent. A small hole, of the girth of one's wrist, sunk like a telescope three feet through the masonry into the cell, served at once for ventilation, and to push through food to the prisoner. This hole opening into the chapel also enabled the poor solitaire, as intended, to over-hear the religious services at the altar; and, without being present, take part in the same. It was deemed a good sign of the state of the sufferer's soul, if from the gloomy recesses of the wall was heard the agonized groan of his dismal response. This was regarded in the light of a penitent wail from the dead, because the customs of the order ordained that when any inmate should be first incarcerated in the wall, he should be committed to it in the presence of all the brethren, the chief reading the burial service as the live body was sepulchred Sometimes several weeks elapsed ere the disentombment, the penitent being then usually found numb and congealed in all his extremities, like one newly stricken with paralysis.

This coffin-cell of the Templars had been suffered to remain in the demolition of the general edifice, to make way for the erection of the new, in the reign of Queen Elizabeth. It was enlarged somewhat, and altered, and additionally ventilated, to adapt it for a place of concealment in times of civil dissension.

With this history ringing in his solitary brain, it may readily be conceived what Israel's feelings must have been. Here, in this very darkness, centuries ago, hearts, human as his, had mildewed in despair; limbs, robust as his own, had stiffened in immovable torpor.

At length, after what seemed all the prophetic days and years of Daniel, morning broke. The benevolent light entered the cell, soothing his frenzy, as if it had been some smiling human face—nay, the Squire himself, come at last to redeem him from thrall. Soon his dumb ravings entirely left him, and gradually, with a sane, calm mind, he revolved all the circumstances of his condition.

He could not be mistaken; something fatal must have befallen his friend. Israel remembered the Squire's hinting that in case of the discovery of his clandestine proceedings it would fare extremely hard with him. Israel was forced to conclude that this same unhappy discovery had been made; that owing to some untoward misadventure his good friend had been carried off a State-prisoner to London; that prior to his going the Squire had not apprised any member of his household that he was about to leave behind him a prisoner in the wall; this seemed evident from the circumstance that, thus far, no soul had visited that prisoner. It could not be otherwise. Doubtless the Squire, having no opportunity to converse in private with his relatives or friends at the moment of his sudden arrest, had been forced to keep his secret, for the present, for fear of involving Israel in still worse calamities. But would he leave him to perish piecemeal in the wall? All surmise was baffled in the unconjecturable possibilities of the case. But some sort of action must speedily be determined upon. Israel would not additionally endanger the Squire, but he could not in such uncertainty consent to perish where he was. He resolved at all hazards to escape, by stealth and noiselessly, if possible; by violence and outcry, if indispensable.

Gliding out of the cell, he descended the stone stairs, and stood before the interior of the jamb. He felt an immovable iron knob, but no more. He groped about gently for some bolt or spring. When before he had passed through the passage with his guide, he had omitted to notice by what precise mechanism the jamb was to be opened from within, or whether, indeed, it could at all be opened except from without.

He was about giving up the search in despair, after sweeping with his two hands every spot of the wall-surface around hiim, when chancing to turn his whole body a little to one side, he heard a creak, and saw a thin lance of light. His foot had unconsciously pressed some spring laid in the floor. The jamb was ajar. Pushing it open, he stood at liberty in the Squire's closet.

CHAPTER XIII

HIS ESCAPE FROM THE HOUSE, WITH VARIOUS ADVENTURES FOLLOWING

HE started at the funereal aspect of the room, into which, since he last stood there, undertakers seemed to have stolen. The curtains of the window were festooned with long weepers of crape. The four corners of the red cloth on the round table were knotted with crape.

Knowing nothing of these mournful customs of the country, nevertheless, Israel's instinct whispered him that Squire Woodcock lived no more on this earth. At once the whole three days' mystery was made clear. But what was now to be done? His friend must have died very suddenly; most probably struck down in a fit, from which he never more rose. With him had perished all knowledge of the fact that a stranger was immured in the mansion. If discovered then, prowling here in the inmost privacies of a gentleman's abode, what would befall the wanderer, already not unsuspected in the neighborhood of some underhand guilt as a fugitive? If he adhered to the strict truth, what could he offer in his own defence without convicting himself of acts which, by English tribunals, would be accounted flagitious crimes? Unless, indeed, by involving the memory of the deceased Squire Woodcock in his own self-acknowledged proceedings, so ungenerous a charge should result in an abhorrent refusal to credit his extraordinary tale, whether as referring to himself or another, and so throw him open to still more grievous suspicions?

While wrapped in these dispiriting reveries, he heard a step not very far off in the passage. It seemed approaching. Instantly he flew to the jamb, which remained unclosed, and disappearing within, drew the stone after him by the iron knob. Owing to his hurried violence the jamb closed with a dull, dismal and singular noise. A shriek followed from within the room. In a panic, Israel fled up the dark stairs, and near the top, in his eagerness, stumbled and fell back to the last step with a rolling din, which, reverberated by the arch overhead, smote through and through the wall, dying away at last indistinctly, like low muffled thunder among the clefts of deep hills. When raising himself instantly, not seriously bruised by his fall, Israel instantly listened, the echoing sounds of his descent were mingled with added shrieks from within the room. They seemed some nervous female's, alarmed by what must have appeared to her supernatural, or at least unaccountable, noises in the wall. Directly he heard other voices of alarm undistinguishably commingled, and then they retreated together, and all again was still.

Recovering from his first amazement, Israel revolved these occurrences. "No creature now in the house knows of the cell," thought he. "Some woman, the housekeeper, perhaps, first entered the room alone. Just as she entered the jamb closed. The sudden report made her shriek; then, afterwards, the noise of my fall prolonging itself, added to her fright, while her repeated shrieks brought every soul in the house to her, who aghast at seeing her lying in a pale faint, it may be, like a corpse, in a room hung with crape for a man just dead, they also shrieked out, and then with blended lamentations they bore the fainting person away. Now this will follow; no doubt it *has* followed ere now:— they believe that the woman saw or heard the spirit of Squire Woodcock. Since I seem then to understand how all these strange events have occurred, since I seem to know that they have plain common causes, I begin to feel cool and calm again. Let me see. Yes. I have it. By means of the idea of the ghost prevailing among the frightened household, by that means I will this very night make good my escape. If I can but lay hands on some of the late Squire's clothing, if but a coat and hat of his, I shall be certain to succeed. It is not too early to begin now. They will hardly come back to the room in a hurry. I will return to it and see what I can find to serve my purpose. It is the Squire's private closet, hence it is not unlikely that here some at least of his clothing will be found."

With these thoughts, he cautiously sprung the iron under foot, peeped in, and, seeing all clear, boldly re-entered the apartment. He went straight to a high, narrow door in the opposite wall. The key was in the lock. Opening the door, there hung several coats, small-clothes, pairs of silk stockings, and hats of the deceased. With little difficulty Israel selected from these the complete suit in which he had last seen his once jovial friend. Carefully closing the door, and carrying the suit with him, he was returning towards the chimney, when he saw the Squire's silver-headed cane leaning against a corner of the wainscot. Taking this also, he stole back to his cell.

Slipping off his own clothing, he deliberately arrayed himself in the borrowed raiment, silk small-clothes and all, then put on the cocked hat, grasped the silver-headed cane in his right hand, and moving his small shaving-glass slowly up and down before him, so as by piecemeal to take in his whole figure, felt convinced that he would well pass for Squire Woodcock's genuine phantom. But after the first feeling of self-satisfaction with his anticipated success had left him, it was not without some superstitious embarrassment that Israel felt himself encased in a dead man's broadcloth; nay, in the very coat in which the deceased had no doubt fallen down in his fit. By degrees he began to feel almost as unreal and shadowy as the shade whose part he intended to enact.

Waiting long and anxiously till darkness came, and then till he thought it was fairly midnight, he stole back into the closet, and standing for a moment uneasily in the middle of the floor, thinking over all the risks he might run, he lingered till he felt himself resolute and calm. Then groping for the door leading into the hall, put his hand on the knob and turned it. But the door refused to budge. Was it locked? The key was not in. Turning the knob once more, and holding it so, he pressed firmly against the door. It did not move. More firmly still, when suddenly it burst open with a loud crackling report. Being cramped, it had stuck in the sill. Less than three seconds passed when, as Israel was groping his way down the long wide hall towards the large staircase at its opposite end, he heard confused hurrying noises from the neighboring rooms, and in another instant several persons, mostly in night-dresses, appeared at their chamber-doors, thrusting out alarmed faces, lit by a lamp held by one of the number, a rather elderly lady in widow's weeds, who by her appearance seemed to have just risen from a sleepless chair, instead of an oblivious couch. Israel's heart beat like a hammer; his face turned like a sheet. But bracing himself, pulling his hat lower down over his eyes, settling his head in the collar of his coat, he advanced along the defile of wildly staring faces. He advanced with a slow and stately step, looked neither to the right nor the left, but went solemnly forward on his now faintly illuminated way, sounding his cane on the floor as he passed. The faces in the doorways curdled his blood by their rooted looks. Glued to the spot, they seemed incapable of motion. Each one was silent as he advanced towards him or her, but as he left each individual, one after another, behind, each in a frenzy shrieked out, "The Squire, the Squire!" As he passed the lady in the widow's weeds, she fell senseless and crosswise before him. But forced to be immutable in his purpose, Israel, solemnly stepping over her prostrate form, marched deliberately on.

In a few minutes more he had reached the main door of the mansion, and withdrawing the chain and bolt, stood in the open air. It was a bright moonlight night. He struck slowly across the open grounds towards the sunken fields beyond. When midway across the grounds, he turned towards the mansion, and saw three of the front windows filled with white faces, gazing in terror at the wonderful spectre. Soon descending a slope, he disappeared from their view.

Presently he came to hilly land in meadow, whose grass having been lately cut, now lay dotting the slope in cocks; a sinuous line of creamy vapor meandered through the lowlands at the base of the hill; while beyond was a dense grove of dwarfish trees, with here and there a tall tapering dead trunk, peeled of the bark, and overpeering the rest. The vapor wore the semblance of a deep stream of water, imperfectly descried; the grove looked like some closely-clustering town on its banks, lorded over by spires of churches.

The whole scene magically reproduced to our adventurer the aspect of Bunker Hill, Charles River, and Boston town, on the well-remembered night of the 16th of June. The same season; the same moon; the same new-mown hay on the shaven sward; hay which was scraped together during the night to help pack into the redoubt so hurriedly thrown up.

Acted on as if by enchantment, Israel sat down on one of the cocks, and gave himself up to reverie. But, worn out by long loss of sleep, his reveries would have soon merged into slumber's still wilder dreams, had he not rallied himself, and departed on his way, fearful of forgetting himself in an emergency like the present. It now occurred to him that, well as his disguise had served him in escaping from the mansion of Squire Woodcock, that disguise might fatally endanger him if he should be discovered in it abroad. He might pass for a ghost at night, and among the relations and immediate friends of the gentleman deceased; but by day, and among indifferent persons, he ran no smal risk of being apprehended for an entry-thief. He bitterly lamented his omission in not pulling on the Squire's clothes over his own, so that he might now have reappeared in his former guise.

As meditating over this difficulty, he was passing along, suddenly he saw a man in black standing right in his path, about fifty yards distant, in a field of some growing barley or wheat. The gloomy stranger was standing stock-still; one outstretched arm, with weird intimation pointing towards the deceased Squire's abode. To the brooding soul of the now desolate Israel, so strange a sight roused a supernatural suspicion. His conscience morbidly reproaching him for the terrors he had bred in making his escape from the house, he seemed to see in the fixed gesture of the stranger something more than humanly significant. But somewhat of his intrepidity returned; he resolved to test the apparition. Composing itself to the same deliberate stateliness with which it had paced the hall, the phantom of Squire Woodcock firmly advanced its cane, and marched straight forward towards the mysterious stranger.

As he neared him, Israel shrunk. The dark coat-sleeve flapped on the bony skeleton of the unknown arm. The face was lost in a sort of ghastly blank. It was no living man.

But mechanically continuing his course, Israel drew still nearer and saw a scarecrow.

AN ENCOUNTER OF GHOSTS

Not a little relieved by the discovery, our adventurer paused, more particularly to survey so deceptive an object, which seemed to have been constructed on the most efficient principles; probably by some broken-down wax-figure costumer. It comprised the complete wardrobe of a scarecrow, namely: a cocked hat, bunged; tattered coat; old velveteen breeches; and long worsted stockings, full of holes; all stuffed very nicely with straw, and skeletoned by a framework of poles. There was a great flapped pocket to the coat—which seemed to have been some laborer's—standing invitingly opened. Putting his hands in, Israel drew out the lid of an old tobacco-box, the broken bowl of a pipe, two rusty nails, and a few kernels of wheat. This reminded him of the Squire's pockets. Trying them, he produced a handsome handkerchief, a spectacle-case, with a purse containing some silver and gold, amounting to a little more than five pounds. Such is the difference between the contents of the pockets of scarecrows and the pockets of well-to-do squires. Ere donning his present habiliments, Israel had not omitted to withdraw his own money from his own coat, and put it in the pocket of his own waistcoat, which he had not exchanged.

Looking upon the scarecrow more attentively, it struck him that, miserable as its wardrobe was, nevertheless here was a chance for getting rid of the unsuitable and perilous clothes of the Squire. No other available opportunity might present itself for a time. Before he encountered any living creature by daylight, another suit must somehow be had. His exchange with the old ditcher, after his escape from the inn near Portsmouth, had familiarized him with the most deplorable of wardrobes. Well, too, he knew, and had experienced it, that for a man desirous of avoiding notice, the more wretched the clothes, the better. For who does not shun the scurvy wretch, Poverty, advancing in battered hat, and lamentable coat?

Without more ado, slipping off the Squire's raiment, he donned the scarecrow's, after carefully shaking out the hay, which, from many alternate soakings and bakings in rain and sun, had become quite broken up, and would have been almost dust, were it not for the mildew which damped it. But sufficient of this wretched old hay remained adhesive to the inside of the breeches and coat-sleeves, to produce the most irritating torment.

The grand moral question now came up, what to do with the purse. Would it be dishonest under the circumstances to appropriate that purse? Considering the whole matter, and not forgetting that he had not received from the gentleman deceased the promised reward for his services as courier, Israel concluded that he might justly use the money for his own. To which opinion surely no charitable judge will demur. Besides, what should he do with the purse, if not use it for his own? It would have been insane to have returned it to the relations. Such mysterious honesty would but have resulted in his arrest as a rebel, or rascal. As for the Squire's clothes, handkerchief, and spectacle-case, they must be put out of sight with all dispatch. So, going to a morass not remote, Israel sunk them deep down, and heaped tufts of the rank sod upon them. Then returning to the field of corn, sat down under the lee of a rock, about a hundred yards from where the scarecrow had stood, thinking which way he now had best direct his steps. But his late ramble coming after so long a deprivation of rest, soon produced effects not so easy to be shaken off, as when reposing upon the haycock. He felt less anxious, too, since changing his apparel. So before he was aware, he fell into deep sleep.

When he awoke, the sun was well up in the sky. Looking around he saw a farm-laborer with a pitchfork coming at a distance into view, whose steps seemed bent in a direction not far from the spot where he lay. Immediately it struck our adventurer that this man must be familiar with the scarecrow; perhaps had himself fashioned it. Should he miss it then, he might make immediate search, and so discover the thief so imprudently loitering upon the very field of his operations.

Waiting until the man momentarily disappeared in a little hollow, Israel ran briskly to the identical spot where the scarecrow had stood, where, standing stiffly erect, pulling the hat well over his face, and thrusting out his arm, pointed steadfastly towards the Squire's abode, he awaited the event. Soon the man reappeared in sight, and marching right on, paused not far from Israel, and gave him an one earnest look, as if it were his daily wont to satisfy that all was right with the scarecrow. No sooner was the man departed to a reasonable distance, than, quitting his post, Israel struck out across the fields towards London. But he had not yet quite quitted the field when it occurred to him to turn round and see if the man was completely out of sight, when, to his consternation, he saw the man returning towards him, evidently by his pace and gesture in unmixed amazement. The man must have turned round to look before Israel had done so. Frozen to the ground, Israel knew not what to do; but next moment it struck him that this very motionlessness was the least hazardous plan in such a strait. Thrusting out his arm again towards the house, once more he stood stock still, and again awaited the event.

It so happened that this time, in pointing towards the house, Israel unavoidably pointed towards the advancing man. Hoping that the strangeness of this coincidence might, by operating on the man's superstition, incline him to beat an immediate retreat, Israel kept cool as he might. But the man proved to be of a braver metal than anticipated. In passing the spot where the scarecrow had stood, and perceiving, beyond the possibility of mistake, that by some unaccountable agency it had suddenly removed itself to a distance, instead of being terrified at this verification of his worst apprehensions, the man pushed on for Israel, apparently resolved to sift this mystery to the bottom.

Seeing him now determinately coming, with pitchfork valiantly presented, Israel, as a last means of practising on the fellow's fears of the supernatural, suddenly doubled up both fists, presenting them savagely towards him at a distance of about twenty paces, at the same time showing his teeth like a skull's, and demoniacally rolling his eyes. The man paused bewildered, looked all round him, looked at the springing grain, then across at some trees, then up at the sky and satisfied at last by those observations that the world at large had not undergone a miracle in the last fifteen minutes, resolutely resumed his advance; the pitchfork, like a boarding-pike, now aimed full at the breast of the object. Seeing all his stratagems vain, Israel now threw himself into the original attitude of the scarecrow, and once again stood immovable. Abating his pace by degrees almost to a mere creep, the man at last came within three feet of him, and, pausing, gazed into Israel's eyes. With a stern and terrible expression Israel resolutely returned the glance, but otherwise remained like a statue, hoping thus to stare his pursuer out of countenance. At last the man slowly presented one prong of his fork towards Israel's left

eye. Nearer and nearer the sharp point came, till no longer capable of
enduring such a test, Israel took to his heels with all speed, his tattered coat-
tails streaming behind him. With inveterate purpose the man pursued. Darting blindly on, Israel, leaping a gate, suddenly found himself in a field where
some dozen laborers were at work, who recognizing the scarecrow—an old
acquaintance of theirs, as it would seem—lifted all their hands as the astounding apparition swept by, followed by the man with the pitchfork. Soon all
joined in the chase, but Israel proved to have better wind and bottom than
any. Outstripping the whole pack he finally shot out of their sight in an
extensive park, heavily timbered in one quarter. He never saw more of these
people.

Loitering in the wood till nightfall, he then stole out and made the best of
his way towards the house of that good-natured farmer in whose corn-loft he
had received his first message from Squire Woodcock. Rousing this man up
a little before midnight, he informed him somewhat of his recent adventures,
but carefully concealed his having been employed as a secret courier, together
with his escape from Squire Woodcock's. All he craved at present was a
meal. The meal being over, Israel offered to buy from the farmer his best
suit of clothes, and displayed the money on the spot.

"Where did you get so much money?" said his entertainer in a tone of
surprise; "your clothes here don't look as if you had seen prosperous times
since you left me. Why, you look like a scarecrow."

"That may well be," replied Israel, very soberly. "But what do you say?
will you sell me your suit?—here's the cash."

"I don't know about it," said the farmer, in doubt; "let me look at the
money. Ha!—a silk purse comes out of a beggar's pocket!—Quit the house,
rascal, you've turned thief."

Thinking that he could not swear to his having come by his money with
absolute honesty—since indeed the case was one for the most subtle casuist—
Israel knew not what to reply. This honest confusion confirmed the farmer,
who with many abusive epithets drove him into the road, telling him that he
might thank himself that he did not arrest him on the spot.

In great dolor at this unhappy repulse, Israel trudged on in the moonlight
some three miles to the house of another friend, who also had once succored
him in extremity. This man proved a very sound sleeper. Instead of succeeding in rousing him by his knocking, Israel but succeeded in rousing his
wife, a person not of the greatest amiability. Raising the sash, and seeing so
shocking a pauper before her, the woman upbraided him with shameless impropriety in asking charity at dead of night, in a dress so improper too. Looking down at his deplorable velveteens, Israel discovered that his extensive
travels had produced a great rent in one loin of the rotten old breeches, through
which a whitish fragment protruded.

Remedying this oversight as well as he might, he again implored the woman
to wake her husband.

"That I sha'n't!" said the woman, morosely. "Quit the premises, or I'll
throw something on ye."

With that she brought some earthenware to the window, and would have
fulfilled her threat, had not Israel prudently retreated some paces. Here he
entreated the woman to take mercy on his plight, and since she would not
waken her husband, at least throw to him (Israel) her husband's breeches, and
he would leave the price of them, with his own breeches to boot, on the sill of
the door.

"You behold how sadly I need them," said he; "for heaven's sake befriend me."

"Quit the premises!" reiterated the woman.

"The breeches, the breeches! here is the money," cried Israel, half furious with anxiety.

"Saucy cur " cried the woman, somehow misunderstanding him; "do you cunningly taunt me with *wearing* the breeches? begone!"

Once more poor Israel decamped, and made for another friend. But here a monstrous bull-dog, indignant that the peace of the quiet family should be disturbed by so outrageous a tatterdemalion, flew at Israel's unfortunate coat, whose rotten skirts the brute tore completely off, leaving the coat razeed to a spencer, which barely came down to the wearer's waist. In attempting to drive the monster away, Israel's hat fell off, upon which the dog pounced with the utmost fierceness, and thrusting both paws into it, rammed out the crown and went snuffling the wreck before him. Recovering the wretched hat, Israel again beat a retreat, his wardrobe sorely the worse for his visits. Not only was his coat a mere rag, but his breeches, clawed by the dog, were slashed into yawning gaps, while his yellow hair waved over the top of the crownless beaver, like a lonely tuft of heather on the highlands.

In this plight the morning discovered him dubiously skirmishing on the outskirts of a village.

"Ah!" what a true patriot gets for serving his country!" murmured Israel. But soon thinking a little better of his case, and seeing yet another house which had once furnished him an asylum, he made bold to advance to the door. Luckily he this time met the man himself, just emerging from bed. At first the farmer did not recognize the fugitive, but upon another look, seconded by Israel's plaintive appeal, beckoned him into the barn, where directly our adventurer told him all he thought prudent to disclose of his story, ending by once more offering to negotiate for breeches and coat. Having ere this emptied and thrown away the purse which had played him so scurvy a trick with the first farmer, he now produced three crown-pieces.

"Three crown-pieces in your pocket, and no crown to your hat!" said the farmer.

"But I assure you, my friend," rejoined Israel, "that a finer hat was never worn, until that confounded bull-dog ruined it."

"True," said the farmer, "I forgot that part of your story. Well, I have a tolerable coat and breeches which I will sell you for your money."

In ten minutes more Israel was equipped in a gray coat of coarse cloth, not much improved by wear, and breeches to match. For half-a-crown more he procured a highly respectable looking hat.

"Now, my kind friend," said Israel, "can you tell me where Horne Tooke and John Bridges live?"

Our adventurer thought it his best plan to seek out one or other of those gentlemen, both to report proccedings and learn confirmatory tidings concerning Squire Woodcock, touching whose fate he did not like to inquire of others.

"Horne Tooke? What do you want with Horne Tooke," said the farmer. "He was Squire Woodcock's friend, wasn't he? The poor Squire! Who would have thought he'd have gone off so suddenly. But apoplexy comes like a bullet."

"I was right," thought Israel to himself. "But where does Horne Tooke live?" he demanded again.

"He once lived in Brentford, and wore a cassock there. But I hear he's sold out his living, and gone in his surplice to study law in Lunnon."

This was all news to Israel, who, from various amiable remarks he had heard from Horne Tooke at the Squire's, little dreamed he was an ordained clergyman. Yet a good-natured English clergyman translated Lucian; another, equally good-natured, wrote Tristram Shandy; and a third, an ill-natured appreciator of good-natured Rabelais, died a dean; not to speak of others. Thus ingenious and ingenuous are some of the English clergy.

"You can't tell me, then, where to find Horne Tooke?" said Israel, in perplexity.

"You'll find him, I suppose, in Lunnon."

"What street and number?"

"Don't know. Needle in a haystack."

"Where does Mr. Bridges live?"

"Never heard of any Bridges, except Lunnon bridges, and one Molly Bridges in Bridewell."

So Israel departed; better clothed, but no wiser than before.

What to do next? He reckoned up his money, and concluded he had plenty to carry him back to Doctor Franklin in Paris. Accordingly, taking a turn to avoid the two nearest villages, he directed his steps toward London, where, again taking the post-coach for Dover, he arrived on the channel shore just in time to learn that the very coach in which he rode brought the news to the authorities there that all intercourse between the two nations was indefinitely suspended. The characteristic taciturnity and formal stolidity of his fellow-travellers—all Englishmen, mutually unacquainted with each other, and occupying different positions in life—having prevented his sooner hearing the tidings.

Here was another accumulation of misfortunes. All visions but those of eventual imprisonment or starvation vanished from before the present realities of poor Israel Potter. The Brentford gentleman had flattered him with the prospect of receiving something very handsome for his services as courier. That hope was no more. Doctor Franklin had promised him his good offices in procuring him a passage home to America. Quite out of the question now. The sage had likewise intimated that he might possibly see him some way remunerated for his sufferings in his country's cause. An idea no longer to be harbored. Then Israel recalled the mild man of wisdom's words—"At the prospect of pleasure never be elated; but without depression respect the omens of ill." But he found it as difficult now to comply, in all respects, with the last section of the maxim, as before he had with the first.

While standing wrapped in afflictive reflections on the shore, gazing towards the unattainable coast of France, a pleasant-looking cousinly stranger, in seamen's dress, accosted him, and, after some pleasant conversation, very civilly invited him up a lane into a house of rather secret entertainment. Pleased to be befriended in this his strait, Israel yet looked inquisitively upon the man, not completely satisfied with his good intentions. But the other, with good-humored violence, hurried him up the lane into the inn, when, calling for some spirits, he and Israel very affectionately drank to each other's better health and prosperity.

"Take another glass," said the stranger affably.

Israel, to drown his heavy-heartedness, complied. The liquor began to take effect.

"Ever at sea?" said the stranger, lightly.

"Oh, yes; been a whaling."

"Ah!" said the other, "happy to hear that, I assure you. Jim! Bill! And beckoning very quietly to two brawny fellows, in a trice Israel found himself kidnapped into the naval service of the magnanimous old gentleman of Kew Gardens—his Royal Majesty, George III.

"Hands off!" said Israel, fiercely, as the two men pinioned him.

"Reglar game-cock," said the cousinly-looking man. "I must get three guineas for cribbing him. Pleasant voyage to ye, my friend," and, leaving Israel a prisoner, the crimp, buttoning his coat, sauntered leisurely out of the inn.

"I'm no Englishman," roared Israel, in a foam.

"Oh! that's the old story," grinned his jailers. "Come along. There's no Englishman in the English fleet. All foreigners. You may take their own word for it."

To be short, in less than a week Israel found himself at Portsmouth, and, ere long, a foretopman in his Majesty's ship of the line, *Unprincipled*, scudding before the wind down channel, in company with the *Undaunted*, and the *Unconquerable*, all three haughty Dons bound to the East Indian waters as reinforcements to the fleet of Sir Edward Hughs.

And now, we might shortly have to record our adventurer's part in the famous engagement off the coast of Coromandel, between Admiral Suffrien's fleet and the English squadron, were it not that fate snatched him on the threshold of events, and, turning him short round whither he had come, sent him back congenially to war against England, instead of on her behalf. Thus repeatedly and rapidly were the fortunes of our wanderer planted, torn up, transplanted, and dropped again, hither and thither, according as the Supreme Disposer of sailors and soldiers saw fit to appoint.

CHAPTER XIV

IN WHICH ISRAEL IS SAILOR UNDER TWO FLAGS, AND IN THREE SHIPS, AND ALL IN ONE NIGHT

As running down channel at evening, Israel walked the crowded main-deck of the seventy-four, continually brushed by a thousand hurrying wayfarers, as if he were in some great street in London, jammed with artisans, just returning from their day's labor, novel and painful emotions were his. He found himself dropped into the naval mob without one friend; nay, among enemies, since his country's enemies were his own, and against the kith and kin of these very beings around him, he himself had once lifted a fatal hand. The martial bustle of a great man-of-war, on her first day out of port, was indescribably jarring to his present mood. Those sounds of the human multitude disturbing the solemn natural solitudes of the sea, mysteriously afflicted him. He murmured against that untowardness which, after condemning him to long sorrows on the land, now pursued him with added griefs on the deep. Why should a patriot, leaping for the chance again to attack the oppressor, as at Bunker Hill, now be kidnapped to fight that oppressor's battles on the endless drifts of the Bunker Hills of the billows? But like many other repiners, Israel was perhaps a little premature with upbraidings like these.

Plying on between Scilly and Cape Clear, the *Unprincipled*—which vessel somewhat outsailed her consorts—fell in, just before dusk, with a large revenue cutter close to, and showing signals of distress. At the moment, no other sail was in sight.

Cursing the necessity of pausing with a strong fair wind at a juncture like this, the officer-of-the-deck shortened sail, and hove to; hailing the cutter, to know what was the matter. As he hailed the small craft from the lofty poop of the bristling seventy-four, this lieutenant seemed standing on the top of Gibraltar, talking to some lowland peasant in a hut. The reply was, that in a sudden flaw of wind, which came nigh capsizing them, not an hour since, the cutter had lost all four foremast men by the violent jibing of a boom. She wanted help to get back to port.

"You shall have one man," said the officer-of-the-deck morosely.

"Let him be a good one then, for heaven's sake," said he in the cutter; "I ought to have at least two."

During this talk, Israel's curiosity had prompted him to dart up the ladder from the main-deck, and stand right in the gangway above, looking out on the strange craft. Meantime the order had been given to drop a boat. Thinking this a favorable chance, he stationed himself so that he should be the foremost to spring into the boat; though crowds of English sailors, eager as himself for the same opportunity to escape from foreign service, clung to the chains of the as yet imperfectly disciplined man-of-war. As the two men who had been lowered in the boat hooked her, when afloat, along to the gangway, Israel dropped like a comet into the stern-sheets, stumbled forward, and seized an oar. In a moment more, all the oarsmen were in their places, and with a few strokes the boat lay alongside the cutter.

"Take which of them you please," said the lieutenant in command, addressing the officer in the revenue-cutter, and motioning with his hand to the boat's crew, as if they were a parcel of carcasses of mutton, of which the first pick was offered to some customer. "Quick and choose. Sit down, men"—to the sailors. "Oh, you are in a great hurry to get rid of the king's service, ain't you? Brave chaps indeed!—Have you chosen your man?"

All this while the ten faces of the anxious oarsmen looked with mute longings and appealings towards the officer of the cutter; every face turned at the same angle, as if managed by one machine. And so they were. One motive.

"I take the freckled chap with the yellow hair—him," pointing to Israel.

Nine of the upturned faces fell in sullen despair, and ere Israel could spring to his feet, he felt a violent thrust in his rear from the toes of one of the disappointed behind him.

"Jump, dobbin!" cried the officer of the boat.

But Israel was already on board. Another moment, and the boat and cutter parted. Ere long, night fell, and the man-of-war and her consorts were out of sight.

The revenue vessel resumed her course towards the nighest port, worked by but four men: the captain, Israel, and two officers. The cabin-boy was kept at the helm. As the only foremast man, Israel was put to it pretty hard. Where there is but one man to three masters, woe betide that lonely slave. Besides, it was of itself severe work enough to manage the vessel thus short of hands. But to make matters still worse, the captain and his officers were ugly-tempered fellows. The one kicked, and the others cuffed Israel. Whereupon, not sugared with his recent experiences, and maddened by his present hap, Israel seeing himself alone at sea, with only three men, instead of a thousand, to contend against, plucked up a heart, knocked the captain into the lee scuppers, and in his fury was about tumbling the first-officer, a small wash of a fellow, plumb overboard, when the captain, jumping to his feet, seized him by his long yellow hair, vowing he would slaughter him. Meanwhile the cutter flew foaming through the channel, as if in demoniac glee at this uproar on her imperilled deck. While the consternation was at its height, a dark body suddenly loomed at a moderate distance into view, shooting right athwart the stern of the cutter. The next moment a shot struck the water within a boat's length.

"Heave to, and send a boat on board!" roared a voice almost as loud as the cannon.

"That's a war-ship," cried the captain of the revenue vessel, in alarm; "but she ain't a countryman."

Meantime the officers and Israel stopped the cutter's way.

"Send a boat on board, or I'll sink you," again came roaring from the stranger, followed by another shot, striking the water still nearer the cutter.

"For God's sake, don't cannonade us. I haven't got the crew to man a boat," replied the captain of the cutter. "Who are you?"

"Wait till I send a boat to you for that," replied the stranger.

"She's an enemy of some sort, that's plain," said the Englishman now to his officers; "we ain't at open war with France; she's some bloodthirsty pirate or other. What d'ye say, men?" turning to his officers; "let's outsail her, or be shot to chips. We can beat her at sailing, I know."

With that, nothing doubting that his counsel would be heartily responded to, he ran to the braces to get the cutter before the wind, followed by one officer, while the other, for a useless bravado, hoisted the colors at the stern.

But Israel stood indifferent, or rather all in a fever of conflicting emotions. He thought he recognized the voice from the strange vessel.

"Come, what do ye standing there, fool? Spring to the ropes here!" cried the furious captain.

But Israel did not stir.

Meantime the confusion on board the stranger, owing to the hurried lowering of her boat, with the cloudiness of the sky darkening the misty sea, united to conceal the bold manoeuvre of the cutter. She had almost gained full headway ere an oblique shot, directed by mere chance, struck her stern, tearing the upcurved head of the tiller in the hands of the cabin-boy, and killing him with the splinters. Running to the stump, the captain huzzaed, and steered the reeling ship on. Forced now to hoist back the boat ere giving chase, the stranger was dropped rapidly astern.

All this while storms of maledictions were hurled on Israel. But their exertions at the ropes prevented his shipmates for the time from using personal violence. While observing their efforts, Israel could not but say to himself, "These fellows are as brave as they are brutal."

Soon the stranger was seen dimly wallowing along astern, crowding all sail in chase, while now and then her bow-gun, showing its red tongue, bellowed after them like a mad bull. Two more shots struck the cutter, but without materially damaging her sails, or the ropes immediately upholding them. Several of her less important stays were sundered, however, whose loose tarry ends lashed the air like scorpions. It seemed not improbable that owing to her superior sailing, the keen cutter would yet get clear.

At this juncture Israel, running towards the captain, who still held the splintered stump of the tiller, stood full before him, saying, "I am an enemy, a Yankee, look to yourself."

"Help here, lads, help," roared the captain, "a traitor, a traitor!"

The words were hardly out of his mouth when his voice was silenced for ever. With one prodigious heave of his whole physical force, Israel smote him over the taffrail into the sea, as if the man had fallen backwards over a teetering chair. By this time the two officers were hurrying aft. Ere meeting them midway, Israel, quick as lightning, cast off the two principal halyards, thus letting the large sails all in a tumble of canvas to the deck. Next moment one of the officers was at the helm, to prevent the cutter from capsizing by being without a steersman in such an emergency. The other officer and Israel interlocked. The battle was in the midst of the chaos of blowing canvas. Caught in a rent of the sail, the officer slipped and fell near the sharp iron edge of the hatchway. As he fell he caught Israel by the most terrible part in which mortality can be grappled. Insane with pain, Israel dashed his adversary's skull against the sharp iron. The officer's hold relaxed, but himself stiffened. Israel made for the helmsman, who as yet knew not the issue of the late tussle. He caught him round the loins, bedding his fingers like grisly claws into his flesh, and hugging him to his heart. The man's ghost, caught like a broken cork in a gurgling bottle's neck, gasped with the embrace. Loosening him suddenly, Israel hurled him from him against the bulwarks. That instant another report was heard, followed by the savage hail—"You down sail at last, do ye? I'm a good mind to sink ye for your scurvy trick. Pull down that dirty rag there, astern!"

With a loud huzza, Israel hauled down the flag with one hand, while with the other he helped the now slowly gliding craft from falling off before the wind.

In a few moments a boat was alongside. As its commander stepped to the deck he stumbled against the body of the first officer, which, owing to the sudden slant of the cutter in coming to the wind, had rolled against the side near the gangway. As he came aft he heard the moan of the other officer, where he lay under the mizzen shrouds.

"What is all this?" demanded the stranger of Israel.

"It means that I am a Yankee impressed into the king's service, and for their pains I have taken the cutter."

Giving vent to his surprise, the officer looked narrowly at the body by the shrouds, and said, "This man is as good as dead, but we will take him to Captain Paul as a witness in your behalf."

"Captain Paul?—Paul Jones?" cried Israel.

"The same."

"I thought so. I thought that was his voice hailing. It was Captain Paul's voice that somehow put me up to this deed."

"Captain Paul is the devil for putting men up to be tigers. But where are the rest of the crew?"

"Overboard."

"What?" cried the officer; "come on board the *Ranger*. Captain Paul will use you for a broadside."

Taking the moaning man along with them, and leaving the cutter untenanted by any living soul, the boat now left her for the enemy's ship. But ere they reached it the man had expired.

Standing foremost on the deck, crowded with three hundred men, as Israel climbed the side, he saw, by the light of battle-lanterns, a small, smart, brigandish-looking man, wearing a Scotch bonnet, with a gold band to it.

"You rascal," said this person, "why did your paltry smack give me this chase? Where's the rest of your gang?"

"Captain Paul," said Israel, "I believe I remember you. I believe I offered you my bed in Paris some months ago. How is Poor Richard?"

"God! Is this the courier? The Yankee courier? But how now? in an English revenue cutter?"

"Impressed, sir; that's the way."

"But where's the rest of them?" demanded Paul, turning to the officer.

Thereupon the officer very briefly told Paul what Israel told him.

"Are we to sink the cutter, sir?" said the gunner, now advancing towards Captain Paul. "If it is to be done, now is the time. She is close under us, astern; a few guns pointed downwards will settle her like a shotted corpse."

"No. Let her drift into Penzance, an anonymous earnest of what the whitesquall in Paul Jones intends for the future."

Then giving directions as to the course of the ship, with an order for himself to be called at the first glimpse of a sail, Paul took Israel down with him into his cabin.

"Tell me your story now, my yellow lion. How was it all? Don't stand, sit right down there on the transom. I'm a democratic sort of sea-king. Plump on the woolsack, I say, and spin the yarn. But hold; you want some grog first."

As Paul handed the flagon, Israel's eye fell upon his hand.

"You don't wear any rings now, Captain, I see. Left them in Paris for safety."

"Aye, with a certain marchioness there," replied Paul, with a dandyish look of sentimental conceit, which sat strangely enough on his otherwise grim and Fejee air.

"I should think rings would be somewhat inconvenient at sea," resumed Israel. "On my first voyage to the West Indies, I wore a girl's ring on my middle finger here, and it wasn't long before, what with hauling wet ropes, and what not, it got a kind of grown down into the flesh, and pained me very bad, let me tell you, it hugged the finger so."

"And did the girl grow as close to your heart, lad?"

"Ah, Captain, girls grow themselves off quicker than we grow them on."

"Some experience with the countesses as well as myself, eh? But the story; wave your yellow mane, my lion—the story."

So Israel went on and told the story in all particulars.

At its conclusion Captain Paul eyed him very earnestly. His wild, lonely heart, incapable of sympathizing with cuddled natures made humdrum by long exemption from pain, was yet drawn towards a being, who in desperation of friendlessness, something like his own, had so fiercely waged battle against tyrannical odds.

"Did you go to sea young, lad?"

"Yes, pretty young."

"I went at twelve, from Whitehaven. Only so high," raising his hand some four feet from the deck. "I was so small, and looked so queer in my little blue jacket, that they called me the monkey. They'll call me something else before long. Did you ever sail out of Whitehaven?"

"No, Captain."

"If you had, you'd have heard sad stories about me. To this hour they say there that I—bloodthirsty, coward dog that I am—flogged a sailor, one

Mungo Maxwell to death. It's a lie, by Heaven! I flogged him, for he was a mutinous scamp. But he died naturally, some time afterwards, and on board another ship. But why talk? They didn't believe the affidavits of others taken before London courts, triumphantly acquitting me; how then will they credit *my* interested words? If slander, however much a lie, once gets hold of a man, it will stick closer than fair fame, as black pitch sticks closer than white cream. But let 'em slander. I will give the slanderers matter for curses. When last I left Whitehaven, I swore never again to set foot on her pier, except, like Cæsar, at Sandwich, as a foreign invader. Spring under me, good ship; on you I bound to my vengeance!"

Men with poignant feelings, buried under an air of care-free self-command, are never proof to the sudden incitements of passion. Though in the main they may control themselves, yet if they but once permit the smallest vent, then they may bid adieu to all self-restraint, at least for that time. Thus with Paul on the present occasion. His sympathy with Israel had prompted this momentary ebullition. When it was gone by, he seemed not a little to regret it. But he passed it over lightly, saying, "You see, my fine fellow, what sort of a bloody cannibal I am. Will you be a sailor of mine? A sailor of the Captain who flogged poor Mungo Maxwell to death?"

"I will be very happy, Captain Paul, to be sailor under the man who will yet, I dare say, help flog the British nation to death."

"You hate 'em, do ye?"

"Like snakes. For months they've hunted me as a dog," half howled and half wailed Israel, at the memory of all he had suffered.

"Give me your hand, my lion; wave your wild flax again. By Heaven, you hate so well, I love ye. You shall be my confidential man; stand sentry at my cabin door; sleep in the cabin; steer my boat; keep by my side whenever I land. What do you say?"

"I say I'm glad to hear you."

"You are a good, brave soul. You are the first among the millions of mankind that I ever naturally took to. Come, you are tired. There, go into that state-room for to-night—it's mine. You offered me your bed in Paris."

"But you begged off, Captain, and so must I. Where do you sleep?"

"Lad, I don't sleep half a night out of three. My clothes have not been off now for five days."

"Ah, Captain, you sleep so little and scheme so much, you will die young."

"I know it: I want to: I mean to. Who would live a doddered old stump? What do you think of my Scotch bonnet?"

"It looks well on you, Captain."

"Do you think so? A Scotch bonnet, though, ought to look well on a Scotchman. I'm such by birth. Is the gold band too much?"

"I like the gold band, Captain. It looks something as I should think a crown might on a king."

"Aye?"

"You would make a better-looking king than George III."

"Did you ever see that old granny? Waddles about in farthingales, and carries a peacock fan, don't he? Did you ever see him?"

"Was as close to him as I am to you now, Captain. In Kew Gardens it was, where I worked gravelling the walks. I was all alone with him, talking for some ten minutes."

"By Jove, what a chance! Had I but been there! What an opportunity for kidnapping a British king, and carrying him off in a fast sailing smack to

Boston, a hostage for American freedom. But what did you? Didn't you try to do something to him?"

"I had a wicked thought or two, Captain; but I got the better of it. Besides, the King behaved handsomely towards me; yes, like a true man. God bless him for it. But it was before that, that I got the better of the wicked thought."

"Ah, meant to stick him, I suppose. Glad you didn't. It would have been very shabby. Never kill a king, but make him captive. He looks better as a led horse, than a dead carcass. I propose now, this trip, falling on the grounds of the Earl of Selkirk, a privy counsellor and particular friend of George III. But I won't hurt a hair of his head. When I get him on board here, he shall lodge in my best state-room, which I mean to hang with damask for him. I shall drink wine with him, and be very friendly; take him to America, and introduce his lordship into the best circles there; only I shall have him accompanied on his calls by a sentry or two disguised as valets. For the Earl's to be on sale, mind; so much ransom; that is, the nobleman, Lord Selkirk, shall have a bodily price pinned on his coat-tail, like any slave up at auction in Charleston. But, my lad with the yellow mane, you very strangely draw out my secrets. And yet you don't talk. Your honesty is a magnet which attracts my sincerity. But I rely on your fidelity."

"I shall be a vice to your plans, Captain Paul. I will receive, but I won't let go, unless you alone loose the screw."

"Well said. To bed now; you ought to. I go on deck. Good night, ace-of-hearts."

"That is fitter for yourself, Captain Paul, lonely leader of the suit."

"Lonely? Aye, but number one cannot but be lonely, my trump."

"Again I give it back. Ace-of-trumps may it prove to you, Captain Paul; may it be impossible for you ever to be taken. But for me—poor deuce, a trey, that comes in your wake—any king or knave may take me, as before now the knaves have."

"Tut, tut, lad; never be more cheery for another than for yourself. But a fagged body fags the soul. To hammock, to hammock! while I go on deck to clap on more sail to your cradle."

And they separated for that night.

CHAPTER XV

THEY SAIL AS FAR AS THE CRAG OF AILSA

NEXT morning Israel was appointed quartermaster—a subaltern selected from the common seamen, and whose duty mostly stations him in the stern of the ship, where the captain walks. His business is to carry the glass on the lookout for sails; hoist or lower the colors; and keep an eye on the helmsman. Picked out from the crew for their superior respectability and intelligence, as well as for their excellent seamanship, it is not unusual to find the quartermasters of an armed ship on peculiarly easy terms with the commissioned officers and captain. This birth, therefore, placed Israel in official contiguity to Paul, and without subjecting either to animadversion, made their public intercourse on deck almost as familiar as their unrestrained converse in the cabin.

It was a fine cool day in the beginning of April. They were now off the coast of Wales, whose lofty mountains, crested with snow, presented a Norwegian aspect. The wind was fair, and blew with a strange, bestirring power. The ship—running between Ireland and England, northwards towards the Irish Sea, the inmost heart of the British waters—seemed, as she snortingly shook the spray from her bow. to be conscious of the dare-devil defiance of the soul which conducted her on this anomalous cruise. Sailing alone from out a naval port of France, crowded with ships-of-the-line, Paul Jones, in his small craft, went forth in single-armed championship against the English host. Armed with but the sling-stones in his one shot-locker, like young David of old, Paul bearded the British giant of Gath. It is not easy, at the present day, to conceive the hardihood of this enterprise. It was a marching up to the muzzle; the act of one who made no compromise with the cannonadings of danger or death; such a scheme as only could have inspired a heart which held at nothing all the prescribed prudence of war, and every obligation of peace; combining in one breast the vengeful indignation and bitter ambition of an outraged hero, with the uncompunctious desperation of a renegade. In one view, the Coriolanus of the sea; in another, a cross between the gentleman and the wolf.

As Paul stood on the elevated part of the quarterdeck, with none but his confidential quartermaster near him, he yielded to Israel's natural curiosity to learn something concerning the sailing of the expedition. Paul stood lightly, swaying his body over the sea, by holding on to the mizzen-shrouds, an attitude not inexpressive of his easy audacity; while near by, pacing a few steps to and fro, his long spy-glass now under his arm, and now presented at his eye, Israel, looking the very image of viligant prudence, listened to the warrior's story. It appeared that on the night of the visit of the Duke de Chartres and Count D'Estaing to Doctor Franklin in Paris—the same night that Captain Paul and Israel were joint occupants of the neighboring chamber—the final sanction of the French king to the sailing of an American armament against England, under the direction of the Colonial Commissioner, was made known to the latter functionary. It was a very ticklish affair. Though swaying on the brink of avowed hostilities with England, no verbal declaration had as yet been made by France. Undoubtedly, this enigmatic position of things was highly advantageous to such an enterprise as Paul's.

Without detailing all the steps taken through the united efforts of Captain Paul and Doctor Franklin, suffice it that the determined rover had now attained his wish—the unfettered command of an armed ship in the British waters; a ship legitimately authorized to hoist the American colors, her commander having in his cabin-locker a regular commission as an officer of the American navy. He sailed without any instructions. With that rare insight into rare natures which so largely distinguished the sagacious Franklin, the sage well knew that a prowling *brave*, like Paul Jones, was, like the prowling lion, by nature a solitary warrior. "Let him alone," was the wise man's answer to some statesman who sought to hamper Paul with a letter of instructions.

Much subtle casuistry has been expended upon the point, whether Paul Jones was a knave or a hero, or a union of both. But war and warriors, like politics and politicians, like religion and religionists, admit of no metaphysics.

On the second day after Israel's arrival on board the *Ranger*, as he and Paul were conversing on the deck, Israel suddenly levelling his glass towards the Irish coast, announced a large sail bound in. The *Ranger* gave chase. and soon, almost within sight of her destination—the port of Dublin—the stranger was taken, manned, and turned round for Brest.

The *Ranger* then stood over, passed the Isle of Man towards the Cumberland shore, arriving within remote sight of Whitehaven about sunset. At dark she was hovering off the harbor, with a party of volunteers all ready to descend. But the wind shifted and blew fresh with a violent sea.

"I won't call on old friends in foul weather," said Captain Paul to Israel. "We'll saunter about a little, and leave our cards in a day or two."

Next morning, in Glentinebay, on the south shore of Scotland, they fell in with a revenue wherry. It was the practice of such craft to board merchant vessels. The *Ranger* was disguised as a merchantman, presenting a broad drab-colored belt all round her hull; under the coat of a Quaker, concealing the intent of a Turk. It was expected that the chartered rover would come alongside the unchartered one. But the former took to flight, her two lug sails staggering under a heavy wind, which the pursuing guns of the *Ranger* pelted with a hail-storm of shot. The wherry escaped, spite the severe cannonade.

Off the Mull of Galoway, the day following, Paul found himself so nigh a large barley-freighted Scotch coaster, that, to prevent her carrying tidings of him to land, he dispatched her with the news, stern foremost, to Hades; sinking her, and sowing her barley in the sea broadcast by a broadside. From her crew he learned that there was a fleet of twenty or thirty sail at anchor in Lochryan, with an armed brigantine. He pointed his prow thither; but at the mouth of the lock, the wind turned against him again in hard squalls. He abandoned the project. Shortly after, he encountered a sloop from Dublin. He sank her to prevent intelligence.

Thus, seeming as much to bear the elemental commission of Nature, as the military warrant of Congress, swarthy Paul darted hither and thither; hovering like a thunder cloud off the crowded harbors; then, beaten off by an adverse wind, discharging his lightnings on uncompanioned vessels, whose solitude made them a more conspicuous and easier mark, like lonely trees on the heath. Yet all this while the land was full of garrisons, the embayed waters full of fleets. With the impunity of a Levanter, Paul skimmed his craft in the land-locked heart of the supreme naval power of earth; a torpedo-eel, unknowingly swallowed by Britain in a draught of old ocean, and making sad havoc with her vitals.

Seeing next a large vessel steering for the Clyde, he gave chase, hoping to cut her off. The stranger proving a fast sailer, the pursuit was urged on with vehemence, Paul standing, plank-proud, on the quarter-deck, calling for pulls upon every rope, to stretch each already half-burst sail to the uttermost.

While thus engaged, suddenly a shadow, like that thrown by an eclipse, was seen rapidly gaining along the deck, with a sharp defined line, plain as a seam of the planks. It involved all before it. It was the domineering shadow of the Juan Fernandez-like crag of Ailsa. The *Ranger* was in the deep water which makes all round and close up to this great summit of the submarine Grampians.

The crag, more than a mile in circuit, is over a thousand feet high, eight miles from the Ayrshire shore. There stands the cove, lonely as a foundling, proud as Cheops. But, like the battered brains surmounting the Giant of Gath, its haughty summit is crowned by a desolate castle, in and out of whose arches the aerial mists eddy like purposeless phantoms, thronging the soul of some ruinous genius, who, even in overthrow, harbors none but lofty conceptions.

As the *Ranger* shot nigher under the crag, its height and bulk dwarfed both pursuer and pursued into nut-shells. The main-truck of the *Ranger* was nine hundred feet below the foundations of the ruin on the crag's top.

While the ship was yet under the shadow, and each seaman's face shared in the general eclipse, a sudden change came over Paul. He issued no more sultanical orders. He did not look so elate as before. At length he gave the command to discontinue the chase. Turning about, they sailed southward.

"Captain Paul," said Israel, shortly afterwards, "you changed your mind rather queerly about catching that craft. But you thought she was drawing us too far up into the land, I suppose."

"Sink the craft," cried Paul; "it was not any fear of her, nor of King George, which made me turn on my heel; it was yon cock of the walk."

"Cock of the walk?"

"Aye, cock of the walk of the sea; look—yon Crag of Ailsa."

CHAPTER XVI

THEY LOOK IN AT CARRICKFERGUS, AND DESCEND ON WHITEHAVEN

NEXT day, off Carrickfergus, on the Irish coast, a fishing boat, allured by the Quaker-like look of the incognito craft, came off in full confidence. Her men were seized, their vessel sunk. From them Paul learned that the large ship at anchor in the road, was the ship-of-war *Drake*, of twenty guns. Upon this he steered away, resolving to return secretly, and attack her that night.

"Surely, Captain Paul," said Israel to his commander, as about sunset they backed and stood in again for the land, "surely, sir, you are not going right in among them this way? Why not wait till she comes out?"

"Because, Yellow-hair, my boy, I am engaged to marry her to-night. The bride's friends won't like the match; and so, this very night, the bride must be carried away. She has a nice tapering waist, hasn't she, through the glass? Ah! I will clasp her to my heart."

He steered straight in like a friend; under easy sail, lounging towards the *Drake,* with anchor ready to drop, and grapnels to hug. But the wind was high; the anchor was not dropped at the ordered time. The *Ranger* came to a stand three biscuits' toss off the unmisgiving enemy's quarter, like a peaceful merchantman from the Canadas, laden with harmless lumber.

"I sha'n't marry her just yet," whispered Paul, seeing his plans for the time frustrated. Gazing in audacious tranquillity upon the decks of the enemy, and amicably answering her hail, with complete self-possession, he commanded the cable to be slipped, and then, as if he had accidentally parted his anchor, turned his prow on the seaward tack, meaning to return again immediately with the same prospect of advantage possessed at first—his plan being to crash suddenly athwart the *Drake's* bow, so as to have all her decks exposed point-blank to his musketry. But once more the winds interposed. It came on with a storm of snow; he was obliged to give up his project.

Thus, without any warlike appearance, and giving no alarm, Paul, like an invisible ghost, glided by night close to land, actually came to anchor, for an instant, within speaking-distance of an English ship-of-war; and yet came, anchored, answered hail, reconnoitered, debated, decided, and retired, without exciting the least suspicion. His purpose was chain-shot destruction. So easily may the deadliest foe—so he be but dexterous—slide, undreamed of, into human harbors of hearts. And not awakened conscience, but mere prudence, restrain such, if they vanish again without doing harm. At daybreak no soul in Carrick-fergus knew that the devil, in a Scotch bonnet, had passed close that way over night.

Seldom has regicidal daring been more strangely coupled with octogenarian prudence, than in many of the predatory enterprises of Paul. It is this combination of apparent incompatibilities which ranks him among extraordinary warriors.

Ere daylight, the storm of the night blew over. The sun saw the *Ranger* lying midway over channel at the head of the Irish Sea; England, Scotland, and Ireland, with all their lofty cliffs, being as simultaneously as plainly in sight beyond the grass-green waters, as the City Hall, St. Paul's, and the Astor House, from the triangular Park in New York. The three kingdoms lay covered with snow, far as the eye could reach.

"Ah, Yellow-hair," said Paul, with a smile, "they show the white flag, the cravens. And, while the white flag stays blanketing yonder heights, we'll make for Whitehaven, my boy. I promised to drop in there a moment ere quitting the country for good. Israel, lad, I mean to step ashore in person, and have a personal hand in the thing. Did you ever drive spikes?"

"I've driven the spike-teeth into harrows before now," replied Israel; "but that was before I was a sailor."

"Well, then, driving spikes into harrows is a good introduction to driving spikes into cannon. You are just the man. Put down your glass; go to the carpenter, get a hundred spikes, put them in a bucket with a hammer, and bring all to me."

As evening fell, the great promontory of St. Bee's Head, with its lighthouse, not far from Whitehaven, was in distant sight. But the wind became so light that Paul could not work his ship in close enough at an hour as early as intended. His purpose had been to make the descent and retire ere break of day. But though this intention was frustrated, he did not renounce his plan, for the present would be his last opportunity.

As the night wore on, and the ship, with a very light wind, glided nigher and nigher the mark, Paul called upon Israel to produce his bucket for final inspection. Thinking some of the spikes too large, he had them filed down a little. He saw to the lanterns and combustibles. Like Peter the Great, he went into the smallest details, while still possessing a genius competent to plan the aggregate. But oversee as one may, it is impossible to guard against carelessness in subordinates. One's sharp eyes can't see behind one's back. It will yet be noted that an important omission was made in the preparations for Whitehaven.

The town contained, at that period, a population of some six or seven thousand inhabitants, defended by forts.

At midnight, Paul Jones, Israel Potter, and twenty-nine others, rowed in two boats to attack the six or seven thousand inhabitants of Whitehaven. There was a long way to pull. This was done in perfect silence. Not a sound was heard except the oars turning in the row-locks. Nothing was seen except the two lighthouses of the harbor. Through the stillness and the darkness, the two deep-laden boats swam into the haven, like two mysterious whales from the Arctic Sea. As they reached the outer pier, the men saw each other's faces. The day was dawning. The riggers and other artisans of the shipping would before very long be astir. No matter.

The great staple exported from Whitehaven was then, and still is, coal. The town is surrounded by mines; the town is built on mines; the ships moor over mines. The mines honeycomb the land in all directions, and extend in galleries of grottoes for two miles under the sea. By the falling of the more ancient colleries numerous houses have been swallowed, as if by an earthquake, and a consternation spread, like that of Lisbon, in 1755. So insecure and treacherous was the site of the place now about to be assailed by a desperado, nursed, like the coal, in its vitals.

Now, sailing on the Thames, nigh its mouth, of fair days, when the wind is favorable for inward-bound craft, the stranger will sometimes see processions of vessels, all of similar size and rig, stretching for miles and miles, like a long string of horses tied two and two to a rope and driven to market. These are colliers going to London with coal.

About three hundred of these vessels now lay, all crowded together, in one dense mob, at Whitehaven. The tide was out. They lay completely helpless, clear of water, and grounded. They were sooty in hue. Their black yards were deeply canted, like spears, to avoid collision. The three hundred grimy hulls lay wallowing in the mud, like a herd of hippopotami asleep in the alluvium of the Nile. Their sailless, raking masts, and canted yards, resembled a forest of fish-spears thrust into those same hippopotamus hides. Partly flanking one side of the grounded fleet was a fort, whose batteries were raised from the beach. On a little strip of this beach, at the base of the fort, lay a number of small rusty guns, dismounted, heaped together in disorder, as a litter of dogs. Above them projected the mounted cannon.

Paul landed in his own boat at the foot of this fort. He dispatched the other boat to the north side of the haven, with orders to fire the shipping there. Leaving two men at the beach, he then proceeded to get possession of the fort.

"Hold on to the bucket, and give me your shoulder," said he to Israel.

Using Israel for a ladder, in a trice he scaled the wall. The bucket and the men followed. He led the way softly to the guard-house, burst in, and bound the sentinels in their sleep. Then arranging his force, ordered four men to spike the cannon there.

"Now, Israel, your bucket, and follow me to the other fort."

The two went alone about a quarter of a mile.

"Captain Paul," said Israel, on the way, "can we two manage the sentinels?"

"There are none in the fort we go to."

"You know all about the place, Captain?"

"Pretty well informed on that subject, I believe. Come along. Yes, lad, I am tolerably well acquainted with Whitehaven. And this morning intend that Whitehaven shall have a slight inkling of me. Come on. Here we are."

Scaling the walls, the two involuntarily stood for an instant gazing upon the scene. The gray light of the dawn showed the crowded houses and thronged ships with a haggard distinctness.

"Spike and hammer, lad;—so—now follow me along, as I go, and give me a spike for every cannon. I'll tongue-tie the thunderers. Speak no more!" and he spiked the first gun. "Be a mute," and he spiked the second. "Dumb-founder thee," and he spiked the third. And so, on, and on, and on, Israel following him with the bucket, like a footman, or some charitable gentleman with a basket of alms.

"There, it is done. D'ye see the fire yet, lad, from the south? I don't."

"Not a spark, Captain. But day-sparks come on in the east."

"Forked flames into the hounds! What are they about? Quick, let us back to the first fort; perhaps something has happened, and they are there."

Sure enough, on their return from spiking the cannon, Paul and Israel found the other boat back, the crew in confusion, their lantern having burnt out at the very instant they wanted it. By a singular fatality the other lantern, belonging to Paul's boat, was likewise extinguished. No tinder-box had been brought. They had no matches but sulphur matches. Locofocos were not then known.

The day came on apace.

"Captain Paul," said the lieutenant of the second boat, "it is madness to stay longer. See!" and he pointed to the town, now plainly discernible in the gray light.

"Traitor or coward!" howled Paul, "how came the lanterns out? Israel, my lion, now prove your blood. Get me a light—but one spark!"

"Has any man here a bit of pipe and tobacco in his pocket?" said Israel.

A sailor quickly produced an old stump of a pipe, with tobacco.

"That will do," and Israel hurried away towards the town.

"What will the loon do with the pipe?" said one. "And where goes he?" cried another.

"Let him alone," said Paul.

The invader now disposed his whole force so as to retreat at an instant's warning. Meantime the hardy Israel, long experienced in all sorts of shifts and emergencies, boldly ventured to procure, from some inhabitant of Whitehaven, a spark to kindle all Whitehaven's habitations in flames.

There was a lonely house standing somewhat disjointed from the town, some poor laborer's abode. Rapping at the door, Israel, pipe in mouth, begged the inmates for a light for his tobacco.

"What the devil," roared a voice from within, "knock up a man this time of night to light your pipe? Begone!"

"You are lazy this morning, my friend," replied Israel, "it is daylight. Quick, give me a light. Don't you know your old friend? Shame! open the door."

In a moment a sleepy fellow appeared, let down the bar, and Israel, stalking into the dim room, piloted himself straight to the fire-place, raked away the cinders, lighted his tobacco, and vanished.

All was done in a flash. The man, stupid with sleep, had looked on bewildered. He reeled to the door, but, dodging behind a pile of bricks, Israel had already hurried himself out of sight.

"Well done, my lion," was the hail he received from Paul, who, during his absence, had mustered as many pipes as possible, in order to communicate and multiply the fire.

Both boats now pulled to a favorable point of the principal pier of the harbor, crowded close up to a part of which lay one wing of the colliers.

The men began to murmur at persisting in an attempt impossible to be concealed much longer. They were afraid to venture on board the grim colliers, and go groping down into their hulls to fire them. It seemed like a voluntary entrance into dungeons and death.

"Follow me, all of you but ten by the boats," said Paul, without noticing their murmurs. "And now, to put an end to all future burnings in America, by one mighty conflagration of shipping in England. Come on, lads! Pipes and matches in the van!"

He would have distributed the men so as simultaneously to fire different ships at different points, were it not that the lateness of the hour rendered such a course insanely hazardous. Stationing his party in front of one of the windward colliers, Paul and Israel sprang on board.

In a twinkling they had broken open a boatswain's locker, and, with great bunches of oakum, fine and dry as tinder, had leaped into the steerage. Here, while Paul made a blaze, Israel ran to collect the tar-pots, which being presently poured on the burning matches, oakum and wood, soon increased the flame.

"It is not a sure thing yet," said Paul, "we must have a barrel of tar."

They searched about until they found one, knocked out the head and bottom, and stood it like a martyr in the midst of the flames. They then retreated up the forward hatchway, while volumes of smoke were belched from the after one. Not till this moment did Paul hear the cries of his men, warning him that the inhabitants were not only actually astir, but crowds were on their way to the pier.

As he sprang out of the smoke towards the rail of the collier, he saw the sun risen, with thousands of the people. Individuals hurried close to the burning vessel. Leaping to the ground, Paul, bidding his men stand fast, ran to their front, and, advancing about thirty feet, presented his own pistol at now tumultuous Whitehaven.

Those who had rushed to extinguish what they had deemed but an accidental fire, were now paralyzed into idiotic inaction at the defiance of the incendiary, thinking him some sudden pirate or fiend dropped down from the moon.

While Paul thus stood guarding the incipient conflagration, Israel, without a weapon, dashed crazily towards the mob on the shore.

"Come back, come back," cried Paul.

"Not till I start these sheep, as their own wolves many a time started me!"

As he rushed bare-headed like a madman, towards the crowd, the panic spread. They fled from unarmed Israel, farther than they had from the pistol of Paul.

The flames now catching the rigging and spiralling around the masts, the whole ship burned at one end of the harbor, while the sun, an hour high, burned at the other. Alarm and amazement, not sleep, now ruled the world. It was time to retreat.

They re-embarked without opposition, first releasing a few prisoners, as the boats could not carry them.

Just as Israel was leaping into the boat, he saw the man at whose house he had procured the fire, staring like a simpleton at him.

"That was good seed you gave me," said Israel, "see what a yield," pointing to the flames. He then dropped into the boat, leaving only Paul on the pier.

The men cried to their commander, conjuring him not to linger.

But Paul remained for several moments, confronting in silence the clamors of the mob beyond, and waving his solitary hand, like a disdainful tomahawk, towards the surrounding eminences, also covered with the affrighted inhabitants.

When the assailants had rowed pretty well off, the English rushed in great numbers to their forts, but only to find their cannon no better than so much iron in the ore. At length, however, they began to fire, having either brought down some ship's guns, or else mounted the rusty old dogs lying at the foot of the first fort.

In their eagerness they fired with no discretion. The shot fell short; they did not the slightest damage.

Paul's men laughed aloud, and fired their pistols in the air.

Not a splinter was made, not a drop of blood spilled throughout the affair. The intentional harmlessness of the result, as to human life, was only equalled by the desperate courage of the deed. It formed, doubtless, one feature of the compassionate contempt of Paul towards the town, that he took such paternal care of their lives and limbs.

Had it been possible to have landed a few hours earlier not a ship nor a house could have escaped. But it was the lesson, not the loss, that told. As it was, enough damage had been done to demonstrate—as Paul had declared to the wise man of Paris—that the disasters caused by the wanton fires and assaults on the American coasts, could be easily brought home to the enemy's doors. Though, indeed, if the retaliators were headed by Paul Jones, the satisfaction would not be equal to the insult, being abated by the magnanimity of a chivalrous, however unprincipled a foe.

CHAPTER XVII

THEY CALL AT THE EARL OF SELKIRK'S, AND AFTERWARDS FIGHT THE SHIP-OF-WAR "DRAKE"

THE Ranger now stood over the Solway Firth for the Scottish shore, and at noon on the same day, Paul, with twelve men, including two officers and Israel, landed on St. Mary's Isle, one of the seats of the Earl of Selkirk.

In three consecutive days this elemental warrior either entered the harbors or landed on the shores of each of the Three Kingdoms.

The morning was fair and clean. St. Mary's Isle lay shimmering in the sun. The light crust of snow had melted, revealing the tender grass and sweet buds of spring mantling the sides of the cliffs.

At once, upon advancing with his party towards the house, Paul augured ill for his project from the loneliness of the spot. No being was seen. But cocking his bonnet at a jaunty angle, he continued his way. Stationing the men silently round about the house, followed by Israel, he announced his presence at the porch.

A gray-headed domestic at length responded.

"Is the Earl within?"

"He is in Edinburgh, sir."

"Ah—sure?—Is your lady within?"

"Yes, sir—who shall I say it is?"

"A gentleman who calls to pay his respects. Here, take my card."

And he handed the man his name, as a private gentleman, superbly engraved at Paris, on gilded paper.

Israel tarried in the hall while the old servant led Paul into a parlor.

Presently the lady appeared.

"Charming Madame, I wish you a very good morning."

"Who may it be, sir, that I have the happiness to see?" said the lady, censoriously drawing herself up at the too frank gallantry of the stranger.

"Madame, I sent you my card."

"Which leaves me equally ignorant, sir," said the lady, coldly, twirling the gilded pasteboard.

"A courier dispatched to Whitehaven, charming Madame, might bring you more particular tidings as to who has the honor of being your visitor."

Not comprehending what this meant, and deeply displeased, if not vaguely alarmed, at the characteristic manner of Paul, the lady, not entirely unembarrassed, replied, that if the gentleman came to view the isle, he was at liberty so to do. She would retire and send him a guide.

"Countess of Selkirk," said Paul, advancing a step, "I call to see the Earl. On business of urgent importance, I call."

"The Earl is in Edinburgh," uneasily responded the lady, again about to retire.

"Do you give me your honor as a lady that it is as you say?"

The lady looked at him in dubious resentment.

"Pardon, Madame, I would not lightly impugn a lady's slightest word, but I surmised that, possibly, you might suspect the object of my call, in which case it would be the most excusable thing in the world for you to seek to shelter from my knowledge the presence of the Earl on the isle."

"I do not dream what you mean by all this," said the lady with a decided alarm, yet even in her panic courageously maintaining her dignity, as she retired, rather than retreated, nearer the door.

"Madame," said Paul, hereupon waving his hand imploringly, and then tenderly playing with his bonnet with the golden band, while an expression poetically sad and sentimental stole over his tawny face; "it cannot be too poignantly lamented that, in the profession of arms, the officer of fine feelings and genuine sensibility should be sometimes necessitated to public actions which his own private heart cannot approve. This hard case is mine. The Earl, Madame, you say is absent. I believe those words. Far be it from my soul, enchantress, to ascribe a fault to syllables which have proceeded from so faultless a source."

This probably he said in reference to the lady's mouth, which was beautiful in the extreme.

He bowed very lowly, while the lady eyed him with conflicting and troubled emotions, but as yet all in darkness as to his ultimate meaning. But her more immediate alarm had subsided, seeing now that the sailor-like extravagance of Paul's homage was entirely unaccompanied with any touch of intentional disrespect. Indeed, hyperbolical as were his phrases, his gestures and whole carriage were most heedfully deferential.

Paul continued: "The Earl, Madame, being absent, and he being the sole object of my call, you cannot labor under the least apprehension, when I now inform you, that I have the honor of being an officer in the American Navy, who, having stopped at this isle to secure the person of the Earl of Selkirk as a hostage for the American cause, am, by your assurances, turned away from that intent; pleased, even in disappointment, since that disappointment has served to prolong my interview with the noble lady before me, as well as to leave her domestic tranquillity unimpaired."

"Can you really speak true?" said the lady in undismayed wonderment.

"Madame, through your window you will catch a little peep of the American colonial ship-of-war *Ranger*, which I have the honor to command. With my best respects to your lord, and sincere regrets at not finding him at home, permit me to salute your ladyship's hand and withdraw."

But feigning not to notice this Parisian proposition, and artfully entrenching her hand, without seeming to do so, the lady, in a conciliatory tone, begged her visitor to partake of some refreshment ere he departed, at the same time thanking him for his great civility. But declining these hospitalities, Paul bowed thrice and quitted the room.

In the hall he encountered Israel, standing all agape before a Highland target of steel, with a claymore and foil crossed on top.

"Looks like a pewter platter and knife and fork, Captain Paul."

"So they do, my lion; but come, curse it, the old cock has flown; fine hen, though, left in the nest; no use; we must away empty-handed."

"Why, ain't Mr. Selkirk in?" demanded Israel in roguish concern.

"Mr. Selkirk? Alexander Selkirk, you mean. No, lad, he's not on the Isle of St. Mary's; he's away off, a hermit, on the Isle of Juan Fernandez—the more's the pity; come."

In the porch they encountered the two officers. Paul briefly informed them of the circumstances, saying, nothing remained but to depart forthwith.

"With nothing at all for our pains?" murmured the two officers.

"What, pray, would you have?"

"Some pillage, to be sure—plate."

"Shame. I thought we were three gentlemen."

"So are the English officers in America; but they help themselves to plate whenever they can get it from the private houses of the enemy."

"Come, now, don't be slanderous," said Paul; "these officers you speak of are but one or two out of twenty, mere burglars and light-fingered gentry, using the king's livery but as a disguise to their nefarious trade. The rest are men of honor."

"Captain Paul Jones," responded the two, "we have not come on this expedition in much expectation of regular pay; but we *did* rely upon honorable plunder."

"Honorable plunder! That's something new."

But the officers were not to be turned aside. They were the most efficient in the ship. Seeing them resolute, Paul, for fear of incensing them, was at last, as a matter of policy, obliged to comply. For himself, however, he resolved to have nothing to do with the affair. Charging the officers not to allow the men to enter the house on any pretence, and that no search must be made, and nothing must be taken away, except what the lady should offer them upon making known their demand, he beckoned to Israel and retired indignantly towards the beach. Upon second thoughts, he dispatched Israel back, to enter the house with the officers, as joint receiver of the plate, he being, of course, the most reliable of the seamen.

The lady was not a little disconcerted on receiving the officers. With cool determination they made known their purpose. There was no escape. The lady retired. The butler came; and soon, several silver salvers, and other articles of value, were silently deposited in the parlor in the presence of the officers and Israel.

"Mister Butler," said Israel, "let me go into the dairy and help to carry the milk-pans."

But, scowling upon this rusticity, or roguishness—he knew not which—the butler, in high dudgeon at Israel's republican familiarity, as well as black as a thundercloud with the general insult offered to an illustrious household by a party of armed thieves, as he viewed them, declined any assistance. In a quarter of an hour the officers left the house, carrying their booty.

At the porch they were met by a red-cheeked, spiteful-looking lass, who, with her brave lady's compliments, added two child's rattles of silver and coral to their load.

Now, one of the officers was a Frenchman, the other a Spaniard.

The Spaniard dashed his rattle indignantly to the ground. The Frenchman took his very pleasantly, and kissed it, saying to the girl that he would long preserve the coral, as a memento of her rosy cheeks.

When the party arrived on the beach, they found Captain Paul writing with pencil and paper held up against the smooth tableted side of the cliff. Next moment he seemed to be making his signature. With a reproachful glance towards the two officers, he handed the slip to Israel, bidding him hasten immediately with it to the house and place it in Lady Selkirk's own hands.

The note was as follows:

"Madame:

"After so courteous a reception, I am disturbed to make you no better return than you have just experienced from the actions of certain persons under my command—actions, lady, which my profession of arms obliges me not only to brook, but, in a measure, to countenance. From the bottom of my heart, my dear lady, I deplore this most melancholy necessity of my delicate position. However unhandsome the desire of these men, some complaisance seemed due them from me, for their general good conduct and bravery on former occasions. I had but an instant to consider. I trust, that in unavoidably gratifying them, I have inflicted less injury on your ladyship's property than I have on my own bleeding sensibilities. But my heart will not allow me to say more. Permit me to assure you, dear lady, that when the plate is sold I shall, at all hazards, become the purchaser, and will be proud to restore it to you, by such conveyance as you may hereafter see fit to appoint.

"From hence I go, Madame, to engage, to-morrow morning, his Majesty's ship, *Drake*, of twenty guns, now lying at Carrickfergus. I should meet the enemy with more than wonted resolution, could I flatter myself that, through this unhandsome conduct on the part of my officers, I lie not under the disesteem of the sweet lady of the Isle of St. Mary's. But unconquerable as Mars should I be, could I but dare to dream, that in some green retreat of her charming domain, the Countess of Selkirk offers up a charitable prayer for, my dear lady countess, one, who coming to take a captive, himself has been captivated.

"Your ladyship's adoring enemy,
"John Paul Jones."

How the lady received this super-ardent note, history does not relate. But history has not omitted to record, that after the return of the *Ranger* to France, through the assiduous efforts of Paul in buying up the booty, piece by piece, from the clutches of those among whom it had been divided, and not without a pecuniary private loss to himself, equal to the total value of the plunder, the plate was punctually restored, even to the silver heads of two pepper-boxes; and, not only this, but the Earl, hearing all the particulars, magnanimously wrote Paul a letter, expressing thanks for his politeness. In the opinion of the noble Earl, Paul was a man of honor. It were rash to differ in opinion with such high-born authority.

Upon returning to the ship, she was instantly pointed over towards the Irish coast. Next morning Carrickfergus was in sight. Paul would have gone straight in; but Israel, reconnoitring with his glass, informed him that a large ship, probably the *Drake*, was just coming out.

"What think you, Israel, do they know who we are? Let me have the glass."

"They are dropping a boat now, sir," replied Israel, removing the glass from his eye, and handing it to Paul.

"So they are—so they are. They don't know us. I'll decoy that boat alongside. Quick—they are coming for us—take the helm now yourself, my lion, and keep the ship's stern steadily presented towards the advancing boat. Don't let them have the least peep at our broadside."

The boat came on, an officer in its bow all the time eyeing the *Ranger* through a glass. Presently the boat was within hail.

"Ship ahoy! Who are you?"

"Oh, come alongside," answered Paul through his trumpet, in a rapid off-hand tone, as though he were a gruff sort of friend, impatient at being suspected for a foe.

In a few moments the officer of the boat stepped into the *Ranger's* gangway. Cocking his bonnet gallantly, Paul advanced towards him, making a very polite bow, saying: "Good morning, sir, good morning; delighted to see you. That's a pretty sword you have; pray, let me look at it."

"I see," said the officer, glancing at the ship's armament, and turning pale. "I am your prisoner."

"No—my guest," responded Paul, winningly. "Pray, let me relieve you of your—your—cane."

Thus humorously he received the officer's delivered sword.

"Now tell me, sir, if you please," he continued, "what brings out his Majesty's ship *Drake* this fine morning? Going a little airing?"

"She comes out in search of you, but when I left her side half an hour since she did not know that the ship off the harbor was the one she sought."

"You had news from Whitehaven, I suppose, last night, eh?"

"Aye: express; saying that certain incendiaries had landed there early that morning."

"What?—what sort of men were they, did you say?" said Paul, shaking his bonnet fiercely to one side of his head, and coming close to the officer. "Pardon me," he added derisively, "I had forgot you are my *guest*. Israel, see the unfortunate gentleman below, and his men forward."

The *Drake* was now seen slowly coming out under a light air, attended by five small pleasure-vessels, decorated with flags and streamers, and full of gaily-dressed people, whom motives similar to those which drew visitors to the circus, had induced to embark on their adventurous trip. But they little dreamed how nigh the desperate enemy was.

"Drop the captured boat astern," said Paul; "see what effect that will have on those merry voyagers."

No sooner was the empty boat descried by the pleasure-vessels than forthwith, surmising the truth, they with all diligence turned about and re-entered the harbor. Shortly after, alarm-smokes were seen extending along both sides of the channel.

"They smoke us at last, Captain Paul," said Israel.

"There will be more smoke yet before the day is done," replied Paul, gravely.

The wind was right under the land, the tide unfavorable. The *Drake* worked out very slowly.

Meantime, like some fiery-heated duellist calling on urgent business at frosty daybreak, and long kept waiting at the door by the dilatoriness of his antagonist, shrinking at the idea of getting up to be cut to pieces in the cold— the *Ranger*, with a better breeze, impatiently tacked to and fro in the channel.

At last, when the English vessel had fairly weathered the point, Paul, ranging ahead, courteously led her forth, as a beau might a belle in a ballroom, to mid-channel, and then suffered her to come within hail.

"She is hoisting her colors now, sir," said Israel.

"Give her the stars and stripes, then, my lad."

Joyfully running to the locker, Israel attached the flag to the halyards. The wind freshened. He stood elevated. The bright flag blew around him, a glorified shroud, enveloping him in its red ribbons and spangles, like upspringing tongues, and sparkles of flame.

As the colors rose to their final perch, and streamed in the air, Paul eyed them exultingly.

"I first hoisted that flag on an American ship, and was the first among men to get it saluted. If I perish this night, the name of Paul Jones shall live. Hark! they hail us."

"What ship are you?"

"Your enemy. Come on! What wants the fellow of more prefaces and introductions?"

The sun was now calmly setting over the green land of Ireland. The sky was serene, the sea smooth, the wind just sufficient to waft the two vessels steadily and gently. After the first firing and a little manœuvring, the two ships glided on freely, side by side; in that mild air exchanging their deadly broadsides, like two friendly horsemen walking their steeds along a plain, chatting as they go. After an hour of this running fight, the conversation ended. The *Drake* struck. How changed from the big craft of sixty short minutes before! She seemed now, above deck, like a piece of wild western woodland into which choppers had been. Her masts and yards prostrate, and hanging in jack-straws; several of her sails ballooning out, as they dragged in the sea, like great lopped tops of foliage. The black hull and shattered stumps of masts, galled and riddled, looked as if gigantic woodpeckers had been tapping them.

The *Drake* was the larger ship; more cannon; more men. Her loss in killed and wounded was far the greater. Her brave captain and lieutenant were mortally wounded.

The former died as the prize was boarded, the latter two days after.

It was twilight, the weather still severe. No cannonade, naught that mad man can do, molests the stoical imperturbability of Nature, when Nature chooses to be still. This weather, holding on through the following day, greatly facilitated the refitting of the ships. That done, the two vessels, sailing round the north of Ireland, steered towards Brest. They were repeatedly chased by English cruisers, but safely reached their anchorage in the French waters.

"A pretty fair four weeks' yachting, gentlemen," said Paul Jones, as the *Ranger* swung to her cable, while some French officers boarded her. "I bring two travellers with me, gentlemen," he continued. "Allow me to introduce you to my particular friend Israel Potter, late of North America, and also to his Britannic Majesty's ship *Drake*, late of Carrickfergus, Ireland."

This cruise made loud fame for Paul, especially at the court of France, whose king sent Paul a sword and a medal. But poor Israel, who also had conquered a craft, and all unaided too—what had he?

CHAPTER XVIII

THE EXPEDITION THAT SAILED FROM GROIX

THREE months after anchoring at Brest, through Dr. Franklin's negotiations with the French king, backed by the bestirring ardor of Paul, a squadron of nine vessels, of various force, were ready in the road of Groix for another descent on the British coasts. These craft were miscellaneously picked up, their crews a mongrel pack, the officers mostly French, unacquainted with each other, and secretly jealous of Paul. The expedition was full of the elements of insubordination and failure. Much bitterness and agony resulted to a spirit like Paul's. But he bore up, and though in many particulars the sequel more than warranted his misgivings, his soul still refused to surrender.

The career of this stubborn adventurer signally illustrates the idea that since all human affairs are subject to organic disorder, since they are created in and sustained by a sort of half-disciplined chaos, hence he who in great things seeks success must never wait for smooth water, which never was and never will be, but, with what straggling method he can, dash with all his derangements at his object, leaving the rest to Fortune.

Though nominally commander of the squadron, Paul was not so in effect. Most of his captains conceitedly claimed independent commands. One of them in the end proved a traitor outright; few of the rest were reliable.

As for the ships, that commanded by Paul in person will be a good example of the fleet. She was an old Indiaman, clumsy and cranky, smelling strongly of the savor of tea, cloves, and arrack, the cargoes of former voyages. Even at that day she was, from her venerable grotesqueness, what a cocked hat is, at the present age, among ordinary beavers. Her elephantine bulk was houdahed with a castellated poop like the leaning tower of Pisa. Poor Israel, standing on the top of this poop, spy-glass at his eye, looked more an astronomer than a mariner, having to do, not with the mountains of the billows, but the mountains in the moon. Galileo on Fiesole. She was originally a single-decked ship, that is, carried her armament on one gun-deck; but cutting ports below, in her after part, Paul rammed out there six old eighteen-pounders, whose rusty muzzles peered just above the water-line, like a parcel of dirty mulattoes from a cellarway. Her name was the *Duras*, but, ere sailing, it was changed to that other appellation, whereby this sad old hulk became afterwards immortal. Though it is not unknown, that a compliment to Doctor Franklin was involved in this change of titles, yet the secret history of the affair will now for the first time be disclosed.

It was evening in the road of Groix. After a fagging day's work, trying to conciliate the hostile jealousy of his officers, and provide, in the face of endless obstacles (for he had to dance attendance on scores of intriguing factors and brokers ashore), the requisite stores for the fleet, Paul sat in his cabin in a half-despondent reverie, while Israel, cross-legged at his commander's feet, was patching up some old signals.

"Captain Paul, I don't like our ship's name.—Duras? What's that mean? —Duras? Being cribbed up in a ship named Duras! a sort of makes one feel as if he were in durance vile."

"Gad, I never thought of that before, my lion. Duras—Durance vile. I

suppose it's superstition, but I'll change it.   Come, Yellow-mane, what shall
we call her?"

"Well, Captain Paul, don't you like Doctor Franklin?   Hasn't he been the
prime man to get this fleet together?   Let's call her the Doctor Franklin."

"Oh, no, that will too publicly declare him just at present; and Poor
Richard wants to be a little shady in this business."

"Poor Richard!—call her Poor Richard, then," cried Israel, suddenly struck
by the idea.

" 'Gad, you have it," answered Paul, springing to his feet, as all trace
of his former despondency left him;—"Poor Richard shall be the name, in
honor to the saying, that 'God helps them that help themselves,' as Poor
Richard says."

Now this was the way the craft came to be called the *Bon Homme Richard;*
for it being deemed advisable to have a French rendering of the new title, it
assumed the above form.

A few days after, the force sailed.   Ere long, they captured several vessels;
but the captains of the squadron proving refractory, events took so deplorable
a turn, that Paul, for the present, was obliged to return to Groix.   Luckily,
however, at this junction a cartel arrived from England with upwards of a
hundred exchanged American seamen, who almost to a man enlisted under the
flag of Paul.

Upon the resailing of the force, the old troubles broke out afresh.   Most
of her consorts insubordinately separated from the *Bon Homme Richard*.
At length Paul found himself in violent storms beating off the rugged south-
eastern coast of Scotland, with only two accompanying ships.   But neither
the mutiny of his fleet, nor the chaos of the elements, made him falter in
his purpose.   Nay, at this crisis, he projected the most daring of all his
descents.

The Cheviot Hills were in sight.   Sundry vessels had been descried bound
in for the Firth of Forth, on whose south shore, well up the Firth, stands
Leith, the port of Edinburgh, distant but a mile or two from that capital.   He
resolved to dash at Leith and lay it under contribution or in ashes.   He called
the captains of his two remaining consorts on board his own ship to arrange
details.   Those worthies had much of fastidious remark to make against the
plan.   After losing much time in trying to bring to a conclusion their sage
deliberations, Paul, by addressing their cupidity, achieved that which all appeals
to their gallantry could not accomplish.   He proclaimed the grand prize of
the Leith lottery at no less a figure than £200,000, that being named as the
ransom.   Enough: the three ships enter the Firth, boldly and freely, as if
carrying Quakers to a Peace-Congress.

Along both startled shores the panic of their approach spread like the
cholera.   The three suspicious crafts had so long lain off and on, that none
doubted they were led by the audacious viking, Paul Jones.   At five o'clock, on
the following morning, they were distinctly seen from the capital of Scotland,
quietly sailing up the bay.   Batteries were hastily thrown up at Leith, arms
were obtained from the castle at Edinburgh, alarm fires were kindled in all
directions.   Yet with such tranquillity of effrontery did Paul conduct his ships,
concealing as much as possible their warlike character, that more than once
his vessels were mistaken for merchantmen, and hailed by passing ships as
such.

In the afternoon, Israel, at his station on the tower of Pisa, reported a
boat with five men coming off to the *Richard.* from the coast of Fife.

"They have hot oat-cakes for us," said Paul; "let 'em come. To encourage them, show them the English ensign, Israel, my lad."

Soon the boat was alongside.

"Well, my good fellows, what can I do for you this afternoon?" said Paul, leaning over the side with a patronizing air.

"Why, captain, we come from the Laird of Crokarky, who wants some powder and ball for his money."

"What would you with powder and ball, pray?"

"Oh! haven't you heard that that bloody pirate, Paul Jones, is somewhere hanging round the coasts?"

"Aye, indeed, but he won't hurt you. He's only going round among the nations, with his old hat, taking up contributions. So, away with ye; ye don't want any powder and ball to give him. He wants contributions of silver, not lead. Prepare yourselves with silver, I say."

"Nay, captain, the Laird ordered us not to return without powder and ball. See, here is the price. It may be the taking of the bloody pirate, if you let us have what we want."

"Well, pass 'em over a keg," said Paul, laughing, but modifying his order by a sly whisper to Israel: "Oh, put up your price, it's a gift to ye."

"But ball, captain; what's the use of powder without ball?" roared one of the fellows from the boat's bow, as the keg was lowered in. "We want ball."

"Bless my soul, you bawl loud enough as it is. Away with ye, with what you have. Look to your keg, and hark ye, if ye catch that villain, Paul Jones, give him no quarter."

"But, captain, here," shouted one of the boatmen, "there's a mistake. This is a keg of pickles, not powder. Look," and poking into the bung-hole, he dragged out a green cucumber dripping with brine. "Take this back, and give us the powder."

"Pooh," said Paul, "the powder is at the bottom, pickled powder, best way to keep it. Away with ye, now, and after that bloody embezzler, Paul Jones."

This was Sunday. The ships held on. During the afternoon, a long tack of the *Richard* brought her close towards the shores of Fife, near the thriving little port of Kirkaldy.

"There's a great crowd on the beach, Captain Paul," said Israel, looking through his glass. "There seems to be an old woman standing on a fish-barrel there, a sort of selling things at auction to the people, but I can't be certain yet."

"Let me see," said Paul, taking the glass as they came nigher. "Sure enough, it's an old lady—an old quack-doctress, seems to me, in a black gown, too. I must hail her."

Ordering the ship to be kept on towards the port, he shortened sail within easy distance, so as to glide slowly by, and seizing the trumpet, thus spoke:

"Old lady, ahoy! What are you talking about? What's your text?"

"The righteous shall rejoice when he seeth the vengeance. He shall wash his feet in the blood of the wicked."

"Ah, what a lack of charity. Now hear mine:—God helpeth them that help themselves, as Poor Richard says."

"Reprobate pirate, a gale shall yet come to drive thee in wrecks from our waters."

"The strong wind of your hate fills my sails well. Adieu," waving his bonnet—"tell us the rest at Leith."

Next morning the ships were almost within cannon-shot of the town. The men to be landed were in the boats. Israel had the tiller of the foremost one, waiting for his commander to enter, when just as Paul's foot was on the gangway, a sudden squall struck all three ships, dashing the boats against them, and causing indescribable confusion. The squall ended in a violent gale. Getting his men on board with all dispatch, Paul essayed his best to withstand the fury of the wind, but it blew adversely, and with redoubled power. A ship at a distance went down beneath it. The disappointed invader was obliged to turn before the gale, and renounce his project.

To this hour, on the shores of the Firth of Forth, it is the popular persuasion, that the Rev. Mr. Shirrer's (of Kirkaldy) powerful intercession was the direct cause of the elemental repulse experienced off the endangered harbor of Leith.

Through the ill qualities of Paul's associate captains: their timidity, incapable of keeping pace with his daring; their jealousy, blind to his superiority to rivalship; together with the general reduction of his force, now reduced by desertion, from nine to three ships; and last of all, the enmity of seas and winds; the invader, driven, not by a fleet, but a gale, out of the Scottish waters, had the mortification in prospect of terminating a cruise, so formidable in appearance at the onset, without one added deed to sustain the reputation gained by former exploits. Nevertheless, he was not disheartened. He sought to conciliate fortune, not by despondency, but by resolution. And, as if won by his confident bearing, that fickle power suddenly went over to him from the ranks of the enemy—suddenly as plumed Marshal Ney to the stubborn standard of Napoleon from Elba, marching regenerated on Paris. In a word, luck—that's the word—shortly threw in Paul's way the great action of his life: the most extraordinary of all naval engagements; the unparalleled deathlock with the *Serapis*.

CHAPTER XIX

THEY FIGHT THE "SERAPIS"

THE battle between the *Bon Homme Richard* and the *Serapis* stands in history as the first signal collision on the sea between the Englishman and the American. For obstinacy, mutual hatred, and courage, it is without precedent or subsequent in the story of ocean. The strife long hung undetermined, but the English flag struck in the end.

There would seem to be something singularly indicatory in this engagement. It may involve at once a type, a parallel, and a prophecy. Sharing the same blood with England, and yet her proved foe in two wars—not wholly inclined at bottom to forget an old grudge—intrepid, unprincipled, reckless, predatory, with boundless ambition, civilized in externals but a savage at heart, America is, or may yet be, the Paul Jones of nations.

Regarded in this indicatory light, the battle between the *Bon Homme Richard* and the *Serapis*—in itself so curious—may well enlist our interest.

Never was there a fight so snarled. The intricacy of those incidents which defy the narrator's extrication, is not illy figured in that bewildering intertanglement of all the yards and anchors of the two ships, which confounded them for the time in one chaos of devastation.

Elsewhere than here the reader must go who seeks an elaborate version of the fight, or, indeed, much of any regular account of it whatever. The writer is but brought to mention the battle because he must needs follow, in all events, the fortunes of the humble adventurer whose life he records. Yet this necessarily involves some general view of each conspicuous incident in which he shares.

Several circumstances of the place and time served to invest the fight with a certain scenic atmosphere casting a light almost poetic over the wild gloom of its tragic results. The battle was fought between the hours of seven and ten at night; the height of it was under a full harvest moon, in view of thousands of distant spectators crowning the high cliffs of Yorkshire.

From the Tees to the Humber, the eastern coast of Britain, for the most part, wears a savage, melancholy, and Calabrian aspect. It is in course of incessant decay. Every year the isle which repulses nearly all other foes, succumbs to the Attila assaults of the deep. Here and there the base of the cliffs is strewn with masses of rock, undermined by the waves, and tumbled headlong below, where, sometimes, the water completely surrounds them, showing in shattered confusion detached rocks, pyramids, and obelisks, rising half-revealed from the surf—the Tadmores of the wasteful desert of the sea. Nowhere is this desolation more marked than for those fifty miles of coast between Flamborough Head and the Spurm.

Weathering out the gale which had driven them from Leith, Paul's ships for a few days were employed in giving chase to various merchantmen and colliers; capturing some, sinking others, and putting the rest to flight. Off the mouth of the Humber they ineffectually manœuvred with a view of drawing out a king's frigate, reported to be lying at anchor within. At another time a large fleet was encountered, under convoy of some ships of force. But their panic caused the fleet to hug the edge of perilous shoals very nigh the land, where, by reason of his having no competent pilot, Paul durst not approach to molest them. The same night he saw two strangers farther out at sea, and chased them until three in the morning, when, getting pretty nigh, he surmised that they must needs be vessels of his own squadron, which, previous to his entering the Firth of Forth, had separated from his command. Daylight proved this supposition correct. Five vessels of the original squadron were now once more in company. About noon a fleet of forty merchantmen appeared coming round Flamborough Head, protected by two English men-of-war, the *Serapis* and *Countess of Scarborough*. Descrying the five cruisers sailing down, the forty sail, like forty chickens, fluttered in a panic under the wing of the shore. Their armed protectors bravely steered from the land, making the disposition for battle. Promptly accepting the challenge, Paul, giving the signal to his consorts, earnestly pressed forward. But, earnest as he was, it was seven in the evening ere the encounter began. Meantime his comrades, heedless of his signals, sailed independently along. Dismissing them from present consideration, we confine ourselves, for a while, to the *Richard* and the *Serapis*, the grand duellists of the fight.

The *Richard* carried a motley crew, to keep whom in order one hundred and thirty-five soldiers—themselves a hybrid band—had been put on board, commanded by French officers of inferior rank. Her armament was similarly heterogeneous; guns of all sorts and calibres; but about equal on the whole to those of a thirty-two-gun frigate. The spirit of baneful intermixture pervaded this craft throughout.

The *Serapis* was a frigate of fifty guns, more than half of which individually

exceeded in calibre any one gun of the *Richard*. She had a crew of some
three hundred and twenty trained man-of-war's men.

There is something in a naval engagement which radically distinguishes it
from one on the land. The ocean, at times, has what is called its *sea* and its
trough of the sea; but it has neither rivers, woods, banks, towns, nor mountains.
In mild weather it is one hammered plain. Stratagems, like those of disciplined
armies—ambuscades, like those of Indians, are impossible. All is clear, open,
fluent. The very element which sustains the combatants, yields at the stroke
of a feather. One wind and one tide at one time operate upon all who here
engage. This simplicity renders a battle between two men-of-war, with their
huge white wings, more akin to the Miltonic contests of archangels than to
the comparatively squalid tussles of earth.

As the ships neared, a hazy darkness overspread the water. The moon
was not yet risen. Objects were perceived with difficulty. Borne by a soft
moist breeze over gentle waves, they came within pistol-shot. Owing to the
obscurity, and the known neighborhood of other vessels, the *Serapis* was uncertain who the *Richard* was. Through the dim mist each ship loomed forth
to the other vast, but indistinct, as the ghost of Morven. Sounds of the
trampling of resolute men echoed from either hull, whose tight decks dully
resounded like drum-heads in a funeral march.

The *Serapis* hailed. She was answered by a broadside. For half an hour
the combatants deliberately manœuvred, continually changing their position,
but always within shot fire. The *Serapis*—the better sailer of the two—kept
critically circling the *Richard*, making lounging advances now and then, and
as suddenly steering off; hate causing her to act not unlike a wheeling cock
about a hen, when stirred by the contrary passion. Meantime, though within
easy speaking distance, no further syllable was exchanged; but an incessant
cannonade was kept up.

At this point, a third party, the *Scarborough*, drew near, seemingly desirous
of giving assistance to her consort. But thick smoke was now added to the
night's natural obscurity. The *Scarborough* imperfectly discerned two ships,
and plainly saw the common fire they made; but which was which, she could
not tell. Eager to befriend the *Serapis*, she durst not fire a gun, lest she might
unwittingly act the part of a foe. As when a hawk and a crow are clawing
and beaking high in the air, a second crow flying near, will seek to join the
battle, but finding no fair chance to engage, at last flies away to the woods;
just so did the *Scarborough* now. Prudence dictated the step; because several
chance shot—from which of the combatants could not be known—had already
struck the *Scarborough*. So, unwilling uselessly to expose herself, off went for
the present this baffled and ineffectual friend.

Not long after, an invisible hand came and set down a great yellow lamp
in the east. The hand reached up unseen from below the horizon, and set
the lamp down right on the rim of the horizon, as on a threshold; as much
as to say, Gentlemen warriors, permit me a little to light up this rather gloomy
looking subject. The lamp was the round harvest moon; the one solitary
foot-light of the scene. But scarcely did the rays from the lamp pierce that
languid haze. Objects before perceived with difficulty, now glimmered am-
biguously. Bedded in strange vapors, the great footlight cast a dubious, half
demoniac glare across the waters, like the phantasmagoric stream sent athwart
a London flagging in a night-rain from an apothecary's blue and green window. Through this sardonical mist, the face of the Man-in-the-Moon—looking
right towards the combatants, as if he were standing in a trapdoor of the

sea, leaning forward leisurely with his arms complacently folded over upon
the edge of the horizon—this queer face wore a serious, apishly self-satisfied
leer, as if the Man-in-the-Moon had somehow secretly put up the ships to
their contest, and in the depths of his malignant old soul was not unpleased
to see how well his charms worked. There stood the grinning Man-in-the-Moon,
his head just dodging into view over the rim of the sea:—Mephistopheles
prompter of the stage.

Aided now a little by the planet, one of the consorts of the *Richard,* the
Pallas, hovering far outside the fight, dimly discerned the suspicious form of
a lonely vessel unknown to her. She resolved to engage it, if it proved a foe.
But ere they joined, the unknown ship—which proved to be the *Scarborough*—
received a broadside at long gun's distance from another consort of the *Richard,*
the *Alliance.* The shot whizzed across the broad interval like shuttlecocks
across a great hall. Presently the battledores of both batteries were at work,
and rapid compliments of shuttlecocks were very promptly exchanged. The
adverse consorts of the two main belligerents fought with all the rage of those
fiery seconds who in some desperate duels make their principal's quarrel their
own. Diverted from the *Richard* and the *Serapis* by this little by-play, the
Man-in-the-Moon, all eager to see what it was, somewhat raised himself from
his trapdoor with an added grin on his face. By this time, off sneaked the
Alliance, and down swept the *Pallas,* at close quarters engaging the *Scarborough;*
an encounter destined in less than an hour to end in the latter ship's striking her
flag.

Compared to the *Serapis* and the *Richard,* the *Pallas* and the *Scarborough*
were as two pages to two knights. In their immature way they showed the same
traits as their fully developed superiors.

The Man-in-the-Moon now raised himself still higher to obtain a better
view of affairs.

But the Man-in-the-Moon was not the only spectator. From the high cliffs
of the shore, and especially from the great promontory of Flamborough Head,
the scene was witnessed by crowds of the islanders. Any rustic might be par-
doned his curiosity in view of the spectacle presented. Far in the indistinct distance fleets of frightened merchantmen filled the lower air with their sails, as
flakes of snow in a snowstorm by night. Hovering undeterminedly, in another
direction, were several of the scattered consorts of Paul, taking no part in
the fray. Nearer, was an isolated mist, investing the *Pallas* and *Scarborough*
—a mist slowly adrift on the sea, like a floating isle, and at intervals irradiated
with sparkle of fire and resonant with the boom of cannon. Farther away, in
the deeper water, was a lurid cloud, incessantly torn in shreds of lightning, then
fusing together again, once more to be rent. As yet this lurid cloud was neither
stationary nor slowly adrift, like the first-mentioned one; but, instinct with
chaotic vitality, shifted hither and thither, foaming with fire, like a valiant
water-spout careering off the coast of Malabar.

To get some idea of the events enacting in that cloud, it will be necessary
to enter it; to go and possess it, as a ghost may rush into a body, or the devils
into the swine, which running down the steep place perished in the sea; just
as the *Richard* is yet to do.

Thus far the *Serapis* and the *Richard* had been manœuvring and chasséing
to each other like partners in a cotillion, all the time indulging in rapid repartee.

But finding at last that the superior manageableness of the enemy's ship
enabled him to get the better of the clumsy old Indiaman, the *Richard,* in taking position, Paul, with his wonted resolution, at once sought to neutralize this,

by hugging him close. But the attempt to lay the *Richard* right across the head of the *Serapis* ended quite otherwise, in sending the enemy's jib-boom just over the *Richard's* great tower of Pisa, where Israel was stationed; who, catching it eagerly, stood for an instant holding to the slack of the sail, like one grasping a horse by the mane prior to vaulting into the saddle.

"Aye, hold hard, lad," cried Paul, springing to his side with a coil of rigging. With a few rapid turns he knitted himself to his foe. The wind now acting on the sails of the *Serapis* forced her, heel and point, her entire length, cheek by jowl, alongside the *Richard*. The projecting cannon scraped; the yards interlocked; but the hulls did not touch. A long lane of darkling water lay wedged between, like that narrow canal in Venice which dozes between two shadowy piles, and high in air is secretly crossed by the Bridge of Sighs. But where the six yard-arms reciprocally arched overhead, three bridges of sighs were both seen and heard, as the moon and wind kept rising.

Into that Lethean canal—pond-like in its smoothness as compared with the sea without—fell many a poor soul that night; fell, forever forgotten.

As some heaving rent coinciding with a disputed frontier on a volcanic plain, that boundary abyss was the jaws of death to both sides. So contracted was it, that in many cases the gun-rammers had to be thrust into the opposite ports, in order to enter to muzzles of their own cannon. It seemed more an intestine feud, than a fight between strangers. Or, rather, it was as if the Siamese Twins, oblivious of their fraternal bond, should rage in unnatural fight.

CHAPTER XIX (*Continued*)

THEY FIGHT THE "SERAPIS"

Ere long, a horrible explosion was heard, drowning for the instant the cannonade. Two of the old eighteen-pounders—before spoken of, as having been hurriedly set up below the main deck of the *Richard*—burst all to pieces, killing the sailors who worked them, and shattering all that part of the hull, as if two exploded steam-boilers had shot out of its opposite sides. The effect was like the fall of the walls of a house. Little now upheld the great tower of Pisa but a few naked crow stanchions. Thenceforth, not a few balls from the *Serapis* must have passed straight through the *Richard* without grazing her. It was like firing buck-shot through the ribs of a skeleton.

But, farther forward, so deadly was the broadside from the heavy batteries of the *Serapis*—levelled point-blank, and right down the throat and bowels, as it were, of the *Richard*—that it cleared everything before it. The men on the *Richard's* covered gundeck ran above, like miners from the fire-damp. Collecting on the forecastle, they continued to fight with grenades and muskets. The soldiers also were in the lofty tops, whence they kept up incessant volleys, cascading their fire down as pouring lava from cliffs.

The position of the men in the two ships was now exactly reversed. For while the *Serapis* was tearing the *Richard* all to pieces below deck, and had swept that covered part almost of the last man, the *Richard's* crowd of musketry had complete control of the upper deck of the *Serapis*, where it was almost impossible for man to remain unless as a corpse. Though in the beginning, the tops of the *Serapis* had not been unsupplied with marksmen, yet they had long since been cleared by the overmastering musketry of the *Richard*. Several, with leg or arm broken by a ball, had been seen going dimly downward from their giddy perch, like falling pigeons shot on the wing.

As busy swallows about barn-eaves and ridge-poles, some of the *Richard's* marksmen, quitting their tops, now went far out on their yard-arms, where they overhung the *Serapis*. From thence they dropped hand-grenades upon her decks, like apples, which growing in one field fall over the fence into another. Others of their band flung the same sour fruit into the open ports of the *Serapis*. A hail-storm of aerial combustion descended and slanted on the *Serapis*, while horizontal thunderbolts rolled crosswise through the subterranean vaults of the *Richard*. The belligerents were no longer, in the ordinary sense of things, an English ship and an American ship. It was a co-partnership and joint-stock combustion-company of both ships; yet divided, even in participation. The two vessels were as two houses, through whose party-wall doors have been cut; one family (the Guelphs) occupying the whole lower story; another family (the Ghibellines) the whole upper story.

Meanwhile, determined Paul flew hither and thither like the meteoric corposant-ball, which shiftingly dances on the tips and verges of ships' rigging in storms. Wherever he went, he seemed to cast a pale light on all faces. Blacked and burnt, his Scotch bonnet was compressed to a gun-wad on his head. His Parisian coat, with its gold-laced sleeve laid aside, disclosed to the full the blue tattooing on his arm, which sometimes in fierce gestures streamed in the haze of the cannonade, cabalistically terrific as the charmed standard of Satan. Yet his frenzied manner was less a testimony of his internal commotion than intended to inspirit and madden his men, some of whom seeing him, in transports of intrepidity stripped themselves to their trowsers, exposing their naked bodies to the as naked shot. The same was done on the *Serapis*, where several guns were seen surrounded by their buff crews as by fauns and satyrs.

At the beginning of the fray, before the ships interlocked, in the intervals of smoke which swept over the ships as mist over mountain-tops, affording open rents here and there—the gun-deck of the *Serapis*, at certain points, showed, congealed for the instant in all attitudes of dauntlessness, a gallery of marble statues—fighting gladiators.

Stooping low and intent, with one braced leg thrust behind, and one arm thrust forward, curling round toward the muzzle of the gun, there was seen the *loader*, performing his allotted part; on the other side of the carriage, in the same stooping posture, but with both hands holding his long black pole, pikewise, ready for instant use—stood the eager *rammer and sponger;* while at the breech, crouched the wary *captain of the gun*, his keen eye, like the watching leopard's, burning along the range; and behind all, tall and erect, the Egyptian symbol of death, stood the *matchman*, immovable for the moment, his long-handled match reversed. Up to their two long death-dealing batteries, the trained men of the *Serapis* stood and toiled in mechanical magic of discipline. They tended those rows of guns, as Lowell girls the rows of looms in a cotton factory. The Parcæ were not more methodical; Atropos not more fatal; the automaton chess-player not more irresponsible.

"Look, lad; I want a grenade, now, thrown down their main hatchway. I saw long piles of cartridges there. The powder monkeys have brought them up faster than they can be used. Take a bucket of combustibles, and let's hear from you presently."

These words were spoken by Paul to Israel. Israel did as ordered. In a

few minutes, bucket in hand, begrimed with powder, sixty feet in air, he hung
like Apollyon from the extreme tip of the yard over the fated abyss of the
hatchway. As he looked down between the eddies of smoke into that slaughter-
ous pit, it was like looking from the verge of a cataract down into the yeasty
pool at its base. Watching his chance, he dropped one grenade with such faultless precision, that, striking its mark, an explosion rent the *Serapis* like a volcano. The long row of heaped cartridges was ignited. The fire ran horizontally, like an express on a railway. More than twenty men were instantly
killed: nearly forty wounded. This blow restored the chances of battle, before
in favor of the *Serapis*.

But the drooping spirits of the English were suddenly revived, by an event
which crowned the scene by an act on the part of one of the consorts of the
Richard, the incredible atrocity of which has induced all humane minds to impute it rather to some incomprehensible mistake than to the malignant madness
of the perpetrator.

The cautious approach and retreat of a consort of the *Serapis*, the *Scarborough*, before the moon rose, has already been mentioned. It is now to be related how that, when the moon was more than an hour high, a consort of the
Richard, the *Alliance*, likewise approached and retreated. This ship, commanded
by a Frenchman, infamous in his own navy, and obnoxious in the service to
which he at present belonged; this ship, foremost in insurgency to Paul hitherto,
and which, for the most part, had crept like a poltroon from the fray; the
Alliance now was at hand. Seeing her, Paul deemed the battle at an end. But
to his horror, the *Alliance* threw a broadside full into the stern of the *Richard*,
without touching the *Serapis*. Paul called to her, for God's sake to forbear destroying the *Richard*. The reply was, a second, a third, a fourth broadside,
striking the *Richard* ahead, astern, and amidships. One of the volleys killed
several men and one officer. Meantime, like carpenters' augers, and the sea-
worm called Remora, the guns of the *Serapis* were drilling away at the same
doomed hull. After performing her nameless exploit, the *Alliance* sailed away,
and did no more. She was like the great fire of London, breaking out on the
heel of the great Plague. By this time, the *Richard* had so many shot-holes
low down in her hull, that like a sieve she began to settle.

"Do you strike?" cried the English captain.

"I have not yet begun to fight," howled sinking Paul.

This summons and response were whirled on eddies of smoke and flame.
Both vessels were now on fire. The men of either knew hardly which to do;
strive to destroy the enemy, or save themselves. In the midst of this, one hun-
drd human beings, hitherto invisible strangers, were suddenly added to the rest.
Five score English prisoners, till now confined in the *Richard's* hold, liberated
in his consternation by the master at arms, burst up the hatchways. One of
them, the captain of a letter of marque, captured by Paul, off the Scottish coast,
crawled through a port, as a burglar through a window, from the one ship to the
other, and reported affairs to the English captain.

While Paul and his lieutenants were confronting these prisoners, the gunner,
running up from below, and not perceiving his official superiors, and deeming
them dead, believing himself now left sole surviving officer, ran to the tower of
Pisa to haul down the colors. But they were already shot down and trailing
in the water astern, like a sailor's towing shirt. Seeing the gunner there, groping
about in the smoke, Israel asked what he wanted.

At this moment the gunner, rushing to the rail, shouted "Quarter! quarter!"
to the *Serapis*.

"I'll quarter ye," yelled Israel, smiting the gunner with the flat of his cutlass.

"Do you strike?" now came from the *Serapis.*

"Aye, aye, aye!" involuntarily cried Israel, fetching the gunner a shower of blows.

"Do you strike?" again was repeated from the *Serapis;* whose captain, judging from the augmented confusion on board the *Richard,* owing to the escape of the prisoners, and also influenced by the report made to him by his late guest of the port-hole, doubted not that the enemy must needs be about surrendering.

"Do you strike?"

"Aye!—I strike *back*," roared Paul, for the first time now hearing the summons.

But judging this frantic response to come, like the others, from some unauthorized source, the English captain directed his boarders to be called, some of whom presently leaped on. the *Richard's* rail, but, throwing out his tattooed arm at them, with a sabre at the end of it, Paul showed them how boarders repelled boarders. The English retreated, but not before they had been thinned out again, like spring radishes, by the unfaltering fire from the *Richard's* tops.

An officer of the *Richard,* seeing the mass of prisoners delirious with sudden liberty and fright, pricked them with his sword to the pumps, thus keeping the ship afloat by the very blunder which had promised to have been fatal. The vessels now blazed so in the rigging that both parties desisted from hostilities to subdue the common foe.

When some faint order was again restored upon the *Richard* her chances of victory increased, while those of the English, driven under cover, proportionably waned. Early in the contest, Paul, with his own hand, had brought one of his largest guns to bear against the enemy's main-mast. That shot had hit. The mast now plainly tottered. Nevertheless, it seemed as if, in this fight, neither party could be victor. Mutual obliteration from the face of the waters seemed the only natural sequel to hostilities like these. It is, therefore, honor to him as a man, and not reproach to him as an officer, that, to stay such carnage, Captain Pearson, of the *Serapis,* with his own hands hauled down his colors. But just as an officer from the *Richard* swung himself on board the *Serapis,* and accosted the English captain, the first lieutenant of the *Serapis* came up from below inquiring whether the *Richard* had struck, since her fire had ceased.

So equal was the conflict that, even after the surrender, it could be, and was a question to one of the warriors engaged (who had not happened to see the English flag hauled down) whether the *Serapis* had struck to the *Richard,* or the *Richard* to the *Serapis.* Nay, while the *Richard's* officer was still amicably conversing with the English captain, a midshipman of the *Richard,* in act of following his superior on board the surrendered vessel, was run through the thigh by a pike in the hand of an ignorant boarder of •the *Serapis.* While, equally ignorant, the cannons below deck were still thundering away at the nominal conqueror from the batteries of the nominally conquered ship.

But though the *Serapis* had submitted, there were two misanthropical foes on board the *Richard* which would not so easily succumb—fire and water. All night the victors were engaged in suppressing the flames. Not until daylight were the flames got under; but though the pumps were kept continually going, the water in the hold still gained. A few hours after sunrise the *Richard* was deserted for the *Serapis* and the other vessels of the squadron of Paul. About ten o'clock the *Richard,* gorged with slaughter, wallowed heavily, gave a long roll, and blasted by tornadoes of sulphur, slowly sank, like Gomorrah, out of sight.

The loss of life in the two ships was about equal; one-half of the total number of those engaged being either killed or wounded.

In view of this battle one may ask—What separates the enlightened man from the savage? Is civilization a thing distinct, or is it an advanced stage of barbarism?

CHAPTER XX

THE SHUTTLE

FOR a time back, across the otherwise blue-jean career of Israel, Paul Jones flits and re-flits like a crimson thread. One more brief intermingling of it, and to the plain old homespun we return.

The battle won, the squadron started for the Texel, where they arrived in safety. Omitting all mention of intervening harassments, suffice it, that after some months of inaction as to anything of a warlike nature, Paul and Israel (both, from different motives, eager to return to America) sailed for that country in the armed ship *Ariel*, Paul as commander, Israel as quartermaster.

Two weeks out, they encountered by night a frigate-like craft, supposed to be an enemy. The vessels came within hail, both showing English colors, with purposes of mutual deception, affecting to belong to the English Navy. For an hour, through their speaking trumpets, the captains equivocally conversed. A very reserved, adroit, hoodwinking, statesman-like conversation, indeed. At last, professing some little incredulity as to the truthfulness of the stranger's statement, Paul intimated a desire that he should put out a boat and come on board to show his commission, to which the stranger very affably replied, that unfortunately his boat was exceedingly leaky. With equal politeness, Paul begged him to consider the danger attending a refusal, which rejoiner nettled the other, who suddenly retorted that he would answer for twenty guns, and that both himself and men were knock-down Englishmen. Upon this, Paul said that he would allow them exactly five minutes for a sober, second thought. That brief period passed, Paul, hoisting the American colors, ran close under the other ship's stern, and engaged her. It was about eight o'clock at night that this strange quarrel was picked in the middle of the ocean. Why cannot men be peaceable on that great common? Or does nature in those fierce night-brawlers, the billows, set mankind but a sorry example?

After ten minutes' canonading, the stranger struck, shouting out that half his men were killed. The *Ariel's* crew hurrahed. Boarders were called to take possession. At this juncture, the prize shifting her position so that she headed away, and to leeward of the *Ariel*, thrust her long spanker-boom diagonally over the latter's squarter; when Israel, who was standing close by, instinctively caught hold of it—just as he had grasped the jib-boom of the *Serapis*—and, at the same moment, hearing the call to take possession, in the valiant excitement of the occasion, he leaped upon the spar, and made a rush for the stranger's deck, thinking, of course, that he would be immediately followed by the regular boarders. But the sails of the strange ship suddenly filled; she began to glide through the sea; her spanker-boom, not having at all entangled itself, offering no hindrance. Israel, clinging midway along the boom, soon found himself divided from the *Ariel* by a space impossible to be leaped. Meantime, suspecting foul play, Paul set every sail; but the stranger, having already the advantage, contrived to make good her escape, though perseveringly chased by the cheated conqueror.

In the confusion, no eye had observed our hero's spring. But, as the vessels separated more, an officer of the strange ship spying a man on the boom, and taking him for one of his own men, demanded what he did there.

"Clearing the signal halyards, sir," replied Israel, fumbling with the cord which happened to be dangling near by.

"Well, bear a hand and come in, or you will have a bow-chaser at you soon," referring to the bow guns of the *Ariel*.

"Aye, aye, sir," said Israel, and in a moment he sprang to the deck, and soon found himself mixed in among some two hundred English sailors of a large letter of marque. At once he perceived that the story of half the crew being killed was a mere hoax, played off for the sake of making an escape. Orders were continually being given to pull on this and that rope, as the ship crowded all sail in flight. To these orders Israel, with the rest, promptly responded, pulling at the rigging stoutly as the best of them; though Heaven knows his heart sank deeper and deeper at every pull which thus helped once again to widen the gulf between him and home.

In intervals he considered with himself what to do. Favored by the obscurity of the night and the number of the crew, and wearing much the same dress as theirs, it was very easy to pass himself off for one of them till morning. But daylight would be sure to expose him, unless some cunning plan could be hit upon. If discovered for what he was, nothing short of a prison awaited him upon the ship's arrival in port.

It was a desperate case, only as desperate a remedy could serve. One thing was sure, he could not hide. Some audacious parade of himself promised the only hope. Marking that the sailors, not being of the regular navy, wore no uniform, and perceiving that his jacket was the only garment on him which bore any distinguishing badge, our adventurer took it off, and privily dropped it overboard, remaining now in his dark blue woollen shirt and blue cloth waistcoat.

What the more inspirited Israel to the added step now contemplated, was the circumstance that the ship was not a Frenchman's or other foreigner, but her crew, though enemies, spoke the same language that he did.

So very quietly, at last, he goes aloft into the maintop, and sitting down on an old sail there, beside some eight or ten topmen, in an off-handed way asks one for tobacco.

"Give us a quid, lad," as he settled himself in his seat.

"Halloo," said the strange sailor, "who be you? Get out of the top! The fore and mizzen-top men won't let us go into their tops, and blame me if we'll let any of their gangs come here. So, away ye go."

"You're blind, or crazy, old boy," rejoined Israel. "I'm a topmate; ain't I, lads?" appealing to the rest.

"There's only ten maintopmen belonging to our watch; if you are one, then there'll be eleven," said a second sailor. "Get out of the top!"

"This is too bad, maties," cried Israel, "to serve an old topmate this way. Come, come, you are foolish. Give us a quid." And, once more, with the utmost sociability, he addressed the sailor next to him.

"Look ye," returned the other, "if you don't make away with yourself, you skulking spy from the mizzen, we'll drop you to deck like a jewel-block."

Seeing the party thus resolute, Israel, with some affected banter, descended.

The reason why he had tried the scheme—and, spite of the foregoing failure, meant to repeat it—was this: As customary in armed ships, the men were in companies allotted to particular places and functions. Therefore, to escape final detection, Israel must some way get himself recognized as belonging to some one of those bands; otherwise, as an isolated nondescript, discovery ere long would be certain, especially upon the next general muster. To be sure, the hope in question was a forlorn sort of hope, but it was his sole one, and must therefore be tried.

Mixing in again for a while with the general watch, he at last goes on the forecastle among the sheet-anchor-men there, at present engaged in critically discussing the merits of the late valiant encounter, and expressing their opinion that by daybreak the enemy in chase would be hull-down out of sight.

"To be sure she will," cried Israel, joining in with the group, "old ballyhoo that she is, to be sure. But didn't we pepper her, lads? Give us a chew of tobacco, one of ye. How many have we wounded, do ye know? None killed that I've heard of. Wasn't that a fine hoax we played on 'em? Ha! ha! But give us a chew."

In the prodigal fraternal patriotism of the moment, one of the old worthies freely handed his plug to our adventurer, who, helping himself, returned it, repeating the question as to the killed and wounded.

"Why," said he of the plug, "Jack Jewboy told me, just now, that there's only seven men been carried down to the surgeon, but not a soul killed."

"Good, boys, good!" cried Israel, moving up to one of the gun-carriages, where three or four men were sitting—"slip along, chaps, slip along, and give a watchmate a seat with ye."

"All full here, lad; try the next gun."

"Boys, clear a place here," said Israel, advancing, like one of the family, to that gun.

"Who the devil are *you*, making this row here?" demanded a stern-looking old fellow, captain of the forecastle, "seems to me you make considerable noise. Are you a forecastleman?"

"If the bowsprit belongs here, so do I," rejoined Israel, composedly.

"Let's look at ye, then!" and seizing a battle-lantern, before thrust under a gun, the old veteran came close to Israel before he had time to elude the scrutiny.

"Take that!" said his examiner, and fetching Israel a terrible thump, pushed him ignominiously off the forecastle, as some unknown interloper from distant parts of the ship.

With similar perseverance of effrontery, Israel tried other quarters of the vessel. But with equal ill success. Jealous with the spirit of class, no social circle would receive him. As a last resort, he dived down among the *holders*.

A group of them sat round a lantern, in the dark bowels of the ship, like a knot of charcoal burners in a pine forest at midnight.

"Well, boys, what's the good word?" said Israel, advancing very cordially, but keeping as much as possible in the shadow.

"The good word is," rejoined a censorious old *holder*, "that you had best go where you belong—on deck—and not be a skulking down here where you *don't* belong. I suppose this is the way you skulked during the fight."

"Oh, you're growly to-night, shipmate," said Israel, pleasantly—"supper sits hard on your conscience."

"Get out of the hold with ye," roared the other. "On deck, or I'll call the master-at-arms."

Once more Israel decamped.

Sorely against his grain, as a final effort to blend himself openly with the crew, he now went among the *waisters*: the vilest caste of an armed ship's company, mere dregs and settlings—sea-Pariahs, comprising all the lazy, all the inefficient, all the unfortunate and fated, all the melancholy, all the infirm, all the rheumatical scamps, scapegraces, ruined prodigal sons, sooty faces, and swine-herds of the crew, not excluding those with dismal wardrobes.

An unhappy, tattered, mopping row of them sat along dolefully on the gun-deck, like a parcel of crestfallen buzzards, exiled from civilized society.

"Cheer up, lads," said Israel, in a jovial tone, "homeward-bound, you know. Give us a seat among ye, friends."

"Oh, sit on your head!" answered a sullen fellow in the corner.

"Come, come, no growling; we're homeward-bound. Whoop, my hearties!"

"Workhouse bound, you mean," grumbled another sorry chap, in a darned shirt.

"Oh, boys, don't be down-hearted. Let's keep up our spirits. Sing us a song, one of ye, and I'll give the chorus."

"Sing if ye like, but I'll plug my ears, for one," said still another sulky varlet, with the toes out of his sea-boots, while all the rest with one roar of misanthropy joined him.

But Israel, not to be daunted, began:

" 'Cease, rude Boreas, cease your growling!' "

"And you cease your squeaking, will ye?" cried a fellow in a banged tarpaulin. "Did ye get a ball in the windpipe, that ye cough that way, worse nor a broken-nosed old bellows? Have done with your groaning, it's worse nor the death-rattle."

"Boys, is this the way you treat a watchmate," demanded Israel reproachfully, "trying to cheer up his friends? Shame on ye, boys. Come, let's be sociable. Spin us a yarn, one of ye. Meantime, rub my back for me, another," and very confidently he leaned against his neighbor.

"Lean off me, will ye?" roared his friend, shoving him away.

"But who *is* this ere singing, leaning, yarn-spinning chap? Who are ye? Be you a waister, or be you not?"

So saying, one of this peevish, sottish band staggered close up to Israel. But there was a deck above and a deck below, and the lantern swung in the distance. It was too dim to see with critical exactness.

"No such singing chap belongs to our gang, that's flat," he dogmatically exclaimed at last, after an ineffectual scrutiny. "Sail out of this!"

And with a shove once more, poor Israel was ejected.

Blackballed out of every club, he went disheartened on deck. So long, while night screened him at least, as he contented himself with promiscuously circulating, all was safe; it was the endeavor to fraternize with any one set which was sure to endanger him. At last, wearied out, he happened to find himself on the berth deck, where the watch below were slumbering. Some hundred and fifty hammocks were on that deck. Seeing one empty, he leaped in, thinking luck might yet some way befriend him. Here, at last, the sultry confinement put him fast asleep. He was awakened by a savage whiskerando óf the other watch, who, seizing him by his waistband, dragged him most in-decorously out, furiously denouncing him for a skulker.

Springing to his feet, Israel perceived from the crowd and tumult of the berth deck, now all alive with men leaping into their hammocks, instead of being full of sleepers quietly dosing therein, that the watches were changed. Going above, he renewed in various quarters his offers of intimacy with the fresh men there assembled; but was successively repulsed as before. At length, just as day was breaking, an irascible fellow whose stubborn opposition our adventurer had long in vain sought to conciliate—this man suddenly perceiving, by the gray morning light, that Israel had somehow an alien sort of general look, very savagely pressed him for explicit information as to who he might be. The answers increased his suspicion. Others began to surround the two. Presently, quite a circle was formed. Sailors from distant parts of the ship drew near. One, and then another, and another, declared that they, in their quarters, too, had been molested by a vagabond claiming fraternity, and seeking to palm himself off upon decent society. In vain Israel protested. The truth, like the day, dawned clearer and clearer. More and more closely he was scanned. At length the hour for having all hands on deck arrived; when the other watch which Israel had first tried, reascending to the deck, and hearing the matter in discussion, they endorsed the charge of molestation and attempted imposture through the night, on the part of some person unknown, but who, likely enough, was the strange man now before them. In the end, the master-at-arms appeared with his bamboo, who, summarily collaring poor Israel, led him as a mysterious culprit to the officer of the deck, which gentleman having heard the charge, examined him in great perplexity, and saying that he did not at all recognize that countenance, requested the junior officers to contribute their scrutiny. But those officers were equally at fault.

"Who the deuce *are* you?" at last said the officer-of-the-deck, in added be-wilderment. "Where did you come from? What's your business? Where are you stationed? What's your name? Who are you, anyway? How did you get here? and where are you going?

"Sir," replied Israel very humbly, "I am going to my regular duty, if you will but let me. I belong to the maintop, and ought to be now engaged in preparing the topgallant stu'n'-sail for hoisting."

"Belong to the maintop? Why, these men here say you have been trying to belong to the foretop, and the mizzentop, and the forecastle, and the hold, and the waist, and every other part of the ship. This is extraordinary," he added, turning upon the junior officers.

"He must be out of his mind," replied one of them, the sailing-master.

"Out of his mind?" rejoined the officer-of-the-deck. "He's out of all reason; out of all men's knowledge and memories! Why, no one knows him; no one has ever seen him before; no imagination, in the wildest flight of a morbid night-mare, has ever so much as dreamed of him. Who *are* you?" he again added, fierce with amazement. "What's you name? Are you down in the ship's books, or at all in the records of nature?"

"My name, sir, is Peter Perkins," said Israel, thinking it most prudent to conceal his real appellation.

"Certainly, I never heard that name before. Pray, see if Peter Perkins is down on the quarter-bills," he added to a midshipman. "Quick, bring the book here."

Having received it, he ran his fingers along the columns, and dashing down the book, declared that no such name was there.

"You are not down, sir. There is no Peter Perkins here. Tell me at once who are you?"

"It might be, sir," said Israel, gravely, "that seeing I shipped under the effects of liquor, I might, out of absent-mindedness like, have given in some other person's name instead of my own."

"Well, what name have you gone by among your shipmates since you've been aboard?"

"Peter Perkins, sir."

Upon this the officer turned to the men around, inquiring whether the name of Peter Perkins was familiar to them as that of a shipmate. One and all answered no.

"This won't do, sir," now said the officer. "You see it won't do. Who are you?"

"A poor persecuted fellow at your service, sir."

"*Who* persecutes you?"

"Every one, sir. All hands seem to be against me; none of them willing to remember me."

"Tell me," demanded the officer earnestly, "how long do you remember yourself? Do you remember yesterday morning? You must have come into existence by some sort of spontaneous combustion in the hold. Or were you fired aboard from the enemy, last night, in a cartridge? Do you remember yesterday?"

"Oh, yes, sir."

"What was you doing yesterday?"

"Well, sir, for one thing, I believe I had the honor of a little talk with yourself."

"With *me?*"

"Yes, sir; about nine o'clock in the morning—the sea being smooth and the ship running, as I should think, about seven knots—you came up into the main-top, where I belong, and was pleased to ask my opinion about the best way to set a topgallant stu'n'-sail."

"He's mad! He's mad!" said the officer, with delirious conclusiveness. "Take him away, take him away, take him away—put him somewhere, master-at-arms. Stay, one test more. What mess do you belong?"

"Number 12, sir."

"Mr. Tidds," to a midshipman, "send mess No. 12 to the mast."

Ten sailors replied to the summons, and arranged themselves before Israel.

"Men, does this man belong to your mess?"

"No, sir; never saw him before this morning."

"What are those men's names?" he demanded of Israel.

"Well, sir, I am so intimate with all of them," looking upon them with a kindly glance, "I never call them by their real names, but by nicknames. So, never using their real names, I have forgotten them. The nicknames that I know them by, are Towser, Bowser, Rowser, Snowser."

"Enough. Mad as a March hare. Take him away. Hold," again added the officer, whom some strange fascination still bound to the bootless investigation. "What's *my* name, sir?"

"Why, sir, one of my messmates here called you Lieutenant Williamson, just now, and I never heard you called by any other name."

"There's method in his madness," thought the officer to himself. "What's the captain's name?"

"Why, sir, when we spoke the enemy, last night, I heard him say, through his trumpet, that he was Captain Parker; and very likely he knows his own name."

"I have you now. That ain't the captain's real name."

"He's the best judge himself, sir, of what his name is, I should think."

"Were it not," said the officer, now turning gravely upon his juniors, "were it not that such a supposition were on other grounds absurd, I should certainly conclude that this man, in some unknown way, got on board here from the enemy last night."

"How could he, sir?" asked the sailing-master.

"Heaven knows. But our spanker-boom geared the other ship, you know, in manœuvring to get headway."

"But supposing he *could* have got here that fashion, which is quite impossible under all the circumstances, what motive could have induced him voluntarily to jump among enemies?"

"Let him answer for himself," said the officer, turning suddenly upon Israel, with the view of taking him off his guard, by the matter of course assumption of the very point at issue.

"Answer, sir. Why did you jump on board here, last night, from the enemy?"

"Jump on board, sir, from the enemy? Why, sir, my station at general quarters is at gun No. 3, of the lower deck, here."

"He's cracked—or else I am turned—or all the world is;—take him away!"

"But where am I to take him, sir?" said the master-at-arms. "He don't seem to belong anywhere, sir. Where—where am I to take him?"

"Take him out of sight," said the officer, now incensed with his own perplexity. "Take him out of sight, I say."

"Come along, then, my ghost," said the master-at-arms. And collaring the phantom, he led it hither and thither, not knowing exactly what to do with it.

Some fifteen minutes passed, when the captain coming from his cabin, and observing the master-at-arms leading Israel about in this indefinite style, demanded the reason of that procedure, adding that it was against his express orders for any new and degrading punishments to be invented for his men.

"Come here, master-at-arms. To what end do you lead that man about?"

"To no end in the world, sir. I keep leading him about because he has no final destination."

"Mr. Officer-of-the-deck, what does this mean? Who is this strange man? I don't know that I remember him. Who is he? And what is signified by his being led about?"

Hereupon the officer-of-the-deck, throwing himself into a tragical posture, set forth the entire mystery; much to the captain's astonishment, who at once indignantly turned upon the phantom.

"You rascal—don't try to deceive me. Who are you? and where did you come from last?"

"Sir, my name is Peter Perkins, and I last came from the forecastle, where the master-at-arms last led me, before coming here."

"No joking, sir, no joking."

"Sir, I'm sure it's too serious a business to joke about."

"Do you have the assurance to say, that you, as a regularly shipped man, have been on board this vessel ever since she sailed from Falmouth, ten months ago?"

"Sir, anxious to secure a berth under so good a commander, I was among the first to enlist."

"What ports have we touched at, sir?" said the captain, now in a little softer tone.

"Ports, sir, ports?"

"Yes, sir, *ports*."

Israel began to scratch his yellow hair.

"What *ports*, sir?"

"Well, sir:—Boston, for one."

"Right there," whispered a midshipman.

"What was the next port, sir?"

"Why, sir, I was saying Boston was the *first* port, I believe; wasn't it? —and"—

"The *second* port, sir, is what I want."

"Well—New York."

"Right again," whispered the midshipman.

"And what port are we bound to, now?"

"Let me see—homeward-bound—Falmouth, sir."

"What sort of a place is Boston?"

"Pretty considerable of a place, sir."

"Very straight streets, ain't they?"

"Yes, sir; cow-paths cut by sheep-walks, and intersected with hen-tracks."

"When did we fire the first gun?"

"Well, sir, just as we were leaving Falmouth, ten months ago—signal-gun, sir."

"Where did we fire the first *shotted* gun, sir?—and what was the name of the privateer we took upon that occasion?"

" 'Pears to me, sir, at that time I was on the sick list. Yes, sir, that must have been the time; I had the brain fever, and lost my mind for a while."

"Master-at-arms, take this man away."

"Where shall I take him, sir?" touching his cap.

"Go, and air him on the forecastle."

So they resumed their devious wanderings. At last, they descended to the berth-deck. It being now breakfast-time, the master-at-arms, a good-humored man, very kindly introduced our hero to his mess, and presented him with breakfast, during which he in vain endeavored, by all sorts of subtle blandishments, to worm out his secret.

At length Israel was set at liberty; and whenever there was any important duty to be done, volunteered to it with such cheerful alacrity, and approved himself so docile and excellent a seaman, that he conciliated the approbation of all the officers, as well as the captain; while his general sociability served, in the end, to turn in his favor the suspicious hearts of the mariners. Perceiving his good qualities, both as a sailor and man, the captain of the maintop applied for his admission into that section of the ship; where, still improving upon his former reputation, our hero did duty for the residue of the voyage.

One pleasant afternoon, the last of the passage, when the ship was nearing the Lizard, within a few hours' sail of her port, the officer-of-the-deck, happening to glance upwards towards the maintop, descried Israel there, leaning very leisurely over the rail, looking mildly down where the officer stood.

"Well, Peter Perkins, you seem to belong to the maintop, after all."

"I always told you so, sir," smiled Israel benevolently down upon him, "though, at first, you remember, sir, you would not believe it."

CHAPTER XXI

SAMSON AMONG THE PHILISTINES

At length, as the ship, gliding on past three or four vessels at anchor in the roadstead—one, a man-of-war just furling her sails—came nigh Falmouth town, Israel, from his perch, saw crowds in violent commotion on the shore, while the adjacent roofs were covered with sightseers. A large man-of-war cutter was just landing its occupants, among whom were a corporal's guard and three officers, besides the naval lieutenant and boat's crew. Some of this company having landed, and formed a sort of lane among the mob, two trim soldiers, armed to the teeth, rose in the stern-sheets; and between them, a martial man of Patagonian stature, their ragged and handcuffed captive, whose defiant head overshadowed theirs, as St. Paul's dome its inferior steeples. Immediately the mob raised a shout, pressing in curiosity towards the colossal stranger; so that, drawing their swords, four of the soldiers had to force a passage for their comrades, who followed on, conducting the giant.

As the letter of marque drew still nigher, Israel heard the officer in command of the party ashore shouting, "To the castle! to the castle!" and so, surrounded by shouting throngs, the company moved on, preceded by the three drawn swords, ever and anon flourished at the rioters, towards a large grim pile on a cliff about a mile from the landing. Long as they were in sight, the bulky form of the captive was seen at times swayingly towering over the flashing bayonets and cutlasses, like a great whale breaching amid a hostile retinue of sword-fish. Now and then, too, with barbaric scorn, he taunted them with cramped gestures of his manacled hands.

When at last the vessel had gained her anchorage, opposite a distant detached warehouse, all was still; and the work of breaking out in the hold immediately commencing, and continuing till nightfall, absorbed all further attention for the present.

Next day was Sunday; and about noon Israel, with others, was allowed to go ashore for a stroll. The town was quiet. Seeing nothing very interesting there, he passed out, alone, into the fields alongshore, and presently found himself climbing the cliff whereon stood the grim pile before spoken of.

"What place is yon?" he asked of a rustic passing.

"Pendennis Castle."

As he stepped upon the short crisp sward under its walls, he started at a violent sound from within, as of the roar of some tormented lion. Soon the sound became articulate, and he heard the following words bayed out with an amazing vigor:

"Brag no more, Old England; consider you are but an island! Order back your broken battalions! home, and repent in ashes! Long enough have your hired tories across the sea forgotten the Lord their God, and bowed down to Howe and Kniphausen—the Hessian!——Hands off, red-skinned jackal! Wearing the king's plate, as I do, I have treasures of wrath against you British."

Then came a clanking, as of a chain; many vengeful sounds, all confusedly together; with strugglings. Then again the voice:

"Ye brought me out here, from my dungeon to this green—affronting yon Sabbath sun—to see how a rebel looks. But I show ye how a true gentleman and Christian can conduct himself in adversity. Back, dogs! Respect a gentleman and a Christian, though he *be* in rags and smell of bilge-water."

Filled with astonishment at these words, which came from over a massive wall, enclosing what seemed an open parade-space, Israel pressed forward, and soon came to a black archway, leading far within, underneath, to a grassy tract, through a tower. Like two boar's tusks, two sentries stood on guard at either side of the open jaws of the arch. Scrutinizing our adventurer a moment, they signed him permission to enter.

Arrived at the end of the arched-way, where the sun shone, Israel stood transfixed at the scene.

Like some baited bull in the ring, crouched the Patagonian-looking captive, handcuffed as before; the grass of the green trampled, and gored up all about him, both by his own movements and those of the people around. Except some soldiers and sailors, these seemed mostly townspeople, collected here out of curiosity. The stranger was outlandishly arrayed in the sorry remains of a half-Indian, half-Canadian sort of a dress, consisting of a fawn-skin jacket —the fur outside and hanging in ragged tufts—a half-rotten, bark-like belt of wampum; aged breeches of sagathy; bedarned worsted stockings to the knee; old moccasins riddled with holes, their metal tags yellow with salt-water rust; a faded red woollen bonnet, not unlike a Russian night-cap, or a portentous, ensanguined full-moon, all soiled, and stuck about with bits of half-rotted straw. He seemed just broken from the dead leases in David's outlawed Cave of Adullam. Unshaven, beard and hair matted, and profuse as a corn-field beaten down by hailstorms, his whole marred aspect was that of some wild beast; but of a royal sort, and unsubdued by the cage.

"Aye, stare, stare! Though but last night dragged out of a ship's hold, like a smutty tierce; and this morning out of your littered barracks here, like a murderer; for all that, you may well stare at Ethan Ticonderoga Allen, the unconquered soldier, by ——! You Turks never saw a Christian before. Stare on! I am he, who, when your Lord Howe wanted to bribe a patriot to fall down and worship him by an offer of a major-generalship and five thousand acres of choice land in old Vermont—(Ha! three-times-three for glorious old Vermont, and my Green-Mountain boys! Hurrah! Hurrah! Hurrah!) I am he, I say, who answered your Lord Howe, 'You, *you* offer *our* land? You are like the devil in Scripture, offering all the kingdoms in the world, when the d——d soul had not a corner-lot on earth! Stare on!"

"Look you, rebel, you had best heed how you talk against General Lord Howe," here said a thin, wasp-waisted, epauletted officer of the castle, coming near and flourishing his sword like a schoolmaster's ferule.

"General Lord Howe? Heed how I talk of that toad-hearted king's lickspittle of a scarlet poltroon; the vilest wriggler in God's worm-hole below? I tell you, that herds of red-haired devils are impatiently snorting to ladle Lord Howe with all his gang (you included) into the seethingest syrups of tophet's flames!'

At this blast, the wasp-waisted officer was blown backwards as from before the suddenly burst head of a steam boiler.

Staggering away, with a snapped spine, he muttered something about its being beneath his dignity to bandy further words with a low-lived rebel.

"Come, come, Colonel Allen," here said a mild-looking man in a sort of clerical undress, "respect the day better than to talk thus of what lies beyond. Were you to die this hour, or what is more probable, be hung next week at Tower-wharf, you know not what might become, in eternity, of yourself."

"Reverend Sir," with a mocking bow, "when not better employed braiding my beard, I have a little dabbled in your theologies. And let me tell you, Reverend Sir," lowering and intensifying his voice, "that as to the world of spirits, of which you hint, though I know nothing of the mode or manner of that world, no more than do you, yet I expect when I shall arrive there to be treated as well as any other gentleman of my merit. That is to say, far better than you British know how to treat an American officer and meek-hearted Christian captured in honorable war, by ——! Every one tells me, as you yourself just breathed, and as, crossing the sea, every billow dinned into my ear, that I, Ethan Allen, am to be hung like a thief. If I am, the great Jehovah and the Continental Congress shall avenge me; while I, for my part, shall show you, even on the tree, how a Christian gentleman can die. Meantime, sir, if you are the clergyman you look, act out your consolatory function, by getting an unfortunate Christian gentleman about to die, a bowl of punch."

The good-natured stranger, not to have his religious courtesy appealed to in vain, immediately dispatched his servant, who stood by, to procure the beverage.

At this juncture, a faint rustling sound, as of the advance of an army with banners, was heard. Silks, scarfs, and ribbons fluttered in the background. Presently, a bright squadron of fair ladies drew nigh, escorted by certain out-riding gallants of Falmouth.

"Ah," sighed a soft voice, "what a strange sash, and furred vest, and what leopard-like teeth, and what flaxen hair, but all mildewed;—is that he?"

"Yea, is it, lovely charmer," said Allen, like an Ottoman, bowing over his broad, bovine forehead, and breathing the words out like a lute; "it is he— Ethan Allen, the soldier; now, since ladies' eyes visit him, made trebly a captive."

"Why, he talks like a beau in a parlor, this wild, mossed American from the woods," sighed another fair lady to her mate; "but can this be he we came to see? I must have a lock of his hair."

"It is he, adorable Delilah; and fear not, even though incited by the foe, by clipping my locks, to dwindle my strength. Give me your sword, man," turning to an officer:—"Ah! I'm fettered. Clip it yourself, lady."

"No, no—I am——"

"Afraid, would you say? Afraid of the vowed friend and champion of all ladies all round the world? Nay, nay, come hither."

The lady advanced; and soon, overcoming her timidity her white hand shone like whipped foam amid the matted waves of flaxen hair.

"Ah, this is like clipping tangled tags of gold-lace," cried she; "but see, it is half straw."

"But the wearer is no man-of-straw, lady; were I free, and you had ten thousand foes—horse, foot, and dragoons—how like a friend I could fight for you! Come, you have robbed me of my hair; let me rob your dainty hand of its price. What, afraid again?"

"No, not that; but——"

"I see, lady; I may do it, by your leave, but not by your word; the wonted way of ladies. There, it is done. Sweeter that kiss, than the bitter heart of a cherry."

When at length this lady left, no small talk was had by her with her companions about some way relieving the hard lot of so knightly an unfortunate. Whereupon a worthy, judicious gentleman, of middle-age, in attendance, suggested a bottle of good wine every day, and clean linen once every week. And these the gentle Englishwoman—too polite and too good to be fastidious—did indeed actually send to Ethan Allen, so long as he tarried a captive in her land.

The withdrawal of this company was followed by a different scene.

A perspiring man in top-boots, a riding-whip in his hand, and having the air of a prosperous farmer, brushed in, like a stray bullock, among the rest, for a peep at the giant; having just entered through the arch, as the ladies passed out.

"Hearing that the man who took Ticonderoga was here in Pendennis Castle, I've ridden twenty-five miles to see him; and to-morrow my brother will ride forty for the same purpose. So let me have first look. Sir," he continued, addressing the captive, "will you let me ask you a few plain questions, and be free with you?"

"Be free with me? With all my heart. I love freedom of all things. I'm ready to die for freedom; I expect to. So be free as you please. What is it?"

"Then, sir, permit me to ask what is your occupation in life—in time of peace, I mean?"

"You talk like a tax-gatherer," rejoined Allen, squinting diabolically at him; "what is my occupation in life? Why, in my younger days I studied divinity, but at present I am a conjurer by profession."

Hereupon everybody laughed, equally at the manner as the words, and the nettled farmer retorted:

"Conjurer, eh? well, you conjured wrong that time you were taken."

"Not so wrong, though, as you British did, that time I took Ticonderoga, my friend."

At this juncture the servant came with the punch, when his master bade him present it to the captive.

"No!—give it me, sir, with your own hands, and pledge me as gentleman to gentleman."

"I cannot pledge a state-prisoner, Colonel Allen; but I will hand you the punch with my own hands, since you insist upon it."

"Spoken and done like a true gentleman, sir; I am bound to you."

Then receiving the bowl into his gyved hands, the iron ringing against the china, he put it to his lips, and saying, "I hereby give the British nation credit for half a minute's good usage," at one draught emptied it to the bottom.

"The rebel gulps it down like a swilling hog at a trough," here scoffed a lusty private of the guard, off duty.

"Shame to you!" cried the giver of the bowl.

"Nay, sir; his red coat is a standing blush to him, as it is to the whole scarlet-blushing British army." Then turning derisively upon the private: "You object to my way of taking things, do ye? I fear I shall never please ye. You objected to the way, too, in which I took Ticonderoga, and the way in which I meant to take Montreal. Selah! But pray, now that I look at you, are not you the hero I caught dodging round, in his shirt, in the cattlepen, inside the fort? It was the break of day, you remember."

"Come, Yankee," here swore the incensed private; "cease this, or I'll darn your old fawn-skins for ye with the flat of this sword;" for a specimen, laying it lashwise, but not heavily, across the captive's back.

Turning like a tiger, the giant, catching the steel between his teeth, wrenched it from the private's grasp, and striking it with his manacles, sent it spinning like a juggler's dagger into the air, saying, "Lay your dirty coward's iron on a tied gentleman again, and these," lifting his handcuffed fists, "shall be the beetle of mortality to you!"

The now furious soldier would have struck him with all his force, but several men of the town interposed, reminding him that it were outrageous to attack a chained captive.

"Ah," said Allen, "I am accustomed to that, and therefore I am beforehand with them; and the extremity of what I say against Britain, is not meant for you, kind friends, but for my insulters, present and to come." Then recognizing among the interposers the giver of the bowl, he turned with a courteous bow, saying, "Thank you again and again, my good sir; you may not be the worse for this; ours is an unstable world; so that one gentleman never knows when it may be his turn to be helped of another."

But the soldier still making a riot, and the commotion growing general, a superior officer stepped up, who terminated the scene by remanding the prisoner to his cell, dismissing the townspeople, with all strangers, Israel among the rest, and closing the castle gates after them.

CHAPTER XXII

SOMETHING FURTHER OF ETHAN ALLEN; WITH ISRAEL'S FLIGHT TOWARDS THE WILDERNESS

AMONG the episodes of the Revolutionary War, none is stranger than that of Ethan Allen in England; the event and the man being equally uncommon.

Allen seems to have been a curious combination of a Hercules, a Joe Miller, a Bayard, and a Tom Hyer; had a person like the Belgian giants; mountain music in him like a Swiss; a heart plump as Cœur de Lion's. Though born in New England, he exhibited no trace of her character. He was frank, bluff, companionable as a Pagan, convivial, a Roman, hearty as a harvest. His spirit was essentially Western; and herein is his peculiar Americanism; for the Western spirit is, or will yet be (for no other is, or can be), the true American one.

For the most part, Allen's manner while in England was scornful and ferocious in the last degree; however, qualified by that wild, heroic sort of levity, which in the hour of oppression or peril seems inseparable from a nature like his; the mode whereby such a temper best evinces its barbaric disdain of adversity, and how cheaply and waggishly it holds the malice, even though triumphant, of its foes! Aside from that inevitable egotism relatively pertaining to pine trees, spires, and giants, there were, perhaps, two special incidental reasons for the Titanic Vermonter's singular demeanor abroad. Taken captive while heading a forlorn hope before Montreal, he was treated with inexcusable cruelty and indignity; something as if he had fallen into the hands of the Dyaks. Immediately upon his capture he would have been deliberately suffered to have been butchered by the Indian allies in cold blood on the spot, had he not, with desperate intrepidity, availed himself of his enormous physical strength, by twitching a British officer to him, and using him for a living target, whirling him round and round against the murderous tomahawks of the savages. Shortly afterwards, led into the town, fenced about by bayonets of the guard, the commander of the enemy, one Colonel McCloud, flourished his cane over the captive's head, with brutal insults promising him a rebel's halter at Tyburn. During his passage to England in the same ship wherein went passenger Colonel Guy Johnson, the implacable tory, he was kept heavily ironed in the hold, and in all ways treated as a common mutineer; or, it may be, rather as a lion of Asia; which, though caged, was still too dreadful to behold without fear and trembling, and consequent cruelty. And no wonder, at least for the fear; for on one occasion, when chained hand and foot, he was insulted on shipboard by an officer; with his teeth he twisted off the nail that went through the mortise of his handcuffs, and so, having his arms at liberty, challenged his insulter to combat. Often, as at Pendennis Castle, when no other avengement was at hand, he would hurl on his foes such howling tempests of anathema as fairly to shock them into retreat. Prompted by somewhat similar motives, both on shipboard and in England, he would often make the most vociferous allusions to Ticonderoga, and the part he played in its capture, knowing, that of all American names, Ticonderoga was, at that period, by far the most famous and galling to Englishmen.

Parlor-men, dancing-masters, the graduates of the Albe Bellgarde, may shrug their laced shoulders at the boisterousness of Allen in England. True, he stood upon no punctilios with his jailors; for where modest gentlemanhood is all on one side, it is a losing affair; as if my Lord Chesterfield should take off his hat, and smile, and bow, to a mad bull, in hopes of a reciprocation of politeness. When among wild beasts, if they menace you, be a wild beast. Neither is it unlikely that this was the view taken by Allen. For, besides the exasperating tendency to self-assertion which such treatment as his must have bred on a man like him, his experience must have taught him, that by assuming the part of a jocular, reckless, and even braggart barbarian, he would better sustain himself against bullying turnkeys than by submissive quietude. Nor should it be forgotten, that besides the petty details of personal malice, the enemy violated every international usage of right and decency, in treating a distinguished prisoner of war as if he had been a Botany-Bay convict. If, at the present day, in any similar case between the same States, the repetition of such outrages would be more than unlikely, it is only because it is among nations as among individuals: imputed indigence provokes oppression and scorn; but that same indigence being risen to opulence, receives a politic consideration even from its former insulters.

As the event proved, in the course Allen pursued, he was right. Because, though at first nothing was talked of by his captors, and nothing anticipated by himself, but his ignominious execution, or at the least, prolonged and squalid incarceration, nevertheless, these threats and prospects evaporated, and by his facetious scorn for scorn, under the extremest sufferings, he finally wrung repentant usage from his foes; and in the end, being liberated from his irons, and walking the quarter-deck where before he had been thrust into the hold, was carried back to America, and in due time, at New York, honorably included in a regular exchange of prisoners.

It was not without strange interest that Israel had been an eye-witness of the scenes on the Castle Green. Neither was this interest abated by the painful necessity of concealing, for the present, from his brave countryman and fellow-mountaineer, the fact of a friend being nigh. When at last the throng was dismissed, walking towards the town with the rest, he heard that there were some forty or more Americans, privates, confined on the cliff. Upon this, inventing a pretence, he turned back, loitering around the walls for any chance glimpse of the captives. Presently, while looking up at a grated embrasure in the tower, he started at a voice from it familiarly hailing him:

"Potter, is that you? In God's name how came you here?"

At these words, a sentry below had his eye on our astonished adventurer. Bringing his piece to bear, he bade him stand. Next moment Israel was under arrest. Being brought into the presence of the forty prisoners, where they lay in litters of mouldy straw, strewn with gnawed bones, as in a kennel, he recognized among them one Singles, now Sergeant Singles, the man who, upon our hero's return home from his last Cape Horn voyage, he had found wedded to his mountain Jenny. Instantly a rush of emotions filled him. Not as when Damon found Pythias. But far stranger, because very different. For not only had this Singles been an alien to Israel (so far as actual intercourse went), but impelled to it by instinct, Israel had all but detested him, as a successful, and perhaps insidious rival. Nor was it altogether unlikely that Singles had reciprocated the feeling. But now, as if the Atlantic rolled, not between two continents, but two worlds—this, and the next—these alien souls, oblivious to hate, melted down into one.

At such a juncture, it was hard to maintain a disguise, especially when it involved the seeming rejection of advances like the Sergeant's. Still, converting his real amazement into affected surprise, Israel, in presence of the sentries, declared to Singles that he (Singles) must labor under some unaccountable delusion; for he (Potter) was no Yankee-rebel, thank Heaven, but a true man to his king; in short, an honest Englishman, born in Kent, and now serving his country, and doing what damage he might to her foes, by being first captain of a carronade on board a letter of marque, that moment in the harbor.

For a moment the captive stood astounded, but observing Israel more narrowly, detecting his latent look, and bethinking him of the useless peril he had thoughtlessly caused to a countryman, no doubt unfortunate as himself, Singles took his cue and, pretending sullenly to apologize for his error, put on a disappointed and crestfallen air. Nevertheless, it was not without much difficulty, and after many supplemental scrutinies and inquisitions from a board of officers before whom he was subsequently brought, that our wanderer was finally permitted to quit the cliff.

This luckless adventure not only nipped in the bud a little scheme he had been revolving, for materially befriending Ethan Allen and his comrades, but resulted in making his further stay at Falmouth perilous in the extreme. And as if this were not enough, next day, while hanging over the side, painting the hull, in trepidation of a visit from the castle soldiers, rumor came to the ship that the man-of-war in the haven purposed impressing one-third of the letter of marque's crew; though, indeed, the latter vessel was preparing for a second cruise. Being on board a private armed ship, Israel had little dreamed of its liability to the same governmental hardships with the meanest merchantman. But the system of impressment is no respecter either of pity or person.

His mind was soon determined. Unlike his shipmates, braving immediate and lonely hazard, rather than wait for a collective and ultimate one, he cunningly dropped himself overboard the same night, and after the narrowest risk from the muskets of the man-of-war's sentries (whose gangways he had to pass), succeeded in swimming to shore, where he fell exhausted; but recovering, fled inland, doubly hunted by the thought, that whether as an Englishman, or whether as an American, he would, if caught, be now equally subject to enslavement.

Shortly after the break of day, having gained many miles, he succeeded in ridding himself of his seaman's clothing, having found some mouldy old rags on the banks of a stagnant pond, nigh a rickety building, which looked like a poorhouse—clothing not improbably, as he surmised, left there on the bank by some pauper suicide. Marvel not that he should with avidity seize these rags; what the suicides abandon, the living hug.

Once more in beggar's garb, the fugitive sped towards London, prompted by the same instinct which impels the hunted fox to the wilderness; for solitudes befriend the endangered wild beast, but crowds are the security, because the true desert, of persecuted man. Among the things of the capital, Israel for more than forty years was yet to disappear, as one entering at dusk into a thick wood. Nor did ever the German forest, nor Tasso's enchanted one, contain in its depths more things of horror than eventually were revealed in the secret clefts, gulfs, caves and dens of London.

But here we anticipate a page.

CHAPTER XXIII

ISRAEL IN EGYPT

IT was a gray, lowering afternoon that, worn out, half starved, and haggard, Israel arrived within some ten or fifteen miles of London, and saw scores and scores of forlorn men engaged in a great brickyard.

For the most part, brickmaking is all mud and mire. Where, abroad, the business is carried on largely, as to supply the London market, hordes of the poorest wretches are employed, their grimy tatters naturally adapting them to an employ where cleanliness is as much out of the question as with a drowned man at the bottom of the lake in the Dismal Swamp.

Desperate with want, Israel resolved to turn brickmaker, nor did he fear to present himself as a stranger, nothing doubting that to such a vocation his rags would be accounted the best letters of introduction.

To be brief, he accosted one of the many surly overseers, or taskmasters of the yard, who, with no few pompous airs, finally engaged him at six shillings a week, almost equivalent to a dollar and a half. He was appointed to one of the mills for grinding up the ingredients. This mill stood in the open air. It was of a rude, primitive, Eastern aspect, consisting of a sort of hopper, emptying into a barrel-shaped receptacle. In the barrel was a clumsy machine turned round at its axis by a great bent beam, like a well-sweep, only it was horizontal; to this beam, at its outer end, a spavined old horse was attached. The muddy mixture was shovelled into the hopper by spavined-looking old men, while, trudging wearily round and round, the spavined old horse ground it all up till it slowly squashed out at the bottom of the barrel, in a doughy compound, all ready for the moulds. Where the dough squeezed out of the barrel a pit was sunken, so as to bring the moulder here stationed down to a level with the trough, into which the dough fell. Israel was assigned to this pit. Men came to him continually, reaching down rude wooden trays, divided into compartments, each of the size and shape of a brick. With a flat sort of big ladle, Israel slapped the dough into the trays from the trough; then, with a bit of smooth board, scraped the top even, and handed it up. Half buried there in the pit, all the time handing those desolate trays, poor Israel seemed some gravedigger, or churchyard man, tucking away dead little innocents in their coffins on one side, and cunningly disinterring them again to resurrectionists stationed on the other.

Twenty of these melancholy old mills were in operation. Twenty heart-broken old horses, rigged out deplorably in cast-off old cart harness, incessantly tugged at twenty great shaggy beams; while from twenty half-burst old barrels, twenty wads of mud, with a lava-like course, gouged out into twenty old troughs, to be slapped by twenty tattered men into the twenty-times-twenty battered old trays.

Ere entering his pit for the first, Israel had been struck by the dismally devil-may-care gestures of the moulders. But hardly had he himself been a moulder three days, when his previous sedateness of concern at his unfortunate lot, began to conform to the reckless sort of half jolly despair expressed by the others. The truth indeed was, that this continual, violent, helter-skelter slapping of the dough into the moulds, begat a corresponding disposition in the moulder, who, by heedlessly slapping that sad dough, as stuff of little worth, was thereby taught, in his meditations, to slap, with similar heedlessness, his own sadder fortunes, as of still less vital consideration. To these muddy philosophers, men and bricks were equally of clay. "What signifies who we be—dukes or ditchers?" thought the moulders; "all is vanity and clay." So slap, slap, slap, care-free and negligent, with bitter unconcern, these dismal desperadoes flapped down the dough. If this recklessness were vicious of them, be it so; but their vice was like that weed which but grows on barren ground; enrich the soil, and it disappears.

For thirteen weary weeks, lorded over by the task-master, Israel toiled in his pit. Though this condemned him to a sort of earthly dungeon, or grave-digger's hole, while he worked, yet even when liberated to his meals, naught of a cheery nature greeted him. The yard was encamped, with all its endless rows of tented sheds, and kilns, and mills, upon a wild waste moor, belted round by bogs and fens. The blank horizon, like a rope, coiled round the whole.

Sometimes the air was harsh and bleak; the ridged and mottled sky looked scourged, or cramping fogs set in from sea, for leagues around, ferreting out each rheumatic human bone, and racking it; the sciatic limpers shivered; their aguish rags sponged up the mists. No shelter, though it hailed. The sheds were for the bricks. Unless, indeed, according to the phrase, each man was a "brick," which, in sober scripture, was the case; brick is no bad name for any son of Adam; Eden was but a brickyard; what is a mortal but a few luckless shovelfuls of clay, moulded in a mould, laid out on a sheet to dry, and ere long quickened into his queer caprices by the sun? Are not men built into communities just like bricks into a wall? Consider the great wall of China: ponder the great populace of Pekin. As man serves bricks, so God him, building him up by billions into edifices of his purposes. Man attains not to the nobility of a brick, unless taken in the aggregate. Yet is there a difference in brick whether quick or dead; which, for the last, we now shall see.

CHAPTER XXIII (*Continued*)

ISRAEL IN EGYPT

ALL night long, men sat before the mouth of the kilns, feeding them with fuel. A dull smoke—a smoke of their torments—went up from their tops. It was curious to see the kilns under the action of the fire, gradually changing color, like boiling lobsters. When, at last, the fires would be extinguished, the bricks being duly baked, Israel often took a peep into the low vaulted ways at the base, where the flaming fagots had crackled. The bricks immediately lining the vaults would be all burnt to useless scrolls, black as charcoal, and twisted into shapes the most grotesque; the next tier would be a little less withered, but hardly fit for service; and gradually, as you went higher and higher along the successive layers of the kiln, you came to the midmost ones, sound, square, and perfect bricks, bringing the highest prices; from these the contents of the kiln gradually deteriorated in the opposite direction, upward. But the topmost layers, though inferior to the best, by no means presented the distorted look of the furnace-bricks. The furnace-bricks were haggard, with the immediate blistering of the fire—the midmost ones were ruddy with a genial and tempered glow—the summit ones were pale with the languor of too exclusive an exemption from the burden of the blaze.

These kilns were a sort of temporary temples constructed in the yard, each brick being set against its neighbor almost with the care taken by the mason. But as soon as the fire was extinguished, down came the kiln in a tumbled ruin, carried off to London, once more to be set up in ambitious edifices, to a true brickyard philosopher, little less transient than the kilns.

Sometimes, lading out his dough, Israel could not but bethink him of what seemed enigmatic in his fate. He whom love of country made a hater of her foes—the foreigners among whom he now was thrown—he who, as soldier and sailor, had joined to kill, burn and destroy both them and theirs—here he was at last, serving that very people as a slave, better succeeding in making their bricks than firing their ships. To think that he should be thus helping, with all his strength, to extend the walls of the Thebes of the oppressor, made him half mad. Poor Israel! well-named—bondsman in the English Egypt. But he drowned the thought by still more recklessly spattering with his ladle: "What signifies who we be, or where we are, or what we do?" Slap-dash! "Kings, as clowns are codgers—who ain't a nobody?" Splash! "All is vanity and clay."

CHAPTER XXIV

IN THE CITY OF DIS

AT the end of his brickmaking, our adventurer found himself with a tolerable suit of clothes—somewhat darned—on his back, several blood-blisters in his palms, and some verdigris coppers in his pocket. Forthwith, to seek his fortune, he proceeded on foot to the capital, entering, like the king, from Windsor, from the Surrey side.

It was late on a Monday morning, in November—a Blue Monday—a Fifth of November—Guy Fawkes' Day!—very blue, foggy, doleful and gunpowdery, indeed, as shortly will be seen, that Israel found himself wedged in among the greatest every-day crowd which grimy London presents to the curious stranger: that hereditary crowd—gulf-stream of humanity—which, for continuous centuries, has never ceased pouring, like an endless shoal of herring, over London Bridge.

At the period here written of, the bridge, specifically known by that name, was a singular and sombre pile, built by a cowled monk—Peter of Colechurch —some five hundred years before. Its arches had long been crowded at the sides with strange old rookeries of disproportioned and toppling height, converting the bridge at once into the most densely occupied ward and most jammed thoroughfare of the town, while, as the skulls of bullocks are hung out for signs to the gateways of shambles, so the withered heads and smoked quarters of traitors, stuck on pikes, long crowned the Southwark entrance.

Though these rookeries, with their grisly heraldry, had been pulled down some twenty years prior to the present visit, still enough of grotesque and antiquity clung to the structure at large to render it the most striking of objects, especially to one like our hero, born in a virgin clime, where the only antiquities are the forever youthful heavens and the earth.

On his route from Brentford to Paris, Israel had passed through the capital, but only as a courier; so that now, for the first time, he had time to linger, and loiter, and lounge—slowly absorb what he saw—meditate himself into boundless amazement. For forty years he never recovered from that surprise—never, till dead, had done with his wondering.

Hung in long, sepulchral arches of stone, the black, besmoked bridge seemed a huge scarf of crape, festooning the river across. Similar funeral festoons spanned it to the west, while eastward, towards the sea, tiers and tiers of jetty colliers lay moored, side by side, fleets of black swans.

The Thames, which far away, among the green fields of Berks, ran clear as a brook, here, polluted by continual vicinity to man, curdled on between rotten wharves, one murky sheet of sewerage. Fretted by the ill-built piers, awhile it crested and hissed, then shot balefully through the Erebus arches, desperate as the lost souls of the harlots, who, every night, took the same plunge. Meantime, here and there, like awaiting hearses, the coal-scows drifted along, poled broadside, pell-mell to the current.

And as that tide in the water swept all craft on, so a like tide seemed hurrying all men, all horses, all vehicles on the land. As ant-hills, the bridge arches crawled with processions of carts, coaches, drays, every sort of wheeled, rumbling thing, the noses of the horses behind touching the backs of the vehicles in advance, all bespattered with ebon mud—ebon mud that stuck like Jews' pitch. At times the mass, receiving some mysterious impulse far in the rear, away among the coiled thoroughfares out of sight, would start forward with a spasmodic surge. It seemed as if some squadron of centaurs, on the thither side of Phlegethon, with charge on charge, was driving tormented humanity, with all its chattels, across.

Whichever way the eye turned, no tree, no speck of any green thing was seen—no more than in smithies. All laborers, of whatsoever sort, were hued like the men in foundries. The black vistas of streets were as the galleries in coal mines; the flagging, as flat tomb-stones, minus the consecration of moss, and worn heavily down, by sorrowful tramping, as the vitreous rocks in the cursed Gallipagos, over which the convict tortoises crawl.

As in eclipses, the sun was hidden; the air darkened; the whole dull, dismayed aspect of things, as if some neighboring volcano, belching its premonitory smoke, were about to whelm the great town, as Herculaneum and Pompeii, or the Cities of the Plain. And as they had been upturned in terror towards the mountain, all faces were more or less snowed or spotted with soot. Nor marble, nor flesh, nor the sad spirit of man, may in this cindery City of Dis abide white.

As retired at length, midway, in a recess of the bridge, Israel surveyed them, various individual aspects all but frighted him. Knowing not who they were; never destined, it may be, to behold them again; one after the other, they drifted by, uninvoked ghosts in Hades. Some of the wayfarers wore a less serious look; some seemed hysterically merry; but the mournful faces had an earnestness not seen in the others: because man, "poor player," succeeds better in life's tragedy than comedy.

Arrived, in the end, on the Middlesex side, Israel's heart was prophetically heavy; foreknowing, that being of this race, felicity could never be his lot.

For five days he wandered and wandered. Without leaving statelier haunts unvisited, he did not overlook those broader areas—hereditary parks and manors of vice and misery. Not by constitution disposed to gloom, there was a mysteriousness in those impulses which led him at this time to rovings like these. But hereby stoic influences were at work, to fit him at a soon-coming day for enacting a part in the last extremities here seen; when by sickness, destitution, each busy ill of exile, he was destined to experience a fate, uncommon, even to luckless humanity—a fate whose crowning qualities were its remoteness from relief and its depth of obscurity—London, adversity, and the sea, three Armageddons, which, at one and the same time, slay and secrete their victims.

CHAPTER XXV

FORTY-FIVE YEARS

For the most part, what befell Israel during his forty years' wanderings in the London deserts, surpassed the forty years in the natural wilderness of the outcast Hebrews under Moses.

In that London fog, went before him the ever-present cloud by day, but no pillar of fire by the night, except the cold column of the monument, two hundred feet beneath the mocking gilt flames on whose top, at the stone base, the shiverer, of midnight, often laid down.

But these experiences, both from their intensity and his solitude, were necessarily squalid. Best not enlarge upon them. For just as extreme suffering, without hope, is intolerable to the victim, so, to others, is its depiction without some corresponding delusive mitigation. The gloomiest and truthfulest dramatist seldom chooses for his theme the calamities, however extraordinary, of inferior and private persons; least of all, the pauper's; admonished by the fact, that to the craped palace of the king lying in state, thousands of starers shall throng; but few feel enticed to the shanty, where, like a pealed knucklebone, grins the unupholstered corpse of the beggar.

Why at one given stone in the flagging does man after man cross yonder street? What plebeian Lear or Œdipus, what Israel Potter, cowers there by the corner they shun? From this turning point, then, we too cross over and skim events to the end; omitting the particulars of the starveling's wrangling with rats for prizes in the sewers; or his crawling into an abandoned doorless house in St. Giles', where his hosts were three dead men, one pendant; into another of an alley nigh Houndsditch, where the crazy hovel, in phosphoric rottenness, fell sparkling on him one pitchy midnight, and he received that injury, which, excluding activity for no small part of the future, was an added cause of his prolongation of exile, besides not leaving his faculties unaffected by the concussion of one of the rafters on his brain.

But these were some of the incidents not belonging to the beginning of his career. On the contrary, a sort of humble prosperity attended him for a time; insomuch that once he was not without hopes of being able to buy his homeward passage so soon as the war should end. But, as stubborn fate would have it, being run over one day at Holborn Bars, and taken into a neighboring bakery, he was there treated with such kindliness by a Kentish lass, the shop-girl, that in the end he thought his debt of gratitude could only be repaid by love. In a word, the money saved up for his ocean voyage was lavished upon a rash embarkation in wedlock.

Originally he had fled to the capital to avoid the dilemma of impressment or imprisonment. In the absence of other motives, the dread of those hardships would have fixed him there till the peace. But now, when hostilities were no more, so was his money. Some period elapsed ere the affairs of the two governments were put on such a footing as to support an American consul at London. Yet, when this came to pass, he could only embrace the facilities for a return here furnished, by deserting a wife and child, wedded and born in the enemy's land.

The peace immediately filled England, and more especially London, with hordes of disbanded soldiers; thousands of whom, rather than starve, or turn highwaymen (which no few of their comrades did, stopping coaches at times in the most public streets), would work for such a pittance as to bring down the wages of all the laboring classes. Neither was our adventurer the least among the sufferers. Driven out of his previous employ—a sort of porter in a riverside warehouse—by this sudden influx of rivals, destitute, honest men like himself, with the ingenuity of his race, he turned his hand to the village art of chair-bottoming. An itinerant, he paraded the streets with the cry of "Old chairs to mend!" furnishing a curious illustration of the contradictions of human life; that he who did little but trudge, should be giving cosy seats to all the rest of the world. Meantime, according to another well-known Malthusian enigma in human affairs, his family increased. In all, eleven children were born to him in certain sixpenny garrets in Moorfields. One after the other, ten were buried.

When chair-bottoming would fail, resort was had to match-making. That business being overdone in turn, next came the cutting of old rags, bits of paper, nails and broken glass. Nor was this the last step. From the gutter he slid to the sewer. The slope was smooth. In poverty,

—"Facilis descensus Averni."

But many a poor soldier had sloped down there into the boggy canal of Avernus before him. Nay, he had three corporals and a sergeant for company.

But his lot was relieved by two strange things, presently to appear. In 1793 war again broke out, the great French war. This lighted London of some of its superfluous hordes, and lost Israel the subterranean society of his friends, the corporals and sergeant, with whom wandering forlorn through the black kingdoms of mud, he used to spin yarns about sea prisoners in hulks, and listen to stories of the Black Hole of Calcutta; and often would meet other pairs of poor soldiers, perfect strangers, at the more public corners and intersections of sewers—the Charing-Crosses below; one soldier having the other by his remainder button, earnestly discussing the sad prospects of a rise in bread, or the tide; while through the grating of the gutters overhead, the rusty skylights of the realm came the hoarse rumblings of bakers' carts, with splashes of the flood whereby these unsuspected gnomes of the city lived.

Encouraged by the exodus of the lost tribes of soldiers, Israel returned to chair-bottoming. And it was frequently in Covent-Garden market, at early morning, for the purchase of his flags, that he experienced one of the strange alleviations hinted of above. The chatting with the ruddy, aproned, huckster-women, on whose moist cheeks yet trickled the dew of the dawn on the meadows; that being surrounded by bales of hay, as the raker by cocks and ricks in the field; those glimpses of garden produce, the blood-beets, with the damp earth still tufting the roots; that mere handling of his flags, and bethinking him of whence they must have come, the green hedges through which the wagon that brought them had passed; that trudging home with them as a gleaner with his sheaf of wheat;—all this was inexpressibly grateful. In want and bitterness, pent in, perforce, between dingy walls, he had rural returns of his boyhood's sweeter days among them; and the hardest stones of his solitary heart (made hard by bare endurance alone) would feel the stir of tender but quenchless memories, like the grass of deserted flagging, upsprouting through its closest seams. Sometimes, when incited by some little incident, however trivial in itself, thoughts of home would—either by gradually working and working upon him, or else by an impetuous rush of recollection—overpower him for a time to a sort of hallucination.

Thus was it:—One fair half-day in the July of 1800, by good luck, he was employed, partly out of charity, by one of the keepers, to trim the sward in an oval enclosure within St. James' Park, a little green but a three-minutes' walk along the gravelled way from the brick-besmoked and grimy Old Brewery of the palace which gives its ancient name to the public resort on whose borders it stands. It was a little oval, fenced in with iron palings, between whose bars the imprisoned verdure peered forth, as some wild captive creature of the woods from its cage. And alien Israel there—at times staring dreamily about him— seemed like some amazed runaway steer, or trespassing Pequod Indian, impounded on the shores of Narraganset Bay, long ago; and back to New England our exile was called in his soul. For still working, and thinking of home; and thinking of home, and working amid the verdant quietude of this little oasis, one rapt thought begat another, till at last his mind settled intensely, and yet half humorously, upon the image of Old Huckleberry, his mother's favorite old pillion horse; and, ere long, hearing a sudden scraping noise (some hob-shoe without, against the iron paling), he insanely took it to be Old Huckleberry in his stall, hailing him (Israel) with his shod fore-foot clattering against the planks—his customary trick when hungry—and so, down goes Israel's hook, and with a tuft of white clover, impulsively snatched, he hurries away a few paces in obedience to the imaginary summons. But soon stopping midway, and forlornly gazing round at the enclosure, he bethought him that a far different oval, the great oval of the ocean, must be crossed ere his crazy errand could be done; and even then, Old Huckleberry would be found long surfeited with clover, since, doubtless, being dead many a summer, he must be buried beneath it. And many years after, in a far different part of the town, and in far less winsome weather too, passing with his bundle of flags through Red-Cross street, toward Barbican, in a fog so dense that the dimmed and massed blocks of houses, exaggerated by the gloom, seemed shadowy ranges on ranges of midnight hills, he heard a confused pastoral sort of sounds—trampling, lowings, halloos—and was suddenly called to by a voice to head off certain cattle, bound to Smithfield, bewildered and unruly in the fog. Next instant he saw the white face—white as an orange-blossom—of a black-bodied steer, in advance of the drove, gleaming ghost-like through the vapors; and presently, forgetting his limp, with rapid shout and gesture, he was more eager, even than the troubled farmers, their owners, in driving the riotous cattle back to Barbican. Monomaniac reminiscences were in him—"To the right, to the right!" he shouted, as, arrived at the street corner, the farmers beat the drove to the left, towards Smithfield: "To the right! you are driving them back to the pastures— to the right! that way lies the barnyard!" "Barnyard?" cried a voice; "you are dreaming, old man." And so, Israel, now an old man, was bewitched by the mirage of vapors; he had dreamed himself home into the mists of the Housatonic mountains; ruddy boy on the upland pastures again. But how different the flat, apathetic, dead, London fog now seemed from those agile mists which, goat-like, climbed the purple peaks, or in routed armies of phantoms, broke down, pell-mell, dispersed in flight upon the plain, leaving the cattle-boy loftily alone, clear-cut as a balloon against the sky.

In 1817 he once more endured extremity; this second peace again drifting its discharged soldiers on London, so that all kinds of labor were overstocked. Beggars, too, lighted on the walks like locusts. Timber-toed cripples stilted along, numerous as French peasants in *sabots*. And, as thirty years before, on all sides, the exile had heard the supplicatory cry, not addressed to him, "An honorable scar, your honor, received at Bunker Hill, or Saratoga, or Trenton, fighting for his most gracious Majesty, King George!" so now, in presence of the still surviving Israel, our Wandering Jew, the amended cry was anew taken up, by a succeeding generation of unfortunates, "An honorable scar, your honor, received at Corunna, or at Waterloo, or at Trafalgar!" Yet not a few of these petitioners had never been outside of the London smoke; a sort of crafty aristocracy in their way, who, without having endangered their own persons much if anything, reaped no insignificant share both of the glory and profit of the bloody battles they claimed; while some of the genuine working heroes, too brave to beg, too cut-up to work, and too poor to live, laid down quietly in corners and died. And here it may be noted, as a fact nationally characteristic, that however desperately reduced at times, even to the sewers, Israel, the American, never sank below the mud, to actual beggary.

Though henceforth elbowed out of many a chance threepenny job by the added thousands who contended with him against starvation, nevertheless, somehow he continued to subsist, as though tough old oaks of the cliffs, which, though hacked at by hail-stones of tempests, and even wantonly maimed by the passing woodman, still, however cramped by rival trees and fettered by rocks, succeed, against all odds, in keeping the vital nerve of the tap-root alive. And even towards the end, in his dismallest December, our veteran could still at intervals feel a momentary warmth in his topmost boughs. In his Moorfields' garret, over a handful of reignited cinders (which the night before might have warmed some lord), cinders raked up from the streets, he would drive away dolor, by talking with his one only surviving, and now motherless child— the spared Benjamin of his old age—of the far Canaan beyond the sea; rehearsing to the lad those well-remembered adventures among New England hills, and painting scenes of nestling happiness and plenty, in which the lowliest shared. And here, shadowy as it was, was the second alleviation hinted of above.

To these tales of the Fortunate Isles of the Free, recounted by one who had been there, the poor enslaved boy of Moorfields listened, night after night, as to the stories of Sinbad the Sailor. When would his father take him there? "Some day to come, my boy," would be the hopeful response of an unhoping heart. And "Would God it were to-morrow!" would be the impassioned reply.

In these talks Israel unconsciously sowed the seeds of his eventual return. For with added years, the boy felt added longing to escape his entailed misery, by compassing for his father and himself a voyage to the Promised Land. By his persevering efforts he succeeded at last, against every obstacle, in gaining credit in the right quarter to his extraordinary statements. In short, charitably stretching a technical point, the American Consul finally saw father and son embarked in the Thames for Boston.

It was the year 1826; half a century since Israel, in early manhood, had sailed a prisoner in the *Tartar* frigate from the same port to which he now was bound. An octogenarian as he recrossed the brine, he showed locks besnowed as its foam. White-haired old Ocean seemed as a brother.

CHAPTER XXVI

REQUIESCAT IN PACE

It happened that the ship, gaining her port, was moored to the dock on a Fourth of July; and half an hour after landing, hustled by the riotous crowd near Faneuil Hall, the old man narrowly escaped being run over by a patriotic triumphal car in the procession, flying a broidered banner, inscribed with gilt letters:

"BUNKER-HILL
1775
GLORY TO THE HEROES THAT FOUGHT!"

It was on Copps' Hill, within the city bounds, one of the enemy's positions during the fight, that our wanderer found his best repose that day. Sitting down here on a mound in the graveyard, he looked off toward Charles River towards the battle-ground, whose incipient monument, at that period, was hard to see, as a struggling sprig of corn in a chilly spring. Upon those heights, fifty years before, his now feeble hands had wielded both ends of the musket. There too he had received that slit upon the chest, which afterwards, in the affair with the *Serapis,* being traversed by a cutlass wound, made him now the bescarred bearer of a cross.

For a long time he sat mute, gazing blankly about him. The sultry July day was waning. His son sought to cheer him a little ere rising to return to the lodging for the present assigned them by the ship-captain. "Nay," replied the old man, "I shall get no fitter rest than here by the mounds."

But from this true "Potter's Field," the boy at length drew him away; and encouraged next morning by a voluntary purse made up among the reassembled passengers, father and son started by stage for the country of the Housatonic. But the exile's presence in these old mountain townships proved less a return than a resurrection. At first, none knew him, nor could recall having heard of him. Ere long it was found, that more than thirty years previous, the last known survivor of his family in that region, a bachelor, following the example of three-fourths of his neighbors, had sold out and removed to a distant country in the west; where exactly, none could say.

He sought to get a glimpse of his father's homestead. But it had been burnt down long ago. Accompanied by his son, dim-eyed and dim-hearted, he next went to find the site. But the roads had years before been changed. The old road was now browsed over by sheep; the new one ran straight through what had formerly been orchards. But new orchards, planted from other suckers, and in time grafted, throve on sunny slopes near by, where blackberries had once been picked by the bushel. At length he came to a field waving with buckwheat. It seemed one of those fields which himself had often reaped. But it turned out, upon inquiry, that but three summers since a walnut grove had stood there. Then he vaguely remembered that his father had sometimes talked of planting such a grove, to defend the neighboring fields against the cold north wind; yet where precisely that grove was to have been, his shattered mind could not recall. But it seemed not unlikely that during his long exile, the walnut grove had been planted and harvested, as well as the annual crops preceding and succeeding it, on the very same soil.

Ere long, on the mountain side, he passed into an ancient natural wood, which seemed some way familiar, and midway in it, paused to contemplate a strange, mouldy pile, resting at one end against a sturdy beech. Though wherever touched by his staff, however lightly, this pile would crumble, yet here and there, even in powder, it preserved the exact look, each irregularly defined line, of what it had originally been—namely, a half-cord of stout hemlock (one of the woods least affected by exposure to the air), in a foregoing generation chopped and stacked up on the spot, against sledging-time, but, as sometimes happens in such cases, by subsequent oversight, abandoned to oblivious decay —type now, as it stood there, of forever arrested intentions, and a long life still rotting in early mishap.

"Do I dream?" mused the bewildered old man, "or what is this vision that comes to me of a cold, cloudy morning, long, long ago, and I heaving yon elbowed log against the beech, then a sapling? Nay, nay, I cannot be so old."

"Come away, father, from this dismal, damp wood," said his son, and led him forth.

Blindly ranging to and fro, they next saw a man ploughing. Advancing slowly, the wanderer met him by a little heap of ruinous burnt masonry, like a tumbled chimney, what seemed the jambs of the fireplace, now aridly stuck over here and there, with thin, clinging, round, prohibitory mosses, like executors' wafers. Just as the oxen were bid stand, the stranger's plough was hitched over sideways, by sudden contact with some sunken stone at the ruin's base.

"There, this is the twentieth year my plough has struck this old hearthstone. Ah, old man,—sultry day, this."

"Whose house stood here, friend?" said the wanderer, touching the half-buried hearth with his staff, where a fresh furrow overlapped it.

"Don't know; forget the name; gone West, though, I believe. You know 'em?"

But the wanderer made no response; his eye was now fixed on a curious natural bend or wave in one of the bemossed stone jambs.

"What are you looking at so, father?"

" *'Father!'* Here," raking with his staff, *"my* father would sit, and here, my mother, and here I, little infant, would totter between, even as now, once again, on the very same spot, but in the unroofed air, I do. The ends meet. Plough away, friend."

Best followed now is this life, by hurrying, like itself, to a close.

Few things remain.

He was repulsed in efforts after a pension by certain caprices of law. His scars proved his only medals. He dictated a little book, the record of his fortunes. But long ago it faded out of print—himself out of being—his name out of memory. He died the same day that the oldest oak on his native hills was blown down.